CELLULAR RADIATION BIOLOGY

A Symposium Considering Radiation Effects in the Cell and Possible Implications for Cancer Therapy

A Collection of Papers Presented at the Eighteenth Annual Symposium on Fundamental Cancer Research, 1964

Published for
The University of Texas M. D. Anderson Hospital and Tumor Institute

Baltimore
The Williams and Wilkins Company
1965

Library of Congress Catalog Card No. 65-15703

Manufactured in the United States of America
by the Printing Division of The University of Texas

Acknowledgments

We acknowledge with appreciation the efforts of Robert J. Shalek, chairman of the 1964 Symposium, and his committee members: Drs. Daniel Billen, Arthur Cole, Murray M. Copeland, Russell W. Cumley, William C. Dewey, Leon Dmochowski, Charles O. Doudney, Gilbert H. Fletcher, Ronald M. Humphrey, Herman D. Suit, Darrell N. Ward, and Mr. Joe E. Boyd, Jr. and Miss Frances Goff. Also, members of the advisory committee: Drs. M. Demerec, Alexander Hollaender, Franklin Hutchinson, Henry S. Kaplan, Henry Quastler, and Warren K. Sinclair.

Co-sponsor of the symposium is The University of Texas Graduate School of Biomedical Sciences at Houston. We gratefully acknowledge the assistance of the American Cancer Society, Texas Division, and the National Cancer Institute in making this meeting possible.

We also wish to acknowledge the efforts of the following members of the Department of Publications of The University of Texas M. D. Anderson Hospital and Tumor Institute who assisted in preparing the volume for publication: R. W. Cumley, Joan McCay, Dorothy Aldridge Beane, Maureen Cronin, Carolyn Crowder, Marilyn Heimann, Arabella Miner, and Wendelyn White.

Table of Contents

THE CRITICAL STRUCTURES IN RADIATION PHENOMENA

MODIFICATION OF RADIATION RESPONSE

RADIOSENSITIVITY IN THE REPLICATION CYCLE OF CELLS AND THE RELATION TO FRACTIONATION IN RADIOTHERAPY

RESPONSES IN MAMMALIAN CELLS AND THE IMPLICATIONS FOR RADIOTHERAPY OF CANCER

Symposium Committee

Robert J. Shalek, *Chairman*
Daniel Billen
Joe E. Boyd, Jr.
Arthur Cole
Murray M. Copeland
Russell W. Cumley
William C. Dewey
Leon Dmochowski
Charles O. Doudney
Gilbert H. Fletcher
Frances Goff
Ronald M. Humphrey
Herman D. Suit
Darrell N. Ward

Advisory Committee

M. Demerec, Department of Biology, Brookhaven National Laboratory, Upton, L. I., New York

Alexander Hollaender, Biology Division, Oak Ridge National Laboratory, Oak Ridge, Tennessee

Franklin Hutchinson, Department of Molecular Biology and Biophysics, Yale University, New Haven, Connecticut

Henry S. Kaplan, Department of Radiology, Stanford University School of Medicine, Palo Alto, California

Henry Quastler, Department of Biology, Brookhaven National Laboratory, Upton, L. I., New York

Warren K. Sinclair, Division of Biological and Medical Research, Argonne National Laboratory, Argonne, Illinois

Session Chairmen

Peter Alexander, Chester Beatty Research Institute, Institute of Cancer Research, Royal Cancer Hospital, London, England

Arthur Cole, Department of Physics, The University of Texas M. D. Anderson Hospital and Tumor Institute, Houston, Texas

FRANKLIN HUTCHINSON, Department of Molecular Biology and Biophysics, Yale University, New Haven, Connecticut

HENRY S. KAPLAN, Department of Radiology, Stanford University School of Medicine, Palo Alto, California

R. F. KIMBALL, Biology Division, Oak Ridge National Laboratory, Oak Ridge, Tennessee

WARREN K. SINCLAIR, Division of Biological and Medical Research, Argonne National Laboratory, Argonne, Illinois

Invited Discussants

In addition to the speakers invited to present formal papers at the Symposium and to take part in the discussions, the following individuals were invited as discussants.

LEROY AUGENSTEIN, Biophysics Department, Biology Research Center, Michigan State University, East Lansing, Michigan

G. W. BARENDSEN, Radiobiological Institute of the Organization for Health Research TNO, Rijswijk (ZH), The Netherlands

DANIEL BILLEN, Department of Biology, The University of Texas M. D. Anderson Hospital and Tumor Institute, Houston Texas

ANNA GOLDFEDER, Cancer and Radiobiological Research Laboratory, The City of New York Department of Hospitals, New York, New York

FELIX L. HAAS, Department of Biology, The University of Texas M. D. Anderson Hospital and Tumor Institute, Houston, Texas

T. C. HSU, Department of Biology, The University of Texas M. D. Anderson Hospital and Tumor Institute, Houston, Texas

ROBERT F. KALLMAN, Department of Radiology, Stanford University School of Medicine, Stanford Medical Center, Palo Alto, California

JOHN S. LAUGHLIN, Division of Biophysics, Sloan-Kettering Institute for Cancer Research, New York, New York

HARALD H. ROSS, Department of Radiology, Radiological Research Laboratories, Columbia University, New York, New York

PAUL TODD, Donner Laboratory, University of California, Berkeley, California

THOMAS H. WOOD, Physics Department, University of Pennsylvania, Philadelphia, Pennsylvania

CELLULAR RADIATION BIOLOGY

Introduction

R. LEE CLARK

Director and Surgeon-in-Chief,
The University of Texas M. D. Anderson Hospital and Tumor Institute,
Houston, Texas

In 1906, Bergonié and Tribondeau made the broad statement that: "All physicians have observed with the same interest, mixed with surprise, that x-irradiation can kill the cells of a neoplasm without impairing the neighboring healthy tissues or even the tissues invaded by the tumor. But experiments on animals have shown that x-rays have a selective action between healthy tissues. For example, in our experiments on the testicles of the rat, we have been able to destroy the germinal cells whereas the interstitial gland and the sertolie syncytium were unimpaired. As a result of these experiments, it has been possible to formulate the following law: x-irradiations are more effective on cells which have a greater reproductive activity; the effectiveness is greater on those cells which have a longer dividing future ahead; on those cells the morphology and the function of which are least fixed. From this law it is easy to understand that roentgen irradiation destroys tumors without destroying healthy tissue."

Since that statement was made, 60 years have passed and they have been filled with vigorous research in attempts to evaluate and separate the conditions and factors that contribute to radiobiological lesions. How ironic it is that radiation—such an effective agent in managing cancer—is also capable of causing cancer. Still, it is only one of many factors, including viruses and a variety of chemicals, that have cancer-inducing abilities.

The earliest known case of radiation-induced cancer was reported in 1902, less than 10 years after Roentgen discovered the X ray. Marie Curie conducted the first course on radioactivity and published a lengthy book on the subject in 1910. A new era in radiotherapy was opened when the Curies discovered that radium salts could burn and cause skin ulcers. Madame Curie herself died of aplastic anemia thought to have been brought on by prolonged exposure to radiation.

Even then, it was thought that these conditions resulted from the irradiated cells' altered status which produced prolific cell growth—thus giving birth to the mutagen theory. We now know that the primary effect of radiation merely introduces limited defects into the whole mechanism. The final outcome depends upon whether these defects are repaired or amplified.

We could not properly advance into a discussion on "Cellular Radiation Biology" without taking note of the outstanding work of Henri Coutard. For it was the method that this talented investigator helped to develop that established the biological fundamentals of radiotherapy. While at the Curie Foundation, he had observed the biologic effects of daily irradiation and prolonged treatments. From this evolutionary period in radiology, he developed "protracted-fractional" radiation. This involves administering daily fractional doses of X and gamma rays so that a large quantity of radiation may be given in "the most effective period of time,"—the purpose being to destroy the tumor yet create minimal permanent damage to the skin and normal tissues. This procedure is now an integral part of radiotherapy.

A few years later, Jacob Furth irradiated mice and produced leukemia in the animals. Mice who received one dose of 400 r or smaller doses at frequent intervals developed a much higher incidence of leukemia than the unirradiated mice. The myeloid cells infiltrated bone marrow, liver, and spleen. Subpassages were easily made by injection of cell emulsion from these infected spleens.

Different types of cells, organisms, and tissues vary in the amount of radiation they can tolerate and the amount of radiation required to initiate change. As outlined by Titus C. Evans, criteria for radiosensitivity are:

1) the median effective dose
2) the threshold dose required to produce injury
3) the dose needed for 100 per cent lethality
4) the time required for injury after irradiation
5) the duration and extent of injury.

Our knowledge of the cellular unit, what it affects, how it is affected, is only as valuable as is our ability to relate this knowledge to the service of man. Here at M. D. Anderson Hospital, we are especially concerned with applying this information to the treatment of the cancer patient. Proper treatment to the cancer patient could not be accomplished until absorbed doses of ionizing radiation could be accurately determined. Louis Harold Gray, this year's recipient of the Bertner Award, participated in the development of a fundamental theory for determining the dosage of radiation which is now known as the Bragg-Gray Law. His interest in, and experiments with oxygen tension in the tissues led to the first clinical trial of high oxygen pressure in radiotherapy.

The late Leonard Grimmet with the head of the Radiotherapy Section at our institution, Gilbert Fletcher, pioneered the development of supervoltage teletherapy units using radioactive isotopes. As a result, supervoltage radiation therapy was made available for the first time at the community level. The advantages of megavoltage therapy for many types of cancer are well documented; however, we are unable to explain why certain other types remain radioresistant. Perhaps when we fully understand the biological and biochemical modifications that occur in an irradiated cell, we shall be able to increase the radiosensitivity of resistant tumors. Certainly no other known agent or chemical applied at the cellular level has been so effective in its selective action of retarding or destroying the cancer cell.

We have acquired much pertinent information in the short period of time since Bergonié and Tribondeau formulated their law, yet many fundamental questions concerning radiation effects remain to be answered:

- How can a latent leukemogenic "virus" be activated?
- How can we determine relative radiosensitivity under various conditions?
- Why do some cells repair themselves after irradiation, while others fail to do so and then propagate their defect?
- What physiochemical processes take place within the cell before lesions become visible?
- How can we influence the recovery processes and re-establish balanced physiological status after irradiation?
- What is the specific dose level at which hematological damage, leukemia induction, shortened life span, genetic, and other injurious effects occur?
- What is the process by which radiation produces effects that lead to malignant change in the cell?

The answers to these questions, while essential to the better understanding of and improvement in the treatment of patients with cancer, assume great significance to all living things in this age of atomic energy and of man's ventures into the profound radiation hazards of space travel.

Most certainly the problems that perplex us now will be solved. It is hoped that cellular radiation research will ultimately lead to: understanding the biological control in cancer therapy; controlling radiation injury resulting from accidental radiation exposure; and determining the types and the amount of genetic damage caused by various types of ionizing radiation. The welfare of future generations is involved, and for that matter, the continuation of the human race and life upon this earth may well depend on the understanding of radiation effects. We must never cease to look beyond, to question, and to search.

BERTNER FOUNDATION AWARD LECTURE

Radiation Biology and Cancer

L. H. Gray

British Empire Cancer Campaign Research Unit in Radiobiology, Mount Vernon Hospital, Northwood, Middlesex, England

In choosing "Radiation Biology and Cancer" as the title of the Bertner Foundation Lecture, I had in mind not only that one special purpose of this lecture is to honor the name of the former Acting Director of The University of Texas M. D. Anderson Hospital and Tumor Institute and the first President of the Texas Medical Center, but also that the title might symbolize the subject matter of the whole symposium.

My subject falls naturally into two parts, and I propose first to say what answer I, myself, would give to the question:

What Has Radiation Biology to Say Concerning the Treatment of Cancer?

The radiotherapist is faced by a person and not by a mass of tissue. Inevitably, therefore, many of his decisions are in fact value judgments, but in as far as he wishes to base his treatment on scientific principles, I think he will not go far wrong by assuming that his objective is no less than to destroy the reproductive integrity of *all* the tumor cells, and that under irradiation these will behave in accordance with the information which can be derived either by the in vitro methods of Puck (1959) or by the in vivo methods of Hewitt (1958).

The number of reproductive cells actually present in the tumor (even in an animal tumor) is usually unknown at the present time. Hewitt's methods can, in principle, be used to evaluate this number, and I hope that in due course this will become practicable in more cases than at present; but in the meantime, the methods of Mendelsohn (1962a, b) are capable of giving us a useful guide.

It may well be that, more frequently than we think, a small proportion of cells of an irradiated tumor retains reproductive integrity even when no local recurrence is observed within a period of, say, five years. Suit and

Shalek (1963a, b) contemplate the possibility that 10, or even 100, cells may have retained reproductive integrity in apparently cured tumors, although their experimental data for the doses needed to control 50 per cent of tumors grown from first generation isotransplants of a C3H mammary adenocarcinoma or the spontaneous tumors themselves, irradiated under anoxia, agree rather exactly with Hewitt and Wilson's original survival curve (see Hewitt, 1963) for a murine leukemia (now known to hold for tumors in seven different strains of animal) if it is assumed that a single surviving cell will in general regenerate the tumor. Such caution is commendable in the present state of ignorance of (1) the total number of cells having reproductive integrity in the original tumor, and (2) the chances that a single isolated cell which retains reproductive integrity and remains among the debris of an irradiated tumor would be able to continue active proliferation within a given period of time. Even should it turn out that as many as 100 cells do not constitute a serious recurrence hazard within a period of five years, the estimated single-exposure sterilizing x-ray dose for the tumor will only be reduced by about 500 r if adequate steps have been taken to secure full aeration of the tumor cells at the time of irradiation. Radiobiologically, we would expect tumors composed of cells with a long intermitotic time to regress slowly, and those composed of cells with short intermitotic times (in which the cells which have lost reproductive integrity immediately lyse or are phagocytosed) to regress rapidly. This distinction may be important, not only, to avoid premature depression and some ill-advised "remedial" action on the part of the radiotherapist, but also because it may be undesirable to make a tumor melt away too quickly.

Within the last decade we have come to recognize anoxia as one factor which may depress the curability of a tumor to a clinically significant degree. While there were still many lacunae in the experimental evidence, Churchill-Davidson boldly accepted the thesis and, as you know, has been treating patients for many years with high pressure oxygen as an adjunct to radiotherapy. Others have followed suit. I confess to being very impressed by the clinical results which have been obtained (Churchill-Davidson *et al.*). Although I am in no position to pass critical judgment on these clinical results I regard the radiobiological evidence on the existence of anoxic cells in animal tumors to be as unequivocable and as dependable a guide to clinical practice as radiobiological evidence can ever be.

Perhaps the most direct evidence comes from the application of Hewitt's technique, whereby the proportion of cells composing a tumor may be assayed for reproductive integrity—the very quantity we are interested in—by isogenic transplantation, provided the cells can be extracted from the original host and obtained as a single cell suspension without gross cellular trauma (minimal trauma is automatically allowed for by Hewitt's technique). Powers and Tolmach (1963) have arrived in this way at an estimate of 1 per cent for the proportion of anoxic cells in a solid growing murine lymphosarcoma.

Before discussing the observations of Powers and Tolmach, I would like to emphasize that none of the tumors which Hewitt examined after irradiating *in situ*, showed any evidence of a "resistant fraction" of the cell population. He has published (Hewitt, 1963) a survival curve for a leukemia irradiated as an ascites in the peritoneal cavity—a situation which we know to be nearly anoxic when the ascites is well advanced (Deschner and Gray, 1959)—which is linear right down to surviving fractions of 10^{-7} and in which the curvature below 10^{-7}, if any, must be downward rather than upward.

The survival curve obtained by Powers and Tolmach is, in my view, sufficiently important to warrant reproduction in this volume (Figure 1). It is for a solid growing lymphosarcoma irradiated *in situ*, in the living animal breathing air. Immediately after irradiation the tumor was excised. A single cell suspension was obtained, and the proportion of survivors was assayed by Hewitt's method. It is evident that the survival curve breaks into two segments having a 2.5:1 difference in slope. Not only do the slopes agree with the slopes of survival curves obtained when the cells were irradiated in vitro under aerobic and anaerobic conditions, respectively, but the possibility that the smaller slope corresponded to cells of an intrinsically lower sensitivity was removed when it was shown that if some of those cells which survived a heavy irradiation were used to grow a second tumor and if this tumor were irradiated and analyzed in the same way, the survival curve was again found to be composed of two segments representing populations of cells differing by a factor of 2.5 in sensitivity. The experiment leaves no doubt about the fact that anoxic cells normally exist in this tumor to the extent of about 1 per cent of the tumor cell population. In subsequent experiments, Powers and Tolmach were able to reduce the proportion of

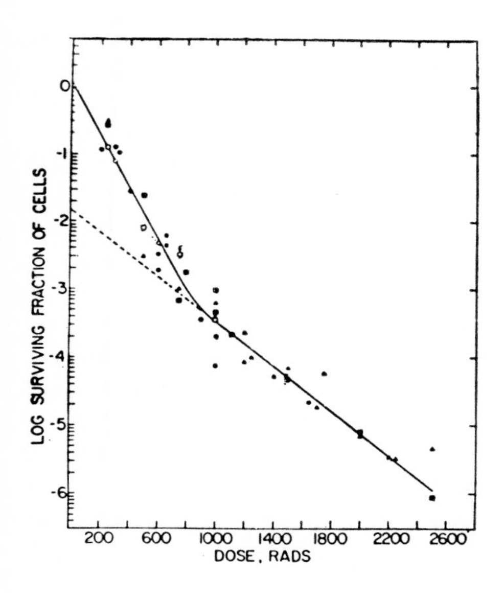

FIGURE 1. Survival of 6C3HED mouse lymphosarcoma cells irradiated in vivo. The curve has been fitted by eye. Each symbol refers to a separate experiment. Each point involved determination of the number of cells required to produce tumors in 50 per cent of 30 mice, using the end-point dilution method of Hewitt (1959). This number for unirradiated cells was generally in the range 2 to 5 cells. The arrows indicate minimum values. (Reproduced from Powers and Tolmach, 1963.)

anoxic cells by a factor of about 10 by the administration of oxygen to the animal. Their experiments thus provide rather direct evidence (1) of the existence of anoxic cells in the tumor when the mouse is breathing air, and (2) of the value of the administration of oxygen at three atmospheres pressure to a mouse during irradiation, thereby confirming and illuminating the observations of workers who have used mice or rats (Thomlinson, 1960) as their experimental animals.

On numerous occasions, from Hollcroft, Lorenz, and Matthews (1952) and Scott (in Gray *et al.*, 1953; Scott, 1963) onwards, some improvement in the resolution of animal tumors has been obtained by the use of oxygen at one atmosphere pressure. In contrast to this evidence, there is a dearth of reports that the administration of oxygen at one atmosphere pressure has been of benefit to patients. It must be remembered that many physiological factors combine to control tissue oxygen tension, some of which may be appreciably different in mouse and man.

Figure 2 shows the difference between the hemoglobin dissociation curves of man and of mouse and rat. The mouse curve, at least according to measurements which Steadman and I have made (Gray and Steadman, in preparation) at carbon dioxide tension of 40 mm Hg and pH of 7.45, (1) is shifted to the right, indicating a lower oxygen affinity; (2) has a different shape, indicating that the lesser oxygen affinity of mouse blood relative to that of man is more pronounced at low oxygen tensions; and (3) is

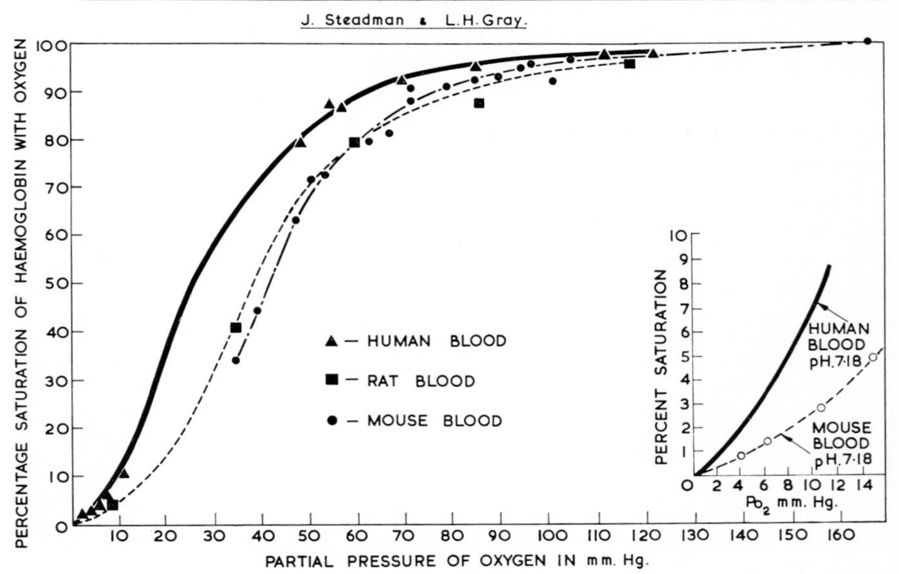

FIGURE 2. Oxyhemoglobin dissociation curves for human, mouse, and rat blood. Insert: o = Experimental observations for mouse blood at pH 7.18. (Gray and Steadman, 1964.)

such that the blood of a mouse would be significantly less completely saturated (at 40 mm Hg CO_2 and at pH 7.45) than human blood at an oxygen tension of 100 mm Hg (alveolar tension for a man breathing air). These differences would seem to be in a direction likely to make it easier to raise the tissue oxygen tension of a mouse by the administration of oxygen at one atmosphere pressure than it would be in the case of a man.

In view of current research into the relation between the structure and function of hemoglobin (Benesch, 1963), it is conceivable that it may become possible to change the shape of the dissociation curve reversibly, for the duration of each radiation treatment, in favor of an increase in tissue oxygen tension when the patient is breathing oxygen at one atmosphere pressure. It might be advantageous to depress the oxygen affinity of the blood. There would be no difficulty in saturating the hemoglobin since the alveolar tension can easily be raised from, say, 100 to 700 mm Hg. Unless there are healthy tissues of the body normally at an oxygen tension low enough to be comparable with the Michaelis constant for the cytochrome oxidase of the respiring cells, this elevation in arterial tension will not affect the total consumption, but, on account of the decreased oxygen affinity, the oxygen will be off-loaded at a higher tension.

Simple acidity is a way of achieving this. Perhaps it should be tried, but I fear it might introduce compensatory changes so that no net increase in oxygen tension would result.

Since cancer patients commonly have low hemoglobin values at the time of admission, one practical step, which as far as I know has never been tested systematically, would be to administer a blood transfusion in such cases immediately before irradiation, *i.e.* at an interval insufficient for the readjustment of the pattern of necrosis.

You will recall that, even in the mouse, Powers and Tolmach observed only a tenfold reduction in the percentage of anoxic cells as a result of administering oxygen at three atmospheres pressure for a brief period before and during irradiation. Their mice were anesthetized. This, and the fact that the pretreatment period was only five minutes in oxygen at atmospheric pressure followed by 10 minutes in oxygen at three atmospheres pressure, may have restricted the rise in tissue oxygen tension to values below those which might otherwise have been achieved. In the meantime, useful information has been contributed by the experiments of Du Sault (1963). These data clearly show that, in the case of mice, there are great advantages in adding 5 per cent carbon dioxide to oxygen at one atmosphere pressure. Indeed, when only comparatively short preconditioning periods were employed, the cure rate actually observed by Du Sault with the oxygen/carbon dioxide mixture at one atmosphere pressure were nearly as good as those produced by the administration of oxygen at 45 pounds per square inch gauge pressure. This point deserves a fuller investigation.

A skeptical radiotherapist will ask about the effect of hyperbaric oxygen on the reaction of normal tissues. The answer must, of course, depend on which tissues he has in mind and on the degree of damage, *i.e.* on the dose. If it is skin, and if desquamation is the measure of damage, then the experimental answer seems to be that in mice the dose enhancement factor lies between 1.25 and 1.35 for a dose of 1,600 rads delivered in oxygen at three atmospheres pressure. I say this in the light of an extensive investigation (Withers, in preparation) involving some 168 animals, in which Withers has compared the desquamation produced on the thighs of mice by 250 kv X rays delivered at the end of 10 minutes pre-treatment time, during which some groups of mice were breathing air while others (unanesthetized) were breathing oxygen at three atmospheres pressure. The dose delivered to the animals breathing oxygen was, 1,600 r, and that to groups of animals breathing air was varied until the skin reaction matched that of the oxygen group. The average value, say 1.3, of the factor which they have observed is just a little lower than the figure arrived at by Chase and Hunt in our laboratory of years ago (1959) for damage to the pigment cells at the base of the hair follicles in mice when air and oxygen at two atmospheres pressure were compared. In other tissues, quite other factors have been observed —or would be expected to be observed.

On the basis of the observations of Hewitt and Wilson (1959), it would seem that the liver of a mouse is normally well oxygenated. The cells of the bone marrow, which determine the hemopoietic death of a mouse, also seem to be at approximately their maximum sensitivity when the animal is breathing air. At the other extreme, the mature sperm, either of *Drosophila* or the mouse, seem normally to be almost completely anoxic and therefore capable of as much elevation in sensitivity as tumor cells would be. One of the most important tissues clinically is probably cartilage, which is subject to an elevation in sensitivity which, though not accurately known, seems to be considerable.

The purpose of Figure 3—an old curve but with new data—is to remind ourselves that the oxygen tensions with which we are chiefly concerned lie in the range 0 to 20 mm Hg.

The sensitivity measurements shown in this figure are based on the scores of abnormal anaphases, which were determined by Miss Hawes (Hawes, Howard, and Gray, in preparation). The data are more extensive and allow for possible artifacts which might have been present in the earlier measurements which Deschner and I made (Deschner and Gray, 1959)—without, however, changing K_{O_2} to a greater extent than from five to four micromoles per liter. The new data also confirm that this quantity is, as nearly as we can determine, independent of temperature. Since respiration measurements for the same cells have become available in the interval (Froese, 1962), I have shown them on the same figure so that you can see that a cell may be radiobiologically insensitive at an oxygen tension at which respiration is proceeding at almost maximum rate. The oxygen tension of a tissue can in fact be judged approximately if it is possible to determine the ratio of the normal to the maximum and minimum sensitivities

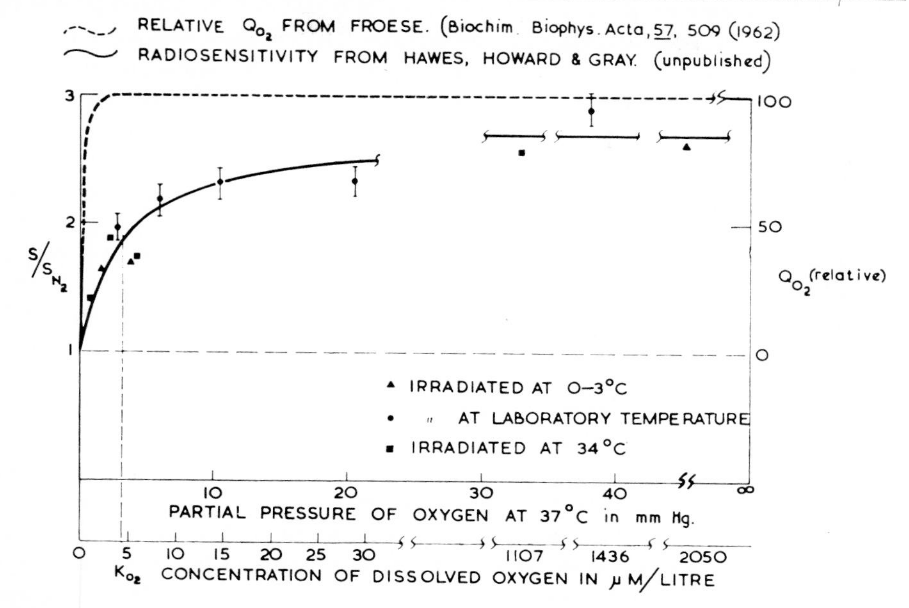

FIGURE 3. Radiosensitivity and respiration of Ehrlich ascites tumor cells as a function of oxygen concentration at the temperature indicated against the experimental points, and of oxygen tension at 37 °C. ⌒ = Respiration as a percentage of that when oxygen is abundant (right hand ordinate). (Redrawn from Froese, 1962.) ∼ = Radiosensitivity defined as the reciprocal of the dose required to produce a given percentage of abnormal anaphase figures at the first mitosis after irradiation. (Hawes, Howard, and Gray, In preparation).

which may be induced by varying the oxygen content of the blood.

The purpose of oxygen administration is to eliminate the obstacle arising out of the existence of anoxic foci in tumors. It does not in itself provide the favorable therapeutic ratio as between damage to malignant and healthy tissue which we desire. The radiation response of proliferating normal tissues, under in vivo conditions, has as yet been comparatively little explored (Till, 1963). Such data as we have suggest that the transformation to a malignant state has little effect on the vulnerability of the proliferative capacity of a cell. If, in order to cure a tumor, we deliver a single dose sufficient to reduce the surviving fraction of aerobic cells to 10^{-12}, we must expect a comparable surviving fraction among any proliferating normal cells which are exposed to the same dose. This would not be tolerated, as far as I know, on any considerable scale by any "cell renewal system" of the body (Patt and Quastler, 1963). Under the term "proliferating cell" I include not only the cells which are normally in constant proliferation, but also those which may be called upon to proliferate in an irradiated tissue in order to restore the organism to a healthy condition. I have in mind, for instance, cells composing the blood capillaries.

As the possibilities inherent in an appropriate fractionation of the dose have been rather fully discussed by Till (1963) and others, and as I have no new data to add, I will only suggest that we press on in the belief that fractionation *is* important and that it is therefore worthwhile trying to find ways of raising oxygen tension which could be used routinely and repeatedly when a favorable fractionation scheme has been devised.

What Has Radiation Biology to Say about Carcinogenesis?

Descriptively, radiobiology has contributed many facts of the utmost practical importance. The large number of x-ray martyrs during the first quarter of the century, the small but significant number of dial painters who died of cancer as a result of their occupational hazard during the first world war, and the infinitesimal proportion of those exposed to radiation hazards who have developed cancer as a result of exposure since the beginning of the second world war is a diminishing series of numbers which pays tribute to our increasing understanding of radiation carcinogenesis as an occupational hazard. Nevertheless, the mass of empirical data which has been accumulated has not, as far as I know, yielded to a definitive analysis in terms of mechanism.

Theories of carcinogenesis abound, and I do not propose to bore you with one more nor shall I attempt a review of radiation carcinogenesis. Good ones already exist (Glucksman, Lamerton, and Mayneord, 1957; Furth and Lorenz, 1954; Upton, 1959). I would like only to ruminate upon some of the older work and to draw attention to one or two recent experiments which appear to provide definitive evidence on important points.

For the purpose of discussion, I shall take it as agreed that most cancers are clones derived from a single cell which has undergone the full transformation from the normal to the malignant state. Although many examples of this are on record, it is perhaps worth reminding ourselves of some recent evidence on this point, provided by Wakonig-Vaartaja (1962).

In the table beneath Figure 4, you will see that, out of 168 analyzable cells from a human adenocarcinoma of the corpus uteri, all but one contained the long marker chromosome shown in the metaphase and anaphase photographs reproduced in the figure. I find this evidence very impressive. Wakonig-Vaartaja points out that most of the cells had the normal number (46) of chromosomes, in agreement with her own previous conclusion that the abnormal chromosome numbers which are often, but by no means invariably, found in human and animal tumors are to be regarded as a consequence, and not as a cause, of the neoplasia.

While it would be generally agreed that experiments such as those of Kaplan (1952) clearly demonstrate that whole-body irradiation may induce tumors in unirradiated tissue, it has often been debated whether the trans-

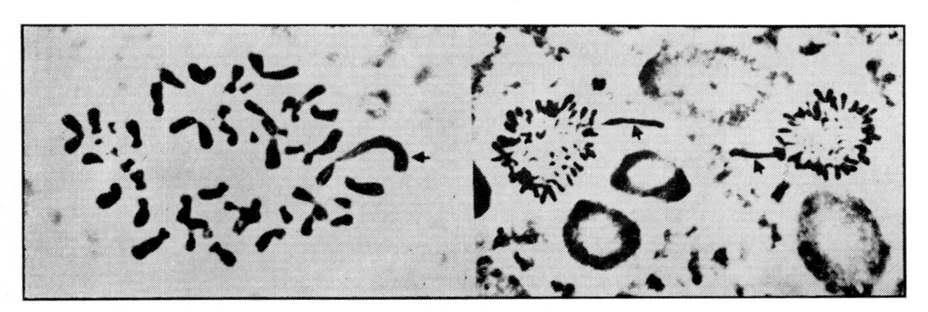

Metaphase with Marker (2n = 46) Anaphase with Two Markers

FIGURE 4. Frequency of occurrence of the marker (= identifiable) chromosome in the cells from a human adenocarcinoma of the corpus uteri. (From R. Wakonig-Vaartaja, 1962.)

MATERIAL	TOTAL NUMBER OF CELLS	MARKER PRESENT
Metaphase	38	37
Anaphase-telophases	130	130
Total	168	167

formation of a given cell from a normal, to a malignant condition can be provoked by the energy of ionizing radiation deposited in the cell itself. It seems to me that an answer comes from the experiments of Baserga, Lisco, and Kisieleski (1962), who have obtained tumors by a single injection of tritiated thymidine. An injection of about 1 μc/g of body weight at a specific activity of 360 μc/mmole to newborn animals seems to be very effective. They obtained a greater variety of tumors in the experimental animals than in the controls. Since they scored the percentages of tumors seen in control and irradiated animals of the same age, an artifact which could have arisen through the influence of longevity was eliminated. The authors ran an "inactive" thymidine as well as saline controls, to make sure that the modifications in tumor incidence which they observed were, in fact, caused by the radioactivity. A statistically significant yield of tumors was also observed by the administration of C^{14} thymidine, but I prefer to concentrate on the tritiated thymidine experiment. I think we can safely neglect the whole-body dose of about 0.2 rad, which may have been delivered during the interval before the thymidine was incorporated into deoxyribonucleic acid (DNA). Tritiated thymidine in the amount of 0.1 μc/g of body weight was uniformly ineffective; 10 μc/g of body weight was hardly more effective than was 1 μc/g of body weight. Six injections of 1.7 μc/g of body weight, spaced over eight days, seemed to be the most effective regimen of those tested.

Although a "metabolic" DNA has been postulated (see Pelc, 1958; Pelc and Gahan, 1959), many hold strongly that thymidine is solely incorporated into the DNA of cells which are preparing for division (see Baserga and Kisieleski, 1962). Since the purpose of such cell proliferation in a normal adult is to keep pace with loss, it might appear to be a problem to see how cells which had incorporated tritium, and in which the carcinogenic process was proceeding, failed to be shed from the body or destroyed in some way (e.g. skin, intestine, or the lymphocytes). It therefore seems of great interest that a number of authors, including Messier and Leblond (1960) and the late Henry Quastler, in collaboration with Lipkin, noticed that occasional cells which had incorporated thymidine remained in the body long after the time when they would normally have been sloughed off. Lipkin and Quastler's original observations referred to the intestinal tract of mice, rats, and frogs (Lipkin and Quastler, 1962), in which isolated labeled cells were seen along almost the whole length of the intestine. They were never seen, however, in the duodenum where cancer rarely, if ever, occurs. These data have been confirmed by Deschner, who tells me she finds a similar interesting correlation with the cancer-free sites for the intestinal tract in hamsters (Deschner, Personal communication).

Returning to consideration of the induction of tumors by tritiated thymidine, the dose rate distribution is very relevant. This is a quantity which is notoriously difficult to calculate. Figure 5 shows the best estimates which my colleague, F. S. Stewart, and I have been able to make and is based on the following parameters: Administered dose 30 μc of 360 mc/mmole to mice weighing 30 g. Thymidine pool = 50 μg (Baserga and Kisieleski, 1962). Administration is at the beginning of S, and the tritiated thymidine remains at full strength for the duration of S, so that the mass of tritiated thymidine incorporated per nucleus is a quarter of the mass of DNA per nucleus, *i.e.* 1.5×10^{-12} g. Nuclear radius = 3 μ.

The estimated maximum dose rate at the center of the nucleus is large, but the value shown in the figure is probably an overestimate. The data upon which it was based were deliberately chosen to give an estimate of the largest conceivable dose rate in and around the nucleus of a cell which completes one round of synthesis entirely in the presence of thymidine which has retained its full activity. Both the absolute values and the shape of the curve agree rather closely with the calculations of Goodheart (1961), although Stewart's theoretical treatment differs from Goodheart's. Each cell which incorporates thymidine thus irradiates itself and, allowing for the possible eccentric position of the nucleus, one neighboring cell. It is inconceivable that it should irradiate several of its various neighbors since the maximum range of the beta particle is only about 5 μ. We can conceive of the possibility that in some rapidly proliferating zone of certain organs about half of all the cells might be in some part of S while the circulating thymidine is active, but I would regard this as a very special case. In many cell renewal systems (e.g. skin and liver in which tumors arise), only a very small proportion of the cells are in S at any one time. Moreover, the authors found no very great difference between the yield of tumors in mice irradiated when newborn or at 2, 6, or 12 months of age. Various organs must have been of very different size and stage of development at these times. I therefore do not think we can reasonably ascribe all the tumors obtained by the administration of tritiated thymidine to generalized damage in organs which are not necessarily the ones in which the tumors arose. A specific action of the radiation on the cell from which the tumor arose seems to me to be indicated. This action alone need not, of course, establish complete independence of homeostatic control. Since tumors arise in controls, especially later in life, a biological mechanism must exist independently of the irradiation which is capable of effecting the transformation from a normal to a malignant condition. The chance of this happening may be the product of the probabilities that a number of

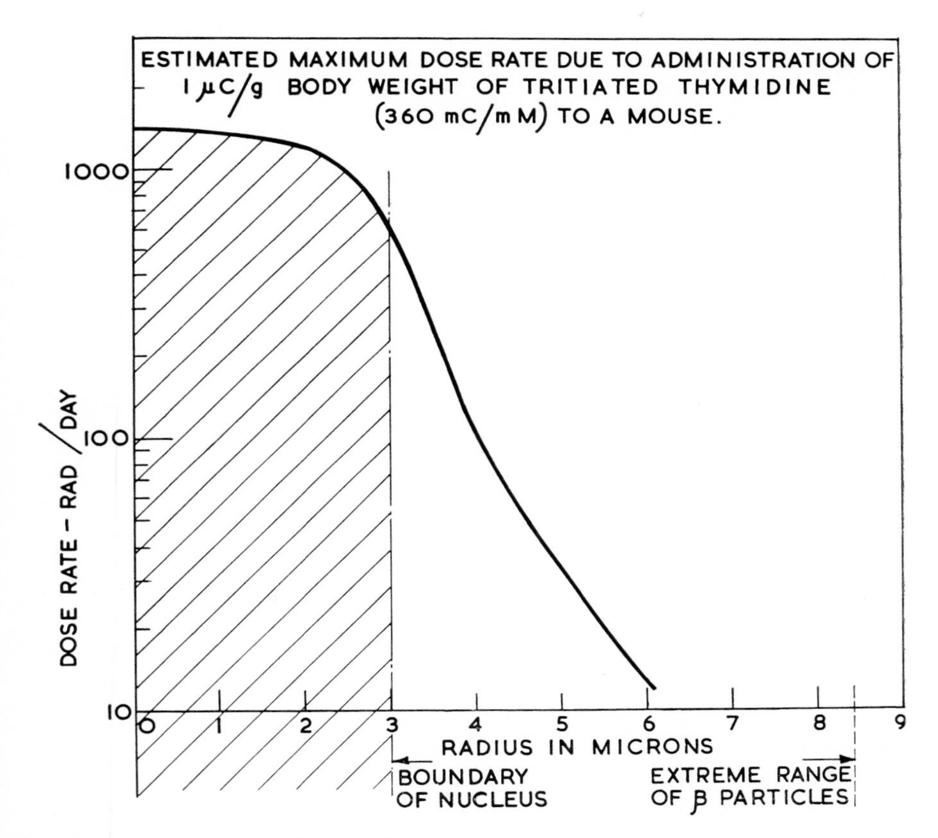

FIGURE 5. Estimated upper limit of dose rate due to tritium incorporated in DNA under conditions of the experiment by Baserga, Lisco, and Kisieleski (1962) (Stewart, Personal communication). Ordinate: Dose rate in rads per day. Abscissa: Distance in microns from the center of the nucleus.

unusual events happen, and one or more of these events may be of such a nature that it can be brought about by ionizing radiation. The irradiation may increase the number of cells "at risk" to the full transformation (e.g. by inducing in them the right kind of genetic defect), or, it may shorten the time required for the completion of the transformation because this has been partly accomplished by radiation damage within the cell.

Survival of the Induced Cell

The existence of a detectable tumor has necessarily involved extensive proliferation of the fully transformed cell. Hence, whatever sequence of changes has taken place in the course of the transformation, the changes must have been such as to leave the cell capable of indefinite proliferation, *i.e.* with full reproductive integrity.

In looking through the literature for evidence of the manner in which tumors are induced by radiation, I was struck by the frequency with which it has been noted that radiation *decreases* the yield below the so-called "spontaneous" level. Thus, Nowell and Cole (1959) comment on the fact that, after whole-body irradiation with either neutron or X-radiation, they observed a decrease in the incidence of those tumors which arose spontaneously with fairly high frequency, e.g. pulmonary adenomas, leukemias, and miscellaneous sarcomas. Of course, account must be taken of the fact that generally an irradiated animal will die earlier than a control animal, but they were of the opinion that the observed decrease in lymphoma incidence, for example from 22 per cent to 9 per cent as a result of exposure to a dose of between 300 and 600 rads of neutrons, could not be ascribed to this cause.

I thought it might be of interest to analyze some of the experimental data in detail from this point of view. I chose a curve published by Upton *et al.* (see Upton, 1961) for the induction of myeloid leukemia by a single dose of whole-body X-radiation. The experimental data (not shown in Figure 6) are fairly complete at the low as well as at the higher doses.

Knowing that most survival curves have rather flat shoulders, *i.e.* little killing at very low doses, I proceeded by assuming that the part of the experimental curve (Figure 6, solid line) between 0 and 150 r might be used to define the dose relation for the induction processes. The extrapolation of this curve to higher doses is shown as an interrupted line. By comparing it with the observed incidence one can infer, at any given dose, the probability that an induced cell will survive (broken line and insert). It seemed remarkable to me that the survival curve derived in this way should so closely resemble the curves with which we are all familiar. In this case I found $n = 3$ and $D_0 = 120$ r. The points shown in the insert diagram are the ratios of the experimentally observed numbers of animals with tumors to the number given by the assumed curve for the induction process (referred to above). If, alternatively, we read survival figures off the curve shown as a broken line in the insert, we obtain either the full or open squares of the main diagram, according to whether we do or do not assume that the survival function should operate on the spontaneous as well as the radiation-induced tumors. The difference is small. In a figure published elsewhere by Upton (1959), he attempted to correct the full line of Figure 6 for the shortening of lifespan which resulted from deaths other than leukemia attributable to the radiation. I did not consider it worthwhile to recalculate my curves on this ac-

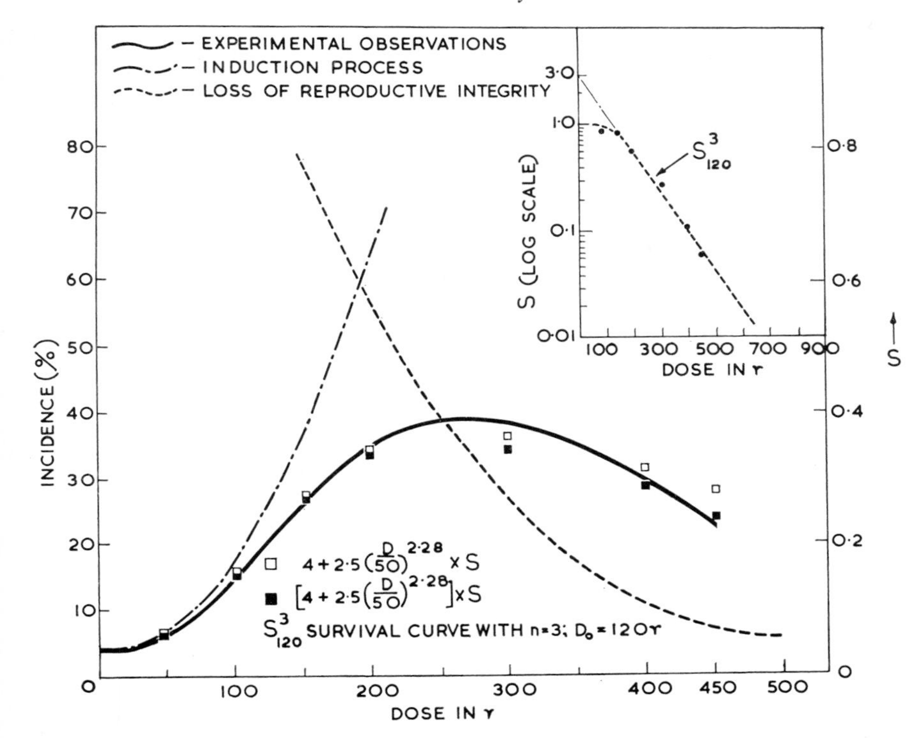

FIGURE 6. Dose response relations for the induction of myeloid leukemia. (Experimental curve redrawn from Upton, 1961; calculated curves from Gray, Unpublished data.)

count. It would not change the shape of the survival curve appreciably but would only increase the estimate of D_0 somewhat. The shape of the curve which I have derived for S does, of course, depend on the validity of my extrapolation of the function

$$I = 4 + 2.5 \left(\frac{T}{50}\right)^{2.28}$$

to doses higher than 150 r.

Another demonstration of the apparent killing of potential tumor cells by radiation is provided by the experiments of Foley and Cole (1963) who found that a whole-body dose of 880 r reduced the yield of urethan-induced lung tumors by a factor of about 50.

The number of animals with tumors in both the unirradiated and irradiated groups (Table 1) accords fairly closely with a random distribution of the total number of tumors among the total number of animals, as we should expect if each induced cell responds to radiation independently.

Since the carcinogenic action of urethan in producing lung tumors is believed to be by way of some interference with DNA synthesis (Rogers, 1957), and radiation itself interferes with DNA synthesis, it is, in principle, possible that the effect of irradiation in suppressing the induction of tumors

TABLE 1

Inhibition of Urethan Pulmonary Tumor Induction in Mice by 880 rad Whole-Body Irradiation

Treatment	No. of mice in group	No. of mice with tumor	Total tumors	Tumors relative to urethan only
None	9	0	0	0
X only	10	1	1	0.012
U only	16	16	89	1.00
U + X at 3 hours	15	2	2	0.02_2
U + X at 24 hours	15	2	2	0.02_2
U + X at 1 week	15	8	12	0.13_5
X + U at 3 hours	15	3	4	0.04_5

Abbreviations: X = 880 rads of 250 kvp X rays 0.5 mm Cu + 1 mm Al filter; U = Urethan: ethyl carbamate (U.S.P.) 1 mg/g body weight. (After Foley and Cole, 1963.)

by urethan is not a matter of cell survival as I have suggested. Though this possibility must be granted, I believe cell killing is the more likely explanation.

If tumor incidence is represented (Figure 7) by the product of a power law of induction and a survival function, which I write $S^n_{D_0}$, then in the simplest case of n = 1, the maximum incidence occurs when the differential coefficient of $D^N e^{-D}/_{D_0} = 0$, *i.e.* when $D = N\ D_0$. If n is not equal to 1, our ignorance of the exact shape of the shoulder of the survival curve makes an accurate evaluation of the general case impossible, but it will almost always happen that, unless n is very large indeed, $N\ D_0$ corresponds to a point on the linear part of the survival curve which is given by $S = NE^{-D}/_{D_0}$, so that the *yield* of tumors is increased by a factor equal to the extrapolation number, but the maximum still occurs when $D = N\ D_0$. It is perhaps worth noting that a protective agent which affects incidence and survival equally would leave the height of the maximum unchanged but move its position to a higher absolute dose. In an experiment in radiation carcinogenesis, carried

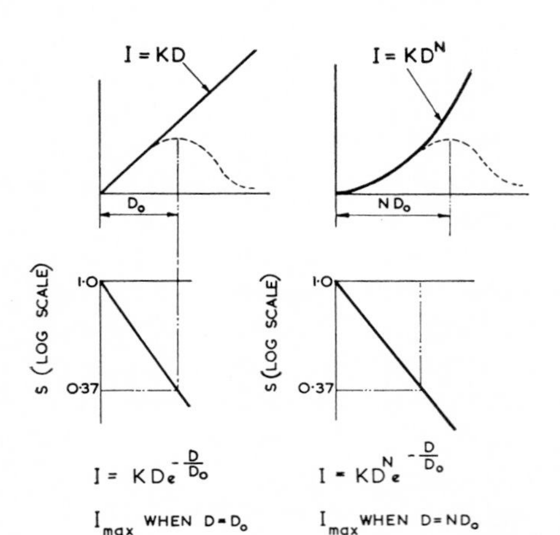

FIGURE 7. Types of dose-response relation for tumor incidence.

out in our laboratories during the past two or three years, anoxia appeared to reduce papilloma incidence, but the results were on the borderline of significance. In undertaking this experiment I had in mind that, in eliciting skin tumors, a strictly local irradiation might be called upon to serve two functions, which we may broadly call initiation and promotion, and that these two functions might be separated by the employment of an independent promoting agent. Croton oil (a well-known chemical cocarcinogen) was chosen because Shubick and co-workers (Shubick, Goldfarb, Ritchie, and Lisco, 1953) had obtained a good yield of papillomas by painting irradiated skin twice weekly with croton oil, whereas virtually no tumors had been obtained in similar circumstances, either by the radiation alone or by croton oil alone. Shubick and associates exposed small areas of skin to about 800 rads* of thallium beta rays delivered in the period of an hour.

We (Hawes, Boag, and Gray, Unpublished data) used very high dose rates (pulsed). The croton oil was kindly supplied by Dr. Shubick.

In the first experiment we used the range of doses shown in Table 2 because it was my hope that we should define a dose-response curve. For technical reasons the skin was rendered almost anoxic by suction during the irradiation, and control skin on the opposite flank was similarly treated.

TABLE 2

Papilloma Induction by Irradiation Followed by Croton Oil

	Irradiated flank 1.8 Mev electrons + croton oil twice weekly				
Control flank Croton oil twice weekly	Dose (rad)	Papillomas arising in nearly anoxic skin (1.3 cm²)		Papillomas arising in aerobic skin (1.3 cm²)	
	200	2/18			
	400	0/10			
4/63 = 0.06			Mean 0.09		
	600	3/16			
	800	1/19			
	Second Experiment				
2/28 = 0.07	800	2/25 = 0.05		8/25 = 0.3	p = 0.06 relative to controls

Abbreviation: p = probability. (Hawes, Boag, and Gray, Unpublished data.)

Since we obtained no papillomas attributable to the irradiation, we repeated the 800 rad exposure to skin which was either open to the air or had oxygen flowing gently over it. A small number of papillomas attributable to the radiation were obtained, but the difference between the number on the ir-

* It was subsequently noticed that the applicator was not uniformly loaded, with the result that the dose rate at some points will have been much higher and that at others correspondingly lower than the mean value quoted above (Shubick, Personal communication).

radiated side and control side was on the borderline of significance. The result is therefore equivocal without additional data.

It seems to be of considerable interest to know whether, in particular circumstances, irradiation can suppress tumor incidence in accordance with survival kinetics for the following reason.

We know that forms of chromosome structural damage which are lethal to the cell may be induced by radiation delivered when a cell is in a nonproliferating stage, provided that proliferation is subsequently induced. For example, Bender and Gooch (1963) saw about the same amount of chromosome damage in lymphocytes which had been irradiated as they occurred in a sample of circulating blood and subsequently induced to divide by the phytohemoglutanin technique, as in, say, a culture of human kidney or skin cells irradiated in vitro. Or again, a considerable amount of chromosome structural damage is seen in liver cells brought into division by a partial hepatectomy performed months after the irradiation (Stevenson and Curtis, 1961; Curtis and Crowley, 1963).

It is therefore not surprising that Foley and Cole (Table 1) observed that irradiation was about equally effective in suppressing urethan-induced tumors when given shortly before, or up to 24 hours after, the urethan treatment. The fact that irradiation was found to be somewhat less effective when given one week after the urethan treatment would receive a natural explanation if the urethan acted quickly enough for two or three cycles of cell division to have taken place in the induced or potential cancer cells in the interval before irradiation.

If irradiation is itself the carcinogenic agent, or if a tissue is irradiated virtually simultaneously with the application of a carcinogen such as urethan, it would seem that the yield of tumors must inevitably be reduced in accordance with cell survival kinetics; but if the carcinogenic factor is applied or arises after irradiation at an interval long enough for a cell division to have intervened, then two possibilities exist: 1. Only a finite number of potential tumor cells exist at any one time upon which the carcinogen can act, e.g. only those cells which already have a certain genetic defect. 2. All cells can be considered as "at risk" and the carcinogen acts with a probability dependent only on the type of cell and its phase of development in relation to mitosis and differentiation. In the second case, a mitosis following irradiation will clear away most, if not all, of the lethal injuries induced by the radiation. The proliferation of neighbors will make good the actual loss of tissues which has been caused by the irradiation, and there should remain the same number of cells at risk to the action of the carcinogenic factor. Hence, in this case, the irradition would not be expected to have reduced the yield of tumors.

It is appropriate that I should end on a note of uncertainty. To do otherwise would be almost immodest when discussing a subject which poses some very elementary questions which the best radiobiological intellects collectively have so far failed to answer.

ACKNOWLEDGMENTS

I would like to acknowledge the help I have received from all my colleagues at the R.U.R., more especially Dr. Scott and Dr. Hewitt, who have both thought deeply about their first-hand experience of cancer in man and experimental animals. I am grateful to Dr. Boag for examining the rigor with which certain concepts can be held to be consistent with the facts, and to Dr. Withers for allowing me to present some of his unpublished data.

REFERENCES

Baserga, R., H. Lisco, and W. Kisieleski. 1962. Further Observations on Induction of Tumors in Mice with Radioactive Thymidine. *Proceedings of the Society for Experimental Biology and Medicine*, 110:687–690.

Baserga, R., and W. E. Kisieleski. 1962. Recent Observations on Cell Proliferation and Metabolism by Radioautography with Tritiated Compounds. *Atompraxis*, 8:386–391.

Bender, M. A., and P. C. Gooch. 1963. Chromatid-Type Aberrations Induced by X-Rays in Human Leukocyte Cultures. *Cytogenetics*, 2:107–116.

Benesch, R. 1963. Some Relations between Structure and Function in Hemoglobin. *Journal of Molecular Biology*, 6:498–505.

Chase, H. B., and J. W. Hunt. 1959. "Pigment Cell Damage in Hair Follicles with Relation to X-Rays and Oxygen," *Pigment Cell Biology* (Proceedings of the Fourth Conference on the Biology of Normal and Atypical Pigment Cell Growth), M. Gordon, Ed. New York, New York: Academic Press, Inc. Pp. 537–547.

Churchill-Davidson, I., C. A. Foster, D. B. L. Skeggs, G. Wiernik, C. D. Collins, R. J. Healey, and P. R. Purser. 1964. The Place of Oxygen in Radiotherapy. (In preparation.)

Curtis, H., and C. Crowley. 1963. Chromosome Aberrations in Liver Cells in Relation to the Somatic Mutation Theory of Aging. *Radiation Research*, 19:337–344.

Deschner, E. E. Personal communication.

Deschner, E. E., and L. H. Gray. 1959. Influence of Oxygen Tension on X-Ray Induced Chromosome Damage in Ehrlich Ascites Tumor Cells Irradiated *in vitro* and *in vivo*. *Radiation Research*, 11:115–146.

Du Sault, L. A. 1963. The Effect of Oxygen on the Response of Spontaneous Tumours in Mice to Radiotherapy. *British Journal of Radiology*, 36:749–754.

Foley, W. A., and L. J. Cole. 1963. Inhibition of Urethan Lung Tumor Induction in Mice by Total-Body X-Radiation. *Cancer Research*, 23:1176–1180.

Froese, G. 1962. The Respiration of Ascites Tumour Cells at Low Oxygen Concentrations. *Biochimica et biophysica acta*, 57:509–519.

Furth, J., and E. Lorenz. 1954. "Carcinogenesis by Ionizing Radiations," *Radiation Biology*, A. Hollaender, Ed. New York, New York: McGraw-Hill Book Company, Inc. Vol. I. Pp. 1145–1201.

Glucksman, A., L. F. Lamerton, and W. V. Mayneord. 1957. "Carcinogenic Effects of Radiation," *Cancer*, R. W. Raven, Ed. London, England: Butterworth and Company, Ltd. Vol. I. Pp. 497–539.

Goodheart, C. R. 1961. Radiation Dose Calculation in Cells Containing Intranuclear Tritium. *Radiation Research*, 15:767–773.

Gray, L. H. Unpublished data.

Gray, L. H., A. D. Conger, M. Ebert, S. Hornsey, and O. C. A. Scott. 1953. The Concentration of Oxygen Dissolved in Tissues at the Time of Irradiation as a Factor in Radiotherapy. *British Journal of Radiology*, 26:638–648.

Gray, L. H., and J. M. Steadman. 1964. Determination of the Oxyhaemoglobin, Dissociation Curves for Mouse and Rat Blood. *The Journal of Physiology*, (in press).

Hawes, C. A., J. W. Boag, and L. H. Gray. Unpublished data.

Hawes, C. A., A. Howard, and L. H. Gray. (in preparation.)

Hewitt, H. B. 1958. Studies of the Dissemination and Quantitative Transplantation of a Lymphocytic Leukaemia of CBA Mice. *The British Journal of Cancer*, 12:378–401.

————. 1963. "Effects on Organized Systems in the Light of Cellular Radiobiology," *Radiation Effects in Physics, Chemistry and Biology*, M. Ebert and A. Howard, Eds. Amsterdam, The Netherlands: North-Holland Publishing Company. Pp. 234–252.

Hewitt, H. B., and C. W. Wilson. 1959. The Effect of Tissue Oxygen Tension on the Radiosensitivity of Leukaemia Cells Irradiated *in situ* in the Livers of Leukaemic Mice. *The British Journal of Cancer*, 13:675–684.

Hollcroft, J. W., E. Lorenz, and M. Matthews. 1952. Factors Modifying the Effect of X-Irradiation on Regression of a Transplanted Lymphosarcoma. *Journal of the National Cancer Institute*, 12:751–763.

Kaplan, H. S. 1952. Radiation-Induced Lymphoid Tumors of Mice. *Acta unio internationalis contra cancrum*, 7:849–859.

Lipkin, M., and H. Quastler. 1962. Cell Retention and Incidence of Carcinoma in Several Portions of the Gastrointestinal Tract. *Nature*, London, 194:1198–1199.

Mendelsohn, M. L. 1962a. Chronic Infusion of Tritiated Thymidine into Mice with Tumors. *Science*, 135:213–215.

————. 1962b. Autoradiographic Analysis of Cell Proliferation in Spontaneous Breast Cancer of C3H Mouse. III. The Growth Fraction. *Journal of the National Cancer Institute*, 28:1015–1029.

Messier, B., and C. P. Leblond. 1960. Cell Proliferation and Migration as Revealed by Radioautography after Injection of Thymidine-H^3 into Male Rats and Mice. *American Journal of Anatomy*, 106:247–285.

Nowell, P. C., and L. J. Cole. 1959. Late Effects of Fast Neutrons versus X-Rays in Mice: Nephrosclerosis, Tumors, Longevity. *Radiation Research*, 11:545–546.

Patt, H. M., and H. Quastler. 1963. Radiation Effects on Cell Renewal and Related Systems. *Physiological Reviews*, 43:357–396.

Pelc, S. R. 1958. Nuclear Uptake of Labelled Adenine in the Seminal Vesicle of the Mouse. *Experimental Cell Research*, 14:301–315.

Pelc, S. R., and P. B. Gahan. 1959. Incorporation of Labelled Thymidine in the Seminal Vesicle of the Mouse. *Nature*, London, 183:335–336.

Powers, W. E., and L. J. Tolmach. 1963. A Multicomponent X-Ray Survival Curve for Mouse Lymphosarcoma Cells Irradiated *in vivo*. *Nature*, London, 197:710–711.

Puck, T. T. 1959. Quantitative Studies on Mammalian Cells *in vitro*. *Reviews of Modern Physics*, 31:433–448.

Rogers, S. 1957. Studies of the Mechanism of Action of Urethane in Initiating Pulmonary Adenomas in Mice. II. Its Relation to Nucleic Acid Synthesis. *Journal of Experimental Medicine*, 105:279–306.

Scott, O. C. A. 1963. The Modification of Tissue Response to Radiation Injury. *Annual Review of Medicine*, 14:371–380.

Shubick, P. Personal communication.

Shubick, P., A. R. Goldfarb, A. C. Ritchie and H. Lisco. 1953. Latent Carcinogenic Action of Beta-Irradiation on Mouse Epidermis. *Nature*, London, 171:934–935.

Stevenson, K. G., and H. J. Curtis. 1961. Chromosomal Aberrations in Irradiated and Nitrogen Mustard-Treated Mice. *Radiation Research*, 15:774–784.

Stewart, F. S. Personal Communication.

Suit, H. D., and R. J. Shalek. 1963a. Response of Anoxic C3H Mouse Mammary Carcinoma Isotransplants (1–25mm) to X-Irradiation. *Journal of the National Cancer Institute*, 31:479–495.

———. 1963b. Response of Spontaneous Mammary Carcinoma of the C3H Mouse to X-Irradiation given under Conditions of Local Tissue Anoxia. *Journal of the National Cancer Institute*, 31:497–509.

Thomlinson, R. H. 1960. An Experimental Method for Comparing Treatments of Intact Malignant Tumours in Animals and its Application to Use of Oxygen in Radiotherapy. *The British Journal of Cancer*, 14:555–576.

Till, J. E. 1963. Quantitative Aspects of Radiation Lethality at the Cellular Level. *The American Journal of Roentgenology, Radium Therapy and Nulear Medicine*, 90:917–927.

Upton, A. C. 1959. "Studies on the Mechanism of Leukaemogenesis by Ionizing Radiation," *Ciba Foundation Symposium on Carcinogenesis: Mechanisms of Action*, G. E. W. Wolstenholme and M. O'Connor, Eds. London, England: J. and A. Churchill, Ltd. Pp. 249–273.

———. 1961. The Dose Response Relation in Radiation-Induced Cancer. *Cancer Research*, 21:717–729.

Wakonig-Vaartaja, R. 1962. A Human Tumour with Identifiable Cells as Evidence for the Mutation Theory. *The British Journal of Cancer*, 16:616–618.

Withers, H. R. 1964. The Oxygen Enhancement Factor in Response of Normal Mouse Skin to Radiation. (in preparation.)

RADIATION EFFECTS ON MACROMOLECULES

The Effects of Ultraviolet Light on Thymine, Uracil and Their Derivatives

H. E. JOHNS, M. L. PEARSON, C. W. HELLEINER, AND D. M. LOGAN

Department of Medical Biophysics, University of Toronto, Toronto, and Biochemistry Department, Dalhousie University, Halifax, Canada

It has long been known that when deoxyribonucleic acid (DNA) or ribonucleic acid (RNA) are irradiated with ultraviolet light in the range 200 to 300 mμ, the main absorption of radiation takes place in the purine and the pyrimidine bases which have peak absorption between 250 to 280 mμ. However, the main photochemical changes seem to occur only in the pyrimidines (thymine, cytosine, and uracil). Sinsheimer (1954, 1957) showed that when uracil and cytosine solutions were irradiated, a loss in optical density was observed which was reversible by acid and heat treatments. In the case of uracil, Moore (1958) was able to demonstrate that this reversible photoproduct of uracil was 5-hydro-6-hydroxyuracil (Figure 1), which was formed by the addition of water across the 5,6 double bond. This greatly reduces the absorption maximum at 262 mμ. By analogy, it is believed that the main photoproduct of cytosine is a similar hydrate, although its synthesis has not been achieved because of the extreme thermal lability of this compound (Fikus, Wierzchowski, and Shugar, 1962). Moore and Thomson (1957) and Wang (1958a, b, 1962a, b) have studied the similar hydration of 1,3-dimethyluracil, while Wierzchowski and Shugar (1959, 1961, 1962) have demonstrated hydrate formation in a variety of uracil- and cytosine-containing oligonucleotides. A definitive proof for the hydration of thymine has not yet been found.

Beukers and Berends (1961) showed that when thymine is irradiated in frozen solution, a new photoproduct is formed which is stable to both heat and acid treatment. This product is a dimer of thymine (Figure 1). In this dimer, two thymines are held together by a cyclobutane ring. Since the 5,6 double bonds in both thymines are now saturated, the dimer shows very little absorption at 267 mμ. If thymine is irradiated as a liquid, it is relatively insensitive to UV, but when frozen, it is rapidly converted to the dimer. Presumably, in frozen solution, as opposed to liquid solution, the thymine rings are stacked in such a position relative to each other that the absorption of a photon favors dimerization (Wang, 1961). In addition, Beukers and Berends (1960), Wacker, Weinblum, Träger, and Moustafa (1961), and Smith (1963) have demonstrated the formation of mixed "dimers" of thymine and uracil by irradiating frozen solutions containing both thymine and uracil. Another important property of the dimer was discovered by Beukers and Berends (1961), who showed that when the dimer is reirradiated in liquid solution it is converted back to thymine.

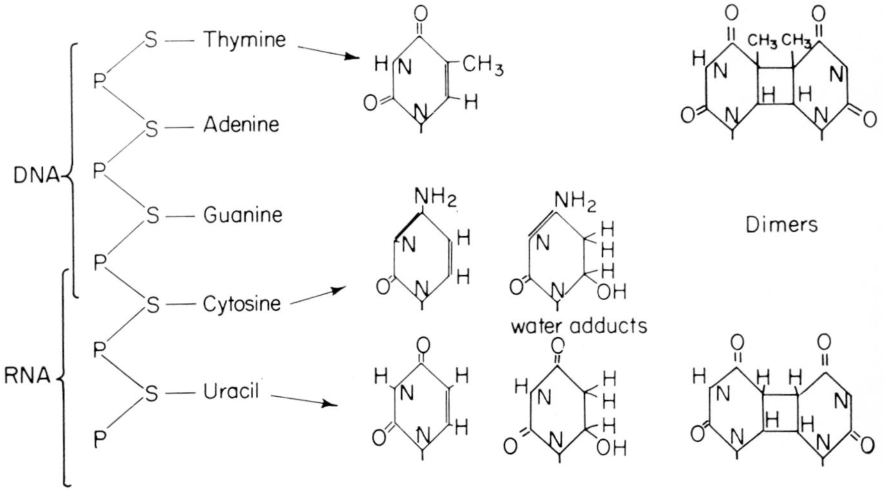

FIGURE 1. Schematic diagram showing the structure of thymine, cytosine, uracil, the water addition products of cytosine and uracil, and the dimer of thymine and uracil.

In ordered structures such as DNA or RNA, adjacent thymines or uracils may be stacked in much the same way as they are in frozen solutions, so that dimers might be produced when DNA or RNA is irradiated in aqueous solution or in vivo. Wulff (1963), and Wacker, Dellweg, and Weinblum (1961) have shown that thymine dimers can indeed be isolated from irradiated DNA. A number of investigators (Setlow and Setlow, 1962; Bollum and Setlow, 1963; Wulff and Rupert, 1962; Wacker, Dellweg, and Weinblum, 1961) have shown that the presence of thymine dimers could be correlated with altered biological function using the *H. influenzae*-transforming principle, a calf thymus DNA polymerase system, *Escherichia coli* DNA photoreactivation, and *E. coli* colony-forming ability.

With this brief discussion it is clear that the formation of dimers and hydrates of uracil and dimers of thymine may be important lesions in UV-irradiated, biologically active nucleic acids. In addition, it is quite possible that other photoproducts produced by UV-irradiation are biologically important. To understand the biological effects of UV-irradiation, it is essential to determine the nature of the photoproducts produced in irradiated RNA and DNA. In the earlier work in this field, the presence of the dimer was inferred by measuring the loss in optical density. This procedure is justified provided it is known that only one photoproduct is involved, and that this photoproduct has negligible absorption at the wavelength used in measuring the optical density. A much more satisfactory technique is to use P^{32}-labeled material, separate the photoproducts chromatographically, and measure the yield of each as a function of dose. This procedure requires the hydrolysis of the polynucleotide, leaving the lesions (dimers, hydrates, or other products) intact so that the yield of each may be determined. Such an approach is technically difficult in complex polynucleotide structures such as DNA and RNA, so initially we have studied the simpler model compounds TpT, dUpU, and UpU shown in Figure 2. In these compounds the two bases are held together in a sugar-phosphodiester linkage. With this linkage the bases are able to move with respect to one another, and at times will be sterically related as they would be in DNA. Since adjacent thymines in such a molecule are relatively close together, it seems reasonable to expect dimers to form between neighboring thymines even in liquid solution. Thymine dimers were indeed found in irradiated solutions of such dinucleotides (Beukers and Berends, 1961; Johns, Rapaport, and Delbrück, 1962; Sztumpf and Shugar, 1962; Deering and Setlow, 1963).

We have studied in detail the effects of UV on TpT, dUpU, and ribo UpU (UpU) by separating their photoproducts chromatographically. In all

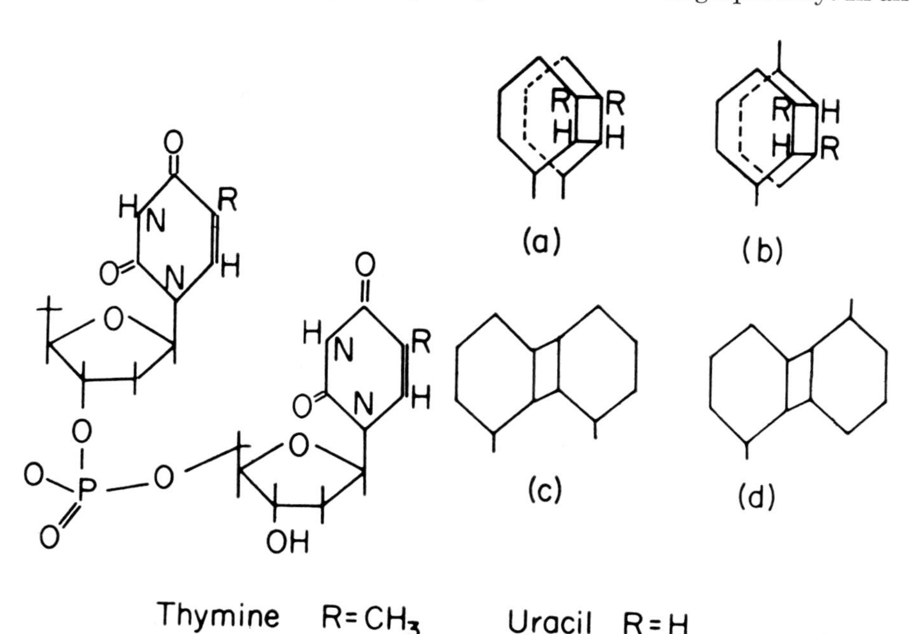

FIGURE 2. Structure of TpT and dUpU, as well as four possible isomeric dimers of these materials.

three materials two kinds of dimers are formed. In dUpU and UpU, hydrate photoproducts are also produced with either one or both of the uracils hydrated. In TpT, two unidentified photoproducts, TpT^3 and TpT^4, have been found and studied. We have been unable to detect a thymine hydrate photoproduct. The details of this work are given elsewhere (Helleiner, Pearson, and Johns, 1963; Johns, Pearson, LeBlanc, and Helleiner, 1964). In the first part of this review paper, we will summarize some of these results, and attempt to compare the photochemistry of dUpU, UpU, and TpT.

A good deal of the interest in the photochemistry of DNA and RNA arises from the work of Grossman (1963), who has investigated the effects of UV-radiation on the ability of poly U to code for the incorporation of phenylalanine into synthetic protein. The last part of this paper will deal with some of our preliminary experiments dealing with the coding problem.

Methods and Materials

Irradiation

Most of the irradiations were carried out in a large UV monochromator (Johns and Rauth, 1964) using two blazed gratings with total area 25.6 × 20.6 cm². The system used entrance and exit slits 15 cm high, and up to 6 mm wide, with a dispersion of 4 mμ/cm at the exit slit. The irradiations of TpT, dUpU, and UpU were performed in quartz cuvettes with a 1 cm light path. The solutions were continually stirred during the irradiation, and the beam was monitored at intervals using a photoelectric cell. After each increment of dose, samples were removed for chromatography and the optical density of the cell at the irradiation wavelength measured. If we assume complete mixing of the solution, it can be shown (Johns, Pearson, LeBlanc, and Helleiner, 1964) that the increment in mean flux density $\Delta\bar{L}$ (microeinsteins/cm²) is given by

$$\overline{\Delta L} = \frac{\Delta N_i \cdot \{1 - e^{-2.303 D_\lambda \bar{l}/l_o}\}}{2.303\, D_\lambda \cdot \dfrac{V}{l_o}} \qquad (1)$$

where ΔN_i is the increment of incident flux on the solution inside the cell expressed in microeinsteins (μE), V is the volume irradiated, l_o is the thickness of the cell D_λ is the optical density at wavelength λ of the solution as measured in the parallel beam of a spectrophotometer, and l is the mean path length of the rays through the cell. This value of $\bar{l}$ (1.10 ± 0.01 cm) is greater than l_o (1 cm), because the beam is made to converge at the center of the cell by a quartz lens. The quantity ΔN_i was determined using malachite green leukocyanide (Calvert and Rechen, 1952).

After any increment of flux ΔN_i, $\Delta\bar{L}$ was calculated using expression (1) with D_λ replaced by the average optical density during this dose interval. After a series of doses the cumulated flux $\bar{L}$ was obtained from

$$\bar{L} = \Sigma \, \Delta \bar{L} \tag{2}$$

In our work the dose is expressed in units of $\mu E/cm^2$, which corresponds to a μmole (6.02×10^{17}) of photons/cm^2. When doses are expressed in this way, it effectively converts the dosimetry to the case where an infinitely thin solution of the material is exposed to a parallel beam of radiation in such a way that every molecule of the solution is exposed to the same radiation flux. When doses are given in terms of incident flux, this is not the case for now the flux increment throughout the solution, added in each unit of time from a constant source, will vary as the optical density of the cell changes. If the solution becomes more dense with irradiation, the mean flux seen by each molecule per unit time will decrease with dose, while the reverse will be the case when the solution becomes less dense with irradiation.

When doses are expressed in $\mu E/cm^2$, it is convenient to express the corresponding cross sections in cm^2/μmole, since 1 μmole of photons equals 1 μE. (A dose of 1 $\mu E/cm^2$ corresponds to an energy flux of 4.7×10^4 ergs/mm^2 at 254 mμ.)

Irradiation of the poly U was performed in a small cell (area 1.2 cm^2) with a path length of 1 mm which was stirred by an oscillating fine probe. The solutions of poly U had optical densities of about 12 (1 cm path) at 262 mμ. The radiation from the exit slit was concentrated on this small cell with a quartz lens of short focal length.

The TpT was irradiated in aqueous air-saturated solutions. Irradiation in buffered solutions in the pH range 3.5 to 8.5 gave the same yield of major photoproducts. dUpU and UpU were irradiated in 0.005 M potassium tartrate buffer at pH 4.5 containing 0.02 M NaCl. Poly U was irradiated in 0.007 M NaCl at pH 7.5 to 8.0.

Separation of Photoproducts

100 μ liter samples of TpT, dUpU, and UpU were removed from the irradiation vessel and spotted on acetic acid washed tartrate buffered (pH 4.5) Whatman 3HR paper (Moscarello, Lane, and Hanes, 1961). This was developed as a descending chromatogram in solvent 1 (isopropyl alcohol-ethyl alcohol-0.05 M tartrate pH 4.5, 30:40:30, v/v). For some of the chromatograms, unbuffered paper was used with solvent 2 (isopropyl alcohol-ammonia-water, 7:1:2, v/v). The positions of the P^{32}-labeled photoproducts were located by autoradiography on Kodak KK industrial x-ray film. The activity was measured by cutting out the spots and measuring their activity in a liquid scintillation counter.

Preparation of TpT, dUpU, and UpU

Radioactive TpT and dUpU were made by condensing suitably blocked nucleotides with the corresponding blocked nucleosides (Michelson and Todd, 1953; Smrt and Sorm, 1960; Tener, 1961) in the presence of dicyclohexylcarbodiimide (Gilham and Khorana, 1958). Radioactive UpU was made by allowing radioactive uridine-2′,3′ cyclic phosphate and uridine at high concentrations to react under ribonuclease catalysis (Heppel, Whitfeld, and Markham, 1955). The products were obtained as ammonium or triethylammonium salts, and characterized by their spectral and chromatographic properties.

Amino Acid Incorporation

Preparation of Poly U

Poly U was prepared according to Grossman (1963), using polynucleotide phosphorylase extracted by a modification of the procedure of Steiner and Beers (1961) from *Micrococcus lysodeikticus*. Bentonite was used to inhibit the action of ribonuclease (RNase), and the final poly U preparation showed essentially no hydrolysis after 3 hours incubation at 37C. The poly U preparation was fractionated using 0.1 M NaCl on a Sephadex G-100 column, and the leading peak of high molecular weight poly U was used for all experiments.

Incorporating Fraction

An *E. coli* B/1/2 extract, which was capable of incorporating C^{14} amino acids, was prepared according to the method of Nirenberg and Matthaei (1961) for the preparation of their S-30 fraction. The extract was fractionated using Nirenberg's standard buffer on a Sephadex G-25 column to remove low molecular weight contaminants, and the leading peak was used for all incorporation experiments.

sRNA

E. coli unfractionated sRNA was prepared according to Zubay (1962).

Reaction Mixture for Amino Acid Incorporation

The reaction mixture had a total volume of 0.5 ml and contained the following in μmoles/ml: Tris-HCl pH 7.8, 100.0; magnesium acetate, 20.0; KCl, 50.0; mercaptoethanol, 6.0; adenosine triphosphate (ATP), 4.0; phosphoenol pyruvate, 5.0; guanosine triphosphate (GTP), 0.02; C^{14}-phenylalnanine, 0.1 (specific activity 24.3 mC/mM) plus S-30 fraction, 3 mg; sRNA, 1 mg; pyruvate kinase, 10 μg; and poly U 40 μg. The reaction mixture was incubated at 37C for approximately 24 minutes after the addition of the S-30 fraction. At this point, poly U-directed poly-L phenylalanine synthesis was essentially complete, and the reaction was halted by the addition of 5 ml of 5 per cent trichloroacetic acid. The reaction mixture was then heated at 90C for 15 minutes (Barondes and Nirenberg, 1962) to release C^{14}-phenylalanine oligopeptides and polypeptides from ribosomal and sRNA attachment (Gilbert, 1963), and C^{14}-phenylalanine from sRNA attachment (Siekevitz, 1952). In this way specific C^{14} amino acid oligo- and polypeptides were precipitated and counted. Nonspecific counts, *i.e.* those resistant to heating, incorporated in the absence of poly U corresponded to about 1 to 2 per cent of the unirradiated controls. After cooling, the reaction mixture was collected by filtration on a Millipore filter (.45 μ pore size), and washed with trichloroacetic acid (5 per cent). The filters were oven dried and counted in a liquid scintillation counter.

Results and Discussion

Photoproducts of TpT

When TpT is irradiated, four major photoproducts $\widehat{\mathrm{TpT}}^1$, $\widehat{\mathrm{TpT}}^2$, TpT^3, and TpT^4 are formed. Their chromatographic separation is illustrated in Figure 3. It is seen from this diagram that the complete separation of the parent TpT and its four major photoproducts requires the use of two sol-

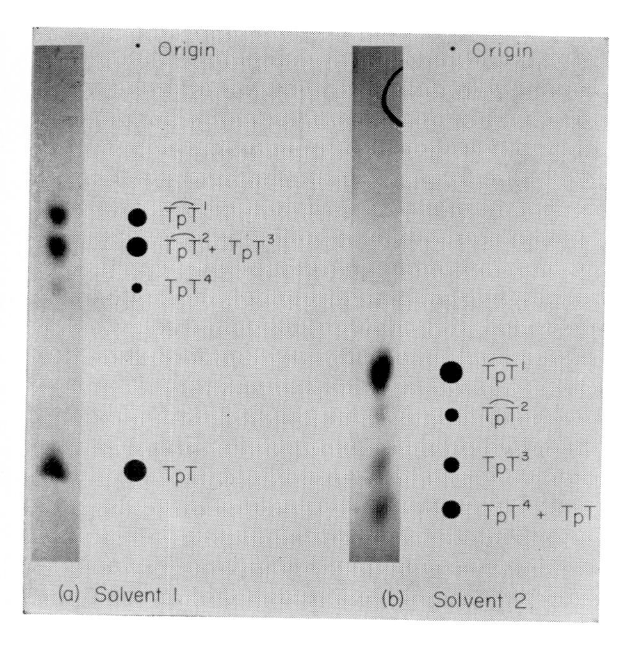

Figure 3. The separation of TpT and its photoproducts by paper chromatography: a—Tartrate buffered paper developed by solvent 1 (isopropyl alcohol-ethyl alcohol-0.05 M tartrate pH 4.5, 30:40:30, v/v); b—unbuffered paper developed by solvent 2 (isopropyl alcohol-ammonia-water, 7:1:2, v/v).

vents. The main photoproducts are the two dimers which we will refer to as $\widehat{\mathrm{TpT}}^1$ and $\widehat{\mathrm{TpT}}^2$ in the order of increasing R_f. The bar joining the thymines is meant to represent the linkage of the two thymines by the cyclobutane ring (see Figure 1). These are presumed to be dimers because they can be converted back to the parent TpT by reirradiation when they are separated from TpT. They are stable to the action of venom phosphodiesterase, but are not completely stable to the action of 0.1 N HCl or 0.1 N KOH at 85C for several hours. The two dimers are probably stereoisomers. There may be as many as 12 possible types of isomeric dimers of TpT (see Johns, Pearson, LeBlanc, and Helleiner, 1964), four of which are shown in Figure 2.

In addition to the dimers, two other photoproducts of unknown structure, TpT^3 and TpT^4 are produced. Our evidence indicates that TpT^4 is probably formed directly from TpT, and that TpT^3 is formed from TpT^4. We will also show that TpT^4 can be converted back to TpT^3 by reirradiation at a suitable wavelength, and that TpT^3 is probably the dimer form of TpT^4.

Reaction Scheme and Cross Sections

Our studies on TpT indicate that the reaction scheme of Figure 4 describes the photochemical behavior of TpT. From this diagram it is seen that TpT may be converted to $\widehat{TpT}^1$, $\widehat{TpT}^2$, and TpT^4 with cross sections

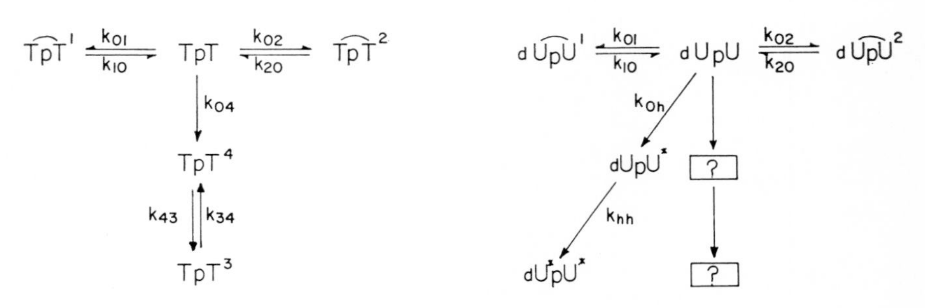

FIGURE 4. Reaction scheme for TpT and dUpU.

k_{01}, k_{02}, and k_{04}. The two dimers can be reversed to the parent TpT with cross sections k^{10} and k^{20}. After long irradiations an "equilibrium" is established between TpT and $\widehat{TpT}^1$, and between TpT and $\widehat{TpT}^2$, so that the rate of the forward and reverse reactions are equal. Under these circumstances

$$(k_{10})\ [\widehat{TpT}^1]_e = (k_{01})\ [TpT]_e \qquad (3)$$

where $[\widehat{TpT}^1]_e$ and $[TpT]_e$ stand for the concentrations of $\widehat{TpT}^1$ and TpT at equilibrium. A similar expression applies to the second dimer, $\widehat{TpT}^2$. From equation (3), it is evident that a knowledge of the cross sections determines the relative concentrations of dimer and parent at "equilibrium." It should be noted in the scheme that k_{04}, which determines the rate of production of TpT^4, is the only cross section which leads irreversibly away from TpT. Thus, after long irradiations TpT will all be converted to TpT^3 and TpT^4. This conversion of TpT to TpT^3 and TpT^4 is illustrated in Figure 5, which will be discussed later. It is also evident that one must know all the cross sections, k_{01}, k_{10}, k_{02}, k_{20}, k_{04}, k_{43} and k_{34} shown in Figure 4, to completely describe the photochemical behavior of TpT. Their cross sections may be determined by isolating a given photoproduct, irradiating it with monochromatic ultraviolet light, and measuring the rate at which it is converted to other photoproducts. For example, to determine k_{10} one would isolate $\widehat{TpT}^1$, irradiate it at a given wavelength, and measure the yields of $\widehat{TpT}^1$ and TpT as a function of dose. The differential equation describing the conversion of $\widehat{TpT}^1$ to TpT is

$$-\,d\,\frac{[\widehat{TpT}^1]}{d\bar{L}} = k_{10}\,[\widehat{TpT}^1] - k_{01}\,[TpT] \tag{4}$$

Since initially $[TpT] = 0$, the cross section k_{10} may be determined from

$$k_{10} = -\left\{\frac{d[\widehat{TpT}^1]}{d\bar{L}}\right\}_{\text{initially}} \times \frac{1}{[\widehat{TpT}^1]} \tag{5}$$

In this expression the first term is the initial slope of the curve describing the conversion of $\widehat{TpT}^1$ to TpT. It should be emphasized that since all the k's of Figure 4 depend upon wavelength, monochromatic radiation must be used to determine these cross sections.

Dependence of Equilibrium on Wavelength for TpT

The effect of wavelength on the photochemical behavior of TpT is illustrated in Figure 5. The total amounts of dimer, $\widehat{TpT}^1 + \widehat{TpT}^2$, the photoproducts $TpT^3 + TpT^4$ and TpT is plotted as a function of dose at 280 mμ. After a dose of about 15 $\mu E/cm^2$, it is evident that the amount of dimer reaches about 88 per cent, the amount of TpT about 6 per cent, and the amount of $TpT^3 + TpT^4$ about 6 per cent. Further dose at 280 mμ will not alter these values much since the main effect will be the continued production and reversion of dimer. However, some $TpT^3 + TpT^4$ will always be produced irreversibly from TpT, so that the amount of TpT present will slowly decline, and with it, the amount of dimer. If, after a dose of 18 $\mu E/cm^2$ at 280 mμ, the wavelength is shifted to 235 mμ, TpT is rapidly regenerated from the dimer until the new equilibrium characteristic of 235 mμ is established. At 235 mμ the new equilibrium has 90 per cent in the TpT form and about 3 per cent as dimer. However, at this wavelength the side reaction leading to TpT^4 is more important (since much more TpT is present), so that the amount of $TpT^3 + TpT^4$ increases with dose. Eventually all of the TpT will be converted to this product, or some daughter of it.

It can be shown that the growth and decay curves of Figure 5 are not exponential, but are the combination of three exponential terms whose coefficients are a function of k_{01}, k_{02}, k_{04}, k_{10}, and k_{20} (Johns, Unpublished data). The equilibrium condition described by equation 3 is approximately correct, provided the cross section for the side reaction k_{04} is small compared with the other k's. If it is large (as is the case in dUpU), the equilibrium in the sense of equation 3 is not established.

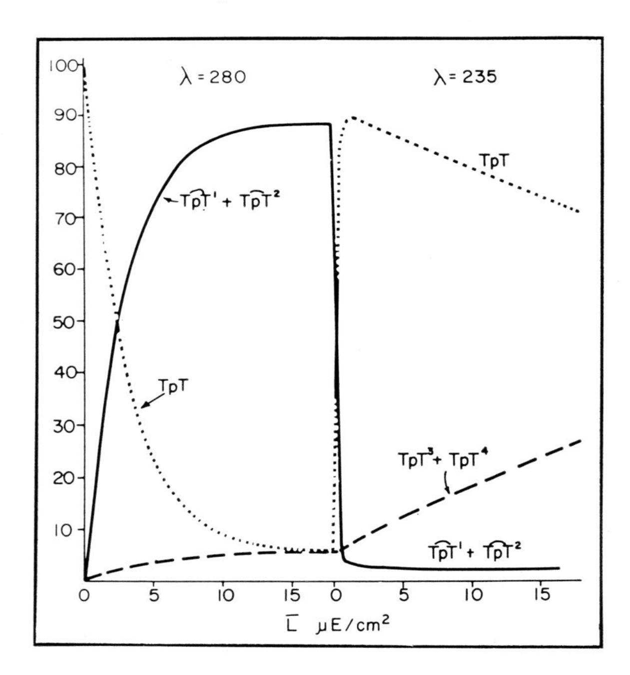

FIGURE 5. Growth of TpT dimers ($\widehat{\text{TpT}}^1 + \widehat{\text{TpT}}^2$) upon irradiation at 280 mμ as calculated from experimentally determined cross sections. After a dose of 18 μE/cm² the wavelength was changed to 235 mμ. The second half of the diagram shows the conversion of the dimers back to TpT. At all wavelengths TpT is irreversibly converted to TpT^3 and TpT^4.

Photoproducts of dUpU

Irradiation of dUpU gives rise to two dimers which run in our chromatographic systems in much the same way as the dimers of TpT. In addition, there is produced a single hydrate (dUpU*) where water is added across the 5,6 double bond of one of the uracils, and the double hydrate (dU*pU*), which is produced from the single hydrate by the addition of a water molecule across the remaining unsaturated uracil moiety (Helleiner, Pearson, and Johns, 1963). The proposed photochemical reaction scheme for dUpU is given in Figure 4. In addition to the four known dimer and hydrate photoproducts shown in Figure 4, it appears that other photoproducts are produced in small yield which are probably analogous to TpT^3 and TpT^4, but we have no detailed data on these at the moment. To date we have measured the cross sections k_{01}, k_{02}, k_{0h}, and k_{hh}, and have preliminary data on the reverse reactions k_{10} and k_{20}.

Although the over-all reaction scheme for dUpU (Figure 4) may appear similar to TpT, the presence of the hydration reaction with a rather large cross section k_{0h} alters the photochemistry of dUpU considerably from that of TpT. This is illustrated in Figure 6, where data for TpT (left) are compared with dUpU (right). The diagram on the right shows the rapid initial production of the single hydrate dUpU* and the dimer $d\widehat{UpU}^1$ as dUpU is destroyed. The double hydrate dU*pU*, which is formed from dUpU*, rises along an S-shaped curve and would be the major photoproduct after long irradiations. Since dUpU* is continually converted to dU*pU*, it will eventually decrease with dose for doses larger than those shown in Figure 6. Both dimers, $d\widehat{UpU}^1$ and $d\widehat{UpU}^2$, reach a maximum and then decline as their parent dUpU is continually drained off by the irreversible production of the single hydrate.

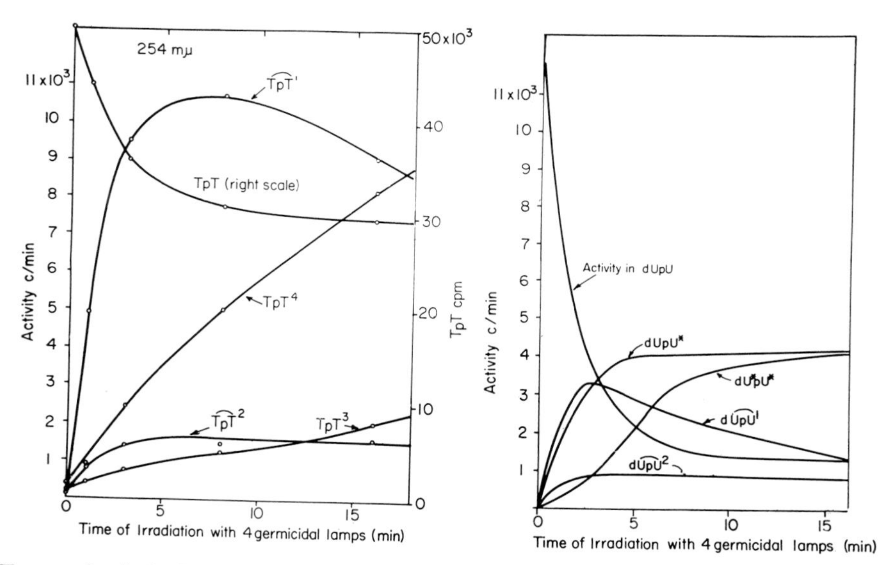

FIGURE 6. Left, P^{32} activity in TpT and its photoproducts as a function of irradiation time with four germicidal lamps. Right, similar data for dUpU. Irradiation for one minute with four germicidal lamps corresponds to a mean flux density of 0.3 $\mu E/cm^2$. The scale on the right of the left diagram applies to the TpT activity.

A comparison of the two sets of curves of Figure 6 will illustrate the much greater sensitivity of dUpU than TpT. After 10 minutes exposure, only 40 per cent of the TpT is converted, while over 90 per cent of the dUpU is altered. For the irradiation at 254 mμ illustrated in Figure 6, the maximum amount of TpT in the form of dimers (25 per cent) is about the same as in dUpU (30 per cent), and the maximum concentrations are achieved after about the same dose. In the case of dUpU, the decline from the peak value is rapid because of side reaction (k_{oh}) leading to hydrate; in TpT the decline is slow because the smaller cross section of k_{04} leads to TpT^4.

Quantum Yields and Absorption Cross Sections

The cross section k_{ij} which we have been discussing give the rate of production of the photo product j in terms of the incident flux of photons. The fraction of i converted to j is the product of the cross section in $cm^2/\mu E$ and the flux in $\mu E/cm^2$. The cross section gives one a measure of the amount of photoproduct j produced when the sample i is exposed to a given flux of photons.

If, however, one is interested in describing the photochemical conversion of i *per photon absorbed* in the parent j, then it is convenient to speak of the quantum yield Φ_{ij}. The quantum yield is the probability that an absorbed photon will convert i to j. The quantum yield Φ_{ij} and the cross section k_{ij} are related by the cross section k_a for the absorption of an incident photon according to

$$\Phi_{ij} = k_{ij}/k_a \quad (6)$$

The cross-section for absorption k_a, in $cm^2/\mu mole$, is related to the molar extinction coefficient of the parent i by

$$k_a = 2.303 \times 10^{-3}\, \varepsilon_\lambda\ cm^2/\mu mole \quad (7)$$

For example, a quantum yield of 0.02 would mean that for every 100 photons absorbed by a molecule of the material, two molecules would be converted to the new photoproduct.

Quantum Yields for the Production of Photoproducts of TpT and dUpU

The quantum yields for the production of the dimers of TpT and dUpU are compared in Figures 7a and 7b. At short wavelengths, the yields of both dimers in dUpU are about 3 times as great as the corresponding dimer yields in TpT. At long wavelengths the yields of dimers in dUpU and in TpT are about the same. At all wavelengths the yield of dimer 1 is 3 to 5 times that of dimer 2 in both TpT and dUpU. The quantum yield for the production of the single hydrate in dUpU is 7 to 30 times as great as the yield of TpT^4 (Figure 7c). Because of the large quantum yield for hydrate production in dUpU which does not occur in TpT, dUpU is much more sensitive to UV than TpT at all wavelengths. The fraction of TpT which can be converted to dimer forms, $\widehat{Tp}T^1$ and $\widehat{Tp}T^2$, is very dependent on the wavelength of irradiation, as illustrated in Figure 5. At short wavelengths (230 mμ), equilibrium is established in TpT with about 3.0 per cent of the TpT in the dimer form, while at long wavelengths (280 mμ) the corresponding value is about 90 per cent. In dUpU these percentages would be about 9 per cent and 70 per cent if the hydration reaction did not remove dUpU from possible dimerization. The hydration of dUpU alters these values by greatly reducing the percentage of dimer at long wavelength, but having little effect at short wavelength. This follows from the fact that at long wavelengths the quantum yield for hydration is relatively large compared to that for dimerization, and at short wavelengths it is relatively small. The net result is that the maximum amount of dimer which may be produced in dUpU is 9 to 30 per cent, and almost independent of wavelength.

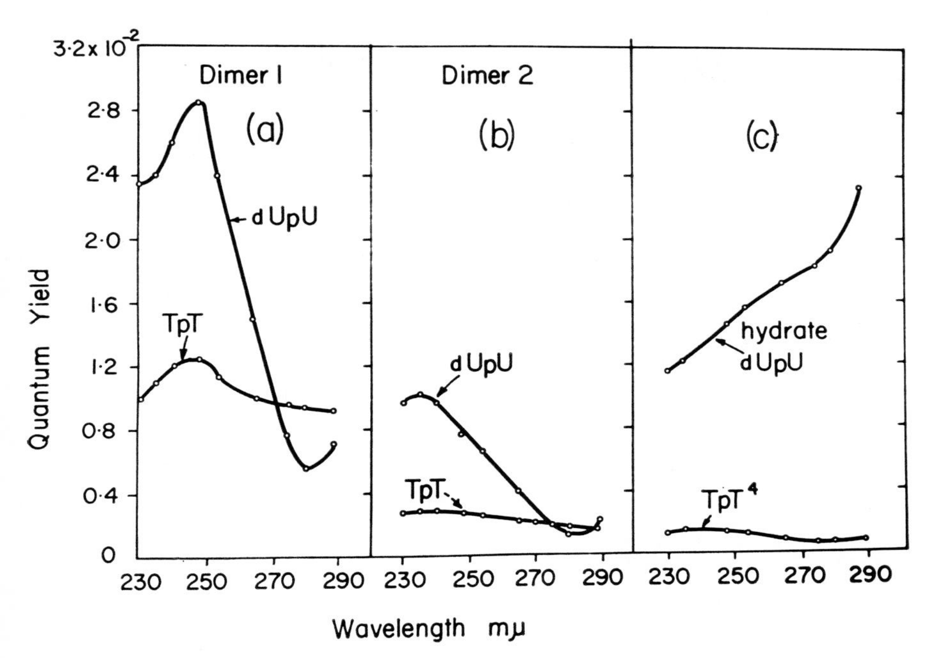

FIGURE 7. (a) Quantum yields for the production of dimer 1 of dUpU and TpT. (b) Quantum yields for the production of dimer 2 of dUpU and TpT. (c) Quantum yield for the production of the single hydrate in dUpU and for the production of TpT^4.

Photoproducts of ribo UpU

Irradiation of ribo UpU gives rise to two dimers and the single and double hydrate, as well as other photoproducts in smaller yield. The photoproducts run in our chromatographic system in the same way as the products of dUpU. The yield of the dimers and hydrates in ribo UpU varies with wavelength in much the same way as in dUpU. Detailed results for ribo UpU will be presented elsewhere.

Photoproducts TpT^3 and TpT^4

Our evidence that TpT^3 and TpT^4 can be converted one to the other is given in Figure 8. Upon irradiation at 313 mμ, TpT^4 is converted to TpT^3, while irradiation of TpT^3 at 240 mμ converts TpT^3 to TpT^4. Thus TpT^4 and TpT^3 behave in many ways like TpT and TpT dimer. The idea that TpT^3 may be the dimer of TpT^4 is further strengthened by the extinction coefficients given in Figure 9. TpT^4 has a maximum absorption at 325 mμ, and TpT^3 has negligible absorption at this wavelength, while at 280 mμ and at shorter wavelengths they have very similar extinction coefficients.

At 270 mμ TpT has a large extinction compared with $\widehat{\mathrm{TpT}}^1$, while at wavelengths below 230 mμ, the two have very similar extinctions. Assuming that the peak extinction coefficient of TpT is increased from 267 mμ to 325 mμ when TpT is converted to TpT^4, we are tempted to suggest that in TpT^4 the ring structure has been altered so that the conjugation has increased. The thymine moiety of TpT^4 may be very similar to the structure 5-methyl-pyrimidin-2-one deoxyriboside produced by Laland and Serck-Hanssen (1964). These authors produced this material by the reduction of thymidine by sodium amalgam in dilute acetic acid. This compound is similar to thymidine with the oxygen at C-4 replaced by hydrogen and a double bond between N-3 and C-4. Such a structure absorbs strongly at 320 mμ, fluoresces, and is alkali and acid labile. TpT^4 has these same properties.

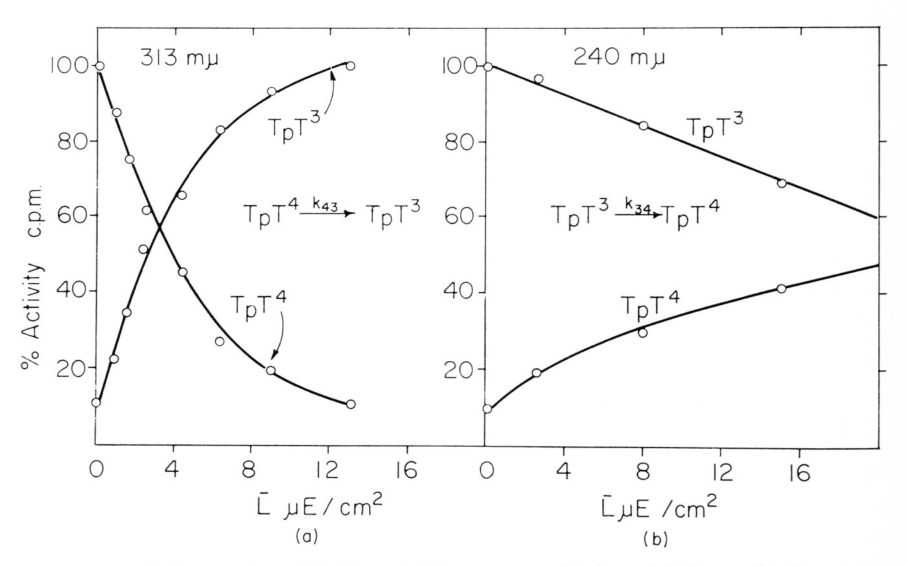

FIGURE 8. (a) Conversion of TpT^4 to TpT^3 upon irradiation of 313 mμ. (b) Conversion of TpT^3 to TpT^4 upon irradiation of 240 mμ.

Another compound which has similar properties to TpT^4 has been produced by Barszcz and Shugar (1961) by irradiating 1,3-dimethyluracil using Co^{60}. This compound also fluoresces, and gives a positive test with potassium iodide indicative of a peroxide. TpT^4 is resistant to the action of venom phosphodiesterase under conditions where an equivalent amount of TpT is completely hydrolyzed. Since venom phosphodiesterase appears *not* to attack $\widehat{\mathrm{TpT}}$ (Johns *et al.*, 1964) or $\mathrm{pXp}\widehat{\mathrm{TpT}}$ where X is any deoxyribonucleoside (Bollum and Setlow, 1963), one could postulate that the two thymine moieties in TpT^4 are somehow linked together to prevent the attack of the enzyme. Both rings in TpT^4 must be altered from that in the

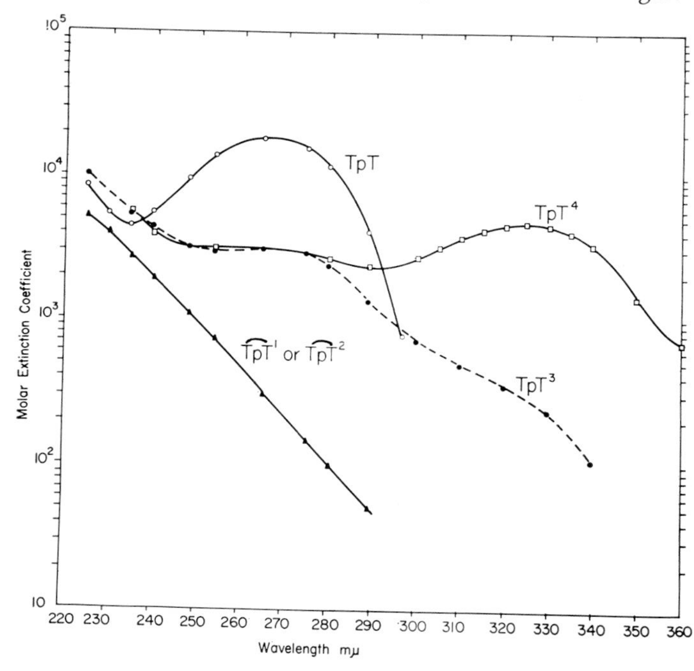

FIGURE 9. Molar extinction coefficient for TpT, $\widehat{TpT}^1$, $\widehat{TpT}^2$, TpT^3, and TpT^4 as a function of wavelength.

parent TpT since the extinction of TpT^4 at 267 mμ is less than that of one intact thymine ring. We have tentatively postulated that in TpT^4, the two thymine rings are held together by a peroxide bridge between the two carbons in the 4 position. We also speculate that in TpT^3 the two thymine rings are, in addition, coupled together by the cyclobutane ring of Figure 1 (Johns, Pearson, LeBlanc, and Helleiner, 1964).

Setlow and Carrier (1963) found a small increase in absorption at 320 mμ in irradiated DNA which could be reversed by irradiation at 310 mμ, but not at 239 mμ. In addition, Smith (1963) observed an increase in optical density at 320 mμ on irradiating frozen solutions of thymine. These materials may well be closely related to TpT^4.

Inactivation by UV of the Ability of poly U to Code for Phenylalanine

Grossman (1962, 1963) demonstrated that UV-irradiation of poly U can alter its ability to act as a messenger in directing the incorporation of phenylalanine into synthetic polypeptides in an in vitro system. We have been interested in trying to correlate this alteration in the coding properties of poly U with the formation of dimers and hydrates of uracil residues in the polynucleotide. To do this, we have calculated the number of hydrates and dimers produced in a poly U chain using our cross sections for hydration and dimerization in dUpU. Such a calculation is by no means simple since the production of hydrates and dimers in the chain can isolate single unaffected U's, which cannot then be dimerized. Even if two adjacent uracils are isolated, the probability of dimerizing one of these U's is reduced by a factor of two since it has half as many unaffected neighbors. We have not succeeded in deriving a differential equation which describes this situation, so we have resorted to a Monte Carlo method for solving the problem.

Monte Carlo Calculations of the Photoproducts Produced in poly U

In the Monte Carlo method one imagines a poly U chain being bombarded by photons one at a time. The interaction of each photon with the poly U is recorded, and the altered chain is then bombarded by the next photon. At each interaction a random number is selected to determine what happens. This must be repeated many times to give a meaningful answer. Such calculations are possible with a high speed computer. For these calculations a poly U chain of 100 nucleotides length was bombarded in sequence by 1,000 photons. It was assumed that initially every photon is absorbed, giving rise to either a hydrate or dimer. However, as the uracil bases are converted to photoproducts, each photon has an increasingly smaller probability of being absorbed by a uracil. Assuming the initial absorption of every photon is, of course, incorrect, this assumption does not alter the conclusions since it merely reduces the number of photons required to alter completely the poly U. The bombardment of a poly U chain by 1,000 photons is called a case history. In order to obtain results of statistical significance, we have averaged the results of 3,000 such histories.

For each interaction, a random number R_1 between 1 and 100 was first selected to determine the nucleotide in the chain in which the interaction was to occur. If the site contained U (as it would initially but not necessarily after some U's have been altered), a second random number R_2 was selected to determine if the photoproduct produced was to be a hydrate or a dimer. If R_2 lay between 0 and 50, a hydrate was assumed to have been produced; while if R_2 lay between 50 and 100 a dimer was assumed to have resulted. Thus, for this calculation, dimer and hydrate are assumed to be produced, each with a probability of 0.5 which is roughly the case for $\lambda = 265$ mμ in dUpU (see Figure 7). If a hydrate resulted from this choice of R_2, a hydrate was placed at this point in the chain, and the procedure was repeated by selecting the next random number R_1. If a dimer resulted from the choice of R_2, then a third random number R_3 was chosen to determine whether the dimer was to be formed with the U to the left or to the right. If the chosen neighbor was an unhydrated or undimerized U, then the dimer was considered to be formed and was placed in the chain. However, if this neighboring U was already hydrated or dimerized, it was assumed that this photon produced no effect. The photon was counted and the next random number R_1 selected. If the initial choice of R_1 selected a site in which a hydrate had been formed by a previous interaction, the photon was counted but the hydrate was not altered. If the choice of R_1 selected a site already occupied by a dimer, then a random number R_4 was chosen to decide whether this dimer was to be reversed. Calculations were performed for dimer reversal probabilities of 0.25, 0.5 and 0.75.

This procedure was carried out on the IBM 7090 computer at the University of Toronto, and the results of one such calculation are shown in Figure 10. The lower curve shows the fraction of the uracils coupled into dimers as a function of the number of times R_1 was selected, that is, the number of photons or dose. This graph indicates that the number of uracils coupled into dimers increases with dose to a maximum of 26 per cent after 80 photons, and then decreases on the assumption that the probability for reversal of the dimer was equal to 0.5. The upper curves of Figure 10 show the fraction of uracils not affected as a function of dose for three different dimer reversal probabilities. In all cases the number of unaffected uracils

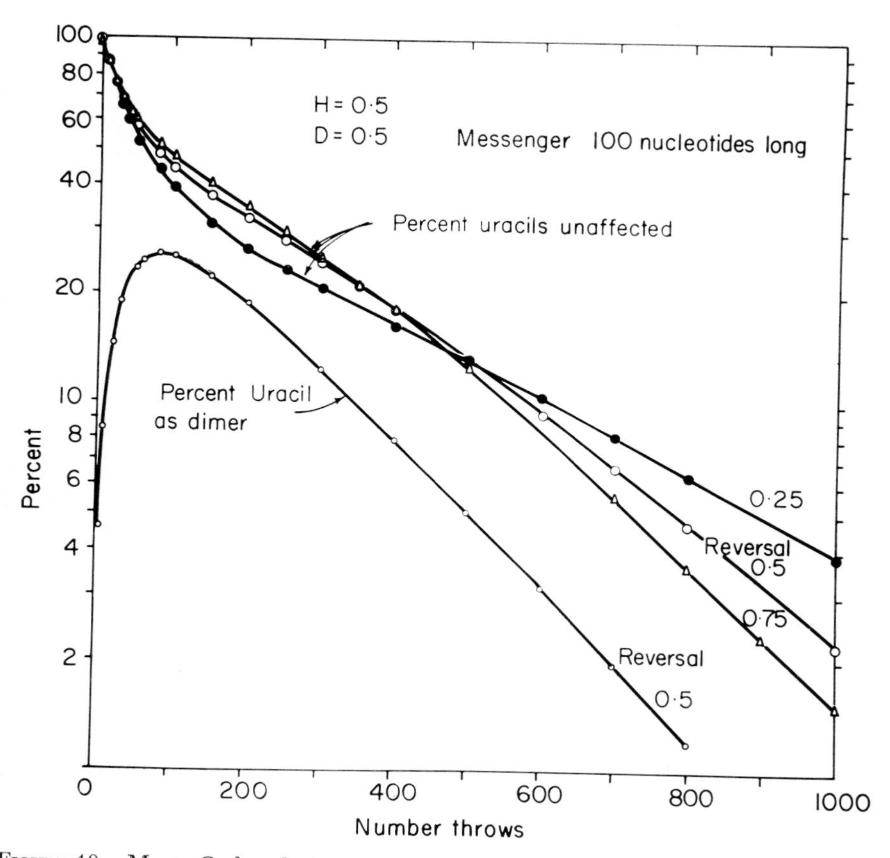

FIGURE 10. Monte Carlo calculations giving the percentage of uracils as dimers, and the percentage of unaffected uracils as a function of dose when poly U chains consisting of 100 nucleotides are irradiated. For the calculation we have assumed that the probability of dimer formation D = 0.5, and that the probability of hydrate formation H = 0.5. Three curves are shown for dimer reversal probabilities of 0.25, 0.5, and 0.75. Data are based on the average result after 3,000 repetitions involving the interaction of 1,000 photons with the poly U chain.

initially drops rapidly with dose, then tends to level off, and finally becomes concave downward. It is evident that the dose response curve of Figure 10 is S-shaped.

Inactivation of poly U-directed Phenylalanine Incorporation

Figure 11 shows some of our preliminary data, giving the amount of phenylalanine incorporated into synthetic polypeptide as a function of the dose to the poly U. The amount of incorporation is expressed as a percentage of the amount incorporated at zero dose. The precision of these data is not great, and it is difficult to draw the best fit curve to it. If a straight line is drawn through the points, the second and third points (50 to 70 per cent incorporation) are usually low and the point for 5 per cent incorporation is also very low. A much better fit could be obtained by fitting an S-shaped curve as indicated in agreement with our Monte Carlo calculations.

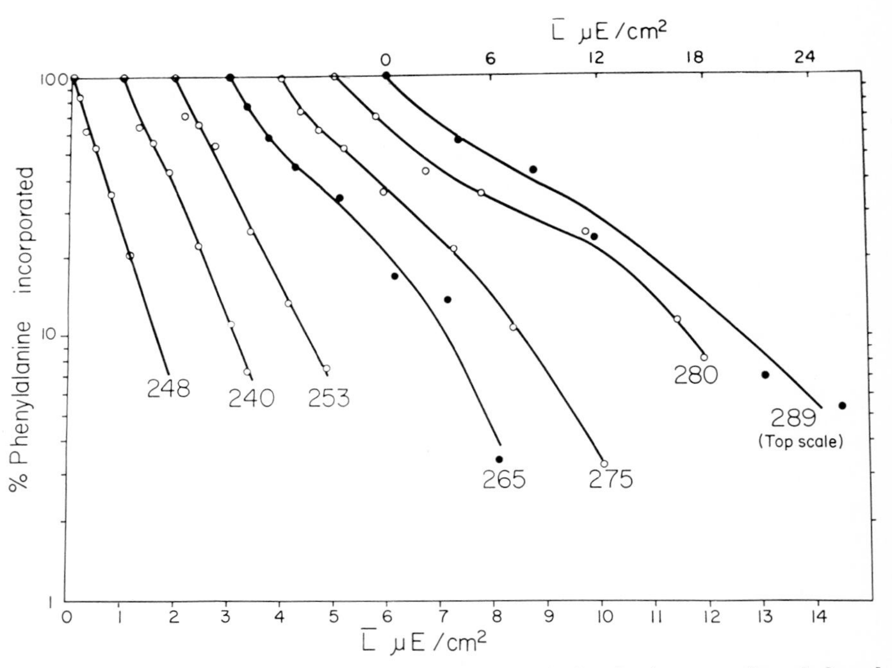

FIGURE 11. Inactivation of the ability of poly U to code for the incorporation of phenylalanine as a function of dose at a variety of wavelengths. The curves have been moved horizontally 1 μE/cm^2 to avoid overlap. The scale for $\lambda = 289$ is shown at the top.

In Figure 12 the results of our Monte Carlo calculations are compared with the data for $\lambda = 265$ mμ of Figure 10. By adjusting the dose scale of the Monte Carlo curve, fair agreement between the two sets of data is obtained. Further experimental work is required to establish the dose-effect curve in the amino acid incorporation system, but it appears that the ability of poly U to code for phenylalanine is correlated with the total number of unaffected uracils present in the poly U chain.

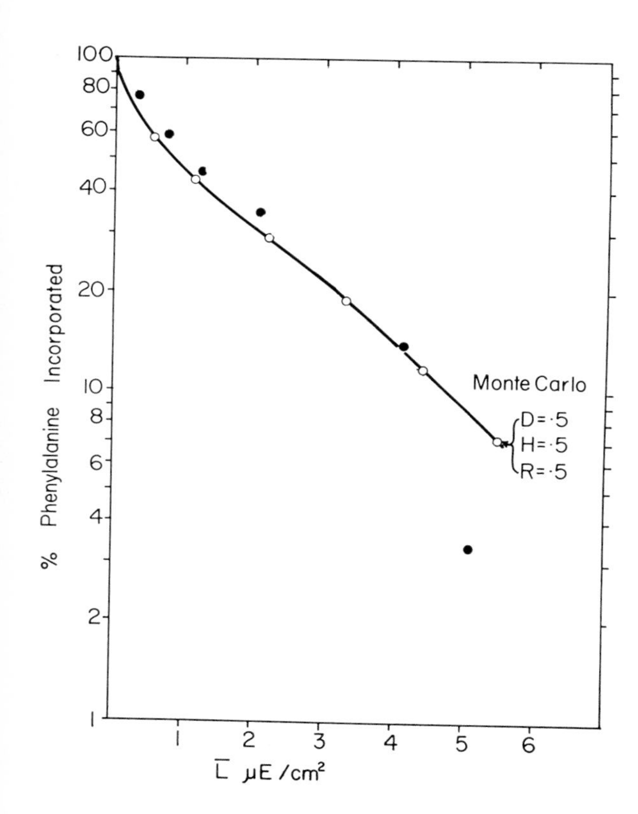

FIGURE 12. Attempt to fit the 265 mμ inactivation data of Figure 10 to a curve based on the Monte Carlo calculation. The Monte Carlo calculations are the solid curve through the open circles. Calculations are for dimer (D), hydrate (H), and reversal (R) probabilities of 0.5.

However, our data present one very serious difficulty which is illustrated in Figure 13; the per cent loss in phenylalanine incorporation is plotted on a linear scale against the loss in optical density of the poly U. If we ignore for the moment any difference between the curves for different wavelengths, we see that for wavelengths near 265 mμ, an 80 per cent loss in optical density corresponds to a 90 per cent loss in coding ability. While this may not at first appear surprising, it must be remembered that the incorporation of *one* phenylalanine is assumed to require *three* adjacent undamaged uracils. At a dose where 80 per cent of the uracils are altered (80 per cent loss in optical density), the chances of finding three adjacent unaltered uracils is very small (1 per cent); yet we still observe 10 per cent incorporation ability. It is yet to be determined whether this implies that three adjacent uracils are not required for phenylalanine incorporation, or whether it implies the presence in the amino acid incorporating system of a UV lesion repair mechanism or some other possibility.

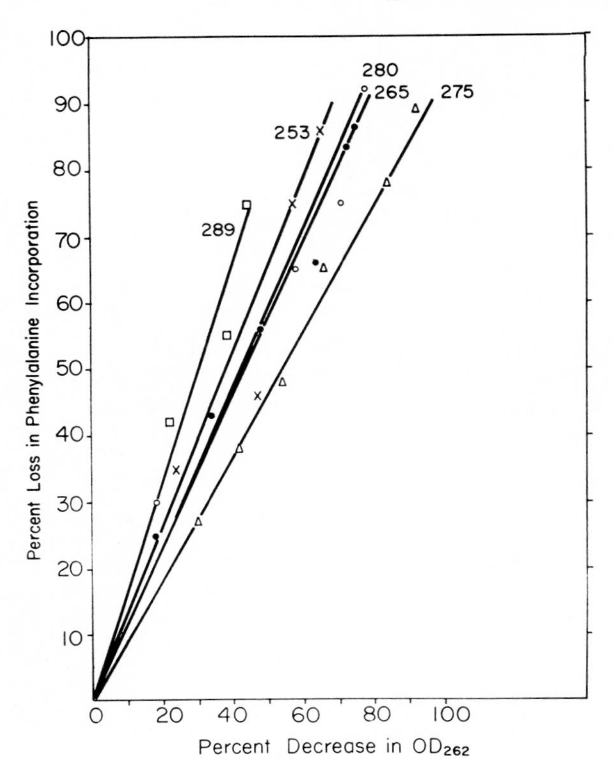

FIGURE 13. Percentage loss in phenylalanine incorporation plotted against the percentage loss in optical density for a number of different wavelengths.

SUMMARY

(1) In TpT, dUpU, and UpU, two isomeric dimers are produced in relative yields of about 5:1. It is not known whether one or both of these dimers are important biologically. Since Wulff (1963) has shown that in $T4v_1$ about 4.8 dimers are formed per lethal hit, it may be that the dimer which appears in low yield is the biologically lethal one.

(2) The single hydrate is formed in both dUpU and UpU with about the same yield, but further experiments are required to look into the details of the photochemical reactions in UpU. No hydrates were found in TpT.

(3) At short wavelengths (225 to 240 mμ) the yield of dimers in dUpU is about 2.5 times that in TpT, while at long wavelengths the two yields are about the same. The maximum amount of dimer which can be produced in TpT is very wavelength dependent. In dUpU the wavelength dependence is much less.

(4) In dUpU the ratio of the yield of hydrate to dimer at short wavelengths is about 0.5, while at long wavelengths it is about 3. The yields are equal at 265 mμ.

(5) In TpT an unidentified photoproduct TpT^4 with peak absorption at 325 mμ is produced irreversibly from TpT in low yield. This photo-

product can be converted to another unidentified product TpT^3 upon irradiation at 313 mμ. TpT^3 can be converted back to TpT^4 by irradiation at 240 mμ. TpT^4 has a peak absorption at 325 mμ which TpT^3 lacks. TpT^3 behaves as if it were the dimer form of TpT^4. Photoproducts with peak absorption at 325 mμ have been found in DNA by others, and may have biological significance.

(6) The effects of monochromatic UV on the ability of poly U to code for phenylalanine are being investigated. Preliminary data indicate that the loss of coding ability may be related to the total number of hydrates and dimers which are formed in poly U, and that the coding ability depends upon the number of unaffected uracils left in the chain.

(7) Monte Carlo calculations have been performed on poly U chains to determine the number of hydrates and dimers which are produced as a function of dose.

ACKNOWLEDGMENTS

The authors take pleasure in acknowledging the work of Professor G. F. Whitmore, who was responsible for setting up the amino acid incorporating system in our laboratory. We are indebted to Dr. A. M. Rauth and Professor L. Siminovitch for many helpful discussions. Two of us (M.L.P. and D.M.L.) are grateful to the National Cancer Institute of Canada for Fellowships in Biophysics.

The financial support of the National Cancer Institute and the Medical Research Council of Canada is appreciated.

REFERENCES

Barondes, S. M., and M. W. Nirenberg. 1962. Fate of a Synthetic Polynucleotide Directing Cell-Free Protein Synthesis. II. Association with Ribosomes. *Science*, 138:813–817.

Barszcz, D., and D. Shugar. 1961. Radiation Chemistry of Nucleic Acids and Their Derivatives. I. Some Pyrimidines, Dehydropyrimidines and Hydrated Pyrimidines. *Acta biochimica polonica*, 8:455–471.

Beukers, R., and W. Berends. 1960. Isolation and Identification of the Irradiation Product of Thymine. *Biochimica et biophysica acta*, 41:550–551.

———. 1961. The Effects of U.V.-Irradiation on Nucleic Acids and their Components. *Biochimica et biophysica acta*, 49:181–189.

Bollum, F. J., and R. B. Setlow. 1963. Ultraviolet Inactivation of DNA Primer Activity. I. Effects of Different Wavelengths and Doses. *Biochimica et biophysica acta*, 68:599–607.

Calvert, J. G., and H. J. L. Rechen. 1952. Precision Actinometry at Low Light Intensities with Malachite Green Leucocyanide. *Journal of the American Chemical Society*, 74:2101–2103.

Deering, R. A., and R. B. Setlow. 1963. Effects of Ultraviolet Light on Thymidine Dinucleotide and Polynucleotide. *Biochimica et biophysica acta*, 68:526–534.

Fikus, M., K. L. Wierzchowski, and D. Shugar. 1962. Photochemistry of Cytosine Nucleotides. III. Mono- and Di-Methylamino Analogues. *Photochemistry and Photobiology*, 1:323–335.

Gilbert, W. 1963. Polypeptide Synthesis in *Escherichia coli*. II. The Polypeptide Chain and S-RNA. *Journal of Molecular Biology*, 6:389–403.

Gilham, P. T., and H. G. Khorana. 1958. Studies on Polynucleotides. I. A New and General Method for the Chemical Synthesis of the C_5'-C_3' Internucleotidic Linkage. Syntheses of Deoxyribo-dinucleotides. *Journal of the American Chemical Society*, 80:6212–6222.

Grossman, L. 1962. The Effects of Ultraviolet-Irradiated Polyuridylic Acid in Cell-Free Protein Synthesis in *E. coli*. *Proceedings of the National Academy of Sciences of the U.S.A.*, 48:1609–1614.

————. 1963. The Effects of Ultraviolet-Irradiated Polyuridylic Acid in Cell-Free Protein Synthesis in *Escherichia coli*. II. The Influence of Specific Photoproducts. *Proceedings of the National Academy of Sciences of the U.S.A.*, 50:657–664.

Helleiner, C. W., M. L. Pearson, and H. E. Johns. 1963. The Ultraviolet Photochemistry of Deoxyuridylyl (3'→5') Deoxyuridine. *Proceedings of the National Academy of Sciences of the U.S.A.*, 50:761–767.

Heppel, L. A., P. R. Whitfeld, and R. Markham. 1955. Nucleotide Exchange Reactions Catalysed by Ribonuclease and Spleen Phosphodiesterase. II. Synthesis of Polynucleotides. *Biochemical Journal*, 60:8–15.

Johns, H. E. Unpublished data.

Johns, H. E., M. L. Pearson, J. C. LeBlanc, and C. W. Helleiner. 1964. The Ultraviolet Photochemistry of Thymidylyl-(3'→5')-Thymidine. *Journal of Molecular Biology*, 9:503–524.

Johns, H. E., S. A. Rapaport, and M. Delbrück. 1962. Photochemistry of Thymine Dimers. *Journal of Molecular Biology*, 4:104–114.

Johns, H. E., and A. M. Rauth. 1964. (a) Theory and Design of High Intensity U.V. Monochromators for Photobiology and Photochemistry. (b) Comparison of Spectral Purity and Intensity of Different U.V. Monochromators. (Submitted to *Photochemistry and Photobiology*.)

Laland, S. G., and G. Serck-Hanssen. 1964. Synthesis of Pyrimidin-2-one Deoxyribosides and Their Ability to Support the Growth of the Deoxyriboside-Requiring Organism *Lactobacillus acidophilus* R26. *Biochemical Journal*, 90:76–81.

Michelson, A. M., and A. R. Todd. 1953. Nucleotides. XX. Mononucleotides Derived From Thymidine. Identity of Thymidylic Acid from Natural Sources with Thymidine-5' Phosphate. *Journal of the Chemical Society*, 1:951–956.

Moore, A. M. 1958. Ultraviolet Irradiation of Pyrimidine Derivatives. II. Note on the Synthesis of the Product of Reversible Photolysis of Uracil. *Canadian Journal of Chemistry*, 36:281–283.

Moore, A. M., and C. H. Thomson. 1957. Ultraviolet Irradiation of Pyrimidine Derivatives. I. 1,3-Dimethyluracil. *Canadian Journal of Chemistry*, 35:163–169.

Moscarello, M. A., B. G. Lane, and C. S. Hanes. 1961. Quantitative Chromatographic Methods. VIII. Chromatographic Systems of High Resolving Power for Nucleotides. *Canadian Journal of Biochemistry and Physiology*, 39:1755–1764.

Nirenberg, M. W., and J. H. Matthaei. 1961. The Dependence of Cell-Free Protein Synthesis in *E. coli* upon Naturally Occurring or Synthetic Polyribonucleotides. *Proceedings of the National Academy of Sciences of the U.S.A.*, 47:1588–1602.

Setlow, R. B., and W. L. Carrier. 1963. Identification of Ultraviolet-Induced Thymine Dimers in DNA by Absorbance Measurements. *Photochemistry and Photobiology*, 2:49–57.

Setlow, R. B., and J. K. Setlow. 1962. Evidence that Ultraviolet-Induced Thymine Dimers in DNA Caused Biological Damage. *Proceedings of the National Academy of Sciences of the U.S.A.*, 48:1250–1257.

Siekevitz, P. 1952. Uptake of Radioactive Alanine *in vitro* into the Protein of Rat Liver Fractions. *Journal of Biological Chemistry*, 195:549–565.

Sinsheimer, R. L. 1954. The Photochemistry of Uridylic Acid. *Radiation Research*, 1:505–513.

———. 1957. The Photochemistry of Cytidylic Acid. *Radiation Research*, 6:121–125.

Smith, K. C. 1963. Photochemical Reactions of Thymine, Uracil, Uridine, Cytosine and Bromouracil in Frozen Solution and in Dried Films. *Photochemistry and Photobiology*, 2:503–517.

Smrt, J., and F. Šorm. 1960. Komponenten der Nucleinsäuren und ihre Analoga. V. Synthese von 5-Bromuridin-5′-Phosphat und 5-Bromodeoxyuridin-5′-Phosphat. *Collection of Czechoslovak Chemical Communications*, 25:553–558.

Steiner, R. F., and R. F. Beers, Jr. 1961. Appendix P. "Preparation of Polyribonucleotide Phosphorylase from M. lysodeikticus," *Polynucleotides: Natural and Synthetic Acids*. Amsterdam, The Netherlands; London, England; New York, New York; and Princeton, New Jersey: Elsevier Publishing Co. Pp. 374–376.

Sztumpf, E., and D. Shugar. 1962. Photochemistry of Model Oligo- and Polynucleotides. VI. Photodimerization and Its Reversal in Thymine Dinucleotide Analogues. *Biochimica et biophysica acta*, 61:555–566.

Tener, G. M. 1961. 2-Cyanoethyl Phosphate and Its Use in the Synthesis of Phosphate Esters. *Journal of the American Chemical Society*, 83:159–168.

Wacker, A., H. Dellweg, and D. Weinblum. 1961. Über die strahlensensibilisierende Wirkung des 5-Bromuracils. *Journal of Molecular Biology*, 3:787–789.

Wacker, A., D. Weinblum, L. Träger, and Z. H. Moustafa. 1961. Photochemische Reaktionen von Uracil und Uridin. *Journal of Molecular Biology*, 3:790–793.

Wang, S. Y. 1958a. Photochemistry of Nucleic Acids and Related Compounds. I. The First Step in the Ultraviolet Irradiation of 1,3-Dimethyluracil. *Journal of the American Chemical Society*, 80:6196–6198.

———. 1958b. Photochemistry of Nucleic Acids and Related Compounds. II. The Ultraviolet Irradiation of the First Product from 1,3-Dimethyluracil. *Journal of the American Chemical Society*, 80: 6199–6201.

———. 1961. Photochemical Reactions in Frozen Solutions. *Nature*, London, 190: 690–694.

———. 1962a. Irradiation of Uridine with Ultraviolet Light. *Photochemistry and Photobiology*, 1:37–40.

———. 1962b. Analysis of the Rate of the Ultraviolet Irradiation and Reconstitution Reactions of 1,3-Dimethyluracil and Uridine. *Photochemistry and Photobiology*, 1:135–145.

Wierzchowski, K. L., and D. Shugar. 1959. Studies of Reversible Photolysis in Oligo- and Poly-uridylic acids. *Acta biochimica polonica*, 6:313–334.

———. 1961. Photochemistry of Cytosine Nucleosides and Nucleotides. II. *Acta biochimica polonica*, 8:219–234.

———. 1962. Photochemistry of Model Oligo- and Polynucleotides. IV. Hetero-Oligonucleotides and High Molecular Weight Single and Twin-Stranded Polymer Chains. *Photochemistry and Photobiology*, 1:21–36.

Wulff, D. L. 1963. Kinetics of Thymine Photodimerization in DNA. *Biophysical Journal*, 3:355–362.

Wulff, D. L., and C. S. Rupert. 1962. Disappearance of Thymine Photodimer in Ultraviolet Irradiated DNA upon Treatment with a Photoreactivating Enzyme from Baker's Yeast. *Biochemical and Biophysical Research Communications*, 7:237–240.

Zubay, G. 1962. The Isolation and Fractionation of Soluble Ribonucleic Acid. *Journal of Molecular Biology*, 4:347–356.

The Repair of Ultraviolet Photoproducts in DNA of Bacteria

PAUL HOWARD-FLANDERS AND RICHARD P. BOYCE

Department of Radiology,
Yale University School of Medicine,
New Haven, Connecticut

The processes of repair in *Escherichia coli* after ultraviolet (UV) irradiation are better understood as the result of the discoveries that thymine dimers are formed in the deoxyribonucleic acid (DNA) of UV-irradiated cells (Beukers and Berends, 1960; Wacker, 1963). It appears that thymine dimers can block the biological activity of transforming DNA (Setlow and Setlow, 1962) and can impair the ability of DNA to act as primer for the calf thymus DNA polymerase in vitro (Bollum and Setlow, 1963). The work to be described here is concerned with one of the mechanisms by which DNA is repaired in UV-irradiated bacteria.

RADIOSENSITIVE MUTANTS OF *E. Coli* K12

Because of an initial interest in the genetics of repair mechanisms, the work was carried out with a strain of *E. coli* K12 that would be convenient for genetic analysis. This is a female or F^- genetic recipient strain that carries 12 markers for amino acid requirement or ability to utilize sugars. The first step was to obtain mutant strains of bacteria unable to repair their DNA, which would therefore be abnormally sensitive to ultraviolet light. This strain with multiple markers was used as the parental stock from which radiosensitive mutants were derived. The bacteria were exposed to the mutagenic action of nitrous acid or UV light, and then to certain selective procedures. Radiosensitive mutants of two kinds were obtained. One kind, the so-called *uvr* mutants, was isolated by contraselection with UV-irradiated T1 bacteriophage (Howard-Flanders and Theriot, 1962). The rationale for this is that when colonies of normal, resistant bacteria are infected, the irradiated DNA is repaired and the phage survive, multiply in the colony, and destroy it. If, however, the colony is of a sensitive mutant of the required type, the irradiated phage DNA is not repaired and the phage fail to multiply, so that many of the cells in the colony survive. In essence, this procedure selects for cells that are unable to repair the UV-irradiated DNA of the T1 bacteriophage. It also selects for T1 resistant cells which were tested for and discarded. In comparison with the parental strain, the required *uvr⁻* strains are very sensitive to ultraviolet light, as is seen in Figure 1. The greater sensitivity of these strains is, however, specific to UV-irradiation, for they are only about 20 per cent more sensitive than the parental strain to X-irradiation.

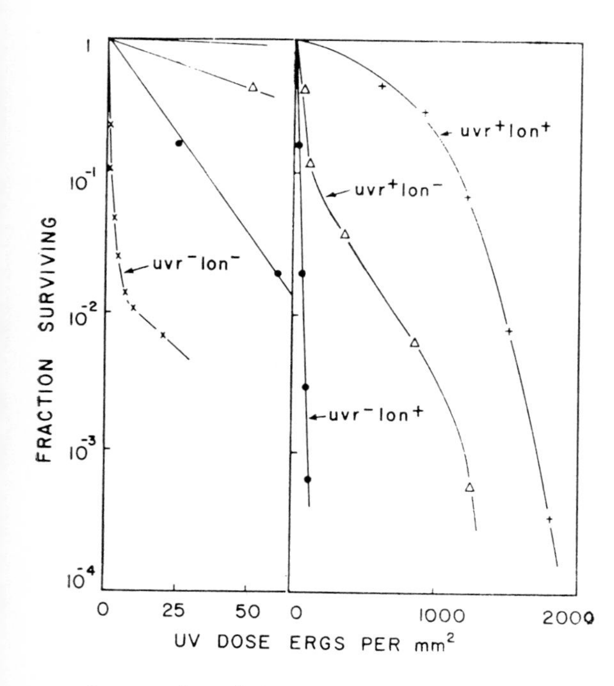

FIGURE 1. The logarithm of fraction of cells that retain the ability to form colonies is plotted as a function of the UV dose. Four strains of *E. coli* K12 were grown overnight on nutrient agar, harvested and washed in buffered saline, exposed to various doses of UV light of 2537 A, plated on nutrient agar, and incubated at 37 C. The fraction surviving was determined from the number of visible colonies seen after incubation for 18 to 24 hours.

It was found that colonies which produced a sloppy mucoid exudate on minimal agar contained radiosensitive mutants of a second type that showed a tendency to grow in long forms and were designated *lon*. When the fraction of cells retaining the ability to form colonies is plotted as a function of the ultraviolet dose, the survival curves obtained for these *lon* mutants are S-shaped and are thus similar to those obtained with *E. coli* B. The double mutants *uvr⁻ lon⁻* are highly sensitive, and are similar to Ruth Hill's strain, *E. coli* B_{S-1} (Hill, 1958; Hill and Simson, 1961).

When these strains of *E. coli* K12 were used as host for plating UV-irradiated T1 bacteriophage, it was found that the apparent sensitivity of the bacteriophage (Ellison, Feiner, and Hill, 1960) was affected by the *uvr* locus, but not by *lon* (Howard-Flanders, Simson, and Theriot, 1964), as shown in Figure 2. These results suggest that the UV-irradiated T1 phage are in some way repaired in the wild type *uvr⁺* resistant bacteria, but that this repair does not occur in the *uvr⁻* strains. There is a close correlation among the various mutants between the resistance of the cell as judged by survival of colony forming ability, judged in turn by the survival of UV-irradiated T1 bacteriophage. About three-fourths of the *uvr⁻*-sensitive mutants so far isolated show a certain apparently maximal sensitivity, but one-fourth retain partial ability for reactivation, as judged both by colony formation and by the survival of UV-irradiated T1 bacteriophage.

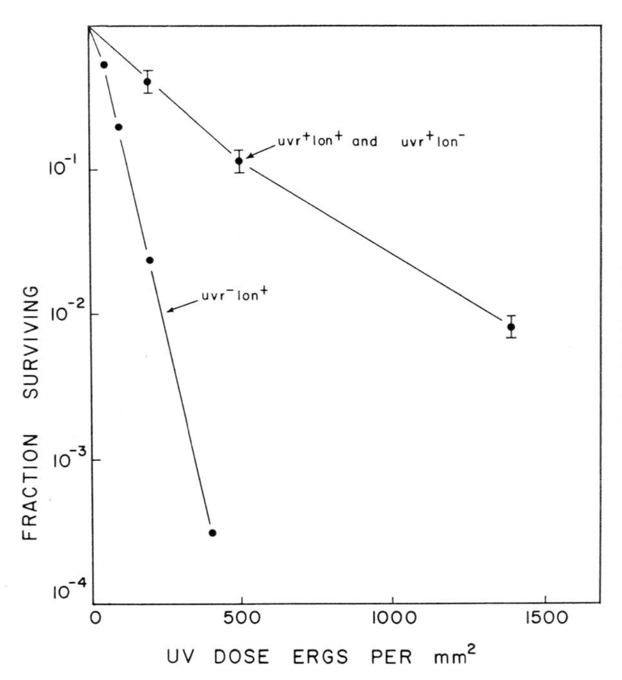

FIGURE 2. The fraction of UV-irradiated T1 bacteriophage that form plaques is plotted against the UV dose when they are plated on *uvr⁺ lon⁺*, *uvr⁺ lon⁻*, and *uvr⁻ lon⁺* strains of *E. coli* K12.

GENETIC ANALYSIS OF RADIOSENSITIVE MUTANTS

The genetic analysis of some of the mutants has shown that the repair of UV-irradiated DNA is controlled by three widely spaced genetic loci. To show this, the sensitive female *uvr⁻* mutants were mated with suitable resistant male strains of the Hfr type, thus giving a high frequency of recombinants (Howard-Flanders, Boyce, Simson, and Theriot, 1962). It is to be expected that in a cross between a resistant Hfr male and a sensitive female, the male chromosome will be transmitted and will carry the locus for radiation resistance into the female at a characteristic time and that this will lead to the development of a higher level of radiation resistance in the recombinants. To test for the time of entry of the marker for resistance, log-phase cultures of the two strains were mixed. Samples of the mating mixture taken at various times were plated on nutrient agar, exposed to ultraviolet light, and incubated. It was found that the number of recombinant cells forming visible colonies after the ultraviolet irradiation increased at a time characteristic of the strains used. Moreover, the time of entry of the *uvr*+ gene was related to the time of entry of certain nutritional markers. Mating experiments of this type have been carried out with a number of independently isolated mutants and certain appropriate Hfr strains. The results show that there are three *uvr* loci, designated *uvr*A, *uvr*B, and *uvr*C, and that all three are needed for the repair of UV-irradiated DNA. They are situated on the chromosome, as seen in Figure 3. Also shown in this figure is the *lon* locus which controls the radiosensitivity and filament formation, but which does not affect the ability to repair UV-irradiated T1 bacteriophage DNA.

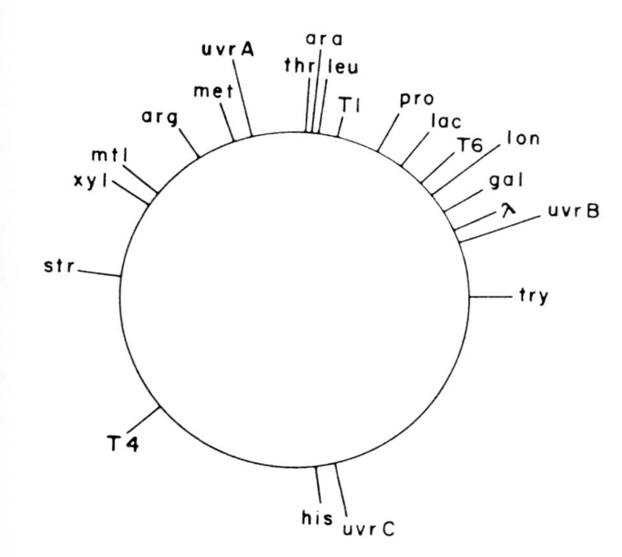

FIGURE 3. The circular chromosome map of *E. coli* K12, showing the position of various well-known biochemical markers as well as the *uvr*A, *uvr*B, *uvr*C, and *lon* loci.

There is a similarity between the characteristics of these various mutants of *E. coli* K12 and certain well-known *E. coli* B strains (Hill and Simson, 1961; Greenberg, 1964), as shown in the table.

Strains of E. coli *B. and K12, Comparable in Regard to Survival After UV-Irradiation*

E. coli B	*E. coli* K12
B/r	*lon*+ *uvr*+
B	*lon*− *uvr*+
......	*lon*+ *uvr*−
B_{S-1}	*lon*− *uvr*−

When a resistant Hfr strain of *E. coli* K12 was crossed with female *uvr*− *lon*− strain, there was a two-step increase in the radiation resistance of the recombinants, as first the *lon*+ and then the *uvr*+ markers entered the female strain and formed recombinants. Of the *uvr* mutants so far tested, it has been found that 12 map at the *uvr*A locus, 6 at *uvr*B, and 3 at *uvr*C. Double mutants of type *uvr*A *uvr*B are not more sensitive than single mutants, although mutants of intermediate sensitivity generally form more sensitive double mutants. No differences in properties have so far been detected between the *uvr*A, *uvr*B, and *uvr*C strains except for the site of the mutation. Further study of their functions is required.

Nature of the Photoproduct Repaired UV-Irradiated DNA

Several observations drew attention to thymine dimers as a photoproduct in DNA that might be repaired when UV-irradiated bacteria are incubated.

It is known that the effects of dark reactivation and photoreactivation overlap, each separately being able to repair more than 80 per cent of the UV injuries (Sauerbier, 1962). Thymine dimers formed in transforming DNA by UV light disappear when the DNA is treated with photoreactivating enzyme from yeast and then exposed to visible light (Wulff and Rupert, 1962). This result suggests that DNA containing thymine dimers may be repaired during incubation of UV-irradiated cells of the resistant strains in the dark, and raises the question as to whether a similar mechanism is involved in the uvr^+ reactivation process. During photoreactivation, the covalent bonds linking the two thymine molecules are split. This led us to ask whether the same type of repair process occurs when UV-irradiated bacteria are incubated in the dark.

Biochemical Investigation of the Mechanism of Repair of UV-Irradiated DNA

In the following experiments (Boyce and Howard-Flanders, 1964) uvr^- strains were used as a control for the resistant uvr^+ strains in the expectation that any differences found might be due to the repair processes. The DNA of uvr^- and uvr^+ strains of *E. coli* K12 was labeled by growth in the presence of tritiated thymidine. The cells were washed and exposed to a dose of 1,000 ergs/mm^2 of UV light from a low pressure mercury germicidal lamp. After irradiation, they were incubated for various times. The cells were then extracted with cold trichloroacetic acid, the acid soluble and acid precipitate fractions were separated at 0 C, and then hydrolyzed in hot trifluoroacetic acid under vacuum. They were finally analyzed by paper chromatography in butanol acetic acid water. When the radiochromatograms of the acid precipitates of UV-irradiated cells were scanned, it was found that nearly all the radioactivity appeared in a single peak at an Rf of 0.6 due to thymine. It was also found that a new peak appeared in the UV-irradiated samples at Rf 0.25. This peak was identified as thymine dimer, both by the comparison of its Rf value with that of dimer made by the UV-irradiation of frozen thymine solution, and by its being reconverted to thymine by UV-irradiation in solution after elution. It was found that in cells that had been incubated for two hours after UV-irradiation, the thymine dimer peak had fallen by about 70 per cent in the *uvr*$^+$ strain while there was no corresponding fall in the *uvr*$^-$ strain given the same treatment. Thus, thymine dimers were retained in the acid-precipitable fraction in the *uvr*$^-$ strain, while they are diminished in this fraction in the resistant strain.

Although this result could be explained by the thymine dimers being monomerized as in photoreactivation, a different conclusion was reached when the acid-soluble fractions were analyzed from the same experiment. No thymine dimers were found in the soluble fraction of cells immediately after irradiation, but they appeared quantitatively in the acid-soluble fractions of the resistant strain if incubated before acid extraction. None were found in the acid-soluble fraction of the sensitive strain. This shows that thymine dimers are cut out of the DNA during incubation of the resistant but not the sensitive strain. In another experiment, the acid-soluble fractions were chromatographed, but the hot acid hydrolysis step was omitted. In this experiment, there was no evidence of there being any free thymine dimer. These results indicate that thymine dimers were excised from the DNA, but as they remained close to the origin of the chromatography paper, they were thought to be still attached to part of the phosphate-diester backbone. Analysis of the products on diethylaminoethyl (DEAE) paper indicates that the dimers may appear in the form of a trinucleotide (Setlow and Carrier, 1964). Thus, excision must occur by cleavage of the DNA phospho-diester backbone.

It has also been found that during incubation after UV-irradiation, there is a release of the radioactive thymine from the DNA in the *uvr*$^+$ but not in the *uvr*$^-$ strains. This breakdown may be as much as 25 per cent of the total counts in the DNA in certain experiments and corresponds to about 200 to 500 nucleotides per thymine dimer. Evidently, a gap is formed in a single strand of the deoxyribonucleic acid by the excision of the thymine dimer and the gap is then widened, presumably through the action of nucleases.

These results show that the repair of DNA during incubation of the UV-irradiated resistant strains of bacteria proceed through an unexpectedly complicated process. In this the thymine dimers still attached to part of the phospho-diester backbone are excised or cut out of the DNA chain, thus breaking the backbone of the single strand. This appears to be accompanied by the release of many nucleotides from the DNA for each dimer excised. This remarkable observation was made first by Setlow and Carrier (1964) and confirmed in our laboratories shortly afterwards (Boyce and Howard-Flanders, 1964).

Evidence for the insertion of new bases into DNA has recently been obtained by incubating UV-irradiated bacteria in the presence of 5-bromouracil (Pettijohn and Hanawalt, 1964), and analyzing the DNA in a CsCl density gradient.

Proposed Mechanism of Repair of UV-Irradiated DNA

These results have led us to suggest that the repair process controlled by the *uvr* loci in *E. coli* K12 proceeds by the mechanism outlined in Figure 4. The top line shows a short segment of the UV-irradiated DNA that con-

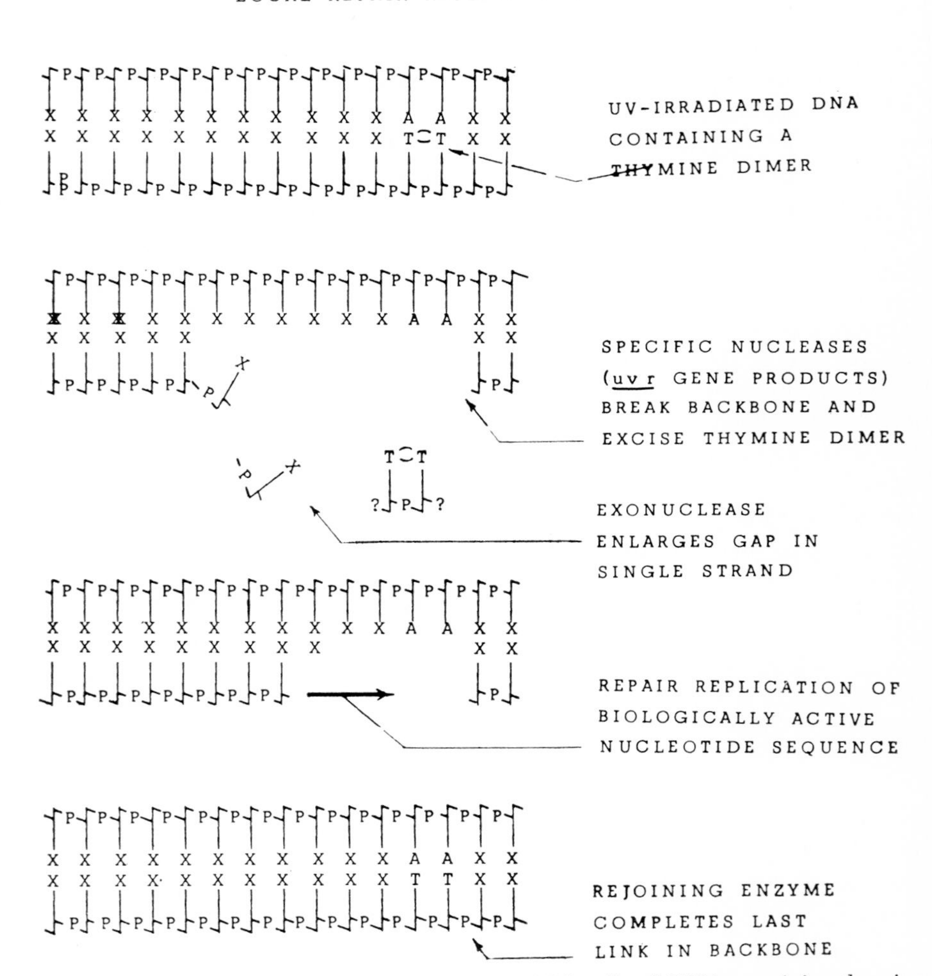

FIGURE 4. Proposed mechanism for the repair of UV-irradiated DNA containing thymine dimers. The thymine dimer is presumably cut out of the DNA by nucleases controlled by the *uvr* loci. The dimer is released while still attached to part of the phosphate-sugar backbone, thus forming a gap in the single strand. This gap is widened, presumably by an exonuclease, with the release of nucleotides. The gap is then filled in by a repair replication enzyme which presumably inserts bases complementary to those in the other strand, thus reconstructing the biologically active nucleotide sequence. Finally, the last link in the backbone is completed by a rejoining enzyme that reconstructs the last phosphate-diester linkage. (After Setlow and Carrier, 1964 and Boyce and Howard-Flanders, 1964.)

tains a thymine dimer. This thymine dimer with an unknown amount of phosphate and other nucleotides attached is cut out of the DNA, leaving a gap in one of the two strands. This gap is subsequently widened with the release of many nucleotides with each dimer. To judge by the recovery of biological activity, bases complementary to those of the other strand must then be inserted into the gap by a repair replicase enzyme and the backbone finally rejoined enzymatically. It is worth noting, however, that many features of the breakdown followed by repair replication and rejoining may also occur during genetic recombination and the termination of DNA synthesis in organisms such as *E. coli* that have a circular chromosome.

Radiosensitization by Base Analogue Substitution

There is a large difference in the fraction of UV-irradiated T1 bacteriophage that forms plaques on uvr^+ and uvr^- strains of *E. coli* K12. When this experiment was repeated with T1 bacteriophage that contained 5-bromouracil in partial substitution for thymine, it was found that there was relatively little difference between the numbers of plaques formed on the uvr^+ and uvr^- strains and that these numbers were comparable to the numbers formed by irradiated normal phage plated on the uvr^- strain (Howard-Flanders, Boyce, Simson and Theriot, 1962). This observation shows that DNA containing 5-bromouracil is not efficiently repaired. While breakdown after UV irradiation occurs normally, the capacity to incorporate radioactive thymidine into acid precipitable DNA after irradiation is much lower in cells with 5-bromouracil containing DNA than in cells with normal DNA (Aoki, Howard-Flanders and Boyce, Unpublished data). This indicates that the reconstruction of the DNA by the insertion of complementary nucleotides may not take place correctly.

ACKNOWLEDGMENTS

This work was supported by grants GM11014, 5-k6-AM-9397, and CA 06519 from the United States Public Health Service.

REFERENCES

Aoki; Howard-Flanders, P., and Boyce, R. P. Unpublished data.

Beukers, R., and W. Berends. 1960. Isolation and Identification of the Irradiation Product of Thymine. *Biochimica et biophysica acta*, 41:550–551.

Bollum, F. J., and R. B. Setlow. 1963. Ultraviolet Inactivation of DNA Primer Activity. I. Effects of Different Wavelengths and Doses. *Biochimica et biophysica acta*, 68:599–607.

Boyce, R. P., and P. Howard-Flanders. 1964. Release of Ultraviolet Light-Induced Thymine Dimers from DNA in *E. coli* K-12. *Proceedings of the National Academy of Sciences of the U.S.A.*, 51:293–300.

Ellison, S. A., R. R. Feiner, and R. F. Hill. 1960. A Host Effect on Bacteriophage Survival after Ultraviolet Irradiation. *Virology*, 11:294–296.

Greenberg, J. 1964. A Locus for Radiation Resistance in *Escherichia coli*. *Genetics*, 49:771–778.

Hill, R. F. 1958. A Radiation-Sensitive Mutant of *Escherichia coli*. *Biochimica et biophysica acta*, 30:636–637.

Hill, R. F., and E. Simson. 1961. A Study of Radiosensitive and Radioresistant Mutants of *Escherichia coli* Strain B. *The Journal of General Microbiology*, 24:1–14.

Howard-Flanders, P., R. P. Boyce, E. Simson, and L. Theriot. 1962. A Genetic Locus in *E. coli* K-12 that Controls the Reactivation of UV-Photoproducts Associated with Thymine in DNA. *Proceedings of the National Academy of Sciences of the U.S.A.*, 48:2109–2115.

Howard-Flanders, P., E. Simson, and L. Theriot. 1964. A Locus that Controls Filament Formation and Sensitivity to Radiation in *Escherichia coli* K-12. *Genetics*, 49:237–246.

Howard-Flanders, P., and L. Theriot. 1962. A Method for Selecting Radiation-Sensitive Mutants of *Escherichia coli*. *Genetics*, 47:1219–1224.

Pettijohn, D., and P. Hanawalt. 1964. Evidence for Repair—Replication of Ultraviolet Damaged DNA in Bacteria. *Journal of Molecular Biology*, 9:395–410.

Sauerbier, W. 1962. The Bacterial Mechanism Reactivating UV-Irradiated Phage in the Dark (Host-Cell Reactivation). *Zeitschrift für Vererbungslehre*, 93:220–228.

Setlow, R. B., and W. L. Carrier. 1964. The Disappearance of Thymine Dimers from DNA: An Error-Correcting Mechanism. *Proceedings of the National Academy of Sciences of the U.S.A.*, 51:226–231.

Setlow, R. B., and J. K. Setlow. 1962. Evidence that Ultraviolet-Induced Thymine Dimers in DNA Caused Biological Damage. *Proceedings of the National Academy of Sciences of the U.S.A.*, 48:1250–1257.

Wacker, A. 1963. "Molecular Mechanisms of Radiation Effects," *Progress in Nucleic Acid Research*, J. N. Davidson and W. E. Cohn, Eds. New York, New York, and London, England: Academic Press. Vol. I. Pp. 369–399.

Wulff, D. L., and C. S. Rupert. 1962. Disappearance of Thymine Photodimer in Ultraviolet Irradiated DNA upon Treatment with a Photoreactivating Enzyme from Baker's Yeast. *Biochemical and Biophysical Research Communications*, 7:237–240.

DISCUSSION

Dr. Daniel Billen, The University of Texas M. D. Anderson Hospital and Tumor Institute, Houston, Texas: Dr. Roger Hewitt and I are currently using an isotope marker and a density label to follow new DNA synthesis. We have observed that low doses of ultraviolet rays (UV) (50 to 100 ergs/mm^2) will distort the replication kinetics of the isotope-labeled region once the DNA synthesizing system is restored. The period after thymine dimer repair is followed by DNA replication at these low doses. Our results indicate that although removal of thymine dimers does occur, there is at least one additional region of replication introduced which was not present before UV exposure. If repair occurs, are protein and RNA synthesis blocked following the UV challenge?

Dr. Paul Howard-Flanders, Yale University School of Medicine, New Haven, Connecticut: Dr. Robert Shuster in our laboratory has been able to show that at least the first stage in the repair process, dimer excision, proceeds under conditions of starvation and even under conditions of thymine deprivation. What happens in the later stages in repair is more difficult to observe.

Dr. Franklin Hutchinson, Yale University, New Haven, Connecticut: Dr. Johns, is there any evidence that the cross sections for the formation of various products are dependent upon the chain length of the material? In order to form the dimers, the material has to be held together in some way, and one might expect that the chain length might be involved, as well as spatial relationships if the bases are held in position by a double helical structure. Has any progress been made in identifying the different dimers by study of the photoproducts formed in the radiation of crystals of bases?

Dr. Harold E. Johns, The Ontario Cancer Institute, and University of Toronto, Toronto, Canada: At the present time we do not know what happens when poly U of various lengths is irradiated. The Monte Carlo calculations which I showed are not sensitive to the length of this chain. It does not matter if the calculations are based on 100 or

1,000 nucleotides per chain. We have not been able to isolate the products of irradiated poly U, but we are working on this. We would like to enzymatically isolate dimers and hydrates from irradiated poly U and measure the amount of each of these that is produced as a function of doses. We also hope to measure the length of poly U in our amino acid incorporating system using electron microscopy.

We have started to look into the nature of the photoproducts formed on irradiation in frozen solution, and have found a host of photoproducts which we are now trying to identify. We have not looked at crystals.

Dr. Manley Mandel, The University of Texas M. D. Anderson Hospital and Tumor Institute, Houston, Texas: Dr. Johns, in studying the phenylalanine incorporation of the irradiated and nonirradiated poly U, have you checked the rate of incorporation of leucine which is coded for also? It would be of particular interest to determine the relative rates of incorporation of each of the amino acids at different concentrations of Mg^{++} with the irradiated and normal primer.

Dr. Johns: We have looked at leucine and found no increase in incorporation with dose; the only other amino acid that we have looked at is serine. In five experiments, we have found that the amount of serine incorporated decreased with dose to the poly U. This is opposite to the results obtained by Dr. Grossman about a year ago. Our results on leucine agree with Grossman's findings.

Dr. Waclaw Szybalski, McArdle Memorial Laboratory, University of Wisconsin, Madison, Wisconsin: Do you have any idea about the chemical nature of the cross-links between the complementary DNA strands induced by UV light?

Dr. Johns: We have no information in our laboratory on cross-linking.

Dr. L. Grossman, Brandeis University, Waltham, Massachusetts: I would like to answer Dr. Szybalski's question concerning the UV-induced cross-links and Dr. Mandel's question on serine incorporation. Polydeoxy AT, because of its alternating adenine-thymine sequence in which two thymine residues are separated by an adenine residue, has been used as a "target" for induced cross-linking. Following irradiation, most of the polydeoxy AT polymers become cross-linked, whereas poly dA$\overline{BU}$ and polydeoxy GC remain unlinked. Polydeoxy AT was also prepared in which the thymine residues were labeled and following irradiation subsequent isolation of labeled thymine dimer could be demonstrated. By analogy, therefore, one must presume that an isomer which differs from intrastrand dimers had been produced. Since it is in very small quantity, it has not been possible to determine its properties. That Dr. John's group was observing serine incorporation with unirradiated poly U is indicative of the degeneracy of the amino acid incorporating system. It is imperative under such circumstances to isolate and purify the polyphenylalamine from the reaction mixtures. This procedure reduces incorporation "noise" to zero and permits evaluation of the low levels of serine incorporation following irradiation.

Dr. L. Grossman: From our data, the quantum yield for the dimers isolated from labeled polydeoxy AT is almost 1,000 times lower than those found for intrastrand thymine dimer. If one calculates back, one can argue that it is highly unlikely that intrastrand or cross-link formation is very important biologically.

Chairman Peter Alexander, Chester Beatty Research Institute, Institute of Cancer Research, Royal Cancer Hospital, London, England: Since there are no further discussions on the photochemical aspects, perhaps we can turn to the general problem of repair following ultraviolet irradiation.

Dr. Howard-Flanders, do you think that the effect, reported by J. H. Stuy (*Radiation Research*, 14:56–65, 1961), that very soon after irradiation of *E. coli* the total amount of DNA in the cell decreases, could be attributable to this exonuclease enzyme?

Dr. Howard-Flanders: The only evidence for the nuclease is that breakdown occurs in the resistant but not in the sensitive mutants. This is, at first sight, the wrong-way-round. You might expect that after ultraviolet irradiation the DNA would break down more rapidly in the sensitive rather than in the resistant strains. In fact, the contrary is true. Under the conditions we have used, only one or two per cent DNA breakdown occurs in the sensitive strain during the first half hour after irradiation, while in the resistant strain there is 10 or 12 per cent breakdown. We suggest that this breakdown, which probably occurs in association with the excision of thymine dimers, is an integral part of the repair process.

Chairman Alexander: This would seem to provide satisfactory resolution of a paradox which I think worried the Yugoslav group who extended the original observation of Stuy. They found that there is no correlation between radiosensitivity and the amount of DNA disappearing soon after irradiation and they also found that this degradation depends on the energy source in the medium (Kos and Drakulic, *Radiation Research*, 19:439–466, 1963). I believe that the phenomena you report may be linked to their observation.

Dr. R. F. Kimball, Biology Division, Oak Ridge National Laboratory, Oak Ridge, Tennessee: As a postscript to Dr. Howard-Flanders' paper, I might mention Dr. Setlow's work (*Science*, 142:1464–1466, 1963). He has been able to show in the sensitive strain *E. coli* B_S that the presence of the dimers, which are not removed, completely blocks DNA synthesis. This is of some interest in connection with earlier work of Bollum and Setlow (*Biochimica et biophysica acta*, 68:599–607, 1963), which seems to show that in the in vitro system there is not a complete blockage of polymerization, but some polymerization at a very low rate around the dimer. Apparently in the B_S, so far, there is no real evidence for such a mechanism. I might also re-emphasize something that came up in connection with Dr. Howard-Flanders' remarks, that there can be considerable differences in colony-forming ability in those strains that remove the thymine dimers by cutting. Dr. Setlow (*Proceedings of the National Academy of Sciences of the U.S.A.*, 51:226–231, 1964), has shown that strains B and B/r both remove most of the thymine dimers by cutting. Yet they are very different in sensitivity for colony-forming ability.

Dr. Howard-Flanders: A point of interest in this connection is the greater sensitivity in the filament-forming strains of B or K12. With the four strains of K12 shown in the first figure (Figure 1, page 53), the greater sensitivity of the filament-forming *lon* mutants is found both in the uvr^+ and the uvr^- strains. The conclusion that I draw from this is that in some way the *lon* mutants are more disturbed by a given number of defects in their DNA. A given number of defects may result from a high dose largely repaired in a uvr^+ strain, or a small dose given to a uvr^- strain.

Dr. Kimball: In connection with the filament-forming strains, and going now to X rays, Dr. Adler at the Oak Ridge laboratory has some evidence that suggests to him that the main block in some of the filament-forming strains to colony-forming formation is the failure to form cross-walls. This failure seems to be the really sensitive thing and perhaps has nothing very much to do directly with the DNA.

Dr. Mortimer Elkind, National Cancer Institute, National Institutes of Health, Bethesda, Maryland: Dr. Howard-Flanders, in connection with the appearance of thymine dimers in the acid-soluble material of irradiated resistant strains, have you examined the temperature dependence, and if so, could you give us some idea of how the rate of appearance of dimers depends on temperature?

Dr. Howard-Flanders: Dr. Richard Boyce investigated the effect of heating the cells to 75 C for 10 minutes before UV-irradiation. He then looked for the excision of thymine dimers during subsequent incubation. This short heat treatment had very little effect on the DNA, but completely inhibited the excision of thymine dimers. We have no data on the temperature coefficients at low temperatures that I think you were interested in.

Dr. William B. Looney, University of Virginia School of Medicine, Charlottesville, Virginia: Would Dr. Howard-Flanders comment on the depression of synthesis in *E. coli* and the depression of synthesis in mammalian cells following irradiation? For instance, on DNA synthesis we note that the depression after irradiation does not occur until between 30 and 60 minutes and this continues to be depressed. If we assume that thymine dimerization is a major mechanism for DNA depression, then it would seem this depression in mammalian cells should occur very quickly and recover, whereas the reverse seems to be true. I would like for Dr. Howard-Flanders to comment on his findings in *E. coli* and on this finding in mammalian cells following X-radiation.

Dr. Howard-Flanders: I think it is difficult to answer these questions because what happens in *E. coli* may or may not happen in mammalian cells. Moreover, the thymine dimers seem to be an important radiation product affecting biological activity following UV-irradiation, but they are not formed in appreciable quantities following X-irradiation when various different products are formed.

Dr. Grossman: One of the interesting biological effects of UV is the increased rate of genetic recombination. I wonder whether, since the mechanisms which have been proposed for such recombinations involve breakage and reunion which is analogous to the selective removal of dimers, you have any experimental evidence relating to this problem?

Dr. Howard-Flanders: Genetic recombination in the absence of radiation occurs in *uvr*+ and in *uvr*− cells to about the same extent. We have investigated UV-induced genetic recombination in two situations—between T1 bacteriophage mutants and between markers on the Hfr chromosome and female chromosome. In each case, UV increased the frequency of recombination more rapidly in the *uvr*− strain than in the *uvr*+ strain. Thus, in the *uvr*− strains, the UV products form a block that leads to a genetic switch, whereas in the resistant strains, there is repair and a reduced frequency of UV-induced genetic recombination. The mechanism that we suggested for dark repair is almost identical with the mechanism that one would write down for the later stages of genetic recombination between homologous DNA strands.

Dr. Tikvah Alper, Medical Research Council, Hammersmith Hospital, London, England: I would like to follow up the point made by Dr. Kimball about *E. coli* B and B/r. Dr. Howard-Flanders was saying that there are different considerations applying to *E. coli* B because it forms filaments and different mechanisms come into play. I should like to remind him of the observation that if you treat *E. coli* with chloramphenicol after UV, or for that matter after X rays, you get the maximum effect of the rescuing treatment if the cells have been metabolizing in very vigorous growth conditions. You get the maximum rescuing effect if you start chloramphenicol treatment at about the end of the lag phase when the filament formation is, of course, just about at its maximum, or at any rate, filaments are present in very great numbers. So it does appear that you have rescue mechanisms that can operate even after filament formation has taken place. I should like also to mention some results of Dr. Neil Gillies which he very kindly gave me permission to use. I mention these because they are relevant to some of Dr. Howard-Flanders' data on the BUdR phage which he showed were not capable of being rescued in the host cells. Dr. Gillies has found that *E. coli* B incorporating 5-BU are capable of a greater amount of chloramphenicol rescue than are the thymine-grown cells. I think that this is an important observation. I had thought of mentioning it tomorrow, but there is a very general idea that the incorporation of BU interferes with reactivation or repair, and I think that these observations of Dr. Gillies should be borne in mind.

Dr. Thomas Wood, University of Pennsylvania, Philadelphia, Pennsylvania: I should like to comment on a previous question concerning the effects of UV on genetic recombination in the *E. coli* K12 mating system. We have studied this system rather extensively, using not only UV but X rays and alpha rays, and the following general comments can be made. Irradiation of female cells before mating results in a preferential utilization in the recombinational process of the nonirradiated male genetic information. However, if the male is irradiated before the mating, a preferential utilization of the female genetic information is observed. In general then, we have found that irradiation results in recombinants whose genetic information comes primarily from the nonirradiated parent. These results can be explained by either a copy choice or a break-and-reunion hypothesis. If the recombination process is due to copy choice, these results can be explained in terms of switches on the irradiated material that would cause a preferential utilization of the nondamaged material. If it is a break-and-reunion process, the linkage between the lethal elements produced by the irradiation and the genetic markers on the irradiated parent would cause a bias in favor of the nonirradiated chromosomal material. In addition, I would like to suggest that one has to be fairly cautious about the very interesting model Dr. Howard-Flanders suggested for the repair of UV damage, because there may be many other effects of UV-radiation even in the relatively simple K12 system. We have found at least three types of radiation lesions in this system. The first, which I have previously mentioned, affects genetic recombination *per se*; a second effect of UV is on the transfer process and reduces the ability of the donor to transfer markers to the female; and the third type of lesion affects the ability of the irradiated cell to mate. There may be other types of lesions, but we have positively identified only these three types.

Transient Chemical Species Formed by Radiation

John W. Boag and Gerald E. Adams

Research Unit in Radiobiology, British Empire Cancer Campaign, Mount Vernon Hospital, Northwood, England

The nature and extent of radiation damage produced in living cells can be greatly influenced by the chemical environment of the cells at the instant of irradiation (Gray, 1957; Howard-Flanders, 1957; Howard-Flanders and Moore, 1958; Powers, Webb, and Kaleta, 1960; Scott, 1963). This fact alone is strong confirmation of the important role which radiation-chemical reactions play in the development of cellular damage. Even more direct evidence implicating free radical intermediates in the development of biological damage has been obtained in dry systems (Powers, Ehret, and Smaller, 1961; Hunt, Till, and Williams, 1962; Zimmer, Köhnlein, Hotz, and Müller, 1963) and in frozen solutions (Henriksen, 1962) by the method of electron spin resonance (ESR). This technique, which is uniquely sensitive and specific for radicals, has been used to study the radicals formed in nonpolar liquids (Fessenden and Schuler, 1963) but it is technically more difficult in aqueous systems. In studying the nature and behavior of the transient species formed in irradiated aqueous systems at room temperature, the method of optical absorption spectroscopy has proved to be particularly productive. Before describing the results obtained by this method, some attention will be given to the experimental techniques and apparatus used.

All the results presented have been obtained by pulse radiolysis, that is, by firing into the solution to be studied an electron pulse lasting from one half of a microsecond to a few microseconds and measuring the subsequent optical absorption of the solution as a function of wavelength and of time. In favorable instances, the nature and concentrations of the initial species formed can be determined, their rate of disappearance by reaction followed, the growth and decay of any longer-lived transients observed, and the permanent products identified. Frequently, some of the reacting species have no significant optical absorption throughout the visible and ultraviolet regions, and their presence then has to be inferred from the kinetics of those other species which have identifiable absorption spectra.

Experimental Techniques

Two methods of recording the spectra are commonly employed, which may be called "flash spectroscopy" and "kinetic spectroscopy," respectively. The former is particularly suitable for observing what transients are present in a given system, the latter for accurate measurement of reaction orders and rate constants.

Flash Spectroscopy

This method uses a short, intense flash of light to record the complete absorption spectrum of the solution photographically at a chosen instant (Porter, 1950; Matheson and Dorfman, 1960; McCarthy and MacLachlan, 1960; Boag and Steele, 1961; Boag, Steele, and Hart, 1963). An illustration of a set of spectra obtained in this way is presented in Figure 1, and the evaluation of these spectra by means of a densitometer is shown in

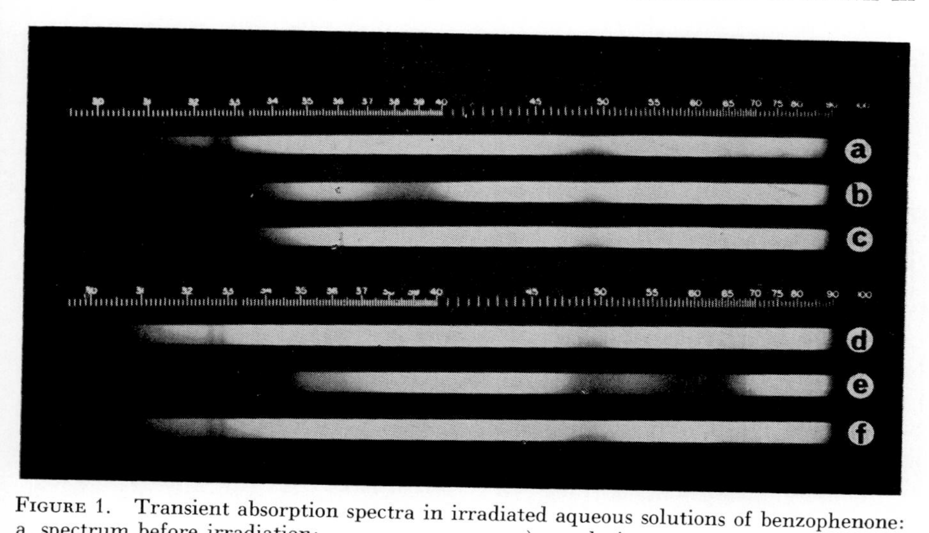

FIGURE 1. Transient absorption spectra in irradiated aqueous solutions of benzophenone:

a, spectrum before irradiation;) —solution
b, spectrum with 2 μsec trigger delay;) contained
) 10^{-2} N
c, spectrum 1 min after irradition.) H_2SO_4

d, spectrum before irradiation;
e, spectrum with 2 μsec trigger delay;) —solution
) contained
f, spectrum 1 min after irradiation.) 0.05 M Na_2CO_3

(Note: When these spectra were taken, copper electrode tips were in the underwater spark light source; this accounts for the pair of strong reversed lines between 3,200 and 3,300 A. Generally, uranium tips were used; these gave an almost perfect continuum.) (From Adams, Baxendale, and Boag, 1964b. Reproduced by permission of the Royal Society.)

Figure 2. The light source used in taking these was an underwater spark (Boag, 1957, 1963a). This gives a very intense continuum relatively free from superimposed lines, and thus makes it easy to obtain accurate difference curves. If the electrode tips are made of uranium, the continuum is practically perfect (Boag, 1957); copper, silver, or gold tips are also fairly satisfactory, each showing only two strong reversed lines. The duration of the underwater spark depends upon the electric circuit constants and upon the afterglow in the spark channel.

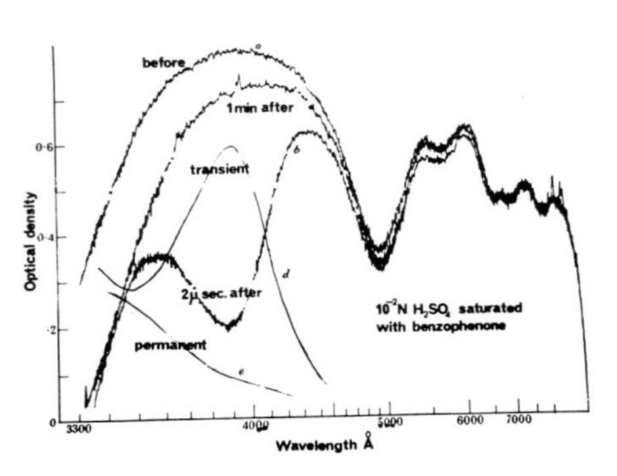

FIGURE 2. Densitometer traces from the spectra a—b—c shown in Figure 1.

Oscillograms showing the light output from three different light sources as a function of time are given in Figure 3. With a 0.05 μf low-inductance condenser charged to 20 kv, an effective duration of 5 μsec is readily ob-

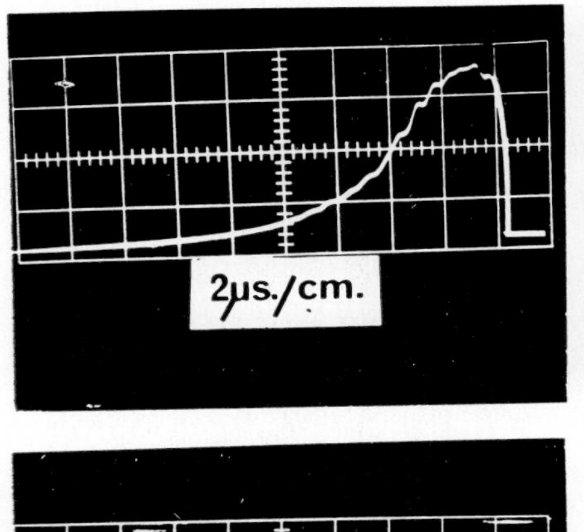

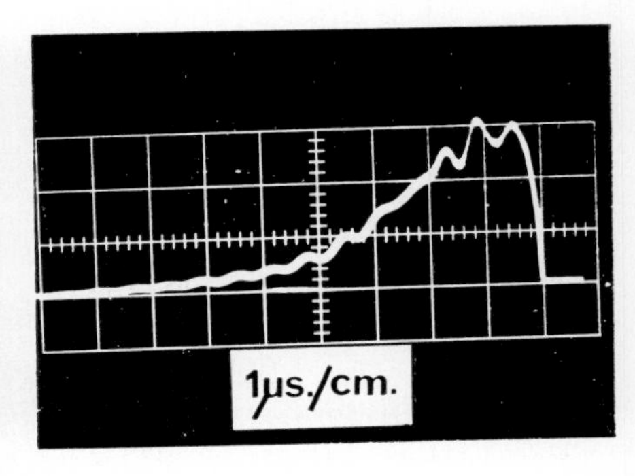

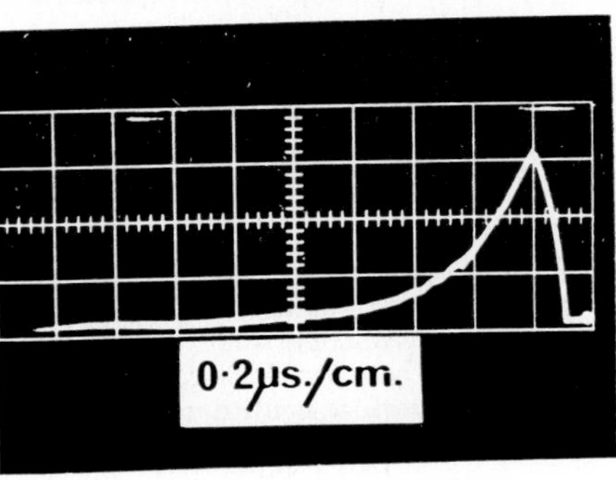

FIGURE 3. Duration of light output from spark light sources used. Top left, underwater spark between uranium electrodes fed by 0.05 μf low inductance capacitor 20 kv. Top right, underwater spark between uranium tips fed by barium titanate cylinder 0.018 μf 20 kv. Bottom left, spark in argon jet between copper tips fed by barium titanate cylinder 0.018 μf 20 kv.

tained. The same spark gap fed by a barium titanate condenser of 0.018 μf capacity gave an effective spark duration of some 2.5 μsec. A much faster spark is obtained with an argon jet spark gap. In the latter case, the effective duration is less than 0.5 μsec, but the spectrum has many strong lines superimposed on the continuum, and this makes it difficult to plot smooth difference curves. With any of these spark light sources, it is usually possible to take a good spectrogram on a medium-resolution spectrograph with a single flash. When slower infrared emulsions are used, several sparks may be required to build up an adequate blackening, but the technique is still a remarkably rapid one in view of the great amount of information which a single plate can yield.

The solution to be irradiated is introduced into a quartz cell, using the syringe method of handling solutions under controlled gas tension (Senvar and Hart, 1958). The optical path through the cell is made as long as possible by producing a ribbon-shaped electron beam which can irradiate the whole length of a relatively long cell, and using multiple-pass by reflection from the partially aluminized ends of the cell. A general view of the equipment is given in Figure 4.

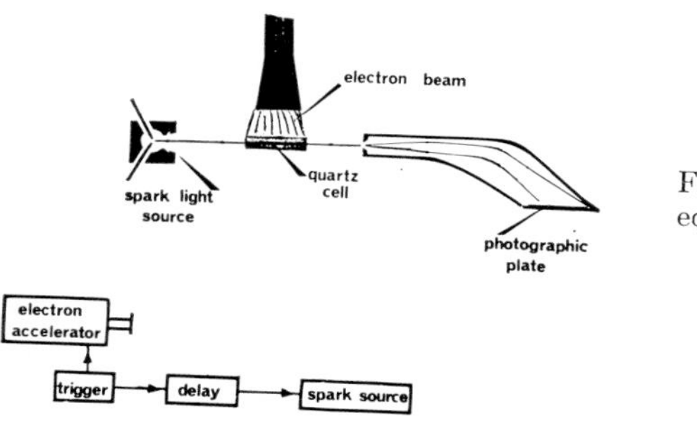

FIGURE 4. Diagrammatic view of the equipment for flash spectroscopy.

Kinetic Spectroscopy

This technique employs a continuous light source, a monochromator, and a photomultiplier, the output of the latter being displayed and photographed on an oscillograph (Dorfman, Taub, and Bühler, 1962; Gordon *et al.*, 1963; Keene, 1963a, 1964a). At the present time, this method yields better time resolution than does flash spectroscopy. It is also much more sensitive, since an absorption smaller than one per cent of the incident light can be amplified and recorded accurately, whereas flash spectroscopy demands at least 50 per cent absorption for accurate work. This higher sensitivity can be used to explore reaction rates for very low radiation doses. Keene (1963b) has studied the rate of disappearance of the electron spectrum for a dose as low as 10 rads. An oscillogram showing the buildup of the hydrated electron absorption at 5,430 A during a 2 μsec pulse of 600 rads of fast electron radiation, and the subsequent disappearance of the electron by recombination with H^+ in a 50 micromolar solution of sulfuric acid is shown in Figure 5 (Keene, 1964a): The reaction order and rate constant for a simple reaction such as this may be determined directly from the shape of the decay curve. In any complex system, it is necessary to check carefully that no other transient species are formed which absorb at the wavelength selected.

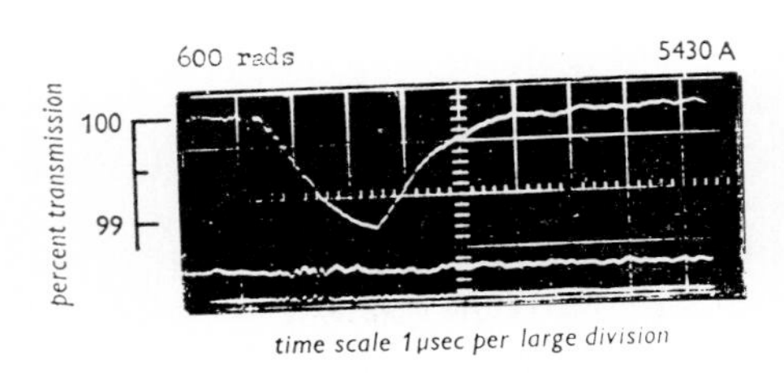

FIGURE 5. Oscilloscope trace of absorption in 50×10^{-6} N sulfuric acid at 5,430 A after a dose of 600 rads. The buildup of absorption during the 2 μsec pulse and its disappearance due to reaction of hydrated electrons with H^+ are observed. (From Keene, 1964a.)

Transient Species Observed

In looking for new transient species by the method of absorption spectroscopy, it has to be borne in mind that absorption spectra in liquids are generally broad bands having a half width of hundreds of Ångstroms. Since the total wavelength range readily accessible to optical spectroscopy extends only from some 2,000 A to 9,000 A, overlapping of absorption bands is to be expected, and the spectra obtained must, therefore, be subjected to many tests before a particular absorption band can be identified with a known chemical species. The flash spectroscopic method, which yields a complete spectrogram is particularly useful in this respect, since small changes in shape of spectra under varying conditions are readily detected.

The Hydrated Electron

One interesting new species found by the method of flash spectroscopy was the hydrated electron (Hart and Boag, 1962; Boag and Hart, 1963; Keene, 1963a). This species had been predicted on theoretical grounds some 10 years earlier (Platzman, 1953; Stein, 1952), but little attention was paid to the prediction at that time. However, within the past five years, radiation chemists have found it necessary to postulate a second reducing species, different from the hydrogen atom, in irradiated aqueous solutions. By varying the ionic strength, it was shown that this species carried a unit negative charge (Czapski and Schwarz, 1962; Collinson, Dainton, Smith, and Tazuké, 1962), and it was, therefore, considered to be an electron stabilized in some way. The physical nature of this species was not clear, however.

Experimental

The first observation leading to the recognition of the absorption spectrum of the hydrated electron (Hart and Boag, 1962) was made in a deaerated aqueous solution of sodium carbonate of strength 0.5 M on a panchromatic plate sensitive to 6,500 A. The complete absorption band was then obtained by using an infrared emulsion, sensitive to 9,000 A, and its identification with the hydrated electron was confirmed by testing the influence of several known electron scavengers, including oxygen, N_2O, CO_2. The same band was then found in pure deaerated water, but not in acid solutions, since the hydrogen ion rapidly captures the electron. The shape of the complete absorption spectrum is shown in Figure 6 as determined photographically, and for comparison a recent careful plot of the spectrum by means of the photomultiplier technique is shown (Baxendale *et al.*, 1964). The peak of the absorption band lies near 7,000 A, and is thus quite close to the value predicted by Platzman on theoretical grounds (2 ev).

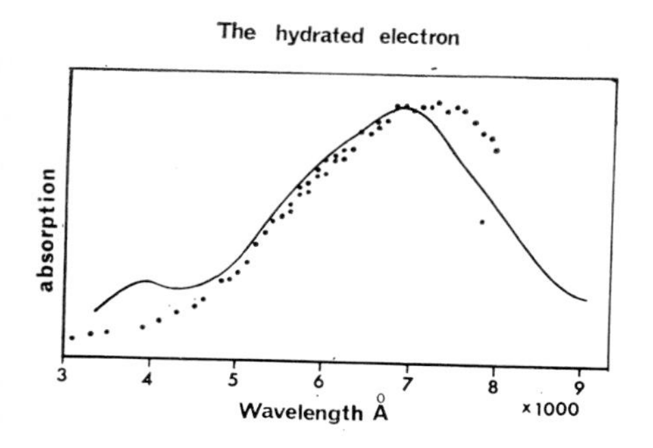

FIGURE 6. The absorption spectrum of the hydrated electron: The spectrum determined by flash spectroscopy (Hart and Boag, 1962) is compared with that plotted out by kinetic spectroscopy (Baxendale, *et al.*, 1964).

In the initial photographic work, we did not attribute significance to the ripples on the absorption curves, since these appeared to be caused almost entirely by variations in the emulsion gamma, for which no corrections were applied. There was, however, some indication that in sodium carbonate solutions, the elimination of the electron spectrum by oxygen or its decay with time was accompanied by a shift of the peak towards 6,000 A.

Further evidence for the existence of the hydrated electron has been obtained by conductivity measurements in deaerated water. These showed an enhanced initial conductivity which decayed within a few microseconds of the electron pulse (Boag, 1963b; Boag, Adams, and Hart, 1964a).

Theoretical

The physical description and properties of the hydrated electron are best discussed in relation to the theory of solvated electrons in other polar media such as liquid ammonia or methylamine (Das, 1962; Yost and Russell, 1944). It has been known for more than 100 years (Weyl, 1864) that a solution of sodium or other alkali metal in liquid ammonia possesses peculiar properties. Dilute solutions show a blue color which increases in intensity as the concentration of dissolved sodium increases, and ultimately becomes bronze with a metallic luster. Dilute solutions also show high electrical conductance, while concentrated solutions conduct almost as readily as a metal. More recently, it has been shown (Hutchison and Pastor,

1951, 1953) that these solutions have an ESR spectrum consisting of an exceedingly narrow line centered at the value for a free electron. All these properties suggested that electrons, free or loosely bound, must be present in the solution, and it was an obvious hypothesis that the phenomena were due to the dissociation of the sodium atom into a positive ion and a free electron. Attempts to treat these electrons as if they were a free electron gas, as in a metal, were, however, unsuccessful.

It was known that the addition of sodium to liquid ammonia caused a considerable increase in volume, and Ogg (1946) suggested that the electrons might be considered to be trapped in cavities in the liquid. Crude as this model was, it permitted a quantum theoretical treatment to be used which predicted discrete energy levels, transitions between which could yield the observed optical absorption.

The first suggestion of a more satisfactory theoretical model for these liquid ammonia solutions was made by Davidov (1948). His approach was based on Landau's proposal (1933) that electrons might be trapped in ionic crystals by their own polarization field. Traps of this kind were called "polarons" by Pekar (1954), who continued Landau's work. In liquids, as distinct from crystals, it was possible for the molecules to orient themselves freely around the charged species. Davidov's suggestion was taken up by Deigen, and a fairly detailed quantum mechanical theory of the optical electrical and magnetic properties of these liquid ammonia solutions was worked out by him (Deigen, 1954).

Independently of this work, and at the same time, Platzman had studied the problem of how an electron, which had been slowed down to thermal energies in a polar solvent, could be stabilized by polarization, working it out for the case of water (Platzman, 1953). He called the trapped electron in water the "hydrated electron," by analogy with the hydration of an ion. Weiss (1960, 1963) introduced the term "polaron" into aqueous radiation chemistry and drew attention to Pekar's work.

The theoretical model discussed above is illustrated in Figure 7. The electron ejected from an ionized molecule, after it has been slowed down to thermal energies, eventually succeeds in imposing an average radial polarization on the surrounding polar solvent molecules, those remote from it as well as those adjacent to it, and thereby creates for itself a positive potential well from which it cannot readily escape. In such a trap the elec-

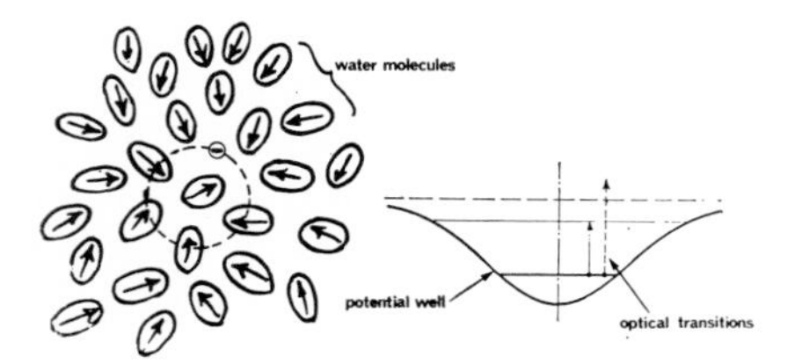

FIGURE 7. Physical model of the hydrated electron. The electron polarizes the medium, and is then trapped in the potential well thus set up (Platzman, 1953; Davidov, 1948; Deigen, 1954).

tron will have one or more quantized energy levels, and transitions between these or from these to the ionization continuum will give rise to the observed optical absorption spectrum.

Reactions of the Hydrated Electron

The importance of the hydrated electron to radiobiology lies in the specificity of its reactions. Although it may not look like a radical, it is in fact a transient species which reacts in entirely characteristic ways with any solutes present. Being negatively charged, it may react preferentially with any regions of excess positive charge on large organic molecules. Although the electron absorption spectrum is most readily seen in a solution at high pH, this does not indicate that the hydrated electron is only formed under these conditions. On the contrary, a high proportion of all the electrons ejected from ionized molecules in an aqueous solution will first become "hydrated" and will then react with whatever solutes are present or with the water itself in a manner determined by the relative solute concentrations and the rate constants for the reactions. Under acidic conditions, most of the hydrated electrons will be captured by H^+ to form hydrogen atoms which will then react with other solutes present. At neutral pH, as in living cells, the reactions undergone by the electron will be determined by the solute concentrations and rate constants. The fact that the hydrated electron may not live more than a microsecond is irrelevant, if its disappearance is caused in part by reactions with important biological molecules. Attacking organic molecules, it will often form a charged ion, which may live much longer than the electron and may itself be highly reactive, and thus damaging to biological molecules. It is possible that the enhancement of radiation damage in the presence of chemical sensitizers such as oxygen may be caused in part by just such an effect—the formation of a charged ion (Adams and Dewey, 1963).

The experiment described below with benzophenone as solute, which demonstrates clearly the different reaction pathways followed by the electron and by the hydrogen atom, was devised by Baxendale before the discovery of the absorption spectrum of the electron itself, although the experiment was only carried out some time later (Adams, Baxendale, and Boag, 1964b).

Electron Reactions with Benzophenone

It was shown by Porter and Wilkinson that the molecule of benzophenone splits up under photolysis to give either the radical $(C_6H_5)_2\,\dot{C}\text{-}OH$, or the radical ion $(C_6H_5)_2\,\dot{C}\text{-}O^-$, depending upon pH (Porter and Wilkinson, 1961). They determined the absorption spectrum of the radical; that of the ion was already known (Carter, McClelland, and Warhurst, 1960). The pK of the equilibrium was found to be 9.2 ± 0.1.

Baxendale expected that the hydrated electron would attack the benzophenone molecule to give the ketyl radical ion, while the hydrogen atom—

when this was the reducing species present—would produce the ketyl radical. The absorption spectra of the two species, and of benzophenone itself in solution, are shown in Figure 8. To test this hypothesis, we prepared saturated aqueous solutions of benzophenone, carefully deaerated, and irradiated them at three values of pH. On irradiating benzophenone in acid solution where the H atom is the predominant reducing species, we expected to find the transient absorption spectrum of the ketyl radical. Instead we found no trace of either spectrum, but only a transient absorption in the ultraviolet with a peak at 3,900 A, as shown in Figure 9.

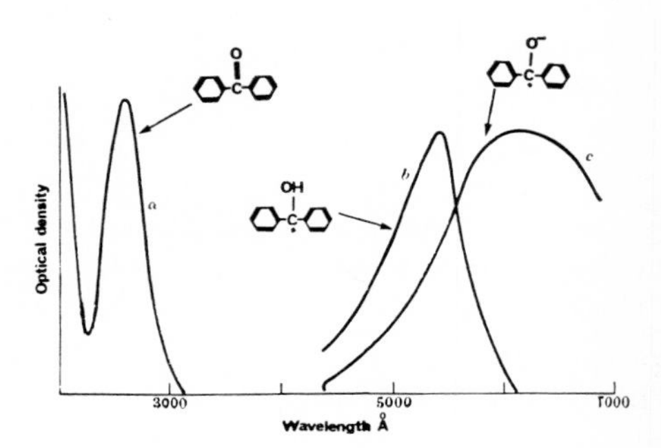

FIGURE 8. Absorption spectra in aqueous solutions of benzophenone: a, absorption spectrum of benzophenone; b, absorption spectrum of the ketyl radical (Porter and Wilkinson, 1961); c, absorption spectrum of the ketyl radical ion (Carter, McClelland, and Warhurst, 1960).

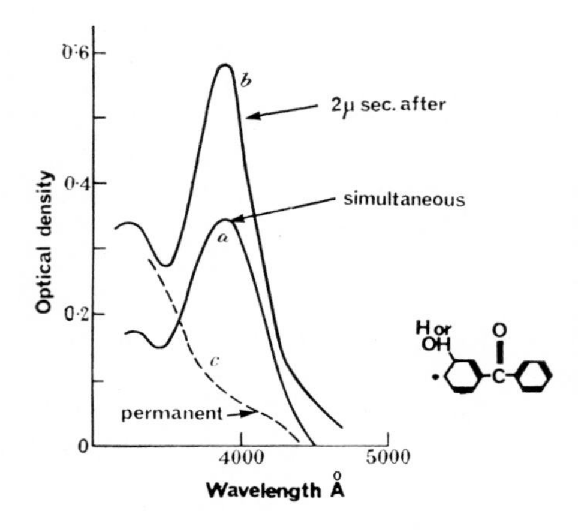

FIGURE 9. Transient absorption spectrum in saturated solution of benzophenone in 10^{-2} N H_2SO_4 after a pulse of radiation. a, spectrum taken simultaneously with the pulse; b, spectrum with 2 μsec delay; c, permanent absorption one minute after irradiation.

The lower spectrum was taken with a simultaneous flash, and the upper one with a delay of 2 μsec. Evidently the species responsible for this absorption was still growing after a few microseconds. In addition, a permanent absorption was found in a spectrogram taken one minute after the electron pulse. We deduce from this that the hydrogen atom formed when the hydrated electron is captured by a hydrogen ion does not attack the benzophenone molecule at the bond between carbon and oxygen, but instead probably adds on to the ring (Dorfman, Taub, and Bühler, 1962). Not only the H atom but also the OH radical may add on to the ring in this way, and the radicals so formed are believed to be the species which absorb at

3,900 A. These probably dimerize, and the dimer is likely to be responsible for the permanent absorption.

Proceeding to alkaline solutions, Figure 10 shows the spectra obtained in a 0.05 M solution of sodium carbonate saturated with benzophenone. Spectra taken simultaneously with the electron pulse, and with 2 μsec delay, are practically identical. For comparison, the spectrum of the hydrated electron has been drawn in, and also the permanent absorption persisting one minute after irradiation. In this instance, the absorption spectrum of the transient species found is identical with that of the ketyl radical ion, as had been expected. The peak is at 6,200 A and, as before, there is some transient absorption in the 3,000 to 4,000 A region, in addition to the permanent absorption there.

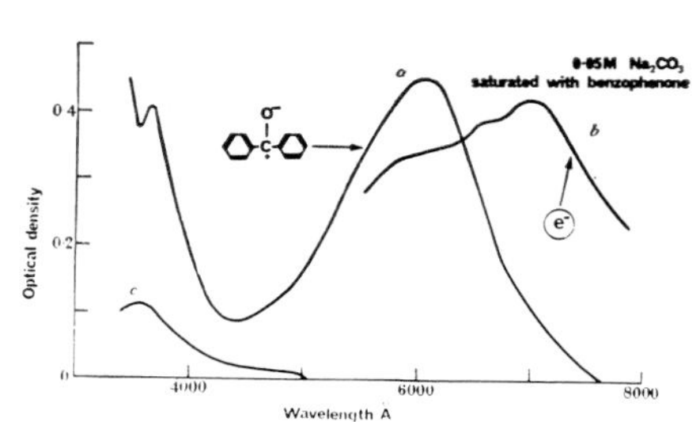

FIGURE 10. Transient absorption spectrum in aqueous solution of benzophenone containing 0.05 M Na_2CO_3 after a pulse of radiation. a, spectrum taken with 2 μsec delay; b, absorption peak of the hydrated electron, for comparison; c, permanent absorption one minute after irradiation.

The most interesting results, however, were obtained in neutral solution. These are shown in Figure 11. In this case the absorption spectrum obtained by triggering the spark and the electron pulse simultaneously is a compound one, consisting of a mixture of the spectra of radical and radical ion. A delay of 2 μsec before triggering the spark is sufficient to eliminate the component corresponding to the radical ion, leaving only the spectrum of the acid form of the radical, which is the stable form at neutral pH. The neutralization is clearly a very fast reaction, since it must have been proceeding even during the 2 μsec pulse. A resolution of the simultaneous spectrum into its two components is given in the inset picture in the upper half of Figure 11. The fact that the spectrum of the radical ion is present initially can be taken as direct evidence for the attachment of the hydrated electron to benzophenone, since the radical ion cannot be formed indirectly by ionization of the neutral radical, the pK of this is 9.2.

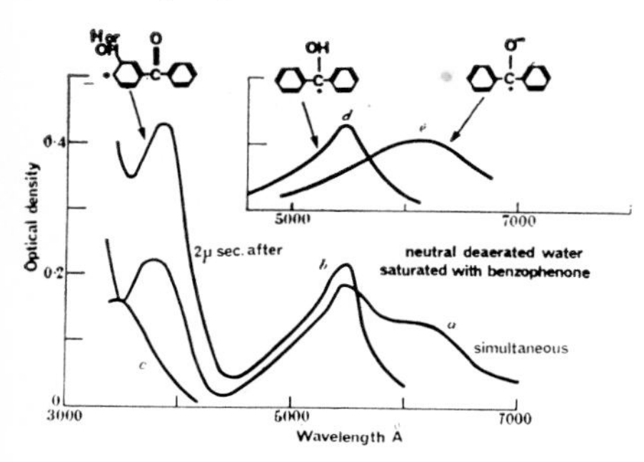

FIGURE 11. Absorption spectra in neutral aqueous solutions of benzophenone after a pulse of radiation. a, spectrum taken simultaneously with the pulse; b, spectrum with 2 μsec trigger delay; c, permanent absorption one minute after irradiation; d and e, resolution of a into the two components corresponding to the absorption of the radical and of the radical ion, respectively.

We have carried out a similar survey on solutions of benzophenone in methanol, either neutral, acidified with 0.01 N sulfuric acid, or rendered alkaline with sodium methoxide. These methanolic solutions yield almost identical absorption spectra, except that the peak at 3,900 A is not found in methanol. We attributed this peak to a transient formed by H or OH addition to the ring. In methanol, however, any hydrogen atoms formed, either initially or by neutralization of the hydrated electron, should react preferentially with the solvent, as will also the OH radicals.

In pure deaerated methanol, and in ethanol, transient spectra have been found corresponding to the electron solvated in these media. In methanol the peak is at 6,200 A, in ethanol at 6,700 A (Adams, Baxendale, and Boag, 1964a; Adams and Boag, 1964a; Dorfman, 1964).

Electron Reactions with Metal Ions

Another example of the specific reactivity of the electron is provided by its reactions with metal ions in solution. When aqueous solutions containing cadmium, zinc, manganese, or cobalt, for example, are irradiated, the transient spectra obtained are shown in Figure 12 (Adams, Baxendale, and Boag, 1963). In all there is a strong transient spectrum with a peak at

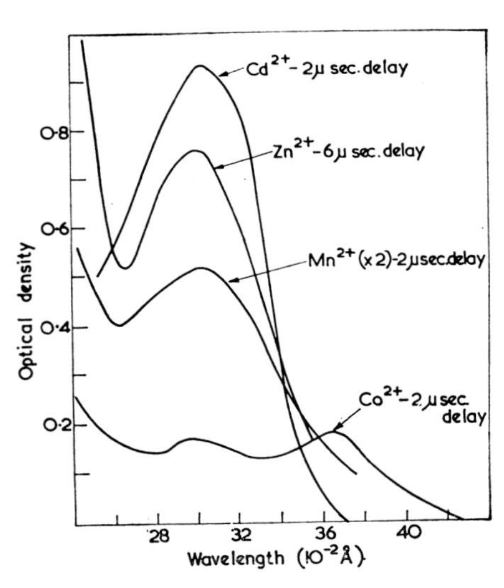

FIGURE 12. Transient absorption spectra of metal ions (10^{-3}M for zinc, and 10^{-2}M for the others) in 0.1 M deaerated aqueous solutions of methanol after an electron pulse.

3,000 A, which we attribute to the formation of an abnormal valency state of these divalent ions due to the capture of an electron. The rising absorption below 2,800 A is probably attributable to the further reduction of the metal ions to uncharged atoms by the capture of a second electron. Metallic zinc has been found as a final product (Baxendale and Dixon, 1963). With zinc, the duration of the transient spectrum at 3,000 A is about 50 μsec, and is considerably reduced in the presence of 0.01 N sulfuric acid, owing to the competition of the hydrogen ion for the electron. The acid also removes the far ultraviolet absorption, presumably by reoxidizing the singly charged ion instead of allowing it to be further reduced to the metal.

Rate Constants for Reactions Involving the Hydrated Electron

The discovery of the absorption spectrum of the electron opened the way to a convenient exploration of the rate constants of electron reactions, and this has been pursued with great vigor by the groups who are using kinetic spectroscopy (Gordon *et al.*, 1963; Hart, Thomas, and Gordon, 1964; Hart, Gordon, and Thomas, 1964; Dorfman and Taub, 1963; Baxendale, *et al.*, 1964).

Table 1 shows rate constants for electron reactions obtained by kinetic spectroscopy. The wide range of values for the rate constants again emphasizes the specificity of electron reactions. Since these rate constants have all been obtained by measuring the disappearance of absorption at a particular wavelength (generally between 5,000 A and 6,000 A) not far from the absorption maximum of the electron at 7,000 A, care has to be taken that no additional transients are occurring which might give absorption in this region.

REACTIONS OF THE OH RADICAL

It has already been mentioned that the absorption spectrum of the hydrated electron was first discovered in a deaerated alkaline solution con-

TABLE 1

*Rate Constants for Electron Reactions Determined by Kinetic Spectroscopy**

10^6		10^7		10^8		10^9		10^{10}	
$SO_4^=$		NH_2OH	< 2 (M)	Y^{3+}	< 2 (M)	Zn^{2+}	1.5 (M)	C^{2+}	1.2 (M)
ClO_4^-		Eb^{3+}	<7 (M)	Lu^{3+}	2.5 (A)			$Co(Ox)_3^{3-}$	1.2 (M)
CNS^-		Mn^{2+}	7.7 (M)	Fe^{2+}	3.5 (M)	$Co(Cn)_6^{3-}$	2.7 (M)	H_2O_2	1.3 (A)
$CO_3^=$				La^{3+}	3.4 (A)	NO_2^-	3.5 (M)		1.4 (M)
Cl^-							4.6 (A)	CrO_4^{2-}	1.8 (M)
					6.9 → 12 (M) pH dependent	$PtCl_4^{2-}$	9 (M)	O_2	1.9 (A)
						$S_2O_8^{2-}$	7.6 (M)		2.2 (M)
							10.6 (A)	Ni^{2+}	2.2 (M)
	< 1.0 (A and M)			Dy^{3+}	4.6 (A)			H^+	2.1 (M)
				Gd^{3+}	5.5 (A)				2.4 (A)
				Nd^{3+}	5.9 (A)			Cu^{2+}	2.9 (M)
									3.3 (A)
								$Co(en)_2Cl_2^+$	3.2 (M)
								Yb^{3+}	3.7 (M)
									4.3 (A)
								$Cr_2O_7^{2-}$	4.4 (A)
								UO_2^{2+}	7.4 (M)
								Cr^{3+}	4 to 7 (M)
								Eu^{3+}	6.1 (A)
								$Co(NH_3)_6^{3+}$	9.0 (M)

*Those determined at the Argonne National Laboratory are indicated by (A), those at the Christie Hospital, Manchester, by (M). A number of substances have been omitted where the discrepancy between (A) and (M) was very large.

taining sodium carbonate, and that there was some suggestion in the early spectrograms that the peak in the absorption spectrum moved towards 6,000 A when electron scavengers such as oxygen were added to the solution. From very recent work (Adams and Boag, 1946b), it now appears that the major part of the absorption discovered on the original plate was not due to the electron at all, but to a carbonate radical ion formed by reaction with OH.

$$CO_3^{=} + OH \rightarrow CO_3^{\overline{\cdot}} + OH^-$$

In retrospect, it was exceedingly fortunate that we misread the signpost and proceeded along the road which did lead to the correct electron spectrum. When an oxygenated solution of sodium carbonate is irradiated, the oxygen removes the hydrated electrons so rapidly that their absorption spectrum is not seen, under our experimental conditions, but the absorption spectrum shown in Figure 13 then remains. This has a peak at 6,000 A, and its lifetime extends over tens of microseconds. It disappears by a second-order reaction. Evidence that this absorption spectrum is due to a reaction of the carbonate ion with the OH or its alkaline form, O^-, is afforded by competition reactions with other OH scavengers. The following OH scavengers have been used: Methanol, ethanol, bromide, chloride, iodide, nitrite, sulfite, thiosulfate, bisulfite, potassium ferrocyanide, glycerol, and potassium thiocyanate. In all cases, these reduce the spectrum formed with

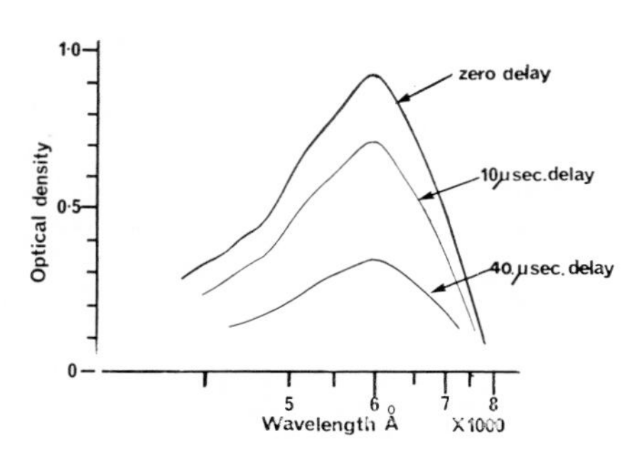

FIGURE 13. Transient absorption spectrum produced in 0.05 M aqueous solution of sodium carbonate saturated with oxygen. This is attributed to the carbonate radical ion, $CO_3^{\overline{\cdot}}$.

carbonate in a manner characteristic of a competition reaction. In many cases, other transients characteristic of the competing solute are produced; a few of these are illustrated in Figure 14. These were obtained by setting a fixed time delay of some 5 μsec on the flash light source and photographing the absorption spectrum at this delay for different concentrations of the competing solute. The disappearance of the one peak, and the rise of the other, in Figure 14, is not a change with time, but a change with varying concentrations of the competing solutes. This type of experiment, therefore, gives a direct method of obtaining relative rate constants of all these solutes with the OH radical, and if the absolute value of its reaction with the carbonate ion can be determined, these relative rate constants can thus be converted to absolute values. There are many advantages of this competition technique. The relative values obtained should be independent of dose rate, dose distribution, and extinction coefficient of the radicals in question. Moreover, by choosing a suitable one from among the other transients found, similar competition studies can be carried out at acid pH, and in this way relative rate constants for reactions of the OH radical determined over the whole pH range.

Finally, absolute values of these rate constants can be determined di-

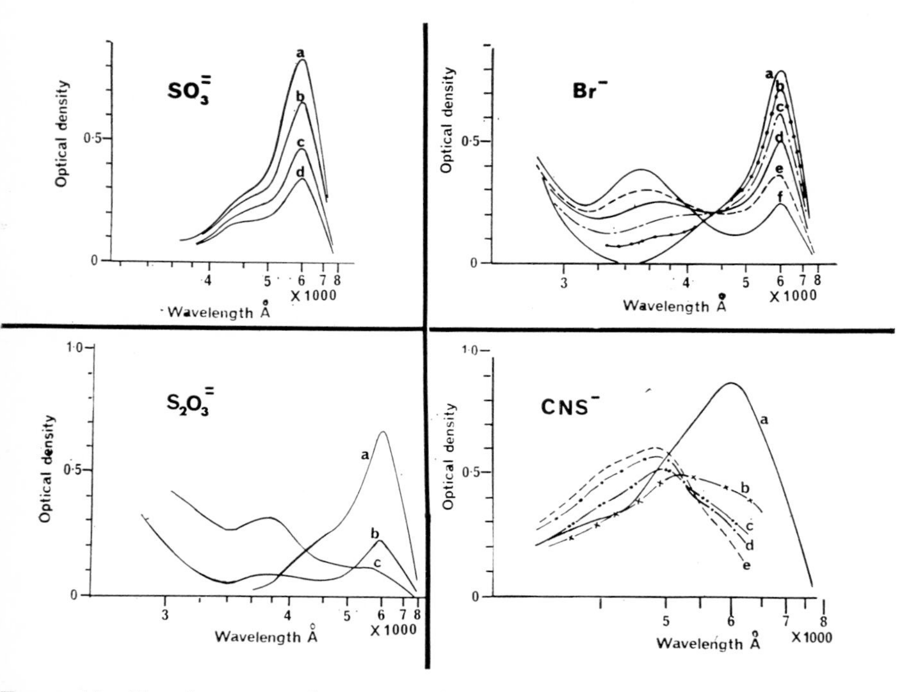

FIGURE 14. Transient spectra in oxygenated aqueous solutions containing 0.04 M Na_2CO_3 with various anions competing for the OH radical. Delay on all spectra, 5 μsec. Concentrations:

$SO_3^=$	a	b	c	d		
	0	1	2	4mM		
Br^-	a	b	c	d	e	f
	0	6	10	16	24	36mM
$S_2O_3^=$	a	b	c			
	0	2	10mM			
CNS^-	a	b	c	d	e	
	0	2.4	4	6	10mM	

rectly from observations on the rate of buildup of the transient spectra at low values of dose per pulse. For this purpose the high sensitivity of the photomultiplier technique is required.

The object of such studies must be to build up a "vocabulary" of rate constants for all the transient species commonly encountered in irradiated aqueous solutions. Once these are known, the influence of pH or of particular solutes upon the course of any radiation-chemical reaction will be predictable.

Transient Species in Oxygenated Water

In oxygenated water, the possible transient species are much more numerous than in deaerated water, since the reactions of the oxygen molecule with the electron, and with the other transient species formed, have to be considered. Recent work by kinetic spectroscopy (Dorfman and Czapski, 1964) and by flash spectroscopy (Adams and Boag, 1964) has provided much new evidence on the absorption spectra of the species which occur in oxygenated water and on their rate constants.

The absorptions observed are illustrated in Figure 15. At acid pH, there is some ultraviolet absorption which disappears fairly rapidly with second-order kinetics. In alkaline solutions, the situation is more complex. The ultraviolet absorption is much stronger, and lives longer. In addition, at high pH a new, relatively narrow absorption band with a peak at 4,300 A appears. This is shown in Figure 16 (Adams and Boag, 1964b) as it appears in a series of delayed spectrograms, and also as plotted out by the kinetic spectroscopy technique (Czapski and Dorfman, 1964). This band appears only at high pH, and is probably caused by an attack of O^-, the ionized form of the OH radical, on the oxygen molecule to form O_3^-. The band at 4,300 A is eliminated by OH scavengers such as carbonate, bromide, or methanol. With carbonate alone competing, the carbonate radical ion band with a peak at 6,000 A appears instead of the 4,300 A band. Since the OH radical is clearly involved in the formation of the 4,300 A band, and is evidently effective only in the form of O^-, this 4,300 A absorption band gives a convenient method of determining the pK of the OH radical.

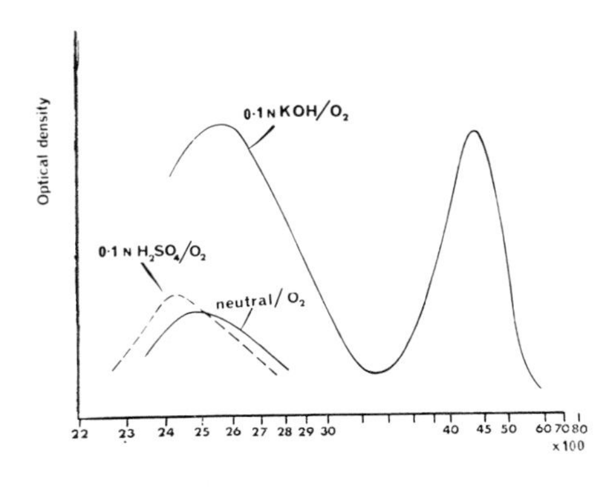

FIGURE 15. Transient spectra observed in oxygenated water at acid, neutral, and alkaline pH. The optical density scale is an arbitrary one.

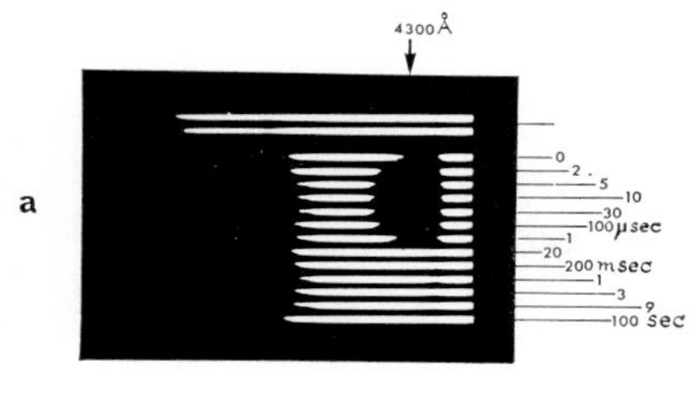

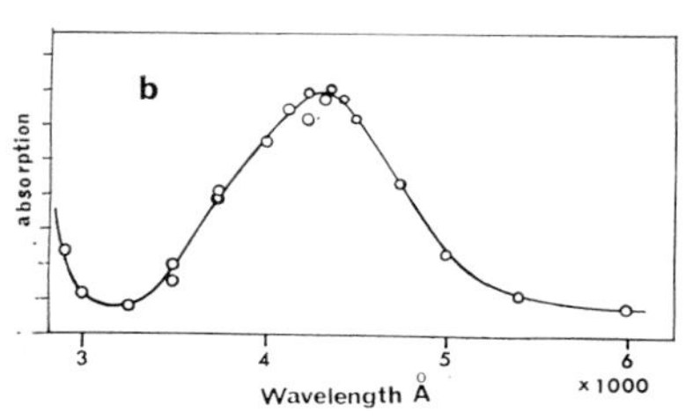

FIGURE 16. Transient absorption band in oxygenated water attributed to the O_3^- ion. a, the band as recorded by flash spectroscopy, (Adams and Boag, 1964b); b, the same band as determined by kinetic spectroscopy (Czapski and Dorfman, 1964).

We have, however, carried out a detailed survey over a wide range of the several parameters—pH, oxygen concentration, and dose—and have shown that the factor determining the yield of O_3^- is not the dissociation of the OH radical but the competition between OH recombination and the reaction of OH with OH^-, leading to O^- (Adams and Boag, 1964b).

The nature of the ultraviolet absorption band in alkali and neutral solutions (Boag, Steele, and Hart, 1963; Boag, 1963b) is not yet certain, but it appears to be caused, at least in part, by the HO_2 radical or its dissociated form O_2^-. In acid solution, the absorption peak is reported to be at 2,300 A (Czapski and Dorfman, 1964) or at 2,400 A (Adams and Boag, 1964b). In alkaline solution, it shifts by about 100 A towards longer wavelengths. A peak at 2,500 A is reported by Baxendale *et al.* (1964), but the pH at which this was found is not specified.

Another species whose absorption spectrum would be extremely interesting to observe directly is the O^-, the ionized form of the OH radical. We have looked for this by flash spectroscopy during the electron pulse, and within the first few microseconds thereafter. While we cannot claim a firm identification, we have observed a short-lived absorption in the ultraviolet in deaerated 0.1 N KOH which remains after the electron absorption in the visible has vanished.

TRANSIENTS IN BIOLOGICAL MOLECULES

Some preliminary studies have already been made on many biological molecules, using either the kinetic or the flash spectroscopic technique. Table 2 gives rate constants of organic molecules with the hydrated electron. These were determined by kinetic spectroscopy using the disappearance of the electron absorption spectrum at 5,750 A as a criterion for the speed of the reaction (Gordon *et al.*, 1963; Baxendale *et al.*, 1964).

TABLE 2

*Rate Constants for the Reaction of the Hydrated Electron with Organic Molecules Determined by Kinetic Spectroscopy**

10^6		10^7		10^8		10^9		10^{10}	
Methane		Aniline	< 2 (A)	Naphthalene	3.1 (A)	Benzoquinone	1.25 (A)	Adenosine	1.0 (A)
Methanol		Formic acid	4.2 (A)	Indole	7 (M)	β-naphthol	1.8 (A)	Styrene	1.3 (A)
Phenylalanine	< 1 (A)	Acetate ion		Tryptophan	8 (M)	Phthalate ion	2.0 (A)	Tetracyano-ethylene	1.5 (A)
Hydroquinone			< 10 (M)						
Glycine		Oxalate ion							
Formaldehyde	(A)					Thiourea	2.9 (A)	Orotic acid	1.5 (A)
Benzene	< 7 (A)					Acetaldehyde	3.5 (A)	Acrylamide	1.8 (A)
Ethylene	7.6 (M)					Methacrylate ion	7.8 (A)	Carbon tetrachloride	3.0 (A)
								Methylene blue	34 (M)

* Those determined at the Argonne National Laboratory are indicated by (A), those at the Christie Hospital, Manchester, by (M).

DNA itself, and a series of natural and synthetic pyrimidines have been investigated by flash spectroscopy and several interesting transient spectra observed (Figure 17) (Adams, Boag, and Shugar, Unpublished data). Further work will be required in order to identify the nature of these transients. In such work the use of synthetic analogues of the naturally occurring molecules is of great value, as particular sites can be blocked by nonreactive side groups, e.g. methyl, in an attempt to locate the source of the observed spectra; we have used synthetic analogues prepared by Dr. D. Shugar.

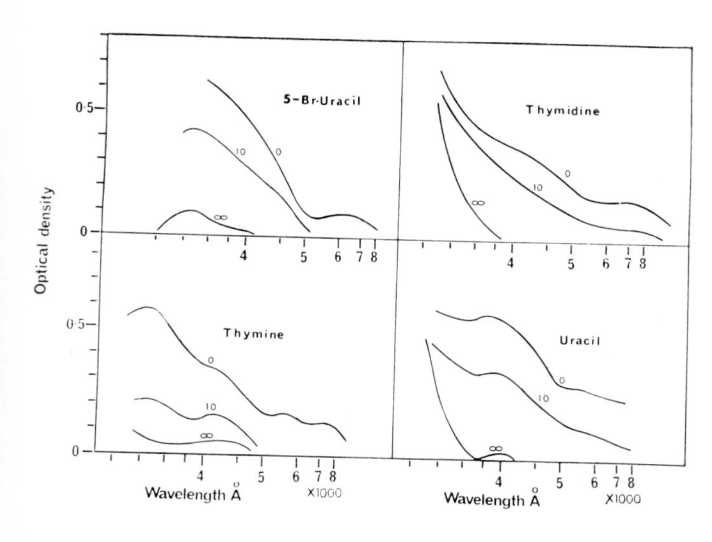

FIGURE 17. Transient absorption spectra observed in aqueous solutions of pyrimidines after a pulse of radiation. Curves labeled O were taken with no delay between pulse and flash, those labeled 10 with 10 μsec delay, and those labeled ∞ approximately one minute after irradiation.

SUMMARY

We have given a short survey of some of the very numerous results which the techniques of kinetic spectroscopy and flash spectroscopy have already produced in the short period of some 18 months since the discovery of the absorption spectrum of the hydrated electron. These methods will continue to be productive, even with their present time resolution, for a lengthy period, and we may look forward to their ultimate extension to a shorter time scale as the technical methods are further improved. It should then be possible to detect even shorter-lived transient intermediates, such as excited states, and to build the bridge further toward the fundamental physical processes in the one direction, and toward complicated biological systems in the other.

ADDENDUM

Subsequent to the work described above, a new series of absorption spectra arising from reactions of the hydroxyl radical have been observed. These spectra are produced in aqueous solutions of some anions and reducing oxyanions of groups 4, 5, 6 and 7 of the periodic table. It is concluded that these spectra are due to unstable oxidation states produced in reactions formally equivalent to that between OH and carbonate ion. In particular, absorption maxima have been observed in solutions containing silicate, nitrite, arsenite, selenite, tellurite, thiosulphate and thiocyanate.

The above conclusion is supported by the fact that these spectra are removed by typical OH scavengers, e.g. alcohols, and furthermore, the absorption intensities are increased by saturation of the solution with nitrous oxide prior to irradiation, i.e. the conversion of e_{aq}^- to OH.

Absolute Rate Constants: Using the technique of kinetic spectroscopy, several absorptions have been studied in more detail, and absolute rate constants for the reactions of OH have been obtained for carbonate, selenite and thiocyanate. These three absorption maxima were used as reference standards by means of which absolute rate constants have been obtained by competitive methods for methanol and ethanol. The agreement between the three independent methods, as expressed by the values for methanol and ethanol, is good, verifying the conclusion that one radiation-induced precursor is responsible for all these spectra, and also confirming the reliability of competition methods.

Due to its greater sensitivity, kinetic spectroscopy has proved to be particularly useful for competition studies in systems where the rate of decay of the transient absorption is sufficiently great as to affect the density recorded spectrographically, even when the light source and electron pulse are triggered as close together as possible.

Absolute rate constants for OH reactions

Solute	k ($M^{-1}sec^{-1}$)
Carbonate	2.2×10^8
Methanol	4.9×10^8
Ethanol	1.08×10^9
Hypophosphite	1.08×10^9
Phosphite	2.1×10^9
Tellurite	2.2×10^9
Selenite	2.7×10^9
Nitrite	3.9×10^9
Arsenite	5.0×10^9
Thiocyanate	6.5×10^9

REFERENCES

Adams, G. E., J. H. Baxendale, and J. W. Boag. 1963. The Formation of Abnormal Valency States in the Radiolysis of Aqueous Metal-Ion Solutions. *Proceedings of the Chemical Society*. Pp. 241–242.

———. 1964a. Absorption Spectrum of the Electron Solvated in Methanol. *Discussions of the Faraday Society*. (in press.)

———. 1964b. Electron Attachment in Irradiated Solutions. *Proceedings of the Royal Society*. (in press.)

Adams, G. E., and J. W. Boag. 1964a. Absorption Spectrum of the Electron Solvated in Ethanol. *Discussions of the Faraday Society*. (in press.)

———. 1964b. Transient Species in Irradiated Oxygenated Water. (in press.)

Adams, G. E., J. W. Boag, and D. Shugar. Unpublished data.

Adams, G. E., and D. L. Dewey. 1963. Hydrated Electrons and Radiobiological Sensitization. *Biochemical and Biophysical Research Communications,* 12:473–477.

Baxendale, J. H., and H. Dixon. 1963. Some Unusual Reactions of The Hydrated Electron. *Proceedings of the Chemical Society.* P. 148.

Baxendale, J. H., E. M. Fielden, and J. P. Keene. 1963. Absolute Rate Constants for the Reactions of Some Metal Ions with the Hydrated Electron. *Proceedings of the Chemical Society.* Pp. 242–243.

Baxendale, J. H., and G. Hughes. 1958. The X-Irradiation of Aqueous Methanol Solutions I and II. *Zeitschrift für physikalische Chemie,* 14:306, 323.

Baxendale, J. H., E. M. Fielden, C. Capellos, J. M. Francis, J. V. Davies, M. Ebert, C. W. Gilbert, J. P. Keene, E. J. Land, A. J. Swallow, and J. M. Nosworthy. 1964. Pulse Radiolysis. *Nature,* London, 201:468–470.

Boag, J. W. 1957. A Spark Light Source for Absorption Spectroscopy. *Proceedings of the Second International Congress of Photobiology.* Minerva fisioterapica Series. Turin, Italy: Edizioni Minerva medica.

———. 1963a. U. V. Absorption Spectroscopy. *Actions Chimiques et Biologiques des Radiations,* M. Haissinsky, Ed., Paris, France: Masson et Cie. Pp. 25–34.

———. 1963b. Primary Processes of Deposition of Radiant Energy and Initial Radiochemical Events. *American Journal of Roentgenology, Radium Therapy and Nuclear Medicine,* 90:896–906.

Boag, J. W., G. E. Adams, and E. J. Hart. 1964a. Evidence for the Hydrated Electron from Optical Absorption and Electrical Conductivity. *International Symposium on Physical Processes in Radiation Biology.* (in press.)

Boag, J. W., and E. J. Hart. 1963. Absorption Spectra of Hydrated Electron. *Nature,* London, 197:45–47.

Boag, J. W., and R. E. Steele. 1961. Kinetics of Radiation-Induced Chemical Reactions. British Empire Cancer Campaign Report No. P. 38, Pt. 2, pp. 251–252.

Boag, J. W., R. E. Steele, and E. J. Hart. 1963. "Absorption Spectroscopy of Irradiated Liquids," *Radiation Effects in Physics, Chemistry and Biology,* M. Ebert and A. Howard, Eds., Amsterdam, The Netherlands: North-Holland Publishing Co. P. 38.

Carter, H. V., B. J. McClelland, and E. Warhurst. 1960. Studies of Organo-alkali Metal Complexes. Part 4. Absorption Spectra in the Visible Region. *Transactions of the Faraday Society,* 56:455–458.

Collinson, E., F. S. Dainton, D. R. Smith, and S. Tazuké. 1962. Evidence for the Unit Negative Charge on the "Hydrogen Atom" Formed by the Action of Ionising Radiation on Aqueous Systems. *Proceedings of the Chemical Society.* Pp. 140–141.

Czapski, G., and L. M. Dorfman. 1964. Pulse Radiolysis Studies. V. Transient Spectra and Rate Constants in Oxygenated Aqueous Solutions. *Journal of Physical Chemistry.* 68:1169–1177.

Czapski, G., and H. A. Schwartz. 1962. The Nature of the Reducing Radical in Water Radiolysis. *Journal of Physical Chemistry,* 66: 471–474.

Das, T. P. 1962. Structure and Properties of Metal-Ammonia Solutions. *Advances in Chemical Physics,* 4:303–388.

Davidov, A. S. 1948. On the Theory of the Optical Absorption Spectra of Metal-Ammonia Solutions. *Zhurnal eksperimental' noi i teoreticheskoi fiziki,* 18:913.

Deigen, M. F. 1954. (a) On the Theory of the Optical Properties and Electrical Conductivity of Metal-Ammonia Solutions. (b) The Magnetic Properties of Metal-Ammonia Solutions and the Equilibrium Concentration of Trapping Centres in the Dielectric. *Trudy Institut Fiziki,* Akademy Sciences, Ukraine. No. 5. 105:119.

Dorfman, L. M. 1964. Absorption Spectrum of the Electron Solvated in Ethanol. *Discussions of the Faraday Society.* (in press.)

Dorfman, L. M., R. E. Bühler, and I. A. Taub. 1962. Absolute Rate Constant for the Reaction of Hydroxyl Radicals with Benzene in Water. *Journal of Chemical Physics,* 36:549–550.

Dorfman, L. M., and I. A. Taub. 1963. Pulse Radiolysis Studies. III. Elementary Reactions in Aqueous Ethanol Solution. *Journal of the American Chemical Society,* 85:2370–2374.

Dorfman, L. M., I. A. Taub, and R. E. Bühler. 1962. Pulse Radiolysis Studies. I. Transient Spectra and Reaction-Rate Constants in Irradiated Aqueous Solutions of Benzene. *Journal of Chemical Physics,* 36:3051–3061.

Fessenden, R. W., and R. H. Schuler. 1963. Electron Spin Resonance Studies of Transient Alkyl Radicals. *Journal of Chemical Physics,* 39:2147–2195.

Gordon, S., E. J. Hart, M. S. Matheson, J. Rabani, and J. K. Thomas. 1963. Reaction Constants of the Hydrated Electron. *Journal of the American Chemical Society,* 85:1375.

Gray, L. H. 1957. "The Influence of Oxygen on the Response of Cells and Tissues to Ionizing Radiation," *Lectures on the Scientific Basis of Medicine.* London, England: The Athlone Press. Vol. VII. Pp. 314–347.

Hart, E. J., and J. W. Boag. 1962. Absorption Spectrum of the Hydrated Electron in Water and in Aqueous Solutions. *Journal of the American Chemical Society,* 84:4090–4095.

Hart, E. J., S. Gordon, and J. K. Thomas. 1964. Rate Constants of the Hydrated Electron-Reactions with Organic Compounds. *The Journal of Physical Chemistry,* 68: 1271–1274.

Hart, E. J., J. K. Thomas, and S. Gordon. 1964. A Review of the Radiation Chemistry of Single Carbon Compounds and Some Reactions of the Hydrated Electron in Aqueous Solution. *Radiation Research,* Supplement 4:74–88.

Henriksen, T. 1962. Radiation-Induced Radicals in Water, Deuterium Oxide and Aqueous Solutions of Glycine at Low Temperatures. *Nature,* London, 193:371–372.

Howard-Flanders, P. 1957. Effect of Nitric Oxide on the Radiosensitivity of Bacteria. *Nature,* London, 180:1191–1192.

Howard-Flanders, P., and D. Moore. 1958. The Time Interval after Pulsed Irradiation within which Injury to Bacteria can be Modified by Dissolved Oxygen. 1. A Search for an Effect of Oxygen 0.02 Second after Pulsed Irradiation. *Radiation Research,* 9: 422–428.

Hunt, J. W., J. E. Till, and J. F. Williams. 1962. Radiation Damage and Free Radical Production in Irradiated Ribonuclease. *Radiation Research,* 17:703–711.

Hutchison, C. A., Jr., and R. C. Pastor. 1951. Paramagnetic Resonance Absorption in Potassium Dissolved in Liquid Ammonia. *Physical Review,* 81:282.

———. 1953. Paramagnetic Resonance Absorption in Solutions of K in Liquid NH_3. *Reviews of Modern Physics,* 25:285–290.

Keene, J. P. 1963a. Optical Absorptions in Irradiated Water. *Nature,* London, 197:47–48.

———. 1963b. Pulse Radiolysis of Aqueous Solutions. In Review by F. S. Dainton, "Primary Species in Water." *Radiation Effects in Physics, Chemistry and Biology.* M. Ebert and A. Howard, Eds. Amsterdam, The Netherlands: North-Holland Publishing Co. Pp. 34–49.

———. 1964a. Pulse Radiolysis Studies. *Discussions of the Faraday Society.* (in press.)

———. 1964b. Technique of Pulse Radiolysis. *Review of Scientific Instruments.* (in press.)

Landau, L. 1933. Electron Traps in Ionic Crystals. *Soviet Physics,* 3:664.

Matheson, M. S., and L. M. Dorfman. 1960. Detection of Short-Lived Transients in Radiation Chemistry. *Journal of Chemical Physics,* 32:1870–1871.

Matheson, M. S., W. A. Mulac, and J. Rabani. 1964. Formation of the Hydrated Electron in the Flash Photolysis of Aqueous Solutions. *Journal of Physical Chemistry*, 67:2613–2617.

McCarthy, R. L., and A. MacLachlan. 1960. Transient Benzyl Radical Reactions Produced by High-Energy Radiation. *Transactions of the Faraday Society*, 56:1187–1200.

Ogg, R. A., Jr. 1946. Physical Interaction of Electron with Liquid Dielectric Media. The Properties of Metal-Ammonia Solutions. *Physical Review*, 69:668–669.

Pekar, S. I. 1954. Researches on the Electron Theory of Crystals. Berlin, Germany: *Akadamie-Verlag*. 184 pp.

Platzman, R. L. 1953. "Energy Transfer from Secondary Electrons to Matter," *Physical and Chemical Aspects of Basic Mechanisms in Radiobiology*, J. L. Magee, M. D. Kamen, and R. L. Platzman, Eds. (National Academy of Sciences, National Research Council Publication No. 305). Washington, D. C.: National Research Council. Pp. 22–50.

Porter, G. 1950. The Absorption Spectroscopy of Substances of Short Life. *Discussions of the Faraday Society*, 9:60–69.

Porter, G., and F. Wilkinson. 1961. Primary Photochemical Processes in Aromatic Molecules. Part 5. Flash Photolysis of Benzophenone in Solution. *Transactions of the Faraday Society*, 57:1686–1691.

Powers, E. L., C. F. Ehret, and B. Smaller. 1961. "The Role of Free Radicals in the Lethal Effects of X-Rays in Dry Bacterial Spores," *Free Radicals in Biological Systems* (Proceedings of a Symposium at Stanford University, March, 1960), M. S. Blois, Jr., H. W. Brown, R. M. Lemmon, R. O. Lindblom, and M. Weissbluth, Eds. New York, New York, and London, England: Academic Press. Pp. 351–366.

Powers, E. L., R. B. Webb, and B. F. Kaleta. 1960. Oxygen and Nitric Oxide as Modifiers of Radiation Injury in Spores of *Bacillus megatherium*. *Proceedings of the National Academy of Sciences of the U. S. A.*, 46:984–995.

Scott, O. C. A. 1963. The Modification of Tissue Response to Radiation Injury. *Annual Review of Medicine*, 14:371–380.

Senvar, C. B., and E. J. Hart. 1958. "Decomposition of Aqueous Solutions by Alpha Particles." *Proceedings of the Second United Nations International Conference on the Peaceful Uses of Atomic Energy*. Geneva, Switzerland: United Nations Publication. Vol. 29. Pp. 19–23.

Stein, G. 1952. Contributions to the Discussion. *Discussions of the Faraday Society*, 12:289.

Taub, I. A., and L. M. Dorfman. 1962. Pulse Radiolysis Studies. II. Transient Spectra and Rate Processes in Irradiated Ethanol and Aqueous Ethanol Solution. *Journal of the American Chemical Society*, 84:4053–4059.

Thomas, J. K., S. Gordon, and E. J. Hart. 1964. The Rates of Reaction of the Hydrated Electron in Aqueous Inorganic Solutions. *The Journal of Physical Chemistry*, 68: 1524–1527.

Weiss, J. 1960. Primary Processes in the Action of Ionizing Radiations on Water: Formation and Reactivity of Self-Trapped Electrons (Polarons). *Nature*, London, 186:751–752.

———. 1963. Behaviour of Polarons Produced by the Action of Ionizing Radiation in Aqueous Media. *Nature*, London, 199:589–590.

Weyl, W. 1864. Solutions of Sodium in Liquid Ammonia. *Annalen der Physik und Chemie* (Poggendorff), 121:601–612.

Yost, D. M., and H. Russell. 1944. *Systematic Inorganic Chemistry of the Fifth-and-Sixth-Group Nonmetallic Elements*. New York: Prentice Hall, Inc., 423 pp.

Zimmer, K. G., W. Köhnlein, G. Hotz, and A. Müller. 1963. Elektron-Spin-Resonanzen in bestrahlten Bakteriophagen und deren Bestandteilen. I. Mitteilung. *Strahlentherapie*, 120:161–190.

The Inactivation of DNA and Other Biological Molecules by Ionizing Radiations

FRANKLIN HUTCHINSON

Department of Molecular Biology and Biophysics, Yale University, New Haven, Connecticut

The aim of this article is to review certain work covering the action of ionizing radiations on the biological molecules of which the cell is composed.

The interest in connecting the actions of ionizing radiation at the molecular level with the complex events which occur in the living cell on irradiation is partly a recognition of the advantages of generalizing on the basis of established fundamental mechanisms. Many radiobiological papers suggest explanations in terms of free radical mechanisms, destruction of deoxyribonucleic acid (DNA), etc., often on inadequate evidence. Also, the progress in molecular biology within the past few years has been spectacular, and there are very real reasons to want to connect radiobiology with the vast increase in our knowledge of biology on the molecular level.

By and large, studies of the molecular basis of the action of ionizing radiation are not progressing as well as we would like in giving a clear and unambiguous view on the mechanisms at work. Nevertheless, there are certain general rules which appear to be obeyed well enough that I think there is some validity to them, even while recognizing certain difficulties.

It is generally considered that the mechanisms involved in the loss of biological activity of molecules inside irradiated cells can be divided into two categories: those which take place almost instantaneously, and those which depend on complex biochemical sequences after irradiation. We are concerned here only with the first. These immediate changes can again be divided into two types: those events mediated through diffusing free radicals, mainly those produced by the action of radiations on intracellular water; and the events produced by the radiations directly in macromolecules without other chemical intermediates. Such "direct effect" is thought to be similar to the damage produced in the irradiation of dry samples. It is doubtful if these two types of damage can be strictly separated, but for lack of any better procedure they are usually treated as though they were entirely independent of each other. Recent reviews (Hutchinson, 1961, 1963) have indicated that the results of irradiating molecules in intact cells can be reasonably well correlated with results of irradiation in vitro by assuming that the damage in cells is a simple sum of the direct effect as measured by irradiation of samples in the dry state, and the indirect effect of diffusing radicals as studied in very dilute solutions. It is further shown by such studies that the two processes are of about the same importance in typical living cells, with the indirect effect tending to be somewhat more important for smaller molecules, and direct effect for the larger ones.

The rest of this paper will be concerned almost entirely with the direct effect, and with efforts to bring inactivation data on nucleic acids in line with results for proteins.

Simple Target Theory

For the loss of specific biological activity of proteins (the loss of enzymatic activity, for example), a good correlation has been found between the molecular weight and the slope of the exponential inactivation curve when the irradiation is in the dry state (Pollard, Guild, Hutchinson, and Setlow, 1955; Pollard, 1959; Hutchinson and Pollard, 1961). One way of expressing this is to say that empirically the product of the molecular weight (MW) and the D_{37} dose expressed in rads is a constant.

$$(MW)(D_{37}) = 0.72 \times 10^{12} \qquad (1)$$

A physical picture can be readily obtained by using the fact that ionizing radiation releases energy in an irradiated material in individual events of considerable energy, with a mean energy release the order of magnitude of 60 ev per primary event (Rauth and Hutchinson, 1962). This order of energy release is so much larger than chemical bonding energies that there is considerable likelihood of enough disruption in the vicinity of the energy loss event to cause the loss of biological activity of the molecule within which the event takes place. This is the essence of the target theory as developed by Lea (1946) and by Timofeev-Resovskii and Zimmer (1947). If it is assumed that an average of 75 ev are expended per inactivating event, then equation (1), above, follows directly.

Alternatively, equation (1) may be assumed, and a radiation target molecular weight may be calculated for a variety of molecules. From the simple target theory, the target molecular weight should equal the molecular weight as determined by physicochemical methods. Figure 1, with data mainly from Pollard, Guild, Hutchinson, and Setlow (1955), shows that this is approximately true.

The situation is not, in fact, as simple as it has been made here, in that by various means it is possible to vary the calculated target molecular weight by a factor the order of a magnitude of ten. This should indicate that the correlations shown in Figure 1 were not very meaningful.

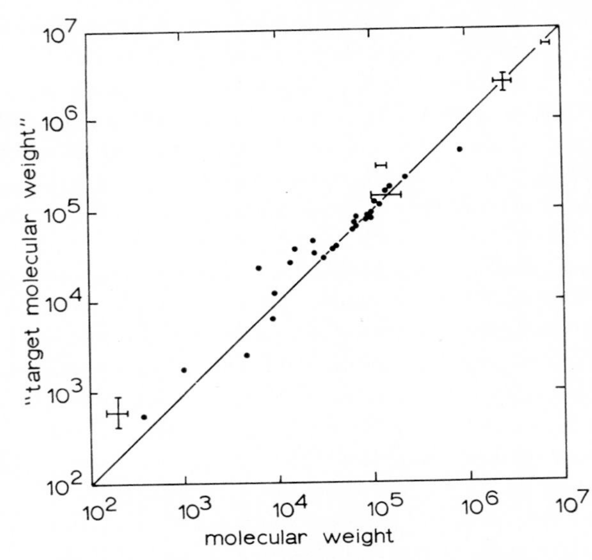

FIGURE 1. A plot of the radiation-sensitive molecular weight against the known molecular weight as determined by physicochemical methods. Much of the data are from Pollard, Guild, Hutchinson, and Setlow, (1955). Note the logarithmic scale. The line drawn is that assuming that the radiation molecular weight equals the chemical molecular weight.

The situation is too complicated to be dealt with satisfactorily here. The reader is referred to other reports for a more complete discussion (Hutchinson, 1960, 1962a), since the main concern here is to show the general agreement between proteins and nucleic acids. In general, it appears to be an oversimplification to think of inactivation following every primary energy loss event. Additional events beyond the primary ones can be created by the electrons released in the primary energy loss events, and in the presence of oxygen gas additional events apparently become evident as manifested by an increase in radiosensitivity the order of a factor of two. Conversely, at liquid nitrogen temperatures radiation damage is appreciably reduced, perhaps because of increased effectiveness of a cage effect in reducing the chance of new configurations arising afterwards. Drying the proteins in certain protective materials, such as sulfhydryl compounds, can also protect by a factor the order of two; but such protection occurs only in the presence of a large excess of such protective agents. However, certain metallic ions at low concentrations also give considerable protection.

Much more needs to be learned about the protective mechanisms at work. Nevertheless, it is possible in most cases to estimate the D_{37} dose for a protein irradiated in the dry state to within a factor of two, using equation (1) and then modifying the the calculated dose in an empirical way to take into account the specific conditions under which the irradiation is conducted. To this extent, then, it appears that the correlation between molecular weight and radiation sensitivity in the dry state is meaningful.

NUCLEIC ACID INACTIVATION BY SIMPLE TARGET THEORY

Several years ago Norman and Ginoza (1957) showed that the radiosensitive target of tobacco mosaic virus was quite accurately equal to the amount of ribonucleic acid (RNA) in the virus; furthermore, the radiosensitivity of the RNA irradiated in the frozen state after extraction from the virus was exactly the same. In a recent paper Ginoza (1963) has extended this work to the bacterial RNA virus R17 and to the single-stranded DNA virus ΦX174. In both cases, he shows that the radiosensitivity of these viruses is that expected on the basis of simple target theory, the nucleic acid being considered to be the radiosensitive material. Schambra (1961) has also shown the same for ΦX174.

The situation is much more complicated when the effect of ionizing radiation on DNA is considered. For one thing, there is in some cases the problem of identifying an assayable property of DNA with the molecular weight of the piece of DNA responsible for the property. There is general agreement that DNA, as usually prepared from living cells, is greatly degraded in the process of extraction; and in bacterial cells, at least, it usually exists in the cell in the form of very long strands of molecular weight the order of hundreds of millions.

Viruses having double-stranded DNA, such as the T series of bacteriophages attacking *Escherichia coli*, have a definite size, and the biological activity can readily be assayed for by plaque counting. As a representative virus, the irradiation of T1 in the dry state has been studied by a number of workers (Pollard and Forro, 1951; Fluke and Forro, 1960; Fluke, Brustad, and Birge, 1960) who all find an exponential inactivation with a dose of 0.5 megarads required to inactivate to 37 per cent survival. This corresponds to a radiation-sensitive molecular weight of only 1.4×10^6 against a known molecular weight for the DNA of 42×10^6. In general (Terzi, 1961), it seems to be true that double-stranded DNA is much more resistant to the action of ionizing radiation than would be expected on the basis of simple target theory.

Inactivation of DNA Viruses with Radiation of High LET

Information about this has been obtained from some recent experiments by Schambra and myself in which a single-stranded virus ΦX174, and a double-stranded virus, T1, were irradiated with radiations of various linear energy transfer (LET) (Schambra, 1961). Dry samples were irradiated with beams of ions of several elements lying between helium, atomic number 2, and argon, atomic number 18. The beams were obtained from the Yale heavy ion linear accelerator at an energy of 10 Mev/atomic mass unit. Dosimetry was fundamentally based on determining the number of incident particles incident per square centimeter on the samples, and energy absorption was calculated from the rate of energy loss as determined by both theory and experiment.

The results at high LET obtained for T1 were in very good agreement with previous work (Pollard and Forro, 1951; Fluke and Forro, 1960; Fluke, Brustad, and Birge, 1960). No similar data seem to have been obtained before with ΦX174.

Instead of presenting the results in the usual form of the dose in rads plotted against LET, or relative biological effectiveness (RBE) plotted against LET, it will be more informative to plot the radiosensitivity per incident particle against Z^2, where Z is the atomic number of the accelerated ion. For a measure of the radiosensitivity, we will use the reciprocal of the D_{37} measured in particles/unit area. This reciprocal has the units of an area, and in physical terms represents the apparent size of the target area which must be struck by a particle to inactivate. For this reason, it is frequently referred to as an inactivation cross section.

The utility of plotting against Z^2 instead of LET, which is, of course, directly proportional to Z^2, is to emphasize that on this plot the effect produced by delta electrons is directly proportional to Z^2 if all of the incident particles have the same velocity. As first pointed out by Dolphin (Dolphin and Hutchinson, 1960), particles of the same velocity (or same energy per unit mass) all produce secondary electrons having the same spectrum in energy, but in numbers proportional to Z^2. Thus, a measure of the radiosensitivity per incident particle, such as inactivation cross section, will be linear in Z^2 for damage done by the delta electrons from beams used in this experiment, all having an energy of 10 Mev/atomic mass unit. Any damage produced in excess of this linearly increasing dose will be ascribed to the heavily ionizing core of the track, as shown schematically in Figure 2. If it is assumed that energy transfer is not an important mechanism, then the track core must pass through a molecule to inactivate it.

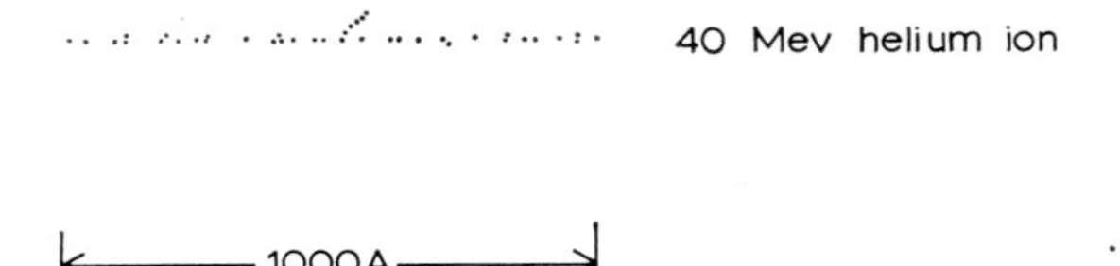

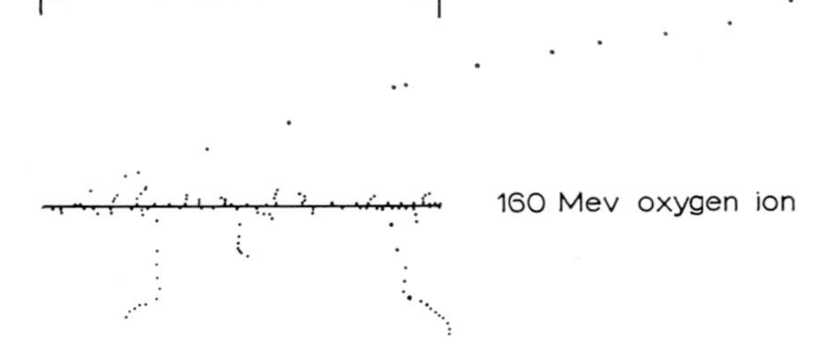

FIGURE 2. A schematic diagram of the track and delta electrons from a helium ion and an oxygen ion, both having an energy of 10 Mev/atomic mass unit.

Figure 3 shows a plot of the results for the two viruses. Looking first at the points for ΦX174, it is seen that the points lie along a straight line. The line shown is not that drawn through the points, but that calculated on the basis of the model just discussed.

The calculated inactivation cross section includes one term for the inactivation by the particle track, and another for that caused by the delta rays. It is readily shown to be:

$$S = eS_0 + 1.6 \times 10^{-8} \frac{f\,(dE/dx)\,Z^2}{D_\delta} \tag{2}$$

where S_0 is the physical cross section in square centimeters of the sensitive target; e is the efficiency of the track for inactivating the target in a single pass; f is the fraction of the total energy of the particle going in to delta electrons, equal to 0.40 for heavy ions of 10 Mev/atomic mass unit; dE/dx is rate of loss of energy in Mev-cm²/gm for a *proton* of the same velocity as the heavy ion, equal to 46.7 Mev-cm²/gm (Lea, 1946); and D_δ is the D_{37} dose (in rads) applicable for the delta electrons.

Since it has been shown that the mean LET of the delta electrons from heavy particles of energy 10 Mev/atomic mass unit is about the same as as that for helium ions of this energy (Fluke, Brustad, and Birge, 1960), the value of D_δ has been taken to be equal to that for the helium beam as measured in these experiments.

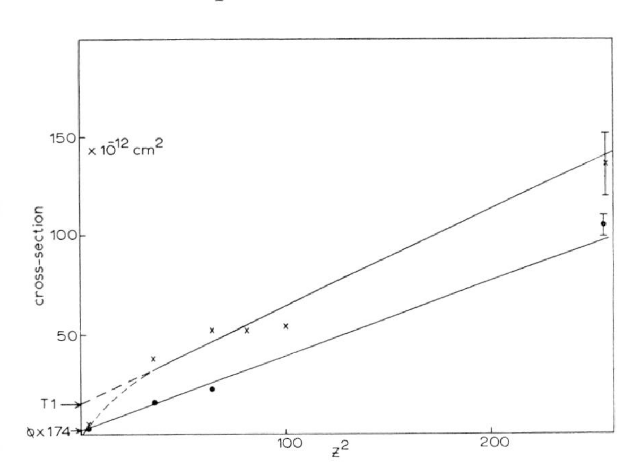

FIGURE 3. The inactivation cross sections for the single-stranded DNA virus ΦX174 and the double-stranded DNA virus T1 plotted against the square of Z, the atomic number of the incident ion. All the ions had an energy of 10 Mev/atomic mass unit. The arrows along the ordinate axis point to the physical cross sections of the DNA in the two viruses. The lines plotted are those calculated from equation 2.

When the expression given above is plotted for ΦX174, the line shown in Figure 3 is obtained. It has been assumed that e in the expression is unity. That is, even for the most lightly ionizing beam used in this experiment (helium), the chance of inactivation is essentially one if the track passes through the target volume. It is seen that the experimental points fall very nicely on the calculated line. This might have been expected, since for sparsely ionizing radiation the inactivation of this virus was in good agreement with that expected on target theory considerations.

Looking at the results for T1, it is seen that a line drawn in according to equation 2 fits the points only at sufficiently high LET. To interpret the results, it is worthwhile to reconsider the assumptions involved in the cross-section calculation.

They are (1) that energy transfer over large distances is not an important method of inactivation; (2) the effect produced by the delta electrons is proportional to the number of deltas (assuming that the delta spectrum remains the same); and (3) the track of a sufficiently highly ionizing particle is certain to inactivate a virus if it passes through the radiosensitive area. Accepting the reasonableness of these assumptions, we conclude that the T1 data show a case where most of the inactivation events at low LET are not effective, and that the proportion of events which result in the loss of activity rises as the rate of energy loss along the track rises.

A number of viruses with double-stranded DNA seem to be inactivated only with a low efficiency by sparsely ionizing radiations, and a summary of some of the data collected from the literature has been published (Terzi, 1961). Unfortunately, it is probable that many of the figures published represent lower limits to the D_{37} dose, since in most cases quoted it is by no means clear that all the effects of water radicals had been suppressed. However, this does not detract from the conclusion; if the contributions from radical attack were to be subtracted, the efficiency of inactivation would be even lower.

The most obvious hypothesis as to why the efficiency should rise so rapidly with radiations of high LET is that events in both strands of the DNA are needed for inactivation with high efficiency. It might be remarked in this connection that for a particle with a Z^2 equal to nine (from Figure 3, having a LET for which the efficiency factor e is approximately equal to 0.5), an average of 35 events would take place in the DNA of T1. In traversing a single DNA double helix, such a particle would create an average of 1.3 events of mean energy loss of 60 ev. These figures are not inconsistent with the idea of requiring one or two events in each of the adjacent single strands for inactivation, but not enough is known of the details of the energy release from heavy ions to be able to say any more.

Inactivation of Transforming DNA

Another set of studies involving biological assays on DNA have been those involving transforming DNA. These studies have hitherto been complicated by the fact that the inactivation curves are usually complex, with two distinct parts (Marmur and Fluke, 1955; Guild and DeFilippes, 1957; Latarjet, Ephrussi-Taylor, and Rebeyrotte, 1959; Pakula, Walczak, and Shugar, 1961) unless the irradiation is carried out in dilute solution (DeFilippes and Guild, 1959). It has, however, been shown that the survival curves become simple exponentials if the irradiations are carried out with the transforming DNA in the intact cells, and the DNA removed for assay afterwards (Hutchinson and Arena, 1960; Stuy, 1961).

In recent experiments carried out at Yale, pneumococcus cells were irradiated with beams of various rates of LET and then the DNA extracted was assayed for the ability to transform cells (Hutchinson, 1962b). Transformation was for the streptomycin resistance marker. The point I wish to make can be seen in Figure 4, which plots the RBE as a function of LET. For comparison, similar curves are given for the killing of cells and for the two bacterial viruses.

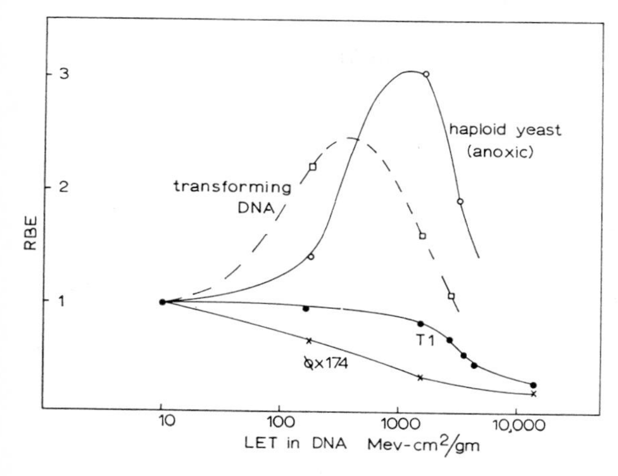

FIGURE 4. The RBE of several biological systems plotted as a function of LET. Data from Schambra (1961) and Hutchinson (1962b).

The virus ΦX174 shows the drop in RBE with increasing LET which is to be expected on the basis of simple target theory, and is similar to curves for enzymes (Dolphin and Hutchinson, 1960). T1 shows a type of behavior intermediate between ΦX174 and the others. If, however, the ratios of the radiosensitivities of T1 to ΦX174 are plotted as a function of LET, a curve very similar to the others is obtained, as shown in Figure 5.

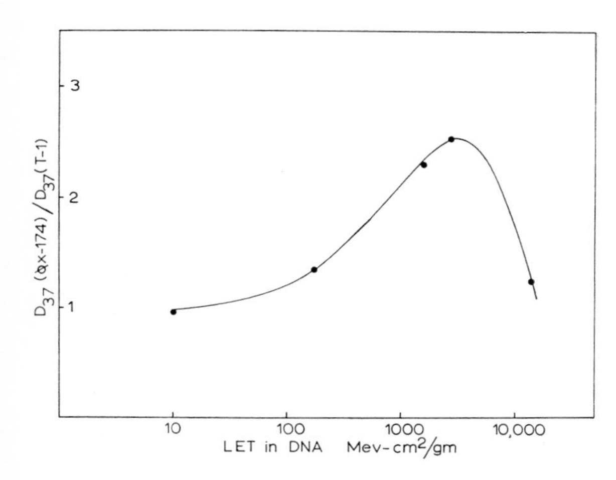

FIGURE 5. The ratios of the radiosensitivity of T1 bacteriophage to the radiosensitivity of ΦX174 bacteriophage as a function of LET.

Some clue as to the mechanism is given by experiments in which different samples of cells were irradiated with electron beams and with beams of 120 Mev carbon ions of LET approximately 1,700 Mev-cm^2/g. The DNA was then extracted from these cells, and the molecular weight determined by sedimentation. Typical results are given in the table. The difficulties with the extraction procedure are seen for the case where the DNA irradiated with carbon ions was run through the procedure twice. The smaller DNA pieces are lost selectively in the process. However, it was necessary to do the experiment in this way to avoid extensive cross-linking, which takes place on the irradiation of DNA in a more or less pure form (Setlow and Doyle, 1954; Alexander, Lett, Kopp, and Itzhaki, 1961). Despite the uncertainties caused by the selective loss of the smaller pieces of DNA in the extraction, it seems quite clear that heavy ion irradiation gives considerably more breakage of the DNA than a larger dose (measured in rads) of lightly ionizing radiations. This strongly suggests that scission of the double helix represents one form of damage to the DNA, a form which becomes more important at high LET. Breakage by radiations of various rates of LET has previously been reported, although the figures given were complicated by simultaneous cross-linking (Alexander, Lett, Kopp, and Itzhaki, 1961). The variation with LET in efficiency of scission in the experiments reported in this paper is greater than the earlier results (Alexander, Lett, Kopp, and Itzhaki, 1961) would indicate.

Effect of Different Radiations on the Molecular Weight of Transforming DNA Extracted by Phenol Procedure from Pneumococcus

RADIATION	MEGARADS	D_{37}	MOLECULAR WEIGHT
None	....	..	7.9×10^6
1 Mev electrons	3.5	1	3.9×10^6
120 Mev carbon ions	2.2	1	1.6×10^6
Same, DNA re-extracted	2.2	1	2.7×10^6

DISCUSSION

It is quite clear that sparsely ionizing radiations do affect double-stranded DNA such as T1. In fact, for T1 the lightly ionizing delta electrons produce most of the inactivation for high energy argon ions (see Figure 1).

It may be asked if all the damage done by radiations of low LET is caused by the densely ionizing tails of slow electrons set in motion by the gamma or X rays. Evidence that this is not so is provided by the RBE plots shown in Figure 4. If the most important part of the damage was caused by the same effect of the heavily ionizing segments, all curves of RBE against LET should be similar. It can be seen that this definitely is not the case. The curves shown indicate that there are at least two, and perhaps more, types of damage; and that different types of DNA suffer from these types of damage to different extents. Thus, the approximate constancy of the RBE of T1 is an accident, resulting from the decrease in one form of damage predominant at low LET and a corresponding increase in another.

The apparent stability to radiation of most DNA, assayed on the basis of various biological activities, is presumably connected with its double-stranded nature. It also seems reasonable to ascribe the stability to biological factors, rather than to mechanisms which dissipate the energy harmlessly without breaking chemical bonds. The best evidence is the recent work of Müller (1962). He found that the formation of free radicals as measured by electron spin resonance to be about the same in proteins and in nucleic acids, with a yield the order of one radical per 100 ev expended.

There is an obvious connection between these experiments in which bacteriophages have been irradiated with ionizing radiations and those in which the "radioactive suicide" of disintegrating radioactive atoms are used as the method of inactivation. It will be remembered that here also there is a division between the single-stranded bacteriophages which are inactivated with an efficiency the order of unity (Tessman, 1959), and the double-stranded viruses which are inactivated with a probability an order of magnitude lower (Stent and Fuerst, 1960).

An interesting result has been reported for the phage alpha of *Bacillus megaterium* (Celano *et al.*, 1960). This virus has a reported inactivation dose of 2.1×10^4 rads, and 30×10^6 molecular weight of DNA. This would indicate an efficiency of inactivation the order of unity. Inactivation by P^{32} suicide also occurs with an efficiency of about one. Although both these results would indicate single-stranded DNA, it has been definitely established that the DNA is double-stranded (Fuller *et al.*, 1963). The reason for this anomaly is not known.

Finally, these results imply, although do not prove, that the biological activity of two-stranded DNA can usually survive if the matching strand directly opposite a lesion is intact. The connection between this suggestion and the repair mechanisms for damage by ultraviolet light discovered by R. B. Setlow and W. L. Carrier (1964) and reported by Howard-Flanders (see pages 52 to 60, this volume) is obvious.

ACKNOWLEDGMENTS

The work on viruses T1 and ΦX174 discussed here was done in collaboration with Dr. P. E. Schambra. The sedimentation measurements on the transforming DNA were carried out by Dr. Frank Gardner. The work reported here and the preparation of the manuscript was supported by contracts from the United States Atomic Energy Commission and the United States Air Force.

REFERENCES

Alexander, P., J. T. Lett, P. Kopp, and R. Itzhaki. 1961. Degradation of Dry Deoxyribonucleic Acid by Polonium Alpha Particles. *Radiation Research,* 14:363–373.

Butler, J. A. V., and A. B. Robins. 1962. Metal Ion Redox Systems as Radiation Protective Agents. *Nature,* London, 193:673–674.

———. 1963. Effects of Certain Metallic Salts on the Inactivation of Solid Trypsin by Ionizing Radiation. *Radiation Research,* 19:582–592.

Celano, A., A. Aurisicchio, A. Coppo, P. Donini, C. Frontali, and F. Graziosi. 1960. Unusual Biophysical Properties of the Temperate Phage α. *Nuovo Cimento,* 18:Serie X, Supplment: 190–196.

DeFilippes, F. M., and W. R. Guild. 1959. Irradiation of Solutions of Transforming DNA. *Radiation Research,* 11:38–53.

Dolphin, G. W., and F. Hutchinson. 1960. The Action of Fast Carbon and Heavier Ions on Biological Material. *Radiation Research,* 13:403–414.

Fluke, D. J., T. Brustad, and A. C. Birge. 1960. Inactivation of Dry T-1 Bacteriophage by Helium Ions, Carbon Ions and Oxygen Ions. Comparison of Effect for Tracks of Different Ion Density. *Radiation Research,* 13:788–808.

Fluke, D. J., and F. Forro, Jr. 1960. Efficiency of Inactivation of Dry T-1 Bacteriophage by Protons, Deuterons and Helium Ions from a 60 Inch Cyclotron. *Radiation Research*, 13:305–317.

Fuller, W., M. Spencer, A. D. Sargentini, F. Sgarlata, and R. Langridge. 1963. Determination by X-Ray Diffraction of the Structure of Deoxyribonucleic Acid from Bacteriophage α. *Journal of Molecular Biology*, 6:510–512.

Ginoza, W. 1963. Radiosensitive Molecular Weight of Single Stranded Virus Nucleic Acids. *Nature*, London, 199:453–459.

Guild, W. R., and F. M. DeFilippes. 1957. Ionizing Radiation and Ultrasonic Evidence for a Minimum Unit of Transforming Principle Deoxyribonucleic Acid. *Biochimica et biophysica acta*, 26:241–251.

Hutchinson, F. 1960. Modifying Factors in the Inactivation of Biological Macromolecules. *Radiation Research*, Supplement 2:49–64.

————. 1961. Molecular Basis for Action of Ionizing Radiations. *Science*, 134:533–538.

————. 1962a. Effects of Milieu on Immediate Radiation Response of Biological Molecules Within the Cell. *Strahlentherapie*, Sonderband 51:58–70.

————. 1962b. "Two kinds of Action of Ionizing Radiation on DNA," *Biological Effects of Ionizing Radiation at the Molecular Level*. Vienna, Austria: International Atomic Energy Agency. Pp. 15–23.

————. 1963. "Effects of Ionizing Radiations on Molecules in Cells," *Actions Chimiques et Biologiques des Radiations*, M. Haissinsky, Ed. Paris, France: Masson et Cie. Pp. 107–146.

Hutchinson, F., and J. Arena. 1960. Destruction of the Activity of Deoxyribonucleic Acid in Irradiated Cells. *Radiation Research*, 13:137–147.

Hutchinson, F., and E. Pollard. 1961. "Target Theory and Radiation Effects on Biological Molecules," *Mechanisms in Radiobiology*, M. Errera and A. Forssberg, Eds. New York, New York, and London, England: Academic Press. Vol. I. Pp. 71–92.

Latarjet, R., H. Ephrussi-Taylor, and N. Rebeyrotte. 1959. On the Target Size of a Transforming Factor Based on X-Ray Inactivation. *Radiation Research*, Supplement 1:417–430.

Lea, D. E. 1946. *Actions of Radiations on Living Cells*. Cambridge, England: University Press, 402 pp.

Marmur, J., and D. J. Fluke. 1955. Uniformity of Ionizing Radiation Action on Several Transforming Factors of *Pneumococcus*. *Archives of Biochemistry and Biophysics*, 57:506–514.

Müller, A. 1962. Efficiency of Radical Production by X-rays in Dry Proteins and Nucleic Acids. *International Journal of Radiation Biology and Related Studies in Physics, Chemistry and Medicine*, 5:199–200.

Norman, A., and W. Ginoza. 1957. Radiosensitive Molecular Weight of Tobacco Mosaic Virus Nucleic Acid. *Nature*, London, 179:520–521.

Pakula, R., W. Walczak, and D. Shugar. 1961. Inactivation of the Streptomycin Resistance Markers of Three Species of Bacteria by Ionizing Radiation. *Acta Biochimica Polonica*, 8:413–425.

Pollard, E. C. 1959. Radiation Inactivation of Enzymes, Nucleic Acids, and Phage Particles. *Reviews of Modern Physics*, 31:273–281.

Pollard, E., and F. Forro, Jr. 1951. The Inactivation of Bacteriophage by Ionizing Radiation. *Archives of Biochemistry and Biophysics*, 32:256–273.

Pollard, E. C., W. R. Guild, F. Hutchinson, and R. B. Setlow. 1955. "The Direct Action of Ionizing Radiation on Enzymes and Antigens," *Progress in Biophysics*. New York, New York: Academic Press, Inc. Pp. 72–108.

Rauth, A. M., and F. Hutchinson. 1962. "Distribution in Energy of the Primary Energy Loss Events of Electrons in Condensed Media," *Biological Effects of Ionizing*

Radiation at the Molecular Level. Vienna, Austria: International Atomic Energy Agency. Pp. 25–36.

Schambra, P. E. 1961. *Effect of Accelerated Heavy Ions on Viruses and Cells*. Ph.D. Dissertation. Yale University, New Haven, Connecticut.

Schambra, P. E., and F. Hutchinson. 1964. The Action of Fast Heavy Ions on Biological Material. II. Effects on T1 and ΦX-174 Bacteriophage and Double and Single Strand DNA. *Radiation Research* (in press).

Setlow, R. B., and W. L. Carrier. 1964. The Disappearance of Thymine Dimers from DNA: An Error-Correcting Mechanism. *Proceedings of the National Academy of Sciences of the U.S.A.*, 51:226–231.

Setlow, R. B., and B. Doyle. 1954. Action of Radiation on Dry DNA. *Biochimica et biophysica acta*, 15:117–125.

Stent, G. S., and C. R. Fuerst. 1960. Genetic and Physiological Effects of the Decay of Incorporated Radioactive Phosphorus in Bacterial Viruses and Bacteria. *Advances in Biological and Medical Physics*, 7:1–76.

Stuy, J. H. 1961. Studies on the Mechanism of Radiation Inactivation of Microorganisms. VII. Inactivation of Intracellular Multiply Marked *Haemophilus Influenzae* Deoxyribonucleic Acid by High Voltage Electrons. *Radiation Research*, 15:45–58.

Terzi, M. 1961. Comparative Analysis of Inactivating Efficiency of Radiation on Different Organisms. *Nature*, London, 191:461–463.

Tessman, I. 1959. Some Unusual Properties of the Nucleic Acid in Bacteriophages S13 and ØX174. Virology, 7:263–275.

Timofeev-Resovskii, N. V., and K. G. Zimmer. 1947. "Das Trefferprinzip (*sic*) in der Biologie," *Biophysik*. I. Leipzig, Germany: S. Hirzel. 317 pp.

DISCUSSION

Dr. Robert J. Shalek, The University of Texas M. D. Anderson Hospital and Tumor Institute, Houston, Texas: Dr. Boag, does this experimental method now indicate that the electron in a condensed system can escape from the parent atom after ionization, thus supporting the Lea-Platzman model?

Dr. John W. Boag, British Empire Cancer Campaign, Mount Vernon Hospital, Northwood, Middlesex, England: In my opinion, it certainly shows that a high proportion of electrons can escape and become stabilized in the "hydrated" form.

Dr. Earle Gregg, Western Reserve University, Cleveland, Ohio: We have been doing some work with pulsed electron beams down around 10 μsec in duration and we have found in the organic liquid dielectrics that we have irradiated that there are always two components in the conductivity: one is around one-tenth μsec half-life and the other is around 4 to 5 μsec, both of which vary with electric field and charge density. Now I would like to ask Dr. Boag whether he has observed this in water (which we have not looked at), whether the optical half-life gives some clue as to the influence of mobility and recombination, and finally, whether this leads to a model of the transport of the hydrated electron?

Dr. Boag: The resolution of our technique is not yet good enough to detect anything which has a half-life of only one tenth of a μsec, but both we and others are hoping to get down to that level in due course. We therefore have no evidence for such a short-lived species as yet. The rate of decay of conductivity which we were able to measure agrees with the duration of the transient optical absorption spectrum, and we attribute it tentatively to the same species. But our conductivity experiments are preliminary. Other work on this matter is in progress by Dr. Klaus Schmidt at the Argonne Laboratory, but he is using a slightly different method.

Dr. Paul Howard-Flanders, Yale University School of Medicine, New Haven, Connecticut: I would like to ask Dr. Boag if he has any data on reaction rates with sulfhydryl compounds. There is, in the literature, a dearth of reaction rates for sulfhydryls although they are widely present in biological systems. If he doesn't at present have data, I plead that he search for them as soon as possible.

Dr. Boag: Most of the work on the OH radical reactions which I have reported here has been done within the last six weeks, and we have a long list of substances whose reaction rates with OH we wish to measure. I believe the method would be quite suitable for the problem you have in mind.

Dr. Ulrich Hagen, University of Freiburg, Freiburg, Germany: I would like to comment on Dr. Hutchinson's statement that the radiation damage of the biological function of the DNA is attributable to a single event in the single nucleotide chains. We irradiated DNA in dilute solutions and determined the number of single breaks, the base destruction, and the priming ability of the DNA in the RNA-polymerase system. According to our data, the number of single breaks in the DNA is linearly related to the dose ($b > \alpha D$). Five krads give about 10 single breaks per molecule of a molecular weight of eight million. The number of double breaks, however, is dependent upon the square of the dose ($B = K1\ \alpha D)^2$. If one measured the incorporation of ATP in the RNA primed by the irradiated DNA, a high radiosensitivity is found, which follows the amount of single breaks in the DNA. Fifty per cent inhibition of the priming ability is found, if one single break has occurred per 1,000 nucleotides; and according to the g values of the base damage, one base per 500 nucleotides is destroyed (Zimmerman, Kröger, Hagen and Keck, *Biochimica et biophysica acta*, in press).

Dr. Thomas Wood, Physics Department, University of Pennsylvania, Philadelphia, Pennsylvania: Dr. Marcovich in Paris and our group have found that X-ray, alpha particle, or UV-irradiation of the donor parent in the *E. coli* K12 mating system prevents the transfer of DNA to the recipient parent. One might therefore conclude that this loss of transferability is caused by double strand breaks in the male DNA. We have tried to support this hypothesis in the following way: If double strand breaks do occur in the male cell, one may assume that it would be possible for transpositions or inversions of the genetic markers to occur. We have carried out experiments in which we have irradiated *Htr* strains to survival levels of 10^{-3} and 10^{-4}, selected surviving cells, and then mated populations grown from these with the female recipient strain; we then look for inversions and transpositions by standard genetic techniques. However, we have found no such effects in the 200 cultures so far tested.

Our negative experiments do not mean that double strand breaks do not occur. However, the additional fact that UV-irradiation also leads to breakage during transfer casts some doubt as to whether the loss of transferability is due to a primary double strand break. We postulate that a single strand break is formed on irradiation which results in an actual breakage during the transfer process due to additional strains put on the system. In general, I think that one should be very careful in assuming that a fragmentation in DNA following extraction is evidence for double strand rupture, as such breakage could be due to a single strand lesion which results in a double strand break when additional strains are put on the system.

Dr. Shalek: I would like to direct a question to Dr. Hutchinson. In the paper by Ginoza (1963) there was one other remarkable point: He indicated that with ΦX174 bacteriophage there was no temperature dependence in the radiation sensitivity between room temperature and liquid nitrogen temperature. Most other things show a marked temperature dependence. We have shown that T2 *E. coli* complexes and dry enzymes are four to five times less sensitive at liquid nitrogen temperature than at room temperature. Vos and Kaalen (*International Journal of Radiation Biology*, 5:609–621, 1962) have shown that with cells in culture there is something greater than a twofold reduction in radiation sensitivity in this temperature range. Would Dr. Hutchinson like to comment on why ΦX174 appears to be different? It appears to be related to the strandedness of the DNA.

Dr. Franklin Hutchinson, Yale University, New Haven, Connecticut: I think that the inference that the inactivation of ΦX174 is independent of temperature is not warranted by the data. The data at room temperature were taken with dry ΦX174 phage; the data at low temperature were taken with a frozen culture. It is quite probable that in frozen cultures the situation is similar to that in dry material. According to the present concepts of drying, what probably happens is that the ΦX174 gets crowded up in little pockets which may be quite similar to dry material. However, they are not identical with dry material, and until the same experiment has been done with identical samples, I think one has to be cautious in interpreting the data. Personally, I would be somewhat surprised if a temperature variation were not found.

Dr. Helen Harrington, Western Reserve University, Cleveland, Ohio: When we irradiate tissue culture cells with 1,000 r and then extract the DNA, we find evidence of single strand breaks, but no evidence of double strand breaks. Under these conditions and also after irradiation of DNA solutions with 1,000 r, we find a marked decrease in priming activity for RNA- and DNA-polymerase. However, I don't think the decrease in priming activity can be attributable to breaks in the phosphodiester chain, because if the DNA is treated with deoxyribonuclease I or II or with ultrasound to decrease the viscosity to the same extent obtained with 1,000 r, the change in priming activity is not similar to that found with 1,000 r. However, heating the DNA changes the priming activity in a manner similar to that obtained with 1,000 r. Therefore, x-irradiation may produce single strand breaks, which are accompanied by local denaturation, which in turn might result in the decreased priming activity.

Dr. Robert J. Rutman, University of Pennsylvania, Philadelphia, Pennsylvania: From a somewhat different line of work dealing with alkylating agents, I would like to point out the fact that the temperature dependency of the various reactions involving DNA can be very different. For instance, the temperature dependency of alkylation itself differs from the effect of temperature on backbone breaks and also differs from the temperature dependency of the cross-linking of the DNA by the alkylating agent. As a consequence, a complex relationship can be expected between the kinds of damage to the DNA, the cytotoxicity and the effect of temperature.

Dr. Hutchinson: I would just like to put on record one point about the solvated electron and its significance to radiobiology. According to current theories of the formation of the hydrated electron, it takes the electron quite a time after it has become thermalized before it is trapped in a hydrated water cage; during this time it will "see" the order of 10,000 atoms. In traversing this long path then, there is a substantial chance in a concentrated solution such as a cell that the electron could perhaps react with the other molecules before becoming solvated. In the experiments that Dr. Boag has been discussing, all the measurements have been done in very dilute solutions for purely technical reasons. I think that there are very good reasons for believing that the solvated electron probably does form in the cell, but I think it would be of extreme interest to try to establish this independently.

Dr. Daniel Billen, The University of Texas M. D. Anderson Hospital and Tumor Institute, Houston, Texas: Perhaps I should defend the cells and suggest that perhaps a single strand break may have some significance for the cell if not for the investigator. Perhaps a replication point in which the strands are dissociated might be a particularly sensitive site in the chromosome. There should be periods in the cell cycle in which single strands do exist, and damage to the strand at that point may be of some consequence to the cell.

RADIATION EFFECTS ON REPLICATION OF CELLULAR STRUCTURES

The Contribution of Water-Free Radicals to the X-Ray Inactivation of Bacteria

Ivar Johansen*

Yale University School of Medicine, New Haven, Connecticut

Since the discovery of the actions of free radicals upon solutes in aqueous solutions, there has been much speculation about the relative importance of direct and radical-mediated or indirect action of X rays upon cells. I will describe experiments, performed in collaboration with Dr. Paul Howard-Flanders, designed to determine whether the reactive species formed by radiolysis of water make any contribution to the lethal injuries sustained by irradiated cells. In order to elucidate this question, we have X-irradiated bacteria in the presence of various substances with known reactivities towards the water-free radicals. Results of the experiments indicate that in regard to X-ray-induced lethal injury, neither hydrogen atoms nor solvated electrons make a significant contribution, while radical intermediates with properties similar to the hydroxyl radical are responsible for about half the effect.

Escherichia coli B/r was grown with aeration in nutrient broth to stationary phase, diluted in buffered saline at pH 6.8 to 10^6 bacteria per ml and kept at 2 to 5C during the experiment. Aliquots of 10 ml were irradiated in a glass vessel with 250 kv, 15 ma X rays at 6.0 krads per minute, and vigorously stirred to maintain the concentration of dissolved gases close to their equilibrium values. Samples were taken, plated on nutrient agar, and incubated for 12 to 24 hours. The fraction of bacteria that survived irradiation was determined from the numbers of visible colonies. The substances tested were not toxic, with the exception of sodium nitrite and sodium nitrate. At 0.8 M, the highest concentration used, these two compounds killed 40 to 50 per cent of the bacteria. The data were corrected for this toxic effect.

* On leave of absence from the Norwegian Defense Research Establishment, Kjeller, Norway.

The main results are summarized in Table 1, and a more detailed presentation will appear elsewhere (Johansen and Howard-Flanders, 1964). As in earlier work (Dale, Davies, and Russell, 1961; Burnett, Stapleton, Morse, and Hollaender, 1951), we found that 10 per cent nitric oxide in nitrogen sensitizes the cells to the same level as does full oxygenation, while at higher concentrations nitric oxide is protective. The sensitivity of the cells in 0.0015 M nitric oxide is only about 50 per cent of the maximum, while higher concentrations do not afford any additional protection. Similarly, ethanol and methanol protect oxygenated cells, but at high concentrations of the substances, the protection levels off to a value of about 50 per cent. Ethanol also affords about the same degree of protection to cells in the presence of widely differing amounts of oxygen, which indicates that the mechanism of protection is independent of the mechanism of the oxygen effect (Johansen and Howard-Flanders, 1964). We tested the effects of nitrite, nitrate, and carbon dioxide, because of their known reactivities towards water-free radicals, and found that nitrite protected oxygenated cells to a degree comparable to the substances listed above, while 0.5 M nitrate and 0.003 M carbon dioxide did not protect bacteria either under anoxia or full oxygenation.

TABLE 1

The Effect of Various Substances on the Radiosensitivity of E. coli *B/r at the 1 Per Cent Survival Level*

Substance	Highest concentration tested (molar)	Gas	Per cent protection	Concentration necessary for half maximum protection (molar)
Nitric oxide	3×10^{-3}	N_2	49	7×10^{-4}
Sodium nitrite	8×10^{-1}	O_2	48	1.4×10^{-1}
Ethanol	2	O_2	53	1.6×10^{-1}
	2	N_2	39	....
Methanol	2	O_2	47	5×10^{-1}
	2	N_2	32	....
Carbon dioxide	3.5×10^{-3}	Air	none	....
	2.8×10^{-3}	N_2	none	....
Sodium nitrate	8×10^{-1}	O_2	none	....
	5×10^{-1}	N_2	none	....
Oxygen	2×10^{-3}	O_2	none	....

In the upper part of Figure 1, the concentration of substances needed for half of maximum protection of bacteria is plotted against the known reactivity of these substances toward each of the water-free radicals in aqueous solutions. It is seen that the substances found to protect bacteria have in common only the ability to react rapidly with the hydroxyl radicals. The lower part of the figure shows the reaction rates of substances without protective effect. These react rapidly with the reducing species, but not with the hydroxyl radicals. Further, if the protection observed is caused by scavenging free radicals, the effective concentration should be in inverse proportion

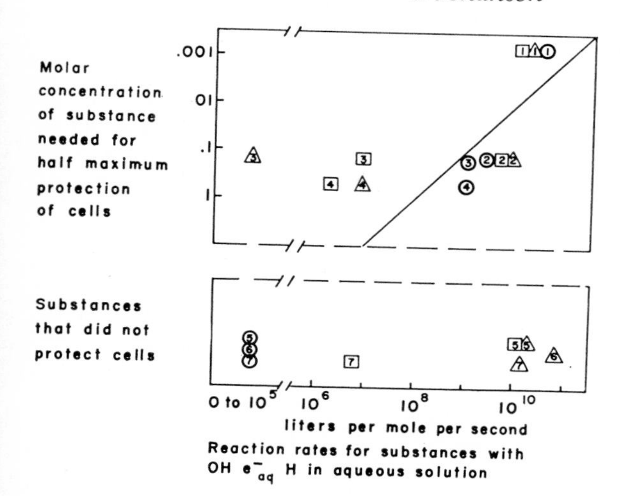

FIGURE 1. The molar concentration of substances 1 through 4 required for half maximum protection against X rays in *Escherichia coli* B/r (from Table 1) plotted against published data for their reactivities towards water-free radicals in aqueous solutions. The reactivities of substances 5 through 7, which did not protect, is shown in the lower half of the figure. Abbreviations: O, OH; Δ, e^-_{aq}; □, H; 1, NO; 2, NO^-_2; 3, CH_3CH_2OH; 4, CH_3OH; 5, O_2; 6, CO_2; 7, NO^-_3. (Johansen and Howard-Flanders, in press.)

to the reactivity towards the free radical. If so, the experimental points would lie on a 45-degree line in the upper figure. Only the points for the hydroxyl radicals fall close to this line. Taken together, these data suggest that radical intermediates with properties similar to the hydroxyl radicals are responsible for half of the radiation injury.

As oxygen is an effective electron scavenger, it could be argued that the reducing species could be important only under anoxia. Table 1 shows that ethanol and methanol afford about the same protection in nitrogen as in oxygen, while carbon dioxide and sodium nitrate are without any protective effect, both in nitrogen and in oxygen. Thus, the experiments have so far failed to demonstrate that any of the lethal effects of X rays can be attributed to the reducing species.

It has been suggested by Adams and Dewey (1963) that the mechanism by which N-ethylmaleimide (NEM) sensitizes cells is in part by capture and stabilization of the electronic charge, and that the radical ion so formed may be more toxic than the solvated electron. If this hypothesis for the action of NEM is correct, the presence of an electron scavenger would be expected to reverse the sensitizing effect of NEM. Table 2 shows the effects of

TABLE 2

The Anoxic Radiosensitivity of E. coli *B/r in the Presence of NEM and Electron Scavengers*

TREATMENT	1 PER CENT SURVIVAL DOSE KRADS	RELATIVE RADIOSENSITIVITY
N_2	137	1.00
N_2 + 0.5 M $NaNO_3$	137	1.00
N_2 + 0.0004 M NEM	71	1.93
N_2 + 0.0004 M NEM + 0.5 M $NaNO_3$	82	1.67
N_2 + 0.0004 M NEM + 0.0028 M CO_2	82	1.67

Abbreviation: NEM, N-ethylmaleimide.

nitrate and carbon dioxide on the colony-forming ability of NEM-sensitized bacteria irradiated under anoxia. The 93 per cent sensitization of anoxic bacteria by NEM is decreased by 26 per cent in the presence of electron scavengers. Evidently not more than one third of the sensitization by NEM can be contributed to this mechanism. An alternative hypothesis that the radiobiological action of NEM is based on its properties as a sulfhydryl binding agent (Bridges, 1962) is supported by the findings that the amount of acid-soluble sulfhydryls in *E. coli* B/r is reduced by more than 90 per cent after treatment with 0.0004 M NEM, and that the anoxic sensitivity is restored if the concentration of endogenous sulfhydryls is restored by addition of mercaptoethanol (Johansen and Howard-Flanders, 1964).

REFERENCES

Adams, G., and D. L. Dewey. 1963. Hydrated Electrons and Radiobiological Sensitization. *Biochemical and Biophysical Research Communications,* 12:473–477.

Bridges, B. A. 1962. The Chemical Sensitization of *Pseudomonas* Species to Ionizing Radiation. *Radiation Research,* 16:232–242.

Burnett, W. T., G. E. Stapleton, M. L. Morse, and A. Hollaender. 1951. Reduction of X-Ray Sensitivity of *Escherichia coli* B/r by Sulfhydryl Compounds, Alcohols, Glycols and Sodium Hydrosulphite. *Proceedings of the Society for Experimental Biology and Medicine,* 77:636–638.

Dale, W. M., J. V. Davies, and C. Russell. 1961. Nitric Oxide as a Modifier of Radiation Effects on *Shigella flexneri. International Journal of Radiation Biology and Related Studies in Physics, Chemistry and Medicine,* 4:1–13.

Johansen, I., and P. Howard-Flanders. 1964. Macromolecular Repair and Free Radical Scavenging in the Protection of Bacteria Against X-Rays. *Radiation Research.* (in press.)

The Effects of Ultraviolet Light on Nucleic Acid Coding Systems

L. GROSSMAN, J. ONO,* AND R. WILSON†

The Graduate Department of Biochemistry, Brandeis University, Waltham, Massachusetts

Ultraviolet light has long been employed as a mutagenic agent in biological systems following the observation that the action spectrum of its effects coincided with the absorbence spectrum of nucleic acids (Franklin, Friedman, and Setlow, 1953). Although a great deal of effort was spent in the ensuing years on the use of ultraviolet light in biological systems, little progress was made until recently on the photochemistry of irradiated nucleic acids and their derivatives. The work which has perhaps stimulated more experimental efforts on this subject was that of Beukers and Berends (1960, 1961) and Wang (1961), which described the photoconversion of thymine to a dimeric product, either in frozen solutions of thymine or in aqueous solutions of deoxyribonucleic acid (DNA) (Wacker, Dellweg, and Weinblum, 1960). The photoproducts formed from the other pyrimidine bases which had been studied before the discovery of dimers attracted less attention, even though little was known concerning the biological roles of these photoproducts. Thus uracil derivatives were shown to be hydrated by ultraviolet light, and the absolute structure of such hydrated derivatives was unequivocably proved by chemical synthesis (Moore and Thomson, 1957; Moore, 1958; and Wang, 1958). It was not until the isolation and characterization of thymine dimers that uracil dimers proved to be a major photoproduct of this ribonucleic acid (RNA) derivative. Cytosine at moderate ultraviolet doses essentially forms only a hydrated derivative, or water adduct (Shugar and Wierzchowski, 1957), the absolute structure of

* Present address: National Institute of Radiological Sciences, Chiba-shi, Japan.
† Present address: National Institutes of Health, Bethesda, Maryland.

which is still under discussion (Wang, 1958; Shugar, 1960).

In the past several years a concentrated effort has been made to relate the biological activities of killing and mutations to specific photoproducts. Setlow and Setlow (1962) have been able to correlate the photochemistry of thymine with survival studies of *Hemophilus influenzae* transforming DNA. The formation of dimers and their photoreversal by lower wavelengths of ultraviolet light (Johns, Rapaport, and Delbrück, 1962) is related quite well with the depression and reversal of the biological activity of the irradiated transforming principle. It can be concluded from these experiments that the lethal effects of ultraviolet light are caused by thymine dimer formation.

The mutational properties of ultraviolet light, as with chemical mutagens in general, should exert their effects at a number of predictable biochemical sites. These loci are (1) the direct coding of amino acids by messenger RNA, (2) the replication of RNA and DNA, and (3) the incorporation of nucleoside triphosphates from a fixed nucleic acid template. The researches of Nirenberg (Matthaei and Nirenberg, 1961; Nirenberg and Matthaei, 1961) and Ochoa and his collaborators (Lengyel, Speyer, and Ochoa, 1961; Speyer, Lengyel, Basilio, and Ochoa, 1962) on the amino acid incorporating systems, and those of Kornberg (Lehman, Bessman, Simms, and Kornberg, 1958; Bessman, Lehman, Simms, and Kornberg, 1958), Weiss (Weiss and Nakamoto, 1961; Nakamoto and Weiss, 1962), and Hurwitz (Furth, Hurwitz, and Goldman, 1961; Furth, Hurwitz, and Anders, 1962) on the nucleic acid replicating systems have contributed to our understanding of these biochemical coding systems and allowed for their isolation and utilization. Moreover, the isolation and characterization of the polynucleotide phosphorylases have permitted the preparation of polyribonucleotides whose base content and sequence can be controlled. These biochemicals provide exact and known messenger and template polymers, so that treatment of such polymers by mutagenic agents permits the direct determination of the effects of mutation in vitro.

The subject of this communication will be to describe experiments in which polyribonucleotides are irradiated with ultraviolet light and their coding and replicating properties examined in isolated and purified enzyme systems.

Results and Discussion

Protein Synthesizing Systems

It has been demonstrated in many laboratories that polyuridylic acid (poly U) acts as a messenger RNA for the synthesis of polyphenylalanine in both bacterial and mammalian amino acid incorporating systems. Irradiation of the polyribonucleotide with ultraviolet light modifies its coding properties, resulting in the synthesis of polyphenylalanyl-serine (Grossman, 1962). Because irradiation products of uracil derivatives result in the formation of hydrated and dimer species, further examination of the photoproducts responsible for the effects of ultraviolet irradiation of poly U was required; this examination revealed a separation of biochemical effects with specific photoproduct formation. It was apparent that the water adduct, or hydrate, was responsible for the code change accompanying irradiation, and that the uracil moieties in poly U which formed dimers resulted in a lethallike effect which induced an irrevocable loss of phenylalanine incorporation not replaced by any other amino acid (Grossman, 1963).

The code change implicit in this mutation in vitro can be expressed in terms of an irradiation-induced pyrimidine-pyrimidine transition of the triplet: U-U-U $\xrightarrow{hv}$ U-U-"C". However, an interpretation of this modification from the amino acid incorporating system is complicated by the coding degeneracies recently reported by a number of workers. Many of the polypeptides formed in such systems do not readily lend themselves to chemical examination. Consequently, these studies were extended to nucleic acid-replicating systems in which induced changes in coding could be followed with less equivocation, and the location of radioactive labels in the polymers produced by the enzyme could also be more easily located.

The RNA polymerase from *Micrococcus leisodeikticus* described by Weiss (Weiss and Nakamoto, 1961; Nakamoto and Weiss, 1962) can utilize as its template, for the synthesis of RNA, either DNA or RNA. Furthermore, polyribonucleotides can substitute as a template for the latter nucleic acid. Thus polycytidylic acid (poly C), as a template, directs the synthesis of polyguanylic acid (poly G) in the presence of guanosine triphosphate (GTP) and enzyme. Poly U in the presence of adenosine triphosphate (ATP) and the same enzyme governs the synthesis of polyadenylic acid (poly A). The present communication describes experiments involving the effects of ultraviolet irradiation on the template properties of poly C catalyzed by the RNA polymerase.

The Effects of Temperature on the Absorbence Properties of Irradiated Poly C

Poly C was exposed to ultraviolet light until 50 per cent of its characteristic absorbence was lost. After this period of irradiation the polymer was placed in quartz cuvettes and housed in a constant temperature block in the Zeiss Spectrophotometer. The return to original absorbence followed as a function of time and temperature. Figure 1 shows the effect of temperature on the initial rates of absorbence restoration.

It is apparent that the photoproducts which are produced in irradiated poly C are unstable at temperatures approaching those normally employed for enzymatic reactions. The ideal temperature, in terms of photoproduct stability, for study with the RNA polymerase enzyme is about 15° to 20°.

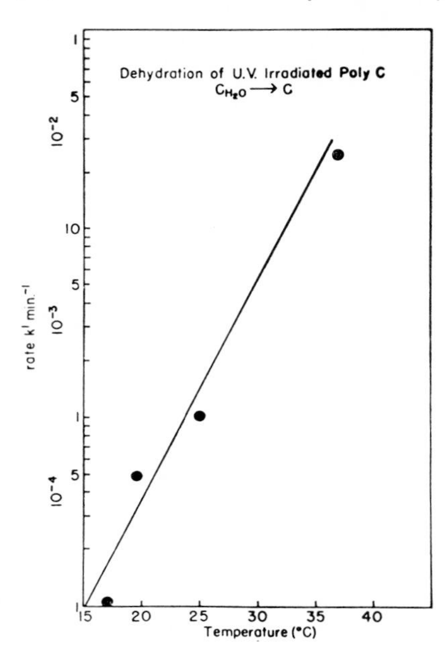

FIGURE 1. Initial rates of dehydration of ultraviolet-irradiated poly C by temperature.

The RNA polymerase from *M. leisodeikticus* functions quite well at such low temperatures, thus permitting study of the photoproducts under reasonably stable conditions.

The Effects of Ultraviolet Irradiation on the Replicating Properties of Poly C

The replication of poly C involves the polymerization of GTP in the presence of Mn^{+2} and enzyme to yield the acid-insoluble poly G (Figure 2). After irradiation of poly C, there is a rapid loss of GTP incorporation (Figure 3) which is almost quantitatively recovered when the irradiated poly C is preincubated at temperatures sufficiently high to cause dehydra-

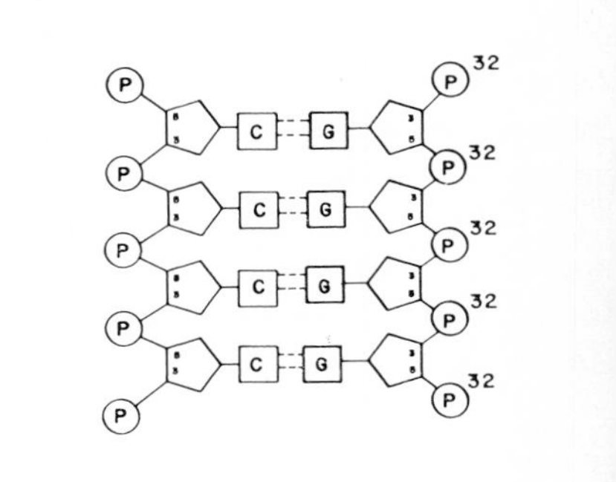

$$\text{Poly C} + \text{GRP}^{32}\text{–P–P} \xrightarrow[\text{Polymerase}]{Mn^{+2}} \text{P}^{32}\text{– Poly G} + \text{P–P}_i$$

FIGURE 2. Diagrammatic representation of the template properties of poly C.

tion of the cytosine water adduct moieties in the irradiated polymer.

The interpretation of this information is that each time a cytosine residue is hydrated by ultraviolet light, the sequential coding properties of the polymer are stopped at the point of lesion. If such a lesion, which can be denoted simply as *X* base replacing cytosine, codes for another purine, then the coding or replicating process should continue in the presence of *X*TP. To test this hypothesis, we performed a series of replacement experi-

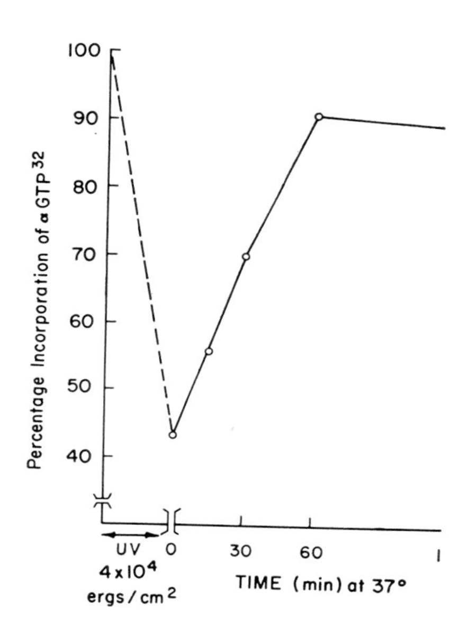

FIGURE 3. Effects of temperature on ultraviolet-irradiated poly C template properties.

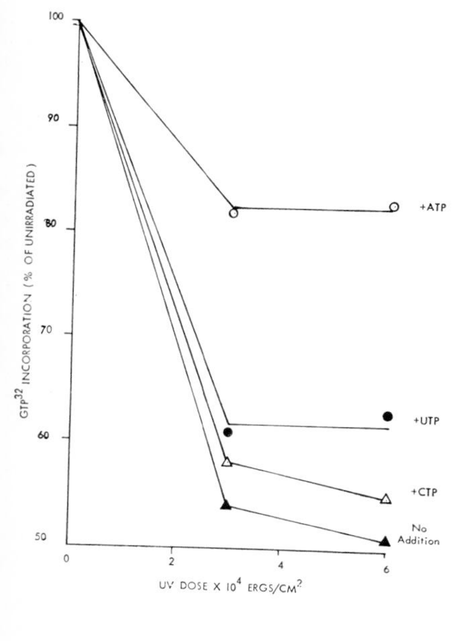

FIGURE 4. Diagrammatic representation of nucleoside triphosphate replacement with ultraviolet-irradiated poly C.

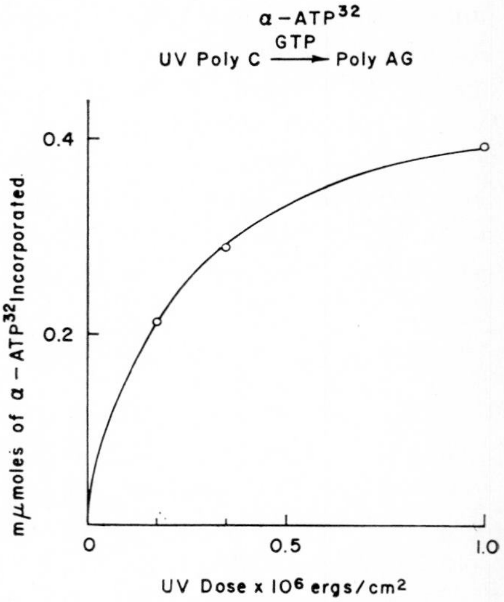

FIGURE 5. Alpha-ATP^{32} incorporation directed by irradiated poly C.

ments in which each of the other nucleoside triphosphates was added separately to the reaction mixture containing the labeled GTP, enzyme, and irradiated poly C. The results of such experiments are shown in Figure 4, in which it can be seen that only unlabeled ATP is capable of partially restoring the depressed incorporation of labeled GTP.

The analagous, but reverse, experiment was performed in which labeled ATP and unlabeled GTP were included in the reaction mixtures in which the poly C was irradiated for varying periods of time (Figure 5). Under these conditions, the other labeled nucleoside triphosphates are not

UV Irradiation of Poly C

$$\text{AR-P}^{32}\text{-P-P} + \text{GTP} \rightleftharpoons \text{P}^{32}\ \text{Poly GA} + \text{P-P}_i$$

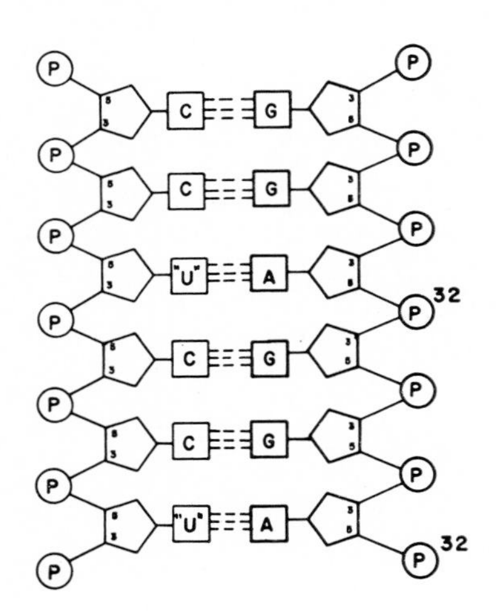

FIGURE 6. Diagrammatic representation of the mixed polymer produced by irradiation and its template properties.

incorporated to any significant extent, implying, from the original hypothesis, that the homopolymer following the irradiation is converted to a mixed polymer, in which the lesion base *X* codes in the replicating system as uracil and now directs the incorporation of labeled ATP. The interpretation of this phenomenon is depicted in Figure 6, in which it is assumed that the irradiated lesion acts as the other pyrimidine, uracil, and that in its replication cycle the ultraviolet light-induced mixed polymer directs the enzymatic synthesis of the mixed polymer poly GA.

Nearest Neighbor Analysis of the Mixed Polymers

In order to determine whether the incorporation of ATP with irradiated poly C and cold GTP represents the inclusion of ATP in internucleotide linkage, a series of nearest neighbor experiments were performed. The basis of such investigations involves the use of P^{32}-labeled ATP, in which the labeled phosphate is esterified to the carbohydrate moiety and the beta and gamma pyrophosphates are unlabeled. Following incorporation of this labeled ATP in the presence of unlabeled GTP, the polymer is degraded with alkali, which causes internucleotide cleavage between the 5′-P^{32} linkage and the adenosine moiety such that the neighboring 2′,(3′)-nucleoside monophosphate bears the labeled phosphate. Such an analysis provided information concerning the formation of internucleotide linkages, as well as determining the frequency in which a specific purine base is a neighbor in the same polynucleotide chain.

An application of this kind of analysis to the template properties of poly C exposed to varying levels of ultraviolet light is shown in Figure 7. In this experiment, ATP^{32} and GTP were included in the reaction mixtures with irradiated poly C and enzyme. After one hour of incubation at 17° C,

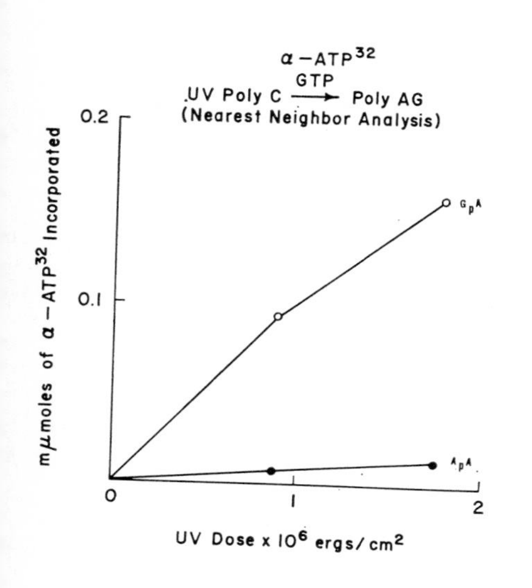

FIGURE 7. Nearest neighbor analysis with α-ATP^{32} and irradiated poly C.

the reaction was terminated and the acid-insoluble material hydrolyzed overnight with 0.3 M KOH. The alkaline hydrolysate was neutralized and subjected to paper electrophoresis, which served to separate the individual 2′(3′) nucleotides. The spots corresponding to the AMP-2′(3′) and GMP-2′(3′) which were well separated, were eluted from the paper and the level of radioactivity was determined.

The extent of labeling in the GMP-2′(3′) is designated as GpA, and the frequency of labeling in AMP-2′(3′) is indicated as ApA. The latter nucleotide represents the frequency in which two adenosine monophosphate (AMP) moieties are next to each other; GpA represents the frequency in which guanine residues are adjacent to the incorporated adenine nucleotide in the same polynucleotide chain.

It is quite evident from Figure 7 that the ATP^{32} incorporated following irradiation of the poly C represents the conversion of a monomer nucleotide into the internucleotide linkage of this RNA-like polymer following ultraviolet irradiation.

This phenomenon is reversible under conditions in which the hydrated species of cytosine is dehydrated by elevated temperatures (Table 1), implicating this species of photoproduct in the coding change induced by irradiation. These experiments are identical to those in Figure 6, with the exception that the irradiated polymer was heated to 70° C for 15 minutes. It is apparent from these data that the ultraviolet-induced code change is reversible and that the probable photoproduct responsible for the template change is the water adduct of cytosine.

TABLE 1

Nearest Neighbor Analysis of α-ATP^{32} Incorporated after Ultraviolet Irradiation of Poly C and Reversal by Heat

Poly C Treatment	Isolated GpA	2′(3′)-Ribonucleotides[1] ApA
None	0	0.006
1.75×10^6 ergs/cm²	0.115	0.022
1.75×10^6 ergs/cm² 70°—15 min	0	0.008

[1] mμmoles of nucleotides per 60-minute incubation. Abbreviations: GpA denotes the sequence of the guanyli acid 3′—to the adenylic acid bearing the α-P^{32}; ApA denotes the sequence of an adenylic acid residue as neighbor to itself.

A series of analagous experiments were performed in which the labele phosphate was associated with the GTP, and the unlabeled nucleoside tri phosphate was ATP. These experiments, shown in Figure 8, were execute with irradiated poly C, in which part of the irradiated polymer was expose to dehydration. The levels of radioactivity associated with the GMP-2′(3′ are represented as GpG nucleotide sequences, whereas the AMP^{32}-2′(3′ include the nearest neighbor groups of GpA. The levels of such incorpora tion into GpA are consistent with those observed in which ATP^{32} label wa

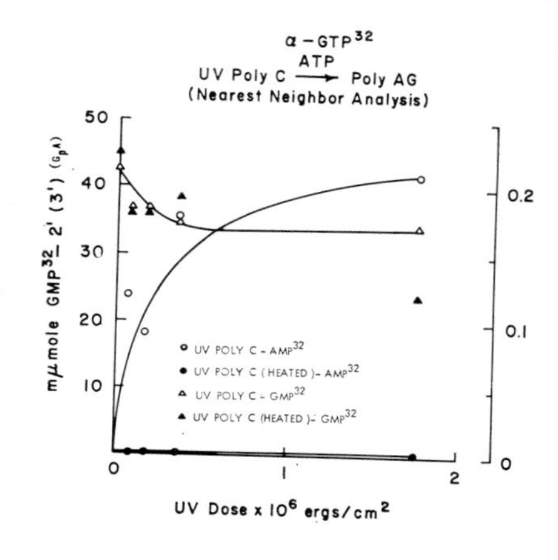

FIGURE 8. Nearest neighbor analyses of α-GTP^{32} and irradiated poly C.

found next to the guanylic acid residues (ApG) in the enzymatically synthesized polymer (Figure 7 and Table 1).

The ability of dehydrating temperatures to reverse completely the label in AMP-2′(3′) from the GTP^{32} implicates the hydrated species of cytosine as the photoproduct responsible for this shift in recognition by the polymerase enzyme and implies that heat stable photoproducts cannot account for the code transition from cytosine to uracil. At very high doses of ultraviolet irradiation, there is a significant deamination of cytosine to uracil (Schuster, Personal communications); however, deamination is an irreversible phenomenon and is certainly not reversible by increases in temperature.

To test whether deamination might contribute to this change in code, C^{14}-poly C was prepared and irradiated. After irradiation, the polymer was hydrolyzed with alkali, and the nucleotides were separated by paper electrophoresis to determine whether any C^{14}-UMP-2′(3) was formed by deamination of the labeled cytosine residues. Significant deamination does occur, however, at doses 100 times greater than those employed in these experiments. The sensitivity of this assay procedure is greater than that of the nearest neighbor analysis, so that if deamination of the cytosine residues contributed to the code change it would have been easily observable by this technique.

pK Changes

It is assumed that the region of the pyrimidine ring most likely to be involved in the transcription of information was that which shared hydrogen bonds with the purines during polymerization and that the photomodification of the opposite side of the pyrimidine must influence the same reacting positions. Such an indirect effect would be expected to modify the pK values for the protonation of the ring nitrogen. Electrometric titrations of cytidine were compared with 5,6-dihydrocytidine rather than the photoproduct for a number of reasons. The photoproduct of cytidine is temperature-unstable, and its reversal to cytidine would complicate the titrations. The -OH group on the 6 position of the water adduct should not influence the protonation of the ring nitrogen because of its distance from the site of proton addition. Also, the lack of aromaticity would not transmit the inductive effects of such a grouping. Thus the pK obtained for the 5,6-dihydrocytidine should be essentially the same as that for the photoproduct. This reduced analog was prepared by catalytic hydrogenation in which rhodium-on-alumina was the catalyst and one mole of hydrogen gas was taken up at atmospheric pressure.

The apparent pK's of the two species of pyrimidine nucleosides indicate a noticeable increase in basicity of the ring nitrogen following reduction of the 5,6-double bond. This change has also been observed for the free nitrogen bases (Janion and Shugar, 1960). Such a large pK change (from 4.2 to 6.1 for dihydrocytidine) would effectively increase the probability of the existence of the cationic species at the pH's of the enzymatic polymerizations. A calculation of such probabilities for the two species at three pH values is given in Table 2.

TABLE 2

Ratio of Protonated Species at Different pH's

$$\mathrm{pH} = 1/\log\left(\frac{\mathrm{N}}{\mathrm{NH}^{+}}\right) + \mathrm{pK}$$

pH	Cytidine (pK = 4.2)	5,6-Dihydrocytidine (pK = 6.1)
7.5	1:2000	1:20
6.5	1:200	1:2
6.0	1:63	1:1

A direct test of the contributions of the protonated species of the photoproduct involved a titration of the incorporation of ATP^{32} with ultraviolet-irradiated poly C employed as the template. Control titrations were performed with GTP^{32} as the sole source of monomeric nucleotides. The results of the experiment are shown in Figure 9. It can be seen from this figure that there is a fourfold increase in ATP^{32} incorporation following exposure to ultraviolet light when the pH of the enzymatic mixture is lowered from pH 7.5 to 6.0. This same pH change had essentially no effect on the control GTP^{32} incorporation, implying that the photoproduct directing the incorporation of ATP was sensitive to this pH change. If it can be assumed that the molecular basis for such an ultraviolet-induced code transition is valid, then it must also be assumed that the protonated species behaves differently in its hydrogen bonding properties to account for its ability to direct the incorporation of ATP rather than GTP as predicted from the Watson-Crick hydrogen bond pairing mechanism.

Since the cationic species of the cytosine photoproduct can exist as two

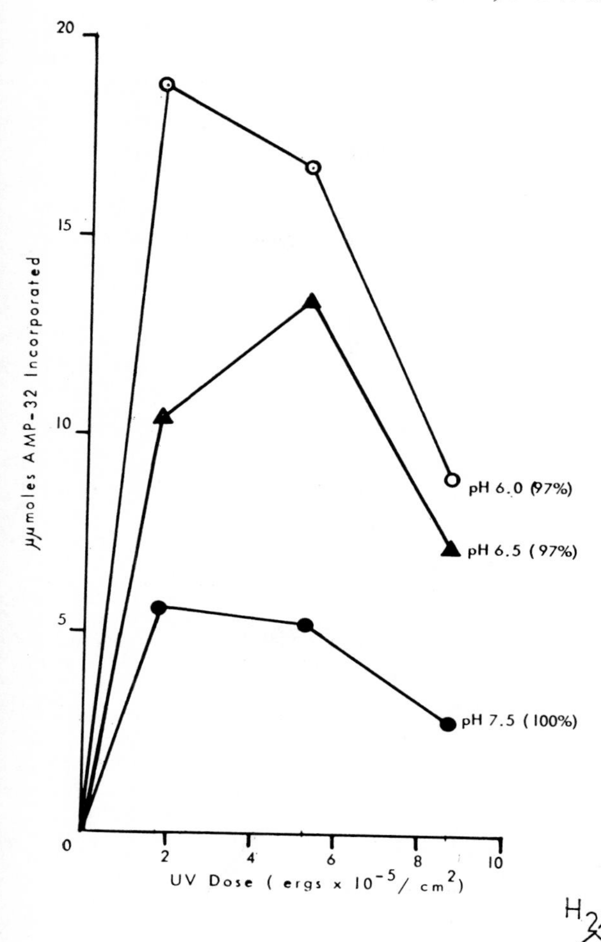

FIGURE 9. The effects of pH on the incorporation of α-ATP[32] with irradiated poly C.

FIGURE 10. Hydrogen bonding properties of protonated cytosine hydrate.

mesomeric species, two possible hydrogen bond pairs with adenine are shown in Figure 10. In the uppermost hydrogen bond pair two hydrogen bonds can exist, whereas only a single hydrogen bond is involved in the mesomer depicted in the lower portion of the same figure. In each case, the hydrogen bonds should be sufficiently stable to account for its coding properties.

ACKNOWLEDGMENTS

Publication No. 311 from the Graduate Department of Biochemistry, Brandeis University, Waltham, Massachusetts.

This work was supported in part by Grant C-5329 from the National Institutes of Health and Grant G-14382 from the National Science Foundation.

REFERENCES

Bessman, M. J., I. R. Lehman, E. S. Simms, and A. Kornberg. 1958. Enzymatic Synthesis of Deoxyribonucleic Acid. II. General Properties of the Reaction. *Journal of Biological Chemistry*, 233:171–177.

Beukers, R., and W. Berends. 1960. Isolation and Identification of the Irradiation Product of Thymine. *Biochimica et biophysica acta*, 41:550–551.

———. 1961. The Effects of U.V. Irradiation on Nucleic Acids and Their Components. *Biochimica et biophysica acta*, 49:181–189.

Franklin, R. M., M. Friedman, and R. B. Setlow. 1953. The Ultraviolet Action Spectrum of a *Bacillus megatherium* Bacteriophage. *Archives of Biochemistry and Biophysics*, 44:259–264.

Furth, J. J., J. Hurwitz, and M. Anders. 1962. The Role of Deoxyribonucleic Acid in Ribonucleic Acid Synthesis. *Journal of Biological Chemistry*, 237:2611–2619.

Grossman, L. 1962. The Effects of Ultraviolet-Irradiated Polyuridylic Acid in Cell Free Protein Synthesis in *E. coli*. *Proceedings of the National Academy of Science of the U.S.A.*, 48: 1609–1614.

———. 1963. The Effects of Ultraviolet-Irradiated Polyuridylic Acid in Cell-Fre Protein Synthesis in *E. coli*. II. The Influence of Specific Photoproducts. *Proceeding of the National Academy of Sciences of the U.S.A.*, 50:657–664.

Janion, C., and D. Shugar. 1960. Absorption Spectra, Structure and Behavior Toward Some Enzymes of Dihydropyrimidines and Dihydrooligonucleotides. *Acta Biochemic Polonica*, 7:309–329.

Johns, H. E., S. A. Rapaport, and M. Delbrück. 1962. Photochemistry of Thymin Dimers. *Journal of Molecular Biology*, 4:104–114.

Lehman, I. R., M. J. Bessman, E. S. Simms, and A. Kornberg. 1958. Enzymatic Sy thesis of Deoxyribonucleic Acid. *Journal of Biological Chemistry*, 233:163–170.

Lengyel, P., J. F. Speyer, and S. Ochoa. 1961. Synthetic Polynucleotides and the Amir Acid Code. *Proceedings of the National Academy of Sciences of the U.S.A.*, 47:1936 1942.

Matthaei, J. H., and M. W. Nirenberg. 1961. Characteristics and Stabilization DNAase-Sensitive Protein Synthesis in *E. Coli* Extracts. *Proceedings of the Nation Academy of Sciences of the U.S.A.*, 47:1580–1588.

Moore, A. M. 1958. Ultraviolet Irradiation of Pyrimidine Derivatives. II. Note on t Synthesis of the Product of Reversible Protolysis of Uracil. *Canadian Journal Chemistry*, 36:281–283.

Moore, A. M., and C. H. Thomson. 1957. Ultraviolet Irradiation of Pyrimidine Deriv tives. I. 1,3-Dimethyluracil. *Canadian Journal of Chemistry*, 35:163–169.

Nakamoto, T., and S. B. Weiss. 1962. The Biosynthesis of RNA: Priming by Pol ribonucleotides. *Proceedings of the National Academy of Sciences of the U.S.A.*, 48:880–887.

Nirenberg, M. W., and J. H. Matthaei. 1961. The Dependence of Cell-Free Protein Synthesis in *E. coli* Upon Naturally Occurring or Synthetic Polyribonucleotides. *Proceedings of the National Academy of Sciences of the U.S.A.*, 47:1588–1602.

Schuster, H. Personal communication.

Setlow, R. B., and J. K. Setlow. 1962. Evidence That Ultraviolet-Induced Thymine Dimers in DNA Cause Biological Damage. *Proceedings of the National Academy of Sciences of the U.S.A.*, 48:1250–1257.

Shugar, D. 1960. "Photochemistry of Nucleic Acids," *The Nucleic Acids*, E. Chargaff and J. N. Davidson, Eds. New York, New York: Academic Press, Inc. Vol. III. Pp. 39–104.

Shugar, D., and K. L. Wierzchowski. 1957. Reversible Protolysis of Pyrimidine Derivatives Including Trials with Nucleic Acids. *Biochimica et biophysica acta*, 23:657–658.

Speyer, J. F., P. Lengyel, C. Basilio, and S. Ochoa. 1962. Synthetic Polynucleotides and the Amino Acid Code. II. *Proceedings of the National Academy of Sciences of the U.S.A.*, 48:63–68.

Wacker, A. H., H. Dellweg, and D. Weinblum. 1960. Strahlenchemische Veränderung der Bakterien-Deoxyribonucleinsäure *in vivo*. *Naturwissenschaften*, 47:477.

Wang, S. Y. 1958. Photochemistry of Nucleic Acids and Related Compounds. I. The First Step in the Ultraviolet Irradiation of 1,3-Dimethyluracil. *Journal of the American Chemical Society*, 80:6196–6198.

———. 1961. Photochemical Reactions in Frozen Solutions. *Nature*, London, 190: 690–694.

Weiss, S. B., and T. Nakamoto. 1961. On the Participation of DNA in RNA Biosynthesis. *Proceedings of the National Academy of Sciences of the U.S.A.*, 47:694–697.

Ultraviolet Light Effects on Deoxyribonucleic Acid Replication

C. O. DOUDNEY

Section of Genetics, Department of Biology, The University of Texas M. D. Anderson Hospital and Tumor Institute, Houston, Texas

This study is a comparison of certain biochemical and biological events after ultraviolet light (UV) exposure of the bacterial cell. These events are (1) ribonucleic acid (RNA), deoxyribonucleic acid (DNA), and protein synthesis; (2) mutation induction; and (3) survival. We are specifically concerned with the recoverable and nonrecoverable blocks to DNA synthesis induced by UV. The recoverable block to DNA synthesis was first observed by Kelner (1953). Recovery of DNA synthesis has been shown to require RNA and protein synthesis but not DNA synthesis (Harold and Ziporin, 1958; Drakulic and Errera, 1959; Doudney, 1959). Recent studies (Setlow and Carrier, 1964; Boyce and Howard-Flanders, 1964) suggest the possibility that this recoverable block to DNA synthesis may be based on the induction of thymine dimers in the DNA and that the enzymatic excision of these dimers, followed by a repair step requiring RNA and protein synthesis, is involved in restitution of DNA synthesis.

MATERIALS AND METHODS

The techniques used have been described elsewhere (Doudney and Young, 1962; Doudney, 1963). For determination of RNA, the orcinol reaction or spectrophotometric measurements of nucleic acid hydrolysates is carried out. The Burton reaction is used to determine DNA. The density gradient analysis technique, in which the bacteria are grown on N^{15} medium and then transferred to N^{14} medium after UV exposure, is basically that of Meselson and Stahl (1958). Survival is determined by plating on minimal agar medium supplemented with 2.5 per cent nutrient broth. Reversion in strain WP2 is determined by plating on the same medium at a higher concentration of cells. Mutations are expressed as the number of prototrophs per 10^5 surviving auxotrophs. The organism used is *Escherichia coli* strain WP2, isolated by Dr. Evelyn Witkin after UV exposure of strain B/r. Strain WP2 requires tryptophan. A Hanovia germicidal lamp is used with an output below 2,800 A of 30 ergs/mm²/sec as measured by a Hanovia UV meter at the position of the cell suspension for the studies which are described in Figures 1 through 7 and Tables 1 through 3. A Gates Raymaster lamp with an output of 10 ergs/min²/sec was used for the studies which are described in Figures 8 through 16.

Results and Discussion

Relation Between UV Dose and Effect on DNA Synthesis

We have investigated a number of different strains of *E. coli* and have found the following relation between dose and effect on DNA synthesis, as illustrated by strain WP2 (Figure 1). Each increment of UV exposure increases the delay in initiation of DNA synthesis; thus the duration of the delay is related to dose. There is little or no effect of UV exposure at lower UV levels on the rate of DNA synthesis, once initiated. However, somewhere between 15 and 17.5 seconds of UV exposure a decreased rate of DNA synthesis is seen, and with increasing dose a corresponding decrease in rate of DNA synthesis is observed. At energy levels above this critical dose level, no further lag in DNA synthesis is observed; the only effect observed is the effect on rate. It is interesting to note that the relative increase in RNA, observed at the point where the effect on rate of DNA synthesis begins, is almost onefold in comparison to that amount present at time of exposure.

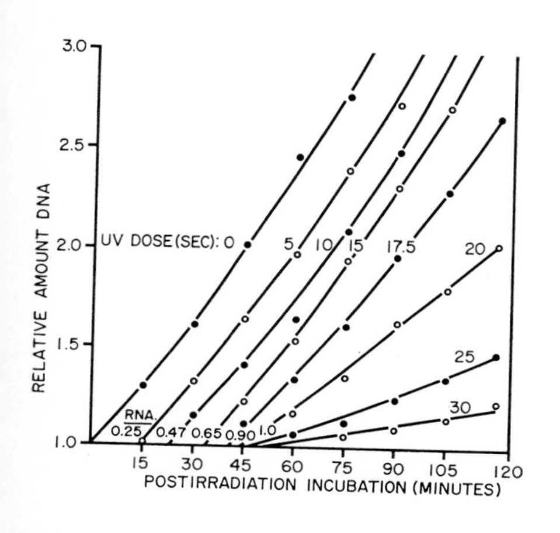

FIGURE 1. Effect of UV on postirradiation DNA replication in *E. coli* strain WP2. Suspensions of the cells were exposed to several doses of UV, then allowed to grow at 37C (1 = 52 μg DNA/ml culture). The values for RNA represent relative increase in RNA related to that amount present in the culture at time of UV exposure (1 = increase of 291 μg RNA/ml culture).

We shall return to this point later. Thus, to summarize, we apparently have two effects of UV exposure on DNA synthesis: (1) below 17.5 seconds there is a lag related to dose but little effect on rate once synthesis starts; (2) above 17.5 seconds, little or no further lag is induced, but an increasing effect on rate is observed.

Density Gradient Analysis of DNA Replication

It is important to establish that DNA replication after UV exposure (in so far as we can determine by distribution of subunits, using the Meselson and Stahl [1958] technique) corresponds to that which would be expected on the basis of the Watson and Crick model for DNA replication. Bacteria are grown on N^{15} medium, irradiated, transferred to N^{14} medium before growth can take place, and allowed to replicate. Figure 2 shows replication at approximately 15 seconds of UV exposure or at that UV dose just before the effect on rate of DNA synthesis is observed. Note the band of N^{15} containing DNA at zero time (at 1.724 density units). The sample extracted at 30 minutes' incubation has this band remaining, showing that no DNA has been formed. At 50 minutes' incubation where synthesis has started, the hybrid band is beginning to appear (at 1.716 density units). At 60 minutes' incubation, the hybrid band has grown relatively higher, and the first suggestion of completely N^{14} DNA band (at 1.710 density units) is observed. At 70 minutes' incubation, the N^{14} DNA band has grown higher. At 90 minutes' incubation, the N^{14} band almost equals the height of the hybrid band; and the N^{15} band or the original DNA has almost completely disappeared, indicating that almost all the DNA is replicating.

The results as to distribution of subunits with replication after 20 seconds' UV exposure more or less compare with those described for the samples taken from the 15 seconds' UV exposure culture, except that the band of N^{15} DNA does not completely disappear with incubation (Figure 3). This

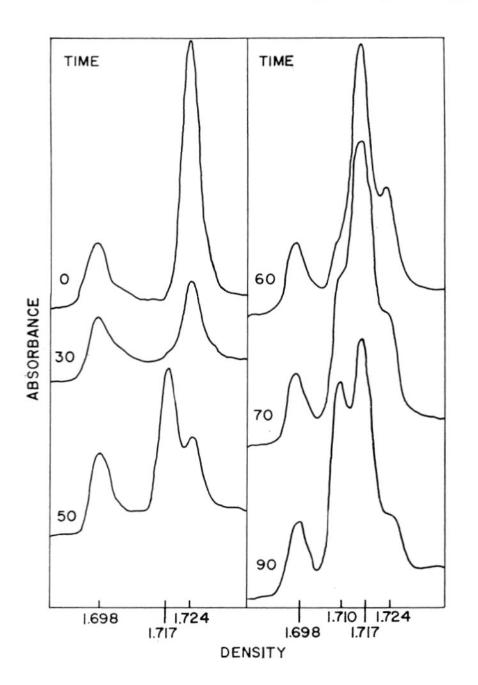

FIGURE 2. Joyce-Loebl microdensitometer tracings of photograph negatives of DNA samples extracted from *E. coli* strain WP2 after varying periods of incubation following 15 seconds of UV exposure and spun in the Spinco model E. analytical ultracentrifuge for 24 hours at 44,750 rpm. The cells were transferred from N^{15} medium to N^{14} medium immediately following UV exposure (see Doudney and Young, 1962). The first band (density = 1.698) is DNA obtained from *Proteus vulgaris* and added as a density reference. The second band (density = 1.710) is that of N^{14} DNA. The third band (density = 1.716) represents hybrid DNA consisting of one N^{15}- and one N^{14}-labeled strand. The final band (density = 1.723) is completely N^{15}-labeled DNA present in the bacteria at the time of UV exposure.

suggests that the basis of the slowed rate of DNA synthesis observed is not an effect interfering with the rate of synthesis of all the DNA, but is a partial inactivation of some of the DNA.

To summarize, after two levels of UV exposure, cells replicate according to the Watson and Crick model. All the DNA observed is at the expected

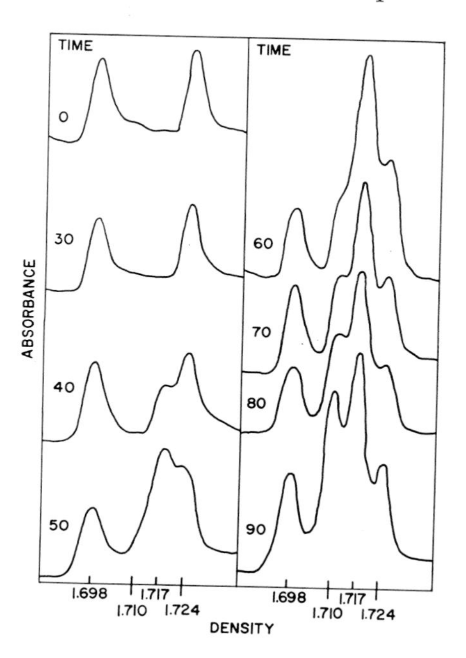

FIGURE 3. Joyce-Loebl microdensitometer tracings of photograph negatives of DNA samples extracted from *E. coli* strain WP2 after varying periods of incubation following 20 seconds of UV exposure (see Figure 2 for details).

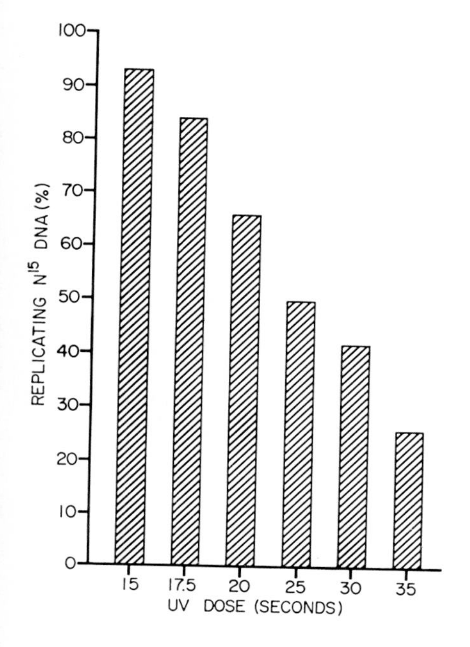

FIGURE 4. Replicating N^{15} DNA from strain WP2 after varying doses of UV grown on N^{14} medium for 180 minutes prior to extraction. The calculation of per cent is based on one-half the height of the Joyce-Loebl microdensitometer tracing of the hybrid DNA band (replicating) plus the full height of the N^{15} DNA band (nonreplicating).

TABLE 1

Comparison of UV Inactivation of DNA Synthesis and Cellular Inactivation in E. coli *Strain WP2*

UV DOSE (SECONDS)	RELATIVE RATE OF DNA SYNTHESIS*	RELATIVE AMOUNT OF REPLICATING N^{15} DNA**	RELATIVE SURVIVAL***
15	1.0	0.94	1.0
17.5	0.88	0.84	0.83
20	0.61	0.66	0.73
25	0.45	0.50	0.53
30	0.39	0.42	0.40

* Based on rate after 15 seconds of UV exposure (Figure 1).
** Hybrid DNA band height divided by 2 relative to sum of N^{15} DNA band height and hybrid DNA band height divided by 2.
*** Survival relative to number of colony-forming organisms at 15 seconds of UV exposure.

densities for replication of *E. coli* N^{15} DNA in N^{14} medium. The data suggest that the basis for the decrease in rate of DNA synthesis at higher UV levels is related to the inactivation of some of the DNA rather than to a decrease in rate of synthesis of all the DNA.

By using the density gradient analysis technique and growing cells for prolonged periods of time (to the point where all N^{15} DNA which is capable of replicating has replicated), the percentage of replicating N^{15} DNA can be determined at various dose levels (Figure 4). Up until 15 seconds of UV exposure, there is little effect in decreasing the amount of replicating DNA. Above this level of UV exposure an increasing amount of DNA is inactivated, as indicated by the observed decrease in replicating N^{15} DNA. This confirms that the basis for the irreversible inactivation causing the decrease in rate of DNA synthesis with increasing UV doses above 17.5 seconds is based on the inactivation of DNA (Table 1).

Effect of Dose of UV on Survival of E. coli *Strain WP2*

As is typical of *E. coli* strain B/r, the dose curve at lower energy levels shows a shoulder (Figure 5). The decrease in number of colony-forming

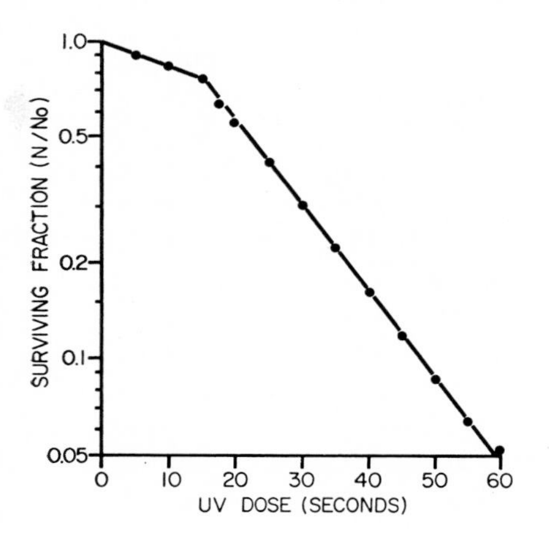

FIGURE 5. Relative surviving fraction (N/No) of *E. coli* strain WP2 exposed to varying doses of UV, based on the number of colonies observed after three days of incubation.

organisms is relatively low per unit dose. Above 17.5 seconds, however, an increase in inactivation rate is observed with dose. The multiplicity of the inactivation curve is approximately two and suggests that two inactivation events are involved in decreasing survival of this organism at the increased rate.

Comparison of Replicating DNA and Relative Survival of E. coli *Strain WP2*

If the relative rate of postirradiation DNA synthesis is calculated based on the rate observed at 15 seconds, it can be compared with calculated relative surviving bacteria based on survival at the same dose. The results (Table 1) show a correspondence at several different energy levels between relative rate of DNA synthesis, relative amount of replicating N^{15} DNA, and relative survival. This suggests that the inactivation event responsible for the increased inactivation rate of *E. coli* strain WP2 is based on the irreversible inactivation of DNA. The initial slower inactivation rate (the "shoulder") may be due to "lethal mutation" or some other mechanism.

The basis for the irreversible inactivation of DNA cannot be predicted at this time. It should be pointed out that the inactivation multiplicity is around two, corresponding to the two strands of DNA. This is in agreement with the survival results. Thus, the amount of UV required to completely inactivate DNA synthesis in the culture (34 to 40 seconds) is roughly double that which produces the maximum lag in DNA synthesis. The possibility exists that one inactivation event in a given region on each strand is repairable, but that a second inactivation event in the same region on the opposite strand irreversibly inactivates the DNA (since there would be no information left to repair the DNA). This idea will be discussed further below.

RNA Formation and Restitution of DNA Synthesis After UV Exposure

It has been shown (Doudney and Haas, 1958; Doudney, 1961a) that in UV-exposed cells, the rate of DNA synthesis is directly related to the amount of RNA formed before chloramphenicol (an antibiotic which blocks protein synthesis) is added (Figure 6). In amino acid-starved cells (Doudney, 1961b), there is a limitation to the amount of DNA which can be formed, but no significant decrease in rate of DNA synthesis (Figure 7).

These findings illustrate a significant difference in the two systems of RNA-protein synthesis involved in the restitution of cellular capacity for DNA synthesis. They indicate that the physiological system which comes into play when the DNA comes to the end of its replication cycle (Maaløe and Hanawalt, 1961) exerts its effect by removing a limitation to DNA synthesis, but does not influence rate of synthesis. It is thus clear from Figure 6 that, with restitution of DNA synthesis after UV exposure, the mode of action of RNA-protein synthesis is not simply the removal of the

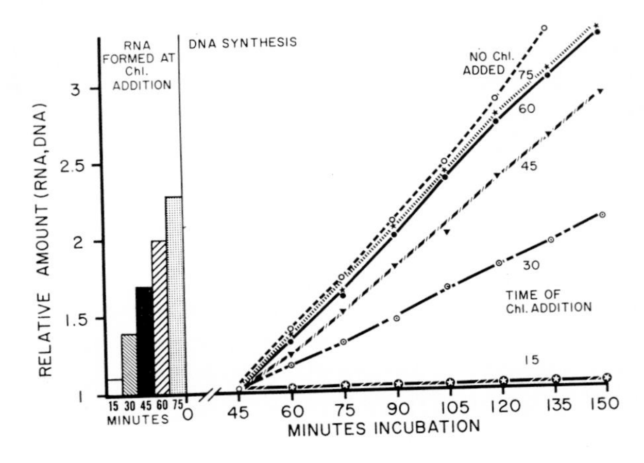

FIGURE 6. DNA synthesis in chloramphenicol (40 μg/ml) added after varying periods of incubation after UV exposure (15 seconds). The values for RNA are the amounts present in the culture at time of chloramphenicol addition relative to that amount present at time of UV exposure (1 = 305 μg/ml). DNA: 1 = 61 μg/ml culture.

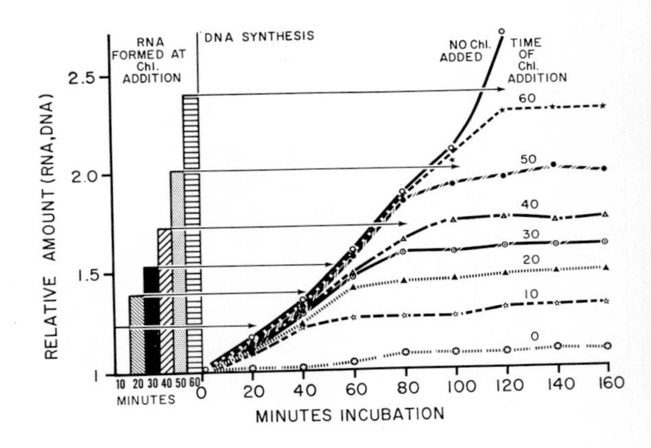

FIGURE 7. DNA synthesis in chloramphenicol (40 μg/ml) added after varying periods of incubation with tryptophan of a culture of *E. coli* strain WP2 starved for one hour without trytophan prior to incubation. The values for RNA are the amounts present in the culture at the time of chloramphenicol addition relative to that amount present at the time of addition of tryptophan (1 = 289 μg/ml). DNA: 1 = 86 μg/ml of culture.

limiting physiological mechanism which has somehow been brought into action by the effect of UV exposure.

Figure 6 shows that, unlike unirradiated cells, cells exposed to UV and then allowed to recover their DNA synthetic system have gained the capacity to replicate their DNA more than one time without protein synthesis. This is in striking contrast to the limitation to DNA synthesis imposed with recovery of amino acid-starved cells, and clearly differentiates the blockage by UV exposure from the blockage imposed on cells through action of the physiological control mechanism. It is hypothesized that the double replication of DNA (confirmed by using the density gradient analysis technique as mentioned below) is based on the cells gaining an additional physiological capacity for DNA synthesis during that period in which DNA synthesis is blocked by UV exposure. In other words, the physiological control mechanism for DNA synthesis has a chance to increase more than one time during the period of blocked DNA synthesis by UV action.

TABLE 2

Accumulation of Capacity for DNA Replication in Chloramphenicol by Thymine-Starved E. coli *Strain 15T⁻ and UV-Exposed* E. coli *Strain WP2*

Incubation prior to chloramphenicol addition (minutes)		Distribution of DNA as to density after 90 minutes incubation in N^{14} medium plus chloramphenicol Per cent (based on relative height of microdensitometer tracing)		
		N^{15} band	Hybrid band	N^{14} band
15T⁻*	0	43	57	0
	60	7	40	53
WP2**	0	38	62	0
	60	4	52	44

* 15T⁻: the culture, grown on N^{15} medium, was incubated without thymine for 60 minutes, then transferred to N^{14} medium containing thymine and chloramphenicol (40 μg/ml) and incubated for 90 minutes. The 0 incubation control was treated identically except that there was no thymineless incubation.
** WP2: the culture, grown on N^{15} medium, was irradiated (15 seconds UV) and incubated for 60 minutes, then transferred to N^{14} medium containing chloramphenicol and incubated for 90 minutes. The 0 culture was not irradiated or incubated prior to transfer to N^{14} medium.

Similar results have been observed with *E. coli* strain 15T⁻ (Table 2). If the culture is starved for thymine for increasing periods of time, an increasing capacity for formation of DNA without protein synthesis is observed. The culture actually accumulates the capacity for more than one round of DNA replication with thymineless incubation. With N^{15} grown cells starved for thymine beyond the period of time required for the accumulation of the capacity for doubling their DNA, an increased capacity for DNA synthesis is accumulated so that the N^{14} band of DNA accumulates in chloramphenicol (Table 2). Similar results are observed for UV-exposed cells. This indicates that cells may accumulate capacity for more than one DNA replication cycle under two conditions of blocked DNA synthesis: blockage by UV exposure and by thyminelessness. These findings have considerable implications as to the nature of the physiological control mechanism for DNA synthesis in bacteria. The physiological control mechanism could simply be a trigger mechanism which is released as a DNA replication cycle is completed. If this is so, then it is difficult to see the basis for the double accumulation of capacity for DNA synthesis with thymine-starved or UV-exposed cultures.

An Examination of Chloramphenicol Blockage of DNA Synthesis in UV-Exposed Cells

As mentioned above, at that dose of UV which delays DNA synthesis to the maximum possible extent without producing irreversible inactivation of synthesis, RNA doubles in the culture before synthesis starts (Figure 1). At any dose of UV, chloramphenicol blocks the recovery of DNA synthesis. At that dose of UV giving maximum delay of DNA synthesis without inactivation, an approximate doubling of RNA takes place before the inhibition of DNA synthesis by chloramphenicol is completely overcome (Figure 6).

If chloramphenicol is added before the doubling of RNA, DNA synthesis proceeds at a linear rate directly related to the amount of RNA made before the antibiotic is added. At any dose of UV, the rate of DNA synthesis in chloramphenicol is quantitatively related to the proportional increase in RNA at the time of chloramphenicol addition.

Using the density gradient technique, it has been found that in UV-exposed cells (at the dose of UV where DNA synthesis is lagged to the maximum possible extent without irreversible inactivation), there is complete disappearance of the N^{15} DNA with N^{15} grown bacteria, which indicates that no DNA has been irreversibly inactivated with UV. If chloramphenicol is added prior to complete recovery, decreasing the rate of DNA synthesis, a part of the N^{15} DNA does not replicate, as shown by the persistence of the N^{15} band in chloramphenicol (Table 3). The rest of the DNA replicates in chloramphenicol, as shown by the appearance of the hybrid and N^{14} DNA bands with incubation. These studies show that the decrease in rate of DNA synthesis in chloramphenicol with cells recovering from the inhibitory effect of UV is not caused by a decrease in rate of formation of all the DNA in the culture, but is the result of prevention of part of the DNA from being replicated by the antibiotic. Whether this blockage is on a per cell basis could only be established by autoradiography of DNA replication under these conditions.

TABLE 3

Effect of Chloramphenicol on DNA Replication In UV-Exposed E. coli *Strain WP2*

Time of chloramphenicol addition (minutes)*	Relative RNA increase**	Relative rate of DNA synthesis***	Relative amount of replicating N^{15} DNA****
0	0	0	0
30	0.41	0.52	0.48
45	0.77	0.81	0.79
60	1.10	0.95	0.87

* Length of incubation between UV exposure (15 seconds) and addition of chloramphenicol.
** Increase over that amount present at time of UV exposure.
*** Based on maximum rate in chloramphenicol (40 μg/ml), observed when chloramphenicol is added at 75 minutes incubation after UV exposure (see Figure 5).
**** Calculated as in Table 1.

General Working Model for Recoverable Inactivation of DNA by UV

Extensive investigation in this area has led us to the following general working model for the recoverable block to DNA synthesis by UV. Whatever its disadvantages, the model does fit all available data and has provided a fruitful basis for further experimentation. The block is a result of the production of damage in the bacterial DNA. Since the block is photoreversible, it is reasonable to expect that the damage is actually the thymine dimer, as suggested by Setlow and Carrier (1964) and by Howard-Flanders (see pages 52 to 60, this volume). DNA synthesis can proceed to the point of one of these lesions, and then must stop. The duration of delay is dependent on the number of lesions induced in the DNA, and thus is directly related to dose. When the maximum delay in DNA synthesis is induced by UV, the DNA chain is damaged to the maximum possible extent for this type of lesion or to the maximum extent that it can be repaired. It is possible that one strand of the DNA at each site must be undamaged if the DNA is to be restituted, to provide the information needed. Thus the recoverable block, observed up until 17.5 seconds of UV exposure, could be caused by the production of hits on either strand of the DNA, as long as they do not overlap in the area required for information for repair of the opposite strand. However, it may be that above 17.5 seconds, the damage begins to overlap in these areas and thus produces the nonreversible inactivation of DNA.

If DNA synthesis has been delayed by UV to the maximum extent before irreversible inactivation occurs, recovery of the DNA synthetic system is correlated with the doubling of cellular RNA. While this has been experimentally verified repeatedly in a number of strains, the significance of this correlation is not known. This is not to imply that all the RNA participates in the recovery process, but that some special component involved in recovery is formed in correlation with total RNA synthesis in the cell. At lower doses of UV involving fewer lesions of the DNA chain, proportionately less RNA need be made for DNA synthesis to proceed. This indicates that repair is specifically at the sites of damage, and that the RNA involved in repair need be formed only to the extent that there is damage of this type. Thus the amount of RNA needed for recovery of DNA synthesis, as measured by total RNA increase, can be taken as a relative measure of the number of DNA lesions produced at any given UV dose. The nature of the RNA involved in recovery of DNA synthesis is not known, but the suggestion can be made that the recovery process may involve formation of complementary RNA on the DNA template. Such complementary RNA might function in restitution of the DNA after enzymatic excision of an undefined region of one strand containing the thymine dimer. Alternatively, a specific protein or enzyme could be formed to effect the repair of the lesions in the DNA macromolecule, allowing synthesis to proceed.

Effect of DNA-Combining Dyes on Response to UV

Witkin (1958, 1961) has studied certain DNA-combining substances (hereafter referred to as "dyes") which increase mutation frequency response. In our studies we have compared the effects of these dyes (acriflavine, crystal violet, caffeine, methyl green) on RNA, DNA and protein synthesis, survival, and mutation induction with UV-exposed bacteria. The results establish that the dyes exert some action on the UV-exposed cells which results in increased mutation frequency response and lethality, as well as blockage of RNA, DNA, and protein synthesis. In this paper we will use caffeine and acriflavine as examples of this type of effect. However, the effects described are comparable for all dyes studied. Acriflavine and caffeine may be taken as examples for the general type of effect induced by these agents.

The effect of incubation in caffeine after UV exposure on survival of *E. coli* strain WP2 is shown in Figure 8. The effect reaches its maximum extent after about 70 minutes of incubation. In Figure 9 is shown the dose relationship of the effect. Note the typical B/r survival curve, as demonstrated earlier. The effect of caffeine apparently is to reduce the inactivation multiplicity from two to one. This suggests that the caffeine is interacting with some site to make it more sensitive. In other words, with caffeine, two UV hits are not necessary as with the inactivation of B/r. The possibility is that caffeine interacts with the thymine dimer (or the damaged region left after thymine dimer excision) to prevent repair, causing inactivation of the cell.

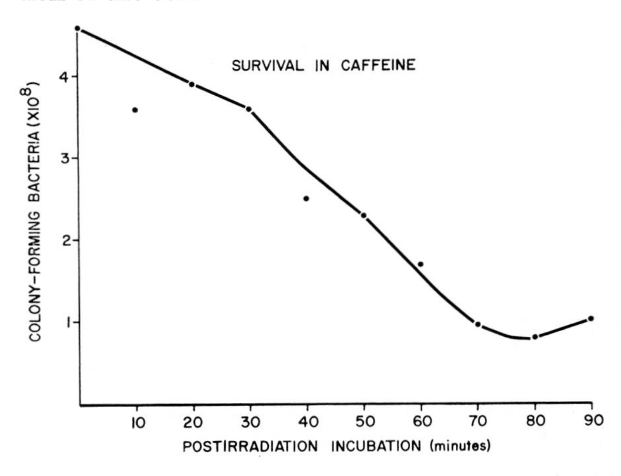

FIGURE 8. Survival of UV-exposed *E. coli* strain WP2 in 0.075 per cent caffeine after exposure to UV. In the dye studies, a dose rate of 10 ergs/mm^2/sec was used instead of 30 ergs/mm^2/sec, as in the above described studies. These bacteria have been exposed to 40 seconds of UV to reduce the number of colony-forming organisms from 8×10^8/ml to around 5×10^8/ml.

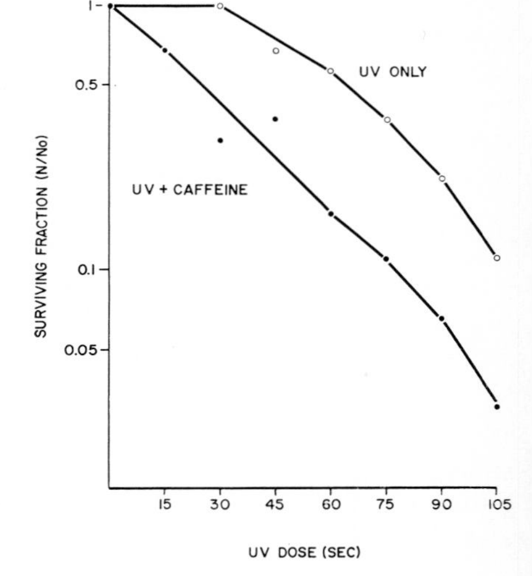

FIGURE 9. Effect of postirradiation incubation for 70 minutes ± caffeine (0.075 per cent) on survival with UV dose of *E. coli* strain WP2 (dose rate = 10 ergs/mm^2/sec).

The effect of caffeine on mutation frequency response in strain WP2 is shown in Figure 10. Caffeine itself does not interfere with the mutation frequency decline process in the absence of amino acids to any great extent, but a marked increase in mutation frequency response with caffeine is observed in the presence of amino acids. In Figure 11 is shown the dose effect on mutation frequency response. Caffeine greatly increases mutation frequency response with increasing dose. Figure 12 shows the effect of varying concentrations of caffeine on mutation frequency response and on survival. Note that roughly the same concentration produces maximum mu-

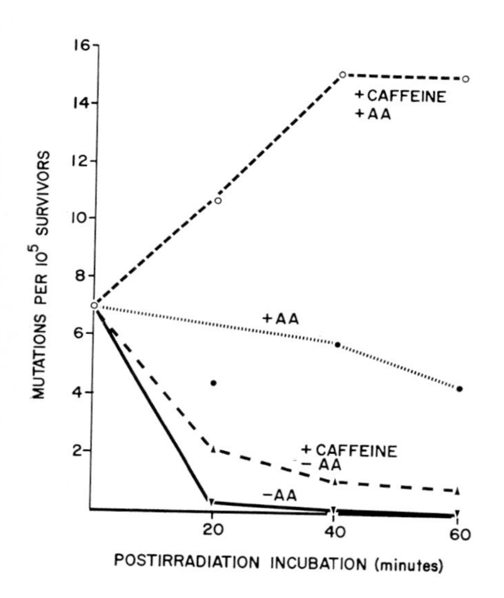

FIGURE 10. Effect of postirradiation incubation of UV-exposed (40 seconds) *E. coli* strain WP2 on production of induced prototrophs. Incubation was with and without an amino acid supplement including trytophane (Doudney and Haas, 1958, 1959) and with and without caffeine (0.075 per cent). In all other postirradiation incubations reported in this paper, the amino acid supplement was added.

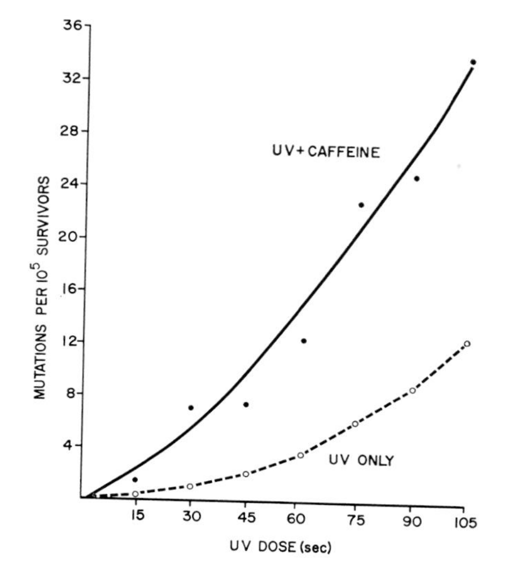

FIGURE 11. Effect of varying doses of UV exposure (10 ergs/mm²/sec) on production of induced prototrophs from a culture of *E. coli* strain WP2. The irradiated subcultures were incubated for 60 minutes with and without caffeine (0.075 per cent) prior to plating.

tation frequency response and the maximum decrease in survival. Similarly, the effects on RNA, DNA, and protein synthesis to be described below have been shown to have their maximum decrease at about the same concentration, which suggests the same site of action for all effects.

The question arose as to whether the mutations induced by UV with caffeine incubation are produced by a mechanism similar to that which produces those induced in the absence of caffeine. An indication would be whether these mutations are photoreversible as are most of the mutations

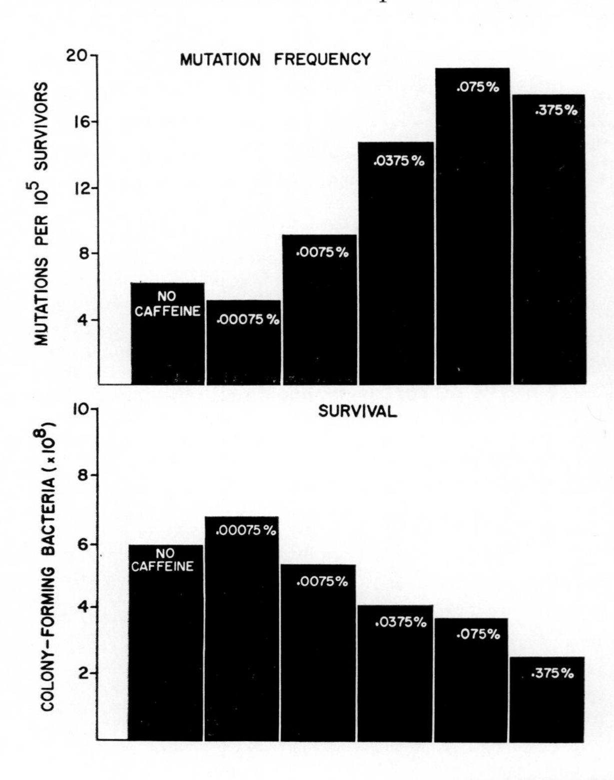

FIGURE 12. Effect of post-irradiation incubation (70 minutes with varying concentrations of caffeine of UV-exposed (40 seconds at 10 ergs/mm²/sec) *E. coli* strain WP2 on production of induced prototrophs and on survival.

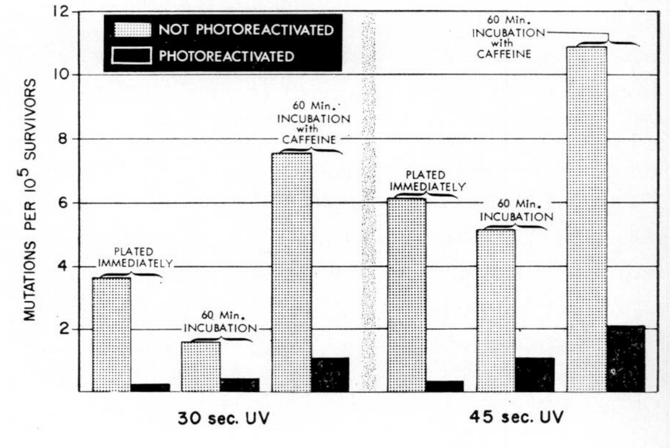

FIGURE 13. Photoreversibility of the induced prototrophs of UV-exposed (40 seconds at 10 ergs/mm²/sec) *E. coli* strain WP2. Photoreversal was attained by exposure for one hour to white light from two 500 watt General Electric projection bulbs located 6 inches from the cellular suspension and while cooling in an ice bath.

observed in the absence of caffeine. Figure 13 shows the results. Most of the mutations plated immediately without any postirradiation treatment are photoreversible. This is true at 30 and 45 seconds of UV exposure (at a dose rate of 10 ergs/mm^2/sec). At 60 minutes of incubation, mutation frequency response is still photoreactivated. Sixty minutes of incubation with caffeine increases the mutation frequency response noticeably, and most mutations remain photoreversible. This shows that most of the mutations induced by a combination of UV and caffeine are photoreversible, and is in line with a report by Shankel (1962).

Acriflavine will be used to illustrate the effects on DNA, RNA, and protein synthesis observed, although the effects with caffeine are identical. The concentration used (1 μg/ml) is the minimum effective concentration. Acriflavine has little effect on DNA synthesis in non-UV-exposed cultures. If the culture is exposed to UV before incubation with acriflavine, DNA synthesis is blocked for over 90 minutes (Figure 14). In UV-exposed cultures without acriflavine, there is a 45-minute lag in DNA synthesis which is followed by complete recovery of DNA synthetic capacity. Similarly, acriflavine has little effect on RNA synthesis in a non-UV-exposed culture. If exposed to UV, the culture has the capacity in acriflavine for an initially slow rate of RNA synthesis (Figure 15). RNA doubles in acriflavine, and then synthesis ceases. Similar results have been observed with protein synthesis.

At the dose of UV used, incubation in the presence of acriflavine increases mutation frequency response from about $5/10^5$ to $13/10^5$ surviving organisms (Figure 16). This increase appears to be correlated with RNA synthesis in the culture. During the first 15 minutes of incubation, there is no change in mutation frequency in acriflavine and little RNA formation. Upon initiation of RNA synthesis at about 15 minutes, a marked increase in mutation frequency occurs. No DNA is formed in the culture during the period of increasing mutation frequency response in acriflavine.

Incubation in acriflavine after UV exposure also decreases survival. This effect also appears to be correlated with RNA synthesis in the culture. Recent studies have shown that the concentration of acriflavine (as with caffeine) producing maximum effect is identical for blockage of RNA, DNA, and protein synthesis, and increased mutation frequency response and lethality, suggesting an identical site of action for all effects.

These results are consistent with a hypothesis in which the dyes react with the UV-damaged site on the DNA (possibly the UV-induced thymine dimer [Setlow and Carrier, 1964]) which is otherwise repairable to prevent replication. Whether the dyes would prevent excision of the thymine dimer region or whether the block is at a later stage preventing restitution of the DNA after excision of the dimer region cannot be decided at this point. However, it would make a great deal of sense if the latter case were true, nucleases present in the cell being responsible for excision of the thymine dimer region and the dyes then fitting into this area to prevent restitution.

One effect of the dyes presumably would be to prevent formation on the DNA template of the component of the RNA synthetic system (presumably the messenger RNA) necessary for total RNA synthesis. This would explain the limitation of RNA synthesis in the culture by acriflavine in UV-exposed cells. The fact that the RNA can double in the culture in the presence of acriflavine would suggest either (1) that the cell has at all times enough gene action product for one round of RNA replication (assuming that the dye reaction with damaged DNA is immediate), or (2) that it is the gene action event itself (messenger RNA formation) which uncovers the DNA to the inhibitory action of the acriflavine on the damaged site.

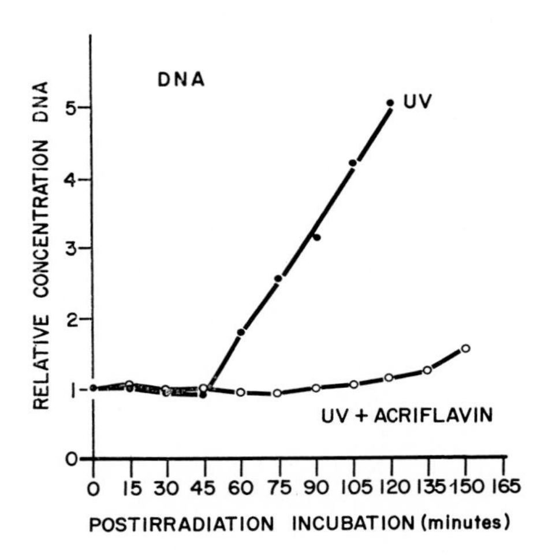

FIGURE 14. Effect of acriflavine (1 μg/ml) on DNA synthesis in UV-exposed cultures of *E. coli* strain WP2 (Doudney, White, and Bruce, 1964). DNA: 1 = 32 μg/ml culture.

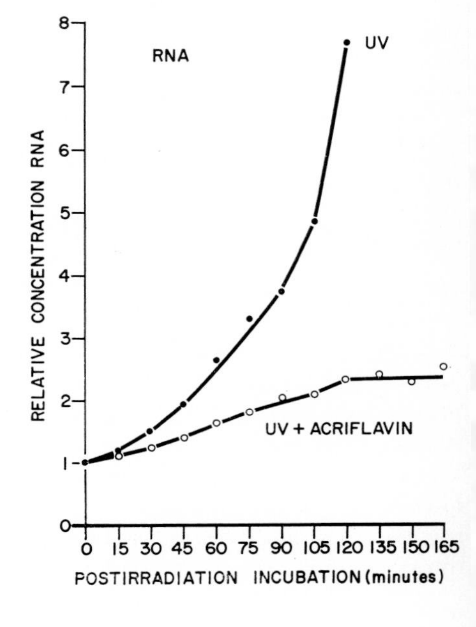

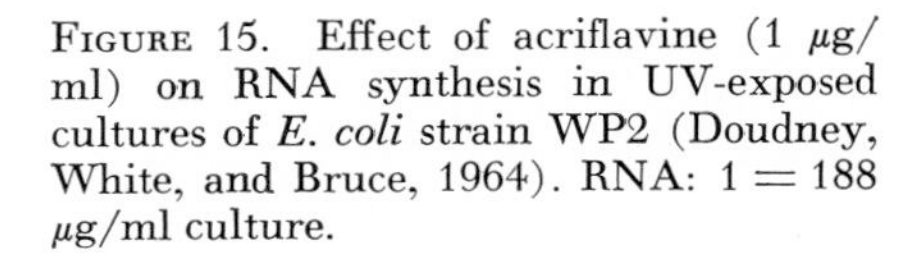

FIGURE 15. Effect of acriflavine (1 μg/ml) on RNA synthesis in UV-exposed cultures of *E. coli* strain WP2 (Doudney, White, and Bruce, 1964). RNA: 1 = 188 μg/ml culture.

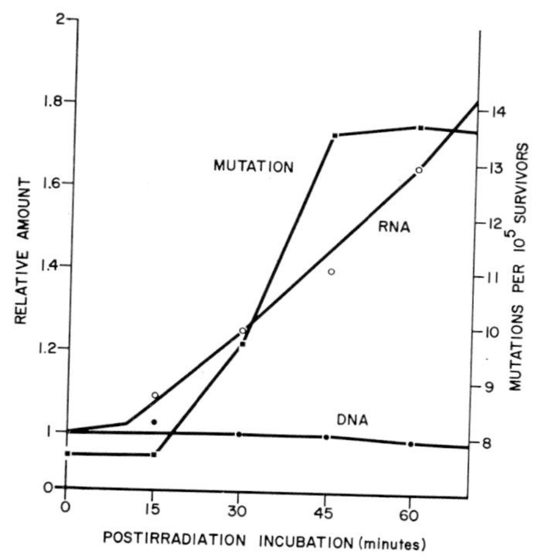

FIGURE 16. Effect of acriflavine on production of induced prototrophs with UV-exposed *E. coli* strain WP2 in comparison to synthesis of RNA and DNA in the culture. RNA: $1 = 188$ μg/ml culture; DNA: $1 = 32$ μg/ml culture. Acriflavine is not measurably mutagenic with non-UV-exposed cultures. (See Doudney, White, and Bruce [1964]).

This would allow one round of RNA formation before inactivation of the DNA template.

The latter possibility is supported by the dye effect on mutation induction. This idea is very attractive from the standpoint of the studies described above, which show correlation of RNA doubling with restitution of the UV-damaged DNA synthetic system and with mutation fixation. All these correlations strongly suggest the significance of the initial round of RNA synthesis after UV exposure in restitution of the DNA synthetic system. It is highly probable that mutation comes about through errors introduced in the DNA during this restitution process.

In view of the correlation of the above described increase in lethal and mutagenic effects of the dyes with RNA synthesis of the culture, it can be proposed that the action of the dyes on the site of damage is uncovered by RNA synthesis. In other words, the DNA is somehow protected until RNA is made. Thus when the damaged site on the DNA interacts with dyes with RNA synthesis, the mutagenic, lethal, and metabolic effects are observed. The reaction of the dyes would appear to be specifically with the DNA-damaged site, explaining the fact that only UV-damaged cells show these effects in the presence of the dyes.

A Thought About Mutation

An interpretation along the same lines can be developed for mutation induced by UV (in the absence of dyes). This could explain the correlation of "mutation fixation" with RNA synthesis as reported by Doudney and Haas (1958, 1959). Thus gene action (RNA synthesis on the DNA template) could uncover the UV-damaged site on the DNA, allowing its reaction (in a manner comparable to the damaged site-dye interaction proposed) with some extra-DNA photoproduct to produce that modification of the DNA which leads to mutation. Of course the hypothetical UV photoproduct would be present in the cell in too low a concentration to produce the lethal effects and the effects on nucleic acid formation observed with dye. This hypothesis is especially attractive from the standpoint of the work of Doudney and Young (1962). This work suggests that actually two hits are required to produce mutation. Doudney and Young proposed that the hits are opposite each other in each DNA strand. The possibility is, however, that one hit is responsible for the production of the thymine dimer and that an extra-DNA photoproduct comparable in mode of action to the dyes is induced in the cell by UV to account for the second hit.

Summary

At the lower dose range of UV, a recoverable block to DNA synthesis is induced in *E. coli*. A relation exists between dose and the duration of delay in DNA synthesis induced. Above a certain critical dose, little further delay in DNA synthesis is induced. The rate of DNA synthesis decreases with increasing dose above this dose level. DNA replication can be followed using the density gradient technique of Meselson and Stahl (1958), with bacteria grown for several generations on N^{15} medium and transferred to N^{14} medium immediately after UV exposure. Replication at various dose levels is semiconservative, in agreement with the findings of Meselson and Stahl for unirradiated bacteria. No intermediate band of DNA of abnormal density is observed with replication in UV-exposed bacteria. Below the critical dose level, all N^{15} DNA replicates after recovery. At doses above the critical level, failure of some part of the N^{15} DNA to replicate, as indicated by the failure of the N^{15} band to disappear, is correlated with the decrease in rate of DNA synthesis, suggesting nonrepairable damage. This suggests that the basis for the decrease in rate of DNA synthesis is the inactivation of a part of the DNA which then does not participate in replication, rather than a decrease in rate of synthesis involving all the DNA. With UV inactivation of *E. coli* strain B/r, two rates are observed. At lower doses of UV, the decrease in number of colony-forming organisms is relatively low per unit dose. Above the critical dose level, however, an increased inactivation rate is observed which is correlated quantitatively with decrease in capacity to replicate DNA, thus suggesting a direct relation between the inactivation of DNA and the inactivation of the bacterial cell by UV.

Studies of the kinetic aspects of recovery of DNA synthesis after UV exposure, utilizing measurement of DNA synthesis by chemical means and the density gradient analysis technique, are described. Control experiments on unirradiated cultures are presented which differentiate blockage of DNA synthesis with amino acid starvation from the UV-induced blockage of DNA synthesis. The data support the following general hypothesis: The recoverable block to DNA synthesis by UV at the lower dose levels is attributable to the production of damage in the bacterial DNA. DNA synthesis can proceed to the point of one of the damaged sites and then must stop.

The duration of the delay in DNA synthesis depends upon the number of lesions induced in the DNA and thus is directly related to dose. When maximum delay in DNA synthesis is induced by UV, the DNA is damaged to the maximum possible extent for this recoverable type of damage. If DNA synthesis has been delayed to this extent by UV, repair of the DNA synthetic system is correlated with the doubling of cellular RNA. At lower doses of UV involving fewer lesions in the DNA chain, proportionately less RNA need be made for DNA synthesis to proceed. This suggests that repair is specifically at the sites of damage and that the RNA involved in repair need be formed only to the extent that there are lesions of this type. The possibility that the damage involved is the production of the thymine dimer and that RNA synthesis is involved in repair of this damage is discussed.

The effects of acriflavine, caffeine, and certain dyes (crystal violet, methyl green) on DNA, RNA and protein synthesis, and survival, and mutation induction with UV-exposed bacteria are described. The results establish that these agents exert some action on UV-exposed cells which results in increased mutation frequency response and lethality as well as in blockage of DNA, RNA, and protein synthesis, while having little effect on non-UV-exposed cells. The results are consistent with a hypothesis in which the agents react with the UV-damaged site on the DNA, which is otherwise repairable, to prevent replication of DNA. The reaction would also prevent formation on the DNA template of the component of the RNA synthetic system (presumably the messenger RNA) necessary for total RNA synthesis. In irradiated cells, RNA doubles in the presence of these agents and then synthesis ceases; this suggests that gene action (messenger RNA formation) uncovers the DNA to the inhibitory action of the dyes on the damaged site, allowing one round of RNA formation before inactivation of the DNA template. Both the increased lethal and mutagenic effects are correlated with RNA synthesis in the culture. It is proposed that when the damaged site of the DNA interacts with the agents with RNA synthesis, the lethal, mutagenic, and metabolic effects are observed. An interpretation along the same lines is developed for mutation induced by UV (in the absence of the dyes). The hypothesis explains the correlation of mutation fixation with RNA synthesis as reported by Doudney and Haas (1958, 1959).

ACKNOWLEDGMENTS

The author wishes to acknowledge the helpful advice and criticism given during the course of these studies by his colleague, Dr. F. L. Haas, and the collaboration of Mrs. Carolyn S. Young in the density gradient analysis studies of DNA replication. The valuable technical assistance of Miss Billie F. White, Miss Betty J. Bruce, and Miss Janet Allison are gratefully acknowledged.

REFERENCES

Boyce, R. P., and P. Howard-Flanders. 1964. Release of Ultraviolet Light-Induced

Dimers from DNA in *E. coli* K-12. *Proceedings of the National Academy of Sciences of the U.S.A.*, 51:292–300.

Doudney, C. O. 1959. Macromolecular Synthesis in Bacterial Recovery from Ultraviolet Light. *Nature*, London, 184:189–190.

———. 1961a. Recovery of Deoxyribonucleic Acid Synthesis in Ultraviolet-Light-Exposed Bacteria. *Biochemical and Biophysical Research Communications*, 5:410–415.

———. 1961b. Recovery of Deoxyribonucleic Acid Synthesis in Bacteria After Amino Acid Starvation. *Biochemical and Biophysical Research Communications*, 5:405–410.

———. 1963. "Ultraviolet Light-Induced Mutation as an Event in the Physiology of the Bacterial Cell," *Repair from Genetic Radiation Damage and Differential Radiosensitivity in Germ Cells*. F. H. Sobels, Ed. Oxford and London, England; New York, New York; and Paris, France: Pergamon Press. Pp. 125–149.

Doudney, C. O., and F. L. Haas. 1958. Modification of Ultraviolet-Induced Mutation Frequency and Survival in Bacteria by Postirradiation Treatment. *Proceedings of the National Academy of Sciences of the U.S.A.*, 44:390–401.

———. 1959. Mutation Induction and Macromolecular Synthesis in Bacteria. *Proceedings of the National Academy of Sciences of the U.S.A.*, 45:709–722.

Doudney, C. O., B. F. White, and B. J. Bruce. 1964. Acriflavine Modification of Nucleic Acid Formation, Mutation Induction and Survival in Ultraviolet Light Exposed Bacteria. *Biochemical and Biophysical Research Communications*, 15:70–75.

Doudney, C. O., and C. S. Young. 1962. Ultraviolet Light Induced Mutation and Deoxyribonucleic Acid Replication in Bacteria, *Genetics*, 47:1125–1138.

Drakulic, M., and M. Errera. 1959. Chloramphenicol Sensitive DNA Synthesis in Normal and Irradiated Bacteria. *Biochimica et biophysica acta*, 31:459–463.

Harold, F. M., and Z. Z. Ziporin. 1958. Synthesis of Protein and of DNA in *Escherichia coli* Irradiated with Ultraviolet Light. *Biochimica et biophysica acta*, 29:439–440.

Kelner, A. 1953. Growth, Respiration, and Nucleic Acid Synthesis in Ultraviolet-Irradiated and in Photoreactivated *Escherichia coli*. *Journal of Bacteriology*, 65:252–262.

Maaløe, O., and P. C. Hanawalt. 1961. Thymine Deficiency and the Normal Replication Cycle. *Journal of Molecular Biology*, 3:144–155.

Meselson, M., and F. W. Stahl. 1958. The Replication of DNA in *Escherichia coli*. *Proceedings of the National Academy of Sciences of the U.S.A.*, 44: 671–682.

Setlow, R. B., and W. J. Carrier. 1964. The Disappearance of Thymine Dimers from DNA, an Error-Correcting Mechanism. *Proceedings of the National Academy of Sciences of the U.S.A.*, 51:226–231.

Shankel, D. M. 1962. "Mutational Synergism" of Ultraviolet Light and Caffeine in *E. coli*. *Journal of Bacteriology*, 84:410–415.

Witkin, E. M. 1958. Post-irradiation Metabolism and the Timing of Ultraviolet-Induced Mutations in Bacteria. *Proceedings of the Tenth International Congress of Genetics*. Toronto, Canada: University of Toronto Press. Vol. I. Pp. 280–299.

———. 1961. Modification of Mutagenesis Initiated by Ultraviolet Light Through Posttreatment of Bacteria with Basic Dyes. *Journal of Cellular and Comparative Physiology*, Suppl. 1, 58:135–144.

DISCUSSION

Dr. Paul Tso, Johns Hopkins University, Baltimore, Maryland: Following the exciting paper of Dr. Grossman about the biological and biochemical consequences of adding water into nucleic acids by photo radiation, I would like to make a comment on this interesting concept. I have found in the past that most of the interests have been placed on the destructive power of radiations, especially in damaging nucleic acids and proteins; but actually radiation can be very effective, too, in synthesizing something new or in attaching organic molecules into nucleic acids. Recently, my group at California Institute of Technology and Johns Hopkins University have demonstrated that by photoradiating the 3,4 benzpyrene-DNA complex at wavelength region of 350 millimicrons, in nitrogen atmosphere, in water and at room temperature, chemical linkage or covalent linkages between benzpyrene and DNA can be formed. These links are permanent and of very high "yield." The implications of these results, in terms of chemical carcinogens of 3,4 benzpyrene or the radiation effect involved, are not yet certain. It nevertheless demonstrates the effectiveness of photochemistry for attaching organic molecules of interest onto nucleic acid. These experiments come from our previous work in hydrophobic and stacking interaction of nucleic acids and have been reported to the *Proceedings of the National Academy of Sciences of the U.S.A.* (51:272–280, Feb., 1964) and at the Biophysical Society Meeting in 1964.

Chairman R. Kimball, Oak Ridge National Laboratory, Oak Ridge, Tennessee: As a geneticist, I should like to make a few comments about Dr. Grossman's very interesting presentation. While he showed clearly that transition-type mutations are mainly responsible for the mutations he detects in transforming principle, there is considerable evidence that nontransition mutations also play an important role in ultraviolet mutagenesis. Drake's work (*Journal of Molecular Biology*, 6:268–283, 1963) with the rII cistron of T4 phage gives evidence, from reversion studies on UV-induced mutations, that something like a third or more of the mutations do not have the reversion pattern one would expect of transition mutations but rather have that of the base addition or base loss type. Drake had evidence for the rII cistron, indicating that the transition class was mainly of the GC to AT class. Somewhat more than half acted like transitions, but this still leaves a large nontransition class. Furthermore, there are four cases known to me in which a large fraction of ultraviolet-induced forward mutations arise in pure clones, which is not what one would expect with transition mutations.

Drake claims in his paper that half of the mutants he obtained with ultraviolet light were of the transition type in which the guanine-hydroxymethylcytosine base pair is the "mutagenic target." Most of the remainder he classified as "nontransition" types and he further suggested that they contain "additions or deletions" at the site of the mutation.

Moreover, the T-even bacteriophage DNA lacks cytosine and is replaced by its derivative 5-hydroxymethylcytosine which does not form the same photoproducts. It is difficult, therefore, to relate our biochemical evidence with this particular biological experiment.

Dr. Franklin Hutchinson, Yale University, New Haven, Connecticut: If I understood the curves that Dr. Grossman showed on the rate at which the hydrated species decays, it would look as though it would have a lifetime the order of magnitude of 10 minutes in cells of 37 C.

Dr. Lawrence Grossman, Brandeis University, Waltham, Massachusetts: The half-life of the cytosine hydrate is between 5 and 10 minutes at this temperature.

Dr. Hutchinson: Yes, if this is the case, an increased mutation rate might be demonstrated in cells which are in rapid DNA synthesis, and I was wondering if anybody has experimental evidence for this.

Dr. Grossman: There has been some evidence that a direct relationship between the rates of mutation and the rates of replication exists. I think there is a need, at least on my part anyway, for a great deal of re-examination of the properties of biological systems with respect to mutations which should include the effects of temperature, and the problem of division rates on rates of mutation.

Dr. Paul Howard-Flanders, Yale University School of Medicine, New Haven, Connecticut: I would like to ask Dr. Grossman if he would enlarge on the problem of distinguishing between the code triplet UUC and UCU in ultraviolet-irradiated poly U.

Dr. Grossman: This problem, of course, is of great interest, and we spent about six months trying to analyze the polymers that were produced to find out the location of the serine residues with respect to phenylalanine. This has been complicated by the physical properties of polyphenylalanine which is totally insoluble in water. One is restricted to working with solvents like glacial acetic acid and HBR or chloroform and formamide which do not lend themselves to enzymatic hydrolysis or C terminal end-group analysis. This is one reason why we went to the RNA polymerase, because one can do a complete nearest neighbor analysis and nucleoside end-group determination. It is difficult to investigate the polyphenylalanine produced in the amino acid-incorporating system with the irradiated poly U coding system. Since the published triplets sometimes include cytosine, we at first thought that leucine should be incorporated following UV. We thought perhaps it might be a sequence effect, for if the coding mechanism came up to the point of the lesion and stopped but did not complete the triplet for leucine, then serine might be included as a C terminal end group directed by a UU"C". And if the triplet, say for leucine, was CUU or UCU and the lesion was "C", then you would never include a complete triplet. But we cannot answer that because the levels of incorporation of serine are very low, and it may simply be for technical reasons that we cannot detect leucine incorporation.

This further emphasizes the importance of examining the isolated polypeptide, since one can observe the incorporation of serine into total acid insoluble material with unirradiated poly U. However, the isolated polypeptide, directed by irradiated poly U has no label. But these are very important questions which we cannot really get a good "handle" for as yet.

Dr. Peter Alexander, Chester Beatty Research Institute, Institute of Cancer Research, Royal Cancer Hospital, London, England: I would like to come back to the point which our Chairman made at the beginning of this discussion. How far can you extend your observations to the "in cell" situation? If the mutations produced as a result of the hydration of C and U play an important part, would one not then expect that a heat shock to 45 C after UV irradiation should greatly reduce the mutation rate? Such a heat shock would not, I think, increase DNA synthesis, which I believe decreases again after the optimum temperature has been passed for the organism. So a heat shock ought to be a very favorable situation for wiping out mutation. Do your methods enable one to distinguish something which I have always naively thought of as the "mutation by loss," where DNA was just rendered useless, and the mutation where the DNA made some new RNA? According to the simplest interpretation of your work, one would expect that the thymine dimer which would not be temperature-sensitive should lead to a "mutations by loss" (*i.e.*, loss of physiological activity of DNA), whereas hydration should give mutations that alter the code.

Dr. Grossman: To answer your second question first—one can picture two possible mechanisms whereby a deletion might occur. One is that because the dimer is reduced at the 5,6-double bond the N-glycosyl linkage is labilized, but we have looked at the hydrolysis rate constants of such compounds and this linkage is labilized but is still more stable than a purine deoxyribose linkage. Thus one cannot envision that the two bases would simply fall off leaving a toothless gap which could be filled in by any nucleoside triphosphate. Also, one might be able to envision a deletion in which a good part of the backbone is removed, analogous to the repair mechanism described by Dr. Howard-Flanders, so that nonsense is inserted again.

Returning to the first question concerning the effect of heat treatments of biological systems, I would be tempted to relate what one observes at a level in vitro to observations at the level in vivo. We know very well, for example, that the stability of many of these photoproducts is different when the pyrimidine is polymerized; presumably, the stacking effects can stabilize the cytidine hydrate. As a result, I cannot anticipate yet the kind of protective devices available to the cell for stabilization.

Dr. Alexander: Are there no experiments in the literature which bear on the effect of postirradiation temperature treatments on the yield of UV-induced mutation?

Dr. Grossman: Dr. Szybalski indicates there are. Perhaps he will answer this question.

Dr. Waclaw Szybalski, McArdle Memorial Laboratory, University of Wisconsin, Madison, Wisconsin: Would Dr. Lieb wish to answer the question?

Dr. M. Lieb, University of Southern California School of Medicine, Los Angeles, California: I just want to refer to the work of Dr. Witkin who has done a lot of work with temperature effects after UV. She reported (*Cold Spring Harbor Symposia on Quantitative Biology*, 21:123, 1956) that heating to 37 C or 45 C immediately after UV-irradiation reduced the mutation frequency below that observed at 24 C, while killing was not affected.

Dr. Grossman: I am sure that it is very difficult to relate the chemical stability, again, of a system in vitro to one in vivo because of the many complexities involved in heating an organism above normal metabolic temperatures.

Dr. C. O. Doudney, The University of Texas M. D. Anderson Hospital and Tumor

Institute, Houston, Texas: Would you predict that these mutations in vivo are photoreversible or not?

Dr. Grossman: It has been demonstrated that the lethal as well as mutational effects of ultraviolet irradiation are photoreparable. If we could then transpose our results in vitro to genotypic systems in vivo, instinctively one would predict that separate photoreactivating enzymes would be required to reverse these two biological effects. The enzyme-catalyzed breakage of a carbon-carbon bond in the dimer would be expected to differ significantly from the dehydration reaction governing the mutational events, since such chemical events are so clearly different.

Dr. Doudney: Photoreversible mutations could be caused by another lesion, of course, and not the dehydration reaction. Do we really expect another photoreactivating enzyme?

Chairman Kimball: Dr. Evelyn Witkin (*Proceedings of the National Academy of Sciences of the U.S.A.*, 50:425–430, 1963), I believe, has evidence that in the phtr⁻ mutant, which is unable to be photoreactivated for cell colony formation, photoreactivation can still occur for mutation production. Thus there may be more than one kind of photoreactivable lesion. This is also indicated by recent work by Dr. Jane K. Setlow (*Photochemistry and Photobiology*, in press).

Dr. Grossman: Yes, I think that such biological evidence warrants concluding that there must be more than one photoreactivating enzyme.

Radiosensitivity of Nuclear ATP Synthesis and its Relation to Inhibition of Mitosis

HERMAN M. KLOUWEN

Radiobiological Institute TNO, Rijswijk, The Netherlands

The isolation of cell organelles from tissues or cell suspensions has enabled the biochemists to study these particles, to unravel their metabolic pathways, and to elucidate major synthetic processes such as the synthesis of proteins and nucleic acids and the synthesis of cellular chemical energy (adenosine triphosphate [ATP]) at subparticle or even at molecular level.

The isolation of pure nuclear preparations has presented more difficulties than the isolation of cytoplasmic organelles; this is one of the reasons that the study of metabolic activities of isolated nuclei has been neglected until recently. Several methods have been described for the isolation of nuclei (Dounce, 1953; Allfrey, 1959; Roodyn, 1963).

Nuclei isolated from different sources show metabolic activities. Nucleic acids, proteins, phospholipids, and nicotinamide adenine dinucleotide (NAD) can be synthesized by nuclear preparations or by enzymes isolated from them (Hogeboom and Schneider, 1952; Griffiths and Pace, 1953; Siebert, Lang, Lucius, and Rossmüller, 1953; Mirsky and Osawa, 1961; Rees and Rowland, 1961; Roodyn, 1963).

As a result of these investigations, the nucleus can now be considered as an important site of synthetic capacities. In vivo the nucleus is the site of deoxyribonucleic acid (DNA) synthesis and of the synthesis of metabolic, highly active ribonucleic acid (RNA), which, in mammalian cells, is transferred to the cytoplasm to instruct and direct microsomal protein synthesis according to the principles which underly this mechanism in microorganisms (Taylor, 1958; Prescott, 1960; Jacob and Monod, 1961).

An exciting discovery in the studies on metabolic activities of isolated nuclei was made by Osawa, Allfrey, and Mirsky in 1957, when they demonstrated that isolated calf thymus nuclei show the ability to resynthesize ATP from adenosine monophosphate (AMP) under aerobic conditions without the addition of any external substrate. They also demonstrated the incorporation of C^{14}-amino acids in protein fractions isolated from thymus nuclei (Allfrey, Mirsky, and Osawa, 1957).

At that time considerable progress had been made in radiobiology. It was well established that the cell nucleus could be considered the most radiosensitive part of mammalian cells, because inhibition or delay of mitosis, the occurrence of chromosome aberrations after irradiation, and pycnosis could be regarded as typical radiation effects originating or localized in the cell nucleus (Upton, 1963).

Attempts have been made radiobiologically to find a biochemical basis for the explanation of the cellular radiation effects mentioned; therefore, several authors have tried to detect early biochemical effects which can be demonstrated within two hours after sublethal doses of irradiation. The studies concerning the effects of X-irradiation on biochemical processes in the cell have revealed some important facts. The results relevant to our experiments will be mentioned briefly.

The synthesis of DNA was found to be inhibited as a result of X-irradiation (Lajtha, 1960); this was assumed to be responsible for the inhibition of mitosis. However, much evidence has accumulated which demonstrates that inhibition of mitosis generally precedes the inhibition of DNA synthesis, although in thymus an immediate effect of X-irradiation on DNA synthesis cannot be excluded (Nygaard and Potter, 1962).

Potter and Bethell (1952) and van Bekkum, Jongepier, Nieuwerkerk, and Cohen (1953) discovered independently the radiosensitivity of mitochondrial oxidative phosphorylation. In subsequent years van Bekkum and co-workers made an extensive study of the effects of X-irradiation on mitochondrial phosphorylation (van Bekkum, *et al.* 1954, 1956, 1957). The irradiation effects were observed only after irradiation in vivo and could be demonstrated within four hours after irradiation with low doses (50 to 100 r), or one to two hours after higher doses. It could not be demonstrated that the observed biochemical effects precede the occurrence of pycnosis and cell death. The evidence obtained from the investigations mentioned is in accord with the concept of a direct effect of irradiation on ATP synthesis.

Using varied experimental conditions, Scaife and Hill (1962) recently confirmed the inhibition of oxidative phosphorylation in mitochondria isolated from thymus and spleen after whole-body irradiation. In mitochondria isolated from irradiated livers, ascites tumor cells, or HeLa cells, no inhibition of oxidative phosphorylation was found.

It must be emphasized that early biochemical effects are demonstrated almost exclusively in lymphatic tissues. The cells from these tissues possess a large nucleus surrounded by a thin layer of cytoplasm, which contains relatively few mitochondria. They usually show moderate mitotic activity, while in thymus glands of young animals the mitotic index is considerable (Klouwen and Betel, 1963). Also the radiation effects described by Ernst and Hagen (1961), Ernst (1962), Hagen, Ernst, and Cepicka (1963), and

Braum, (1963a) are observed in thymus and spleen. These authors demonstrated a sharp decrease of nuclear proteins or enzymes within a few hours after irradiation with relatively high doses (1000 r).

The occurrence of interphase death and an immediate inhibition of mitosis shortly after irradiation are two effects observed in lymphocytes and thymocytes. It is difficult to demonstrate that independent early biochemical effects cause the early cellular effects.

The inhibition of mitosis cannot be attributed to the inhibition of mitochondrial phosphorylation, for in different tumors and in liver no radiosensitivity of mitochondrial oxidative phosphorylation is observed shortly after irradiation in vivo with sublethal doses.

So far, a biochemical explanation for the occurrence of cellular radiation damage seems unavailable. Radiation effects on nuclear ribonucleic acid (RNA) fractions in thymus and in liver have been reported, but these effects cannot be regarded as early biochemical effects (Klouwen, 1960). Although a trigger mechanism in which nuclear RNA synthesis stimulates enzyme synthesis and subsequently DNA synthesis during the development of the mitotic cycle seems attractive, and although some DNA-synthesizing enzymes are inhibited for several hours after doses ranging from 500 to 1000 r, these inhibitions cannot explain the immediate radiation effects on mitosis (Bollum, Anderegg, McElya, and Potter, 1960; Myers, 1962; Sugino, Frenkel, and Potter, 1963).

The demonstration by Creasey and Stocken (1959) of the extreme radiosensitivity of nuclear ATP synthesis in lymphatic and hemopoietic organs opened new possibilities for a biochemical explanation of early cellular radiation effects. In the following years, the results of these investigations were neither confirmed nor denied by other authors; one of the difficulties was that the synthesis of ATP in thymus nuclei proved to be variable under the experimental conditions described by the authors mentioned. Moreover, interference by cytoplasmic contamination could not be excluded. In a previous report (Klouwen and Betel, 1963), we have demonstrated that nuclear preparations do contain some cytoplasmic contamination (5 per cent) which does not interfere with the nuclear phosphorylation studied. In subsequent papers Ord and Stocken (1962a) described research which demonstrated that the time interval between death of the animal and the removal of the glands is critical for obtaining reproducible results. The radiation effects were reconfirmed by them (Ord and Stocken, 1962b).

Conditions of "aging" either of thymus glands in the dead animals or of nuclei incubated in a nitrogen atmosphere were studied in our laboratory. After standardizing the experimental conditions, ATP synthesis in rat thymus nuclei could be reproduced (Klouwen and Betel, 1963).

The effects of X-irradiation in vivo and in vitro on nuclear ATP synthesis were reinvestigated by us and part of the results have been published (Klouwen and Betel, 1963).

It was confirmed that nuclear ATP synthesis is an extremely radiosensitive process after irradiation in vivo. However, immediately after irradiation in vitro, no inhibition of nuclear ATP synthesis could be demonstrated. Kelly has discussed the possibility that the inhibition of nuclear ATP synthesis could be considered as a biochemical basis for interphase death (Kelly, 1961).

In order to evaluate alternative mechanisms (interphase death, inhibition of mitosis) in more detail, our studies on this subject were extended to other tissues, both normal and neoplastic. Nuclear ATP synthesis could be demonstrated only in a restricted number of cell types (thymus, spleen, and lymphosarcomas). The radiosensitivity of nuclear ATP synthesis could be detected only in thymus and lymphatic tissues within one hour after whole-body irradiation with low doses (100 to 500 r). In different lymphosarcomas only 24 hours after a radiation dose of at least 1000 r, an inhibition of nuclear phosphorylation was detected. The implications of the results of the experiments will be discussed in this communication.

Experimental

Isolation of Nuclei

Six-to-seven-week-old male albino rats weighing 130 to 150 g were used in these experiments for the isolation of thymus nuclei, as described by Klouwen and Betel, 1963. Spleen nuclei were isolated from rats or mice. The mice used were CBA, C57BL, (CBA $\times$ C57BL)F_1, seven to ten weeks old and weighing 25 to 35 g. The nuclear preparations isolated from spleens were contaminated with erythrocytes even when precautions were taken, e.g. a rapid differential centrifugation technique. In some experiments, hematopoiesis was stimulated in rat spleens by exposing rats at one-third atmosphere of air during three subsequent days for 12-hour periods. During the night the animals were kept under normal conditions and fed ad libitum. The spleens of these animals will be referred to as stimulated spleens. Bone marrow was obtained from the femurs of rats. Mesenteric lymph nodes from rats were prepared free of contaminating tissue.

Transplantable tumors (CBA, and C57BL 2028) were obtained previously in this laboratory from spontaneously occurring tumors. The (CBA $\times$ C57BL)F_1:30 L lymphoma was obtained from the F_1 mice spontaneously. The tumors were maintained by serial passage or kept at -170 C until needed. For transfer of the tumors, suspensions were prepared from spleens of mice inoculated with tumor cells at least six days before, as was described by de Vries and Vos (1958). Cell suspensions containing 10^6 lymphosarcoma cells in a volume of 0.5 ml were injected into the tail vein. Between the seventh and ninth day after this injection, the spleens of the mice were used for the isolation of nuclei. At that time the spleens consisted predominantly of malignant cells and were about three times the normal size.

The isolation of nuclei from lymphosarcomas was performed according to the method described for the isolation of thymus nuclei.

Final homogenizations in the isolation procedures were carried out with Dounce homogenizers of different clearances. A clearance of 0.01 mm appeared to be effective in the final disruption of lymphatic cells. For the isolation of nuclei from liver, kidney, and a rhabdomyosarcoma, smaller clearances were used (0.008 mm).

The nuclear sediments were resuspended in sucrose solutions containing 0.1875 M sucrose, 0.02 M glucose, 0.02 M NaCl, and 0.008 M $MgCl_2$, buffered with 0.025 M Tris to pH 7.4 (Frenster, Allfrey, and Mirsky, 1961).

The concentrations of the nuclear suspensions were kept between 10 and 12 mg protein/ml; the volumes of the nuclear suspensions were 3 to 4 ml.

Nuclei from a rhabdomyosarcoma, liver, and kidney were isolated by using a layering technique to remove cytoplasmic contaminations.

Purity of Nuclear Preparations

The purity of the isolated nuclei was estimated by microscopic examination without staining or after staining by the methyl green pyronine method; or by estimation of mitochondrial enzymes.

Acid-Soluble Extracts

Acid-soluble extracts were isolated from nuclear sediments as described by Klouwen and Betel (1963). The remaining acidified nuclear sediment was used for the determination of DNA and RNA.

Analyses of Nucleotides and Orthophosphate

In the neutralized acid-soluble extracts, ATP, ADP, and AMP were determined by enzymatic methods (Adams, 1962). If necessary, ATP, ADP, and AMP were separated in these eluates using high voltage electrophoresis (Klouwen, 1962a). Orthophosphate was determined according to the methods described by Klouwen and Betel (1963) or the method of Berenblum and Chain (1938).

DNA, RNA, Protein

DNA and RNA were determined according to the methods described previously (Klouwen and Betel, 1963), protein by the method of Gornall, Bardawill, and David (1949).

Histological Techniques

The tissues were fixed in Bouin's fluid and embedded in paraffin. Sections of 7 μ in thickness were made and stained with hematoxylin and eosin. Mitotic figures were counted in 4 μ sections.

Irradiations

Irradiation of animals was performed in circular perspex cages. The physical constants of the radiation were 250 kv, 30 ma, HVL 2.1 mm Cu., and dose rate 70 r/min for total-body irradiations. The FTD for rats and mice was 51 cm. Nuclear suspensions were irradiated with a dose rate of 70 r/min, FTD 51 cm.

Results

Purity of the Nuclear Preparations

The purity of the nuclear preparations was evaluated from preparations stained with methyl green and pyronin. The enzymes assayed were succinate-cytochrome c reductase and (or) cytochrome oxidase (Table 1).

TABLE 1

Purity of Nuclear Preparations

	Thymus		Lymphosarcoma
	Succinate-cytochrome c reductase	Cytochrome oxidase	Cytochrome oxidase
Nuclei	5	7	10
Total calculated*	79	89	74
Total homogenate**	100	100	100

* The total calculated percentages represent the sum of the percentage activity measured in the separate fractions: nuclei, mitochondria and supernatant. Supernatant includes microsomes.
** Enzyme activities of the nuclear preparations are given as percentages of the activity measured in the total unfractionated homogenate.

From the results presented it can be seen that cytoplasmic contamination is still present in the nuclear preparations. Detailed results described earlier show that a real fractionation of protein and RNA is achieved and that DNA is almost exclusively present in the nuclei, which means that no disruption of nuclei has taken place (Klouwen and Betel, 1963).

Synthesis of ATP in Nuclear Preparations

Two methods which provide critical conditions necessary to obtain nuclear ATP synthesis were used. The common principle of both methods is "aging." When thymus glands are left in decapitated animals for 15 minutes, the amount of ATP in the glands is decreased. This is called "aging in vivo," and it represents the first method used (Klouwen and Betel, 1963). The second method, "aging in vitro," was developed recently by Betel and Klouwen (1963). Isolated nuclei are incubated in a nitrogen atmosphere for 15 minutes at 25 or 30 C; as a result of this treatment, a sharp decrease of ATP is observed.

Only in nuclear preparations in which the ATP content was decreased could a resynthesis of ATP be detected. Therefore, the aging of glands or tissue or of the isolated nuclei is essential in order to obtain reproducible phosphorylations. In the second method the time necessary for the isolation is not critical. Using the first method, ATP synthesis occurs during the isolation so that the net synthesis for ATP seems smaller. Both methods were used in our experiments. The early experiments were usually performed according to the in vivo aging method; the in vitro aging method in later experiments. The available data provide no evidence which points to different metabolic pathways of nucleotide breakdown or synthesis underlying the two methods of aging.

When the in vivo aging method was used, nuclear preparations were divided into two parts directly after a first quick isolation (30 minutes). One part was centrifuged off, $HClO_4$ in a final concentration of 2 per cent was added, and an acid soluble extract was obtained and neutralized. The other part of the nuclear suspension was incubated aerobically at 4 or 25 C, and stirred or shaken mechanically. After the incubation period of 45 minutes, an acid soluble extract was prepared from the sediment of this nuclear suspension. Nuclei isolated from glands left in the dead animals for 15 minutes were previously called "15 minutes nuclei." Nuclei called "0 minutes nuclei" are those isolated from glands directly after killing the animal.

In the in vitro method of aging, the nuclear preparation was divided into three parts after the nuclei were shaken vigorously. From one part an acid soluble extract was prepared, which had a nucleotide composition comparable to the composition of the "0 minutes nuclei." The other two parts were incubated in a nitrogen atmosphere at 25 or 30 C for 15 minutes. From one an acid soluble extract was prepared directly, and the other was incubated aerobically for 30 to 45 minutes at a different temperature (Figure 1).

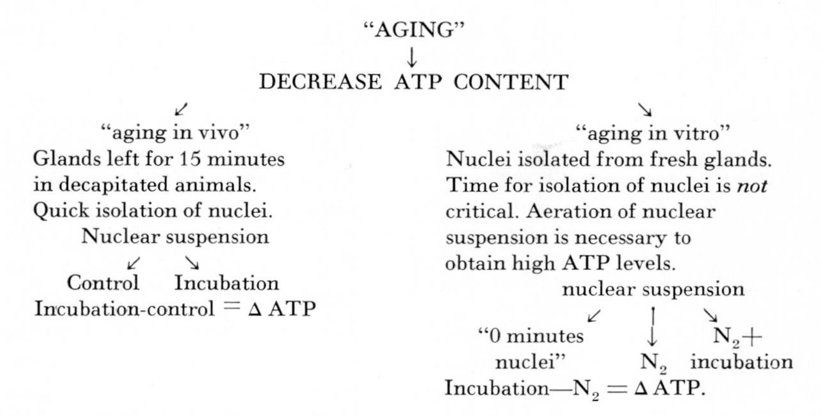
"AGING"
DECREASE ATP CONTENT
"aging in vivo"
Glands left for 15 minutes
in decapitated animals.
Quick isolation of nuclei.
Nuclear suspension
Control
Incubation
Incubation-control = Δ ATP
"aging in vitro"
Nuclei isolated from fresh glands.
Time for isolation of nuclei is *not*
critical. Aeration of nuclear
suspension is necessary to
obtain high ATP levels.
nuclear suspension
"0 minutes
nuclei"
N_2
N_2+
incubation
Incubation—N_2 = Δ ATP.

FIGURE 1. Flow sheet for aging of thymus nuclei.

The results of a number of experiments are summarized in Table 2.

TABLE 2

Synthesis of ATP in Rat Thymus

Aging in vivo* µmole ATP/mg DNA-P		Aging in vitro* µmole ATP/mg DNA-P	
"0 minutes nuclei"	0.45	"0 minutes nuclei"	0.45
"15 minutes nuclei"	0.24	N_2	0.15
Incubation	0.39	Incubation	0.40

* For the aging procedures, see flow sheet (Figure 1).

Synthesis of Nuclear ATP in Different Tissues

The synthesis of nuclear ATP in a number of different tissues was investigated. The results of these experiments are summarized in Table 3.

The results show that only a restricted number of cell types demonstrate nuclear ATP synthesis. Nuclei which do not contain ATP or any other nucleotides are not capable of synthesizing ATP. The inability of nuclei isolated from lymph nodes to synthesize ATP is noteworthy as an exception among the nuclear preparations of lymphatic origin which demonstrate nuclear ATP synthesis.

A direct correlation between ATP-synthesizing capacity and mitotic activity does not exist. The stimulated spleen with a very high mitotic index shows a low ATP synthesis; nuclei isolated from a rhabdomyosarcoma do not synthesize ATP at all.

Effect of X-Irradiation in vivo on Nuclear ATP Synthesis

In Rat Thymus. The first results obtained with rat thymus demonstrated the great radiosensitivity of nuclear ATP synthesis after whole-body irradiation (Creasey and Stocken, 1959; Klouwen and Betel, 1963). Even

TABLE 3

*Nuclear ATP Synthesis in Different Tissues**

Tissue	µmole ATP / mg DNA-P**	Δµmole ATP / mg DNA-P***	Mitotic index****
Thymus	0.55 (8)	0.30	8
Spleen	0.15 (3)	0.01	8
Stimulated spleen	0.19 (3)	0.02	23
CBA lymphoma	1.20 (4)	0.60	14
C57BL lymphoma	1.00 (2)	0.33	13
F_1 lymphoma	1.05 (6)	0.55	15
Myeloid leukemia	0.52 (2)	0.22	15
Rhabdomyosarcoma	0 (1)	0	14
Lymph nodes	0 (3)	0	
Liver	0 (3)	0	< 0.1
Kidney	0 (1)	0	< 0.1

* ATP synthesis in the nuclei was determined after aging in vitro.
** The amounts of ATP present in "0 minutes nuclei." Figures in parenthesis are the number of experiments.
*** The amounts of ATP synthesized after anaerobic incubation are summarized.
**** Mitotic indexes are expressed as the number of mitotic figures per 1,000 cells.

after 50 r, a small effect on nuclear ATP synthesis was observed within 30 minutes after irradiation. In following experiments, this extreme radiosensitivity could not be reproduced. The experimental variations under these conditions are considerable. However, the main objective of the experiments was to study the relationships between the biochemical and histological alterations after irradiation. It can be seen from the data that inhibition of nuclear ATP synthesis in rat thymus precedes the decrease in weight and in DNA and ATP content observed after irradiation (Figures 2 and 3). In histological preparations of irradiated thymus glands, pycnosis becomes visible two hours after irradiation with sublethal doses (Figure 4). The inhibition of nuclear ATP synthesis is observed earlier and precedes cell destruction. From the results obtained in these experiments, it cannot be concluded that inhibition of nuclear ATP synthesis causes inhibition of mitosis, because inhibition of mitosis occurs almost immediately after irradiation.

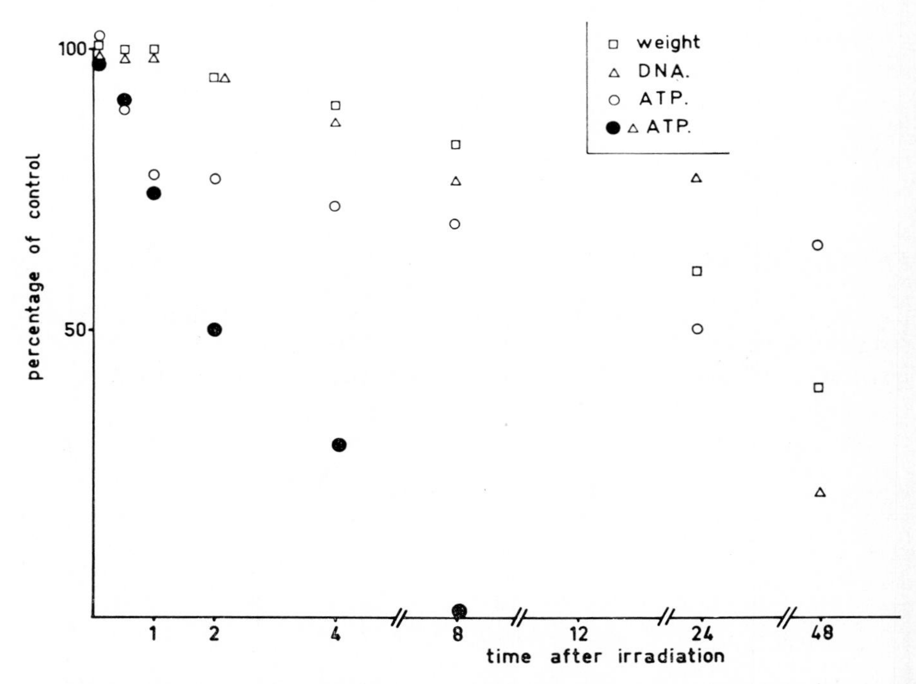

FIGURE 2. Effect of 150 r on thymus nuclei. The effects postirradiation on organ weights (□), DNA content (△), ATP content (○), and ATP synthesis (●) of the nuclear preparations are shown. (Time given in hours.)

Control values (100 per cent) are:

Thymus gland weight: 0.43 g.
DNA content per gland: 11.0 mg.
ATP content: 0.22 μmole per mg DNA-P.
ATP synthesis: 0.19 μmole per mg DNA-P.
The thymus glands of three rats were pooled in each experiment.

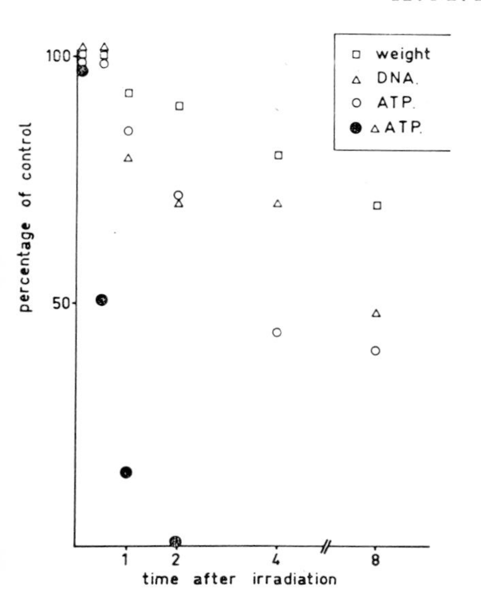

FIGURE 3. Effect of 500 r whole-body irradiation on thymus nuclei. The effects postirradiation on organ weights (□), DNA content (△), ATP content (○) and ATP synthesis (●) of the nuclear preparations are shown. (Time given in hours.) Control values (100 per cent) are:

Thymus gland weight: 0.42 g.

DNA content per gland: 11.7 mg.

ATP content: 0.27 μmole per mg DNA-P.

ATP synthesis: 0.16 μmole per mg DNA-P.

The thymus glands of three rats were pooled in each experiment.

In Spleens from Rats and Mice. Since normal rat spleens show poor and unreproducible ATP-synthesizing capacity, we tried to enhance this synthesis by stimulating erythropoiesis. The mitotic index in these spleens is increased threefold; the weights of the organs are increased from 200 to

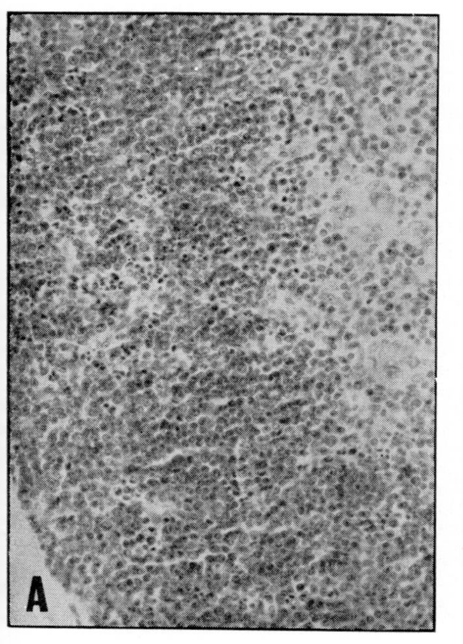

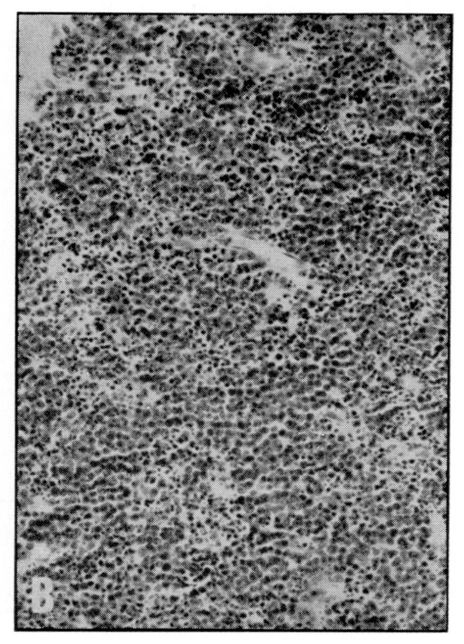

FIGURE 4. Massive pycnosis and karyorrhexis in mouse thymus 2 hours (a) and 4 hours (b) after 500 r whole-body irradiation. Hematoxylin and eosin stain; reduced from × 450.

400 mg for the normal spleens to 600 to 800 mg for the stimulated spleens. Hemopoiesis is greatly enhanced under these conditions; while in normal spleens the contribution of lymphatic cells is about 80 per cent, in stimulated spleens this is about 50 per cent. With these stimulated spleens more reproducible ATP synthesis was obtained, although it remained relatively low. Apparently, nuclei from erythropoietic cells do not contribute to ATP synthesis in these nuclear preparations. The nuclear ATP synthesis is decreased within one hour after 150 r. No pycnosis is observed before two hours after 150 r. From the results obtained, it is tentatively concluded that spleen lymphocytes exhibit the same radiosensitivity as thymocytes (Table 4).

In Lymphosarcomas. In preliminary experiments performed with lymphosarcomas, no inhibition of nuclear ATP synthesis could be demonstrated within one hour after irradiation with doses up to 1,000 r. The preliminary results show that, under conditions in which mitosis is almost completely inhibited, nuclear ATP synthesis still proceeds (Table 5). The experiments were extended in order to study the effect of X-irradiation on nuclear ATP synthesis of these cells for a longer time interval after the irradiation.

Results obtained in experiments performed with lymphosarcoma spleens from (CBA $\times$ C57BL)F_1 mice are shown in Figure 5. Up to 12 to 24 hours after 900 r no severe inhibition of nuclear ATP synthesis is observed. In this period after irradiation, some inhibition of ATP synthesis is detected and can be attributed to a destruction of normal lymphocytes still present in these spleens; however, no decreases in weights and DNA contents are observed.

Severe inhibition of ATP synthesis is observed between 24 and 48

TABLE 4

*Effect of X-Irradiation in Vivo on Synthesis of ATP in Isolated Rat Spleen Nuclei**

	Dose (roentgens)	Time interval between irradiation and decapitation (minutes)	μmole ATP / mg DNA-P
Control	..	..	0.073
Incubation	..	..	0.090
Incubation	150	30	0.075
Control	..	..	0.069
Incubation	.	..	0.093
Incubation	150	45	0.069
Control	..	.	0.073
Incubation	.	..	0.090
Incubation	150	20	0.074
Control	..	..	0.059
Incubation	..	..	0.093
Incubation	100	30	0.081

* Spleens were used from animals which were kept at one-third atmosphere of air for three successive days. Nuclei were aged in vivo.

TABLE 5

*Effect of X-Irradiation in Vivo on ATP Synthesis in Nuclei of Lymphosarcoma Cells**

Exp.	Dose roentgens	Time after irradiation (minutes)	Type of lymphosarcoma	μmole ATP/mg DNA-P
1	100	45	CBA	contr. : 15′ nuclei : 0.65
				incubation : 0.82
				irr. : 15′ nuclei : 0.50
				incubation : 0.66
2	500	60	C57BL	contr. : 15′ nuclei : 0.36
				incubation : 0.72
				irr. : 15′ nuclei : 0.34
				incubation : 0.93
3	1000	60	C57BL	contr. : 15′ nuclei : 0.36
				incubation : 0.71
				irr. : 15′ nuclei : 0.58
				incubation : 0.88

* The tissues were aged in vivo.

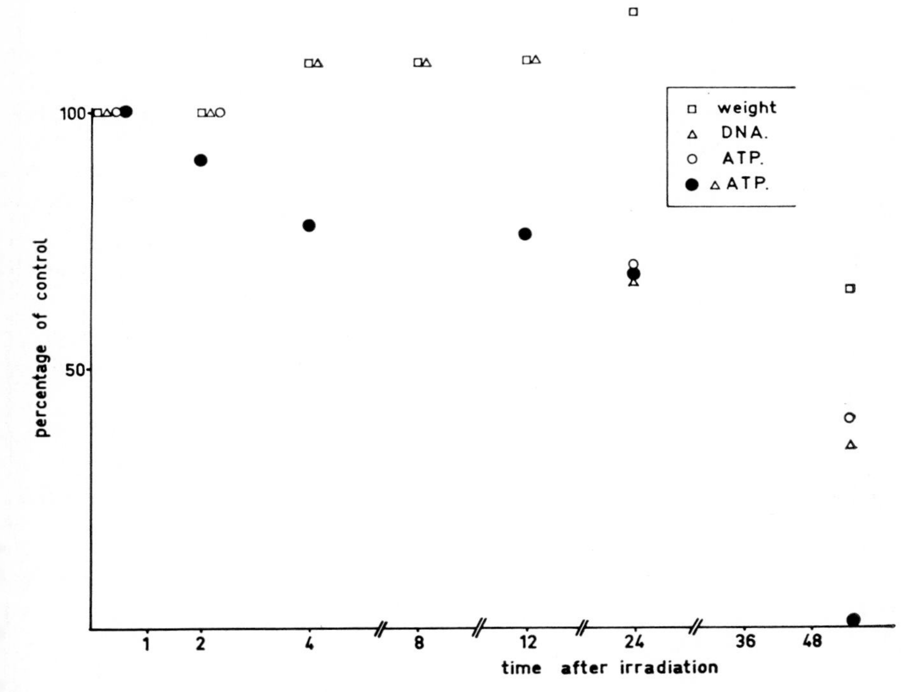

FIGURE 5. Effect of 900 r whole-body irradiation on lymphosarcoma nuclei. The effects postirradiation on organ weights (□), DNA content (△), ATP content (○) and ATP synthesis (●) of the nuclear preparations are shown. (Time given in hours.)
Control values (100 per cent) are:

Spleen weights: 0.39 g.
DNA content per spleen: 4.1 mg.
ATP content: 0.81 μmole ATP per mg DNA-P.
ATP synthesis: 0.55 μmole ATP per mg DNA-P.
The spleens of three mice were pooled in each experiment.

hours after irradiation. In this period a massive loss of weight of the organs and of DNA and ATP content occurs. Histological preparations of the irradiated lymphosarcoma spleens show near total absence of cellular changes up to 12 hours after irradiation (Figure 6). After 12 hours postirradiation, mitotic figures reappear but are all abnormal. Lymphosarcoma cells show the characteristics of mitotic delay and mitotic death, in contrast to thymocytes which undergo interphase death.

After irradiation of lymphosarcoma spleens with 10,000 r, a slightly different picture is obtained (Figure 7). Nuclear ATP synthesis is decreased to 55 per cent of the control preparations; however, no further inhibition is seen up to eight hours after this dose has been applied. Organ weights and

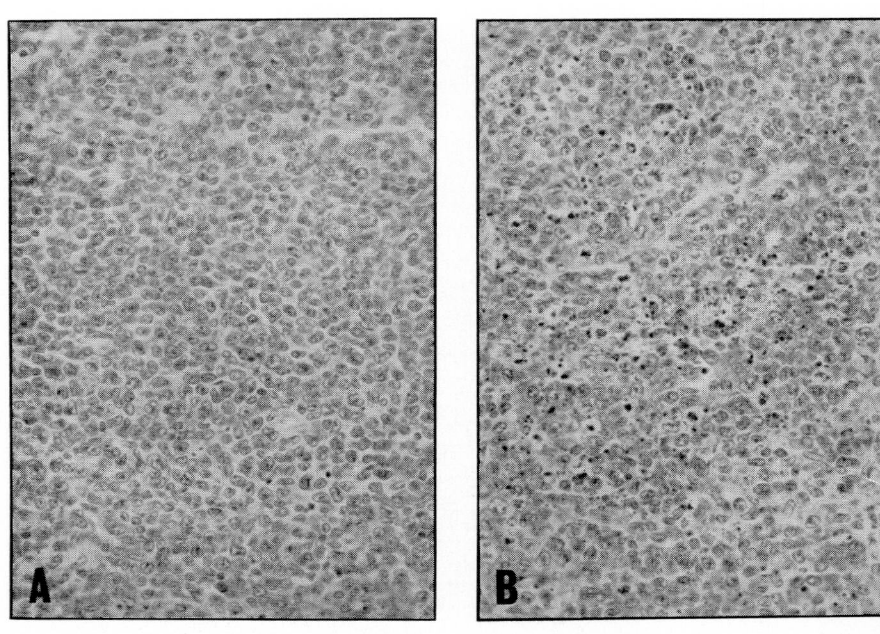

FIGURE 6. Near total absence of cellular changes in lymphosarcomatous mouse spleen 4 hours after 900 r whole-body irradiation. No mitotic figures can be seen (a). Extensive nuclear fragmentation in similar tissue 24 hours after 900 r. Note the occurrence of mitosis (b). Hematoxylin and eosin stain; reduced from × 450.

DNA and ATP contents are also decreased shortly after irradiation and remain constant thereafter. A histological preparation is presented in Figure 8.

Even after irradiation with 10,000 r almost no destruction of the lymphosarcoma cells is observed up to 12 hours after irradiation. Mitotic figures and pycnosis become visible after 12 hours postirradiation. The early sharp decrease of nuclear ATP synthesis (see Figure 7) observed after 10,000 r

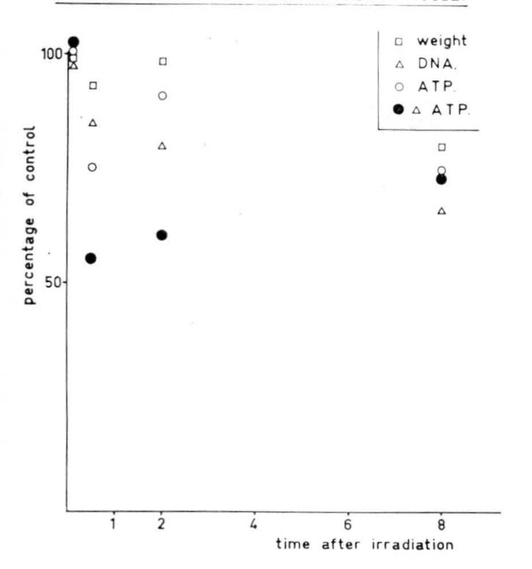

FIGURE 7. Effects of 10,000 r whole-body irradiation on lymphosarcoma nuclei. The effects postirradiation on spleen weights (□), DNA content (△), ATP content (○), and ATP synthesis (●) of the nuclear preparations are shown. (Time given in hours.)
The control values (100 per cent) are:
Spleen weights: 0.60 g.
DNA content per spleen: 5.0 mg.
ATP content: 1.20 µmole per mg DNA-P.
ATP synthesis: 0.70 µmole per mg DNA-P.
The spleens of three mice were pooled in each experiment.

irridation could be attributed to destruction of normal lymphatic cells still present in the invaded spleens. The extent of this decrease (45% is, however, not in agreement with the percentage of normal spleen cells still present in the lymphosarcomatous spleens (15 to 20%).

The results obtained after whole-body irradiation with 1,000 r and with 10,000 r do not show major qualitative differences, and nuclear ATP synthesis appears only partly inhibited in lymphosarcoma cells up to 12 to 24 hours after irradiation.

Since it was demonstrated with rat thymus nuclei that inhibition of nuclear ATP synthesis precedes pycnosis and interphase death, some experiments were performed with the nitrogen mustard compound mustine-HCL (2.2 dichloro-N-methyldimethylamine). Each rat was injected intraperitoneally with 1 mg. Results of a typical experiment are shown in Figure

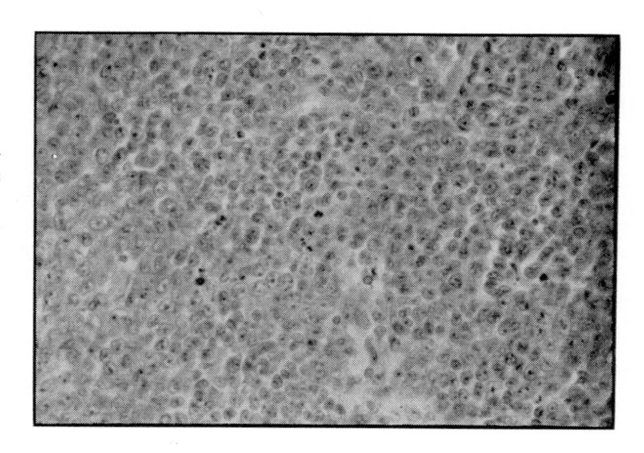

FIGURE 8. Lymphosarcomatous mouse spleen 12 hours after 10,000 r whole-body irradiation. Only few disintegrating cells are present. Hematoxylin and eosin stain; reduced from × 450.

9. Inhibition of ATP synthesis precedes the decrease in weight and DNA and ATP content and the occurrence of pycnosis. Pycnosis is not observed before seven hours after injection of the compound. At that time, inhibition of nuclear ATP synthesis is already evident. From the present evidence it is concluded that in thymocytes and lymphocytes nuclear ATP synthesis is a very radiosensitive process. These cell types show pycnosis and interphase death. In the F_1 lymphoma cells presented here, mitotic death is predominant. In these lymphosarcoma cells, the inhibition of nuclear ATP synthesis is probably not a critical trigger for a change in cellular function but could be regarded as an accompanying phenomenon of cell destruction and mitotic death.

The fact that nuclear ATP synthesis can proceed under conditions in which mitosis is inhibited suggests that nuclear ATP synthesis and the regulation of mitosis are independent processes of cellular activity.

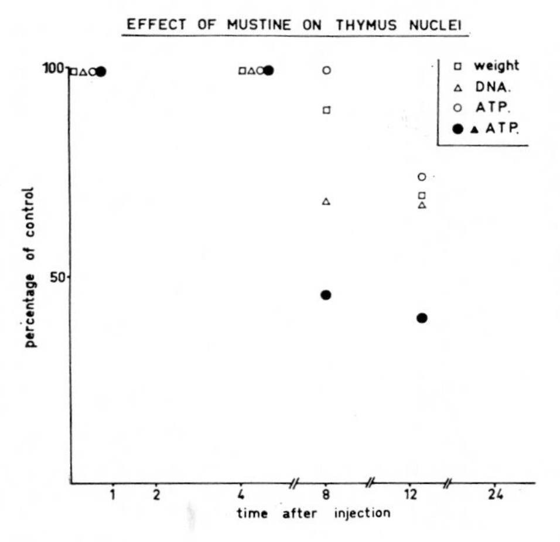

FIGURE 9. Effect of mustine (2.2 dichloro-N-methyldiethylamine) on thymus nuclei.
The effects postintraperitoneal injection of the mustine (2 mg/ml 0.14 M NaCl pH 7.2) on organ weights (□), DNA content (△), ATP content (○), and ATP synthesis (●) of nuclear preparations are shown. (Time given in hours.)
The control values (100 per cent) are:
Thymus gland weight: 0.40 g.
DNA content per gland: 10 mg.
ATP content: 0.40 μmole per mg DNA-P.
ATP synthesis: 0.25 μmole per mg DNA-P.
The thymus glands of three rats were pooled in each experiment.

Effect of X-Irradiation in vitro on Nuclear ATP Synthesis

In a recent report it was stated that irradiation of rat thymus nuclei in vitro did not cause inhibition of ATP synthesis (Klouwen and Betel, 1963). The experiments were performed using the conditions originally described by Creasey and Stocken (1959). These authors were able to demonstrate an inhibition of nuclear ATP synthesis directly after irradiation of isolated nuclei. These results represent the only example, so far, of a direct irradiation effect in vitro on nuclear ATP metabolism or composition.

Experiments in which thymus glands were irradiated locally and the remainder of the animal was shielded with lead demonstrated that inhibition of nuclear ATP synthesis after whole-body irradiation is chiefly due to the action of X rays directly on thymocytes. Therefore, we tried to confirm these results concerning the radiosensitivity of nuclear ATP synthesis by irradiation in vitro under various experimental conditions. The results of these experiments are summarized in Tables 6, 7, and 8.

TABLE 6

Effect of X-Irradiation in Vitro on Nuclear ATP Synthesis

Exp.	Dose in roentgens	Medium	ATP μmole / mg DNA-P		System irradiated
1	500	wash-buffer*	C***	0.28	
			Inc.	0.39	nuclei
			Inc. irr.	0.43	
2	1,000	wash-buffer	C	0.18	
			Inc.	0.23	nuclei
			Inc. irr.	0.25	
3	500	sucrose-$CaCl_2$** tri-ethanolamine	C	0.12	
			Inc.	0.23	nuclei
			Inc. irr.	0.26	
			C	0.25	
4	500	wash-buffer	Inc.	0.36	nuclei
			C. irr.	0.21	
			Inc. irr.	0.35	
5	100	wash-buffer	C	0.23	
			Inc.	0.29	homogenate
			Inc. irr.	0.30	
6	200	wash-buffer	C	0.25	
			Inc.	0.36	thymus
			C. irr.	0.22	glands
			Inc. irr.	0.35	
7	200	wash-buffer	C	0.25	
			Inc.	0.36	thymus
			C. irr.	0.23	glands in
			Inc. irr.	0.31	dead animals

* Wash-buffer: 0.1875 M sucrose; 0.02 M glucose; 0.0235 M NaCl; 0.008 M $MgCl_2$ buffered with Tris to pH 7.4.
** Sucrose-$CaCl_2$-triethanolamine solution: 0.25 M sucrose; 0.0033 M $CaCl_2$; 0.005 M triethanolamine HCl, adjusted with NaOH to give pH 7.1.
*** C: "15 minutes nuclei." C. irr.: irradiated "15 minutes nuclei." Inc.: incubated sample. Inc. irr.: incubated after irradiation.

TABLE 7

*Effect of X-Irradiation in Vitro on Nuclear ATP Synthesis**

Experiment	μmole ATP / mg DNA-P		Δμmole ATP / mg DNA-P
Nonirradiated	N_2	0.08	
	Inc.	0.37	0.29
Incubation for 1 hr at 25C after irradiation with 200 r**	N_2	0.12	
	Inc.	0.40	0.28
Incubation for 2 hrs at 25C after irradiation with 200 r	N_2	0.08	
	Inc.	0.39	0.31

* The nuclear preparations were suspended in a glucose containing Krebs-Ringer medium of the following composition: 0.130 M NaCl; 0.044 M KCl; 0.003 M $CaCl_2$; 0.0011 M $MgSO_4$; 0.0055 M glucose; phosphate buffer 0.006 pH 7.4
** During the period of incubation after irradiation the nuclei were shaken mechanically.

TABLE 8

*Effect of X-Irradiation in Vitro on Nuclear ATP Synthesis**

Experiment	μmole ATP / mg DNA-P		Δμmole ATP / mg DNA-P
Nonirradiated	N_2	0.14	
	Inc.	0.49	0.35
Incubation for 1 hr at 37C after irradiation with 200 r	N_2	0.14	
	Inc.	0.40	0.26
Incubation for 2 hrs at 37C after irradiation with 200 r	N_2	0.14	
	Inc.	0.36	0.22

* See legend, Table 7.

In the experiments, nuclei were isolated both in Ca^{++}- and in Mg^{++}-containing sucrose solutions, and the X-ray doses varied from 100 to 1,000 r; the systems irradiated were as follows: isolated nuclei, thymocytes, thymus homogenate, thymus glands, and thymus glands in decapitated animals. The results presented in Table 6 are a representative selection and merely demonstrate that ATP synthesis determined *immediately* after irradiation in vitro is not inhibited.

Subsequent experiments were designed to find out whether effects on ATP synthesis could be demonstrated after an incubation period of irradiated nuclei. This was done in agreement with whole-body irradiation experiments where radiation effects became manifest after 1 hour post-irradiation.

The nuclear preparations were suspended in a glucose-containing Krebs-Ringer solution and incubated aerobically at 25 C while being shaken gently to prevent sedimentation of the nuclei. ATP synthesis was determined up to two hours after irradiation in vitro; no inhibition could be detected (Table 7).

Since no effect of X-irradiation on nuclear ATP synthesis was observed under these conditions, incubations were performed at 37 C. Myers and Sutherland (1962) demonstrated that radiation effects in thymocytes could be demonstrated after irradiation with low doses in vitro only when the thymocytes were incubated at 37 C. From the results presented in Table 8, it can be seen that this was the case.

The incubation of nuclei in a glucose-containing Krebs-Ringer medium M was necessary because incubation of nuclear suspensions at 37 C in sucrose solutions resulted in a rapid exhaustion of ATP and the capacity to synthesize ATP.

The discrepancies between our results and the results obtained by Creasey and Stocken (1959) remain unexplained for the moment.

Discussion

One of the very confusing trends in radiobiological literature is the tendency of several authors to generalize results obtained under specific experimental conditions and to apply them without restrictions to other systems.

It is well known that major differences exist between cells with regard to their function and organization. Moreover, in different stages of the mitotic cycle, metabolism and cellular structures change profoundly. In spite of the important variations in cellular structure and function, radiation effects on living cells seem to have some characteristics in common, e.g. the inhibition of mitosis, cell death, and genetic aberrations. Whether these cellular effects are caused by the same biochemical alterations is not presently known; however, attempts have been made to detect biochemical effects soon after irradiation. It is relevant to discuss some of the radiobiochemical findings in relation to biochemical aspects of mitosis, a process which requires new synthesis of cellular compounds and of energy and the formation of a structural device for separating the "doubled" cell into two daughter cells.

Mazia and co-workers (1961a) have isolated from sea urchin eggs a mitotic apparatus. They have demonstrated that a major part of the cell, both nucleus and cytoplasm, is involved in the formation of this cellular entity. This organelle was formed from protein SH groups, and its rigid structure was ascribed to the formation of SS linkages. Brachet (1960) and Mazia (1961b) confirmed the fundamental concepts of the Rapkine theory (Rapkine, 1931), which point to cyclical changes in free SH content during cleavage of sea urchin eggs, although glutathione seems not to be involved as was supposed by Rapkine (Neufeld and Mazia, 1957). Brachet (1958) and Mazia, Harris, and Bibring (1960) demonstrated the inhibition of mitosis of sea urchin eggs by β-mercaptoethanol. It can be concluded from this evidence that fluctuations in SH-SS equilibria occur during mitosis.

The role of energy-rich compounds during mitosis was studied by several authors. It was demonstrated that treatment of cells with dinitrophenol (DNP), which uncouples ATP synthesis, leads to a rapid arrest of mitosis (Brachet, 1960). Therefore, the necessity of ATP for cell division seems obvious.

However, Swann (1957) could not demonstrate fluctuations in ATP content during division of sea-urchin eggs, and he speculated about the possible role of a thiolester compound in regulating mitosis.

Scherbaum (1963), Scherbaum, Louderback, and Jahn (1959), and Plesner (1958) reported controversial results with regard to fluctuations of nucleoside triphosphate in synchronized tetrahymena cell populations. Katchman and Fetty (1959), Katchman, Fetty, and Busch (1955), and Baker and Schmidt (1963) have detected fluctuations in polyphosphates, which are supposed to be in equilibrium with ATP, during synchronous division in bacteria. According to Katchman and Fetty (1959), inhibition of mitosis is the result of an inhibition of polyphosphate formation from ATP. Hotta and Stern (1961) have demonstrated that the capacities of *Lilium longiflorum* microspores to phosphorylate deoxyribosides are only manifest during brief intervals adjacent to DNA synthesis.

In the different systems used, fluctuations in ATP, or polyphosphates, or other yet-to-be-defined products could account for the varying energy requirements of cells and microorganisms during the mitotic cycle. During this cycle the amount of DNA has to be doubled, and DNA synthesis can proceed only after the induction of specific enzymes (Bollum, Anderegg, McElya, and Potter, 1960).

Howard and Pelc (1953) and Lajtha, Oliver, and Ellis (1954), using radioactive precursors, have demonstrated that synthesis of DNA occurs only in the synthetic period (S phase) of the interphase. From the labeling experiments performed by these authors, it could be concluded that the mitotic cycle can be divided into several periods (G_1, S, G_2, and M). The duration of the different periods varies for different cell lines. Huntley and Lajtha (1962) studied the incorporation of H^3-thymidine in spleen thymocytes. They demonstrated a much greater radiosensitivity after irradiation in vivo than in vitro. They concluded that if the generation of high-energy phosphate in lymphocytes is mainly intranuclear, then this process could account for the radiosensitivity of the S_0 period, the first part of the biphasic synthetic period. The S_0 process is detectable in vivo but not in vitro. These findings are in agreement with our results which point to important differences in radiation response in vivo and in vitro. Pelc and Howard (1955) demonstrated that P^{32}-incorporation into DNA was effectively inhibited if cells were irradiated during the presynthetic period; in the S phase much higher doses were needed. Although in earlier work it was assumed that inhibition of DNA synthesis will cause inhibition of mitosis, in later experiments it was demonstrated that the converse is true (Kelly, 1957; Harrington, 1960; Lajtha, 1960).

The radiosensitivity of the different phases of the cell cycle has been studied by several authors, and their results show that different cell types respond differently to X-irradiation in the various stages of this cycle (Hsu, Dewey, and Humphrey, 1962; Terasima and Tolmach, 1963; Sinclair and Morton, 1963). Inhibition of mitosis seems to be most effective after irradiation of the cells in G_1 or G_2 phase.

From the biochemical and radiobiological findings presented, it must be concluded that the molecular events underlying mitosis and the effect of X-irradiation on this process are still incompletely understood. Ord and Stocken (1963), discussing the radiosensitivity of dividing cells, especially of the nuclei, mentioned the possibility that inhibition of nuclear ATP synthesis might explain the radiosensitivity of the nucleus. The assumption that inhibition of nuclear ATP synthesis will cause inhibition of mitosis is speculative. From the results shown in Table 3, it can be concluded that no general correlation exists between the mitotic index of the cells and their capacity to exert nuclear phosphorylation. The experiments performed with lymphosarcomas demonstrate that nuclear ATP synthesis is not severely inhibited under conditions in which mitosis is completely blocked.

In these cells, the sharp decline of nuclear ATP synthesis coincides with the occurrence of mitotic death. At the moment of irradiation, a great part of the lymphosarcoma cells is in G_1 or S phase; therefore it can be concluded that in these periods of the mitotic cycle, nuclear ATP synthesis is not severely inhibited, as it is in thymocytes and lymphocytes. The results described by Klouwen and Betel (1963), demonstrate also that in the intact animal nuclear ATP metabolism is affected by low doses of X-irradiation. The early inhibition of incorporation of radiosensitive orthophosphate ($^{32}P_i$) in DNA is noteworthy and in agreement with results obtained by Nygaard and Potter (1962). Apparently, the incorporation of radioactive precursors in DNA in thymocytes is extremely radiosensitive.

From the results presented it can be concluded that, in cells which undergo interphase death, early inhibition of nuclear ATP synthesis is observed. In cells which undergo mitotic death, inhibition of nuclear ATP synthesis cannot be demonstrated before 12 to 24 hours after 1,000 r. In lymphosarcoma cells radiation effects other than inhibition of nuclear ATP synthesis can cause inhibition of mitosis. This is probably also true for thymocytes and lymphocytes, since after irradiation with 100 r, inhibition of nuclear ATP synthesis is still observed when the mitotic index becomes normal again (Klouwen and Betel, 1963).

It has been mentioned that an important part of the cell is involved in the mitotic process, during which profound structural changes occur, e.g. formation of spindles and asters and of a mitotic apparatus. This process is accompanied by formation of SS groups. Until now, no clear evidence could be obtained for oxidation of SH groups after irradiation. Using the DPPH assay (Klouwen, 1962b) for SH groups, no significant decrease in SH content of different tissue fractions, nuclei, mitochondria, microsomes, and supernatant from liver and thymus could be demonstrated within one hour after a dose of 1,000 r (Klouwen, unpublished data). Deakin, Ord, and Stocken (1963), who used a different assay for SH groups recently demonstrated a decrease of thymus nuclear SH content, providing that glutathione reductase was inhibited by Zn^{++}. However, glutathione does not seem to be a critical SH compound during mitosis in sea urchin eggs (Mazia, 1961b). The results concerning the radiosensitivity of SH groups still seem controversial. Changes in SH/SS equilibria in thymus nuclei after irradiation in vivo cannot be excluded; Hagen (1962), Braun (1963a, b), and Ernst (1961) demonstrated alterations in nucleic acid-protein interactions, and they observed changes in enzyme activities. These results indicate that changes in nuclear protein structures might be accompanied by changes in SH/SS equilibria. The effects were demonstrated only in thymocytes and lymphocytes after irradiation in vivo. In comparison with nuclear ATP synthesis, the effects reported by Hagen, Ernst, and Cepicka (1963) seem to coincide with the occurrence of pycnosis; at least they are observed several hours after lethal doses. The decrease in nuclear SH recently reported by Deakin, Ord, and Stocken (1963) was observed within one hour after

1,000 r. Inhibition of nuclear ATP synthesis was observed even after application of 25 r. Possible changes in SH/SS equilibria can probably be regarded as primary biochemical effects although nuclear ATP synthesis is apparently much more radiosensitive.

From the results presented in Table 8, it can be seen that immediate decreases of nuclear ATP synthesis after irradiation in vitro do not occur, and that only after preincubation of irradiated nuclear preparations at 37C could inhibition of the ATP synthesis be detected. This is not the result of cell destruction or cell death, as could be concluded from counting and staining of nuclear preparations after incubation.

The important discrepancies between these results and the results published by Creasey and Stocken (1959) remain. The results do have in common, however, that nuclear ATP synthesis can be inhibited as a result of direct action of irradiation, performed either in vitro or in the intact animal.

Different cell types show important structural differences. Also various cell organelles isolated from different cells show important variations in structure and function. We obtained evidence (Klouwen and Betel, to be published) that liver nuclei are not capable of synthesizing ATP. It may very well be that this is a relatively small and metabolically inactive nucleus that does not possess the capacity of synthesizing ATP, which is generated in the liver cells by hundreds of active mitochondria. Conversely, thymocytes and lymphocytes contain only a small number of mitochondria which are easily uncoupled, and in these cells the nuclear membrane could have taken over the function of ATP synthesis. Lymphosarcoma cells demonstrate more differentiated cytoplasmic structure.

Apparently, the F_1 lymphosarcoma cells possess active mitochondria which are radioresistant (van Bekkum, unpublished data) and demonstrate a high nuclear ATP synthesis. After irradiation, no rapid decrease of ATP content is observed. In thymocytes and lymphocytes, both mitochondria and the nucleus rapidly lose their ATP-synthesizing capacity, and profound structural changes are observed shortly after irradiation in vivo. The nuclear membrane separates from the cytoplasm, and large vacuoles become visible. These vacuoles are not observed in the reticulum cells from the thymus (Braun, 1963b).

From the evidence presented, it is clear that the energy production sites in cells show important variations in radiosensitivity. In cells in which all sites are severely damaged, interphase death is the major radiation effect. Other cell types, which possess relatively active and radioresistant mitochondria and a radioresistant nuclear phosphorylation, are able to survive radiation or die at a later time as a result of mitotic aberrations.

ACKNOWLEDGMENTS

This investigation is part of a study concerning the radiosensitivity and mechanism of nuclear ATP metabolism, in which Miss A. W. M. Appelman and

Dr. I. Betel collaborated. The histological studies were performed in collaboration with Dr. M. J. de Vries.

The author is grateful to Miss C. Arts for her skilled technical assistance.

The many valuable discussions with Dr. D. W. van Bekkum are gratefully acknowledged.

REFERENCES

Adams, H. 1962. "Adenosin-5'Triphosphat. Bestimmung mit Phospho-glycerat-Kinase", *Methoden der enzymatischen Analyse*, H. U. Bergmeyer, Ed. Weinheim, Germany: Verlag Chemie. Pp. 539–558.

Allfrey, V. 1959. "The Isolation of Subcellular Components," *The Cell*, J. Brachet and A. E. Mirsky, Eds. New York, New York, and London, England: Academic Press, Inc. Vol. I. Pp. 193–282.

Allfrey, V. G., A. E. Mirsky, and S. Osawa. 1957. Protein Synthesis in Isolated Cell Nuclei. *Journal of General Physiology*, 40:451–490.

Baker, A. L., and R. R. Schmidt. 1963. Intracellular Distribution of Phosphorus during Synchronous Growth of Chlorella Pyrenoidosa. *Biochimica et biophysica acta*, 74: 75–83.

Berenblum, I., and E. Chain. 1938. An Improved Method for the Colorimetric Determination of Phosphate. *Biochemical Journal*, 32:295.

Betel, I., and H. M. Klouwen. 1963. Adenosine Triphosphate Synthesis in Isolated Rat-Thymus Nuclei. *Biochimica et biophysica acta*, 76:327–329.

Bollum, F. J., J. W. Anderegg, A. B. McElya, and V. R. Potter. 1960. Nucleic Acid Metabolism in Regenerating Rat Liver. VII. Effect of X-Radiation on Enzymes of DNA Synthesis. *Cancer Research*, 20:138–143.

Brachet, J. 1958. Effects of β Mercaptoethanol on Morphogenesis in Amphibian Eggs. *Nature*, London, 181:1736–1737.

———. 1960. *The Biochemistry of Development*. London, England; New York, New York; Paris, France; and Los Angeles, California: Pergamon Press. Pp. 86, 104–107.

Braun, H. 1963a. Beiträge zur Histologie und Zytologie des Bestrahlten Thymus. I. *Strahlentherapie*, 121:567–574.

———. 1963b. Beiträge zur Histologie und Zytologie des Bestrahlten Thymus. II. *Strahlentherapie*, 122:248–257.

Creasey, W. A., and L. A. Stocken. 1959. The Effect of Ionizing Radiation on Nuclear Phosphorylation in the Radiosensitive Tissues of the Rat. *Biochemical Journal*, 72: 519–523.

Deakin, H., M. G. Ord, and L. A. Stocken. 1963. Glucose-6-Phosphate-Dehydrogenase Activity and Thiol Content of Thymus Nuclei from Control and X-Irradiated Rats. *Biochemical Journal*, 89:296–304.

de Vries, M. J., and O. Vos. 1958. Treatment of Mouse Lymphosarcoma by Total Body X-Irradiation and by Injection of Bone Marrow and Lymph Node Cells. *Journal of the National Cancer Institute*, 21:1117–1129.

Dounce, A. L. 1955. The Isolation and Composition of Cell Nuclei and Nucleoli. *The Nucleic Acids*, E. Chargaff and J. N. Davidson, Eds. New York, New York: Academic Press, Inc. Vol. II. Pp. 94–155.

Ernst, H. 1961. Strahlenbedingte Frühveranderungen an Zellkernproteinen. *Zeitschrift für Naturforschung*, 16B:329–333.

Ernst, H. 1962. Vergleichende Untersuchungen über die Konzentration nuclearer Globuline und Histone in lymphatischen und parenchymatischen Geweben. *Zeitschrift für Naturforschung*, 17B:300–306.

Ernst, H., and U. Hagen. 1961. Vergleichende Untersuchung der Zellkernproteine von Leber, Milz und Thymus. *Zeitschrift für Naturforschung*, 15B:597–603.

Frenster, H. H., V. G. Allfrey, and A. E. Mirsky. 1961. In vitro Incorporation of Amino Acids into the Proteins of Isolated Nuclear Ribosomes. *Biochimica et biophysica acta*, 47:130–138.

Gornall, A. G., C. J. Bardawill, and M. M. David. 1949. Determination of Serum Proteins by Means of the Biuret Reaction. *Journal of Biological Chemistry*, 177: 751–766.

Griffiths, M., and N. Pace. 1953. Intracellular Phosphorus Turnover in the Rat Liver Cell. *Proceedings of the Society for Experimental Biology and Medicine*, 83:771–778.

Hagen, U. 1962. Untersuchungen über die Entstehung der Thymusatrophie nach Röntgenbestrahlung. *Strahlentherapie*, 117:119–128.

Hagen, U., H. Ernst, and I. Cepicka. 1963. Radiosensitivity of Glycolytic Enzymes in the Nucleus. *Biochimica et biophysica acta*, 74:598–607.

Harrington, H. 1960. Effect of Irradiation on Cell Division and Nucleic Acid Synthesis in Strain U-12 Fibroblasts. *Biochimica et biophysica acta*, 41:461–469.

Hogeboom, G. H., and W. C. Schneider. 1952. Cytochemical Studies. VI. The Synthesis of Diphosphopyridine Nucleotide by Liver Cell Nuclei. *Journal of Biological Chemistry*, 197:611–620.

Hotta, Y., and H. Stern. 1961. Transient Phosphorylation of Deoxyribosides and Regulation of Deoxyribonucleic Acid Synthesis. *Journal of Biophysical and Biochemical Cytology*, 11:311–319.

Howard, A., and S. R. Pelc. 1953. Synthesis of Deoxyribonucleic Acid in Normal and Irradiated Cells and its Relation to Chromosome Breakage. *Heredity*, 6:Suppl. 261.

Hsu, T. C., W. C. Dewey, and R. M. Humphrey. 1962. Radiosensitivity of Cells of Chinese Hamster in Vitro in Relation to the Cell Cycle. *Experimental Cell Research*, 27:441–452.

Huntley, G. H., and L. G. Lajtha. 1962. The Radiosensitivity of the Processes of DNA Synthesis in Mouse Spleen. *International Journal of Radiation Biology and Related Studies in Physics, Chemistry and Medicine*, 5:447–460.

Jacob, F., and J. Monod. 1961. Genetic Regulatory Mechanisms in the Synthesis of Proteins. *Journal of Molecular Biology*, 3:318–356.

Katchman, B. J., and W. O. Fetty. 1959. Effect of Cell Division Inhibition on the Phosphorus Metabolism of Growing Cultures of *Saccharomyces cerevisiae*. *Journal of Bacteriology*, 77:331–338.

Katchman, B. J., W. O. Fetty, and K. A. Busch. 1955. Phosphorus Metabolism in Growing Cultures of *Saccharomyces cerevisiae*. *Journal of Bacteriology*, 69:607–615.

Kelly, L. 1957. "Effect of Radiation on Deoxyribonucleic Acid Synthesis in Mammalian Cells," *Progress in Biophysics and Biophysical Chemistry*. J. A. V. Butler, H. E. Huxley, and R. E. Zirkle, Eds. Oxford and London, England; New York, New York; and Paris, France: Pergamon Press. Vol. VIII. Pp. 144–163.

Kelly, L. S. 1961. "Fundamental Aspects of Radiosensitivity," Radiosensitivity of Biochemical Processes. *Brookhaven Symposium on Biology*, 14:31–52.

Klouwen, H. M. 1960. Radiosensitivity of Nuclear Ribonucleic Acid. *Biochimica et biophysica acta*, 42:366–368.

———. Unpublished data.

———. 1962a. The Separation of Nucleotides from Acid Soluble Tissue Extracts by High-Voltage Paper Electrophoresis. *Journal of Chromatography*, 7:216–222.

———. 1962b. Determination of Sulfhydryl Content of Thymus and Liver using DPPH. *Archives of Biochemistry and Biophysics*, 99:116–120.

Klouwen, H. M., and I. Betel. 1963. Radiosensitivity of Nuclear ATP Synthesis. *International Journal of Radiation Biology and Related Studies in Physics, Chemistry and Medicine*, 6:441–461.

———. To be published.

Lajtha, L. G. 1960. "The Effects of Radiation on Nucleic Acid Metabolism," *The Nucleic Acids*, E. Chargaff and J. N. Davidson, Eds. New York, New York, and London, England: Academic Press. Vol. III. Pp. 527–545.

Lajtha, L. G., R. Oliver, and F. Ellis. 1954. Incorporation of 32P and Adenine 14C into DNA by Human Bone Marrow Cells in Vitro. *The British Journal of Cancer*, 8:367–379.

Mazia, D. 1961a. "Mitosis and the Physiology of Cell Division," *The Cell*, J. Brachet and A. E. Mirsky, Eds. New York, New York, and London, England: Academic Press. Vol. III. P. 233.

———. 1961b. "Mitosis and the Physiology of Cell Division," *The Cell*, J. Brachet and A. E. Mirsky, Eds. New York, New York, and London, England: Academic Press. Vol. III. P. 250.

Mazia, D., P. J. Harris, and T. Bibring. 1960. The Multiplicity of the Mitotic Centers and the Time Course of their Duplication and Separation. *The Journal of Biophysical and Biochemical Cytology*, 7:1–20.

Mirsky, A. E., and S. Osawa. 1961. "The Interphase Nucleus," *The Cell*, J. Brachet and A. E. Mirsky, Eds. New York, New York, and London, England: Academic Press. Vol. II. P. 750.

Myers, D. K. 1962. Effects of X-Irradiation on Enzymes Synthesis during Liver Regeneration. *Canadian Journal of Biochemistry and Physiology*, 40:619–630.

Myers, D. K., and R. M. Sutherland. 1962. Effect of Temperature on Radiosensitivity of Rat Thymocytes. *Canadian Journal of Biochemistry and Physiology*, 40:413–417.

Neufeld, E., and D. Mazia. 1957. Non-Protein Sulfhydryl Compounds in the Division of Eggs of *Strongylocentrotus purpuratus*. *Experimental Cell Research*, 13:622–624.

Nygaard, O. F., and R. L. Potter. 1962. Effect of Radiation on DNA Metabolism in Various Tissues of the Rat. *Radiation Research*, 16:243–252.

Ord, M. G., and L. A. Stocken. 1962a. Phosphate-Transfer Reactions by Nuclei from Rat Thymus Glands. *Biochemical Journal*, 84:593–600.

———. 1962b. The Effects of 200 r of X-Irradiation in Vivo on Phosphate-Transfer Reactions in Nuclei from Rat Thymus Gland. *Biochemical Journal*, 84:600–601.

———. 1963. Biochemical Effects of X-Irradiation and the Sulfhydryl Hypothesis: A Reappraisal. *Nature*, London, 200:136–138.

Osawa, S., V. Allfrey, and A. E. Mirsky. 1957. Mononucleotides of the Cell Nucleus. *Journal of General Physiology*, 40:491–513.

Pelc, S. R., and A. Howard. 1955. Effect of Various Doses of X-Rays on the Number of Cells Synthesizing Deoxyribonucleic Acid. *Radiation Research*, 3:135–142.

Plesner, P. E. 1958. The Nucleoside Triphosphate Content of *Tetrahymena pyriformis* during the Division Cycle in Synchronously Dividing Mass Cultures. *Biochimica et biophysica acta*, 29:462–463.

Potter, R. L., and F. H. Bethell. 1952. Oxidative Phosphorylation in Spleen Mitochondria. *Federation Proceedings*, 11:270.

Prescott, D. M. 1960. Nuclear Function and Nuclear-Cytoplasmic Interactions. *Annual Review of Physiology*, 22:17–44.

Rabinowitz, M., and B. Bernard. 1957. Studies on the Electron Transport System. X. Preparation and Spectral Properties of a Particulate DPNH and Succinate-Cytochrome C Reductase from Heart Muscle. *Biochimica et biophysica acta*, 26:22–29.

Rapkine, L. 1931. Sur la Processus Chimique au Corps de la Division Cellulaire. *Annales de Physiologie et de Physicochimie Biologique*, 7:382–418.

Rees, K. T., and G. F. Rowland. 1961. The Metabolism of Isolated Rat-Liver Nuclei. *Biochemical Journal*, 78:89–95.

Roodyn, D. B. 1963. "A Comparative Account of Methods for the Isolation of Nuclei," *Methods of Separation of Subcellular Structural Components*, Biochemical Society, London, England: Cambridge University Press. Vol. 23. Pp. 20–39.

Scaife, J. F., and B. Hill. 1962. The Uncoupling of Oxidative Phosphorylation by Ionizing Radiation. *Canadian Journal of Biochemistry and Physiology*, 40:1025–1042.

Scherbaum, O. H. 1963. "Chemical Prerequisites for Cell Division," *The Cell in Mitosis*, Laurence Levine, Ed. New York, New York, and London, England: Academic Press, Inc. Pp. 125–157.

Scherbaum, O. H., A. L. Louderback, and T. L. Jahn. 1959. DNA Synthesis, Phosphate Content and Growth in Mass and Volume in Synchronously Dividing Cells. *Experimental Cell Research*, 18:150–166.

Siebert, G., K. Lang, S. Lucius, and G. Rossmüller. 1953. Untersuchungen über Stoffwechselprozesse in Isolierten Zellkernen. Über den Einbau von Anorganischem Phosphat (P^{32}) in Isolierte Zellkerne in Vitro. *Biochemisches Zeitschrift*, 324:311–324.

Sinclair, W. K., and R. A. Morton. 1963. Variations in X-Ray Response during the Division Cycle of Partially Synchronized Chinese Hamster Cells in Culture. *Nature*, London, 199: 1158–1160.

Smith, L. 1955. "Respiratory Enzymes," *Methods in Enzymology*, S. P. Colowick and N. O. Kaplan, Eds. New York, New York: Academic Press. Vol. II. Pp. 735–736.

Sugino, Y., E. P. Frenkel, and R. L. Potter. 1963. Effect of X-Radiation on DNA Metabolism in Various Tissues of the Rat. V. DNA Metabolism in Regenerating Thymus. *Radiation Research*, 19:682–700.

Swann, M. M. 1957. The Control of Cell Division. A Review. I. General Mechanisms. *Cancer Research*, 17:727–757.

Taylor, J. H., and P. S. Woods. 1958. "In Situ Studies of Polynucleotide Synthesis in Nucleolus and Chromosomes," *Subcellular Particles*, T. Hayashi, Ed. New York, New York: The Ronald Press Company. Pp. 172–185.

Terasima, T., and L. J. Tolmach. 1963. Variations in Several Responses of HeLa Cells to X-Irradiation during the Division Cycle. *Biophysical Journal*, 3:11–33.

Upton, A. C. 1963. The Nucleus of the Cancer Cell: Effects of Ionizing Radiation. *Experimental Cell Research*, Suppl. 9:538–558.

van Bekkum, D. W. 1956. "Oxidative Phosphorylation in Some Radiosensitive Tissues after Irradiation," *Ciba Foundation Symposium on Ionizing Radiations and Cell Metabolism*, G. E. W. Wolstenholme and C. M. O'Connor, Eds. Boston ,Massachusetts: Little, Brown, and Company. Pp. 77–91

———. 1957. The Effects of X-Rays on Phosphorylations in Vivo. *Biochimica et biophysica acta*, 25:487–493.

van Bekkum, D. W., H. J. Jongepier, H. T. M. Nieuwerkerk, and J. A. Cohen. 1953. The Oxidative Phosphorylation by Mitochondria Isolated from the Spleen of Rats after Total Body Exposure to X-Rays. *Transactions of the Faraday Society*, 49:329–334.

———. 1954. XIII. The Oxidative Phosphorylation by Mitochondria Isolated from the Spleen of Rats after Total Body Exposure to X-Rays. *British Journal of Radiology*, 27:127–130.

Radiation Effects as Measured by Chromosome Damage

Sheldon Wolff

Biology Division, Oak Ridge National Laboratory, Oak Ridge, Tennessee

Although studies on the relations between chromosome aberration induction and cell survival have shown that there is not a one-to-one correlation between survival and the production of any given type of aberration (Wolff, 1960; Bender and Wolff, 1961; Davies, 1963), the bulk of the evidence still indicates that at low doses of radiation, cell lethality is caused by nuclear, *i.e.* genetic, damage. Part of the evidence for this is inferential and part is direct.

Inferential Evidence

As an example of the inferential evidence, we might list Patt's calculations (as cited by Gray, 1954) that it would take the ionizations from about one million rads to inactivate certain enzyme systems in the cells. Since far lower doses (96 r exposure) can lead to an average of one lethal event per cell for mammalian cells in culture (Puck and Marcus, 1956), it seems reasonable to assume that a direct physiological effect of the radiation cannot account for cell death. Nuclear damage, mutations and aberrations, however, can be produced at low doses and since the nucleus with its genetic information governs all cell processes, it is logical to expect that many small genetic changes induced by radiation could be magnified to the point at which they would be cell lethal. This leads to the inference that it is the genetic damage induced by low doses of radiation that kills cells.

Direct Evidence

The direct evidence that shows correlations between nuclear damage and cell survival is more striking. For instance, Atwood and Pittenger (1954) made two component heterokaryons of *Neurospora crassa, i.e.* they made *Neurospora* whose conidia had two different types of nuclei. Each nucleus was deficient for the capability to make a specific metabolite that the other could make. Consequently, only those conidia with both nuclei could germinate and survive on minimal medium. When such conidia were irradiated and plated on minimal medium, the survival curves were exponential, or one-hit, as one might expect if death were caused by radiation-induced inactivation of any one nucleus. On doubly supplemented media, the survival curves were sigmoidal as would be expected if two hits were necessary to inactivate the conidia. The final slope was only one half that observed on minimal medium. This is a reflection of the properties of the binucleate heterokaryotic cell, in which the inactivation of either nucleus renders the cell inviable on minimal medium but still allows it to be viable on supplemented medium.

Experiments on the eggs of the wasp *Habrobracon* by Whiting (1955) have also provided a striking demonstration that nuclear damage can kill cells. Fertilized *Habrobracon* eggs, which are diploid, ordinarily develop into females. The unfertilized eggs develop into haploid males that are matroclinous, *i.e.* have all their genotype derived from their mother. When unmated females with oocytes in metaphase I are irradiated with exposures above 10 kr and subsequently mated, the offspring are all haploid, male, and patroclinous, *i.e.* they contain a genome derived from a sperm rather than from an egg. These experiments show that, in a cell that is given a dose beyond that which can cause death, a new nucleus can be substituted and can lead to normal development. The cytoplasm of these cells that have been subjected to high doses of radiation is still perfectly capable of supporting life.

Other experiments on *Habrobracon* (von Borstel and Wolff, 1955; von Borstel and Rogers, 1958) have shown that the *Habrobracon* egg is far more sensitive to radiation when the nucleus is irradiated than when the cytoplasm alone is irradiated.

In plants, too, similar evidence has been accumulated that shows that cell death is caused by nuclear inactivation. For instance, Dr. Sparrow (see pages 199 to 218, this volume) has found strong correlations between cell sensitivity and the nuclear volume of the cells.

It may be concluded that nuclear damage is a major cause of cell death although a one-to-one correlation does not exist between cell death and the most conveniently detected form of nuclear damage, chromosomal aberrations. Indeed, the induction of chromosome aberrations has been a phenomenon that has given us some of our greatest insights into how radiation can interact with biological material. This is because, by studying the aberrations, we see not only the breaks or lesions that radiation has produced, but also how these breaks can either be repaired or interact with other breaks to form new configurations.

Difficulty with Chromatid Aberration Studies

At this point, we might note that there are different types of chromosomal aberrations induced in different parts of the cell cycle. In that portion of interphase known as G_1 or gap 1 that occurs before deoxyribonucleic acid (DNA) synthesis (S), the chromosome reacts to radiation as though single, *i.e.* aberrations (formed by breakage and rejoining) are induced that later replicate when the chromosome doubles. Under these circumstances both chromatids of a chromosome are affected identically. Since both chromatids are affected, these aberrations are called chromosome aberrations. Studies on chromosome aberrations induced in G_1 are relatively straightforward since it has been known from the early work of Sax (1938) with *Tradescantia* that that portion of the cycle in which chromosome aberrations are induced has uniform sensitivity to radiation. We, therefore, do not need to worry about the possible effects of mitotic delay on our results, for all cells will show the same sensitivity.

In late G_1, S, or G_2 stages of the interphase, however, the chromosome reacts to radiation as though already double; *i.e.* the individual chromatid is now the unit of aberration formation giving rise to what are commonly called chromatid aberrations. In these stages, however, the sensitivity to radiation changes markedly according to where the cell is in the cycle. Under these circumstances, therefore, any mitotic delay or mitotic reversion that is induced by radiation or any other treatment can confound the results (Gaulden, Nix, and Moshman, 1953).

Experiments with Chromatid Aberrations

We have recently been involved in experiments that tend to show just how misleading experiments with chromatid aberrations can be. The experiments are of three types: those with combinations of X-radiation and far-red radiation; those with different doses of X rays; and those with combinations of X rays and treatments with antimetabolites such as 5-fluorodeoxyuridine (FUdR) that may have some value in cancer research.

X Rays Plus Far-Red Radiation

It has been known for a long time that far-red radiation given in combination with X rays can increase the number of aberrations (Swanson and Hollaender, 1946). Since the aberrations observed come from both the breakage and the subsequent reunion of the breaks, it has been postulated that the far-red radiation, which by itself cannot break chromosomes, affected either the breakage process or the rejoining process (Swanson, 1949; Kaufmann, 1946; Moh and Withrow, 1959). We, however, have found that in soaked seeds of *Vicia faba* in which all the cells were in G_1 there was no far-red effect. We have similarly found that in G_1 of *Tradescantia* microspores, far red has no effect when given either before or after X-radiation. We then performed an experiment on actively growing lateral roots of *Vicia faba* (Wolff and Luippold, 1960).

Seeds with lateral roots were exposed to either X rays or X rays and far-red when some of the roots were picked at 24 hours to obtain a sample of

G_2 and S cells that had chromatid aberrations, we indeed observed a typical X ray far-red synergistic effect (Table 1). When other lateral roots from the same beans were picked 48 hours after treatment, at which time those cells that had been in G_1 would be in metaphase, the effect had disappeared.

This was an indication that the effect might be caused by a far red-induced shift of the mitotic cycle, for G_1 is a period of uniform sensitivity wherein a shift of the cycle would not be effective, whereas S and G_2 have differential sensitivities. We, therefore, performed an experiment in which we gave either X rays or X rays plus far red and sampled cells every three hours so as to be able to follow the pattern of aberration yield as cells from those close to metaphase through G_2 and S were sampled. The curves obtained (Figure 1) show that the far-red treatment has merely shifted the curve obtained with X rays alone so that a given point is observed some two and one-half to three hours later. We also see a pattern of differential sensitivity according to the time at which the cells were sampled. Close to metaphase we find a period of lower sensitivity, which, after a dose of 150 r, subsequently rises to a maximum at about 12 to 18 hours and then falls. If one compares the two curves at 24 hours, which is usually done in the typical chromatid aberration experiment, one sees an apparent synergistic effect of far red and X rays. If one samples, however, at 15 hours, there is no effect, whereas if one samples at the very early part of the experiment, far red appears to be protective rather than synergistic.

Such results were indicative that far red induced a mitotic delay and shifted the arrival of cells in metaphase so that the two curves were essentially identical with the exception of having been shifted in time.

To make a direct test of the inhibition of mitosis by far-red radiation,

TABLE 1

Effect of Far Red on Radiation-Induced Aberrations

Type	150 r Aberrations Number	150 r Aberrations Per cent	150 r + Far-red Aberrations Number	150 r + Far-red Aberrations Per cent
	24-hr Fixation (chromatid aberrations)			
Chromatid deletions	34	10.2	24	8.7
Isochromatid breaks	38	11.4	25	9.1
Chromatid exchanges	10	3.0	31	11.3
Total chromatid breaks	92	27.5	111	40.4
Cells with chromosome aberrations	48	14.4	26	9.5
Total cells	334		275	
	48-hr Fixation (chromesome aberrations)			
Dicentrics and rings	31	10.3	22	7.3
Interstitial deletions	19	6.3	17	5.7
Terminal deletions	8	2.7	7	2.3
Cells with chromatid aberrations	1	0.3	19	6.3
Total cells	300		300	

(Modified from Wolff and Luippold, 1960.)

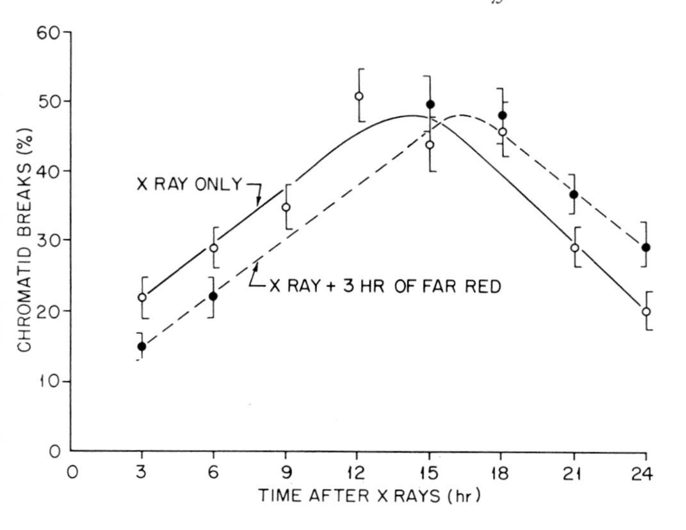

FIGURE 1. Shift in time of appearance of X ray-induced aberrations following treatment with far-red radiation for three hours. (Redrawn from Wolff and Luippold, 1960.)

we labeled S cells in lateral roots of *Vicia faba* by treating for 15 minutes with tritiated thymidine (specific activity 1.9 c/mmole, concentration 16.6 μc/ml). Some roots were kept in the light for three hours, while others were exposed to far-red radiation. After this time roots were picked periodically and autoradiograms prepared by dipping slides in Kodak Nuclear Track Base Emulsion, type NTB. Figure 2a presents the percentage of metaphases that were labeled among all metaphases observed at various times after treatment. The first cells to reach metaphase are unlabeled (G_2). These are followed by labeled S cells. The percentage of labeled metaphases increases as more and more cells from S reach metaphase. Then, as G_1 cells proceed to metaphase, the percentage of labeled cells decreases. It may be seen that with far-red treatment the peak of labeled metaphases occurs later than without far-red treatment. We suspect that the reason there are never 100 per cent labeled metaphases is that the concentration of label used was so high as to have induced delays in mitosis and a disorganization of the orderly progression of cells through the mitotic cycle. Wimber (1964) has shown that treatment with high concentrations of either tritiated thymidine or C^{14}-thymidine can induce mitotic delays in *Tradescantia* root tip nuclei. The far-red effect, however, is over and above the effect caused by the radionucleoside itself, and the curve is shifted to the right in the far red-treated material.

Figure 2b shows a similar experiment in which the material has been treated with 150 r. A radiation-induced delay of mitosis is evident in that the peak occurs later and is broader when no radiation is given, but the far-red effect is still evident over and above the X ray-induced delay.

It is such delays as observed here, coupled with differential radiation sensitivity of the various stages of the cell cycle (Figure 1), that can lead to misinterpretations if aberrations induced by various treatments are com-

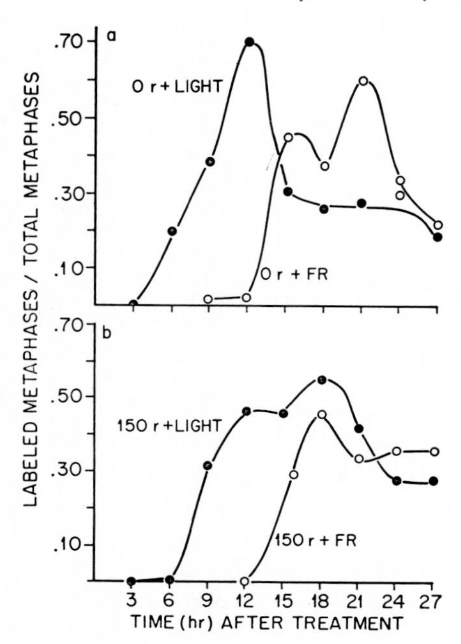

FIGURE 2. Proportion of metaphases that were in S at various times before fixation. a, 0 r plus 3 hours in light or far red (*ca.* 800 mμ 37,000 μW/cm²). b, 150 r plus 3 hours in light or far red.

pared at only one given point in time after the treatment has been administered. We have concluded from these experiments that there is no far red-X ray synergistic effect caused by an effect of far red on either chromosome breakage or rejoining; indeed, there is no far red-X ray synergistic effect at all. Far red merely seems to have changed the time at which a given sequence of cells from various stages of the cell cycle will be sampled. If all the cells showed uniform sensitivity to radiation as they do in G_1, this would not affect the results; but when cells have different radiosensitivity, it often means that we end up comparing a group with one sensitivity to a group with another.

X Rays Alone

Mitotic delays induced by X rays alone can also affect the time of appearance at metaphase of cells from a given part of the cell cycle, and again this can often be misleading. An example of this is seen if one attempts to study the kinetics of production of isolocus breaks that are frequently called isochromatid deletions. This particular type of chromatid aberration affects both chromatids at essentially the same locus. These are true chromatid deletions that are distinguishable from terminal chromosome deletions induced in G_1 by two criteria. The first is that the isochromatid deletions always appear in samples of cells containing chromatid and not chromosome aberrations, *i.e.* they are induced in S and G_2 cells. The second is that they almost always undergo sister-strand reunion that is either complete sister union (SU), or incomplete either proximally (nonunion proximal, NUp) or

TABLE 3

Ratio of Labeled to Total Metaphases and Anaphases

Treatment time (hr)	Colchicine†	Treatment: FUdR‡+ uridine	Treatment: Uridine§ (controls)
3	−	0/101	0/39
3	+	0/72	12/120
4	−	0/30	82/116
4	+	0/42	25/49
5	−	0/5	15/24
5	+	0/33	52/57
6	−	1/5	18/20
6	+	0/21	63/71

† Colchicine added for 1 hour after treatment.
‡ 10^{-5} M 5-fluorodeoxyuridine.
§ 10^{-4} M uridine in spring water.
(Modified from Bell and Wolff, 1964.)

higher concentrations of FUdR, they were able to observe aberrations sooner after treatment. They were even able to observe them one and one-half hours after treatment. These cells certainly were in prophase or late G_2 and not S. It appears, therefore, that the production of breaks is dependent upon the dose of the treatment, and that dose can be measured in the conventional way for radiomimetic compounds as the product of the concentration and the time of treatment. With a high concentration, breaks can appear quickly. With a lower concentration, the time to get an effective dose is increased and it takes longer for cells with breaks to appear at metaphase. The compound seems able to break chromosomes at all stages of the cell cycle.

Bell and I (Bell and Wolff, 1964) further found that if we simultaneously treated cells with either 10^{-5} or 10^{-6} M FUdR and equal concentrations of thymidine, we did not prevent the formation of chromosome lesions. We did, however, circumvent the FUdR-induced block of DNA synthesis. (We have shown such a block does occur in *Vicia* [Bell and Wolff, Unpublished data].) This is shown in Table 4, in which we see that, when FUdR plus an equal concentration of tritiated thymidine is administered, the average numbers of grains per nucleus in autoradiographs are the same as those obtained in the absence of FUdR. The same treatments did not decrease aberrations. In order to decrease the yield of aberrations, we had to administer thymidine at 100 times the concentration of FUdR. It may be concluded, therefore, that the effects of FUdR on DNA synthesis and chromosome breakage are independent of one another in that FUdR can break chromosomes at any time in the cell cycle, and that it can break chromosomes under conditions in which DNA synthesis is not inhibited.

Unfortunately, we do not know how FUdR causes chromosome lesions. Although at first sight the yield of chromatid aberrations led to an interpretation that was compatible with the information we had regarding the mode of action of FUdR, we found that we were misled because the compound is

TABLE 4

Effect of 10^{-6} M FUdR, 10^{-6} M Thymidine, and 10^{-5} M Uridine on Chromosome Breakage and DNA Synthesis†*

TREATMENT	NUMBER OF CELLS SCORED	NUMBER OF CELLS WITH ABERRANT METAPHASES	PER CENT OF CELLS WITH ABERRANT METAPHASES	AVERAGE NUMBER OF GRAINS PER LABELED NUCLEUS§
FUdR + uridine + H^3-thymidine	139	55	40	14.3
FUdR + uridine + thymidine	124	76	61	. .
FUdR + uridine	100	57	57	.
Uridine + H^3-thymidine	118	8	7	14.6

* 5-fluorodeoxyuridine.
† Roots were treated for 4 hours and then metaphases were accumulated for 1 hour in colchicine.
§ Four slides were analyzed for each treatment and grains over 100 labeled nuclei from each slide were counted.
(Modified from Bell and Wolff, 1964.)

a severe mitotic inhibitor, and that a cell that takes four hours to reach metaphase in its presence may actually have taken less time had the compound not been present.

SENSITIVITY AND SITES FOR ABERRATIONS

Up until now, we have considered the increased yields in chromatid aberrations at the different stages of the cell cycle in terms of increased sensitivity. It should be remembered, however, that the aberrations finally observed at metaphase are the result of both breakage and the subsequent rejoining of the breaks. Evidence that has been gathered recently indicates that it is the rejoining of the breaks that leads to the increased yields (Wolff, 1961; Brewen, 1964). If the chromosomes do not rejoin to give an aberration, they will rejoin in the original configuration, *i.e.* restitute, and so not give rise to an aberration. Therefore, although the chromosome strand itself may not differ in its breakability, the spatial relations of the chromosomes that allow their rejoining in new combinations can lead to the apparent changes in sensitivity.

We have found that there are but a limited number of places, called sites, where the chromosomes, by chance, come close enough to one another in the nucleus so that they can exchange if broken (Wolff, 1959, 1962). We have found that the change in sensitivity that occurs when the cell proceeds from G_1 to S (and the type of aberrations induced change from chromosome to chromatid) was really a reflection of these spatial relations. The main increase came from those breaks that ordinarily could only restitute because there was no other broken end near, now having a sister strand close by that, if broken, would allow isochromatid formation.

Brewen (1964) has studied the changes in sensitivity that occur as the cell progresses from S through G_2. He interprets his experiments to indicate that here, too, the change is caused by an alteration in the spatial relations in that there is a change in the numbers of sites available for exchanges.

Just because we have not yet been able to change the basic sensitivity of the chromosome to breakage, however, we should not despair of using combined treatments in the treatment of cancer. Any treatment that results in more aberrations, for whatever reason, will result in more cell death caused by radiation. It, therefore, seems theoretically possible that if one uses compounds that induce G_2 delays so as to accumulate cells in G_2, or uses compounds that synchronize the cells so that they may all be irradiated in G_2 or some other sensitive stage, more radiation damage would result. Any treatment that would tend to synchronize cells in a given radiation-sensitive stage would help in the field of radiotherapy.

Conclusions

Low doses of radiation kill cells. At these doses the effect of radiation is most likely on the nucleus. One good parameter of nuclear damage is the production of chromosome aberrations, although, as yet, a one-to-one kinetic relation between the production of any given chromosome aberration and cell survival has not been obtained. In spite of the value of chromosome aberrations as indicators of radiation-induced cell damage and of their value in studies in basic cellular radiobiology, one must be cautious in interpreting experiments on chromatid (as opposed to chromosome) aberrations. The reason for this is that the parts of the cell cycle in which chromatid aberrations are induced are not uniformly sensitive to X rays, *i.e.* different yields are obtained in cells irradiated in the various portions of the cell cycle. If any adjunctive treatment, e.g. other radiation, higher doses of the same radiation, or chemical compounds, induces changes in the mitotic cycle, one would make comparisons at metaphase between cells that came from different parts of the cell cycle.

ACKNOWLEDGMENTS

The Biology Division of the Oak Ridge National Laboratory is operated by Union Carbide Corporation for the United States Atomic Energy Commission.

REFERENCES

Atwood, K. C., and T. H. Pittenger. 1954. X-Ray Inactivation of a Triple Heterokaryon. *Biology Division Semiannual Progress Report* (Oak Ridge National Laboratory Publication No. 1936). Oak Ridge, Tennessee, pp. 20–24.

Bell, S., and S. Wolff. 1964. Studies on the Mechanism of the Effect of Fluorodeoxyuridine on Chromosomes. *Proceedings of the National Academy of Sciences of the U.S.A.*, 51:195–202.

————. Unpublished data.

Bender, M. A, and S. Wolff. 1961. X-Ray-Induced Chromosome Aberrations and Reproductive Death in Mammalian Cells. *The American Naturalist*, 95:39–52.

Brewen, J. G. 1964. Studies on the Frequencies of Chromatid Aberrations Induced by X Rays at Different Times of the Cell Cycle. *Genetics*, 50:101–107.

————. Unpublished data.

Cohen, S. S., J. G. Flaks, H. D. Barner, M. R. Loeb, and J. Lichtenstein. 1958. The

Mode of Action of 5-Fluorouracil and its Derivatives. *Proceedings of the National Academy of Sciences of the U.S.A.*, 44:1004–1012.

Davies, D. R. 1963. Radiation-Induced Chromosome Aberrations and Loss of Reproductive Integrity in *Tradescantia. Radiation Research,* 20:726–740.

Davies, D. R., and D. E. Wimber. Personal communication.

Gaulden, M. E., M. Nix, and J. Moshman. 1953. Effects of Oxygen Concentration on X-Ray-Induced Mitotic Inhibition in Living Chortophaga Neuroblasts. *Journal of Cellular and Comparative Physiology,* 41:451–470.

Gray, L. H. 1954. Some Characteristics of Biological Damage Induced by Ionizing Radiations. *Radiation Research,* 1:189–213.

Kaufmann, B. P. 1946. Modification of the Frequency of Chromosomal Rearrangements Induced by X-Rays in *Drosophila.* III. Effect of Supplementary Treatment at the Time of Chromosome Recombination. *Genetics,* 31:449–453.

Kirby-Smith, J. S., and D. S. Daniels. 1953. The Relative Effects of X-Rays, Gamma Rays and Beta Rays on Chromosomal Breakage in *Tradescantia. Genetics,* 38:375–388.

Moh, C. C., and R. B. Withrow. 1959. Nonionizing Radiant Energy as an Agent in Altering the Incidence of X-Ray-Induced Chromatid Aberrations. II. Reversal of the Far-Red Potentiating Effect in *Vicia* by Red Radiant Energy. *Radiation Research,* 10:13–19.

Puck, T. T., and P. I. Marcus. 1956. Action of X-Rays on Mammalian Cells. *The Journal of Experimental Medicine,* 103:653–666.

Revell, S. H. 1963. "Chromatid Aberrations—The Generalized Theory," *Radiation-Induced Chromosome Aberrations,* S. Wolff, Ed. New York, New York, and London, England: Columbia University Press. Pp. 41–72.

Rogers, R. W., and R. C. von Borstel. 1957. Alpha-Particle Bombardment of the Habrobracon Egg. I. Sensitivity of the Nucleus. *Radiation Research,* 7:484–490.

Sax, K. 1938. Chromosome Aberrations Induced by X-Rays. *Genetics,* 23:494–516.

———. 1941. Types and Frequencies of Chromosomal Aberrations Induced by X-Rays. *Cold Spring Harbor Symposia on Quantitative Biology,* 9:93–101.

Swanson, C. P. 1949. Further Studies on the Effect of Infra-Red Radiation on X-Ray-Induced Chromatid Aberrations in *Tradescantia. Proceedings of the National Academy of Sciences of the U.S.A.*, 35:237–244.

Swanson, C. P., and A. Hollaender. 1946. The Frequency of X-Ray-Induced Chromatid Breaks in *Tradescantia* as Modified by Near Infrared Radiation. *Proceedings of the National Academy of Sciences of the U.S.A.*, 32:295–302.

Taylor, J. H., W. F. Haut, and J. Tung. 1962. Effects of Fluorodeoxyuridine on DNA Replication, Chromosome Breakage, and Reunion. *Proceedings of the National Academy of Sciences of the U.S.A.*, 48:190–198.

Von Borstel, R. C., and R. W. Rogers. 1958. Alpha-Particle Bombardment of the *Habrobracon* Egg. II. Response of the Cytoplasm. *Radiation Research,* 8:248–253.

Von Borstel, R. C., and S. Wolff. 1955. Photoreactivation Experiments on the Nucleus and Cytoplasm of the *Habrobracon* Egg. *Proceedings of the National Academy of Sciences of the U.S.A.*, 41:1004–1009.

Whiting, A. R. 1955. Androgenesis as Evidence for the Nature of X-Ray-Induced Injury. *Radiation Research,* 2:71–78.

Wimber, D. E. 1964. Effects of Low Levels of X-Rays and Irradiation from C^{14} and H^3 on Cell Population Kinetics in the Root Tip of *Tradescantia. Journal of Cell Biology,* (in press).

Wolff, S. 1959. Interpretation of Induced Chromosome Breakage and Rejoining. *Radiation Research,* Suppl. 1:453–462.

———. 1960. Mechanisms of Chromosome Breakage and Repair. *Research in Radiotherapy, National Academy of Sciences, National Research Council,* 888:70–81.

———. 1961. Some Postirradiation Phenomena that Affect the Induction of Chromosome Aberrations. *The Journal of Cellular and Comparative Physiology*, 58 (suppl. 1): 151–162.

———. 1962. The Kinetics for Two-Break Chromosome Exchanges. *Journal of Theoretical Biology*, 3:304–314.

Wolff, S., and H. E. Luippold. 1960. "On the Apparent Synergistic Effect of Far-Red and X Rays in the Production of Chromatid Aberrations," *Progress in Photobiology, Proceedings of the Third International Congress on Photobiology*, B. Chr. Christensen and B. Buchmann, Eds. Amsterdam, The Netherlands: Elsevier Publishing Company. Pp. 457–460.

DISCUSSION

Dr. Peter Alexander, Chester Beatty Research Institute, Institute for Cancer Research, Royal Cancer Hospital, London, England: In connection with Dr. Klouwen's fine paper, I would like to raise the possibility of effects at a distance (or abscopal effects) as contributing to the early biochemical lesions in the lymphatic organs of whole-body irradiated mammals. The evidence is mounting (Maot and Alexander, *International Journal of Radiobiology*, 6:93, 1963) that many of these early lesions are not the result of irradiation of the cells themselves. A critical paper by Benjamin and Yost (*Radiation Research*, 12:613, 1960) showed that the inhibition of mitochondrial ATP synthesis in the spleen could be inhibited by irradiating the head of the animal only. This is an observation which we have confirmed. Second, there is indication that the increase in ATPase, which is common in the lymphatic organs after irradiation, is also largely abscopal and is not seen when the spleen only is irradiated. P. P. Weyemou (*Radiation Research*, 8:307, 1958) demonstrated one of the most sensitive biochemical changes seen after whole body irradiation was the increase in ribonuclease activity. Following the precedent set by Benjamin and Yost, we also found that this increase could also be achieved by irradiating the head of the animal only (Maot *et al., loc cit.*). With regard to the lymphosarcoma results just reported, our experiments with lymphoma cells irradiated in vivo and in vitro may be relevant: When the lymphoma cells were irradiated in vitro, no inhibition of mitochondrial ATP synthesis was found. When, however, we irradiated the same cells by whole body irradiation of the mouse in which they were growing as a solid tumor subcutaneously they behaved rather like the spleen in that there was inhibition of synthesis. If, however, those same cells were grown intraperitoneally, then following whole body irradiation there was no inhibition of oxidative phosphorylation. Clearly, abscopal effects depend on the site at which the cells under examination are growing. This is to be expected if their abscopal effects are of neuroendocrine origin as we suggested (*cf.* Maot, *et al., loc cit.*). Has Dr. Klouwen any data to rule out that a significant contribution to the inhibition of nuclear ATP synthesis may result from these indirect effects? I refer specifically to those following rather low doses.

Dr. Herman Klouwen, Radiobiological Institute of the Organization for Health Research TNO, Rijswijk, The Netherlands: With regard to what you have called in your book the enzyme release hypothesis, I would like to make some general comments. It is known from the work of de Duve (C. de Duve and H. Beaufay, *Biochemical Journal*, 73:604, 1959) that the cytoplasm contains lysozymes and supposedly high concentrations of proteolytic enzymes are located in these lysozymes. However, so far as I know at the present, there is no direct experimental evidence for the release of these enzymes as a result of X-irradiation. You mentioned the work of Benjamin and Yost. We must go back to the original publication on radiosensitivity published by Potter and Bethell (*Federation Proceedings*, 11:270, 1952). They actually found and described that after X-irradiation of mitochondria in vitro, no inhibition of mitochondrial ATP synthesis could be detected. They concluded in their abstract that: "This means that a reduced phosphorylation of mitochondria irradiated in vivo is due to a physiological response of the animal to the irradiation, rather than a direct effect of the irradiation in the mitochondria." I think this conclusion is highly speculative. Van Bekkum from our laboratory was not able to detect any indirect effects of mitochondrial phosphorylation. He has irradiated the exteriorized spleens and demonstrated an inhibition of mitochondrial phosphorylation soon after X-irradiation. (*Ciba Symposium on Ionizing Radiations and Cell Metabolism*, 1956, pp. 77 to 89). Recently, strong inhibitions of nuclear ATP synthesis were demonstrated after irradiation of the thymus only; the rest of the animal was shielded with lead. Also, irradiation experiments were performed in which only the head was irradiated. After irradiation of the head of the animal, a very slight delayed effect on thymus and spleen was observed. I think all the evidence so far obtained seems to indicate direct irradiation effects on these cells. This is also found by Myers and Sutherland (*Canadian Journal of Biochemistry and Physiology*, 40:413, 1962), and Creasey and Stocken (*Biochemical Journal*, 72:519, 1959). Benjamin and Yost (*Radiation Research*, 12:613, 1960) have studied effects of oxidative phosphorylation in mitochondria 24 hours after the irradiation. This is quite a long time after irradiation. It is well known that at this time biochemical effects are studied in a changed cell population which is partly destroyed, and does not represent the original cell population. An increase of ATPase was detected about 24 hours after irradiation with 500 to 600 r. The effects of X-irradiation on oxidative phosphorylation are observed much earlier, within 2 hours after 200 r. I think that the release of enzymes observed by different authors can be considered as a reflection of the major cellular destruction observed late after irradiation.

Dr. Henry S. Kaplan, Stanford University School of Medicine, Palo Alto, California: Dr. Klouwen has very commendably compared different kinds of cells. I think it is of interest that he does not find the same response in the different classes of cells that he has analyzed. However, he placed a good deal of stress on the very early change in the thymus cells; and left the impression that he regarded this as a strong indication that the alteration in ATP synthesis was itself a causative factor in the subsequent death of these cells. I should like to offer an alternative interpretation of his observations which suggests that the three different responses in these cells may not be so very different in terms of initial molecular reaction. There is a generally accepted dogma that DNA makes RNA and RNA makes protein. I think it would be desirable to interpret such phenomena in the light of this concept. Messenger RNA, which is generally credited with being the template for protein synthesis, may have an extremely rapid turnover in bacterial cells and perhaps also in some mammalian cells. In other mammalian cells, however, it may have a very slow turnover. Very recently, Dr. Helen Harrington (*Proceedings of the National Academy of Sciences of the U.S.A.*, 51:59, 1964) has reported that irradiation damages the ability of DNA to serve as primer for both DNA polymerase and RNA polymerase. If this is generally valid for many classes of cells, then it would follow that the ability to synthesize new messenger RNA would be severely impaired in any cell irradiated with an adequate dose. However, the interval until this injury is manifested in terms of an enzyme or other protein deficit would be expected to depend upon the half-life in each type of cell of the messenger RNA and for the enzyme selected for assay. In those cells with a very long half-life, the expression of the radiation injury would be greatly delayed, and there might actually be time to repair the damage before it could be expressed. I would like to ask Dr. Klouwen whether this alternative hypothesis might not equally well explain his data; if so, there is no compelling reason to regard the loss of the ability to synthesize ATP as a primary cause of death in the thymus cell.

Dr. Klouwen: About four years ago we published on the radiosensitivity of nuclear RNA in thymus and liver (Klouwen, *Biochimica et biophysica acta*, 42:366, 1960). A couple of hours after 700 r irradiation, nuclear RNA metabolism was inhibited in both the thymus and liver. Whether the fractions which were extracted by 1 M NaCl from these nuclei represent messenger RNA is not known. We do not have results concerning specific messenger RNA fractions isolated from mammalian cells and their irradiation responses. An alternative possibility is that messenger RNA is inhibited in different ways in different mammalian cells. In our experiments synthesis of nuclear ATP in some cells, is a very radiosensitive process. Brachet's work (in *The Biochemistry of Development*, Pergamon Press, 1960, p. 87) has shown that treatment of cells with dinitrophenol uncouples ATP synthesis, which leads to rapid cell death. The inhibition of nuclear ATP synthesis after irradiation could offer a biochemical explanation of the interphase death.

Dr. Helen Harrington, Western Reserve University, Cleveland, Ohio: Creasey (*Biochimica et biophysica acta*, 37:179, 1960) has reported that after irradiations of 25 to 50 r, nuclei lose sodium and potassium and the decrease in nuclear phosphorylation might be due to this loss. Do you have any data on loss of K^+ and Na^+ from the nucleus?

Dr. Klouwen: We have not done any analysis on sodium or potassium after X-irradiation.

Dr. Waclaw Szybalski, McArdle Memorial Laboratory, University of Wisconsin, Madison, Wisconsin: Might the inhibition of ATP synthesis by X-irradiation have some trivial explanation? Perhaps it could be a secondary effect of the postirradiation breakdown of either DNA or RNA components of the cell followed by flooding of the intracellular pools with nucleotides or deoxynucleotides. These might upset some control mechanism in your cells and interfere with your measurements of P^{32} incorporation into ATP.

Dr. Klouwen: As far as I know, and I am referring now to the work of Green and co-workers (*Federation Proceedings,* 22:1460, 1963), ATP synthesis can occur in mitochondria without the interference or addition of DNA or RNA. The synthesis of cellular energy (ATP) is apparently not regulated by DNA-RNA complexes. Metabolic mechanisms in the cell can operate without the interference of nucleic acids. Whether this is also true for nuclear phosphorylation remains to be seen.

Dr. Szybalski: I am afraid that I did not make my point clear enough. I am concerned with the effects of the accumulation of the nucleic acid precursors or breakdown products on the nuclear synthesis of ATP.

Dr. Klouwen: As far as we know, no detectable changes in DNA or RNA are observed shortly after irradiation of the nuclei in vivo or in vitro. Moreover, no changes in nucleotide pools are observed (Klouwen and Betel, *International Journal of Radiation Biology,* 6:441, 1963).

Dr. William C. Dewey, The University of Texas M. D. Anderson Hospital and Tumor Institute, Houston, Texas: I would like to add some evidence to that which Dr. Wolff presented on the relationship between cell killing and chromosomal damage. Many of us are aware of the work that Berry recently presented (R. D. Berry, *Radiation Research,* 18:236, 1963) on the survival in tetraploid versus diploid ascites cells. It was shown that the extrapolation number was twice as great in the tetraploid cells as in the diploid cells although the mean lethal dose was the same. There is something else I wanted to mention on the problem of mixing in populations after irradiation. We have been very concerned with this in our work. We labeled hamster cells with both C^{14}-thymidine and H^{3}-thymidine in such a way that we could distinguish between the various phases of the life cycle. The G_2 cells were labeled with only carbon-14, late S with carbon-14 and tritium, early S with tritium only, and G_1 cells were unlabeled. Then we found that following a dose of irradiation, before the G_2 cells had finished dividing the late S cells were dividing; before the late S cells had finished dividing, the early S cells were dividing, and some G_1's were dividing with some middle S's. Thus, there is considerable mixing of the populations and this is indeed a problem. One other thing I wanted to ask Dr. Wolff. I notice from your curve plotting the aberration frequency versus time, that it seems to increase to a maximum at about 12 hours. Do you think that the S cells are more sensitive than the G_2 in this particular cell?

Dr. Sheldon Wolff, Oak Ridge National Laboratory, Oak Ridge, Tennessee: Brewen, who is working in our laboratories, is concerned with this particular problem. I think that he is finding that there is an increase as S progresses and another increase when G_2 occurs in the *Vicia faba* cells. In general, I think most plant cells follow this particular pattern. As for mammalian cells in tissue culture, I understand from some of the abstracts and from some of the work that has been published previously the most sensitive stage may very well depend upon what cell line is used.

Dr. Arnold Sparrow, Brookhaven National Laboratory, Long Island, New York: Dr. Wolff referred to some of our work showing that there is a relationship between nuclear volume and radiosensitivity. Although later I will present material on changes in nuclear chromosome volume as a function of stage (see pages 199 to 218, this volume), it should be mentioned here. There is a progressive increase in nuclear volume or chromosome volume from telephase to G_1 to S to G_2. We can therefore expect an increase in absorbed energy. This should be considered when you talk about differences in basic sensitivity. There is also a difference in target volumes. Have you considered this possibility at all?

Dr. Wolff: At the end of my paper I only alluded to some of the things that we had done in regard to sites because there are so much data and it is such a complicated story in itself. It seems that when we find a shift in the type of aberrations induced and a concurrent increase in the number of aberrations showing up at metaphase (an apparent increase in sensitivity) these are not correlated with an increase in the number of breaks. If we look at comparable types of aberrations we find about equal numbers. In an experiment that we performed in *Tradescantia,* we found that the chromatid exchanges were twice as frequent as chromosome exchanges. Since we can score both symmetrical and asymmetrical chromatid exchanges, but only asymmetrical chromosome exchanges, this indicates that the numbers of breaks that went into exchanges in two stages of different sensitivity were equal. Similarly, the numbers of chromosome terminal deletions were equal to the numbers of chromatid deletions; again this indicated breakage was the same in the two different stages. The large increase in aberration yield came only from the appearance of chromatid aberrations in S and G_2. A chromosome that is broken in G_1 usually restitutes if there is no other broken end nearby for it to rejoin with and so form an aberration. A similar break that is induced after the chromosomes duplicate has another strand (the sister chromatid) within the rejoining distance of it. If this second strand is broken too, then instead of only being able to restitute, the break can rejoin from isochromatids.

It seems that we can explain the whole change in sensitivity in the production of aberrations in terms not of increased breakage, but in terms of changes in the spatial relations of the chromosomes that allow rejoining to form aberrations.

Brewen too has been working with the increased aberration yields observed in various parts of cell cycle. He, too, finds results indicating that a change in site number for exchanges causes the change in the numbers of aberrations.

Doctor Thomas H. Wood, University of Pennsylvania, Philadelphia, Pennsylvania: It might be of some interest to extend Dr. Wolff's generalizations concerning cell survival and chromosomal aberrations to a simpler system, the *Escherichia coli* K12 system. There is no *a priori* reason to associate loss of transfer of the male genetic information into the female with survival of the male cells. However, the sensitivity of a marker located distally on the male chromosome and the survival sensitivity of the donor cells are, within a factor of two, the same. So if you are willing to classify a breakage of this nature as a chromosomal aberration, this system would also tend to support Dr. Wolff's hypothesis.

Dr. Alexander: Some years ago you reported a dramatic increase in chromosome aberrations as the dose rate was increased. I believe a few hundred to a few thousand r/min. Would you expect that the radiosensitivity of the cells killed and rendered incapable of reproduction would also show an increase as the dose rate is increased from a few hundred r/min to a few thousand r/min? In this way the contribution of chromosome damage to cell death might be expected.

Dr. Wolff: I would say that this is another one of these cases in which we just have not been able to say that every time we see an aberration a cell dies. In general, we think, dicentrics are cell lethal, but there are persistent dicentrics to be found in some organisms. It depends on the genetic constitution of the cell as to whether the genes that are lost do cause cell death. This is what I wanted to emphasize; it looks as though the target is the nucleus. I think that there are far more data to support this than the data I presented. In spite of this, we cannot pin death down to any given chromosome aberration; I also do not wish to give the impression that aberrations are the only things that can kill a cell. In studies on survival of irradiated single mammalian cells in tissue culture, the criterion of death is really not death, but the inability to divide and give rise to a colony. People have found that they can irradiate nucleoli, or they can irradiate centrosomes, and both of these will prevent a cell from dividing. The cell might be metabolizing and might grow into a giant cell, and in that sense it is not dead; but it is not going to give a macrocolony and so will be considered dead for the purpose of the experiments. So things other than radiation can kill cells, and I do not want to give the impression that they cannot.

Dr. Tikvah Alper, Medical Research Council, Hammersmith Hospital, London, England: What is the relationship of chromosome damage to sublethal damage from which the cells can recover? There will, of course, be several papers dealing with recovery from sublethal damage. Does Dr. Wolff have any information on recovery from chromosomal damage which is relevant to that phenomenon?

Dr. Wolff: Well, I'm not sure I know what the answer is. I will say this: In order to fit the kinetic picture of aberration induction that we have, many more breaks or lesions have to be present in the cell than ever finally show up as aberrations in metaphase. This is the large class that we say have restituted. I think there is ample evidence to indicate that in irradiated chromosomes, we have this repair phenomenon. A lesion (chromosome break) that is sublethal can interact in some way or another to give an aberration that under some conditions could result in the death of the cell. Under other conditions, the break might restitute. This is the type of repair that has been noted in radiobiological literature for many years.

Dr. Kimball and Dr. Russell have been working on the repair of mutations. They have evidence that there is a premutagenic type of damage that can be repaired. This doesn't seem to be the same type of lesion that is manifested as chromosomal aberrations. They are more likely working with premutagenic damage that is truly intragenic.

Dr. Dewey: I would like to add a few words with regard to the last point that Dr. Wolff and Dr. Alexander have brought up. We did restitution experiments in a cell by studying the frequency of chromatid and chromosome exchanges in hamster cells during various phases of the life cycle. We found that in the cells irradiated in G_1 the breaks appeared to close, or at least restitution was complete within 5 to 10 min. in the G_1 cells. So immediately we thought, "All we have to do now is show the same thing for cell survival." We looked at recovery of the sublethal damage as determined by the return of the shoulder of the survival curve. Recovery does not occur within 5 to 10 minutes; instead, it occurred over a period of about 2 to 3 hours. So here we see a discrepancy between the restitution of chromosomal damage and the restitution of sublethal damage in the hamster cell.

Mr. Paul Todd, Donner Laboratory, University of California, Berkeley, California: In reply to Dr. Alper's question, using a cultured line of pig kidney cells, Ruddle has isolated several sublines from irradiated cultures and found them to have aberrant marker chromosomes. Many of these lines appear to grow normally and retain their marker chromosomes, but I am not aware of any radiation sensitivity studies on such lines of cells. This work is being continued by Agnes Stroud and others.

We have isolated slowly growing clones of diploid hamster cells following irradiation to about 10 per cent survival, following similar experiments reported by Warren Sinclair at the Harrogate Conference (*Radiation Effects in Physics, Chemistry and Biology*, M. Ebert and A. Howard, Eds. North-Holland Publishing Co., 1963). These cell lines are characterized by increased sensitivity to ionizing radiation; that is, they appear to have inherited sublethal damage. Sinclair has been unable to relate this increase in radiosensitivity to chromosome number, and we have so far been unable to identify any abnormal chromosomes in four such sublines of Chinese hamster cells.

Dr. Franklin Hutchinson, Yale University, New Haven, Connecticut: Are there any data which provide good correlation between cell survival and chromosomal aberrations, as opposed to some kind of generalized nuclear damage?

Dr. Wolff: The point of the paper that Bender and I wrote (*American Naturalist*, 95:39, 1961) is essentially that we find none. We get certain aberrations that increase approximately as the square of the dose, and indeed, we get two-hit survival curves. But the extrapolation numbers are not necessarily correlated. In mammalian cell survival curves the curves extrapolate to two, but the curves for cells without real two-hit aberrations in *Tradescantia* extrapolate to about 2^4.

There is one correlation that comes to mind. If we irradiate growing roots and sample immediately at the first division, we see aberrations. If, however, we let the roots grow for long periods of time before sampling, the aberrations seem to disappear. There is the selection against aberrant cells. Cells with aberrations eventually die and normal cells take over.

THE CRITICAL STRUCTURES IN RADIATION PHENOMENA

Disassembly of Mitotic Organelles with Subcellular Microbeams

RAYMOND E. ZIRKLE AND ROBERT B. URETZ

Department of Biophysics, University of Chicago, Chicago, Illinois

During the last half century, partial-cell irradiation by means of microbeams has been used to produce numerous effects on various cell parts and on the cell as a whole. Some of these effects are manifested as functional changes, some as changes in cytochemistry, and some as structural alterations that are revealed by light and electron microscopes. Some of the structural changes may be regarded as *submicroscopic disassemblies*, that is some organelles which can be seen in the living cell with the light microscope can be taken apart to the extent that the components can no longer be revealed by the light microscope in either the living or fixed cell. This paper is restricted to such disassembly of *mitotic* organelles, *i.e.*, those which normally have transitory existence in definite parts of the cell cycle. Many of these disassemblies have interesting functional sequelae, but here we shall forego discussion of these.

The investigations that concern us here have been done during the last decade. So far as our survey of literature reveals, the organelles in question belong to only three classes: chromosomes; nucleoli; and spindles and phragmoplasts. Most of the relevant investigations have been performed with ultraviolet microbeams produced by the type of apparatus described in detail by Uretz and Perry (1957), the beam cross sections ranging from 2 to 8 μ in diameter. There is also some fragmentary information on disassemblies produced by ionizing microbeams of 1.6 Mev protons, as described by Zirkle and Bloom (1953), the effective beam diameter being 2.5 μ.

CHROMOSOMES

The first indication of a submicroscopic disassembly of a chromosome was first observed in tissue culture cells of the newt *Triturus viridescens* (Uretz, Bloom, and Zirkle, 1954). Normal metaphase chromosomes, viewed by medium-dark phase microscopy, appeared black. When a 7 μ linear segment of such a chromosome was irradiated with a heterochromatic ultraviolet microbeam, it became gray or even clear, depending on amount of incident energy. This change in phase-microscopic appearance has been referred to as "paling," a term which involves no interpretative commitments. (If bright phase microscopy had been used, the term "darkening" would probably have been used instead.) Paling of a single chromosome segment is shown in Figure 1.

In view of the properties of phase microscopy, it was evident that the paling was due to a decrease in refractive index. Since no permanent increase in volume of the entire chromosome could be demonstrated, it was concluded that the decrease in refractive index was ascribable to loss of nonaqueous material. To designate such loss, Bloom and Leider (1962) introduced the term "steresis."

Since the original observation of paling in metaphase chromosomes, our group has observed it in all major phases of mitosis. Halftone photographs of some of these phases have been published by Bloom, Zirkle, and Uretz (1955), Zirkle, Bloom, and Uretz (1956), Zirkle (1957) and Bloom and Leider (1962). Paling in the interphase nucleus is also a commonplace demonstration in our laboratories. The chromatin particles in an ultraviolet-irradiated fraction of the nucleus behave very much as do the irradiated segments of condensed chromosomes. Perry (1957) has published halftones showing this.

Paling by ultraviolet microbeams has been reported in a rather wide taxonomic range of material. Izutsu (1961b) has described it in meiotic chromosomes of grasshopper spermatocytes, and Yashima (1962) in various mitotic phases of HeLa cells, while Bajer and Molè-Bajer (1961) have clearly shown it in halftones of mitotic endosperm cells of *Haemanthus*

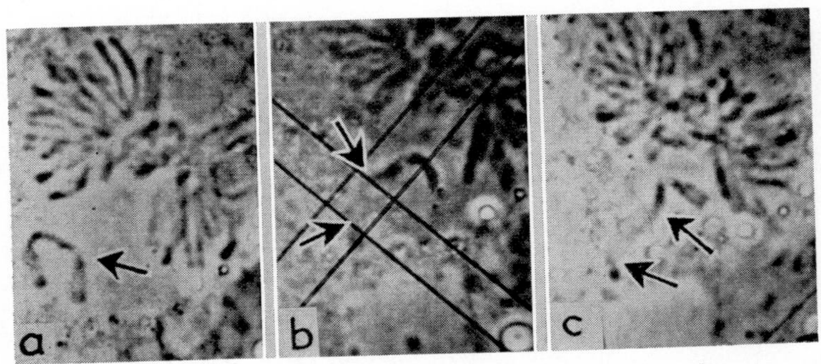

FIGURE 1. Paling of a linear segment of a single metaphase chromosome of *Triturus*. Dark phase-contrast microscopy. Size of each photographed area, 40 by 60 μ. (a) Before irradiation. (b) Two minutes after irradiation with 7-μ microbeam whose circular cross section was located as shown by circumscribing cross-hairs. Pale segment confined to irradiated region. (c) Pale segment now twice as long as the irradiated one. (From Bloom, Zirkle, and Uretz, 1955.)

katherinae. Tchakhotine (1936) irradiated part of a macronucleus of *Paramecium* with a 2,800-A microbeam and observed, in the ultramicroscope, a "hole" that contained a lower concentration of light-scattering particles than in the nonirradiated nuclear surroundings. It is an interesting possibility that, if he had had phase optics, he might have observed paling.

With ionizing microbeams of 1.6-Mev protons, Bloom and Zirkle (Unpublished data) were able to produce, with comparatively large doses to groups of chromosomes, a change in phase-microscopic appearance similar to that seen after ultraviolet microbeam irradiation.

So far as we know, the only attempts to determine the submicroscopic basis for paling and the concomitant steresis have been made by our group at Chicago. The cells were grown in tissue cultures of amphibian heart (*Triturus viridescens* or *Amblystoma tigrinum*, interchangeably) and handled as described by Bloom and Leider (1962). Since the cells were large (metaphase chromosomes about 2 μ in diameter and 25 μ in mean length), it was usually convenient to use fairly large ultraviolet microbeams (usually 4 or 8 μ in diameter). In the following account, the experimental object was the metaphase chromosome, unless otherwise indicated.

After a suitable exposure of a chromosome segment, paling is regularly observed therein within a period of minutes by means of the dark phase-contrast microscope. The greater the exposure, the sooner the paling is detectable and the greater is the degree of paleness ultimately attained. By proper adjustment of exposure, a chromosome segment can be brought to a refractive index practically identical with its cytoplasmic surround (Bloom, Zirkle, and Uretz, 1955, Figures 5 and 8). However, exposures several times greater result in less paling, and sometimes a darkness rather than a paleness is produced (Bloom and Leider, 1962). These various observations suggest that the nonaqueous material, whose loss is responsible for paling, consists chiefly of large molecules or aggregates which can be photochemically detached from the residual chromosome and can then slowly diffuse away, except that this diffusion is inhibited by a second photochemical process (possibly a cross-linking of the detached molecules or aggregates to each other or to the residual chromosome) whose influence becomes manifest with excessive exposure.

Exposure is not the only experimental parameter which, in excess, inhibits the paling process. Another is the fraction of total chromosomal mass irradiated. In general, as the microbeam cross section is enlarged to expose more and more of the chromosomes, the achievement of paling requires more and more incident energy per square micron. In particular, paling is seldom produced when more than half of the chromosomes are exposed and cannot be detected when all of them (or the entire interphase nucleus) are in the irradiated field. The cause of this effect is unknown. So far as detachment of large molecules or aggregates is concerned, it is not easy to see how the irradiation of one or more chromosomes tends to suppress the photochemical action in another. However, if the process of detachment should involve not only a photochemical action but also a "dark" reaction involving some normal diffusible substance that is present either in chromosomes or in the interchromosomal material that is exposed to the beam, then the inactivation of the whole cell's available supply of this substance would be highly augmented by increase in diameter of microbeam. One would expect a substantial fraction of this speculative substance to be inactivated by exposures known to produce barely detectable paling with a microbeam of effective size. Zirkle and Uretz (1963) obtained "just detectable" paling, in the wavelength region 2,500–2,800 A, with exposures ranging from 5.3×10^{10} to 9.9×10^{10} photons/50 μ^2, *i.e.*, of the order of 10^4 ergs mm^{-2}. This is the same order of exposure used by Setlow and Doyle (1957) for 50 per cent inactivation of aldolase (molecular weight 140,000), but it is considerably lower than those required for smaller enzymes. In any case, this comparison of exposures does not seriously discourage the interesting notion that an enzyme may be involved in the mechanism of paling.

Whenever a chromosome segment is substantially paled, the paling first appears in the region that is directly irradiated, then during some tens of minutes extends along the chromosome so that in some cases the ultimate length of the paled segment is two or three times as long as the irradiated segment (Figure 1). We are at a loss to explain this postirradiation spatial progression into nonirradiated portions of chromosomes. Several years ago we briefly had the idea that perhaps all the paling was produced by a diffusible intermediate that was formed either in the irradiated part of the chromosome or in the adjacent nonchromosomal material which was unavoidably irradiated. However, greatly prolonged irradiations, in which the microbeam missed a given chromosome by no more than a micron, failed to produce any paling, whether the exposed region was completely nonchromosomal or contained a segment of a neighboring chromosome. Thus we learned an important fact, *i.e.* that *paling occurs in a chromosome only if part of it is directly irradiated*, but we still have little inkling of the mechanism of spatial progression.

We now turn to some physical and chemical tests on the paled segments. Perry (1957) compared their ultraviolet absorbance with those of normal chromosome segments. For the normal metaphase chromosome he found the optical density at wavelengths 2,400, 2,600 and 2,800 A to have relative values 0.6, 1, and 0.6, respectively, which are close to the comparable figures for nucleic acids. In the paled segment, very nearly the same ratio of absorbances was observed, although in some cases the absolute optical densities were reduced to about 40 per cent of normal. These measurements indicate that paling is accompanied by loss of nucleic-acid bases or by their alteration to less absorbing structures. Published quantum yields for decrease in absorbance of bases, nucleosides and nucleotides (Shugar and Wierzchowski, 1958) are so low that we have calculated (Zirkle and Uretz, 1963) that base alteration cannot account for any substantial fraction of the decrease in absorbance of the chromosome; accordingly, substantial loss of bases must accompany paling.

Bloom and Leider (1962) observed that paling is also accompanied by greatly reduced staining of the chromosome segments by the Feulgen method. This indicates loss or alteration of deoxyribose residues of deoxyribonucleic acid (DNA). In view of the very low absorbance of sugars for most of the wavelength region in question, alteration seems quite unlikely (Shugar and Wierzchowski, 1958, pp. 263–264). If we accordingly accept loss of deoxyribose as the probable explanation of the decrease in Feulgen staining, and couple this idea with our earlier conclusion that nucleic-acid bases are also lost, it appears highly probable that the base and sugar residues are lost together, since the bases are side chains on the sugar-phosphate strand of DNA. Further, if we recall the slowness with which paling develops, it seems possible that the base and sugar residues leave the chromosome in the form of large fragments of DNA molecules.

Bloom and Leider (1962) also demonstrated that paling is accompanied by clearcut reduction of staining by the Alfert-Geschwind method for basic proteins. It therefore appears that a substantial fraction of the histones are lost, in addition to a large fraction of the DNA. At present we have no information concerning loss of any other chemical components.

Paling is also accompanied by a prominent change in appearance of the chromosome by electron microscopy (Bloom and Leider, 1962; Figures 16, 17, 18, 19, 20, and 21). The normal metaphase chromosome, in suitably fixed cells, shows two prominent structural components. One is an irregular reticulum of filaments (or tubules), ranging from 40 to 300 A in diameter, which remains after optimal paling has been produced. The other, noncommitally termed Component A, fills the spaces in the reticulum, appears practically homogeneous at the electron-microscopic resolution used, and is almost completely absent in segments that have been optimally paled. Thus it seems highly probable that Component A contains the DNA and the histones whose removal has been described above.

To gain some concept of the photochemical aspect of the paling mechanism, Zirkle and Uretz (1963) worked out an action spectrum. The relative effectiveness (RE) per incident photon at the various wavelengths (λ) were as follows:

λ(A) :	2,250	2,400	2,500	2,600	2,700	2,800	3,000
RE :	220	30	10	16	19	16	2.2

When this action spectrum is compared with absorption spectra from the literature, we find that DNA fits very poorly. The same is true of its bases, nucleosides, and nucleotides, except for deoxycytidylic acid, which fits well from 2,500 to 3,000 A but deviates widely at lower wavelengths. In general, the spectral absorption of the common tyrosine-containing proteins fits much better. The best fit we have found is provided by histones (perhaps fortuitously). It thus would appear that, although DNA dominates the chromosomal absorbance over most of the wavelength range studied, the process of paling is initiated by the relatively few photons absorbed by some species of chromosomal protein.

Nucleoli

Disassembly of nucleoli has been observed in several types of animal cells. Gaulden and Perry (1958), in their pioneering ultraviolet microbeam experiments on nucleolar function in grasshopper neuroblasts, reported that "the only morphological change observed in the nucleolus after irradiation was an occasional slight decrease in size." Bloom and Zirkle (Unpublished data) also observed occasional decreases in size of *Triturus* nucleoli after ultraviolet microbeam irradiation. After large doses with a proton microbeam, larger decreases in size were observed, amounting in some cases to an eightfold reduction in volume.

In the foregoing investigations, the entire nucleolus was irradiated (plus, of course, the superjacent and subjacent nuclear material and cytoplasm). Yashima (1962) was able to irradiate only a fraction of a nucleolus with a 2μ ultraviolet microbeam by using HeLa cells, which have relatively large nucleoli. Two hours or more after irradiation, he observed by dark phase-contrast microscopy a spot of reduced refractive index at the site of irradiation. Zirkle and Bloom (Unpublished data) also observed decrease of refractive index in a few of the *Triturus* nucleoli which they totally irradiated with a 2.5μ proton microbeam. Whether this nucleolar phenomenon has any basic similarity to chromosomal paling is an open question.

Spindles and Phragmoplasts

So far as we are aware, the first reports of spindle disassembly by irradiation were those of Carlson and Hollaender (1948) and of Carlson (1954), who found that 2,250-A total-cell exposure of grasshopper neuroblasts resulted in decrease of spindle size, the degree of effect depending upon size of exposure and mitotic phase. Shortly afterward, our group at Chicago found that, when the metaphase spindles of *Triturus* tissue culture cells were irradiated at one or both ends with a heterochromatic ultraviolet microbeam (Bloom, Zirkle, and Uretz, 1955), the spindle decreased in size or disappeared entirely, as observed by phase microscopy. Since, in such irradiations, not only a portion of the spindle but also the superjacent and subjacent cytoplasm is exposed, control irradiations of small portions of cytoplasms were performed. The spindle still decreased or disappeared. Moreover, the decrease or disappearance proceeded symmetrically in the two half-spindles, even though in some cases the microbeam was aimed into or near only one of them. Shortly after, these observations were verified by polarization microscopy, which delineates spindles much more accurately than phase-contrast microscopy (Figure 2) (see also Taylor, 1959). Further, it was found that, if a small portion of cytoplasm was irradiated before the spindle was manifest as a birefringent structure (e.g. in prophase), the spindle failed to appear. The foregoing set of basic qualitative results of cytoplasmic irradiation have also been observed by polarization microscopy in two-celled embryos of the sand dollar *Echinarachnius parma* (Uretz and Zirkle, 1955) and in endosperm cells of the African blood lily, *Haemanthus katharinae* (Zirkle, Uretz, and Haynes, 1960; Haynes and Zirkle, Unpublished data).

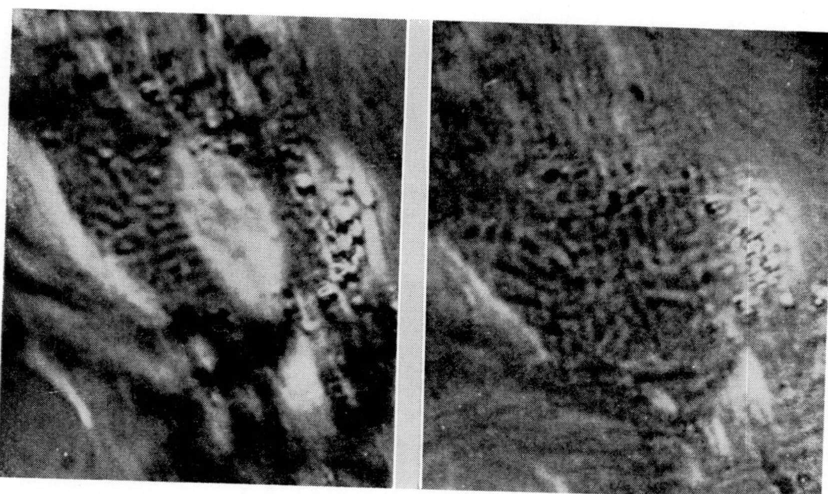

FIGURE 2. Disappearance of spindle in a *Triturus* cell after irradiation of a portion of its cytoplasm with an 8-μ microbeam. Polarization microscopy. Area photographed, 55 by 70 μ. Left, before irradiation; several birefringent areas present, including the spindle. Right, a few minutes after irradiation; the spindle has disappeared, but the birefringence in other areas (probably due to strain orientation) still is seen. From Zirkle, 1959.)

Evidence for spindle disassembly in various other kinds of cells has been reported by a Japanese group at the Mie School of Medicine, which has used a Uretz-type ultraviolet microbeam built by Izutsu (1959, 1961a) and has made observations by phase microscopy. Izutsu (1961b) reported that, in metaphase I of meiosis in grasshopper spermatocytes, "diminution in size of the spindle body" was observed "when any part of the cell was irradiated with a UV microbeam." Since some cytoplasm is unavoidably irradiated when any other cell part is, all of these disassemblies could have been caused by exposure of cytoplasm. In spermatocytes in which spindles had not yet formed, Izutsu (1961a) specifically describes, as a result of exposure of cytoplasm only, complete or partial inhibition of spindle formation. In HeLa cells, Yashima (1962) observed that metaphase and anaphase spindles decreased or disappeared after irradiation of a small region of cytoplasm only or of spindle plus cytoplasm. Thus, both Yashima's and Izutsu's observations appear to agree substantially with ours in *Triturus*, *Echinarachnius* and *Haemanthus*.

In stamen hair cells of *Tradescantia reflexa*, Wada and Izutsu (1961) were able to inhibit spindle formation by irradiating the "polar cap" of the "clear zone" which in plant cells surrounds the nucleus during part of prophase, and is believed to contain material that later forms part or all of the spindle. (Clear zones are shown plainly in the polarization photomicrographs of Inoué and Bajer [1961]). By contrast any irradiation of *Tradescantia* prophase cells which did not impinge upon the polar cap produced no effect on spindle formation. In prometaphase, after the spindle had formed, no clear evidence of spindle decrease or destruction was observed, no matter what part of the cell was irradiated. As the authors point out, in these cells observations of spindles by phase microscopy are difficult because of the large volume of chromosomes and other organelles; they mention no attempt to visualize spindles by polarization microscopy.

At this point, some generalizations can be made about all the foregoing observations on spindles of various kinds of plant and animal cells. In all cases discussed above, except *Tradescantia*, the investigators were able to decrease or destroy metaphase or prometaphase spindles by irradiation in the cytoplasm alone. In all cases where cytoplasm only was irradiated before the spindle formed (*Triturus*, *Echinarachnius*, *Haemanthus*, grasshopper spermatocytes, and *Tradescantia*), spindle formation was inhibited entirely or partially. (In *Tradescantia*, a particular zone of cytoplasm, the polar cap, had to be irradiated in order to produce the effect.) In several kinds of material (*Triturus*, HeLa, grasshopper spermatocytes), the investigators aimed microbeams into parts of the spindle and observed evidence of disassembly. However, since the subjacent and superjacent cytoplasm was also irradiated, the effects could have been caused by cytoplasmic irradiation only. It is still an open question whether the photons absorbed by the spindle itself contributed to its disassembly. Resolution of this question will require a difficult quantitative experiment that nobody has yet reported.

The foregoing generalizations for decrease or disappearance of spindles also hold for phragmoplasts, as studied by polarization microscopy in endosperm cells of *Haemanthus* (Zirkle, Uretz, and Haynes, 1960; Haynes and Zirkle, Unpublished data). This result is to be expected if there is validity in the common view (e.g. Inoué and Bajer, 1961) that the components of spindles and phragmoplasts are similar in nature.

Let us now concentrate on the type of experiment in which the microbeam is limited to a small portion of cytoplasm and the spindle disappears in whole or in part. This is clearly an indirect action, *i.e.* the effect is seen in a microscopic cell part that is not traversed by the beam. Early in the work on *Triturus* cells, we introduced the notion of a chemical intermediate, which we called a "spindle poison" (Zirkle, Bloom, and Uretz, 1956). This was assumed to be an abnormal chemical species which was formed from some normal species present in cytoplasm and could then diffuse to the position of the spindle; there it could react in such fashion as to derange and/or disassemble the elongate components ("fibers") which account for the spindle's birefringence. To get some notion of the nature of the hypothetical precursor, Brown and Zirkle (1963) have recently worked out an action spectrum for disappearance of metaphase spindles after microbeam irradiation of a small fraction of cytoplasm. The spindles were observed by polarization microscopy, and the cells were cultured from heart of *Amblystoma*, which in our laboratories is used interchangeably with *Triturus*. The relative effectiveness (RE) per incident photon at the various wavelengths (λ) were as follows:

λ(A)	2,250	2,345	2,410	2,480	2,535	2,600
RE	110	43	12	9.3	6.9	6.3
λ(A)	2,655	2,755	2,800	2,895	2,967	3,025
RE	10	19	15	11	2.9	0.7

This action spectrum, in its principal features, is shaped much like the absorption spectra of numerous tyrosine-containing proteins. This is in agreement with the results which Carlson (1954) has briefly reported on decrease in spindle size after total-cell irradiation of grasshapper neuroblasts.

We now briefly consider the possible significance of the "protein" action spectrum. There is now little doubt that the dry matter of a spindle is predominantly protein (summarized by Mazia, 1961, pp. 245–247). Taylor (1959) has presented evidence that in *Triturus*, the synthesis of spindle protein is completed about 30 minutes before the start of elongation of the birefringent spindle (see Taylor's polarization photomicrographs in his Figure 1). The growth of the birefringent body is interpreted as due to assembly of elongate parallel elements ("fibers") from molecules of the spindle protein. Quite likely an enzyme system is involved in this assembly. In anaphase of a normal mitosis, the birefringent spindle disappears in orderly fashion; this is attributed to disassembly of the fibers, also a process in which an enzyme system is probably involved.

We can think of the fully formed metaphase spindle in relation to either of two models: (1) the metaphase spindle is a static structure, and its elongate aggregates of spindle protein normally undergo no metabolic changes until their disassembly in anaphase; (2) the metaphase spindle is a dynamic structure in which the elongate aggregates are in equilibrium or steady state with a pool of spindle-protein molecules in the cytoplasm. In terms of these models, we can now make some guesses concerning the cytoplasmic protein species whose alteration could lead to spindle disassembly.

We can guess immediately that this protein may be an enzyme or may be the spindle protein itself. According to the static model, it cannot be the spindle protein. If it is an enzyme, a plausible guess would be that it is the disassembly enzyme (postulated above) which normally functions in anaphase but may be present during metaphase in an inactive or inhibited form; absorption of an ultraviolet photon might activate this enzyme, dissociate an enzyme-inhibitor complex, or destroy the inhibitor (assuming this to be a protein also).

If we use the dynamic model, we are assuming that both the assembly and disassembly enzyme systems are functioning simultaneously. If we further assume that these two enzymes are one and the same, *i.e.* that the fully formed spindle and the spindle protein are in simple equilibrium, it is difficult to explain, on the basis of inactivation of this enzyme, the shift in equilibrium manifested by the observed decrease in spindle size. If we make the assumption that the enzymes for assembly and disassembly are different and maintain a steady state, the manifested shift in equilibrium can be explained on the basis that the assembly enzyme is, for some reason, more readily inactivated by irradiation of cytoplasm than the other.

The dynamic model alternatively permits us to visualize the spindle protein itself as the one indicated by the action spectrum. This molecular species, if it is to form linear aggregates as we have assumed, must have two functional groups. If the ultraviolet radiation should inactivate both groups, the total amount of functional spindle protein in the cell would simply be decreased and the amount in the spindle would correspondingly decrease, thus accounting for the observed reduction in spindle size. However, it would seem to be practically certain that molecules with only one inactivated group would be produced much more rapidly than those with both inactivated. The presence of such monofunctional analogs of the normal spindle protein, even in low relative abundance, could be disastrous for the assembly of long linear aggregates. Here we have a situation for which there are many parallels in current biological research and in which the photo-produced analog can be recognized as a spindle "poison" in a very familiar sense of the word.

The foregoing list of guesses concerning the protein indicated by the action spectrum no doubt can be extended. Conversely, some laborious quantitative work might enable us to rule out some of them.

ACKNOWLEDGMENTS

The above mentioned radiation experiments on *Triturus*, *Amblystoma*, *Haemanthus* and *Echinarachnius* were aided by contracts and grants from the National Institutes of Health of the United States Public Health Service, the U. S. Atomic Energy Commission, the Office of Naval Research, the Damon Runyon Memorial Fund, and the Abbott Research Fund of the University of Chicago.

REFERENCES

Bajer, A., and J. Molè-Bajer. 1961. UV Microbeam Irradiation of Chromosomes During Mitosis in Endosperm. *Experimental Cell Research*, 25:251–267.

Bloom, W., and R. J. Leider. 1962. Optical and Electron Microscopic Changes in Ultraviolet-Irradiated Chromosome Segments. *The Journal of Cell Biology*, 13:269–301.

Bloom, W., and R. E. Zirkle. Unpublished data.

Bloom, W., R. E. Zirkle, and R. B. Uretz. 1955. Irradiation of Parts of Individual Cells. III. Effects of Chromosomal and Extrachromosomal Irradiation on Chromosome Movements. *Annals of the New York Academy of Sciences*, 59:503–513.

Brown, D. Q., and R. E. Zirkle. 1963. Ultraviolet Action Spectra for Mitotic Spindle

Destruction and Anaphase Delay Following Irradiation of Cytoplasm. (Abstract) *Radiation Research*, 19:207.

Carlson, J. G. 1954. Effects of Monochromatic Ultraviolet Radiation on the Spindle and Mitosis. (Abstract) *Proceedings of the First International Photobiology Congress (Fourth International Light Congress)*. H. Veenam & Zonen, Wageningen, pp. 137–138.

Carlson, J. G., and A. Hollaender. 1948. Mitotic Effects of Ultraviolet Radiation of the 2250 Å Region, with Special Reference to the Spindle and Cleavage. *Journal of Cellular and Comparative Physiology*, 31:149–173.

Gaulden, M. E., and R. P. Perry. 1958. Influence of the Nucleolus on Mitosis as Revealed by Ultraviolet Microbeam Irradiation. *Proceedings of the National Academy of Sciences of the U.S.A.*, 44:553–559.

Haynes, R. H., and R. E. Zirkle. Unpublished data.

Inoué, S., and A. Bajer. 1961. Birefringence in Endosperm Mitosis. *Chromosoma (Berlin)*, 12:48–63.

Izutsu, K. 1959. Irradiation of Parts of Single Mitotic Apparatus in Grasshopper Spermatocytes with an Ultraviolet-Microbeam. *Mie Medical Journal*, 9:15–29.

———. 1961a. Effects of Ultraviolet Microbeam Irradiation Upon Division in Grasshopper Spermatocytes. I. Results of Irradiation During Prophase and Prometaphase I. *Mie Medical Journal*, 11:199–212.

———. 1961b. Effects of Ultraviolet Microbeam Irradiation Upon Division in Grasshopper Spermatocytes. II. Results of Irradiation During Metaphase and Anaphase I. *Mie Medical Journal*, 11:213–232.

Mazia, D. 1961. "Mitosis and the Physiology of Cell Division," *The Cell*, J. Brachet and A. E. Mirsky, Eds. New York, New York: Academic Press, Inc. Vol. III. Pp. 77–412.

Perry, R. P. 1957. Changes in the Ultraviolet Absorption Spectrum of Parts of Living Cells Following Irradiation with an Ultraviolet Microbeam. *Experimental Cell Research*, 12:546–559.

Setlow, R., and B. Doyle. 1957. The Action of Monochromatic Ultraviolet Light on Proteins. *Biochimica et biophysica acta*, 24:27–41.

Shugar, D., and K. L. Wierzchowski. 1958. Photochemistry of Nucleic Acids. Nucleic Acid Derivatives and Related Compounds. *Postepy Biochemii, Polska Akademia Nauk*, 4:243–296.

Taylor, E. W. 1959. Dynamics of Spindle Formation and its Inhibition by Chemicals. *The Journal of Biophysical and Biochemical Cytology*, 6:193–196.

Tchakhotine, S. 1936. Effets d'Irradiation Localisée du Noyau des Infusoires par Micropuncture Ultraviolette. *Comptes rendus hebdomadaires des séances de l'Académie des Sciences*, 202:778–781.

Uretz, R. B., W. Bloom, and R. E. Zirkle. 1954. Irradiation of Parts of Individual Cells. II. Effects of an Ultraviolet Microbeam Focused on Parts of Chromosomes. *Science*, 120:197–199.

Uretz, R. B., and R. P. Perry. 1957. Improved Ultraviolet Microbeam Apparatus. *Review of Scientific Instruments*, 28:861–866.

Uretz, R. B., and R. E. Zirkle. 1955. Disappearance of Spindles in Sand-Dollar Blastomeres after Ultraviolet Irradiation of Cytoplasm. (Abstract) *Biological Bulletin*, 109:370.

Wada, B., and K. Izutsu. 1961. Effects of Ultraviolet Microbeam Irradiations on Mitosis Studied in *Tradescantia* Cells *in vivo*. *Cytologia*, 26:480–491.

Yashima, Y. 1962. Effects of Ultraviolet Microbeam Irradiation of Selective Cellular Parts on Mitotic Process of HeLa Cell in Culture. *Mie Medical Journal*, 12:215–233.

Zirkle, R. E. 1957. Partial-Cell Irradiation. *Advances in Biological and Medical Physics*, 5:103–146.

———. 1959. "Structure of the Mitotic Spindle," *A Symposium on Molecular Biology*, R. E. Zirkle, Ed. Chicago, Illinois: University of Chicago Press. Pp. 321–331.

Zirkle, R. E., and W. Bloom. 1953. Irradiation of Parts of Individual Cells, *Science*, 117:487–493.

———. Unpublished data.

Zirkle, R. E., W. Bloom, and R. B. Uretz. 1956. Use of Partial-Cell Irradiation in Studies of Cell Division. *Proceedings of the International Conference on the Peaceful Uses of Atomic Energy*. New York, New York: United Nations. Vol. II. Pp. 273–282.

Zirkle, R. E., and R. B. Uretz. 1963. Action Spectrum for Paling (Decrease in Refractive Index) of Ultraviolet-Irradiated Chromosome Segments. *Proceedings of the National Academy of Sciences of the U.S.A.*, 49:45–52.

Zirkle, R. E., R. B. Uretz, and R. H. Haynes. 1960. Disappearance of Spindles and Phragmoplasts after Microbeam Irradiation of Cytoplasm. *Annals of the New York Academy of Sciences*, 90:435–439.

Relationship between Chromosome Volume and Radiation Sensitivity in Plant Cells

ARNOLD H. SPARROW

Biology Department, Brookhaven National Laboratory,
Upton, Long Island, New York

Comparative radiobiology has long been plagued by the problem of the selection of appropriate end points in a given set of experiments and by the problem of accurate determination of absorbed doses, especially when different kinds of radiation were used or where measurements were made in different laboratories. These problems have been recognized for many years, and much progress has been made in solving them. However, an equally serious dosimetry problem exists because of the variation in nuclear or chromosome size and in chromosome number between different species, or within an organism because of variation with time, stage of development, and type of tissue. Until recently, the dosimetry problem resulting from these variations did not receive much attention, although the main principles of the target theory were worked out more than 25 years ago (Lea, 1947), and it had long been known that the nucleus is a prime target and the major focus of radiation-induced injury. However, the concept of the target theory was not applied at the level of chromosomes or nuclei in higher plants or animals until recently. In fact, many supposedly well-informed biologists (and presumably some radiobiologists, too) are apparently unaware of the great variation in nuclear and/or chromosome size. In this report, some of our recent data on comparative radiosensitivity of plant species will be presented, as well as some new interpretations which it is hoped will throw some light on the understanding of the problem of differential radiosensitivity.

Variations in Nuclear Volume

Variations in both nuclear volume and chromosome volume seem to be potentially or actually of considerable significance in comparative radio-

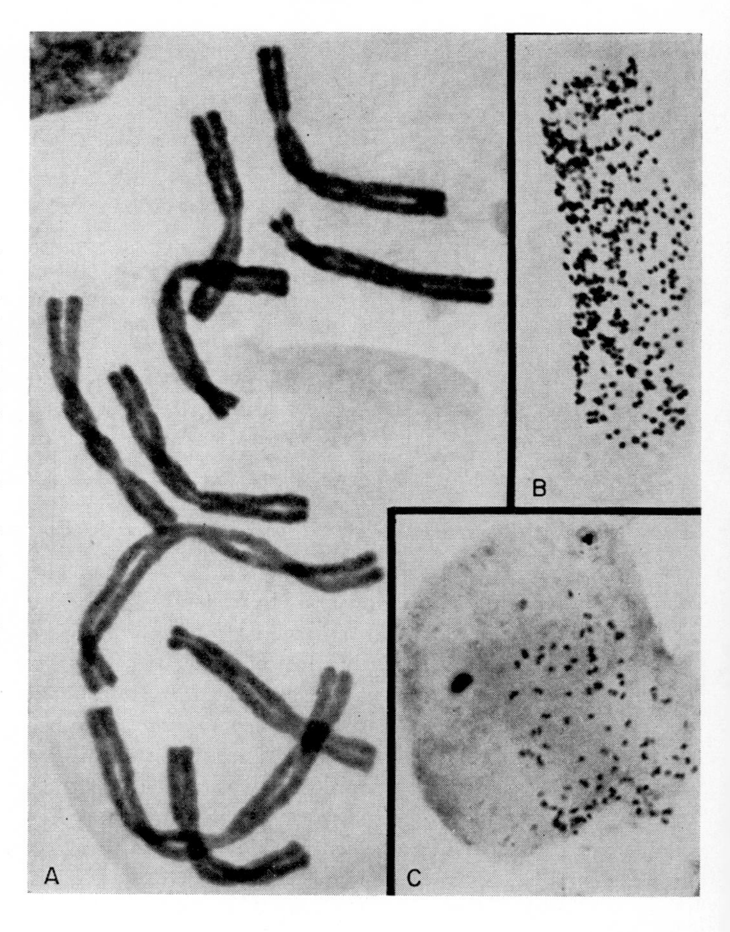

FIGURE 1. Photomicrographs of root-tip metaphase chromosomes in three species of higher plants. A. *Trillium erectum*, B. *Graptopetalum macdougalli*, C. *Sedum rupifragum*. All cells are at the same magnification (× 1330). Note the differences in size and number of chromosomes characteristic of each species (see text and Table 1).

biology, and there is much overlapping of the factors which influence variation in nuclear and chromosomal volumes (Sparrow, 1962). However, it seems best first to consider them separately.

Variations in nuclear volume may be associated with any of the following factors: (1) chromosome number (aneuploidy or polyploidy and meiotic reduction); (2) chromosome size characteristic of the species (Figure 1); (3) stage of cell division; (4) kind of tissue; (5) differentiation, e.g. endopolyploidy and the formation of diplo-chromosomes; (6) degree of physiological activity; (7) degree of hydration; and (8) variations caused by toxic chemicals or physical agents including ionizing radiation. Correlations of sensitivity with some of these variations will be considered.

The range of nuclear volumes in seven different species of higher plants is from 19 to 4265 μ^3 (Table 1). This is a factor of about 225 for the species listed, due partly to polyploidy and partly to larger chromosome volume.

TABLE 1

Somatic Chromosome Numbers and Nuclear and Interphase Chromosome Volumes from Actively Dividing Shoot Meristems of Seven Species of Higher Plants

Species	Chrom. no.	Nuclear volume ($\mu 3$)	Interphase chrom. vol. ($\mu 3$)
Trillium grandiflorum	10	1,452 ± 81.4	145.19 ± 8.14
*Trillium hagae**	30	4,265 ± 245.6	142.17 ± 8.18
Haplopappus gracilis	4	119 ± 9.3	29.81 ± 2.34
Chrysanthemum lacustre	198	1,764 ± 83.6	8.91 ± 0.42
Arabidopsis thaliana	10	19 ± 1.3	1.93 ± 0.13
Graptopetalum macdougalli	384	307 ± 13.6	0.80 ± 0.04
Sedum rupifragum	136	71 ± 3.4	0.52 ± 0.02
Ratio largest/smallest	96	224.5	279

* *Trillium hagae*: the dormant nuclear volume of 2,843 ±163.7 was multiplied by 1.5 to obtain the estimated active volume. The 1.5 factor is the average increase in active shoot meristems compared with dormant shoot meristems as observed in several species (Sparrow, Unpublished data).

Variations in Chromosome Size or Volume

The length of individual metaphase chromosomes in both plants and animals varies from less than 0.5 μ to about 30 μ. A few examples of chromosomes from plant species are illustrated in Figure 1, and the related data for these and several other species are given in Table 1. On the whole, a given species tends to have chromosomes which do not differ from each other by more than a factor of 4 or 5 in metaphase length within a cell, but exceptions to this generalization can be found in certain taxonomic groups, such as birds, and in certain plant genera, e.g. *Gasteria* and *Aloë*. Likewise, certain taxonomic groupings up to, and including, families sometimes tend to follow a pattern of chromosome size, *i.e.* most species within a genus have chromosomes of about the same size. Unfortunately, there are many cases in which species within a genus, and occasionally, different forms within a species, may deviate significantly with respect to chromosome size. For example *Vicia faba* is the only species of *Vicia* with such large chromosomes, and *Oxalis dispar* has exceptionally large chromosomes for *Oxalis* species.

Along with the variation among species in metaphase chromosome length, there is also variation in chromosome or chromatid diameter. Darlington (1937, p. 83) lists the variation in plant chromosome breadth (two chromatids) to be from 0.2 μ for a Myxosporidian to 2 μ for *Hyacinthus*, a factor of 10. Very long chromosomes generally have a much greater diameter at metaphase than do very short ones. This is usually not true for minor variation in length within a karyotype, but it is clearly recognized in extreme cases, e.g. many bird and snake karyotypes and in some plants. Highly localized variation in chromosome or chromatid diameter also occurs at centromeres, secondary constrictions, and in heterochromatic regions commonly found in both plants and animals. Some of these regions are known to influence the probability of breakage by ionizing radiation (Evans, 1962a). The combined effect of variation in length and diameter of chromosomes contributes to the slightly less than 300-fold variation in average interphase chromosome volume in the species so far studied (Table 1). Chromosome size was suggested as a determining factor in radiosensitivity by Sparrow and Christensen (1953) and by Nybom (1956).

The basis of the variation in chromosome size among species of a given taxonomic group is a great mystery. It cannot logically be assumed to represent differences in numbers of unduplicated gene loci. It can be argued that small chromosome size, in some unknown fashion, offers the species having this character some competitive or evolutionary advantage since the great majority of our most successful plants tend to have medium or small chromosomes. Conversely, plants and animals with very large chromosomes (with the exception of some gymnosperms) tend to be economically unimportant and somewhat obscure species. Whatever the basis, however, it is clear that, associated with the variation in total chromosome volume characteristic of a species, there is a corresponding variation in deoxyribonucleic acid (DNA) content (Sparrow and Evans, 1961; Sparrow and Miksche, 1961). This relationship holds for both plants and animals. An increase in DNA per nucleus can be the result of variation either in the basic number (aneuploidy) or in the number of chromosome sets (polyploidy). However, multiplication of chromosome number in the form of polyploidy does not necessarily give a corresponding increase in volume nor in the amount of DNA per nucleus (Sparrow and Miksche, Unpublished data).

With regard to the variation in chromosome size which occurs within a species or within an individual, it may be said that many of the factors which are listed above for variation in nuclear volume will also apply to chromosome volume. However, in this case the reference is not merely to the volume of a metaphase chromosome, but to the space occupied by the chromosome during any stage of cell division or differentiation. Unfortunately, no clear picture of the over-all structure of a chromosome in an interphase nucleus exists; but it does appear from several lines of evidence that, except for the nucleolus, the chromosomes occupy a large fraction of the interphase nucleus. For instance, electron micrographs of nuclei usually show a fairly uniform distribution of chromatin throughout the nuclei, and conventional histological or cytological techniques also generally indicate that the chromatin material, other than that in chromocenters or heterochromatic regions, is fairly uniformly distributed. One can, therefore, visualize the interphase chromosome as a loosely-coiled and apparently irregularly-shaped structure generally considerably longer than it is wide and probably lacking the sharp boundaries characteristic of nuclear membranes. Figure 2 is Pollister's (1952) interpretation of an interphase nucleus. The fact that early prophase chromosomes often exhibit a loose spiral structure with a general arrangement similar to that which existed at the end of telophase suggests that chromosomes maintain roughly the same orientation

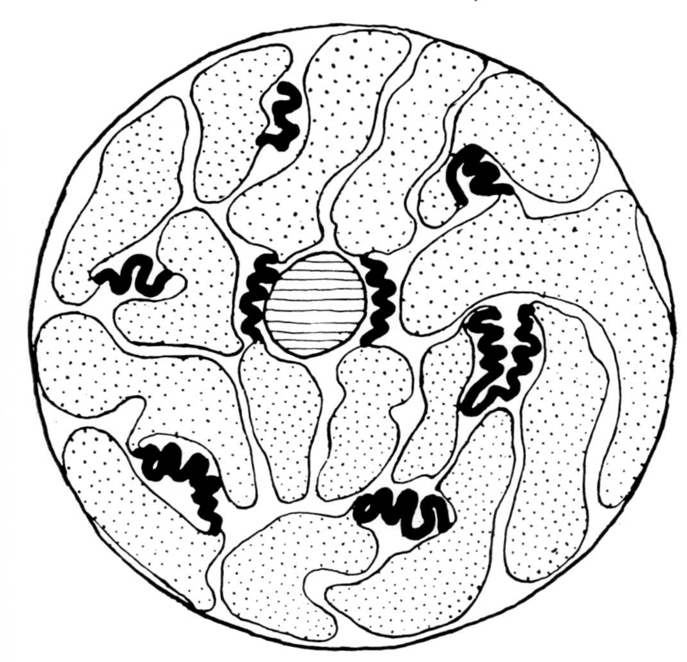

FIGURE 2. Conceptual diagram of the structure of an interphase nucleus showing the chromosomes as swollen structures (except for heterochromatic areas) and relatively small amount of interchromosomal space. (From Pollister, 1952.)

and over-all shape at the end of interphase as at the beginning (see also Manton, 1935). While it seems at this time extremely difficult to reconstruct an interphase chromosome in three dimensions with any degree of accuracy, it would appear that a rough approximation of the average volume available for each chromosome in a nucleus could be obtained by dividing the total nuclear volume by the chromosome number. This procedure admittedly does not correct for the space occupied by the nucleolus, but the relative error introduced by this method is presumably approximately the same for each species. From a practical point of view, the extra effort involved in accurately measuring the nucleoli seemed prohibitive because of the large number of species involved.

Variation in Chromosome Number

Variation in number of chromosomes characteristic of a species is very great in both plants and animals. In plants, haploid chromosome numbers vary from 2 in *Haplopappus gracilis* to about 250 in some flowering plants, and to at least 500 for some species of ferns of the genus *Ophioglossum*. A somewhat similar variation in chromosome number occurs in the lower phyla of the animal kingdom. While it is fairly easy to establish that all of the really high chromosome numbers result from polyploidy, it is often difficult to know in the case of a species with an intermediate chromosome number whether or not polyploidy has occurred at some time in its evolution. In some genera, there is one clear basic chromosome number and all species therein exhibit multiples of this number. However, there are many examples in which several intermediate numbers exist (Darlington and Wylie, 1955).

Variation in chromosome number within a species or within individual organisms is most common as a result of polyploidy (e.g., Partanen, 1959), but it is well known that in many species occasional individuals occur with one or a few extra or missing chromosomes (Smith, Stevenson, and Kehr, 1958; Swanson, 1957). The latter is especially true of polyploids, and actually seems to be quite common in high polyploids (Dawson, 1962). A comparable situation seems to exist in plant cell cultures derived from both normal and abnormal tissue (de Torok and Roderick, 1962; Torrey, 1959). Clinical and cytological evidence is rapidly accumulating regarding variation in chromosome number in man (e.g. McKusick, 1962). It is thus clear that chromosome number is subject to much variation both within and between species. Wherever significant variation does exist, it can be expected that it may influence radiosensitivity (Tsunewaki and Heyne, 1959).

Materials and Methods

Since data on about 50 different species are included in this report, they will not be listed here, but referred to as necessary in the text. Irradiations were made using either Co^{60} gamma radiation or 160 or 250 kvp, 30 ma X rays with 1 mm Al of filtration. The plants were irradiated during active growth. Usually six to eight different exposures were given to groups of 5 to 25 plants. The time between irradiation and scoring varied with growth rate and habit but was generally between three and ten months. The lowest dose at which all plants died was recorded as the lethal dose. Further details of the irradiation procedures have been described elsewhere (Sparrow, 1960; Sparrow and Evans, 1961; Sparrow, Schairer, and Sparrow, 1963).

The degree of growth inhibition was determined by measurements of such characteristics as height, spread, and number of buds or leaves, as well as fresh or dry weight. In the early experiments quantitative measurements were not made, but the group of plants which showed about 15 per cent of the growth of control plants was considered to have been exposed to the critical exposure level, *i.e.* it was considered to have received the exposure required to produce severe growth inhibition. Actually, this value varied between about 5 and 25 per cent of control growth in the earliest experiments as a consequence of the method of determining growth inhibition and because of the fact that exposures were administered in discrete steps. "Slight" growth inhibition was recorded for the first group of plants which showed a recognizable reduction in growth (to about 80 to 90 per cent of controls). Time limitations did not permit dry weight assays on the large number of species studied, although the desirability of such a procedure is recognized and dry weights are currently being obtained in most experiments. In spite of the early lack of sophistication in establishing the end points of severe and slight growth inhibition, the data obtained have been extremely useful, no doubt partly because there were very great differences in sensitivity between the different species studied.

Vegetative shoot meristems of the species used were fixed in Craf III, and after being embedded and sectioned at 8 or 10 μ were stained with safranin and fast green or with methyl violet and orange G. Interphase nuclear volumes of individual cells were calculated from the mean diameter obtained by measuring two diameters at right angles to each other in each of ten nuclei of the tunica or tunica and outer corpus cells of the shoot meristems. Normally two different meristems were measured, and the mean value of volumes was thus obtained. A few measurements were made from sectioned root tips, and such data are clearly identified to distinguish them from shoot-tip data. The chromosome numbers were obtained from Darlington and Wylie (1955) or were determined from root tips or young leaves when the chromosome number was not known.

The volumes were calculated from measurements made on nuclei after they had been through the histological procedure outlined above. For purposes of comparison between species, this procedure is reasonably valid, but it is doubtful that the volumes calculated from the processed slides would be the same as those of living nuclei since the procedures used are known to shrink nuclei to a considerable extent. This fact leads to some difficulties when energy absorption calculations (see pages 207 to 211) are based on the values from histologically processed slides. A correction factor should eventually be determined for calculating absolute values of energy absorption in irradiated living nuclei for specified radiobiological end points.

Observations and Discussion

Tolerance in Relation to Nuclear and Interphase Chromosome Volumes and Calculations of Energy Absorption

Regression lines have been published for nuclear volume versus severe growth inhibition for 23 species with chronic exposures (−0.73) (Sparrow, Cuany, Miksche, and Schairer, 1961), and for lethality versus interphase chromosome volume for 16 species with acute exposures (−0.93) (Sparrow, Schairer, and Sparrow, 1963). These were considered to be close enough to a slope of −1 to be used in predicting the exposures necessary to produce a given effect when nuclear volume and chromosome number were known. The slopes of the sensitivity to acute and chronic radiation based on three end points versus interphase chromosome volume for many species of herbaceous plants have now been calculated. Since none of these deviate significantly from a slope of −1, the regression lines have been plotted with that slope. Tables 2, 3, and 4 give the nuclear and chromosomal volumes and the exposures necessary for lethality, severe growth inhibition, and slight growth inhibition. The tolerance data are plotted against chromosome volume data in Figures 3, 4, and 5. As can be seen, a very high correlation exists, with a small chromosome volume indicating high resistance and a large volume indicating high sensitivity.

TABLE 2

Summary of Nuclear, Chromosomal and Mortality Data for 15 Species of Plants, and Calculated Amount of Energy Absorbed Per Nucleus and Per Interphase Chromosome at the Lethal Exposure. SE, standard error.

Plant number, species and somatic chromosome number (2n)	Nuclear* volume ($\mu^3 \pm$ SE)	Chromosome** volume ($\mu^3 \pm$ SE)	Acute lethal exposure (kr)	Energy† absorbed per nucleus (kev)	Energy† absorbed per chromosome‡ (kev)
33 *Trillium grandiflorum* (10)	1451.9 ± 81.42	145.19 ± 8.142	0.60	50,089	5009
22 *Podophyllum peltatum* (12)	1117.9 ± 56.96	93.16 ± 4.746	0.75	48,211	4018
13 *Hyacinthus orientalis* HV. Innocence§ (27)	1758.3 ± 98.19	65.12 ± 3.637	1.00	101,100	3744
15 *Lilium longiflorum* (24)	1252.3 ± 42.18	52.18 ± 1.758	0.80	57,607	2400
7 *Chlorophytum elatum*§ (28)	422.2 ± 27.58	15.08 ± 0.985	2.00	48,551	1734
36 *Zea mays* HV. Golden Bantam (20)	279.1 ± 11.81	13.95 ± 0.591	4.00	64,181	3209
4 *Aphanostephus skirrobasis* (6)	67.1 ± 5.40	11.19 ± 0.900	8.00	30,882	5147
8 *Crepis capillaris* (6)	63.6 ± 4.95	10.59 ± 0.824	3.75	13,705	2284
29 *Sedum ternatum* (U643) § (32)	148.5 ± 6.22	4.64 ± 0.194	25.00	213,472	6670
9 *Gladiolus* HV. Friendship§ (60)	273.6 ± 9.37	4.56 ± 0.156	25.00	393,305	6555
17 *Mentha spicata*§ (34)	107.0 ± 6.02	3.15 ± 0.177	30.00	184,560	5427
27 *Sedum oryzifolium* (20)	43.3 ± 2.63	2.16 ± 0.132	20.00	49,734	2486
30 *Sedum tricarpum*§ (128)	88.6 ± 4.92	0.69 ± 0.038	75.00	382,177	2985
26 *Sedum alfredi* var. *nagasakianum*§ (128)	78.1 ± 1.87	0.61 ± 0.015	50.00	224,645	1755
28 *Sedum rupifragum*§ (136)	70.8 ± 3.36	0.52 ± 0.025	75.00	305,437	2242
		Mean	144,510 ± 33,761		3711 ± 434

* Average of 20 nuclei from actively dividing shoot meristems.
** Nuclear volume/2n.
† Based on an average value of 32.5 ev per ion pair and 1.77 ionizations per μ^3 of wet tissue per roentgen (*cf.* Table 2, Lea, 1947) times exposure.
‡ Assuming all chromosomes within a karyotype to be the same size.
§ Polyploids.

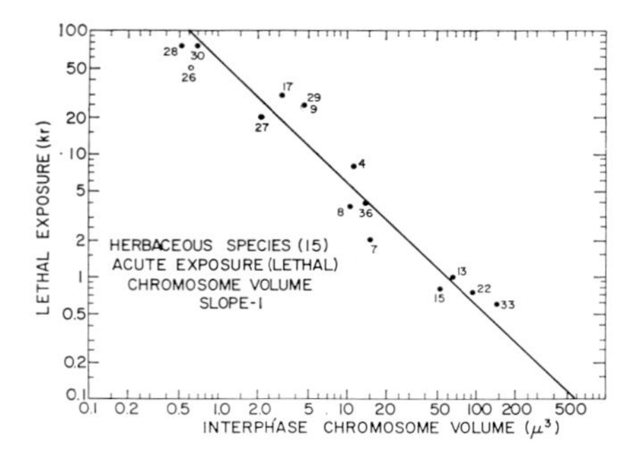

FIGURE 3. Regression of lethal exposure in kr against interphase chromosome volume in μ^3 for 15 herbaceous species following acute irradiation plotted with a slope of — 1. (Data from Table 2.)

With a slope of −1, it can be concluded that the product of the two variables would be a constant if all the points actually fell on the line. It is not sensible or appropriate to multiply the two variables as used in Figures

TABLE 3

Summary of Nuclear, Chromosomal, and Severe Growth Inhibition Data for 14 Species of Plants, and Calculated Amount of Energy Absorbed Per Nucleus and Per Interphase Chromosome at the Exposure which Causes Severe Growth Inhibition

Plant number, species and somatic chromosome number (2n)	Nuclear* volume ($\mu^3 \pm$ SE)	Chromosome** volume ($\mu^3 \pm$ SE)	Severe growth inhibition (kr)	Energy† absorbed per nucleus (kev)	Energy† absorbed per chromosome‡ (kev)
22 *Podophyllum peltatum* (12)	1117.9 ± 56.96	93.16 ± 4.746	0.6	38,569	3214
13 *Hyacinthus orientalis* HV. Innocence§ (27)	1758.3 ± 98.19	65.12 ± 3.637	0.5	50,550	1872
15 *Lilium longiflorum* (24)	1252.3 ± 42.18	52.18 ± 1.758	0.4	28,804	1200
7 *Chlorophytum elatum*§ (28)	422.2 ± 27.58	15.08 ± 0.985	1.0	24,275	867
36 *Zea mays* HV. Golden Bantam (20)	279.1 ± 11.81	13.95 ± 0.591	1.5	24,068	1203
4 *Aphanostephus skirrobasis* (6)	67.1 ± 5.40	11.19 ± 0.900	6.0	23,162	3860
8 *Crepis capillaris* (6)	63.6 ± 4.95	10.59 ± 0.824	2.5	9,137	1523
29 *Sedum ternatum* (U643)§ (32)	148.5 ± 6.22	4.64 ± 0.194	20.0	170,778	5336
9 *Gladiolus* HV. Friendship§ (60)	273.6 ± 9.37	4.56 ± 0.156	15.0	235,983	3933
17 *Mentha spicata*§ (34)	107.0 ± 6.02	3.15 ± 0.177	20.0	123,040	3618
27 *Sedum oryzifolium* (20)	43.3 ± 2.63	2.16 ± 0.132	15.0	37,300	1864
30 *Sedum tricarpum*§ (128)	88.6 ± 4.92	0.69 ± 0.038	40.0	203,828	1592
26 *Sedum alfredi* var. *nagasakianum*§ (128)	78.1 ± 1.87	0.61 ± 0.015	30.0	134,787	1053
28 *Sedum rupifragum*§ (136)	70.8 ± 3.36	0.52 ± 0.025	50.0	203,625	1495
		Mean		93,422 ± 21,868	2331 ± 371

* Average of 20 nuclei from actively dividing shoot meristems.
** Nuclear volume/2n.
† Based on an average value of 32.5 ev per ion pair and 1.77 ionizations per μ^3 of wet tissue per roentgen (*cf.* Table 2, Lea, 1947) times exposure.
‡ Assuming all chromosomes within a karyotype to be the same size.
§ Polyploids.

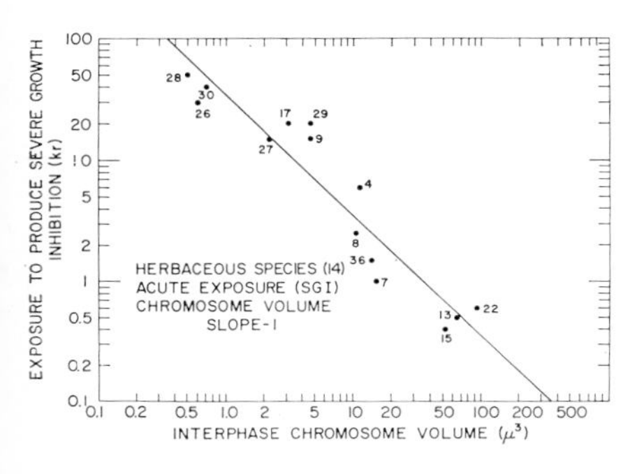

FIGURE 4. Regression of the exposure in kr required to produce severe growth inhibition (SGI) against interphase chromosome volume in μ^3 for 14 herbaceous species following acute irradiation plotted with slope of − 1. (Data from Table 3.)

3, 4, and 5; but if exposure is expressed as energy absorbed per unit volume in tissue, the product of the two variables is the total energy absorbed per

TABLE 4

Summary of Nuclear, Chromosomal, and Slight Growth Inhibition Data for 15 Species of Plants, and Calculated Amount of Energy Absorbed per Nucleus and per Interphase Chromosome at the Exposure which Causes Slight Growth Inhibition

Plant number, species and somatic chromosome number (2n)	Nuclear* volume ($\mu^3 \pm$ se)	Chromosome** volume ($\mu^3 \pm$ se)	Slight effect (kr)	Energy† absorbed per nucleus (kev)	Energy† absorbed per chromosome‡ (kev)
33 *Trillium grandiflorum* (10)	1451.9 ± 81.42	145.19 ± 8.142	0.20	16,696	1670
22 *Podophyllum peltatum* (12)	1117.9 ± 56.96	93.16 ± 4.746	0.25	16,070	1339
13 *Hyacinthus orientalis* HV. Innocence§ (27)	1758.3 ± 98.19	65.12 ± 3.637	0.20	20,220	749
15 *Lilium longiflorum* (24)	1252.3 ± 42.18	52.18 ± 1.758	0.15	10,801	450
7 *Chlorophytum elatum*§ (28)	422.2 ± 27.58	15.08 ± 0.985	0.50	12,138	433
36 *Zea mays* HV. Golden Bantam (20)	279.1 ± 11.81	13.95 ± 0.591	0.75	12,034	602
4 *Aphanostephus skirrobasis* (6)	67.1 ± 5.40	11.19 ± 0.900	2.00	7,721	1287
8 *Crepis capillaris* (6)	63.6 ± 4.95	10.59 ± 0.824	1.00	3,655	609
29 *Sedum ternatum* (U643)§ (32)	148.5 ± 6.22	4.64 ± 0.194	12.00	102,467	3202
9 *Gladiolus* HV. Friendship§ (60)	273.6 ± 9.37	4.56 ± 0.156	5.00	78,661	1311
17 *Mentha spicata*§ (34)	107.0 ± 6.02	3.15 ± 0.177	12.00	73,824	2171
27 *Sedum oryzifolium* (20)	43.3 ± 2.63	2.16 ± 0.132	7.50	18,650	932
30 *Sedum tricarpum*§ (128)	88.6 ± 4.92	0.69 ± 0.038	15.00	76,435	597
26 *Sedum alfredi* var. *nagasakianum*§ (128)	78.1 ± 1.87	0.61 ± 0.015	7.50	33,697	263
28 *Sedum rupifragum*§ (136)	70.8 ± 3.36	0.52 ± 0.025	15.00	61,087	448
		Mean		36,277 ± 8418	1071 ± 206

* Average of 20 nuclei from actively dividing shoot meristems.
** Nuclear volume/2n.
† Based on an average value of 32.5 ev per ion pair and 1.77 ionizations per μ^3 of wet tissue per roentgen (*cf.* Table 2, Lea, 1947) times exposure.
‡ Assuming all chromosomes within a karyotype to be the same size.
§ Polyploids.

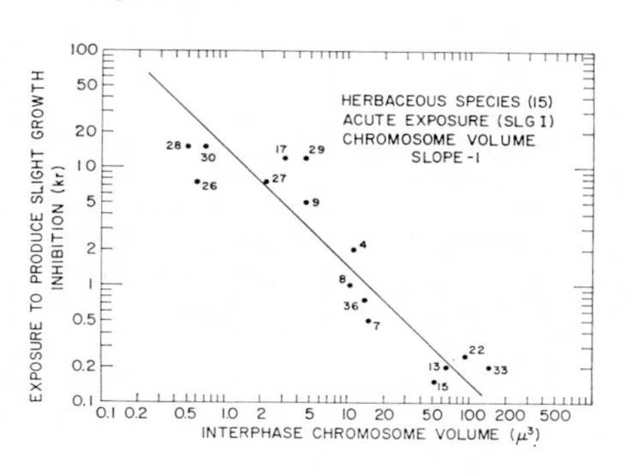

FIGURE 5. Regression of the exposure in kr required to produce slight growth inhibition (SLGI) against interphase chromosome volume in μ^3 for 15 herbaceous species following acute irradiation plotted with slope of − 1. (Data from Table 4.)

chromosome at specified exposures and volumes. The absorbed energy has been expressed in kilo electron volts (or kev), and the average energy absorbed per chromosome for each species for the three end points has been calculated and is presented in Tables 2, 3, and 4 (right hand columns). The average energy absorbed per chromosome for all the species used was 3,711 ± 434 kev for the lethal effect, 2,331 ± 371 kev for severe growth inhibition, and 1,071 ± 206 kev for slight growth inhibition.

If it is assumed that the energy absorption per chromosome at a given end point is a constant, the slope of a line drawn through these points would be 0. The energies absorbed per chromosome versus interphase chromosome volume for each species are plotted for the three end points in Figures 6, 7, and 8. The deviation from 0 of the true slopes of these lines is not significant. It is quite clear that a different relationship exists when the data are considered from the point of view of absorbed energy per chromosome rather than as the exposure in roentgens required to produce a specified effect.

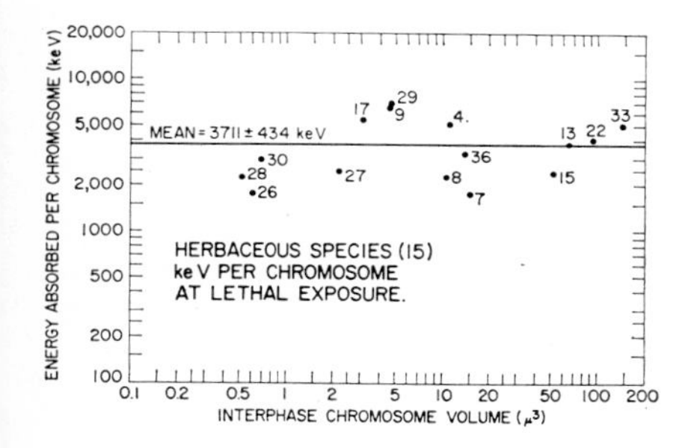

FIGURE 6. The appropriate data from Table 2 and Figure 3 plotted as energy absorbed per chromosome at the lethal exposure for 15 herbaceous species. The mean energy per chromosome at the lethal exposure was 3,711 ± 434 kev.

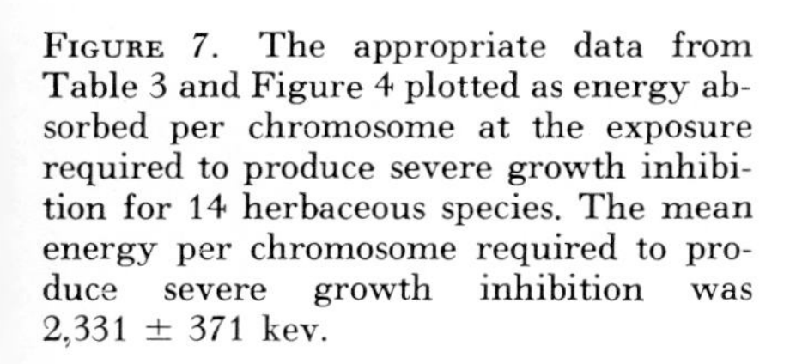

FIGURE 7. The appropriate data from Table 3 and Figure 4 plotted as energy absorbed per chromosome at the exposure required to produce severe growth inhibition for 14 herbaceous species. The mean energy per chromosome required to produce severe growth inhibition was 2,331 ± 371 kev.

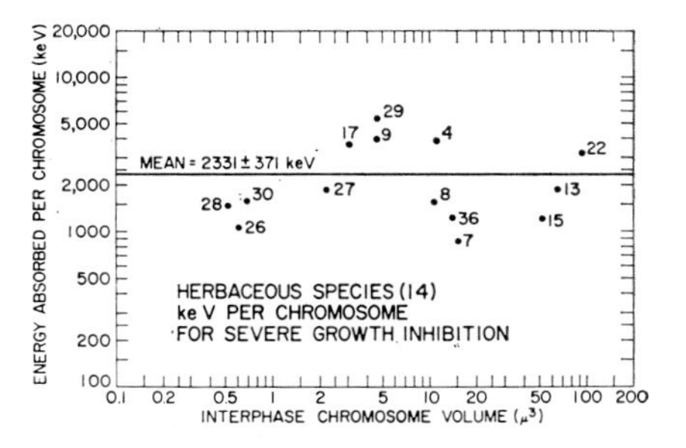

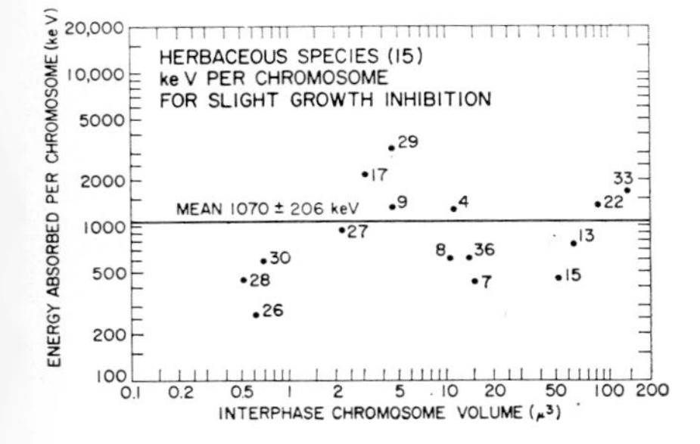

FIGURE 8. The appropriate data from Table 4 and Figure 5 plotted as energy absorbed per chromosome at the exposure required to produce slight growth inhibition for 15 herbaceous species. The mean energy per chromosome required to produce slight growth inhibition was 1,071 ± 206 kev.

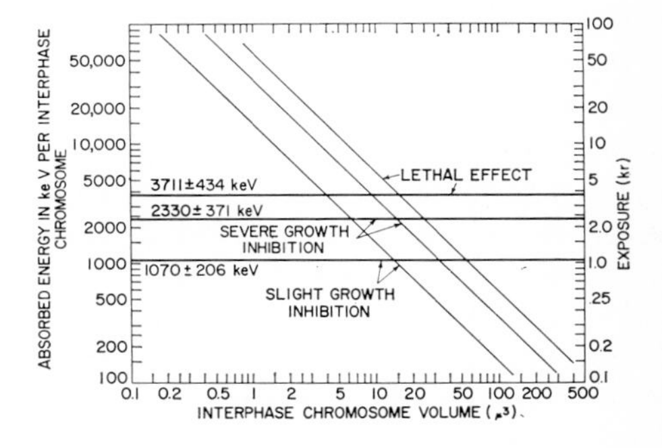

FIGURE 9. Summary of data from Figures 3 through 8 showing the relative positions of the regressions for the three end points and of the energy per interphase chromosome for each of the three effects.

Figure 9 summarizes the sensitivity and energy absorbed versus interphase chromosome volume from the data of Tables 2, 3, and 4.

For purposes of comparison, the total energy absorbed per nucleus for each species at each of these end points is also presented in Tables 2, 3, and 4. As can be seen, there is much more variation in the energy absorbed per nucleus than in the energy absorbed per chromosome. In a comparison of sensitivity versus nuclear volume or chromosome volume, the data were fitted by the method of least squares to the linear regression model:

$$\log Y = \alpha + \beta \log X + \varepsilon$$

where Y is the end-point effect measured in rads and X is the nuclear volume or interphase chromosome volume. A comparison of the two volumes is given in Table 5 in which the slopes and r^2 (the proportion of the Y sum of squares attributable to X) are tabulated for the three end points. It is readily observed that interphase chromosome volume is a better index of radiosensitivity for all three sets of data than nuclear volume.

TABLE 5

Comparisons of Nuclear and Chromosome Volumes as an Index of Radiosensitivity

	Slope of line: exposure vs. volume		Proportion of Y sum of squares due to X	
End point	Nuclear vol.	Interphase chrom. vol.	Nuclear vol.	Interphase chrom. vol.
Lethality	— 1.117	— 0.934	0.68	0.94
Severe growth inhibition	— 1.147	— 0.970	0.65	0.89
Slight growth inhibition	— 1.135	— 0.896	0.69	0.86

The significance of the above relationships has been discussed in previous publications (Evans and Sparrow, 1961; Sparrow, Cuany, Miksche, and Schairer, 1961; Sparrow and Miksche, 1961; Sparrow and Evans, 1961; Sparrow, 1962; Sparrow, Schairer, and Sparrow, 1963; see also Deering, 1959) and will not be discussed in detail here. Only a few points will be mentioned.

It was previously suggested that the effect of chromosome number might be related to the percentage of genes lost per deletion (Sparrow, Cuany, Miksche, and Schairer, 1961; Evans and Sparrow, 1961). As will be shown below (pages 212 to 213), this now seems much less likely than originally thought. It now appears probable that the chromosome-number effect is related to the fact that in plants chromosome size tends to decrease as chromosome number increases, especially within a genus. There are, however, many exceptions. Further, since energy absorption per chromosome seems to be a better index of tolerance than energy absorption per nucleus, and since energy absorption per chromosome is controlled only indirectly by chromosome number (through an effect on volume), there apparently is essentially no interaction between chromosomes with respect to tolerance to or recovery from radiation injury (there is, of course, an interaction in terms of chromosome aberrations of certain types).

It has been shown previously, for a series of species, that DNA content increases as the average nuclear volume per species increases (Sparrow and Miksche, 1961; Van't Hof and Sparrow, 1963). It has also been shown that the amount of DNA per cell is correlated with sensitivity in plant species and in *Escherichia coli* (Bowen, 1962; Deering, 1959). If chromosome number remains constant, DNA per chromosome will increase with an increase in nuclear volume; in other words, an increase in volume of either chromosomes or nuclei (measured at comparable stages in different species) is indicative of increasing DNA content. Thus sensitivity of species will generally increase as average DNA per chromosome increases (Sparrow, 1962). As is shown above, a relatively small degree of variation exists between species in the energy absorbed per chromosome at each of the three end points used (Figures 6, 7, and 8). Since there is wide variation in the DNA content per chromosome of the different species, apparently it is not a constant percentage of the DNA or nucleoprotein injured that is critical, but rather the absolute amount.

The concept that a critical amount of energy must be absorbed in a chromosome as a prerequisite to extensive cellular injury from ionizing radiation is in sharp contrast to the older concept that relatively few sites per cell (probably chromosome breaks) were mainly responsible for cell injury or death. It is too soon, however, to conclude that chromosome breakage can be ruled out as a major mechanism of injury. Much further work will be needed to resolve the conflict, but the above concept should help to decide the relative roles of breakage versus more diffuse and more subtle forms of radiation injury to the genetic system.

That a known amount of energy absorbed per chromosome will, within narrow limits, produce a predictable effect in any one of the species studied is of considerable interest. It suggests, for instance, that each of the genetic systems as represented by the hypothetical interphase chromosome volume has about the same tolerance to radiation injury. Most of the apparent differences in tolerance between species would seem to be spurious and result from inadequate consideration of the dosimetric complexities which result when major changes in target volumes occur. The usual radiation units of roentgens or rads are not readily adaptable to such a situation. Wherever target volumes change significantly, tolerance also will change if it is expressed as a function of rads or roentgens, as found by Deering (1959) in filamentous forms of *E. coli*, but it should change relatively little, if at all, when expressed as electron volts absorbed per chromosome (or per nucleus in some cases), as shown above in plants.

Polyploidy and Radiosensitivity

In the light of the above information, which relates radiosensitivity to interphase chromosome volume, it is apparent that the influence of polyploidy on radiosensitivity must be reinvestigated and re-evaluated. In the past when a comparison was made between the radiation tolerance of diploid and polyploid strains or species, and the polyploid appeared more resistant, e.g. Tables 2, 3, and 4, it has been assumed that the greater resistance was due to the redundancy of genetic information in the polyploid (Nilan, 1956; Révész and Norman, 1960; Sparrow, Cuany, Miksche, and Schairer, 1961). An alternative possibility which must now be considered is that a decrease in the average interphase chromosome volume of polyploid nuclei may be, and often is, concomitant with increased polyploidy.

Keeping the above possibility in mind, we have made a comparison of both nuclear volumes and interphase chromosome volumes of a number of closely related diploid and polyploid pairs of species. The nuclear volume in a tetraploid may be greater than twice that of the diploid, less than twice that of the diploid or even below that of the diploid; also, the interphase chromosome volume of polyploid nuclei may be greater, about the same as, or less than that of a closely related diploid (Table 6). Wherever a decrease in interphase chromosome volume exists in the polyploid, it can be anticipated that a higher dose in roentgens or rads will be required to deliver the same amount of energy in electron volts into the average polyploid chromosome. The apparent increase in resistance expressed in roentgens or rads would actually result from the smaller chromosome volume and not from the protective effect of genetic redundancy.

Since it is clear that in many cases (e.g. Tables 2, 3, and 4) polyploids are more resistant than diploids in terms of roentgen exposures, the important question is to determine whether energy absorption per chromosome, expressed in electron volts, actually is any different for polyploids than it is for diploids. The pertinent evidence from Tables 2, 3, and 4 has been tested by an analysis of variance, from which it can be concluded that the average energy absorbed per chromosome is not significantly greater in polyploids than in diploids, even though the average values for the polyploids are slightly higher. It seems highly probable, therefore, that the previously presumed protective effect of polyploids is, in fact, caused by a change in interphase chromosome volume rather than by the protective effect of redundancy of genetic information. Conversely, if this is true, it will be much more difficult to substantiate the argument that deletion is a major mode of radiation injury unless the loss of a chromosome segment of a given size is equally deleterious to polyploid and diploid cells. Considerable attention should be given to this aspect of cellular radiobiology, as it has some very significant implications regarding the nature of radiation-induced genetic injury.

TABLE 6

Nuclear Volume Ratios and Chromosome Volume Ratios in Diploid-Polyploid Pairs of Species

N.V. RATIO POLYPLOID / DIPLOID	GENUS	SPECIES: POLYPLOID	SPECIES: DIPLOID	VOLUME RATIOS: NUCLEAR	VOLUME RATIOS: CHROMOSOMAL	EXPECTED* SENSITIVITY
>2	*Allium*	*porrum*	*cepa*	2.25	1.13	4x>2x
	Gladiolus	HV. Friendship	*alatus*	3.04	1.53	4x>2x
	Hyacinthus	*orientalis* HV. Delft Blue	*azureus*	6.41	3.84	3.3x>2x
	Ipomoea	*batatas*	*purpurea*	3.30	1.10	6x>2x
	Kalanchoë	*verticillata*	*diagremontiana*	2.50	1.25	4x>2x
	Tradescantia	*virginiana*	*striata*	3.41	1.71	4x>2x
<2,>1	*Allium*	*senescens*	*cepa*	1.53	0.76	4x<2x
	Habranthus	*brachyandrus*	*robustus*	1.42	0.71	4x<2x
	Medicago	*sativa*	*sativa*	1.26	0.63	4x<2x
	Nicotiana	*bigelovi*	*glauca*	1.98	1.00	4x≃2x
	Tradescantia	*occidentalis*†	*occidentalis*	1.40	0.70	4x<2x
	Tradescantia	*paludosa*‡	*paludosa*	1.60	0.80	4x<2x
	Tulipa	*turkestanica*	*coccinea*	1.97	0.99	4x≃2x
<1	*Chrysanthemum*	*indicum*	*nipponicum*	0.78	0.26	6x<2x
	Luzula	*parviflora*	*purpurea*	0.36	0.09	8x<2x
	Oxalis	*stricta*	*dispar*	0.16	0.08	4x<2x
	Tripogandra	*cumanensis*	*rosea*	0.57	0.28	6x<2x
	Tulipa	*turkestanica*	*fosteriana* HV. Red Emperor	0.75	0.38	6x<2x

* Based on amount of energy absorbed per chromosome.
† Naturally occurring polyploid.
‡ Colchicine induced polyploid.

Iversen (1962) has suggested that there might be a correlation between nuclear surface area and sensitivity. The fact that tolerance increases in many polyploids (Sparrow, Cuany, Miksche, and Schairer, 1961; Sparrow and Evans, 1961), while volume and therefore surface area increases, seems to rule out this correlation as being significant.

Changes in Chromosome Volume as a Function of Stage

In view of the obvious significance of chromosome volume in determining sensitivity of a species, it seemed worthwhile to calculate chromosome volumes at different stages of the cell cycle. Preliminary data on such volume changes at different stages of the cell cycle have been obtained for one species. Table 7 gives the nuclear volumes of root-tip cells of *Allium fistulosum* for one complete set of chromatids at metaphase, at early and late telophase, and at early and late interphase (the latter two we assume to be respectively G_1 and late S or G_2). The value for one set of chromatids at metaphase is 35.5 ± 9.0 μ^3, and 145 ± 12.2 μ^3 for early telophase. The nuclear volume increases to a maximum of 1,125 ± 53.5 in the largest nuclei (presumed to be late S or G_2). Thus, the increase in volume between metaphase and G_2 is approximately thirty-twofold, or allowing for the doubled volume of the nuclei during S as reported by Swift (1953), we could consider the 2C volume of G_2 to be half of the measured G_2, or 563 μ^3. These values would indicate that the increase in volume from the 2C value at metaphase to the 2C value at G_2 as approximately sixteenfold. The corresponding maximum increase between early telophase and G_2 is about eight, or, if corresponding 2C values are considered, a volume change from telophase to G_2 of approximately fourfold in this particular case. It is thus clear that major changes in the volume of the genetic material occur between metaphase-telophase stages and late interphase. Prophases were not measured in our material but they appear to be even larger than G_2 (Swift, 1953).

TABLE 7

Comparisons of Nuclear Volumes and Chromatid Volumes of Different Stages of the Mitotic Cycle in Root Tips of* Allium fistulosum (2n = 16)

STAGE	VOLUME (μ^3)	RATIO	RATIO
Metaphase (chromatid)†	35.5 ± 9.0	1	0.24
Telophase, early	145 ± 12.2	4.1	1
Telophase, late	252 ± 8.7	7.1	1.7
Interphase, small (G_1)	396 ± 13.7	11.2	2.7
Interphase, large (S or G_2)	1125 ± 53.5	31.7	7.8
Interphase, large ÷ 2	562.5 ± 26.7	15.8	3.9

* Nuclear volumes were from root tips fixed, sectioned, and stained as indicated under materials and methods. Early telophases were from nuclei before rounding up and before cell wall formation. Late telophases were oval with a nuclear membrane and a clear cell wall. Small interphases are assumed to be G_1 and large interphases late S or G_2 based on Swift's (1953) observations.

† Average of four cells fixed in 3:1 alcohol: acetic and stained by the Feulgen-squash method. Root tips were excised and put into a saturated aqueous solution of α-bromonaphthalene for 2.5 hours before fixation.

No new data are presented here on changes in the frequency of chromosome aberration with stage of division irradiated. Several years ago, however, it was shown that the early interphase following second meiotic division of *Trillium erectum* is a stage of very low sensitivity and that fragment frequency increases by a factor of 24 during approximately the first half of the interphase (Sparrow, 1951). Also aberration frequency in other species is generally greater in G_2 than in G_1 by a factor of three to six (Evans, 1962b). Part of this increase may be attributable to the larger target at G_2, to the presence of two chromatids at G_2, or, as suggested by Evans and Savage (1963), to changes in the spatial distribution of chromosomes within the nucleus. The above data clearly indicate that further investigation along these lines is in order (see pages 376 to 393 and 423 to 441, this volume).

If tolerance is primarily a function of chromosome or nuclear volume at the stages listed above, then the cells most likely to survive irradiation in a tissue containing all stages of cell division would be those cells which have the smallest chromosomes, namely those in early telophase. Conversely, if survival of single cells can lead to regeneration of a tissue, complete killing can be achieved only when the most resistant cells are killed. Since in most tissues these resistant cells are presumably telophase or early interphase nuclei, there might be some operational advantage in tumor therapy in trying to hold up cell division wherever possible in late interphase, prophase or metaphase to avoid having the highly resistant telophase or early interphase cells present. It would be of considerable interest to see whether survival curves are not, in fact, noticeably different under these conditions from those obtained under conditions in which cells in all stages of division are irradiated. It would be of further interest to look for evidence that the cells surviving at the highest exposures are indeed those which had the smallest nuclear volume at the time of exposure.

Summary and Conclusions

1. An inverse relationship between the acute exposure to X or gamma radiation necessary to produce lethality or to inhibit growth and the volume estimated to be associated with interphase chromosomes of shoot meristem cells has been demonstrated using a number of species of higher plants. More specifically, when the log of the exposure required to produce a specified effect is plotted against the log of (nuclear volume) $\div$ (number of chromosomes), a straight line with a slope not significantly different from -1 is obtained.

2. By converting roentgen values to ev per μ^3 it becomes possible to plot absorbed energy per chromosome for an exposure required to produce a specified end point against chromosome volume. Such calculations show that the average energy absorbed in the interphase chromosome of each species approaches a constant for each of three end points in spite of the fact that wide ranges of lethal or growth-inhibiting exposures, apical meristem nuclear volumes and chromosome numbers were involved in the species used.

3. Since DNA content increases with increasing nuclear or chromosomal volume, direct relationships can be presumed to exist between estimated amount of DNA per chromosome and radiosensitivity.

4. Under the conditions of these experiments and using measurements from meristem tissue after histological processing, the average absorbed energy per chromosome was calculated to be about $3.7 \pm 0.43 \times 10^6$ ev for a lethal effect, $2.3 \pm 0.37 \times 10^6$ ev for severe growth inhibition, and $1.07 \pm 0.21 \times 10^6$ ev for slight growth inhibition. Preliminary measurements on

live nuclei indicate that corrections should be made for shrinkage of nuclei during histological processing; these energy values are, therefore, minimum values.

5. If we assume that a given amount of absorbed energy produces the same amount of genetic injury in each of the species studied, we can conclude that the small variation in energy absorbed per chromosome at any of the end points used would indicate that a relatively constant amount of injury per chromosome is a prerequisite to the development of a detectable effect. This would suggest that it is not a constant percentage of the DNA or nucleoprotein injured that is critical with respect to the radiobiological effect, but rather the absolute amount.

6. Most of the apparent differences in radiosensitivity between species studied would seem to be spurious and to result from measuring the dose per unit volume or weight of air or tissue. When energy absorption per chromosome at the growth-inhibiting or lethal exposure is calculated for each species, relatively small interspecific variation is found at each of the three end points. It thus appears that much of the apparent differences in sensitivities between other species or between tissues may likewise be spurious, and would largely disappear when energy absorption per chromosome is measured. This situation is true when polyploids are compared to diploids, suggesting that the greater resistance of some polyploids results more from their reduced interphase chromosome volume than from the protective effect of genetic redundancy. This conclusion would suggest that deletion, at least in organized meristems, is not a major mode of radiation injury.

7. Since any of the three end points measured depends on energy absorption per individual chromosome rather than per nucleus and is largely independent of total chromosome number, there seems to be essentially no interaction between chromosomes.

8. The regression lines presented for each of the three end points can be used to predict the radiosensitivity of other plant species, provided that their nuclear volumes and chromosome numbers are known.

9. The extent of nuclear or chromosomal volume changes in *Allium fistulosum* during the mitotic cycle in root tips is at least fourfold, and may exceed sixteenfold. Such changes should be kept in mind when considering the possible reasons for changes in sensitivity associated with the stage of the nuclear cycle irradiated.

ACKNOWLEDGMENTS

This research was carried out at Brookhaven National Laboratory under the auspices of the United States Atomic Energy Commission.

The author wishes to acknowledge the valuable assistance of Virginia Pond, Anne Rogers, Rhoda C. Sparrow, L. A. Schairer, Eric Klug and Alexandra Jahn. The indispensable assistance with statistical problems given by K. H. Thompson is gratefully acknowledged.

REFERENCES

Bowen, H. J. M. 1962. Radiosensitivity of Higher Plants, and Correlations with Cell Weight and DNA Content. *Radiation Botany*, 1:223–228.

Darlington, C. D. 1937. *Recent Advances in Cytology*. Philadelphia, Pennsylvania: P. Blakiston's Son and Co., Inc., 671 pp.

Darlington, C. D., and A. P. Wylie. 1955. *Chromosome Atlas of Flowering Plants.* London, England: George Allen and Unwin, Ltd., 519 pp.

Dawson, G. W. P. 1962. *An Introduction to the Cytogenetics of Polyploids.* Philadelphia, Pennsylvania: F. A. Davis Company, 96 pp.

Deering, R. A. 1959. Radiation Sensitivity of Filamentous *Escherichia coli. Biochimica et biophysica acta,* 31:11–19.

de Torok, D., and T. H. Roderick. 1962. Associations Between Growth Rate, Mitotic Frequency, and Chromosome Number in a Plant Tissue Culture. *Cancer Research,* 22:174–181.

Evans, H. J. 1962a. Chromosome Aberrations Induced by Ionizing Radiations. *International Review of Cytology*, 13:221–321.

————. 1962b. "Possible Reasons for Variation in Chromosome Radiosensitivity During Mitotic and Meiotic Cycles," *Repair from Genetic Radiation Damage*, F. H. Sobels, Ed. Oxford, England: Pergamon Press. Pp. 31–49.

Evans, H. J., and J. R. K. Savage. 1963. The Relation Between DNA Synthesis and Chromosome Structure as Resolved by X-Ray Damage. *The Journal of Cell Biology,* 18:525–540.

Evans, H. J., and A. H. Sparrow. 1961. Nuclear Factors Affecting Radiosensitivity. II. Dependence on Nuclear and Chromosome Structure and Organization. *Brookhaven Symposia in Biology*, 14:101–127.

Iversen, S. 1962. A Correlation Between Radiation Tolerance and Nuclear Surface Area. *Nature*, London, 195:1216–1217.

Lea, D. E. 1947. *Actions of Radiations on Living Cells.* Cambridge, England: The University Press; New York, New York: The Macmillan Company, 402 pp.

Manton, I. 1935. Some New Evidence on the Physical Nature of Plant Nuclei from Intra-Specific Polyploids. *Proceedings of the Royal Society of London. Series B*, 118: 522–547.

McKusick, V. A. 1962. On the X Chromosome of Man. *Quarterly Review of Biology,* 37:69–175.

Nilan, R. A. 1956. "Factors Governing Plant Radiosensitivity," *A Conference on Radioactive Isotopes in Agriculture.* Washington, D.C.: U. S. Government Printing Office, TID 7512. Pp. 151–162.

Nybom, N. 1956. Some Further Experiments on Chronic Gamma Irradiation of Plants. *Botaniska Notiser*, 109:1–11.

Partanen, C. R. 1959. "Quantitative Chromosomal Changes and Differentiation in Plants," *Developmental Cytology*, D. Rudnick, Ed. New York, New York: Ronald Press Company. Pp. 21–45.

Pollister, A. W. 1952. Nucleoproteins of the Nucleus. *Experimental Cell Research,* Supplement 2:59–74.

Révész, L., and U. Norman. 1960. Relationship Between Chromosome Ploidy and Radiosensitivity in Selected Tumor Sublines of Common Origin. *Journal of the National Cancer Institute*, 25:1041–1060.

Smith, H. H., H. Q. Stevenson, and A. E. Kehr. 1958. Limits and Consequences of Multiple Allopolyploidy in *Nicotiana. The Nucleus*, 1:205–222.

Sparrow, A. H. 1951. Radiation Sensitivity of Cells During Mitotic and Meiotic Cycles with Emphasis on Possible Cytochemical Changes. *Annals of the New York Academy of Sciences*, 51:1508–1540.

———. 1960. "Uses of Large Sources of Ionizing Radiation in Botanical Research and Some Possible Practical Applications," *Large Radiation Sources in Industry*. Vienna, Austria: International Atomic Energy Agency. Vol. II. Pp. 195–219.

———. 1962. *The Role of the Cell Nucleus in Determining Radiosensitivity* (Brookhaven Lecture Series No. 17, Brookhaven National Laboratory Publication No. 766 [T-287]). Upton, New York, 29 pp.

———. Unpublished data.

Sparrow, A. H., and E. Christensen. 1953. Tolerance of Certain Higher Plants to Chronic Exposure to Gamma Radiation from Cobalt-60. *Science*, 118:697–698.

Sparrow, A. H., R. L. Cuany, J. P. Miksche, and L. A. Schairer. 1961. Some Factors Affecting the Responses of Plants to Acute and Chronic Radiation Exposures. *Radiation Botany*, 1:10–34.

Sparrow, A. H., and H. J. Evans. 1961. Nuclear Factors Affecting Radiosensitivity. I. The Influence of Nuclear Size and Structure, Chromosome Complement and DNA Content. *Brookhaven Symposia in Biology*, 14:76–100.

Sparrow, A. H., and J. P. Miksche. 1961. Correlation of Nuclear Volume and DNA Content with Higher Plant Tolerance to Chronic Radiation. *Science*, 134:282–283.

———. Unpublished data.

Sparrow, A. H., L. A. Schairer, and R. C. Sparrow. 1963. Relationship Between Nuclear Volumes, Chromosome Numbers, and Relative Radiosensitivities. *Science*, 141: 163–166.

Swanson, C. P. 1957. *Cytology and Cytogenetics*. Englewood Cliffs, New Jersey: Prentice-Hall, Inc. 596 pp.

Swift, H. 1953. Quantitative Aspects of Nuclear Nucleoproteins. *International Review of Cytology*, 2:1–76.

Torrey, J. G. 1959. "Experimental Modification of Development in the Root," *Cell, Organism and Milieu*, D. Rudnick, Ed. New York, New York: Ronald Press Company. Pp. 189–222.

Tsunewaki, K., and E. G. Heyne. 1959. Radiological Study of Wheat Monosomics. II. Differential Sensitivity of 16 Monosomics and the Disomic to a Single Dosage of X-Irradiation. *Genetics*, 44:947–954.

Van't Hof, J., and A. H. Sparrow. 1963. A Relationship Between DNA Content, Nuclear Volume, and Minimum Mitotic Cycle Time. *Proceedings of the National Academy of Sciences of the U.S.A.*, 49:897–902.

DISCUSSION

Chairman Franklin Hutchinson, Yale University, New Haven, Connecticut: I will call first for discussion on the paper by Drs. Zirkle and Uretz on the disassembly of mitotic organelles.

Dr. R. F. Kimball, Biology Division, Oak Ridge National Laboratory, Oak Ridge, Tennessee: Dr. Zirkle, perhaps wisely, refrained from making many speculations about the structure of the chromosomes. Considering the evidence of Callan and Gall on lampbrush (H. G. Callan and H. C. MacGregor, *Nature*, London, 181:1479, 1958; J. G. Gall, *Nature*, London, 198:36, 1963) suggesting some function of the DNA in the linear continuity of the chromosome, I wonder if Dr. Zirkle's evidence really excludes the possibility that DNA is uncoiled, leaving behind a matrix of electron dense material which maintains the general shape of the metaphase chromosome. In other words, perhaps there is not a true loss of DNA but simply a great spreading out of DNA to the point where it would be very difficult to detect.

Dr. Raymond Zirkle, University of Chicago, Chicago, Illinois: I think that the DNA gets out of that volume which is 2 microns in diameter. I can't get away from that thought. Also, I can't get away from the notion that it does get scattered pretty well throughout the cell after getting away from the residual chromosome or network, or whatever we want to call it. Now, as for the linear structure of a chromosome, the most simple concept would be that it is a single, very long molecule. It is a little difficult to see how the "protein" action spectrum would agree with this completely because it appears that photons absorbed in protein account for the detachment of DNA from the residual chromosome. If we go to the concept that the basic linear structure of a chromosome consists of DNA molecules with protein linkers, then absorption in protein conceivably could break the linear sequence and the chromosome could lose whole DNA molecules that way. One may then ask why we do not immediately observe chromosome breaks in the light microscope. Since the whole long chromosome is tightly coiled, cross-linkages could easily account for maintenance of chromosome continuity at the light microscope level and no visible breaks would be seen.

Dr. Robert Uretz, University of Chicago, Chicago, Illinois: Determining the distribution in the cell of the material lost from the chromosome is a difficult problem. If material diffuses nearby, its density will first fall off with the square of the radius and, as it moves further off, with the cube of the distance. One can clearly tell whether this material is on or near the chromosomal structural unit, but to detect more diffuse gradients would be very difficult indeed.

Dr. Robert J. Shalek, The University of Texas M. D. Anderson Hospital and Tumor Institute, Houston, Texas: Dr. Zirkle, with the proton microbeam, have you observed aberrations or breaks similar to those observed with x-ray radiation in chromosomes?

Dr. Zirkle: Most of our irradiations are done on cells which have already entered mitosis. As we have already heard, the breaks which initiate the aberrations that yield the quantitative data are produced in interphase. We have aimed a proton microbeam right into the middle of a prophase group of chromosomes and in anaphase we observed chromosome fragments. And we have done the same thing to a few interphase nuclei, have followed those into mitosis and have observed fragments. But the nature of these fragments is difficult to interpret and I would not want to draw any parallel, as regards the mechanism of production, between them and the breaks studied by Wolff, Sparrow and others.

Dr. G. Barendsen, Radiobiological Institute of the Organization for Health Research TNO, Rijswijk, The Netherlands: Have you any data on the temperature dependence of the paling process in relation to the time of appearance of the disassembly enzymes?

Dr. Zirkle: We have no information on temperature dependence. So far, we have done all of the experiments in an air-conditioned room at 72 F.

Dr. Arnold H. Sparrow, Brookhaven National Laboratory, Long Island, New York: Is there any pattern of dosages required to produce the effect on the spindle; i.e. do spindles of different species take about the same dose to produce a specified effect, and is there any pattern with respect to dosage required to produce a response when you irradiate the cytoplasm as contrasted to an existing spindle?

Dr. Zirkle: It is hard to get numbers that would be adequate to give a good answer to these questions. However, we have used mostly, for spindle destruction, the amphibian and the *Haemanthus* cells, and here certainly the cytoplasmic exposures necessary to destroy spindles is of the same order of magnitude and probably within a factor of two or three. As for spindle versus cytoplasmic irradiation: When you irradiate spindle you inevitably irradiate cytoplasm because there is cytoplasm above and below the spindle. A good control experiment is to aim the microbeam close to the spindle but not hit it. Then you presumably irradiate cytoplasm only. We have not done any really quantitative dose-effect curves, but I doubt that the irradiation of a spindle has much to do with its destruction. I think the action is probably due to cytoplasmic irradiation only. In some cases, we have irradiated a bit of cytoplasm 30 to 40 microns away from the spindle and still we destroyed it. So, whatever it is, the precursor of the spindle "poison" is well scattered throughout the cell.

Dr. Kosaku Izutsu, The University of Texas, Austin, Texas: Dr. Zirkle, your previous study shows that if the kinetochore of a chromosome is irradiated with a dose which causes chromosome paling, it is deprived of its activity to lead the chromosome movement. Have you obtained any action spectrum for the kinetochore inactivation?

Dr. Zirkle: No. We would love to do that experiment, but we have not gotten to it. These action spectra require much labor. Dr. Izutsu has brought up an effect which I did not mention, namely activation of kinetochores. This requires ultraviolet microbeam exposures of about the same order as those required to produce a fair degree of paling.

But we have as yet no action spectrum.

Dr. Robert Rutman, University of Pennsylvania, Philadelphia, Pennsylvania: Dr. Zirkle, can paling proceed in both directions when it begins centrally in a chromosome? Is there a difference in the threshold dose for the initial paling reaction and for progression, and can the two effects be separated?

Dr. Zirkle: The spatial progression proceeds in both directions. I believe this can be seen in Figure 1. As for the threshold effect, I can't answer that. That would require quantitative data that we do not have.

Dr. Harald Rossi, Columbia University, New York, New York: The question was raised yesterday whether there is any concrete evidence that would implicate chromosome breaks in lethality. I would like to speculate that Dr. Sparrow's very fascinating findings do exactly that, since he not only links lethality to the chromosome but also links it to the amount of energy, rather than to the dose received by the chromosome. The latter observation is, in fact, the most outstanding part of his findings. As has been shown here in the discussions, there is certainly a good deal of question as to what the state of the interphase chromosome is like, but available information is consistent with the notion that it is a very long thread of low strandedness and that a bigger chromosome merely forms a longer thread. If this is indeed the case, one would expect to find that the number of breaks is proportional to the *energy* absorbed per chromosome, since for the same *dose* the number of breaks would go up when the chromosome is longer. In other words, if lethality requires a certain number of breaks, one would expect lethality to occur with the same energy per chromosome rather than the same dose. This leaves one only with the somewhat puzzling question as to why such enormous amounts of energy should be involved; Dr. Sparrow estimates that 3 or 4 Mev of energy are required. There are a number of possible explanations for this. The first, of course, is that many breaks may be required for lethality. The second is that a good deal of the energy must be absorbed in the water and protein of the chromosome, and not in the DNA where it presumably is more likely to cause the break. Finally there is a very important reason for low efficiency which relates to the radiation which was employed. It is well known that X or gamma rays are exceedingly inefficient in inducing chromosome breakage; in the case of plants, the RBE is of the order of one hundredth compared to high LET radiation and there is thus good reason to assume that most x-ray or gamma-ray energy delivered in the form of low LET radiation is wasted, if it is to be expended in the induction of breaks.

Chairman Hutchinson: I would like to bring up a point that I think might be related to what Dr. Rossi has asked Dr. Sparrow. Many of us, here at least, are used to thinking of the effect of irradiation on a per cell basis. That is, a given dose of irradiation has a certain probability of causing the death of a particular cell. In your case the situation is far more complicated in that instead of looking at the effects on a single cell, you are looking at the over-all effect on a rather complicated biological organism. I wonder if you have any way of presenting your results in terms of what they might mean with regard to the survival of the individual cells of which your plants are composed.

Dr. Sparrow: Of course I am aware of this difficulty and the desirability of having my data presented in a manner that could be compared more readily with mammalian and microbial systems. This in part represents the fact that in respect to tissue culture, botanical research is somewhat behind the microbial and mammalian systems, but we hope eventually to be able to express D_{37} doses in terms of cell survival. In terms of cell survival it appears that there are several differences between plants and animal and microbial cell cultures. The first is that when you irradiate plants up to the sublethal dose and then section meristems, you don't find dead or dying cells. Reduction in cell number which does occur apparently results from a reduced rate of cell production or an increased rate of differentiation or both. In terms of getting to have something that can be expressed on a single cell basis, perhaps the closest thing we have is some observations on somatic mutation rate on petal epidermal cells. And in this system, the epidermal cells of the petal are heterozygous for flower color, and when we produce a mutation or deletion in a single cell, if this cell survives and grows, we get a detectable spot on the petal. When mutation rate is determined for flower color loci in several species, the same general relationship is found, as for lethality; that is, the larger the chromosomes characteristic of the species, the higher the mutation rate per roentgen. And again in these data there is relatively little evidence for selective death in most species so far examined. I think the real answer to your question is that in this respect botany has not progressed as far as some other branches of biology. I would, however, like to refer to a recent paper by Davies (*Radiation Research* 20:726, 1963) who has obtained a D_{37} for single cells in *Tradescantia*.

Dr. Kimball: Dr. Rossi's interesting suggestion about chromosome breakage being involved does raise one difficult point in my mind—the death due to chromosome breakage is often thought of as resulting from the loss of chromosome parts. Now Dr. Sparrow's evidence suggests that the redundancy of high "polyploidy" doesn't seriously affect the results. Thus it is very difficult to see how a simple loss of chromosome parts could be involved. This would imply, if you accept a breakage hypothesis, that the breakage was causing death by some different means than loss of chromosome parts.

Dr. Rossi: The microbeam experiments by Dr. Zirkle suggest very clearly that chromosome breakage has a purely mechanical effect. A few broken chromosomes can interfere with division to such an extent that the cell or cells are killed because of mechanical rather than genetic reasons. Polyploidy which, because of redundancy, is a genetic asset, becomes a mechanical liability because it entails a larger number of chromosomes.

Dr. Sparrow: This is a very good point. Obviously before we could cope effectively with the chromosome number variability, we had to have under control the chromosome size variable. When we first found that there seemed to be an effect of chromosome number in diploids, the explanation we gave for this was just what you have suggested, i.e., that the smaller the chromosome number the larger the percentage of genes lost per deletion. And we thought this fitted in with the polyploid story which everybody interpreted to mean that the deletions were losing genetic information and the greater resistance resulted from genetic redundancy. My present interpretation is somewhat different: namely, chromosome number is not important in diploids except as an indirect way at getting at interphase chromosome volume. And this again would indicate that the deletions are not a major mode of radiation damage. Another problem in organized meristems is that there seems to be so much cross-feeding of adjacent cells that potential cell lethals must be kept alive by the cells surrounding them. In other words, cells in a meristem behave quite differently than isolated cells in culture would.

Dr. Henry S. Kaplan, Stanford University, Palo Alto, California: In your abstract you have referred to a similar relationship between radiosensitivity and DNA content. How good is the relationship between DNA content and chromosome volume? When you calculate sensitivity on the basis of DNA content, do you improve the correlation?

Dr. Sparrow: The reason I didn't spend more time discussing the DNA relationship was merely lack of time. It is mentioned in the paper. The lack of discussion does not represent any change of opinion about the relationship between DNA content per chromosome and radiosensitivity (Sparrow and Evans: *Brookhaven Symposia in Biology*, 14:76–100, 1961). We have found that in several species of higher plants the average interphase nuclear volume goes up with a straight line relationship with the average DNA content per cell. (J. Van't Hof and A. H. Sparrow, *Proceedings of the National Academy of Sciences of the U.S.A.*, 49:897, 1963). Now when you consider a series of species, the DNA content can be high because of polyploidy or it can be high because of 2 X large chromosomes. So if you just take the range of nuclear volumes and DNA contents that I have found in different species and try to correlate this to radiosensitivity you get a general trend. But you get a very much better correlation if you plot sensitivity (dose) against DNA content per chromosome (Unpublished data). Now with reference to individual cells and the question of whether the radiosensitivity changes as DNA content changes between G_1 and G_2, I think it does; but this will be discussed in detail by later speakers. I would merely like to point out here again that both DNA content and volume change significantly between early G_1 and late S or G_2. Since the volume changes represent a change in absorbed energy, it is incorrect to talk about changes in sensitivity unless one also considers the changes in nuclear or chromosomal volume in the stages considered.

Dr. Reimut Wette, The University of Texas M. D. Anderson Hospital and Tumor Institute, Houston, Texas: Do I understand you correctly, that in the energy absorbed per nucleus you did not find a significant difference between diploids and polyploids?

Dr. Sparrow: When you compare the energy absorption *per chromosome, not per nucleus*, in diploids and tetraploids, the energy absorption per chromosome is a little higher on the average in polyploids but not statistically significantly so.

Dr. Daniel Billen, The University of Texas M. D. Anderson Hospital and Tumor Institute, Houston, Texas: Is it worthwhile considering the possibility of different metabolic stages in regard to chromosome size (i.e. a larger chromosome could possibly have a greater number of replicating regions as compared to a small chromosome), and that this might be of some importance in determining sensitivity?

Dr. Mortimer Mendelsohn, University of Pennsylvania, Philadelphia, Pennsylvania: Dr. Sparrow, would you comment on the correlation coefficients for some other parameters of the cells, such as the cell volume, the numbers of the cells in the meristem, the growth rates of the plants, or the generation time of the cells?

Dr. Sparrow: Well, there are data on several of these. We have found that as the nuclear volume increases, the average mitotic cycle time increases (Van't Hof and Sparrow, *Proceedings of the National Academy of Sciences of the U.S.A.*, 49:897, 1963). I think this is an important parameter that hasn't been considered as carefully as it should have been. This is important in acute irradiations in terms of how long it takes for a lesion to develop, at least for chromosome aberrations. It is also important with chronic exposures because if you express your dose in r/hr. or r/day, and there is a factor of 5 in the average cycle times, obviously the amount of energy being absorbed per chromosome per mitotic cycle will vary greatly (Van't Hof and Sparrow, *Proceedings of the National Academy of Sciences of the U.S.A.*, 50:855, 1963). With reference to cell volume and cell number in meristems, we haven't any of our own observations on this, but obviously cell size has to increase as nuclear size increases because there would not be enough room for the nucleus otherwise. There are some data on this, mostly unpublished (A. O. Lunden, *Radiation Botany*. In press). He has found that there is a correlation with measured cell size and cell number. Altogether, he has considered nine parameters and he claims he can predict seed radiosensitivity within 10 per cent. It's quite clear that chromosome volume is not the only factor to be considered in determining specific radiosensitivity. One of these factors we certainly would expect to be important would be the amount of protective chemicals, e.g., the ascorbic acid content is known to vary widely in different species of plants. Another factor I would suspect is that you do not get a uniform amount of DNA per cubic micron; or to put it another way, there may be more interchromosomal space in some species than in others. There are a whole series of secondary modifiers that should be considered. We can start to look for these now that we have what I consider the primary one more or less under control.

Dr. David Marrack, The University of Texas M. D. Anderson Hospital and Tumor Institute, Houston, Texas: Since in Dr. Sparrow's studies the nucleus has been sprayed in a random manner with irradiation to a volume much larger than nucleus and since the chromosome is largely water, surely Dr. Sparrow's data mean that the energy absorbed within the volume of the chromosome is handled in a manner differently than that absorbed in the equivalent water volume lying around the chromosome. This makes a slightly different interpretation, I think, from that which he is making.

His data do not explain why you have differences in radiosensitivity between different strains of cells of one species which differ only slightly in their genetic composition.

Dr. William C. Dewey, The University of Texas M. D. Anderson Hospital and Tumor Institute, Houston, Texas: I think that Dr. Sparrow's data show that in diploid and tetraploid cells, for the same amount of killing, the energy absorption per chromosome is the same. This may also mean that the number of breaks per chromosome is the same. Then, in the tetraploid cell which has twice as many chromosomes as the diploid cell, we should have twice as many chromosomal breaks as we have in the diploid cell. Therefore, if you look at it in terms of breaks per cell required for cell killing, it seems reasonable that more breaks are required in the polyploid cell than in the diploid cell.

Dr. Sparrow: The possibility of what you say will hold in some cases. But the point that I was trying to get across about the polyploids was that the only time that the same exposure delivers the same amount of energy into a polyploid chromosome as into a diploid chromosome is when the interphase chromosome volumes are the same. Now if different amounts of energy go into the polyploid and diploid chromosomes, there will be different amounts of genetic injury produced. It does not matter whether one measures growth inhibition, lethality, chromosome aberration, or mutation; the relationship is the same and the effect will be proportional to the absorbed energy per chromosome. So one should not talk about polyploids as a group with respect to their radiosensitivity as compared to diploids. It is highly desirable to talk about specific cases and to know what the volume relationships are between the diploid and polyploid chromosomes. One can then predict what the relative tolerance of diploid and polyploid cells should be.

Radiobiological and Physicochemical Properties of 5-Bromodeoxyuridine-Labeled Transforming DNA as Related to the Nature of the Critical Radiosensitive Structures

WACLAW SZYBALSKI AND ZOFIA OPARA-KUBINSKA

McArdle Memorial Laboratory, University of Wisconsin, Madison, Wisconsin

Replacement of the thymidine in transforming deoxyribonucleic acid (DNA) with 5-bromodeoxyuridine (BUdR) results in enhanced radiosensitivity of the modified DNA (Opara-Kubinska, Lorkiewicz, and Szybalski, 1961; Szybalski and Opara-Kubinska, 1961; Szybalski and Lorkiewicz, 1962). The object of the present study was a systematic evaluation of the relationship between the mode of DNA labeling, unifilar or bifilar, and the sensitivities of several genetic markers located on native, BUdR-labeled (NB and BB) or nonlabeled (NN) DNA molecules exposed to three wavelengths of ultraviolet light, X rays, and other inactivating conditions. It was hoped that this study would serve two complementary purposes: (1) provide better understanding of the sensitizing effects of BUdR labeling, and (2) allow physical and chemical characterization of a series of genetic markers. The latter aim was based on the following reasoning: Since BUdR sensitization depends on the degree of thymidine replacement (Erikson and Szybalski, 1963a,b), the markers located in the regions rich in adenine and thymine (A + T) should exhibit a higher degree of sensitization than those in the DNA regions comparatively poorer in A + T. With a variety of inactivating agents tested, these markers should also exhibit differential sensitivities *per se*, and thus supply additional information as to the molecular structure of the marker regions and different mechanisms of inactivation.

It was hoped also to extend the comparative studies on the BUdR sensitization of transforming DNA versus that of *Bacillus subtilis* cells, since earlier published studies (Opara-Kubinska, Lorkiewicz, and Szybalski, 1961; Szybalski and Opara-Kubinska, 1961; Szybalski and Lorkiewicz,

1962) were based on the radiosensitivity of a single marker only. These studies indicated that the DNA component is the principal target of lethal radiation effects, since BUdR labeling resulted in a similar degree of radiosensitization both of the cells and of the transforming DNA (indole marker) isolated from these cells.

Materials and Methods

Strains and Media

In addition to the previously used prototrophic and indole-requiring (IND^-) strains of *Bacillus subtilis* (Szybalski *et al.*, 1960), two other auxotrophic strains, phenylalanine- and leucine-requiring (PHE^- and LEU^-), kindly provided by Dr. I. Takahashi, were employed in the present study. Strain 31, characterized by two genetically linked deficiencies for indole and histidine (HIS) (Ephrati-Elizur, Srinivasan, and Zamenhof, 1961), was kindly contributed by Dr. S. Greer.

All the media were described in our previous communication (Opara-Kubinska, Borowska, and Szybalski, 1963).

Isolation of DNA and Transformation Procedure

The isolation and fractionation of transforming DNA, nonlabeled (NN), unifilarly (NB), and bifilarly (BB) BUdR-labeled, and the transformation procedures were described earlier (Opara-Kubinska, Borowska, and Szybalski, 1963).

Ultraviolet Irradiation

DNA solutions (5 to 10 μg DNA/ml SSC [0.15 M NaCl + 0.015 M trisodium citrate, pH = 7.6]) were irradiated in 1 mm quartz capillaries, as described earlier (Opara-Kubinska, Borowska, and Szybalski, 1963).

Three sources providing various wavelengths of ultraviolet light were as follows:

1. Short wavelength ultraviolet light, predominantly the 254 mμ mercury line, was provided by a G15T8 Westinghouse Sterilamp delivering 33 ergs/mm^2/sec at a distance of 25 cm from the tube.

2. Medium wavelength ultraviolet light (300 to 340 mμ) was provided by the Westinghouse Fluorescent Sun Lamp (FS2T12, 20 W). With a Pyrex filter, 75 per cent of its energy was emitted at 300 to 340 mμ, 5 per cent at 285 to 300 mμ, and 20 per cent at 340 to 375 mμ, with the peak at 315 mμ and a total flux of 114 ergs/mm^2/sec at a 10 cm distance.

3. Long wavelength ultraviolet light (350 to 390 mμ) was supplied by a General Electric 15 W BLB Black Light lamp. With a filter consisting of a 1 cm layer of a 0.04 per cent solution of Cation X (Kasha, 1948; purchased from Calbiochem, Inc., Los Angeles) contained in a Pyrex dish, 84 per cent of its energy was emitted at 350 to 390 mμ, 10 per cent at 340 to 350 mμ,

and 6 per cent at 390 to 410 mμ, with the peak at 360 mμ and a total flux of 60 ergs/mm^2/sec at a 10 cm distance.

Short and medium wavelength ultraviolet irradiations were performed at room temperature, while long wavelength illumination was performed at 4 to 6 C. Ultraviolet fluxes were determined with the dosimeter described by Jagger (1961).

Bacterial suspensions were irradiated under the conditions described by Opara-Kubinska, Lorkiewicz, and Szybalski (1961).

X-Ray Irradiation

A General Electric Maxitron x-ray machine operated at 250 kv, 30 ma served as the source of x rays. DNA samples (10 μg DNA/ml SSC + 0.2 per cent 2-aminoethylisothiouronium bromide hydrobromide (AET) or bacteria suspended in nutrient broth in 15 $\times$ 20 mm polypropylene cups (0.1 ml/cup) were placed on a 0.2 mm aluminum filter built into the head of the x-ray machine in close proximity to the beryllium window, which was facing upward. The x-ray flux at the level of the sample, measured with the lithium fluoride thermoluminescence dosimeter (Cameron, Daniels, Johnson, and Kenney, 1961), amounted to 11,000 r/min. The irradiation was carried out at room temperature, and the samples were diluted and assayed immediately after irradiation.

Thermal Inactivation of DNA

"Critical" and "subcritical" heat inactivation of *B. subtilis* DNA was carried out in a thermoregulated water bath. For "critical" inactivation, the DNA samples (10 μg DNA/ml of 1.5 $\times$ 10^{-3} M NaCl + 10^{-3} M sodium versenate, pH 7.8) were sealed in glass capillaries, immersed in the water bath, and heated for 10 minutes at each temperature. The temperature was increased from 60 to 80 C by 2° steps. After heating, the samples were rapidly cooled in an ice bath and assayed for transforming activity. "Subcritical" heat inactivation was carried out on a series of identical DNA samples (10 μg DNA/ml SSC, pH 7.5) sealed in glass capillaries and exposed for various periods of time to 85 C. Successive samples were removed from the water bath, rapidly cooled in an ice bath, and assayed for transforming activity. A low ionic strength solvent selected for "critical" inactivation of DNA permits its denaturation at relatively low temperatures with little concomitant depurination of DNA, an unwanted side reaction. To permit exposure of DNA to higher temperatures (85 C) without irreversible strand separation (denaturation) during the "subcritical" inactivation study, the salt concentration was increased approximately 100-fold.

Shear Degradation of DNA

Shear degradation of the DNA molecules was carried out for a twofold purpose: (1) determination of the relationship between the specific transforming activities, as governed by the size of the molecules and their sensitivity to radiation and other inactivating agents, and (2) comparison of normal versus BUdR-labeled DNA with respect to sensitivity to shearing forces.

In earlier experiments, 1 ml of DNA solution (8 to 10 μg/ml) in a 1 ml tuberculin-type syringe was forcefully ejected by manual means through a 27-gauge, 1-inch stainless steel hypodermic needle. To increase reproducibility of the plunger-driving force, a spring-loaded, constant-rate syringe CR 700 with 25-gauge, 1-inch needle (Hamilton Company, Inc., Whittier, California) was used in later experiments. Samples were taken after consecutive ejections for determination of the DNA sedimentation value and the transforming activity, before and after subsequent exposure to various doses of the inactivating agents.

Sedimentation Analysis and CsCl Density Gradient Centrifugation

Sedimentation analysis of normal (not sheared) and sheared DNA preparations was carried out in an analytical Spinco Model E centrifuge equipped with ultraviolet optics. Two ml DNA samples (20 μg/ml SSC) were centrifuged in 30 mm cells at 35,000 rev/min. Pictures were taken every four minutes, using single-coated medical x-ray film. The sedimentation constants, $S^{\circ}_{20,w}$, were corrected for the temperature of 20 C, and for zero concentrations of salt and of DNA (Eigner, 1960, and Personal communication).

Analytical and preparative methods for CsCl and Cs_2SO_4 equilibrium-density-gradient centrifugation (Meselson, Stahl, and Vinograd, 1957), as applied to normal and BUdR-labeled DNA, were outlined earlier (Opara-Kubinska, Borowska, and Szybalski, 1963; Szybalski, 1960; Erikson and Szybalski, 1964).

Results

Sensitivity to Ultraviolet Light

BUdR-labeled DNA exhibited clearly enhanced sensitivity to short and medium wavelength ultraviolet light, the 254 mμ and 300 to 340 mμ bands (Figures 1 and 2, Table), but not to long wavelength ultraviolet light (Figure 3). The quantitative evaluation of the sensitization was based on the comparison of the initial and final slopes of the survival curves (NN versus NB and NN versus BB). These data were further corrected for the specific transforming activities of the three kinds of DNA: NN, NB, and BB, since, as shown earlier by Marmur *et al.* (1961) and in the present study (Figure 4), the slope of the survival curve depends on the size of the DNA molecules, as affected by exposure to hydrodynamic shearing forces and as expressed by the sedimentation value and the specific transforming activity (sTA). These numerical corrections involved (1) determining the initial and final slope ratios (SR) for nonsheared and partially-sheared DNA exposed to various doses of ultraviolet light (Figure 4); (2) plotting these resistance factors as functions of the sTA's for the sheared and nonsheared DNA; (3) interpolating the SR's for the sTA's of the NN, NB, and BB DNA's used in

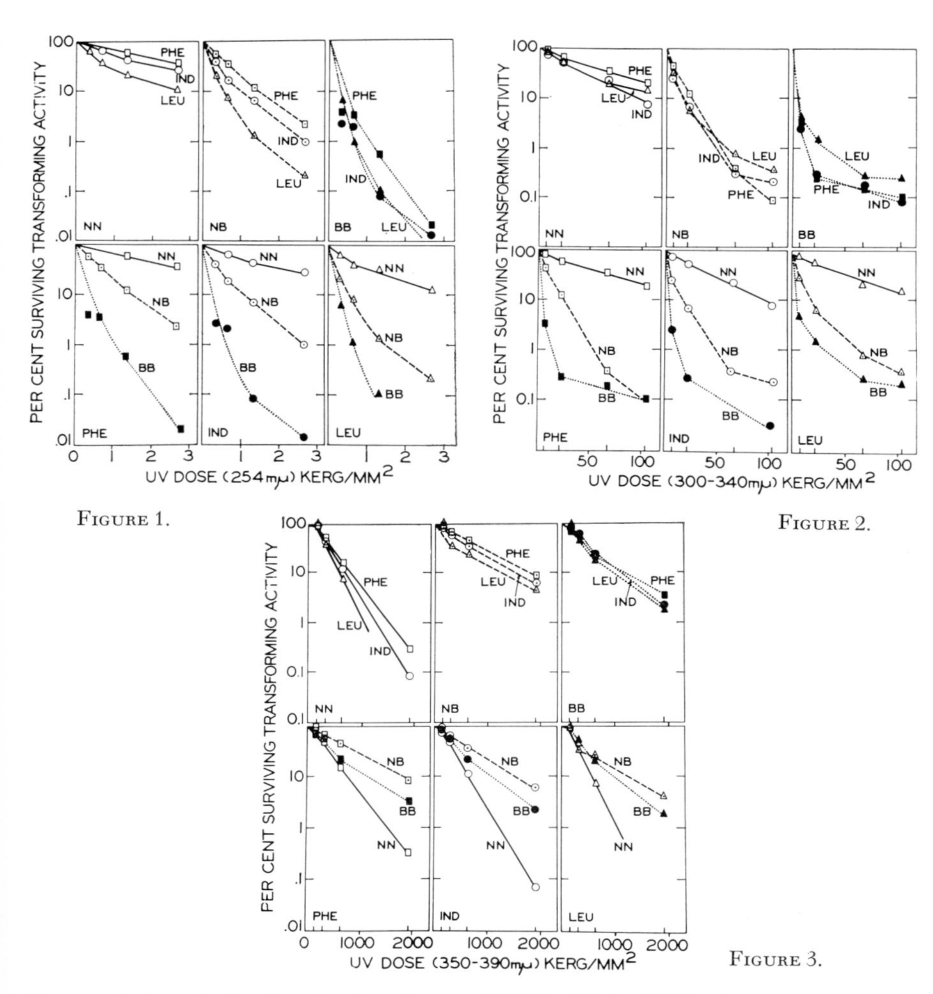

FIGURE 1.

FIGURE 2.

FIGURE 3.

FIGURES 1 through 3. Inactivation of normal DNA (NN-solid lines) and of DNA unifilarly (NB-broken lines) or bifilarly (BB-dotted lines) BUdR-labeled, by three wavelengths of ultraviolet light (254 mμ, Figure 1; 300 to 340 mμ, Figure 2; 350 to 390 mμ, Figure 3), measured as per cent surviving transforming activity assayed with phenylalanine (PHE)-, indole (IND)-, and leucine (LEU)- requiring receptor strains. The specific transforming activities (number of transformants per μg of nonirradiated DNA) of the NB and BB DNA preparations, expressed in relation to the activity of NN DNA defined as 100 per cent, amounted to 83, 85, and 75 per cent (NB; Fig. 1); 52, 61, and 45 per cent (BB; Fig. 1); 35, 33, and 23 per cent (NB; Fig. 2); 73, 57, and 33 per cent (BB; Fig. 2); 47, 32, and 30 per cent (NB; Fig. 3); and 79, 53, and 33 per cent (BB; Fig. 3) for the PHE, IND, and LEU markers, respectively. The degree of thymidine replacement in the BUdR-labeled strands approached 90 to 100 per cent.

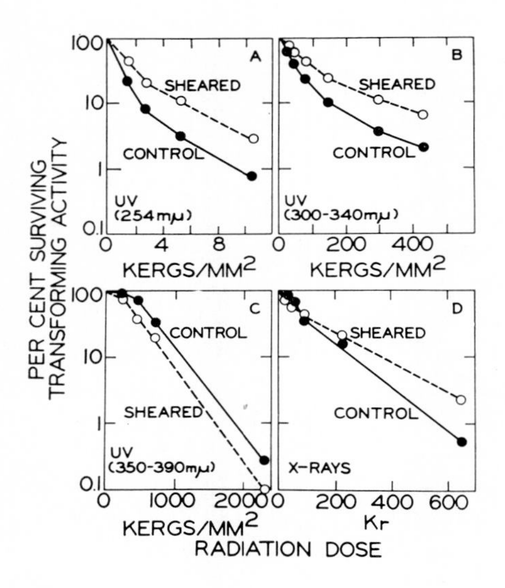

FIGURE 4. Inactivation of control (solid lines) and of sheared (broken lines) transforming DNA by ultraviolet light of three wavelengths (A, B, C) or by X rays (D), as measured by the survival of the IND marker. The specific transforming activities corresponded to: (A) 7.3×10^5 and 6.6×10^4 (9.0 per cent); (B) 2.3×10^5 and 1.7×10^4 (7.4 per cent); (C) 4.5×10^5 and 7.4×10^5 (16.4 per cent); and (D) 5.4×10^5 and 1.2×10^4 (2.2 per cent), for the control and sheared DNA's, respectively. The DNA was exposed to hydrodynamic shear by forcing the solution through a 27-gauge hypodermic needle, three times (A and B), two times (C), or five times (D), as described in the text in the section on materials and methods.

the primary experiment (Figures 1 and 2); and (4) multiplying the BUdR-imposed sensitization factors by the ratios of the SR's determined for the BUdR-labeled and nonlabeled DNA's. The SR's determined for the initial and final slopes of the survival curves were used for correcting the BUdR sensitization ratios based on the initial and final slopes, respectively.

The results of these computations, which admittedly were quite simplified since they were based only on the RF's determined for one marker (IND) carried by the NN DNA, are presented in the table (italicized figures).

Sensitization Factors for Unifilarly and Bifilarly BUdR-Labeled Transforming DNA

		Sensitization factors							
		Unifilarly BUdR labeled				Bifilarly BUdR labeled			
		Initial slope		Final slope		Initial slope		Final slope	
Inactivating agent	Marker		Corrected		Corrected		Corrected		Corrected
Short wave	PHE	4.0	*4.2*	3.0	*3.0*	16.0	*20.9*	6.0	*6.0*
Ultraviolet light	IND	4.5	*4.7*	5.0	*5.0*	13.4	*16.5*	7.0	*7.0*
(254 mμ)	LEU	3.7	*4.1*	2.6	*2.6*	6.4	*8.9*	5.2	*5.2*
Medium wave	PHE	5.2	*6.8*	. .	. .	21.4	*23.2*	. .	. .
Ultraviolet light	IND	6.6	*8.7*	. .	. .	22.4	*26.2*	. .	. .
(300 to 340 mμ)	LEU	5.6	*8.0*	. .	. .	19.0	*25.0*	. .	. .
Long wave	PHE	. .	. .	1/2.7	*1/2.9*	. .	. .	1/2.3	*1/2.4*
Ultraviolet light	IND	. .	. .	1/2.9	*1/3.2*	. .	. .	1/2.4	*1/2.6*
(350 to 390 mμ)	LEU	. .	. .	1/3.5	*1/3.9*	. .	. .	1/2.8	*1/3.2*
	PHE	2.0	*2.0*	1.3	*1.27*	4.5	*4.5*	1.5	*1.65*
X rays	IND	2.1	*2.1*	1.3	*1.2*	4.8	*4.8*	1.5	*1.56*
	LEU	1.4	*1.4*	1.2	*1.1*	2.5	*2.5*	1.5	*1.68*

Abbreviations: BUdR, 5-bromodeoxyuridine; IND, indole; LEU, leucine; PHE, phenylalanine.
Sensitization factor = ratio of the slopes of the semilogarithmic survival curves (Figures 1, 2, 3, 5) determined for the BUdR-labeled and control DNA's. For an outline of the method permitting calculation of the uncorrected and corrected sensitization factors consult the text.

The corrected sensitization factors determined for the initial slopes of the survival curves (short and medium wavelength ultraviolet light) were several times higher for the bifilarly than for the unifilarly labeled DNA. These figures were somewhat higher for the medium wavelength (6.8 to 8.7× for NB and 23.2 to 26.2× for BB) than for the short wavelength ultraviolet light (4.1 to 4.7× for NB and 8.9 to 20.9× for BB).

The sensitization factors computed from the final slopes of the survival curves (254 mμ) were considerably lower than those determined for the initial slopes, especially for the BB DNA, probably reflecting the sensitivity of molecules in which the marker-bearing regions escaped heavy BUdR labeling. This effect, caused most likely by the inhomogeneity of the labeling, was still more pronounced for medium wavelength ultraviolet light; for this reason, the sensitization factors were not computed for the final slopes of the latter curves (table).

The results obtained with long wavelength ultraviolet light were very different from those observed for the shorter wavelengths. The survival curves were sigmoid, with a small shoulder followed by a monophasic exponential curve (Figures 3 and 4C). Reduction of the molecular weight of the transforming DNA resulted in an actual increase in their radiation sensitivity, as evidenced by gradual disappearance of the shoulder and a small change in the final slope of the survival curve (Figure 4C). BUdR-labeling resulted in increased resistance to long wavelength ultraviolet light.

These data indicate that the mechanism of the inactivating effects of long wavelength ultraviolet light must be different from that of the shorter wavelengths. This effect is probably related to the photodynamic inactivation of DNA and not to inactivation by so-called "visible" light, the latter effect being associated with immensely accentuated inactivation of BUdR-labeled phages (Stahl *et al.*, 1961; Fox and Meselson, 1963) probably caused by photochemical dehalogenation (Wacker, Mennigmann, and Szybalski, 1962).

Sensitivity to X Rays

The three markers examined, PHE, IND, and LEU, were progressively more sensitive to X rays (Figure 5) in the same order as observed for the various wavelengths of ultraviolet light (Figures 1, 2, and 3) and other inactivating agents (Figure 6). BUdR-caused sensitization is illustrated in Figure 5 and summarized in the table. The sensitivity factors were calculated as described for ultraviolet light inactivation and corrected for the specific transforming activities, since as with short-to-medium wavelength ultraviolet light, the smaller the DNA molecules, the more radioresistant they were (Figure 4D). As summarized in the table, unifilar BUdR labeling resulted in 1.4 to 2.1-fold sensitization toward X rays, as calculated from the ratios of the initial slopes of the survival curves. These figures were roughly doubled for the bifilarly-labeled DNA. As with ultraviolet

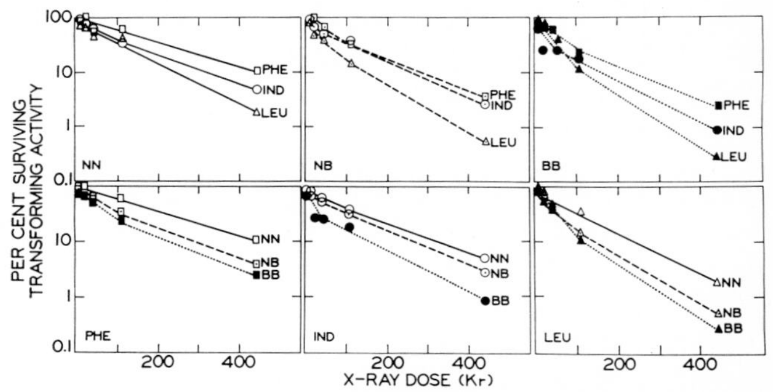

FIGURE 5. X-ray inactivation of normal DNA (NN) and of DNA unifilarly (NB) or bifilarly (BB) BUdR-labeled. The experimental details are outlined in the text section on materials and methods. For symbols, see the legend for Figures 1 through 3. The specific transforming activities of the NB and BB DNA preparations, expressed in relation to the activity of the NN DNA defined as 100 per cent, amounted to 106 and 50 per cent (PHE), to 122 and 57 per cent (IND), and to 120 and 36 per cent (LEU), respectively.

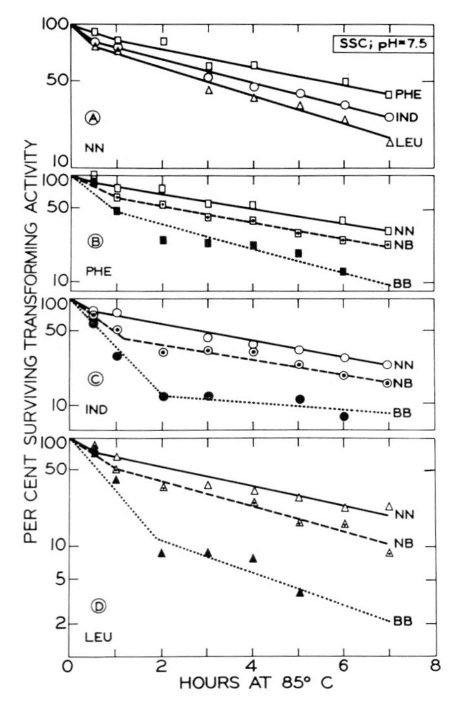

FIGURE 6. "Subcritical" thermal inactivation of normal DNA (NN) and of DNA unifilarly (NB) or bifilarly (BB) BUdR-labeled. The experimental details are outlined in the text section on materials and methods. For symbols, see the legend for Figures 1 through 3.

light (254 to 340 mμ), the sensitization factors calculated for the final slopes of the survival curves were considerably lower.

Sensitivity to "Subcritical" Thermal Inactivation

When heated at temperatures just below the thermal transition point ("melting temperature"), DNA loses progressively its transforming activity (Roger and Hotchkiss, 1961; Ginoza and Zimm, 1961). This inactivation process is most probably the result of heat depurination (Greer and Zamenhof, 1962), although some enzymatic destruction cannot be excluded since thorough deproteinization stabilizes the DNA (Ginoza and Guild, 1961). We have found that *B. subtilis* DNA purified by preparative banding in the CsCl gradient (Szybalski *et al.*, 1960) is more stable than phenol-deproteinized DNA; the chloroform-butanol deproteinization procedure yields DNA most susceptible to "subcritical" thermal inactivation. The rate of thermal inactivation is highly affected by the ionic strength and by the pH of the solvent, which parameters were carefully controlled as described in Materials and Methods.

The results obtained with subcritical heat inactivation were very similar to those obtained with X rays and with short and medium wavelength ultraviolet light (Figures 1, 2, 3, and 5). The order of marker inactivation was again PHE (most resistant), IND, and LEU, with unifilarly and bifilarly BUdR-labeled DNA progressively more sensitive than the nonlabeled control DNA.

Sensitivity to "Critical" Thermal Inactivation

As discussed earlier (Opara-Kubinska and Szybalski, 1962) and as evident in Figure 7, the IND marker is inactivated at the lowest tempera-

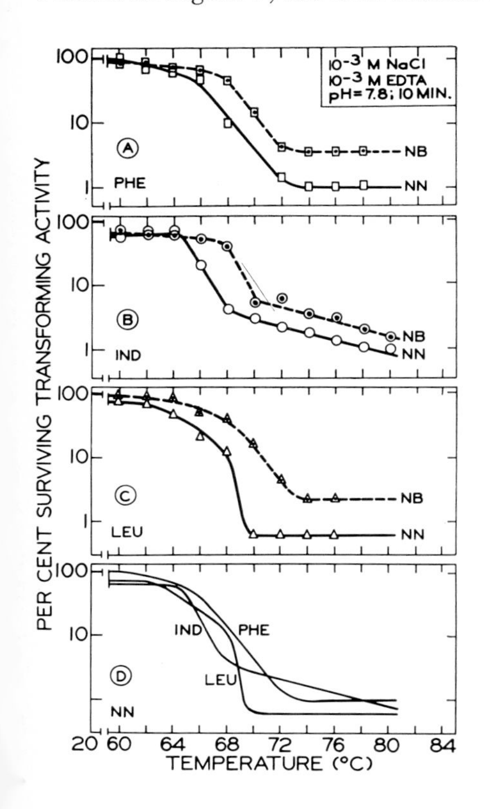

FIGURE 7. "Critical" thermal inactivation of normal (NN) and of unifilarly BUdR-labeled (NB) *B. subtilis* DNA. The experimental details are outlined in the text section on materials and methods.

ture, followed by the LEU and PHE markers. BUdR labeling increases the midpoint of the critical thermal inactivation (= temperature of irreversible denaturation) (Figure 7), in accordance with the increase in melting temperature observed for BUdR-labeled *B. subtilis* DNA (Szybalski, 1961; Szybalski and Mennigmann, 1962).

Discussion

The discussion will be divided into two main parts: (1) the properties of the genetic markers studied as related to the differential effects of a variety of inactivating conditions and agents, and (2) the effect of BUdR labeling on the properties of the markers in question.

As outlined earlier, the complete *B. subtilis* genome most probably consists of a single circular DNA molecule of molecular weight approximately $1{,}000 \times 10^6$ (Szybalski and Opara-Kubinska, 1963). During the extraction procedure, this molecule is usually sheared into 40 to 50 fragments, each of molecular weight approximately 20 to 25×10^6. The markers studied, the positions of which are indicated in Figure 8, are located on separate DNA fragments and thus behave as nonlinked markers. When fractionated by preparative CsCl density gradient centrifugation, the IND marker sediments at the highest density, an indication that the DNA fragment which carries this marker has the highest average guanine (G) + cytosine (C) content. The LEU and PHE markers are characterized by progressively lower buoyant densities (Opara-Kubinska and Szybalski, 1962; Szybalski and Opara-Kubinska, 1963). The temperatures of irreversible thermal inactivation for the individual markers (Figure 7) do not seem to conform to those predicted from the apparent G + C contents based on the buoyant density data. Thus the IND marker, which exhibits the highest buoyant density, is inactivated at a temperature lower than those characteristic of the LEU and PHE markers (Opara-Kubinska and Szy-

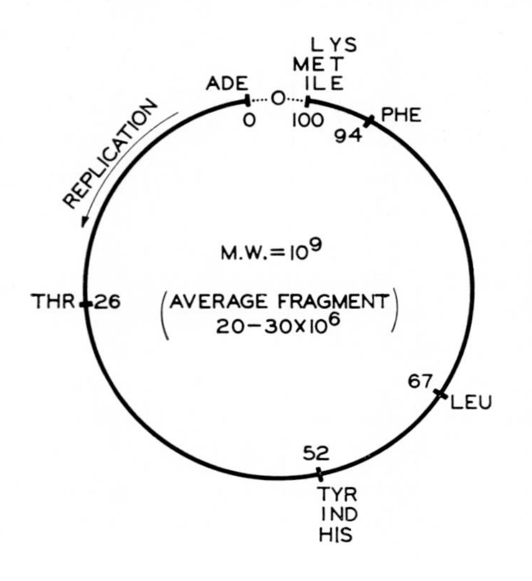

Figure 8. Genetic map of *B. subtilis*, based on data of Yoshikawa and Sueoka (1963).

balski, 1962). These data indicate that buoyant density and critical inactivation temperature are determined by different properties of the DNA fragments on which the individual markers happen to be located: buoyant density indicates the average G + C content of the fragment, whereas the irreversibility of thermal denaturation is governed either by localized G + C rich stretches or by other temperature-resistant bonds between the complementary DNA strands (Szybalski and Opara-Kubinska, 1963).

The sensitivity of the markers studied to all the agents does not seem to bear any relationship to the two hitherto discussed properties of transforming DNA. However, all the markers could be arranged in the specific order of sensitivity, with the PHE marker being most resistant to all the wavelengths of ultraviolet light, X rays, subcritical thermal inactivation, and hydrodynamic shear, followed by the IND and LEU markers. This result would be easier to understand if it reflected the efficiency of transformation as governed by the size of the undamaged DNA region necessary for effective incorporation and integration of each of the individual markers. If sensitivity to X rays is a direct function and sensitivity to ultraviolet an inverse function of the G + C content of the DNA (Haynes, 1954; Kaplan and Zavarine, 1962), then these relationships must be masked by another aspect of the complex radiation survival process, since they do not seem to be corroborated by the present data. For example, the dependence of postradiation repair on the G + C content, and the extent and variety of repair mechanisms all must come into play.

BUdR labeling resulted in definite sensitization of transforming DNA to most of the inactivating agents or conditions. Bifilarly labeled DNA averaged two to four times as much sensitization as did unifilarly BUdR-labeled DNA. This is in contrast to the finding of Fox and Meselson (1963) that unifilarly labeled lambda phage DNA behaves as a mixed population of labeled and nonlabeled molecules when exposed to "visible" light suggesting that mainly the BUdR-labeled DNA strand is photochemically damaged. If the reasoning of Fox and Meselson (1963) is applicable to transforming DNA, our data indicate either that both complementary strands of DNA take part in the transformation process (not necessarily at the same time: Guild and Robison, 1963), or that BUdR-accentuated X-ray and short-to-medium wavelength ultraviolet radiation damage (debromination?) generally is not restricted to one strand only (transbromination?). It is quite possible that the use of AET by Fox and Meselson (1963) eliminated the "transbromination" reaction, since in the absence of this radioprotective radical scavenger both DNA strands of the unifilarly BUdR-labeled lambda phage DNA appeared to be damaged (Meselson, as quoted by Hotz, 1964). As shown by Hotz (1963, 1964) and Hotz and Zimmer (1963), the radioprotectors of the cysteine-cysteamine group, if present during the UV irradiation, abolish the radiosensitizing effects of the BUdR labeling of phage DNA, most probably by interfering with the secondary more drastic chemical modifications of DNA leading to irreparability by the enzymatic host-cell reactivating mechanism. "Transbromination", or other reactions leading to accentuated cross-linking of BUdR-labeled DNA (Opara-Kubinska *et al.*, 1963), might be among these secondary modifications of UV-irradiated DNA, whereas photodehalogenation (Wacker, Mennigmann and Szybalski, 1962) would be the primary reaction, not affected by AET.

Since it was found that the sensitivity of transforming DNA depends directly on its molecular size, and since the size of the molecular fragments varied from preparation to preparation (usually smaller for BUdR-labeled preparations, reflecting the apparently greater fragility of the brominated molecules), it was necessary to correct the actual sensitization factors as calculated from the ratio of the slopes of the survival curves. This was described in an earlier section of this communication. We were primarily interested in the sensitization factors calculated on the basis of the initial slopes determined for unifilarly BUdR-labeled DNA, since most probably these figures could be best related to sensitization of the whole cells from which the transforming DNA was extracted. Since the viability of *B. subtilis* cells containing bifilarly BUdR-labeled DNA is very low, the comparison had to be made between cells and transforming principle containing only unifilarly BUdR-labeled DNA, *i.e.* after one replication cycle in the presence of BUdR. As can be seen in the table, the corrected sensitization factors for unifilarly BUdR-labeled DNA are approximately equal for all the markers, varying from 4.1 to 4.7 for short wavelength ultraviolet light, 6.8 to 8.7 for medium wavelength ultraviolet, and 1.4 to 2.1 for X rays. This relatively small variation in the radiosensitization of various markers permits a comparison between the BUdR-effected radiosensitization factor, both for X rays and for short-to-medium wavelength ultraviolet light, thus corroborating our earlier data (Opara-Kubinska, Lorkiewicz, and Szybalski, 1961; Szybalski and Opara-Kubinska, 1961; Szybalski and Lorkiewicz, 1962) and the conclusion based on these data that in the intact cell DNA is the principal target of lethal radiation effects. A similar conclusion as to the critical role of DNA in determining the radiosensitivity of pneumococcal cells was reached by Hutchinson (1964), on the basis of a comparison of BUdR-effected radiosensitization of pneumococci and of their transforming DNA.

It is difficult to assign any definite order of BUdR-radiosensitizing effects for the three markers studied, although there seems to be a tendency for the IND marker to be most susceptible. If the highest degree of sensitization reflects the highest A + T content of the DNA and thus the potentially heaviest BUdR labeling, it could not correspond to the highest average A + T content of the IND-carrying molecules, since the buoyant density data indicate that the IND marker is associated with the DNA molecules of highest G + C (and thus lowest A + T) content.

If interference with DNA repair is the most important basis for BUdR sensitization (Stahl *et al.*, 1961; Sauerbier, 1961; Howard-Flanders, Boyce, and Theriot, 1962), whereas the natural resistance of the marker reflects its increased reparability, then the naturally most resistant marker (PHE) should be sensitized to the highest degree by the BUdR label, while the most sensitive one (LEU) should be sensitized the least. Only the latter seems to be true in the majority of cases, but any generalizations would most probably be spurious.

All the data presented here were obtained with DNA in which almost 100 per cent of the thymidine residues on one or on both DNA strands was replaced by BUdR. For lower degrees of labeling, the sensitization is usually proportional to the degree of labeling, especially in the case of ultraviolet light; whereas a saturation effect was observed in the case of X rays, as reported earlier by Erikson and Szybalski (1963b) (Figure 9) for human cell cultures, and for *Escherichia coli* by Kaplan, Smith, and Tomlin (1962).

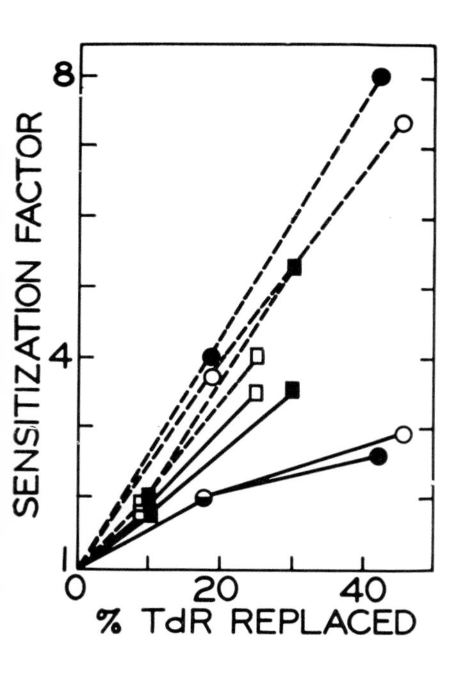

FIGURE 9. Sensitization factors (D_{37} [control]/D_{37}[labeled]) for D98/AG human cell lines inactivated by UV light (broken lines) or by X rays (solid lines) as a function of thymidine replacement by its halogenated analogs, The cells were grown in the presence of BUdR (○); 5-bromodeoxycytidine (BCdR [●]); 5-iododeoxyuridine (IUdR [□]); or 5-iododeoxycytidine (ICdR [■]). Redrawn from Erikson and Szybalski (1963b).

The direct relationship between the degree of DNA labeling and the radiosensitivity of the cells is another indication for the critical role of DNA in determining the radiosensitivity of the cells, relating in this respect mammalian (human) cells to bacteria and DNA viruses. This conclusion as to the nature of the critical radiosensitive structure does not depend on the exact mechanism of the radiosensitization effect, *i.e.* whether BUdR increases the intrinsic radiosensitivity of DNA or affects its repair, in the parental or in the receptor cell. If variation in the repair of DNA affects cell survival, this result still indicates that DNA is the critical radiosensitive structure. Interference of the BUdR label with the DNA repair process is indicated by studies with bacteriophages which were sensitized by BUdR only when tested under conditions involving postirradiation repair (Stahl *et al.*, 1961; Sauerbier, 1961; Howard-Flanders, Boyce, and Theriot, 1962), and by observation that the BUdR label sensitizes "reparable" *E. coli* strains B and B/r, but not the repair-deficient mutant B_s (Hill and Simson, 1961), as indicated in Figure 10. Involvement of the repair mechanism is also compatible with the observation that intracellularly ultraviolet-irradiated

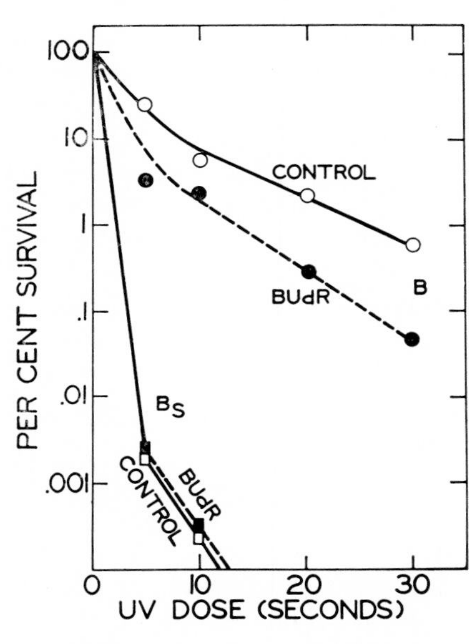

FIGURE 10. UV survival of control (solid line) and BUdR-labeled (broken line) cells of *E. coli* strain B (circles) and repair-impaired mutant B_s (squares). The cells were labeled with BUdR by incubating for three hours in VBE medium (Opara-Kubinska, Borowska, and Szybalski, 1963) supplemented with 100 μg BUdR and 4 μg 5-fluorodeoxyuridine per ml. The cells were suspended in 0.15 M NaCl and irradiated with a UV (254 mμ) flux of 31 ergs/mm²/sec.

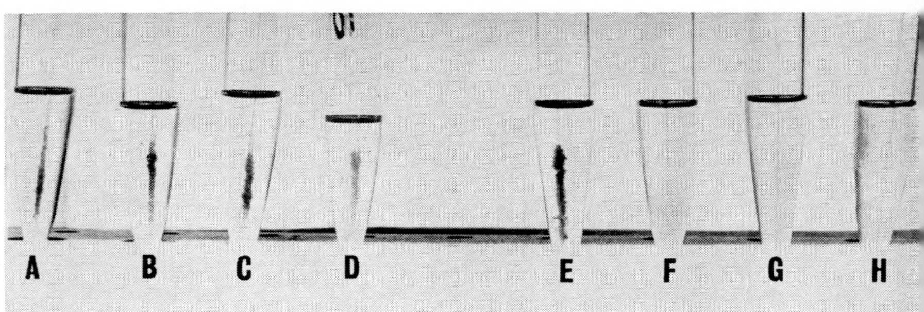

FIGURE 11. The patterns of alcohol precipitation of the *B. subtilis* cell lysate prepared by consecutive exposures of control (A through D) and BUdR-labeled (5 hours, 200 μg/ml BUdR, 4 μg/ml FUdR) (E through H) *B. subtilis* cells to lysozyme (100 μg/ml, 15 min 37 C) and to 1 per cent sodium lauryl sulfate, followed by chloroform-butanol (4:1) deproteinization, and addition of 2 volumes of 95 per cent ethanol. The fibrous precipitate, if formed, was collected on the glass rods visible in the center of the tubes. Prior to lysis the cells were exposed to 0 (A, E), to 6×10^3 (B, F), to 12×10^3 (C, G), or to 24×10^3 (D, H) ergs/mm² of UV light (250 mμ). Under these conditions the survival of the transforming activity (shown by the IND marker) corresponded to 48 per cent (A), 23 per cent (B), 6.5 per cent (C), and 2.1 per cent (D) for the control DNA, and 1.7 per cent (E) and less than 0.2 per cent (F through H) for the BUdR-labeled DNA.

bacterial DNA can be extracted in filamentous form from normal bacteria, whereas under similar conditions BUdR-labeled DNA undergoes gross breakdown (alcohol precipitates it in flocculent form) (Figure 11).

The accentuated sensitivity of BUdR-labeled DNA to subcritical heat inactivation and to hydrodynamic shear seems to confirm the notion that BUdR incorporation leads to generalized fragility of the DNA molecule (Szybalski, 1962; Szybalski and Lorkiewicz, 1962), although one cannot exclude the possibility that BUdR-affected repair processes are operative also on DNA damaged by the two conditions discussed above. One could postulate that the so-called repair phenomenon is a very general process which eliminates single-strand damage to the DNA molecule by the following sequence of reactions similar to those discussed by Howard-Flanders (see pages 52 to 60, this volume): (1) a single-strand break in the DNA molecule in the immediate neighborhood of the damaged nucleotide, (2) limited exonucleolytic digestion of one strand only with simultaneous elimination of the damaged or modified deoxynucleotides, (3) polymerase-mediated resynthesis of the deleted regions by copying the complementary strand, and (4) final closure of the remaining 3′OH to 5′P link. It is obvious that any excessive DNA damage leading to overlapping repairs (= exonucleolytic excision) on the opposite complementary strands would lead to irreparable damage causing double-strand breakage of the DNA molecule, in most cases a lethal event.

Summary

Bacillus subtilis cells grown for two generations in the presence of the thymidine analog, BUdR, yield two classes of DNA: unifilarly labeled ("hybrid") and bifilarly labeled DNA molecules, in which up to 100 per cent of the thymidine residues are replaced by BUdR on only one or on both DNA strands, respectively. The sensitivities of these two classes of labeled DNA molecules to X rays, to three selected wavelengths of ultraviolet light, to "subcritical" heat inactivation, to "critical" heat inactivation ("melting"), and to hydrodynamic shear were assayed and compared with the sensitivity of normal unsubstituted DNA. Genetic transformation toward IND, LEU, and PHE prototrophy served as the assay system for DNA survival. The radiation survival of control and BUdR-labeled *B. subtilis* cells was also determined.

It could be concluded that bifilarly BUdR-labeled DNA is up to 5, 21, and 26 times more sensitive than the unlabeled DNA to X rays, and to short (254 mμ) and medium (300 to 340 mμ) wavelength ultraviolet light, respectively. Similarly, BUdR sensitizes DNA also to "subcritical" heat inactivation and to hydrodynamic shear. Unifilar labeling results in intermediate sensitization. The PHE, IND, and LEU markers, in that order, are progressively more sensitive to all the agents tested with the exception of "critical" heat inactivation, with the IND marker inactivated at the lowest temperature, followed by LEU and PHE. The degree of BUdR sensitization varied somewhat for the individual markers, but differences were small, especially for unifilarly labeled DNA. In contrast to other types of inactivating agents, an actual increase in resistance to long wavelength (350 to 390 mμ) ultraviolet light and to "critical" heat inactivation was observed with BUdR-labeled DNA. Sensitivity of transforming activity to X rays and to short and medium wavelength ultraviolet light depends directly on the size of the DNA fragments.

On the average, cells which survive exposure to BUdR through one replication cycle are sensitized to ultraviolet (254 mμ) and to X rays to the same extent as the unifilarly labeled DNA extracted from these cells, attesting to the role of DNA as the principal radiosensitive cell component. This conclusion is independent of the actual mechanism of radiosensitization by the incorporated BUdR, *i.e.* whether it increases the intrinsic lability of the DNA structure or whether it interferes with some DNA repair process. The notion that DNA is the critical radiosensitive cell component is further corroborated by the observation that the radiosensitivity of bacterial and mammalian cells is a function of the degree of DNA-labeling by BUdR, while BUdR not incorporated into DNA has no effect on the sensitivity of the cells.

ACKNOWLEDGMENTS

These studies were supported in part by Grants CY-5215 and CA-07175 from the National Cancer Institute, United States Public Health Service, Bethesda, Maryland.

The authors are greatly indebted to Dr. H. Vermund for permission to use the X-ray machine, to Drs. J. R. Cameron and G. Kenney for help with its calibration, to Drs. R. B. Setlow and J. Jagger of the Oak Ridge National Laboratory for their help with assembly and calibration of the ultraviolet dosimeter, and to Dr. E. H. Szybalski for the invaluable editorial help.

REFERENCES

Cameron, J. R., F. Daniels, N. Johnson, and G. Kenney. 1961. Radiation Dosimeter Utilizing the Thermoluminescence of Lithium Fluoride. *Science*, 134:333–334.

Eigner, J. 1960. The Native, Denatured, and Renatured States of Deoxyribonucleic Acid. Ph.D. Thesis, Harvard University, Cambridge, Massachusetts. Pp. 1–222.

———. Personal communication.

Ephrati-Elizur, E., P. R. Srinivasan, and S. Zamenhof. 1961. Genetic Analysis, by Means of Transformation, of Histidine Linkage Groups in *Bacillus subtilis*. *Proceedings of the National Academy of Sciences of the U.S.A.*, 47:56–63.

Erikson, R. L., and W. Szybalski. 1963a. Molecular Radiobiology of Human Cell Lines. III. Radiation Sensitizing Properties of 5-Iododeoxyuridine. *Cancer Research*, 23: 122–130.

———. 1963b. Molecular Radiobiology of Human Cell Lines. V. Comparative Radiosensitizing Properties of 5-Halodeoxycytidines and 5-Halodeoxyuridines. *Radiation Research*, 20:252–262.

———. 1964. The Cs_2SO_4 Equilibrium Density Gradient and its Application for the Study of T–even Phage DNA: Glucosylation and Replication. *Virology*, 22:111–124.

Fox, E., and M. Meselson. 1963. Unequal Photosensitivity of the Two Strands of DNA in Bacteriophage λ. *Journal of Molecular Biology*, 7:583–589.

Ginoza, W., and W. R. Guild. 1961. On the Inactivation of Transforming DNA by Temperatures below the Melting Point. *Proceedings of the National Academy of Sciences of the U.S.A.*, 47:633–639.

Ginoza, W., and B. H. Zimm. 1961. Mechanism of Inactivation of Deoxyribonucleic Acids by Heat. *Proceedings of the National Academy of Sciences of the U.S.A.*, 47: 639–652.

Greer, S., and S. Zamenhof. 1962. Studies on Depurination of DNA by Heat. *Journal of Molecular Biology*, 4:123–141.

Guild, W. R., and M. Robison. 1963. Evidence for Message Reading from a Unique Strand of Pneumococcal DNA. *Proceedings of the National Academy of Sciences of the U.S.A.*, 50:106–112.

Haynes, R. H. 1964. "Molecular Localization of Radiation Damage Relevant to Bacterial Inactivation," Augenstein, L., R. Mason, and B. Rosenberg, Eds. *International Symposium on Physical Processes in Radiation Biology*. New York, New York: Academic Press, Inc. Pp. 50–71.

Hill, R. F., and E. Simson. 1961. A Study of Radiosensitive and Radioresistant Mutants of *Escherichia coli* strain B. *Journal of General Microbiology*, 24:1–14.

Hotz, G. 1963. Suppression by Cysteamine of Radiosensitization in 5-Bromodeoxyuridine Substituted Phage T1. *Biochemical and Biophysical Research Communications*, 11: 393–398.

————. 1964. Photoreactivation of UV-Damage in Phage Containing 5-Bromouracil-DNA. *Zeitschrift für Vererbungslehre*, 95:211–214.

Hotz, G., and K. G. Zimmer. 1963. Experiments in Radiation Chemistry of T1-phage. *International Journal of Radiation Biology and Related Studies in Physics, Chemistry and Medicine*, 7:75–86.

Howard-Flanders, P., R. P. Boyce, and L. Theriot. 1962. Mechanism of Sensitization to Ultra-Violet Light of *T*1 Bacteriophage by the Incorporation of 5-Bromodeoxyuridine or by Pre-irradiation of the Host Cell. *Nature*, London, 195:51–54.

Hutchinson, F. 1964. Radiosensitization of *Pneumococcus* Cells and DNA to Ultraviolet Light and X-Rays by Incorporated 5-Bromodeoxyuridine. *Biochimica et biophysica acta*, 91:527–530.

Jagger, J. 1961. A Small and Inexpensive Ultraviolet Dose-Rate Meter Useful in Biological Experiments. *Radiation Research*, 14:394–403.

Kaplan, H. S., K. C. Smith, and P. A. Tomlin. 1962. Effect of Halogenated Pyrimidines on Radiosensitivity of *E. coli*. *Radiation Research*, 16:98–113.

Kaplan, H. S., and R. Zavarine. 1962. Correlation of Bacterial Radiosensitivity and DNA Base Composition. *Biochemical and Biophysical Research Communications*, 8:432–436.

Kasha, M. 1948. Transmission Filters for the Ultraviolet. *Journal of the Optical Society of America*, 38:929–934.

Marmur, J., W. F. Anderson, L. Matthews, K. Berns, E. Gajewska, D. Lane, and P. Doty. 1961. The Effects of Ultraviolet Light on the Biological and Physical Chemical Properties of Deoxyribonucleic Acids. *Journal of Cellular and Comparative Physiology*, Supplement 1, 58:33–55.

Meselson, M., F. W. Stahl, and J. Vinograd. 1957. Equilibrium Sedimentation of Macromolecules in Density Gradients. *Proceedings of the National Academy of Sciences of the U.S.A.*, 43:581–588.

Opara-Kubinska, Z., Z. Borowska, and W. Szybalski. 1963. Genetic Transformation Studies. III. Effect of UV Light on the Molecular Properties of Normal and Halogenated DNA. *Biochimica et biophysica acta*, 72:298–309.

Opara-Kubinska, Z., Z. Lorkiewicz, and W. Szybalski. 1961. Genetic Transformation Studies. II. Radiation Sensitivity of Halogen Labeled DNA. *Biochemical and Biophysical Research Communications*, 4:288–291.

Opara-Kubinska, Z., and W. Szybalski. 1962. Fractionation and Physicochemical Characterization of Genetic Markers in Transforming DNA. *Abstracts, Biophysical Society Sixth Annual Meeting*, February 14–16, 1962, Washington, D.C., p. WA8.

Roger, M., and R. D. Hotchkiss. 1961. Selective Heat Inactivation of Pneumococcal Transforming Deoxyribonucleate. *Proceedings of the National Academy of Sciences of the U.S.A.*, 47:653–669.

Sauerbier, W. 1961. The Influence of 5-Bromodeoxyuridine Substitution on UV Sensitivity, Host-Cell Reactivation, and Photoreactivation in T1 and P22*H5*. *Virology*, 15:465–472.

Stahl, F. W., J. M. Craseman, L. Okun, E. Fox, and C. Laird. 1961. Radiation Sensitivity of Bacteriophage Containing 5-Bromodeoxyuridine. *Virology*, 13:98–104.

Szybalski, W. 1960. Sampling of Virus Particles and Macromolecules Sedimented in an Equilibrium Density Gradient. *Experientia*, 16:164.

————. 1961. "Ultraviolet Light Sensitivity and Other Biological and Physicochemical Properties of Halogenated DNA," *Progress in Photobiology* (Proceedings of the 3rd International Congress on Photobiology. The Finsen Memorial Congress, Copenhagen, 1960), B. C. Christensen and B. Buchmann, Eds. Amsterdam, The Netherlands; London, England; New York, New York; and Princeton, New Jersey: Elsevier Publishing Company. Pp. 542–545.

————. 1962. "Properties and Applications of Halogenated Deoxyribonucleic Acids," *The Molecular Basis of Neoplasia* (The University of Texas M. D. Anderson Hospital and Tumor Institute, Fifteenth Annual Symposium on Fundamental Cancer Research). Austin, Texas: The University of Texas Press. Pp. 147–171.

Szybalski, W., and Z. Lorkiewicz. 1962. On the Nature of the Principal Target of Lethal and Mutagenic Radiation Effects. *Abhandlungen der Deutschen Akademie der Wissenschaften zu Berlin, Klasse für Medizin*, No. 1, pp. 63–71.

Szybalski, W., and H. D. Mennigmann. 1962. The Recording Spectrophotometer, an Automatic Device for Determining the Thermal Stability of Nucleic Acids. *Analytical Biochemistry*, 3:267–275.

Szybalski, W., and Z. Opara-Kubinska. 1961. DNA as Principal Determinant of Cell Radiosensitivity. (Abstract) *Radiation Research*, 14:508–509.

————. 1963. "Physico-chemical and Biological Properties of Genetic Markers in Transforming DNA," *Proceedings of the Symposium on Bacterial Transformation and Bacteriocinogeny*, Budapest, Hungary, Aug. 12–17, 1963.

Szybalski, W., Z. Opara-Kubinska, Z. Lorkiewicz, E. Ephrati-Elizur, and S. Zamenhof. 1960. Transforming Activity of Deoxyribonucleic Acid Labelled with 5-Bromouracil. *Nature*, London, 188:743–745.

Wacker, A., H. D. Mennigmann, and W. Szybalski. 1962. Effects of "Visible" Light on 5-Bromouracil-Labelled DNA. *Nature*, London, 196:685–686.

Yoshikawa, H., and N. Sueoka. 1963. Sequential Replication of *Bacillus subtilis* Chromosome. I. Comparison of Marker Frequencies in Exponential and Stationary Growth Phases. *Proceedings of the National Academy of Sciences of the U.S.A.*, 49:559–566.

Critical Structures Other than DNA as Sites for Primary Lesions of Cell Death Induced by Ionizing Radiations

P. Alexander, C. J. Dean, L. D. G. Hamilton, J. T. Lett, and G. Parkins

Chester Beatty Research Institute, Institute of Cancer Research: Royal Cancer Hospital, London, England

Introduction

The chain of events leading to biological damage after exposure to ionizing radiations has frequently been described in outline. The formation of chemically altered cell substituents as a result of their interaction with radiation is a key step, which we have called the primary lesions (Bacq and Alexander, 1961), since in vegetative cells where the lifetime of radicals is short, the radiation chemical reactions are complete in a fraction of a second. The dose of ionizing radiation which is necessary to modify the chemical constitution of an organic molecule does not vary widely, and radiochemical changes will therefore be distributed nearly at random throughout the cell and one type of substance (such as protein, fat, or nucleic acid) is unlikely to sustain a disproportionate amount of damage. Analysis of the cell immediately after irradiation cannot by itself tell us which reactions are important and which are not, since the key problem is to determine which of the many radiochemical reactions that are occurring are trivial and which constitute "primary lesions" for a particular biological end effect.

We have tried to obtain data for this process of elimination as far as cell death (defined as loss of ability to reproduce indefinitely) is concerned in two ways: (1) from studies on the site of action of treatments that modify sensitivity, and (2) by comparing the biochemistry of cells having different radiosensitivities. This last approach is fraught with difficulties since postirradiation events can prevent a primary lesion from manifesting itself (Alexander, 1962). The importance of postirradiation treatments was demonstrated by Ancel and Vitemberger in 1925. Accurate quantitative data were first provided for microorganisms by Stapleton, Billen, and Hollaender (1953), and, more recently, for mammalian cells by Elkind (see pages 442 to 461, this volume). Postirradiation modification of radiation response may involve either intracellular repair or the metabolic development of the lesion. At the present time it is not possible to distinguish whether a treatment given after irradiation, which reduces the extent of cell death, has assisted repair or hindered development; but for the sake of convenience all such processes will be referred to as recovery repair.

For an end-effect as complex as mitotic cell death, there can be little doubt (e.g. Powers, pages 286 to 304, this volume) that several kinds of radiochemical reactions in the cell can constitute a primary lesion; therefore it is not a question of finding one single "cause." The correct question is, "What are the relative contributions of several different kinds of primary lesions?" The order of importance will probably not be the same for all kinds of cells and may also alter as the conditions of radiation are altered. Certain modifications of DNA, brought about either by an ionization occurring within it or by reaction with radicals formed in the surrounding water, can obviously lead to cell death unless repaired. Several lines of evidence, notably the relationship between radiosensitivity and composition of DNA found by Kaplan and Zavarine (1962) in a series of bacteria, support the widely held view that radiochemical damage to DNA constitutes the principal primary lesion for cell death. The main changes in the macromolecular properties that are seen when DNA is irradiated as a dry substance or as a gel are cross-linking and main-chain scission (Lett and Alexander, 1961). Cross-linking was also found with the simple nucleoprotein in sperm head from salmon (Alexander and Stacey, 1959). These macromolecular changes in DNA did not meet the requirement for a primary lesion for cell death as far as sensitization by oxygen and increased effectiveness with linear energy transfer (LET) was concerned. In this paper we wish to summarize some recent experiments which indicate that for many kinds of cell death, radiochemical reactions which damage the cytoskeleton (for definition see Peters, 1964) constitute an important lesion which may be fatal by itself, or which may prevent important postirradiation repair processes from occurring.

Role of Postirradiation Recovery Processes in the Variation of Radiosensitivity of Mammalian Cells

The cause of the variation in radiosensitivity of different cells, and also between mutants from the same cell line, may be found either at the level of the primary lesion or in postirradiation metabolic process (*i.e.* repair, see p. 250). The dose of radiation necessary to establish a primary lesion may be modified by the presence of intracellular protective agents (e.g. sulfhydryl [SH] compounds) (Alexander, 1962; Alexander and Ormerod, 1962) or the size, shape, and multiplicity of the critical structure. Stapleton,

Billen, and Hollaender (1953) demonstrated that if postirradiation conditions are suitably adjusted, the difference in the radiosensitivity between a number of mutants of *Escherichia coli* largely disappeared; they concluded that the difference in sensitivity to X rays when assayed under standard conditions was mainly attributable to postirradiation phenomena (see Figure 1). Alexander and Mikulski (1961) isolated two strains of murine lymphoma cells derived from L5178Y which differed by a factor of two in radiosensitivity. Since then, a number of other mutants have been isolated (Lett and Leuchars, Unpublished data) in our laboratory. The karyotype (see Table 1) provides no clue to the nature of the differences, and it is interesting that a change from diploid to tetraploid did not alter the radiosensitivity of these mammalian cells. The finding (see Bacq and Alexander, 1961, 1964) that the resistant cells contained more nonprotein SH groups (presumably due to glutathione) suggested that intracellular chemical protection had made it necessary to increase the radiation dose to establish the primary lesion (see also Révész, Glas, and Hilding, 1963). Using the technique of postirradiation storage at a suboptimal temperature, first employed

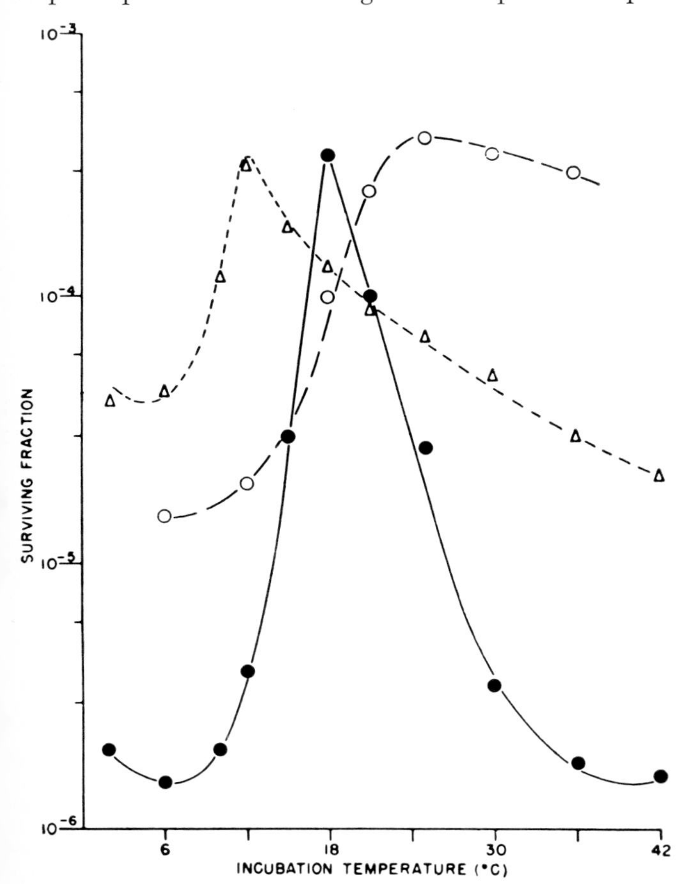

FIGURE 1. Survival of various *E. coli* strains after X-irradiation as a function of incubation temperature. ○, *E. coli* (Texas); △, *E. coli* (Crook); ●, *E. coli* (B/r). Stapleton, Billen, and Hollaender, 1963.)

TABLE 1

Mutants of L5178Y Murine Lymphoma Cells

Type†	DNA content mg/cell	Karyotype of 50 cells <39	39	40	41	>41	SH content ($M \times 10^{-16}$ per cell) Non-protein	Protein bound	Radio-sensitivity (D_0)
Resistant	0.80×10^{-8}	.	3	38	9	.	..	..	105
Sensitive	0.82×10^{-8}	.	3	42	4	1	..	..	50
Sensitive	0.94×10^{-8}	2	34	13	.	1	..	..	35
Resistant	0.82×10^{-8}	.	2	36	12	.	25.4	19.5	84
Sensitive	0.84×10^{-8}	.	4	40	6	.	8.7	19.9	35
Tetraploid from Resistant 2	1.4×10^{-8}	100% tetraploid actual numbers not counted					..	..	81

† "Resistant" lines are those established by taking cells directly from animals into culture. After some months of culturing, sensitive lines appear and are isolated by cloning. "Resistant" lines grow from one cell in adult DBA/2 whereas for "Sensitive" lines an inoculum between 10^3 and 10^4 cells is necessary for tumor growth.

by Stapleton, Billen, and Hollaender (1953), Beer, Lett, and Alexander (1963) found that the difference in sensitivity between the two lymphoma mutants studied so far may be related to postirradiation metabolic processes. Storing after irradiation at 31 C produced much less recovery in the resistant than in the sensitive strain. Consequently, under optimum recovery conditions, the difference in radiosensitivity between these mutants is reduced.

Why are the Micrococci *so Radioresistant?*

Micrococci in general are much more radioresistant than gram negative organisms, but pride of place belongs to *Micrococcus radiodurans* (Figure 2), an organism which was isolated by Anderson *et al.* (1956) from a tin of food which had spoiled after being treated with sterilizing doses of radiation. Table 2 shows that the DNA content and composition of *M. radiodurans* is not very different from that of the most sensitive microorganisms, e.g. *Pseudomonas fluorescens*. The *Micrococci* studied by us do not fit at all into the relationship proposed by Kaplan and Zavarine (1962), according to which D_0 increases with the guanine and cytosine (G-C) content of the cell's DNA. Inspection of the analyses given by Belozersky and Spirin (1960), on which the Kaplan and Zavarine hypothesis was based, shows that two other radioresistant organisms, *Sarcina lutea* ($D_0 = 17$ kr) and *M. lysodeikticus* ($D_0 = 15$ kr), have G-C contents in the same region as *Pseudomonas fluorescens*. By judicious selection, it would not be difficult to find a group of organisms for which the relationship between DNA composition and D_0 was the exact reverse to the one postulated.

If DNA is the site of the primary lesion for the resistant *Micrococci* and for *Pseudomonas fluorescens*, then it would be necessary to postulate that the former were either very heavily protected by an intracellular substance or possessed a quite exceptional capacity for repair. The suggestion has been made (Anderson *et al.*, 1956) that the pigment functions as a protective agent, but this is unlikely to be the whole story since we recently isolated a pigmentless mutant (see also Moseley, 1963) which is still very radioresistant (see Figure 2). In experiments carried out in conjunction with Miss T. Alper, the organism was also shown to be much more resistant to 8 Mev α-particles than was *E. coli* B/r. Chemical protection (Dale, Gray, and Meredith, 1949; Itzhaki and Alexander, 1961) occurs to a lesser extent with high LET radiations, and this is an added reason for rejecting the intracellular protection hypothesis. No experiments have been performed to test whether the *Micrococci* are able to repair damage more

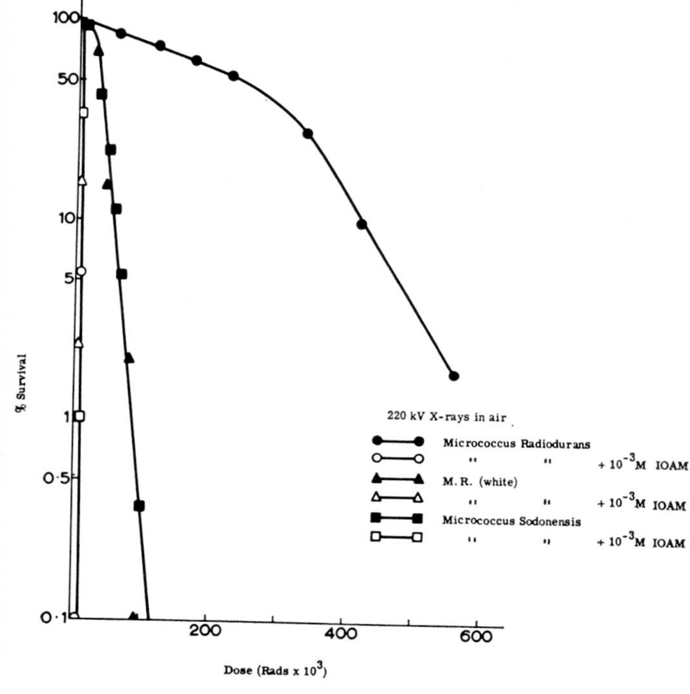

FIGURE 2. Effect of 220 kv X rays on *Micrococcus radiodurans* and a pigmentless mutant (M. R. white) of the same organism. Irradiation with 220 kvp X rays (10^4 r/min) was performed under aerobic conditions either in phosphate buffer at pH 7 or in phosphate buffer containing 10^{-3} M iodoacetamide.

TABLE 2

Relationship between DNA Content and Composition and Radiosensitivity of Some Microorganisms

ORGANISM	Do† (× 10^3)	DNA/CELL MG	BASE COMPOSITION G	A	C	T
Pseudomonas fluorescens	1.6	1.8×10^{-11}	33.0	18.2	30.0	18.8‡
E. coli B/r	5.0	1.5×10^{-11}	26.4	23.1	25.1	25.0‡
Staph. aureus	5.0	7.4×10^{-12}	17.3	32.3	17.4	33.0‡
M. sodonensis	15.0	3.4×10^{-12}	35.4	14.6	35.1	14.9
M. radiodurans	93	1.9×10^{-12}	36.0	18.1	28.3	17.6
M. radiodurans pigmentless mutant	17	9.1×10^{-12}	..	..	..	..

† Irradiated in pH 7.2 phosphate buffer with 220 kv X rays.
‡ Values taken from Belozersky and Spirin.
Abbreviations used above: G, guanine; A, adenine; C, cytosine; T, tyrosine.

effectively than are the more radiosensitive bacteria. If the difference in radiosensitivity is not due to postirradiation repair, then the fact that the dose needed to kill *M. radiodurans* is of the same order as that needed to inactivate viruses, where the primary lesion seems certain to involve DNA, would appear to demand that radiochemical damage of DNA is responsible for the killing of *M. radiodurans* by ionizing radiations. There are two corollaries to such a hypothesis: (1) A radiochemical reaction which does not involve DNA is the chief cause for cell death of the more sensitive microorganisms such as *E. coli* B and *Pseudomonas fluorescens;* and (2) *M. radiodurans* for structural reasons is not susceptible to such a lesion. A very striking inverse relationship between sensitivity to penicillin and sensitivity to X rays (Thornley, 1964) may be an indication that the cell wall and membrane are involved in the mystery lesion in bacteria or in the process involved in postirradiation repair.

Effect of Bromouracil on Postirradiation Recovery Processes

Szybalski's (1962) demonstration that cells grown in the presence of BU or 5-bromodeoxyuridine (BUdR) under conditions in which these bases become incorporated into DNA are much more sensitive to ionizing radiations, has been explained on the basis that DNA was the site of the primary lesion. Szybalski favors the hypothesis that the introduction of a bulky bromine atom makes the DNA more liable to undergo main-chain scission at the phosphate ester bond (see Figure 3). It must not be forgotten that the halogenated pyrimidines and their nucleosides are substances of high biological activity and have many other actions in cells besides being incorporated into DNA. They were originally developed as cytotoxic agents for

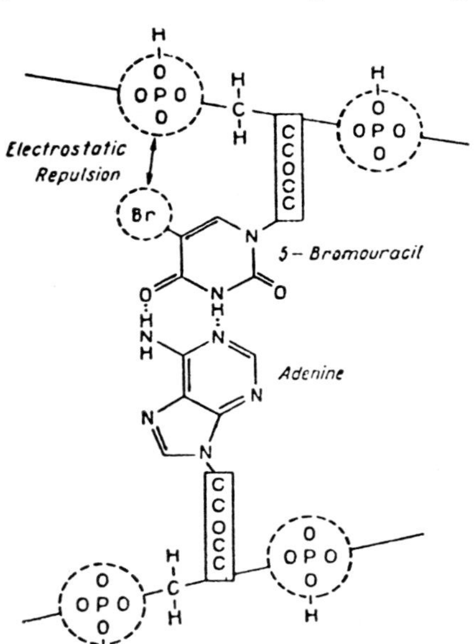

FIGURE 3. Diagrammatic representation of the steric relationship between the phosphate groups and the halogen (the latter replacing the methyl group of thymine) in the DNA molecule, represented by the adenine-5-bromouracil deoxynucleotide pair. The electrostatic repulsion is postulated to render the main-chain-ester link more labile. (Szybalski, 1962.)

the chemotherapy of cancer. Our investigations indicate that their well-established effect as enzyme poisons may play an important part in the radiosensitization of cells.

Using the method described by Kaplan, Smith, and Tomlin (1962), we have prepared DNA from *E. coli* B/r in which 50 per cent of the thymine was replaced by BU and have compared some radiochemical changes following irradiation, both in dilute solution and in the dry state, with those seen in normal DNA. In dilute solution, main-chain scission is produced by OH radical attack and this can be measured by a fall in viscosity (Taylor, Greenstein, and Hollaender, 1948). The substitution of 50 per cent of thymine by BU did not influence the radiation-induced degradation, nor did it render the DNA more susceptible to "spontaneous" scission on standing in solution at 37 C (Figure 4). When DNA is irradiated in the form of dry fibers, a striking change in macromolecular properties is the formation of covalent bonds between different "double strands" until a cross-linked network is produced which is no longer soluble (Lett, Stacey, and Alexander, 1961). Substitution of BU for thymine did not affect this reaction either (Table 3). The possibility that the BU ring system is more sensitive to radiation damage has not been eliminated, and this remains a possibility which can contribute to sensitization by BU, especially at very high levels of incorporation into DNA.

These model experiments are, of course, very far removed from the condition in which DNA is irradiated within the cell; therefore we measured the *in situ* sensitivity of DNA with different BU contents by irradiating *E. coli* B/r which had been grown in BU-containing medium according to the method of Kaplan, Smith, and Tomlin (1962). The cells were ir-

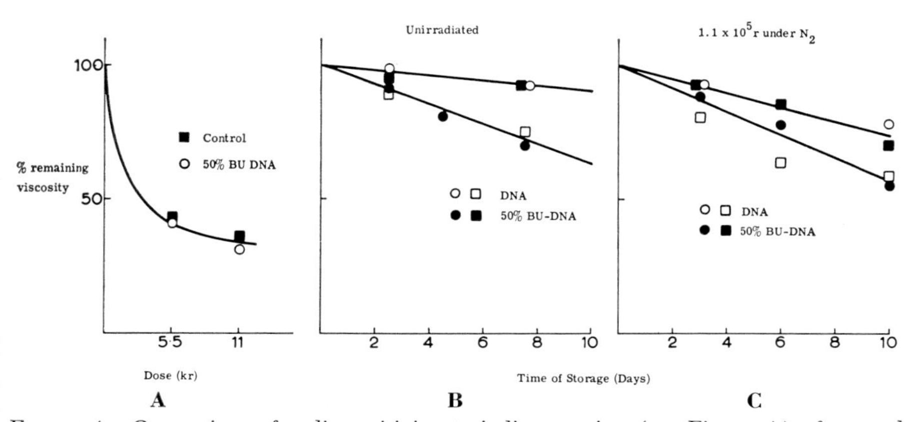

FIGURE 4. Comparison of radiosensitivity to indirect action (see Figure A) of normal DNA and DNA in which 50 per cent of the thymine was replaced by BU as measured by viscosity changes. The DNA was irradiated at a concentration of 0.05 per cent with 220 kvp X rays in nitrogen. Figure (B and C) shows that incorporation of BU does not alter the rate of spontaneous degradation which occurs on standing of dilute solutions of DNA at 37 C (bottom line) and at 0 C (top line). The same applies to irradiated and unirradiated DNA.

TABLE 3

Effect of Incorporation of Bromouracil on Chemical Changes Produced in DNA (Extracted from E. coli *B/r) by Irradiation in the Solid State with* Co^{60} *γ-Rays* in vacuo‡

A: *Cross-linking*	% DNA RENDERED INSOLUBLE* NORMAL DNA	50% THYMINE* REPLACED BY BU
DNA fibers containing 20% of water—3 × 10^6 rads	32%	28%
DNA fibers containing 5% of water—30 × 10^6 rads	48%	52%
B: *Base damage*	RATIO OF THYMINE TO BROMOURACIL†	
Unirradiated	50	50
30 × 10^6 rads	50	50

* Removed as gel by centrifuging solution at 30,000 *g* for 1 hour.
† Determined chromatographically on anion exchange column as nucleotides produced by enzymatic digestion.
‡ Parkins, Unpublished data.

radiated at 0 C at a dose rate of 10^4 r/min and lysed immediately after irradiation. In this way it was hoped to limit changes in the DNA to the initial radiochemical reactions and to avoid postirradiation effects. The DNA was isolated by the method of Kirby (1959), and its viscosity and sedimentation constant determined. Viscosity measurements alone cannot distinguish between a fall in molecular weight caused by main-chain scission and a change in shape caused by cross-linking. Both reactions would lead to a fall in viscosity, but the sedimentation constant decreases with main-chain scission and increases on cross-linking. When the two measurements are considered together, it is clear that when the DNA of *E. coli* B/r is irradiated *in situ* there is no cross-linking and the only change in macromolecular proportion is a reduction in the molecular weight resulting from

TABLE 4

Effect of Bromouracil Incorporation in Degradation of DNA Extracted from E. coli *B/r Immediately after Exposure to X Rays (1.1 × 10^5r delivered at 10^4r/min at 0 C in oxygen)*

PERCENTAGE OF THYMINE REPLACED BY BU	BEFORE IRRADIATION VISCOSITY†	BEFORE IRRADIATION SEDIMENTATION CONSTANT‡	AFTER IRRADIATION VISCOSITY†	AFTER IRRADIATION SEDIMENTATION CONSTANT‡
0	97	28.6	65	22.8
.	106	26.8	. .	. .
7	. .	. .	62	23.0
18	. .	. .	61	. .
31	98	27.0	52	20.8
50	105	28.0	66	20.4
.	103	27.8	63	24.1
Molecular weight based on average values:	1) from viscosity = 11.0 × 10^6 2) from sedimentation = 10.8 × 10^6		1) from viscosity = 7.2 × 10^6 2) from sedimentation = 6.5 × 10^6	

† dl/dg extrapolated to zero sheer and zero concentration using Couette viscometer.
‡ S_{20}w measured with ultraviolet optics.

main-chain scission. Table 4 shows quite unambiguously that the replacement of from 7 to 50 per cent of thymine by BU does not affect the X ray-induced degradation of DNA when irradiated within the cell. These experiments fail to lend support to the hypothesis of Szybalski (1962) that the phosphate ester link is weakened by BU.

We have been unable to show (see Table 5) a direct correlation between the extent of BU incorporation and radiosensitivity with either *E. coli* B/r or murine lymphoma cells in vitro. In the bacteria and in the resistant lymphoma strain, sensitization is initially dependent on the extent of BU incorporation but tends to a maximum after 20 per cent of the thymine residues have been substituted.

TABLE 5

Extent of Bromouracil Incorporation on Radiosensitivity (X rays in air)

	E. coli B/r	Resistant lymphoma cells in vitro			Sensitive lymphoma cells in vitro		
% BU†	Sensitization factor	% BU†	D_0	Sensitization factor	% BU†	D_0	Sensitization factor
0		0	81		0	39	
9	1.7	9	50	1.6	21	33	1.2
18	2.4	31	32	2.5	32	28	1.4
31	2.6	56	31	2.6	.	.	.
50	2.8	.	.	.	.	.	.

† Refers to fraction of thymine in the DNA replaced by bromouracil.

In relation to the mechanism of sensitization by BU incorporation, the finding (Alexander *et al.*, 1963) that incorporation of BU has a far smaller sensitizing effect on the radiosensitive mutant seems particularly important. The difference in radiosensitivity between the two lines disappears almost completely if they have been grown in BUdR-containing medium when the sensitivity of the resistant strain is reduced to that of the sensitive strain (Table 5). Since the greater sensitivity of one of these strains can be ascribed to impairment in postirradiation recovery processes (Beer, Lett, and Alexander, 1963), it is tempting to suggest that the principal effect of BU incorporation is also interference with recovery from radiation. With the radiosensitive mutant growth in BUdR containing medium only leads to sensitization if the incorporation of BU is greater than 20 per cent and the effect increases with increasing substitution. The phenomenon of sensitization with these cells is qualitatively different from the sensitization of the resistant strain which is pronounced at relatively low amounts of incorporation. In the sensitive cells the effect of BU on radiosensitivity is probably due to a radiochemical effect involving a primary lesion in the DNA. This aspect has been discussed by Lett, Parkins, Alexander, and Ormerod (1964).

In principle, BU substitution in DNA could influence postirradiation recovery processes either by interfering with metabolic repair of radiation-damaged DNA (a possibility envisaged by Szybalski [1962]) or by acting as an enzyme inhibitor. The second mechanism implies that BU, when incorporated in DNA, blocks an enzyme or enzymes, which play a part in the physiological process of repairing radiation-damaged DNA. Our data do not enable us to distinguish decisively between these two possibilities, but the fact that sensitization becomes progressively less dependent on the extent of incorporation seems to make it rather less likely that for the sensitization of cells, the important effect of BU is that metabolic repair processes which can restore DNA damaged at a thymine residue cannot repair damage at the site of BU incorporation. Conversely, we have always noticed that treatments with BU (or BUdR) which are sufficient to sensitize give rise to toxic manifestations in the cell culture, shown by both reduced growth rate and loss of colony-forming ability of some of the cells. Halogenated pyrimidines have been shown to poison several enzymes (Delamore and Prusoff, 1962) and to interfere with biosynthetic reactions (Simon, 1963). It is therefore not an unreasonable postulate to suggest that BU incorporated into DNA blocks enzymes that specifically act on DNA. It must be stressed that this discussion is concerned solely with ionizing radiations, and we have carried out no experiments relating to sensitization to ultraviolet light. Also, the sensitization of viruses and transforming principle to ionizing radiations by BU may well occur by a different mechanism from that involved in the sensitization of whole cells.

Influence of Dose-Modifying Treatments on Degradation of Intracellularly Irradiated DNA

The radiosensitivity of *E. coli* B/r to X rays can be varied by a factor greater than 10 by applying various dose-modifying procedures during irradiation. Protection by sulfhydryl compounds and by high concentrations of alcohols and sensitization by oxygen are thought to be the result of a modification of the primary lesion. A radiochemical reaction that is considered as a possibly important primary lesion under aerobic irradiation conditions should accordingly be reduced in magnitude by protective agents and increased in the presence of oxygen. If several lesions contribute, it is quite conceivable that some may be affected to a greater extent than others

TABLE 6

Effect of Dose-Modifying Treatments on Degradation of DNA Extracted from E. coli *B/r (dose 1.1 × 10⁵r; all irradiation at 0 C with gas bubbling)*

Treatment	Radiosensitivity D_o	Viscosity†	Sedimentation constant‡
No irradiation	. .	97	26.1
Irradiated in oxygen	5.0×10^3r	61	21.8
Irradiated in oxygen and 6M glycerol	16×10^3r	59	21.2
Irradiated in nitrogen	17×10^3r	64	23.3
Irradiated in nitrogen and 6M glycerol	40×10^3r	63	22.1

† dl/dg extrapolated to zero sheer and zero concentration using Couette viscometer.
‡ S_{20}w measured with ultraviolet optics.

by dose-modifying treatments. The damage to DNA measured by a fall in molecular weight for cells irradiated under a range of different conditions is summarized in Table 6. In the experiments shown in Table 6, the cells were irradiated at 0 C, and the DNA was extracted immediately after irradiation to reduce the likelihood of postirradiation reactions such as action of DNAse. The viscosity and sedimentation constant of samples which contained less than 1 per cent of protein were measured. The damage produced by an x-ray dose of 1.1×10^5 r was, within experimental error, the same in every case.

If the hypothesis is accepted that the mode of action of the dose-modifying treatments is at the level of the primary lesion, then these experiments would appear to show that the extent of main-chain scission of DNA produced by an initial radiochemical process is not related to cell death. These experiments do not exclude the possibility that a reaction in DNA other than main-chain scission may be the primary lesion. Such a hypothesis would, however, require that the dose-modifying treatments influence the "lethal" kind of radiation damage in DNA without affecting main-chain scission. In the case of sensitization by oxygen, a qualitative difference in reaction product is very likely; but for protection with SH compounds and high concentrations of alcohols, there is no evidence for such selectivity in the radiation chemistry of DNA (Ormerod and Alexander, 1963). The hypothesis we favor is that some dose-modifying agents act in preventing damage to intracellular fine structures and the protectors can then be envisaged to act by preventing damage by radiation to the system in the cell responsible for restoring damage done to the DNA. Such radiation-induced "membrane" damage may reduce the ability of the cell to undergo repair after irradiation.

The Site of Action of Some Radiosensitizers and Radioprotectors in Bacteria

Bacteria are rendered much more sensitive to X rays if they are irradiated in the presence of chemically reactive compounds such as iodoacetamide, divinyl sulphone, and phenylmercuric benzoate (Dean, 1962; Bridges, 1962) which share the property of combining rapidly with sulfhydryl groups. The extent of sensitization increases with the radioresistance of the organisms; for *M. radiodurans*, dose-modifying factors of up to 70 have been reported (Dean and Alexander, 1962; Lee, Anderson, and Elliker, 1963; Bruce, 1963).

The mechanism of action is still quite obscure, but preliminary investigations using electron spin resonance (ESR) (Ormerod, Unpublished data) suggest that these sensitizers combine readily with radiation-induced radicals. In the context of the present paper, the interesting aspect is that these sensitizers do not penetrate throughout the bacterial cell. Iodoacetamide and hydroxymercuric benzoate at a concentration of 10^{-3} M sensitize to radiation (see Figure 2 and Table 7) but do not reduce the ability of *Micrococcus sodonensis* to metabolize pyruvate aerobically, as measured in a Warburg apparatus. The pyruvate oxidase system is known to be extremely sensitive to SH poisons since it contains several SH enzymes (*cf.* Peters, 1964). After the cells had been disrupted in a Hughes press, addition of iodoacetamide completely eliminated the activity of sulfhydryl enzymes. Chemical determination of total SH groups in the cell also shows that in the intact cell only 20 per cent of these groups were accessible to chloromercuric benzoate. The conclusion seems justified that iodoacetamide and mercuric benzoate derivatives, while not able to penetrate the cell, are yet able to modify greatly the radiation response.

TABLE 7

*Radiosensitization by Iodoacetamide**

	LD_{63}† (AEROBIC)	
ORGANISM†	NORMAL	+ 10^{-3}M IODOACETAMIDE
E. coli B/r	13×10^3r	3×10^3r
Micrococcus sodonensis	38×10^3r	3×10^3r
Micrococcus radiodurans	263×10^3r	8×10^3r
Micrococcus radiodurans pigmentless mutant	45×10^3r	3×10^3r

* Dean and Alexander, 1962.
† Irradiated in pH 7 phosphate buffer, exposed to iodoacetamide for 20 min at 20 C before irradiation with 220 kv X rays.

Electron spin resonance studies (Baker, Ormerod, and Alexander, Unpublished data) provide evidence that cysteamine does not permeate throughout *E. coli* B/r under conditions in which it offers a considerable degree of protection. Ormerod and Alexander (1962, 1963) found that in protein and nucleic acids, cysteamine reacted with radiation-produced radicals by a hydrogen transfer process which "repaired" the original radical, and gave rise to a new sulfur radical which could be readily detected in the ESR spectrum:

$$\mathrm{RH} \longrightarrow \underset{\text{(radiation produced organic radical)}}{\mathrm{R^\bullet}} + \mathrm{H^\bullet}$$

$$\mathrm{R^\bullet} + \underset{\text{(SH protector)}}{\mathrm{PSH}} \longrightarrow \underset{\text{("repaired" radical)}}{\mathrm{RH}} + \underset{\text{(new sulphur radical seen in ESR spectrum)}}{\mathrm{PS^\bullet}}$$

If nucleic acids or proteins are mixed with cysteamine and irradiated at −196 C, the sulfur radical appears after irradiation on standing at room temperature, since at the temperature of liquid nitrogen, diffusion of radicals does not occur and the "repair" reaction only takes place on warming. In Figure 5 is shown the appearance of a typical sulfur radical when *E. coli* B/r cells, damaged by repeated freezing and thawing or by being put through a Hughes press, were irradiated in the presence of cysteamine. However, if intact cells are suspended in a solution of cysteamine and then

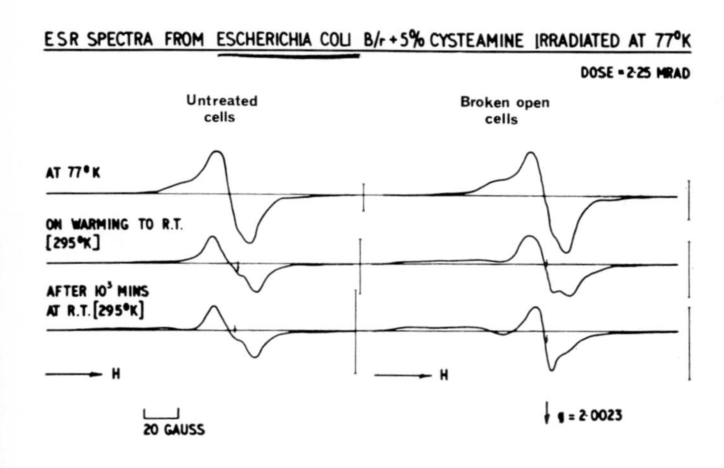

FIGURE 5. Electron spin resonance spectra of dry *E. coli* B/r irradiated at —196 C with Co^{60} γ-rays. The presence of cysteamine gave rise only to —S• radicals if added to cells that had been damaged by repeated freezing and thawing. (—S• radicals give the broad signal on the low "H" side of the spectrum.) (Baker, Ormored, and Alexander, Unpublished data.)

freeze-dried, a sulfur radical cannot be detected; yet under these conditions cysteamine protects the cells against radiation-induced cell death. The inability of cysteamine to react to a measurable extent with the radicals produced in intact cells indicates that this substance is prevented from penetrating into the interior of the cell where, of course, the majority of the radicals are formed, unless the cell has been damaged first.

The fact that both iodoacetamide and cysteamine alter the radiosensitivity of bacteria, while being unable to permeate throughout the cell, suggests that these effects are achieved by reactions that occur at or near the cell membrane. Since there are reasons for believing that these substances modify the initial chemical changes produced by irradiation, the plasma membrane is indicated as the site of an important primary lesion. The possibility must also be considered that the dose-modifying action of SH substances like cysteamine and SH poisons consists in changing the physiological state of the cell, in which case their site of action need not be related to the primary lesion.

"Enzyme Release" in the Nucleus

In mammalian cells the plasma membrane is unlikely to be a critical structure for mitotic cell death, *i.e.* death following after one or two divisions. There are indications that structural elements which regulate enzyme activity in the nucleus, e.g. nuclear membrane or cytoskeleton, may be the site of a primary lesion. Furlan, Hamilton, and Alexander (1962) observed with lymphoma cells that a nuclear ribonuclease (RNase) moved into the cytoplasm. After irradiation, the total RNase content per cell was not changed, but the distribution between the cytoplasm and the nucleus was altered (Table 8). There were indications that exposure to X rays also led to a decrease in high molecular weight nuclear RNA, though the total amount of RNA per nucleus was not detectably altered. Possibly these ex-

TABLE 8

*Influence of Radiation on Distribution of RNase in Nucleus and Cytoplasm of L5178Y Lymphoma Cells**

Treatment	RNase activity (arbitrary units) No irradiation Nucleus	Cytoplasm	After irradiation Nucleus	Cytoplasm	Loss/mm nucleus
Irradiated with 2000r in vivo†					
Analyzed ½ hour later	1.16	2.38	0.98	2.60	—16%
Analyzed 2 hours later	0.93	2.35	0.54	2.38	—42%
Irradiated—under Nitrogen—‡ with 2000r in vitro					
Analyzed ½ hour later	1.11	5.95	0.97	6.39	—13%
Analyzed 1 hour later	1.08	4.33	0.66	5.70	—39%

* Furlan, Hamilton, and Alexander. 1962.
† Animals and cells underwent exactly the same manipulation except the X-ray machine was not turned on.
‡ The cells were in the peritoneal cavity and were probably anoxic.

perimental results represented an example of "enzyme release"; radiation allowed RNase to escape from its "compartment" in the nucleus, and this resulted in degradation of nuclear RNA; there are, of course, other ways in which the distribution of nuclear RNA could be altered.

Technically it proved extremely difficult to prepare sufficient nuclear RNA to characterize fully the changes that had taken place; therefore, a modified technique was employed to follow the effect of radiation on nuclear RNA (Hamilton, 1963). The cells were incubated for five minutes with tritiated uridine. This pulse-labeling technique insured that at the end of this period, only nuclear RNA had become radioactive. In agreement with modern theories of RNA synthesis, no radioactive RNA was found in the cytoplasm (if pulse-labeled cells are incubated after irradiation, the radioactive RNA migrates from the nucleus to the cytoplasm; under normal growth conditions, this movement needs about three hours to be half com-

TABLE 9

Effect of X Rays on Nuclear RNA in Lymphoma Cells

Cells in culture —(*5 min H^3-uridine followed by "cold" uridine*)→ *pulse labeled cells* —(*X rays in aerated suspension*)→ *irradiated cells* —(*incubated for 15 min*)→ *cells for analysis*

RNA fractions‡	Specific activity (c.p.m. × 10^{-3}/mg. RNA) Immediately after "pulse labeling"	15 min incubation† (No irradiation)	15 min incubation after 500r	15 min incubation after 1000r
I: extracted with pH 7.1 buffer	18	46	49	34
II: extracted with 2M NaCl	108	194	184	184
III: Insoluble residue	286	382	324	256

† The total activity increasing during incubation due to utilization of H^3 uridine in acid soluble pool.
‡ Fractions precipitated with acid, washed and hydrolyzed with alkali; prior to assay.

plete) by autoradiography, and the highest radioactivity was associated with fractions (Table 9) in which one would expect to find messenger RNA. Cells that had been pulse labeled were immediately exposed to X rays and then allowed to stand for 15 minutes under normal growth conditions. At the end of this brief incubation period the cells were homogenized, the nuclear RNA was fractionated, and the specific radioactivity of the fractions determined. Table 9 illustrates a typical experiment which shows that X rays cause a loss of labeled RNA from the nucleus. No such change is observed if the cells are maintained at 0 C instead of 37 C during and after irradiation. Evidence for an altered distribution of labeled RNA could already be detected after an incubation of only five minutes; this constitutes perhaps the earliest biochemical lesion seen in irradiated mammalian cells. Mechanisms can readily be envisaged by which damage of messenger RNA could lead to delayed cell death in cultures of rapidly dividing cells. Experiments are now under way to see if there is a relation between the movement of RNase and the changes found in nuclear RNA after irradiation.

These experiments augment the earlier observations by Creasy and Stocken (1959) that soon after irradiation, leakage occurs from the nuclei of lymphocytes. Ten years ago Bacq and Alexander put forward the hypothesis, subsequently called "enzyme release," that an initial radiochemical reaction can disrupt the cytoskeleton of the cell, and can thereby make it possible for enzymes to act on substrates which are normally shielded. The division of the cell into compartments is attained by a variety of structures, and by no means all of them have yet been identified (*cf.* Peters, 1964). Some, like mitochondria (Scaife and Alexander, 1961), are not affected by radiation, and it is our postulate that there are some structures which are altered after doses in the D_0 range. Damage of this type might be lethal on its own or could lead to impairment in the repair capability of the cell. Since the end effect is determined both by the magnitude of the lethal reaction and by the extent of repair, primary radiochemical reactions which interfere with repair are important primary lesions. Damage to the cytoskeleton may well be a primary lesion connected with reduction of repair.

Conclusions

Much research has been directed over the last 60 years to establish the nature of the primary lesions for cell death induced by X rays and related radiations. Recent developments in molecular biology have shown that radiation damage to DNA can result in lethal point mutations; consequently, certain radiochemical changes in DNA must constitute one such primary lesion. The mechanism by which chromosome abnormalities are produced is unknown, but the suggestion has been made that they also are the result of radiochemical changes in DNA. In any case, the radiochemical reaction that initiates the chain of events leading to a large deletion of chromosome material is another primary lesion in mitotic cell death. In this paper we have tried to show that there is no convincing reason for believing that damage to DNA is the primary lesion which determines radiosensitivity. We have some indications that radiochemical damage which affects intracellular fine structures may be an important primary lesion, and for some cells perhaps the most important. It is always a question of the relative contribution of different reactions to the over-all effect, and not a question of whether one particular reaction is or is not *the* cause of cell death. We need experiments that allow us to determine the order of merit of the different lethal reactions and to study how the various dose-modifying procedures affect the different primary lesions. The fact that postirradiation processes have a decisive influence in determining the end effect (e.g. the magnitude of D_0) immensely complicates the situation. When comparing different cells or different dose-modifying treatments, the possibility must always be borne in mind that a change in radiosensitivity need not arise from a change in susceptibility of the lesions which is actually lethal. Indeed, the problem as to the nature of the primary lesions may have to wait until something is known about the kind of reactions that are involved in repair and in injury development. These processes may be radiosensitive themselves, and radiochemical reactions (in primary lesions) which modify postirradiation reactions, may be decisive in determining radiosensitivity. If damage to DNA by irradiation is very effectively restored then interference by radiation with the repair process will be the most important lesion even when the cause of death is damage to DNA.

Summary

This paper is concerned with the question whether radiochemical changes in deoxyribonucleic acid (DNA) constitute the principal primary lesion for mitotic cell death following irradiation with X rays.

Examples are given where variations in the radiosensitivity of mammalian cells can be attributed to postirradiation recovery phenomena and a comparison of cells having different D_0 cannot be used to investigate the primary lesion. It is interesting that tetraploid and diploid mutants of leukemia cells had the same radiosensitivity.

Some very radioresistant *Micrococci* have DNA with base ratios which are very similar to those of the most sensitive microorganisms. The presence of intracellular protective agents does not seem to explain the radioresistance of the *Micrococci*.

Radiochemical experiments show that DNA is not rendered more susceptible to damage (measured physicochemically) if thymine is replaced by bromouracil (BU) when irradiated in solution or within the cell. Sensitization of cells approaches a limit with increasing BU incorporation, and a radiosensitive mutant is sensitized much less. Sensitization by BU seems to be a phenomenon acting primarily at the level of postirradiation recovery.

The effect of irradiation on the molecular weight of DNA extracted from cells immediately after irradiation is the same whether the cells were protected by anoxia, glycerol, or cysteamine or were exposed under normal aerobic conditions.

Under conditions in which microorganisms are sensitized by iodoacetamide or protected by cysteamine, neither of these substances penetrates into the interior of the cell.

Within 15 minutes of irradiation of leukemia cells, changes in nuclear ribonucleic acid (RNA) can be detected which might be caused by a release of nuclear RNase.

ACKNOWLEDGMENTS

This investigation was supported by grants to the Chester Beatty Research Institute (Institute of Cancer Research: Royal Cancer Hospital) from the Medical Research Council, the British Empire Cancer Campaign, and the National Cancer Institute of the National Institutes of Health, United States Public Health Service.

REFERENCES

Alexander, P. 1962. On the Mode of Action of Some Treatments that Influence the Radiation Sensitivity of Cells. *Transactions of the New York Academy of Sciences*, Series II, 24:966–978.

Alexander, P., J. Beer, C. Dean, J. T. Lett, and G. F. Parkins. 1963. The Role of Post-irradiation Recovery Processes in Sensitisation to X-Rays by Bromodesoxyuridine. *British Journal of Radiology*, 36:860.

Alexander, P., and Z. B. Mikulski. 1961. Mouse Lymphoma Cells with Different Radiosensitivities. *Nature*, London, 192:572–573.

Alexander, P., and M. G. Ormerod. 1962. "Repair of the Primary Chemical Lesion: A Unitary Hypothesis for Radiosensitization by Oxygen and Protection by Sulphydryl Compounds," *Biological Effects of Ionizing Radiation at the Molecular Level*. Vienna, Austria: International Atomic Energy Agency. Pp. 399–410.

Alexander, P., and K. A. Stacey. 1959. Crosslinking of Deoxyribonucleic Acid in Sperm Heads by Ionizing Radiations. *Nature*, London, 184:958–960.

Ancel, P., and P. Vitemberger. 1925. Sur la Radiosensibilité Cellulaire. *Compte rendus de Societe Biologie*, Paris, 92:517–520.

Anderson, A. W., H. C. Nordan, R. F. Cain, G. Parrish, and D. Duggan. 1956. Studies on a Radioresistant *Micrococcus*. I. Isolation Morphology. Cultural Characteristics and Resistance to Gamma Radiation. *Food Technology*, 10:575–577.

Bacq, Z. M., and P. Alexander. 1961. *Fundamentals of Radiobiology*. 2nd Ed. Oxford, England: Pergamon Press, 555 pp.

————. 1964. "*Oxygen in the Animal Organism*," Proceedings of a Symposium held in London, 1963. Oxford, England: Pp. 509–535. Pergamon Press.

Baker, A., M. G. Ormerod, and P. Alexander. Unpublished data.

Barendsen, G. W. 1962. Dose Survival Curve of Human Cells in Tissue Culture Irradiated with Alpha-, Beta-, 20-KV. X- and 200-KV. X-Radiation. *Nature*, London, 193:1153–1155.

Beer, J. Z., J. T. Lett, and P. Alexander. 1963. Influence of Temperature and Medium on the X-Ray Sensitivities of Leukaemia Cells *in vitro*. *Nature*, London, 199:193–194.

Belozersky, A. N., and A. S. Spirin. 1960. "Chemistry of the Nucleic Acids of Microorganisms," *The Nucleic Acids*, E. Chargaff and J. N. Davidson, Eds. New York, New York, and London, England: Academic Press. Vol. III. Pp. 147–185.

Bridges, B. A. 1962. The Chemical Sensitization of *Pseudomonas* Species to Ionizing Radiation. *Radiation Research*, 16:232–242.

Bruce, A. K. 1963. Modification of the Radiation Response of a Highly Resistant Bacterium. *Radiation Research*, 18:237–240.

Dale, W. M., L. H. Gray, and J. W. Meredith. 1949. The Inactivation of Carboxypeptidase by X- and α-Radiation. *Philosophical Transactions of the Royal Society*, A, 242: 33–62.

Dean, C. J. 1962. Sensitisation of Bacteria by Iodoacetamide. *British Journal of Radiology*, 35:73–74.

————. Unpublished data.

Dean, C. J., and P. Alexander. 1962. Sensitization of Radio-resistant Bacteria to X-Rays by Iodoacetamide. *Nature*, London, 196:1324–1326.

Dean, C. J., and J. T. Lett. Unpublished data.

Dean, C. J., and G. Parkins. Unpublished data.

Delamore, I. W., and W. H. Prusoff. 1962. Effect of IUDR on the Biosynthesis of Phosphorylated Derivatives of Thymidine. *Biochemical Pharmacology*, 11:101–112.

Furlan, M., L. D. G. Hamilton, and P. Alexander. 1962. Release of RNAse Bound in the Nucleus of Lymphoma Cells Following X-Irradiation. *Abstracts Second International Congress of Radiation Research* (Harrogate), p. 205. (See also Proceedings of Congress. M. Ebert and A. Howard, Eds. Amsterdam, The Netherlands: North-Holland Publishing Company. Pp. 435–436.)

Hamilton, L. D. G. 1963. "Damage of Nuclear RNA by X-Rays," *41st Annual Report of the British Empire Cancer Campaign*. Pp. 61–62.

————. Unpublished data.

Hollaender, A., and G. E. Stapleton. 1954. Modification of Radiation Damage After Exposure to X-Rays. *British Journal of Radiology*, 27:117–121.

Itzhaki, R. F., and P. Alexander. 1961. The Effect of Polonium Alpha Rays on the Physical Properties of Polyethylene and of Polymethyl Methacrylate. *Radiation Research*, 15:553–560.

Kaplan, H. S., K. C. Smith, and P. A. Tomlin. 1962. Effect of Halogenated Pyrimidines on Radiosensitivity of *E. coli*. *Radiation Research*, 16:98–113.

Kaplan, H. S., and R. Zavarine. 1962. Correlation of Bacterial Radiosensitivity and DNA Base Composition. *Biochemical and Biophysical Research Communications*, 8:432–436.

Kirby, K. S. 1959. The Preparation of Deoxyribonucleic Acids by the *p*-Aminosalicylate-Phenol Method. *Biochimica et biophysica acta*, 36:117–124.

Lee, J. S., A. W. Anderson, and P. R. Elliker. 1963. The Radiation-Sensitizing Effects of *N*-Ethylmaleimide and Iodoacetic Acid on a Radiation Resistant *Micrococcus*. *Radiation Research*, 19:593–598.

Lett, J. T., and P. Alexander. 1961. Crosslinking and Degradation of Deoxyribonucleic Acid Gels with Varying Water Contents When Irradiated with Electrons. *Radiation Research*, 15:159–173.

Lett, J. T., K. A. Stacey, and P. Alexander. 1961. Crosslinking of Dry Deoxyribonucleic Acids by Electrons. *Radiation Research*, 14:349–362.

Moseley, B. E. B. 1963. The Variation in X-Ray Resistance of *Micrococcus radiodurans* and Some of its Less-Pigmented Mutants. *International Journal of Radiation Biology and Related Studies in Physics, Chemistry and Medicine*, 6:489.

Ormerod, M. G. Unpublished data.

Ormerod, M. G., and P. Alexander. 1962. Repair of Radiation Damage in a Nucleoprotein by Cysteamine. *Nature*, London, 193:290–291.

————. 1963. On the Mechanism of Radiation Protection by Cysteamine: An Investigation by Means of Electron Spin Resonance. *Radiation Research*, 18:495–509.

Ormerod, M. G., and A. Baker. Unpublished data.

Parkins, G. Unpublished data.

Peters, R. A. 1964. *Lethal Synthesis and the Biochemical Lesion.* Oxford, England: Pergamon Press.

Révész, L., U. Glas, and G. Hilding. 1963. Relationship between Chromosome Number and Radiosensitivity of Tumour Cells. *Nature,* London, 198:260–261.

Scaife, J. F., and P. Alexander. 1961. Inability of X-Rays to Alter the Permeability of Mitochondria. *Radiation Research,* 15:658–674.

Simon, E. H. 1963. Effects of 5-Bromodeoxyuridine on Cell Division and DNA Replication in HeLa Cells. *Experimental Cell Research,* Supplement 9:263–269.

Stapleton, G. E., D. Billen, and A. Hollaender. 1953. Recovery of X-Irradiated Bacteria at Suboptimal Incubation Temperatures. *Journal of Cellular and Comparative Physiology,* 41:345–357.

Szybalski, W. 1962. "Properties and Applications of Halogenated Deoxyribonucleic Acids," *The Molecular Basis of Neoplasia* (The University of Texas M. D. Anderson Hospital and Tumor Institute, Fifteenth Annual Symposium on Fundamental Cancer Research). Austin, Texas: The University of Texas Press. Pp. 147–171.

Taylor, B., J. P. Greenstein, and A. Hollaender. 1948. Effects of X-Radiation on Sodium Thymus Nucleate. *Archives of Biochemistry,* 16:19–31.

Thornley, M. J. 1964. Radiation Resistances among Bacteria. *Applied Bacteriology,* 26:334–338.

DISCUSSION

Dr. Henry S. Kaplan, Stanford University, Palo Alto, California: We have also examined the radiosensitivity of different markers in *B. subtilis* transforming DNA; some of the preliminary aspects of this work were presented at a radiobiological symposium in Brazil about a year and a half ago. Our colleagues, Drs. Ganesan and Lederberg, of the Department of Genetics at Stanford University, selected markers exhibiting concordant shifts in melting temperature and in cesium chloride density gradient equilibrium. We found that the radiosensitivity of different markers to X ray varied with their G-C content when the DNA was irradiated in vitro. The radiosensitivity of the same markers to UV was inversely related. A quadruple mutant was used for the simultaneous scoring of four markers in the same wild type DNA, thus eliminating any possibility that the differences in response could be due to differences in penetrance of the DNA into the organism. I would like to ask Dr. Szybalski whether he would not regard this kind of evidence as consistent with his evidence that the degree of radiosensitization by BU is apparently greater in the high G-C mutants. I would also like to ask Dr. Alexander how he would refute this kind of evidence and that of Dr. Szybalski, in which irradiation is carried out under conditions in which there is no plasma membrane, and only DNA is present.

Dr. Peter Alexander, Chester Beatty Research Institute, Institute of Cancer Research, Royal Cancer Hospital, London, England: If you irradiate pure DNA, then the damage to it must be due to damage to DNA. This I don't think anybody would question, and I have no ax to grind with the fact that high G-C DNA may be more radiosensitive. If DNA containing BU irradiated in isolation is more sensitive, this does not in any way prove that this is the way BU sensitizes cells where there are SH compounds when there are membranes.

Dr. Robert Uretz, University of Chicago, Chicago, Illinois: I would like to raise the question of the kinetics of cellular inactivation by ionizing radiation. Over a wide spectrum of organisms, this inactivation can show a fairly low order of kinetics; that is, exponential or first order dose-effect curves or curves with relatively small shoulders or extrapolation numbers are observed. Would you comment on the relationship of this fact to what I would consider to be the necessary inactivation of a lot of membrane or a lot of SH groups, if the primary effect of the radiation is on such high redundancy systems?

Dr. Alexander: I think survival curves are very difficult to interpret in terms of primary lesions, because repair phenomena change the shape of survival curves. The impressive exponential relationship after the shoulder could be interpreted as damaging a structure by a single event, such as a hole in a plasma in nuclear membrane, opening of some subcellular structure and release of an enzyme.

*Dr. Herman M. Klouwen, Radiobiological Institute of the Organization for Health

Research TNO, Rijswijk, Netherlands: I would like to ask you some questions related with the effects of irradiation on the release of RNase. You have shown that both after irradiation in vitro and in vivo there is a decrease of the nuclear RNase content, since yesterday we discussed indirect and direct radiation effects. I wonder whether you now consider the results of your experiments as strong evidence for direct radiation effects observed in these irradiated lymphomas. Furthermore, I would like to make general comments on the role of SH groups in possible radiation damage. I think it is quite confusing that up until now it has not been possible to prove definitely in radiobiology that a decrease of SH groups is observed after irradiation. Stocken and Ord recently published a paper about the decrease of SH compound after irradiation. The results obtained so far by several authors, however, are not consistent. Dr. Alexander, what is your opinion regarding the possible role of decrease of SH groups after irradiation in vivo as a critical biochemical radiation effect?

Dr. Alexander: With regard to your second question, I have no solid facts to contribute and will not take up the time to speculate on it. The release of nuclear ribonuclease we believe to be a direct effect for the simple reason that it occurs in tissue culture, as well as in vivo. I referred yesterday to the interesting situation discovered by Miss Weymouth, where there was an over-all increase in the ribonuclease content of thymus cells following whole-body irradiation. We did not find this in vitro (*i.e.*, in tissue culture), and this led us to look at the contribution of abscopal effects on early biochemical lesions following irradiation in vivo (see Maor and Alexander, *International Journal of Radiation Biology*, 6:93–103, 1963).

Dr. Arnold H. Sparrow, Brookhaven National Laboratory, Long Island, New York: I would like to address my comments to Dr. Alexander. It is a big jump, taxonomically speaking, from bacteria to higher plant meristems, but I would like to comment on his conclusions regarding the lack of any correlation between DNA content per cell and sensitivity in bacteria. If I tried to correlate DNA content per cell and sensitivity in our plants, it would give a rather poor correlation, depending upon the species used. In higher plants it is necessary to consider polyploidy and/or chromosome numbers. Do you know anything about either the chromosome number or the number of nuclei per cell? If you do not, and bacteria react the same as higher plants, your conclusions may not be valid.

It has been shown on filamentous *E. coli* by Deering (*Biochimica et biophysica acta*, 31:11–19, 1959) that the radiosensitivity changes as the DNA content per cell goes up. This form, I believe, has only one nucleus per cell.

With reference to the possibility that the nuclear membrane may be a sensitive site, in plant cells this seems to be rather improbable because you get increasing sensitivity with increasing nuclear volume in diploids, and the reverse in polyploids. So that in one case, as the surface area of your membrane goes up the sensitivity decreases, and in the other case, it increases. So this would appear to be not a very important site of primary radiation injury in higher plants.

Dr. Daniel Billen, The University of Texas M. D. Anderson Hospital and Tumor Institute, Houston, Texas: I want to make two comments concerning Dr. Alexander's presentation. In regard to his statement that cysteamine may not penetrate the interior of the cell, one has to explain observations which have been made in several laboratories. It is obvious then that cysteamine can influence the DNA synthesis system in the cell as cysteamine will definitely inhibit DNA synthesis both in *Escherichia coli* and in mammalian cells (D. Billen, Unpublished data; C. Doudney, Restoration from an X-Ray Induced Block in Deoxyribonucleic Acid Synthesis in *Escherichia coli*, *Journal of Bacteriology*, 72:488–493, 1956; M. La Salle and D. Billen, Inhibition of DNA Synthesis in Murine Bone Marrow Cells by AET and Cysteamine, *Annals of the New York Academy of Sciences*, in press).

The second point bears on the question as to the necessity of 5-bromouracil being incorporated into DNA in order to behave as a radiosensitizer. If not, then a mechanism involving a general cell poison may be favored. Evidence has been published (D. Billen, Unbalanced Deoxyribonucleic Acid Synthesis: Its Role in X-Ray-Induced Bacterial Death, *Biochimica et biophysica acta*, 72:608–618, 1963) showing that the 5-bromouracil has to be incorporated into the DNA of *Escherichia coli* in order to radiosensitize that organism. If active DNA synthesis occurs while 5-bromouracil is present under conditions in which it may be readily utilized for DNA synthesis in the place of thymine, then radiosensitivity develops. If, however, prior to exposure to 5-bromouracil, the cells have been treated in a manner in which chromosome duplication is apparently completed and DNA synthesis capacity lacking, then exposure to 5-bromouracil does not alter the radiosensitivity of the major portion of the population. This is reasonable evidence that BU must be incorporated into the DNA for radiosensitization to occur.

Dr. Alexander: We did not suggest that in the systems studied by us, BU, as such, sensitized. The BU needs to be incorporated into DNA but in this form we suggest that it acts by interfering with enzymes.

Chairman Franklin Hutchinson, Yale University, New Haven, Connecticut: Relative to the first point that Dr. Billen raised, I can say that if pneumococcus transforming principle is irradiated in pneumococcus cells, the survival of transforming activity in the DNA follows cell survival when the cells are treated with dose-modifying factors such as oxygen, nitrogen, protective agents such as SH compounds, or if the cells are frozen. The data are not comprehensive, but are suggestive.

Dr. Waclaw Szybalski, McArdle Memorial Laboratory, University of Wisconsin, Madison, Wisconsin: I would like to make some general remarks about the points of agreement and disagreement between me and Dr. Alexander. I don't think it would be possible for me to discuss all of Dr. Alexander's experiments since for an intelligent evaluation of the data I would have to know about every single experimental detail, and evaluate each experiment on its own merit. I believe, however, that our disagreement is only of a quantitative nature, since it is quite obvious that all cell components contribute in some way to the cell survival. Our data indicate that in most systems studied, DNA damage contributes much over 50 per cent of the lethal radiation effects, perhaps close to 90 per cent. Dr. Alexander, however, assigns a much smaller role to DNA.

Dr. Tikvah Alper, Medical Research Council, Hammersmith Hospital, London, England: I mentioned the results of Dr. Gillies yesterday as they are relevant; and I think that both Dr. Szybalski and Dr. Alexander might like to take them into consideration. Dr. Gillies has examined the action of "chloramphenicol rescue" on *E. coli* B grown so as to incorporate either 5-bromouracil or thymine, and then exposed to UV or X rays. In a series of experiments with X rays given in aerobic conditions, for example, the thymine grown cells showed almost no evidence of rescue; the 5-BU-sensitized cells, however, were rescued to a considerable extent. The chloramphenicol treatment had the effect of reducing considerably the extent of the BU sensitization. The differential rescuing action of chloramphenicol on cells incorporating 5-BU was even more marked after anoxic irradiation. It seems unlikely, therefore, that sensitization by 5-BU incorporation is attributable to an interference with capacity for "repair."

Dr. Alexander: Dr. Szybalski said exactly what I wanted to say, but I would like to tie it up with a remark to Dr. Sparrow. I really think it is important to stress that we cannot say ,"This is this," or, "It is not." In plants, DNA may be the principal lesion. The relative importance of different primary lesions may well be different in different cells, under different conditions; it may be that under oxygen the relative proportion is not the same as under nitrogen. As far as nuclear volume is concerned, the highly resistant micrococci are rather large cells; they are larger than the *Pseudomonas* or the *E. coli.*

Dr. Helen Harrington, Western Reserve University, Cleveland, Ohio: We reported last year some results which may contrast to those of Dr. Alexander concerning the lability of halogenated DNA after irradiation in vivo. The leukemic lymphoblast, L5178Y, was grown in the presence of IUdR; the cells were irradiated, the DNA was extracted, and its viscosity, its sedimentation rate, and its thermal transition were measured. Of the four types of DNA (control, IU-substituted, irradiated, and IU-substituted-irradiated), only the IU-substituted-irradiated DNA showed a decrease in viscosity and a drop in the melting point of about 3 degrees.

Dr. Kaplan: Dr. Alexander touched on so many different things with such rapidity that he presents a "moving target." I think that he may have left the impression that the results which he presented on the lack of correlation between the degree of incorporation of the halogenated pyrimidine analogue BUdR and its radiosensitizing action are either the only such results or the definitive results. I should like, therefore, to remind the audience that we presented data (*Radiation Research*, 16:98–113, 1962) indicating a good correlation between the extent of incorporation and extent of sensitization; that Erikson and Szybalski have presented similar data for mammalian cells; that Delihas, Rich, and Eidinoff have also observed this phenomenon; that there is competitive inhibition by thymidine of BUdR-induced radiosensitization in either bacteria or mammalian cells. All of these phenomena, together with the data which Dr. Billen will present, seem to me to provide such a convincing correlation between the occurrence and extent of incorporation and the radiosensitization phenomenon that it seems to me the burden of proof is now on Dr. Alexander to indicate that his results have been carried out in such a manner that they do not represent a chance departure rather than a definitive refutation. I think it should also be kept in mind that BUdR is an equally powerful sensitizer in bacteriophage; when the phage is irradiated in the free state where there is nothing comparable to a plasma membrane (there is, of course, a protein coat), the phage is sensitized. It is very difficult to see how one can escape the conclusion that the sensitization is indeed due to the presence of BU in the DNA; thus, although I find this warm shower of "*gemühtlichkeit*" between Szybalski and Alexander a very touching phenomenon, it leaves me from a scientific point of view feeling that a great cloud of fuzziness is being thrown up on what seems to be a rather direct line of evidence.

Dr. Alexander: Dr. Kaplan claims that the weight of the published literature and particularly his own experiments (Kaplan, Smith, and Tomlin, *Radiation Research*, 16:98–113, January, 1962) show that the extent of radiosensitization to X rays increases progressively with increase in BU content of the cells' DNA. Consequently he maintains that our experiments showing that sensitization reaches a limiting value are odd and should not be accepted. This is not how I view the literature; Kaplan's own data (*loc. cit.* p. 105) show that he gets substantial sensitization only after 8 hours growth in BU-containing medium when there had been 41 per cent BU substitution and some cells were killed by the BU treatment. After 4 hours growth in BU, he gets some sensitization and he claims that at this time there was 17 per cent BU replacement. Yet his actual data (Figure 1, p. 100, *loc. cit.*) show that at this time only some 3 per cent of BU had been replaced. His data are thus in no conflict with our findings that sensitization to X rays becomes apparent when the treatment with BU is toxic. Delihas, Rich, and Eidinoff (*Radiation Research*, 17:479–491, October, 1962) as well as Mohler and Elkind (*Experimental Cell Research*, 30:407, 1963), have noted that sensitization to X rays by BUdR in mammalian cells is associated with toxicity. Indeed, Delihas *et al.* had a cell line which was very susceptible to cell killing by BUdR and for them they find sensitization at 1 per cent replacement. The literature data therefore support our contention that sensitization is associated with toxicity.

With regard to Dr. Kaplan's arguments involving phage, I must stress again that in a system where DNA is almost certainly the target, BU must sensitize via DNA. But in cells where we cannot *a priori* assume DNA as being the principal target, BU may act at sites which are absent in phage, e.g. enzymes which are susceptible to BU.

Dr. Szybalski: Just one short comment about phage—in nonprotected medium, the principal lethal X-ray damage is to the tail proteins, not to DNA. However, phage DNA is the principal X-ray target when irradiation is carried out in the presence of radical scavengers.

Dr. Mortimer Elkind, National Cancer Institute, National Institutes of Health, Bethesda, Maryland: I am sure, as Dr. Alexander just demonstrated, that he is quite capable of speaking for himself, even though he may be a "moving target." Still, I would like to make a comment apropos of experiments with mammalian cells in which BU produces apparent sensitization. A critical thing, as Dr. Alexander showed, is that sensitization often sets in when some degree of toxicity is incurred from the drug itself. Now we all know, and will learn more about this tomorrow, that mammalian cells have responses which are not uniform throughout the cell cycle. Almost invariably, the experiments that have been reported with mammalian cells were performed with asynchronous cells. Therefore, once toxicity starts to set in, the question comes up whether we are seeing the response of those cells normally in the population which are among the more responsive anyway, or whether the drug is potentiating.

Dr. Kaplan: We have reported, and Erikson and Szybalski have confirmed, that even one round of DNA replication in the presence of BU is sufficient to sensitize. Under these conditions, there is absolutely no detectable change in the viability of either the bacterial or the mammalian cells. If one allows one additional replication in the presence of thymine, the sensitization is wiped out and there is still no difference in viability. I do not see that carrying the BU incorporation to the point of toxicity refutes the fact that BU incorporation under conditions of no demonstrable toxicity still sensitizes.

Dr. Elkind: I believe Dr. Kaplan has somewhat misinterpreted my remarks. Dr. W. Mohler and I (*Experimental Cell Research*, 30:481–491, 1963) made a study of the influence of BUdR on the X-ray response of Chinese hamster cells in culture. Graded concentrations were used, their effects in time examined, and the resulting alteration in survival parameters observed. From this study, we concluded that the drug did potentiate independently of toxicity-induced changes in population composition. However, I know of reports where the scope of the study was such that changes in response due to BUdR toxicity could not be ruled out. Hence, I feel the point I raised is quite relevant.

Dr. Harold Hewitt, British Empire Cancer Campaign Research Unit in Radiobiology, Northwood, England: In the studies of bacterial radiosensitivity, the bacteria were irradiated in phosphate buffer. Under these conditions, there would be a direct effect and, I believe, a considerable indirect effect from changes in the medium, such as the accumulation of hydrogen peroxide. I do not think that toxic effects from hydrogen peroxide created in the medium by the radiation really have any reference to the concepts we are discussing. So, I would like to ask Dr. Alexander whether he distinguished the effect of hydrogen peroxide in the medium, as a component of his radiosensitivity, because this is an influence that might very well be affected by the quality of the plasma membrane. I can quite believe that different kinds of plasma membranes might be associated with different sensitivities to hydrogen peroxide.

The other comment I would like to make is in relation to the redistribution of ribonuclease in lymphoma cells after a dose, I believe, of 2,000 r. Under these conditions, the overwhelming majority of the cells do, in fact, lose their reproductive integrity. So I do not see how any distinction has been made between a cell which has retained and a cell which has lost its reproductive integrity. It may be that a cell which has not lost its reproductive integrity does not exhibit any redistribution of ribonuclease. Therefore, it appears that no correlation has been demonstrated between ribonuclease redistribution and loss of reproductive integrity. I should like Dr. Alexander to discuss this point.

Dr. Alexander: There are ample data in the literature to show that radiolysis products in water do not contribute substantially to cell death of microorganisms. The most convincing evidence is that the survival curve of microorganisms is independent of the concentration at which they are irradiated.

With regard to the second point: We have demonstrated an early form of biochemical injury, after a given dose of X rays, to the cell. Unfortunately, it is not possible in such biochemical experiments to differentiate between cells that survive and those that do not. All one can hope to do is to find an early biochemical injury and then to carry out ancillary experiments to test its role in cell killing.

Dr. Olga Pierucci, Roswell Park Memorial Institute, Buffalo, New York: An increase in specific and total organ activity of deoxyribonuclease II was detected in the spleen of Ha/ICR Swiss mice 24 hours after 100 and 300 r whole-body radiation. No release of deoxyribonuclease II into the supernatant was detected after 100 r, while the specific activity of the homogenate was 145 per cent of the control value. A release of deoxyribonuclease II into the supernatant was observed after 300 r. This release appeared to be a consequence of cell death.

Chairman Hutchinson: Does either Dr. Alexander or Dr. Szybalski want to add anything to wind up the session? Otherwise I would like to point out that, in my opinion, Dr. Kaplan has issued a very clearly worded challenge. This does not mean that in my opinion he has made his point, that he has settled the issue as to whether it is DNA or not. I think, however, he has stated in a very clear way that there is very good evidence that both the biological activity of DNA *and* cell survival are sensitized to the same extent by the same agent. Dr. Kaplan is calling on the proponents of other radiosensitive structures to give equally good evidence to back up their suggestions. I hope that this is not considered a biased question; it is just simply the impression I have had sitting up here.

MODIFICATION
OF
RADIATION RESPONSE

The Study of Radiosensitive Structures with Low Voltage Electron Beams

Arthur Cole

Department of Physics, The University of Texas M. D. Anderson Hospital and Tumor Institute, Houston, Texas

A summary of work which is reported elsewhere (Cole, 1961, 1964a; Cole, Humphrey, and Dewey, 1963; Cole and Langley, 1963) is relevant to the present discussion of radiosensitive structure. Monoenergetic electron beams of 500 to 150,000 electron volts energy were used to irradiate cellular monolayers on membrane filters. Wet, dry, oxygenated, anoxic, and bromouridine deoxyriboside (BUdR) treatment conditions were utilized in various experiments with T2 bacteriophage, *Streptomyces* spores, *Escherichia coli* cells, haploid yeast cells, and mouse fibroblast cells.

Results of such studies can be analyzed in various ways. One analysis utilizes dependence of the observed cell D_{37} survival dose on the incident beam voltage. In order to calculate the cell dose, we have utilized studies on the energy deposition of low voltage electron beams in solids (Cole, 1962, 1964b). An example of the results of such studies is given in Figure 1, which shows a normalized depth dose plot for 5 to 50 kev electron beams. The data were utilized to estimate, for various beam voltages, the fraction of the total energy absorbed by a cell which is deposited within a given sensitive region configuration. This energy fraction was taken to represent the relative (killing) efficiency of the beam considered and thus to represent a reciprocal measure of the anticipated relative cell D_{37} dose. An example of such calculations is given in Figure 2, in which is plotted the anticipated dependence of the cell D_{37} dose on the incident beam voltage for various spherically symmetrical sensitive regions within a spherical cell.

The plots which were derived exhibited a number of interesting features. For example, thin sensitive shell structures located somewhat below the cell surface yielded calculated responses which exhibited definite minima. This type of dependence was observed for essentially all of the biological systems studied. A typical response is shown in Figure 3 for studies with *E. coli* cells. This plot shows the observed D_{37} doses for wet cells irradiated with or without oxygen. The inactivation cross section is also plotted and represents the area per incident electron for a beam exposure yielding 37 per cent survival.

By combining the analysis outlined with conventional methods of description, the low voltage electron beam results can be utilized to estimate factors such as insensitive coat thicknesses; sensitive region thicknesses, areas, and volumes; and apparent inactivation volumes, cross sections, and thicknesses. Although the results will be presented in detail elsewhere, a short summary is presented in the table. This table lists for the various biological materials studied the apparent insensitive coat thickness and sensitive region thickness, the "corrected" cross section expressed in terms of the fraction (per cent) of the area presented by the sensitive region, the inactivation volume expressed in terms of the fraction (per cent) of the deoxyribonucleic acid (DNA) volume of the cell, and the apparent

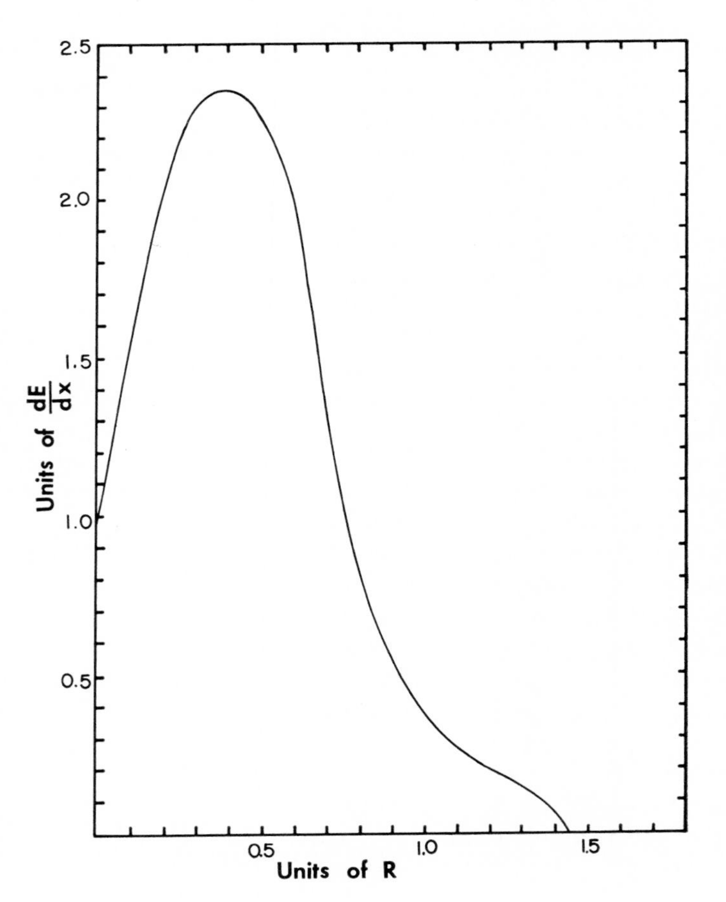

FIGURE 1. Summary plot of dE/dt, the energy deposited per electron per unit absorption thickness versus the absorption thickness, t. The dE/dt is expressed in units of the initial rate of energy loss dE/dx, and t is expressed in units of the range R, appropriate to the beam energies considered.

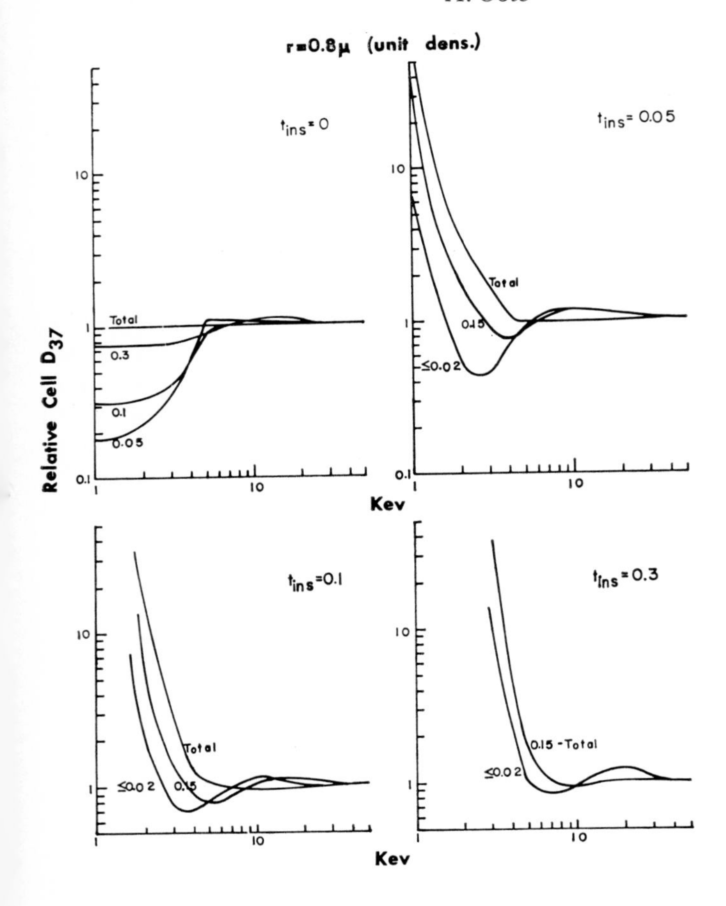

FIGURE 2. Plots of the anticipated dependence of the relative cell D_{37} dose on the incident beam voltage for four values of an outer insensitive coat thickness, t_{ins}. Values of the sensitive region thickness (*i.e.* shell thickness) t_{sens} are given for each curve. The plots labeled "total" refer to sensitive regions which comprise all of the volume within the coat. The plots refer to a spherical cell with a radius, r, of 0.8 μ (unit density).

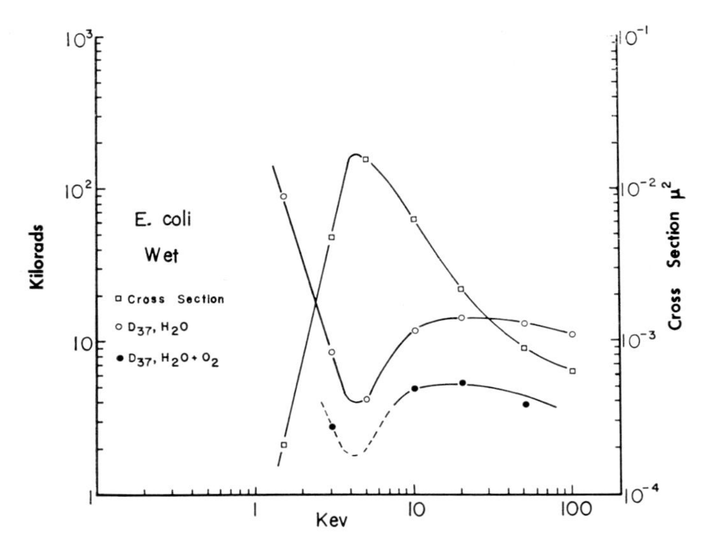

FIGURE 3. Plot of the cell D_{37} dose in kilorads and the inactivation cross section in μ^2 versus the incident electron beam voltage for wet *E. coli* cells with and without oxygen present (the cross-section plot refers to the anoxic situation).

inactivation thickness which equals the inactivation volume divided by the (corrected) inactivation cross section. The listed corrected cross section was derived somewhat arbitrarily as follows: Maximum cross sections were observed for beams which irradiated essentially only the top half of the cell; therefore, the total cell cross section was assumed to be equal to at least twice this value. For electrons with a high linear rate of energy loss (dE/dx), (> 15 kev/μ), the passage of an electron through a sensitive structure is expected to leave sufficient energy to inactivate it with high probability, so that the inactivation cross section may approximate the total area presented to the beam by the sensitive structures. At low dE/dx values the inactivation probability would be expected to decline more or less proportionally with dE/dx. Thus, an additional correction (ranging up to 4.0) applicable to the average dE/dx value expected in the region of the sensitive structures was made.

Estimates of Thickness of Insensitive and Sensitive Regions and of Inactivation Thickness Utilizing Low Voltage Electron Beam Results

System studied	Insensitive coat thickness (microns)	Sensitive region thickness (microns)	Corrected cross section expressed as per cent of sensitive region	Inactivation volume expressed as per cent of DNA volume	Apparent inactivation thickness (A)
DNA* (single strand)				100	
T2 bacteriophage	~0.005	≤0.01	100	11	21
T12 *Streptomyces* spores	~0.1	≤0.05	3.6	0.7	26
E. coli cells	~0.05	≤0.05	1.8	0.7	28
Haploid yeast cells	1.0	~0.1?	0.8	0.4	29
Mouse L-P_{59} cells	1.0	≤0.2	1.8	0.02	16

* Hutcsinson (see pages 86 to 97, this volume).

As shown in the table, the results were consistent with the supposition that, in essentially all of the systems studied, the radiation-sensitive structures appear to be in a thin shell located at a specific depth below the cell surface. Although such a region could correspond to the location of the genetic structures, only a small fraction of the cellular DNA would appear to be implicated. It is interesting that the apparent inactivation thickness, when based on the corrected cross section values, was in the order of 25 A for all the systems studied. This result supports in an independent way the thin-shell sensitive-structure hypothesis. The results indicate that efficient killing of yeast or mouse fibroblast cells requires beam penetration to the nuclear body or to the cell nucleus. Neither the cell wall, cell membrane, nor cytoplasm was radiosensitive, nor does it appear that diffusion of damaging effects from insensitive to sensitive regions can occur within the cell over very great distances. The sensitive region appears to be located on or near the nuclear surface.

In T2 bacteriophage, the protein coat appeared radiation insensitive;

a thin region immediately within the coat appeared to be a major radiosensitive component.

In the bacteria or spore systems, the observed insensitive coat thickness of 0.05 to 0.1 μ could conceivably implicate either plasma membrane or microsomal, enzymatic, or nucleic acid components as the radiosensitive structures.

Although these results are consistent with the DNA target hypothesis, they do not unequivocally support it. If our analysis is correct, it would appear that, at best, only a small peripheral fraction of the DNA is involved in radiosensitive reactions that lead to cell death. Furthermore, if DNA is a prime target, the results illustrate an apparent increase in radioresistance of this component as the complexity of the system increases. Thus, although the inactivation volume of single-stranded DNA in solution corresponds to the molecular volume, the inactivation volume in mammalian cells corresponds to only 0.02 per cent of the DNA volume. This result could reflect the presence of repair mechanisms which become more important or increase in efficiency as the complexity of the organism increases.

REFERENCES

Cole, A. 1961. Study of Radiation Susceptible Structures in Microorganism with Monoenergetic Electron Beams of 0.5 to 150 kev Energies. *Abstracts of International Biophysics Conference.* Pp. 95–96.

———. 1962. Some Physical Properties of Low-Voltage Electrons. (Abstract) *Radiation Research,* 16:597–598.

———. 1964a. The Analysis of Radiosensitive Structure Using Low-Voltage Electron Beams. *Abstracts of Twelfth Annual Radiation Research Meeting.*

———. 1964b. Absorption and Energy Deposition of Electrons of 20 to 80,000 ev Energies. *Journal of Applied Physics.* (in press.)

Cole, A., R. M. Humphrey, and W. C. Dewey. 1963. Low-Voltage Electron Beam Irradiation of Normal and 5-Bromouridine Deoxyriboside-Treated L-P_{59} Mouse Fibroblast Cells *in vitro. Nature,* London, 199:780–782.

Cole, A., and R. Langley. 1963. Study of the Radiosensitive Structure of T2 Bacteriophage Using Low Energy Electron Beams. *Biophysical Journal,* 3:189–197.

Interactions of Modifying Treatments and the Light They Throw on Targets for Cell Death

TIKVAH ALPER

Medical Research Council, Experimental Radiopathology Research Unit, Hammersmith Hospital, London, England

The possibility of modifying radiation damage offers a powerful tool for unraveling mechanisms of action, and much can be learned from studying the interaction of modifying treatments. As is well known, the enhancing action of oxygen is a universal feature of cellular radiobiology, applying not only to all forms of cell, but also to all tests of damage. For a while, there was a tendency to believe in some sort of invariant factor, about three, by which oxygen reduced the dose necessary to achieve a given effect. This could be expected if the oxygen effect were to operate by modifying the decomposition products of water. This mechanism for the oxygen effect is, however, now not much favored. In any event, substantial variations in oxygen enhancement ratios, by no means attributable to inadequacies in techniques, are undoubtedly observed, as is illustrated by the following examples:

1. Differences for the same test of damage in closely related strains: *Escherichia coli* Bs (Hill, 1958), ratio 1.8; *E. coli* B/H (resistant mutant of *E. coli* B), 3.2 to 3.5, depending on conditions (Figures 1 and 2).

2. Differences for different tests of damage in the same organism: (a) Hornsey and Silini's observations (1962) on ratios for induction of chromosome aberrations (2.1) and cell death (3.0) in near-tetraploid mouse ascites tumor cells. (b) Moore's observations (1964) of widely different oxygen enhancement ratios for cell killing and radiation-induced inhibition of the synthesis of β-D-galactosidase in *E. coli* B and some of its mutants. For example, in conditions in which the observed oxygen enhancement ratio for the killing of Bs was about 1.8, it was 3.6 for the inhibition of enzyme synthesis. The ratio for this end point in *E. coli* B was 4.0 and in B/H 4.3 (Figures 3 and 4).

3. Differences occurring by virtue of differences in the physiological or nutritional state of the organism at the time of irradiation, for example: (a) Freshly harvested haploid yeast, which is a mixture of resting and di-

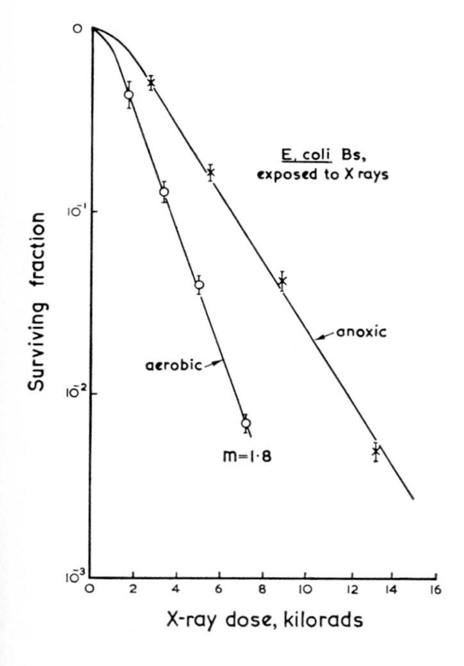

FIGURE 1. Survival curves for *E. coli* Bs, exposed to X rays in the absence of oxygen. O, aerobic irradiation; X, anoxic irradiation; vertical lines show 95 per cent confidence limits.

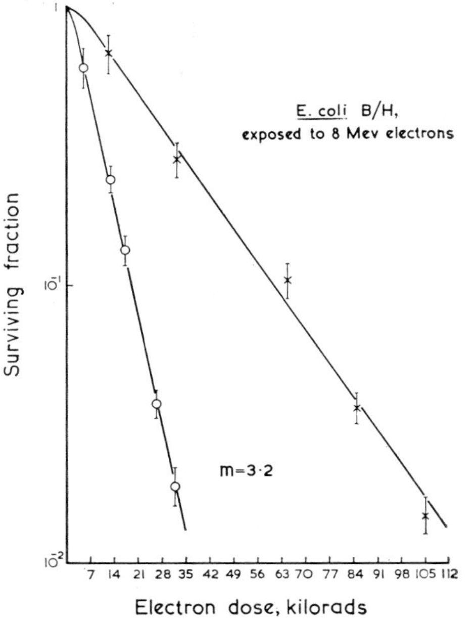

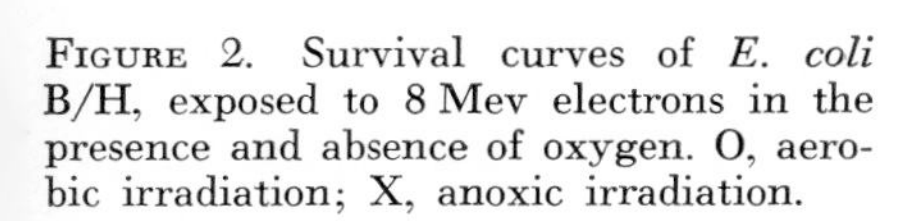
FIGURE 2. Survival curves of *E. coli* B/H, exposed to 8 Mev electrons in the presence and absence of oxygen. O, aerobic irradiation; X, anoxic irradiation.

viding cells. These two populations have different radiosensitivities (Beam, Mortimer, Wolfe, and Tobias, 1954), and also demonstrate different oxygen enhancement ratios, *viz.* 3.4 and 1.7 (Alper, 1959). (b) *E. coli* B grown in the presence of aminopterin, with the addition of either thymine or 5-bromouracil (BU). The ratio is lower for the sensitized cells (Alper and Moore, 1964) (Figures 5 and 6).

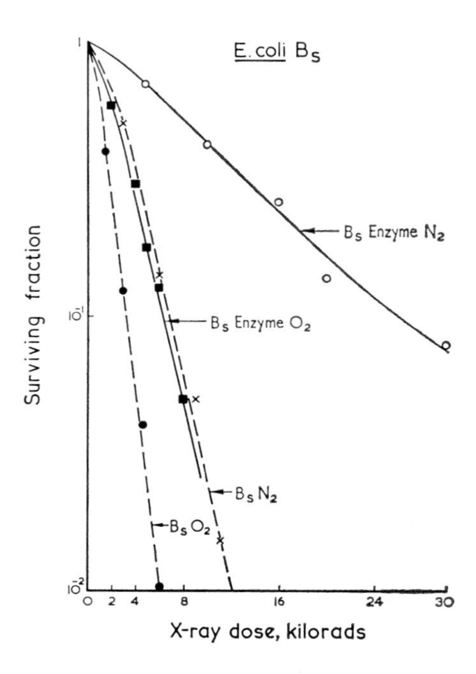

FIGURE 3. Inhibition of the synthesis of β-D-galactosidase after irradiation of *E. coli* Bs in the presence and absence of oxygen (Moore, 1964).
○ anaerobic irradiation, ■ aerobic irradiation: enzyme activity as fraction of control
X anaerobic irradiation, ● aerobic irradiation: colony formers as fraction of control

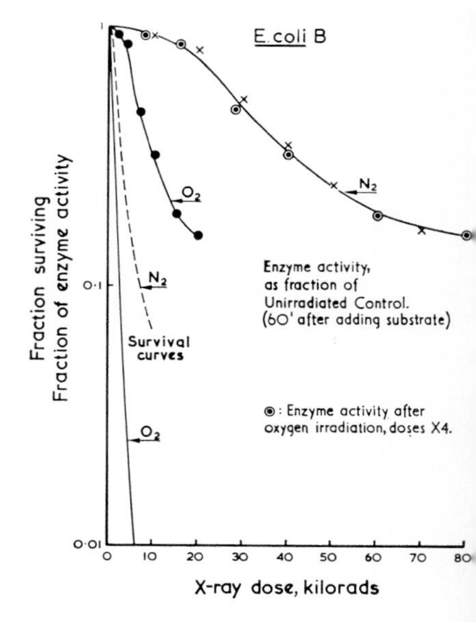

FIGURE 4. Inhibition of the synthesis of β-D-galactosidase after irradiation of *E. coli* B in the presence and absence of oxygen (Moore, 1964). ●, aerobic irradiation; X, anoxic irradiation; ⊙, aerobic irradiation, doses × 4.

4. Differences observed for cells irradiated together, but subjected to different culture conditions after irradiation. When aerobically and anoxically irradiated cells respond differentially to such conditions, the oxygen ratio will vary. For example: (a) The effect on irradiated *E. coli* B/r of incubation at 18 C (Alper, 1963b) (Figure 7). (b) The effect of incubation on

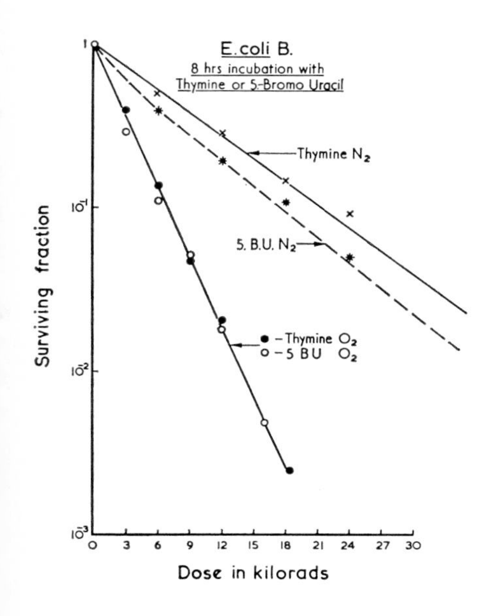

FIGURE 5. *E. coli* B grown for 8 hours in the presence of aminopterin, together with thymine or BU.

○ BU grown ● Thymine	aerobic irradiation
* BU grown X Thymine grown	anaerobic irradiation

FIGURE 6. *E. coli* B grown for 23 hours in the presence of aminopterin, together with thymine or BU.

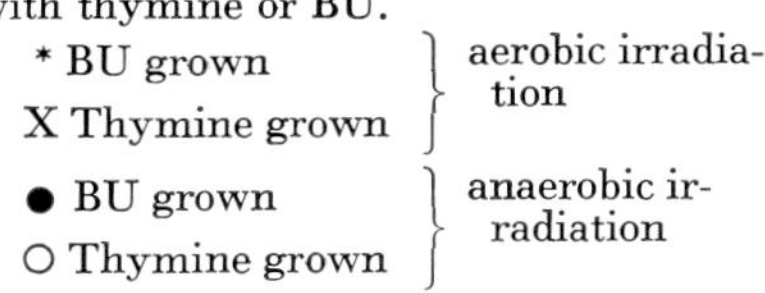

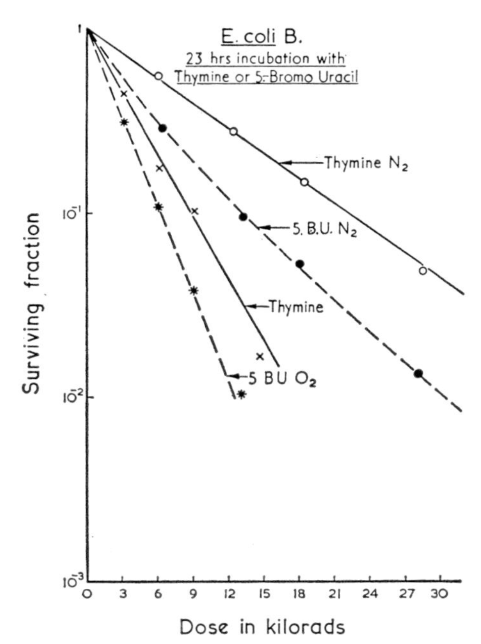

medium containing basic dyes, *e.g. E. coli* B/H grown on medium containing 5 μg/ml of acriflavine (Alper, 1963a) (Figure 8).

Whatever mechanism may be postulated for the cytocidal effect of ionizing radiation and for the involvement of oxygen in this effect, it would have to be a very elaborate one to account for these facts if cell death were ascribed only to *one* mode of action on *one* type of target. If, however, one adopts what seems to me the plausible hypothesis that cell death may oc-

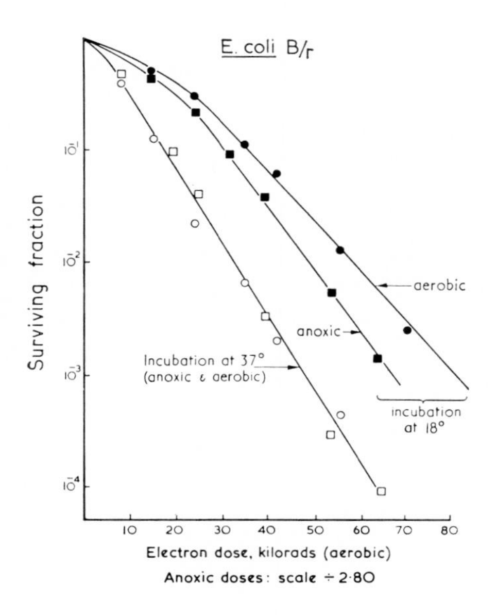

FIGURE 7. Effect of incubating *E. coli* B/r at 18 C after irradiation in the presence or absence of oxygen. Survival curves at 37 C superimposed by using appropriate dosage scales.

○ aerobic irradiation, □ anoxic irradiation — immediate incubation at 37C

● aerobic irradiation, ■ anoxic irradiation — incubation for 14 hours at 18C, then incubation at 37C

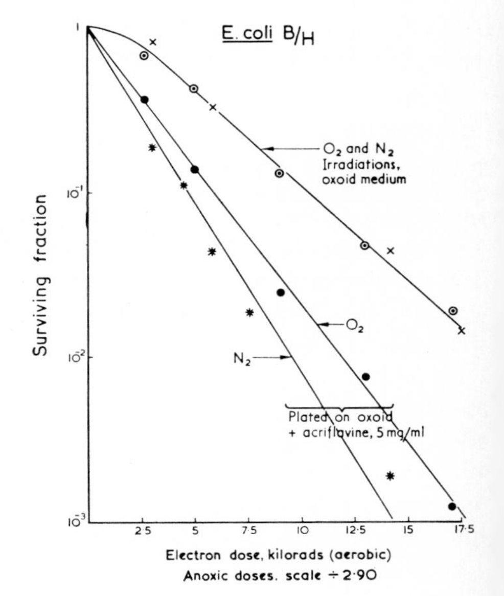

FIGURE 8. Effect of incubating *E. coli* B/H on medium containing acriflavine, 5 μg/ml, after irradiation in the presence and absence of oxygen. Survival curves for growth on normal medium superimposed by using appropriate dosage scales.

⊙ aerobic irradiation, X anaerobic irradiation — oxoid blood agar base

● aerobic irradiation, * anaerobic irradiation — oxoid medium and acriflavine

cur by virtue of more than one type of damage and that these types are differentially modifiable by oxygen as well as by other agents, variability in the over-all modifying action of such agents may be satisfactorily accounted for.

I should like to go over briefly the formal presentation of the concept and show how it seems to be justified by various lines of experimental evidence.

For the sake of simplicity, it will be assumed that there are two components of sensitivity, λ_O and λ_N, with corresponding intrinsic oxygen enhancement ratios m_O and m_N. The over-all, observed, sensitivities are respectively λ and $m\lambda$. Thus

$$\lambda = \lambda_O + \lambda_N \text{ (anoxic)}.$$

In the presence of oxygen

$$m\lambda = m_O\lambda_O + m_N\lambda_N.$$

It is now supposed that *one* of these sensitivity components is modified by some treatment (be it before, during, or after irradiation). If the "low m" component λ_N is modified to λ_N', we have

$$m'\lambda' = m_O\lambda_O + m_N\lambda_N'$$

$$\text{so that } m\lambda - m'\lambda' = m_N(\lambda_N - \lambda_N') = m_N(\lambda - \lambda')$$

$$\text{i.e. } m_N = \frac{m\lambda - m'\lambda'}{\lambda - \lambda'}$$

and m_N may therefore be calculated from four observed parameters. Similarly, if λ becomes λ' because λ_O becomes λ_O',

$$m_O = \frac{m\lambda - m'\lambda'}{\lambda - \lambda'}.$$

In order to calculate m_O or m_N, it is necessary to have observations concerned with modifying treatments which change both sensitivity and oxygen enhancement ratio. Some are here summarized briefly.

Calculation of m_N

Radiation Response of E. coli *B*. This is very dependent on conditions of culture after irradiation. For seven different sets of conditions, seven different values of λ and m were observed. In accordance with the predictions from the simple theory I have set forth, m and D_O (*i.e.* $1/\lambda$) were linearly related, and the mean value of m_N deduced from all these observations was 1.5 (Alper, 1961).

Use of Acriflavine (Alper, 1963a, b). When acriflavine is incorporated in plating medium, more radiation damage is brought to light; the effect after ionizing radiation is more pronounced when this has been delivered in anoxic conditions. For four different strains, the calculated values of m_N were as shown in Table 1.

Incorporation of 5-Bromouracil in E. coli *B*. (Alper and Moore, 1964) (Table 2).

TABLE 1

*Effect of Acriflavine in Growth Medium on Survival of Various Strains, and Calculated Value of m_N**

	Survival curve parameters**				
	Without acriflavine		With acriflavine		
Strain	λ (Kilorad^{-1})	m	λ' (Kilorad^{-1})	m′	m_N***
Shigella flexneri	0.0788	2.97_0	0.1807	2.48_0	1.8_2
E. coli B/H	0.0903	2.90_3	0.1797	2.16_6	1.4_5
E. coli B/r	0.0606	3.06_1	0.0744	2.73_8	1.3_2
E. coli B	0.1971	2.59_3	0.3019	1.92_6	1.3_0

* Acriflavine at 5 μg/ml except with *E. coli* B, for which 3 μg/ml was used.
** Survival curve parameters obtained by Mercury computer (Pike and Alper, 1964).
*** m_N calculated by using equation $m_N = \dfrac{m\lambda - m'\lambda'}{\lambda - \lambda'}$.

TABLE 2

Survival Curve Parameters for E. coli *B Grown in the Presence of Aminopterin + Thymine (100 μg/ml) or 5-Bromouracil (200 μg/ml)**

Time of growth with aminopterin + T or BU	m_T (Thymine)	m_B (BU)	λ_T(Thymine) Kilorad^{-1}	λ_B(BU) Kilorad^{-1}	$m_N = \dfrac{m_T\lambda_T - m_B\lambda_B}{\lambda_T - \lambda_B}$
8 hours	3.10	2.75	0.111	not evaluated (survival curve showed heterogeneity)	
15 hours	3.10	2.38	0.111	0.25	1.73
23 hours	2.63	2.00	0.105	0.200	1.30

* Survival curves fitted by eye.

Calculation of m_0

In terms of the formal treatment set out above, m_0 can be calculated when a given modifying treatment reduces both the sensitivity and the oxygen enhancement ratio. This has been less common in my experience than the converse, in which an increase in sensitivity is accompanied by a reduction in the over-all value of m.

E. coli *B/r Held at 18 C after Irradiation.* m_0 can be calculated from experiments in which B/r was rescued from lethal damage by incubation at 18° for a period after irradiation. Although differing survival curve parameters were observed, depending on methods of growth before and after irradiation, the values of m_0 calculated from different sets of four survival curves are reasonably constant, as shown in Table 3. The mean value of m_0 is 4.5.

Freshly harvested haploid yeast. In this case, there is a modification in radiosensitivity which is connected with the physiological state of the cells. The resting cells have a higher sensitivity than the budding cells (Beam, Mortimer, Wolfe, and Tobias, 1954) and also a higher oxygen enhancement ratio (Alper, 1959). The sensitivity of the single cells is difficult to determine with precision, since resistant budding cells affect the survival curves

TABLE 3

Value of 'm_o' Computed from Survival Curve Parameters for E. coli *B/r, Incubated after Irradiation at 37° and 18°*

Culture conditions before irradiation	Plating medium after irradiation	Survival curve parameters: 37° incubation — Extrap. number	λ (Kilorad^{-1})	m	18° incubation — Extrap. number	λ' (Kilorad^{-1})	m'	m_o**
Stationary, broth without aeration	Rich nutrient medium	4.2	0.0519	3.02_9	2.9	0.0409	2.56_1	4.7_6
	Minimal medium (salts and glucose)	3.3	0.0935	2.82_5	18.0	0.0765	2.37_2	4.8_5
Stationary, with aeration	Rich nutrient medium	6.7	0.0972	2.84_5	4.7	0.0718	2.28_2	4.4_2
Logarithmic, harvested from slant	Rich nutrient medium	1.6	0.0849	2.68_8	1.1	0.0637	2.19_4	4.1_8

* Survival curve parameters obtained by Mercury Computer (Pike and Alper, 1964).

** m_0 calculated by using equation $m_0 = \dfrac{m\lambda - m'\lambda'}{\lambda - \lambda'} = m_2$.

for the sensitive cells at rather high survival levels. However, the figures I published may be used in the calculations as follows: Let λ_b and λ_s be the over-all sensitivities observed for the budding and single cells, respectively, with oxygen enhancement ratios m_b and m_s. Let that component of sensitivity which is reduced in the budding cell have intrinsic oxygen enhancement ratio m_o.

Then

$$m_o = \frac{m_s\lambda_s - m_b\lambda_b}{\lambda_s - \lambda_b} = \frac{m_s.\lambda_s/\lambda_b - m_b}{\lambda_s/\lambda_b - 1}.$$

The parameters observed were

$m_s = 3.4$; $m_b = 1.6$; $\lambda_s/\lambda_b = 3.7$ (Alper, 1959)

$$\therefore m_o = \frac{3.4 \times 3.7 - 1.6}{3.7 - 1} = 4.1.$$

I have recently postulated that type N damage in microorganisms is identifiable with lethal mutational damage or at least is akin to the type of lesion which is expressed as mutation for the following reasons:

1. In the few systems in which estimates have been made, by reliable techniques, of oxygen enhancement ratios for both mutation induction and killing, the ratio is considerably lower for the former end point; m values observed for mutation induction have been from 1.5 to 2.0 (Anderson, 1951; Bridges, 1963; Deering, 1963).

2. There are certain postirradiation treatments which cause "mutation frequency decline" (Doudney and Haas, 1958), e.g. amino acid deprivation

and treatment with chloramphenicol. Such treatments also cause rescue from lethal damage in certain strains. In such strains, the oxygen enhancement ratio for lethal effects is low in conditions in which mutation yields are high; and if those treatments which cause mutation frequency decline also reduce the cytocidal effects of radiation, the oxygen enhancement ratio concomitantly increases (e.g. Figure 9) (Alper, 1963b).

Similarly, the use of acriflavine and basic dyes in growth medium after irradiation has been found to be a powerful tool for "mutation fixation" (Witkin, 1961). These treatments also bring more lethal radiation damage to light (Witkin, 1963; Feiner and Hill, 1963; Alper, 1963a) and concomitantly reduce the oxygen enhancement ratio, as we have seen (Alper, 1963a). Furthermore, they are much more effective in bringing more lethal damage to light in just those strains which normally show little effect of type N damage: for example, our strain *E. coli* B/H, a resistant mutant of *E. coli* B, which in "normal" conditions has an oxygen enhancement ratio of over 3.0, is powerfully affected by acriflavine, whereas the sensitive mutant, Bs, which normally has an oxygen enhancement ratio of only 1.8, is relatively little affected (Alper, 1963a).

Since ultraviolet (UV) irradiation is specifically absorbed by the nucleic acids, it could be expected that type N rather than type O damage would be the more akin to UV damage. This is supported by various observations: UV is more effective than ionizing radiation as a mutagen, in that the dose of UV required for a given absolute yield of mutants kills far fewer cells than does the dose of X rays required for the same yield. With ionizing

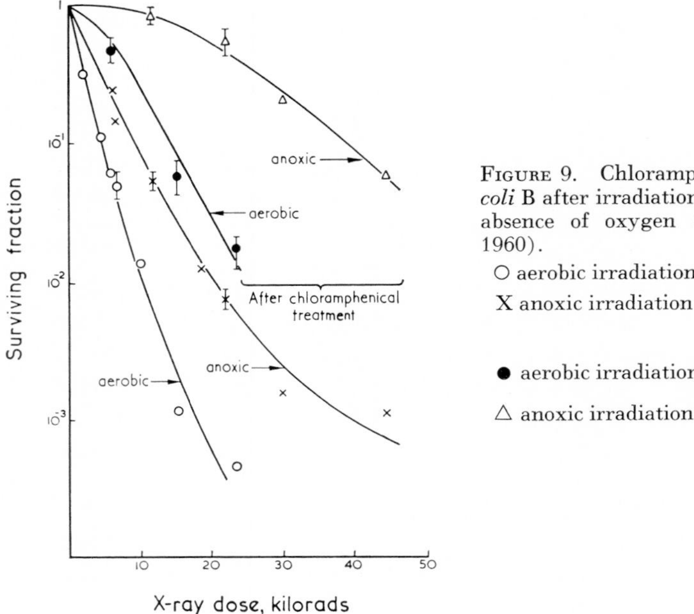

FIGURE 9. Chloramphenicol rescue of *E. coli* B after irradiation in the presence and absence of oxygen (Alper and Gillies, 1960).

○ aerobic irradiation, X anoxic irradiation — plated on oxoid blood agar base

● aerobic irradiation, △ anoxic irradiation — treated with chloramphenicol, then transferred to oxoid blood agar base

radiation, type N damage plays a relatively larger role in anoxic conditions; and ionizing radiation is a more effective mutagen in those conditions. Furthermore, an agent which is preferentially modifying for type N damage will modify UV damage to an even greater extent; whereas one which preferentially modifies type O damage is not modifying for UV damage (Alper, 1963b).

I ought here to mention some observations which do not fit this fairly coherent picture. I showed that the sensitization of *E. coli* B by incorporation of 5-bromouracil causes a decrease in the oxygen enhancement ratio, and that the extra component of sensitivity is indeed subject to an intrinsic m value of about 1.5, in accordance with calculations based on quite independent data. With *Shigella*, however, the incorporation of BU sensitizes without a significant decrease in m (Alper and Moore, 1964), so that the extra component of sensitivity must have the same m value as that observed with thymine-grown cells (about 2.7).

My results with chemical protective agents also do not appear to fit *quantitatively* very well with those I have quoted. Qualitatively, it seems justifiable to assume that protective chemicals act preferentially on type O damage. They are, in general, more effective when irradiations are given in the presence of oxygen (e.g. Figure 10), and more effective when post-irradiation conditions are such as to inhibit type N damage (e.g. Figure 11). However, such survival curves as I have taken with and without chemical protective agents yield parameters from which the calculated m_0 values

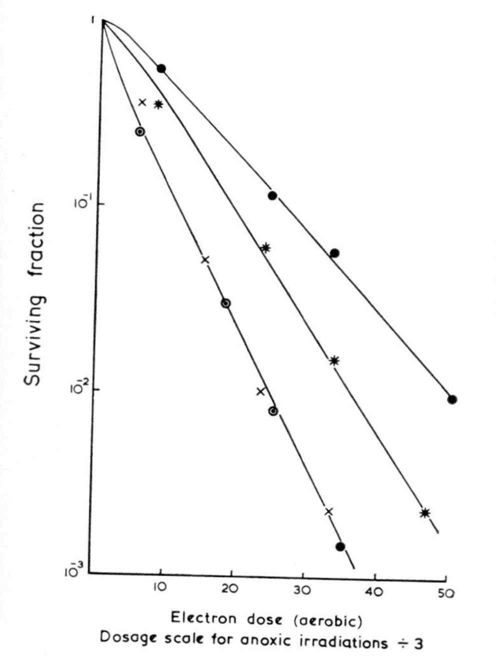

FIGURE 10. Protection of *E. coli* B/r by cysteine (0.15 M). Survival curves for unprotected organisms superimposed by using appropriate dosage scales.
⊙ irradiation under oxygen, unprotected
X irradiation under anoxia, unprotected
● irradiation under oxygen, protected
* irradiation under anoxia, protected

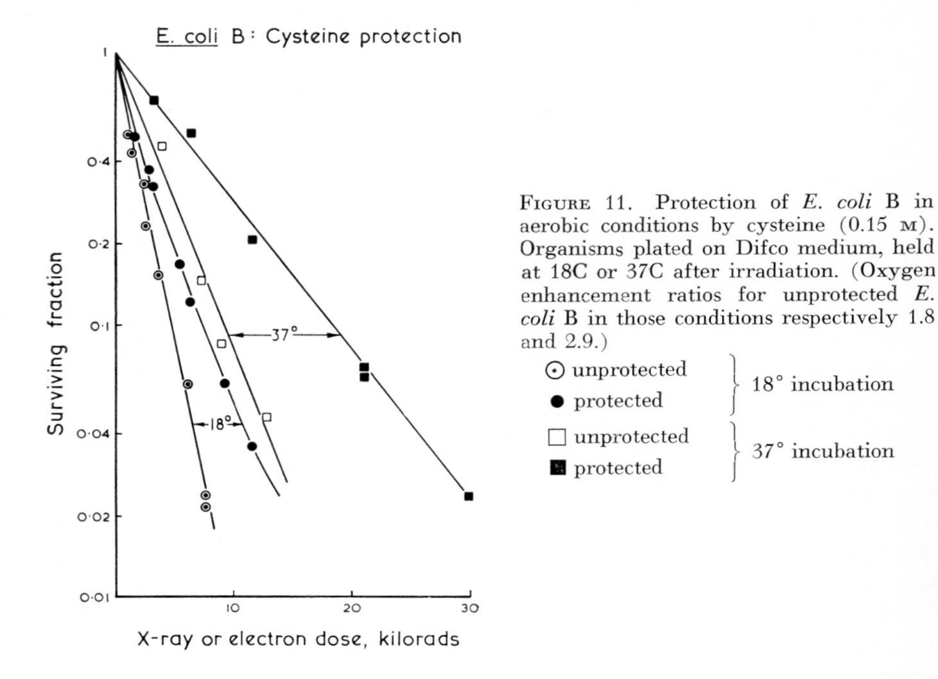

FIGURE 11. Protection of *E. coli* B in aerobic conditions by cysteine (0.15 M). Organisms plated on Difco medium, held at 18C or 37C after irradiation. (Oxygen enhancement ratios for unprotected *E. coli* B in those conditions respectively 1.8 and 2.9.)

⊙ unprotected, ● protected — 18° incubation

□ unprotected, ■ protected — 37° incubation

tend to be rather high, some of them considerably higher than those I have quoted. I regard this as still an open question, however, since the relevant survival curves were not taken with enough points to yield data as precise as are needed for the computation of m_N and m_O, which is based on differences between survival curve parameters. Some of our protection experiments will have to be repeated for this purpose.

It is, of course, particularly relevant to the purpose of this symposium to speculate on whether the model I have put forward for the cytocidal action of radiation can be extrapolated from microorganisms to higher cells, particularly to mammalian cells. There are a few tenuous lines of evidence which show that it might be reasonable; for example, there are closely related strains which show different oxygen enhancement ratios for killing (Silini and Hornsey, 1962; Révész, Glas, and Hilding, 1963).

Recently B. Dixon in our laboratories has been using techniques developed by R. H. Thomlinson (1960) to investigate quantitatively the radiosensitivity of a transplantable tumor which originally arose spontaneously. A dose 2.3 times greater was required to have the same effect on anoxic tumors as on those irradiated while the animals were breathing oxygen at high pressure; in the tumor line originally studied by Thomlinson, this ratio was 3.4 (Thomlinson, 1963). Such a difference suggests that, as with microorganisms, lethal events of different types might be brought to light to a varying extent in different cell lines, perhaps because of biochemical differences.

As far as I know there are no firm data available concerning the oxygen enhancement ratio for mutation induction in mammalian cells. Some preliminary data of Lindop and Rotblat (Personal communication) do, however, suggest that for the induction of leukemia and of lung cancer in mice, after whole-body irradiation, the oxygen enhancement ratio may well be lower than it is for acute death of the hematopoietic type. The dose-effect curves have a maximum which may be accounted for by the combined effects of cancer induction and cell death (Mendes and Lindop, 1964); some observations made after two doses with groups of mice irradiated while anoxic, and while breathing air, show that the maximum is shifted over toward a higher dose and is also at a higher level for the anoxic animals. This higher level is just what could be expected if the anoxia protected better against cell death than against induction of cancer, which is probably akin to mutation induction.

If it is true of mammalian cells, as it is of microorganisms, that there is a different balance in the types of lethal damage inflicted on anoxic and aerobic cells, although the over-all effect is equal for a given pair of doses, there are clear implications for the practice of radiotherapy. It seems to be generally accepted that failures may be due to foci of anoxic cells (Gray *et al.*, 1953), and various methods for overcoming this disadvantage are already in use (Churchill-Davidson, Sanger, and Thomlinson, 1955) or are under active consideration (Fowler, Morgan, and Wood, 1963). If there are sites of lethal cellular damage which are modified to a different extent by oxygen, other approaches are feasible. For example, the use of chemical agents, which appear to protect preferentially against type O damage, would enable the radiotherapist to give greater total doses, since the well-oxygenated normal cells would be much better protected than the anoxic cells. It seems possible, also, that postirradiation treatments might be found which would selectively enhance the damage done to cells which were anoxic during irradiation.

ACKNOWLEDGMENTS

I am most grateful to the following for permission to make use of unpublished results: Dr. P. J. Lindop and Professor J. Rotblat; Mr. J. L. Moore; and Dr. R. H. Thomlinson and Mr. B. Dixon.

REFERENCES

Alper, T. 1959. Variability in the Oxygen Effect Observed with Micro-organisms. I. Haploid Yeast: Single and Budding Cells. *International Journal of Radiation Biology, and Related Studies in Physics, Chemistry and Medicine*, 1:414–419.

———. 1961. Variability in the Oxygen Effect Observed with Micro-organisms. II. *Escherichia coli* B. *International Journal of Radiation Biology and Related Studies in Physics, Chemistry and Medicine*, 3:369–377.

———. 1963a. Effects on Irradiated Micro-organisms in the Presence of Acriflavine. *Nature*, London, 200:534–536.

———. 1963b. Lethal Mutations and Cell Death. *Physics in Medicine and Biology*, 8:365–385.

Alper, T., and N. E. Gillies. 1960. The Relationship between Growth and Survival after Irradiation of *Escherichia coli* Strain B and Two Resistant Mutants. *Journal of General Microbiology*, 22:113–128.

Alper, T., and J. L. Moore. 1964. The Interaction of some Modifying Treatments with the Sensitising Action of 5-Bromouracil in Bacteria. (Abstract) *British Journal of Radiology*, 37:803.

Anderson, E. H. 1951. The Effects of Oxygen on Mutation Induction by X-Rays. *Proceedings of the National Academy of Sciences of the U.S.A.*, 37:340–349.

Beam, C. A., R. K. Mortimer, R. G. Wolfe, and C. A. Tobias. 1954. The Relation of Radioresistance to Budding in *Saccharomyces cerevisiae. Archives of Biochemistry and Biophysics*, 49:110–122.

Bridges, B. A. 1963. Effect of Chemical Modifiers on Inactivation and Mutation-Induction by Gamma Radiation in *Escherichia coli. Journal of General Microbiology*, 31:405–412.

Churchill-Davidson, I., C. Sanger, and R. H. Thomlinson. 1955. High-Pressure Oxygen and Radiotherapy. *Lancet*, i:1091–1095.

Deering, R. 1963. Mutation and Killing of *Escherichia coli* WP-2 by Accelerated Heavy Ions and Other Radiations. *Radiation Research*, 19:169–178.

Doudney, C. O., and F. L. Haas. 1958. Modification of Ultraviolet-Induced Mutation Frequency and Survival in Bacteria by Post-irradiation Treatment. *Proceedings of the National Academy of Sciences of the U.S.A.*, 44:390–401.

Feiner, R. R., and R. F. Hill. 1963. Effect of Basic Dyes on Host-Cell Reactivation of Ultra-violet-Irradiated Phage. *Nature*, London, 200:291–293.

Fowler, J. F., R. L. Morgan, and C. A. P. Wood. 1963. Pretherapeutic Experiments with the Fast Neutron Beam from the Medical Research Council Cyclotron: The Biological and Physical Advantages and Problems of Neutron Therapy. *British Journal of Radiology*, 36:77–80, and papers by other authors in the same symposium.

Gray, L. H., A. D. Conger, M. Ebert, S. Hornsey, and O. C. A. Scott. 1953. The Concentration of Oxygen Dissolved in Tissues at the Time of Irradiation as a Factor in Radiotherapy. *British Journal of Radiology*, 26:638–648.

Hill, R. F. 1958. A Radiation-Sensitive Mutant of *Escherichia coli. Biochimica et biophysica acta*, 30:636–637.

Hornsey, S., and G. Silini. 1962. The Relationship between Chromosome Damage and Cell Viability in Ehrlich Ascites Tumours. (Abstract) *Second International Congress of Radiation Research, Harrogate, England*, p. 111.

Lindop, P. J., and J. Rotblat. Personal communication.

Mendes, J. J. A., and P. J. Lindop. 1964. Characteristics of Tumours in the Lungs of Mice Exposed to Whole-Body Irradiation. (Abstract) *British Journal of Radiology*, 37:161.

Moore, J. L. 1964. An Induced Enzyme in Irradiated *E. coli*: Comparison with Lethal Effects. (Abstract) *British Journal of Radiology*, 37:401.

Pike, M. C., and T. Alper. 1964. A Method for Determining Dose-Modification Factors. *British Journal of Radiology*, 37:458–462.

Révész, L., U. Glas, and G. Hilding. 1963. Relationship between Chromosome Number and Radiosensitivity of Tumour Cells. *Nature*, London, 198:260–261.

Silini, G., and S. Hornsey. 1962. Studies on Cell-Survival of Irradiated Ehrlich Ascites Tumors. III. A Comparison of the X-Ray Survival Curves Obtained with a Diploid and a Tetraploid Strain. *International Journal of Radiation Biology and Related Studies in Physics, Chemistry and Medicine*, 5:147–153.

Thomlinson, R. H. 1960. An Experimental Method for Comparing Treatments of Intact

Malignant Tumours in Animals and its Application to the Use of Oxygen in Radiotherapy. *The British Journal of Cancer*, 14:555–576.

———. 1963. A Comparison of Fast Neutrons and X-Rays in Relation to the "Oxygen Effect" in Experimental Tumours in Rats. *British Journal of Radiology*, 36:89–91.

Witkin, E. M. 1961. Modification of Mutagenesis Initiated by Ultraviolet Light through Posttreatment of Bacteria with Basic Dyes. *Journal of Cellular and Comparative Physiology*, Suppl. 1, 58:135–144.

———. 1963. The Effect of Acriflavine on Photoreversal of Lethal and Mutagenic Damage Produced in Bacteria by Ultraviolet Light. *Proceedings of the National Academy of Sciences of the U.S.A.*, 50:425–430.

Some Physicochemical Bases of Radiation Sensitivity in Cells

E. L. Powers

Division of Biological and Medical Research, Argonne National Laboratory, Argonne, Illinois

This paper is respectfully dedicated to Professor Friedrich Wassermann of Argonne National Laboratory on the occasion of his eightieth birthday, August 13, 1964.

Introduction

One of the goals of radiation biology is comprehension of the events and states intermediate between absorption of energy from high-energy radiation and expression of damage in the cell or organism. The difficulties confronting the investigator seeking this in the dynamic living system are too obvious to repeat. Surely, if transient and ephemeral states and species, and very fast reactions that remove or convert them, are to be recognized and characterized, the metabolizing organism is not the most favorable place to begin the attempt. Nevertheless, to appreciate the biological significance of an induced state or reaction, we are obliged to use biological tests. If one does not know the biological function of an unperturbed state or of the unchanged structure in the normal cell or organism, he cannot know the importance of perturbing or changing them by radiation. For instance, we disturb the capacity of the cell to divide by X-irradiation, now ask, what is the relationship between this damage and damage to molecular deoxyribonucleic acid (DNA) investigated in vitro. No relationship is demonstrable, because we do not know what the relationship is between undisturbed DNA and the capacity of the cell to divide. The relating of a physical or chemical change to biological effects of radiation must be done in a system that performs biologically after it has been disturbed physically or chemically by the radiation.

Since recognition of physical and chemical changes induced by radiations is difficult in metabolizing cells, the investigator must use metabolically inert cells that, even though inert, retain the capability of biological function. With the basic information gained from the inert cell, he can then plot the attack on the metabolizing cell.

In our work at Argonne, we began our series of experiments with dry spores of *Bacillus megaterium*. These cells can be dehydrated and rehydrated to varying degrees, exposed to extremes of cold and heat, bathed in gases that are ordinarily toxic, and can still, after restoration of physiological conditions, exhibit full biological activity. They are able to complete the complex series of biological actions and interactions that result in germination of the spore, morphogenesis of the vegetative cell, and division of this cell through 10 cell generations to produce a visible colony of cells.

In a second series of experiments, we treated the vegetative cells of *Staphylococcus aureus* in the same way, to serve as a transition from the spore to the normal metabolizing cell. In this system, the cell changes from inert in the very dry range to biologically active in the very wet region.

These two systems have allowed description of certain of the early actions of high-energy radiations on biological materials that lead to biological damage.

Another general aspect of our work is our view that the single biological character (in our case, the ability of the cell or the spore to give rise to a macroscopic colony of cells) can be disturbed in a number of physicochemical ways, and that these different ways of inducing damage are not interdependent and do not interact. At least, this is the first premise. Presuming nothing, we suppose at first that there is independence among the modes of injury; that each can be described and characterized separately; that predictions can be made in particular situations from the combined knowledge of the independent behaviors of all; and that it is to the extent to which prediction fails that there is interaction between or among the kinds of damage. Certainly the general biological result from interactions among the different kinds of damage brought about by radiation in a cell or organism is understood only to the extent that the individual kinds of damage are understood separately.

I shall review briefly the descriptions of the components of damage that we recognize in the spore and in the vegetative cell, some of the properties of these kinds of damage, the relationships of some of these findings to more general problems in radiation biology, and the conceptual utility of considering the damage in this compartmentalized manner. I shall then describe some recent experiments with one agent (namely, water, its amount and kind) that operates in different ways on the separate components of damage.

Kinds of Damage

The response measured is the ability of the dry spore or vegetative bacterial cell to give rise to a visible colony of cells after X-irradiation in a variety of experimental circumstances that affect radiation sensitivity. The techniques have been described in several previous papers (Powers, Ehret,

and Bannon, 1957; Kaleta and Powers, 1958; Tallentire and Powers, 196
Webb, 1963; Webb and Powers, 1964).

Each response curve is reduced numerically with the use of the fre
quently used model

$$S = 1 - (1 - e^{-kD})^n \quad (1$$

in which the rate constant k is the number of chief interest to us. The con
stant n is necessary for fits in those situations in which the straight portio
of the line obtained by plotting the logarithm of fractional survival (S
against dose (D) extrapolates to a number greater than 1.0. The constan
are evaluated from each survival curve by the method of Tyler and Dipe
(1962).

We call the rate constant k the "inactivation constant"; it has the di
mensions of reciprocal dose. It is the measure of radiation sensitivity.

It is characteristic that all of the response curves we observe ordinaril
are reducible with this model—a change in radiation sensitivity does n
change the essential exponential nature of the response to dosage (Power
1961b, 1962). Therefore, it is possible for us to describe the kinds of dam
age observed in some circumstances as elements of the rate constant k.

In Figure 1, for instance, the three response curves are of the sam
form. The probability of survival of the individual spore after dose D whe
the gas nitric oxide (NO) is present is

$$e^{-k_{NO}D}$$

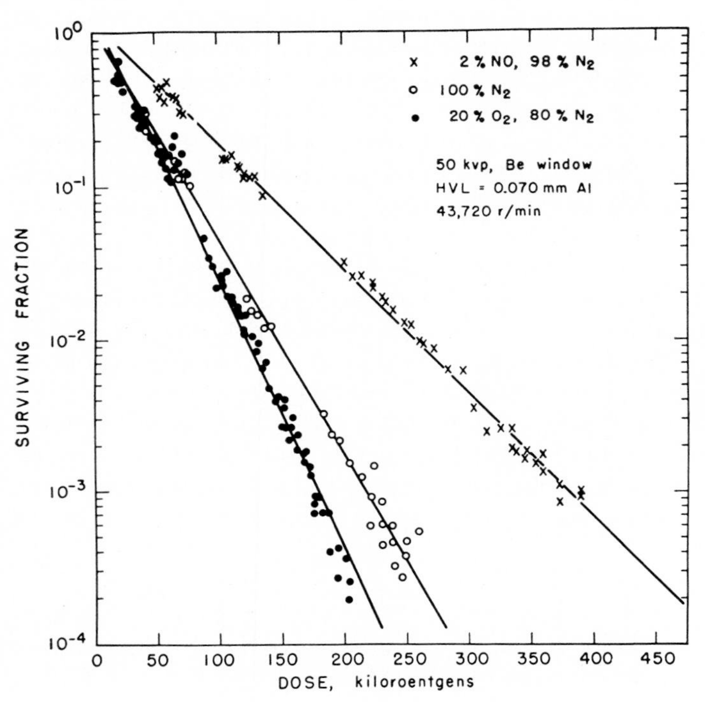

FIGURE 1. Su
vival of spores
Bacillus megate
um after X-irr
diation in the in
cated atmosphere

in which k_{NO} is the rate constant describing the experimental result.* We call the kind of damage that is responsible for death of the cell under these circumstances Class I damage; and in the compartmentalized description the rate constant is k_I. When the spores are irradiated in the absence of oxygen, but are allowed to react with oxygen prior to germination, free radicals formed by the radiation become biologically active (Class III damage). These free radicals are removed when NO is present prior to O_2-exposure. Under these circumstances, the total response includes the free radical component, as well as the k_I component, and is still described by the model (Equation 1). The rate constant, k_{N_2} experimentally, must be $k_I + k_{III}$, with k_{III} being the increase in k necessary to move the curve from the k_{NO} position to the k_{N_2} position. Similarly, when irradiation takes place in the presence of O_2, the damage represented by k_I takes place, that by k_{III} occurs, and the increase in $k_I + k_{III}$ necessary to move the response curve to its new position (from k_{N_2} to k_{O_2}) is represented by a new component, k_{II} (Class II damage). When irradiation takes place in O_2, the rate constant, k_{O_2}, is made up of $k_I + k_{II} + k_{III}$—that part independent of O_2, that part dependent upon O_2 presence during irradiation, and that part brought about by O_2-radical reactions after irradiation.

We have set ourselves the task of describing the properties of each of these three general kinds of damage in the spore and bacterial cell, hoping that we would be led to some understanding of how damage is brought about physicochemically. Figure 2, taken from Webb and Powers (1964), is a recent summary of the over-all response of the spores to 250 kvp X rays. It shows some of the numerical relations existing among the various k's in the dry spore, and spores in suspension, when different experimental conditions are used.

From experiments like those summarized in Figure 2, and from others not represented, we have gathered information concerning certain of these elements of radiation-induced damage. A partial summary is presented in Table 1 as response (+) or nonresponse (0) of the particular component of the inactivation constant to the named agent operating during or after the irradiation period. The arrows represent an increase (↑) or a decrease (↓) of the quantity in the presence of the agent. While some attempt is made to be specific, the table is incomplete, for the information available is too extensive for complete specification in a table of this sort.

This is the kind of information necessary for an understanding of the interaction of radiations and living organisms. To date, the explanations are best for the Class III damage, the free-radical portion. It is clear that in the dry cell free radicals are formed, and that they must react with oxygen to

* The following conventions for describing the experimental conditions under which the particular rate constant is observed are to apply henceforth: The subscript describes the gas present during irradiation with exposure to oxygen following understood. Thus, k_{NO} means irradiation in nitric oxide in the absence of O_2, removal of the nitric oxide, and exposure to O_2. If another procedure has been followed, the atmosphere following irradiation is written second in line; thus, k_{N_2, H_2O} means irradiation in N_2 followed by water treatment in the absence of O_2, followed by exposure to O_2.

become biologically effective (Powers, Ehret, and Smaller, 1961; Ehret, Smaller, Powers, and Webb, 1960; Powers, 1961a). Class II damage in many ways is similar to Class III; it differs mainly in the "immediacy" of its action. It may turn out that the entire oxygen effect is a radical effect, with the Class II radicals differing in their lifetimes. A decision should be possible soon. The nature of Class I damage—the oxygen independent damage—will be revealed also when sufficiently extensive experiments of these kinds (and others) have been done and integrated.

As examples of some of the information not demonstrated by Figure 2 or Table 1, we mention the effect of temperature on the modifying effect of the amount of water and on the effect of kind of water, and the relationship between linear energy transfer (LET) and amount and kind of water, among many others.

The Oxygen Effect

The separate behavior of the kinds of damage must be understood for appreciation of the responses of the cells to radiation. For instance, we have

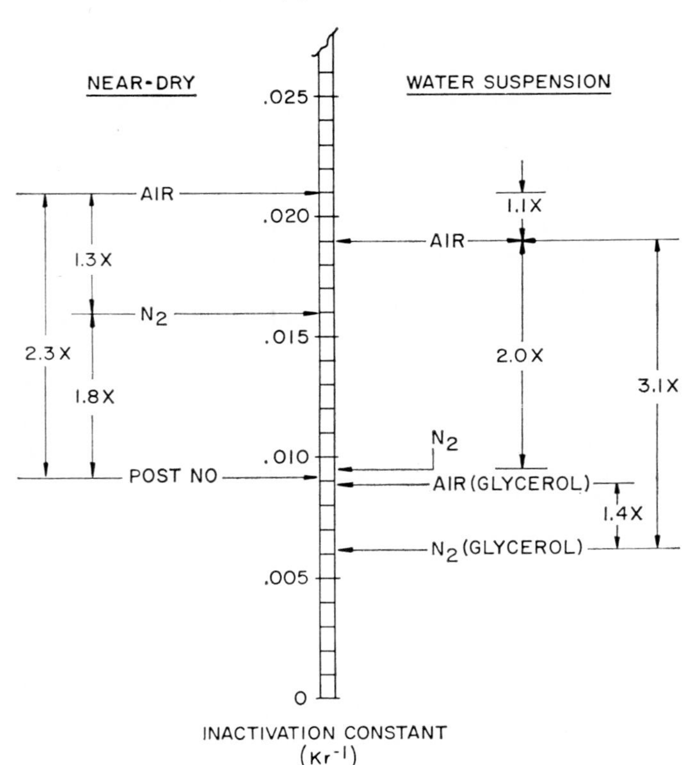

FIGURE 2. Subdivision of the inactivation constant in the dry spore and in water suspension. "Post NO" means postirradiation treatment with nitric oxide. (From Webb and Powers, 1964.)

TABLE 1

A Summary of Some of the Properties of the Three General Classes of Radiation Damage in the Bacterial Spore as They Are Related to the Experimental Variables on the Left

	I		II		III		
Variables	During	After	During	After	During	After	References*
O_2	0	0	$+\uparrow$	0	$+\uparrow$	$+\uparrow$ (<22 torr)	5, 6, 7
H_2S	$+\downarrow$	0	?	0	$+\downarrow$	$+\downarrow$ (<22 torr)	2
NO	?	0	$+(?)\uparrow$	0	$+\downarrow$	$+\downarrow$ (<22 torr)	6, 7
Glycerol	$+\downarrow$	0	$+\downarrow$	0	$+\downarrow$	$+(?)\downarrow$	9, 12, 13
Temp.	$+\uparrow$ (>125 K)	0	$+\uparrow$ (>125 K)	0	$+\downarrow$	$+\downarrow$ (<22 torr)	1, 11, 14
LET	$+\uparrow$	0	$+(>180\ \text{kev}/\mu)\downarrow$ $0(<180\ \text{kev}/\mu)$	0	$+(>180\ \text{kev}/\mu)\downarrow$ $0(<180\ \text{kev}/\mu)$ at 1 torr	0	3, 4
Water amount	$+(>1\ \text{torr})\uparrow$ $0(<1\ \text{torr})$	0	$+\downarrow$	0	$+\downarrow$	$+\downarrow$	8, 10, 13

* 1, Powers, 1961b; 2, Powers and Kaleta, 1960a; 3, Powers, Tobias, Lyman, and Brustad, 1964; 4, Powers, Webb, and Ehret, 1958; 5, Powers, Webb, and Ehret, 1959; 6, Powers, Webb, and Ehret, 1960; 7, Powers, Webb, and Kaleta, 1960; 8, Tallentire and Powers, 1963; 9, Webb, 1963; 10, Webb, 1964; 11, Webb, Ehret, and Powers, 1958; 12, Webb and Powers, 1962; 13, Webb and Powers, 1964; 14, Webb, Powers, and Ehret, 1960.

shown previously that some survival curves obtained under extreme conditions (e.g. high temperature and long radiation periods) appear to depart significantly from the model (Powers, 1961b). When, however, the properties of the separate kinds of damage are taken properly into account, the curves were not departures from exponentials at all, but rather the expectation when three exponential processes are operating simultaneously—two forward and one reverse, and each at a different rate.

As another example of the usefulness of thinking of the components of damage separately, we consider here the enhancing effect of oxygen on radiation damage, and the methods of expressing it. Most commonly the "oxygen enhancement ratio" is used. This is the quotient determined by the dose necessary for a certain effect when the organism is irradiated under anoxic conditions divided by the dose necessary for the same effect when the organism is irradiated in O_2 concentrations that give maximal effects. In our terminology it is k_{O_2}/k_{N_2}, or $k_{O_2}/k_{N_2,\ H_2S}$, depending upon whether the free-radical component is included in the denominator.

I think that the value of the oxygen enhancement ratio recognized by some investigators in particular circumstances does not justify its general use, for in the instances in which mechanisms of damage are being sought attention must be given to the behavior of the individual compartments of damage that are masked when ratios are quoted.

First, we examine the dependence of the oxygen effect on water content in the spore. In Figure 3 (Tallentire and Powers, 1963), we see that total radiation sensitivity in the presence of oxygen decreases from a very high value at low water content for the spore to a minimum value at saturated conditions. The probability of death of the individual spore from oxygen-associated events (both general kinds) is a function of the difference between the total inactivation constant at any degree of dryness and the inactivation constant observed when all oxygen-associated events are prevented (the lowest line of the graph). The oxygen enhancement ratio, in this case, is the inactivation constant observed in the presence of oxygen (k_{O_2}) divided by the inactivation constant after treatment by H_2O (equivalent to H_2S) in the absence of oxygen (k_{N_2} H_2O, or k_I).

Figure 4 demonstrates the change in the oxygen enhancement ratio as the equilibrium vapor pressure of water changes. From 10^{-4} torr H_2O vapor pressure to 22 torr (saturation at 25 C), a steady decrease is observed in the ratio to about 2.0 for the very wet spore. The same general relationship is observed in cells of *Staphylococcus aureus* (Figure 5), with approximately equal values being observed in the water cells. We should infer from this that O_2 effects in the very dry cell are very much larger than they are in wetter cells. The information in Figure 6 (Webb, 1964) bears this out. The O_2 components of damage are very much larger in the dry cell (as in the

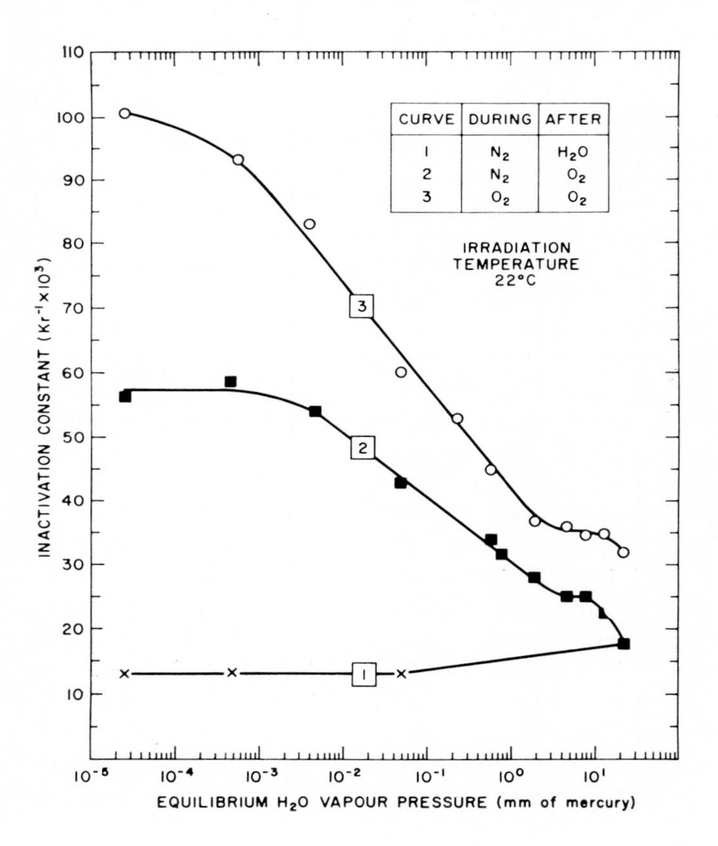

FIGURE 3. Changes in radiation sensitivity of spores related to water content as controlled by equilibrium vapor pressure of H_2O. (From Tallentire and Powers, 1963.)

spore) than they are in the wet cell. Water in some way interferes with the oxygen-associated events of biological importance. The anoxic component (the bottom line in Figures 3 and 6) in each cell is almost invariant over

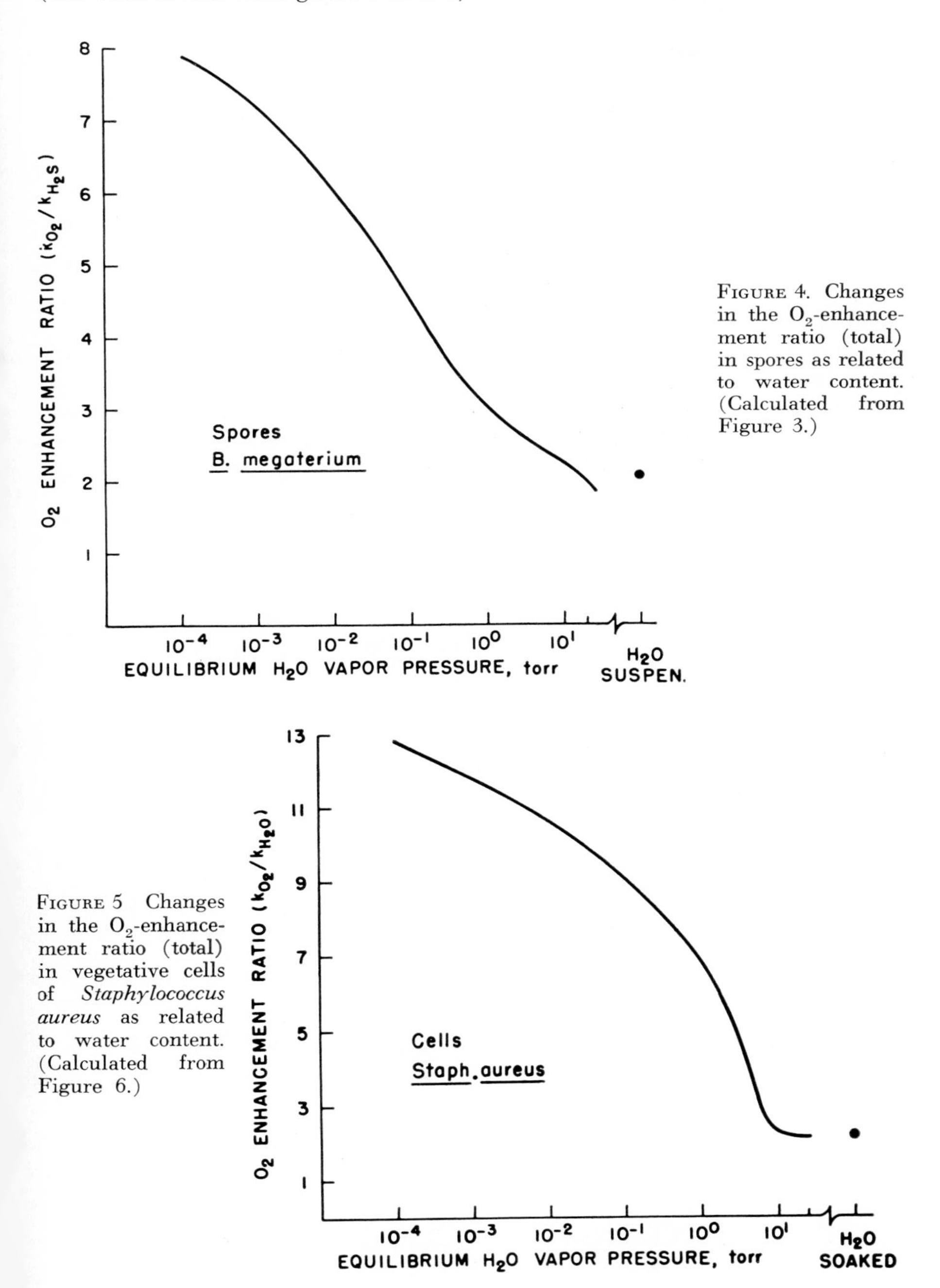

FIGURE 4. Changes in the O_2-enhancement ratio (total) in spores as related to water content. (Calculated from Figure 3.)

FIGURE 5 Changes in the O_2-enhancement ratio (total) in vegetative cells of *Staphylococcus aureus* as related to water content. (Calculated from Figure 6.)

the range, except that, in both systems, the anoxic component increases in the wet region. Statement of the ratio does not reveal that both the numerator and the denominator of the quotient are changing, and important information is hidden.

However, even with this shortcoming the oxygen-enhancement ratio gives the correct general picture in these two instances; it decreases with increasing wetness; and so also does the magnitude of the oxygen-associated components of damage. The ratio suggests the proper interpretation, at least in the dry regions.

Second, let us now consider the oxygen-enhancement ratio as it is influenced by changes in linear energy transfer brought about in the spore with the use of stripped atoms of different atomic number as bombarding ions (Figure 7) (Powers, Tobias, Lyman, and Brustad, 1964). The over-all relationship is the same as that observed for the water situation, namely, that as LET increases there is a decrease in the oxygen-enhancement ratio. If we take our clue from the water circumstance and follow the thought suggested very strongly by the words "oxygen-enhancement ratio," then we might believe that in this instance also there is a decrease in probability of death from oxygen-associated events as LET increases.

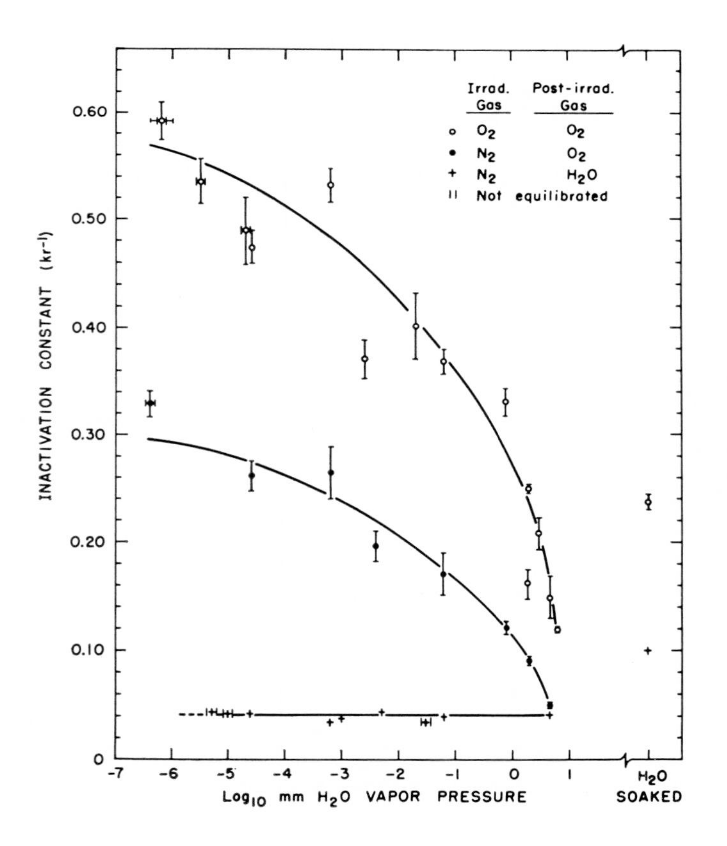

FIGURE 6. Changes in radiation sensitivity of cells of *Staphylococcus aureus* as related to water content. (From Webb, 1964.)

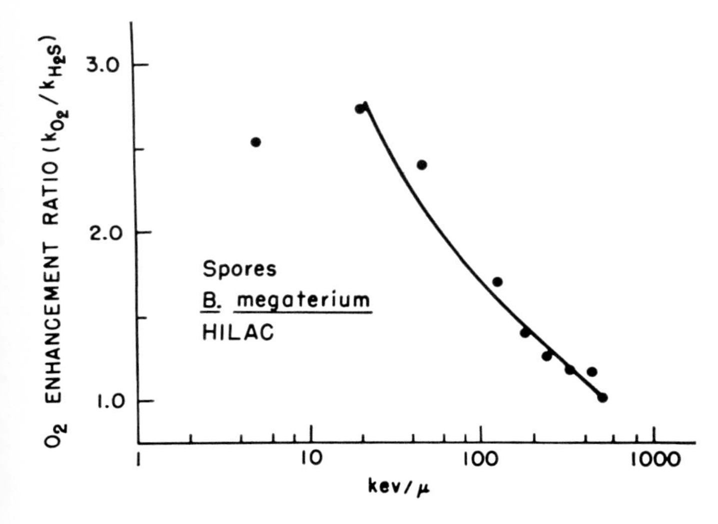

FIGURE 7. The O_2-enhancement ratio in spores as determined by the LET produced by heavy ions. (Calculated from data of Powers, Tobias, and Lyman, 1962; Powers, Tobias, Lyman, and Brustad, 1964.)

For the particles used in this investigation, this is not true, and the conclusion is incorrect. As demonstrated by Figure 8, in which the total effect induced by the individual ion is subdivided into oxygen-dependent portions and oxygen-independent portions, we see that the number proportional to the probability of death from oxygen-associated events is constant from the lowest LET tested to that produced by the carbon ion (about 180 kev/μ); and that over this range the *anoxic portion of the total response increases.* This is saying that the oxygen-enhancement ratio in this instance is decreasing not because the oxygen effect is decreasing in magnitude (as it does as water content increases), but rather because the oxygen-independent part of the effect is increasing in magnitude. (Beyond this point in the LET scale, note that both the oxygen effect and anoxic effect change simultaneously to keep the relation of the ratio to LET on the same functional curve.)

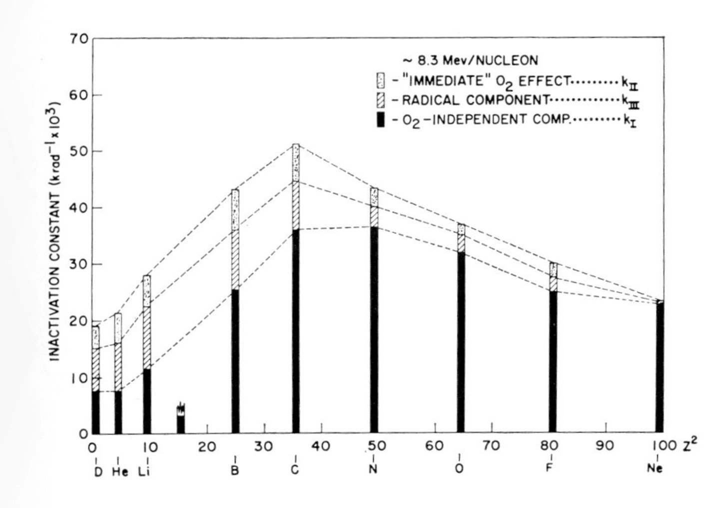

FIGURE 8. The relationship between radiation sensitivity of the bacterial spore and LET produced by heavy ions. The plot is inactivation constant against the square of the atomic number of the ion. (From Powers, Tobias, and Lyman, 1962; Powers, Tobias, Lyman, and Brustad, 1964.)

Now for the understanding of the difference between particle irradiation and X-irradiation as related to oxygen-dependent damage and oxygen-independent damage, is it not very important for us to appreciate that in the one instance the oxygen effect (the numerator) is changing and the anoxic effect (the denominator) is quite constant, and in the other instance the oxygen effect (the numerator) is quite constant and the anoxic effect (the denominator) is changing? By curious circumstance, the same general change in the ratio is observed in the two circumstances, but for reciprocal reasons.

Water

Amount of Water

The general relationship between the amount of water and the magnitude of the kinds of sensitivity to radiation has been described for spores (Tallentire and Powers, 1963) and vegetative cells (Webb, 1964). Water, acting generally as a protective agent, causes a decrease in sensitivity of these cells to oxygen-associated events and appears not to affect the oxygen-independent kind of damage from the very dry to the wet. There are small increases in one oxygen-dependent and the oxygen-independent mode of injury when the two kinds of cells become very wet. The long-lived free-radical component disappears. Current studies are directed to the reasons for the difference in magnitude of these increases in the spore and vegetative cell. These differ in the important aspect of metabolism, or metabolic readiness. The spore is inert; the vegetative cell may be metabolizing in this range of wetness, or, if not actively metabolizing, it is biochemically fit, and the spore is not. The information will bear on an important question not definitely answerable now—is the oxygen effect in the metabolizing cell purely a physicochemical one, or is the fact that the cell is biochemically active the reason for all or a part of the oxygen effect?

Kind of Water

The Deuterium Effect

Among the other water relations we have been investigating is the effect of substituting deuterium for hydrogen in the easily exchangeable positions in the spore. Over a number of years, we have been performing experiments with deuteriated spores along with the experiments on protiated spores that have been described in the literature. The information available is considerable, and has not been compiled and analyzed fully. However, consideration of the results is sufficiently far along to recognize some aspects of this isotope effect in radiation sensitivity, and because of its conceivable importance in the understanding of the early processes, I report some of these to you now. (Some previous announcements were in Powers and Kaleta, 1960b; Powers and Angelus, 1962.)

Deuteriation was accomplished by growing cells and producing spores from these cells on potato extract agar prepared with 100 per cent D_2O. Spores produced in this way contain as much deuterium as possible without our using especially deuteriated metabolites. Spores thus prepared are not different substantially from ordinary spores with respect to germination and colony production, but deuterium substitution has a noticeable effect on radiation sensitivity.

In Figure 9, a distinct difference is seen between protiated and deuteriated spores. Throughout the temperature range tested (from liquid helium temperatures to room temperature), the substitution of deuterium results in lowered radiation sensitivity. When the free-radical component is subtracted by H_2S treatment, the effect of deuterium is still evident. Deuterium presence clearly affects the Class I (oxygen independent part of) radiation damage. (These experiments do not reveal any effect in Class III that changes with temperature.)

One other important fact is demonstrated in Figure 9. Temperature independence is demonstrated by both kinds of spores up to certain temperatures, and then the dependence described by Webb, Ehret, and Powers (1958) is observed. The degree of dependence appears to be the same for both kinds of spores, but the temperature at which dependence begins is different. For the protiated spore it is 120 K; for the deuteriated it is 150 K.

Recall that removal of water from the bacterial spore increases radiation sensitivity (Tallentire and Powers, 1963). The evidence that deuterium ice is more stable structurally than protium ice suggests that these

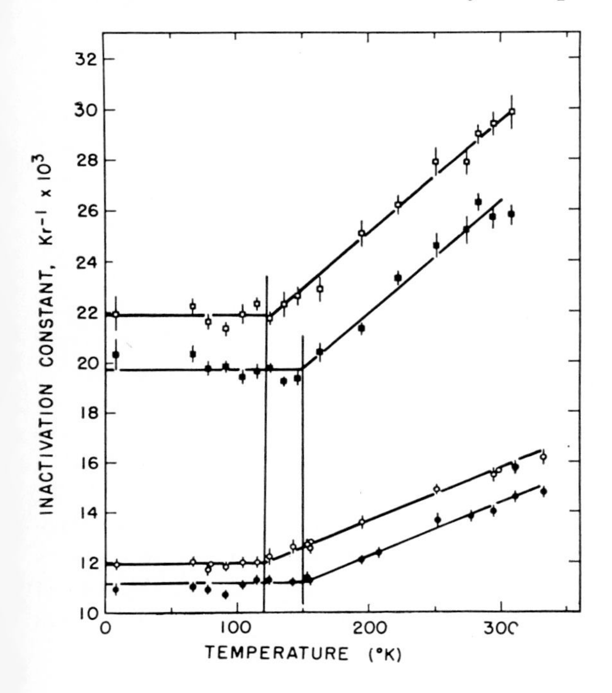

FIGURE 9. The radiation sensitivities of bacterial spores containing only protium (H) (open points) and those of spores containing a large number of deuterium atoms (D) (closed points). The two upper lines are sensitivities observed when irradiation in a N_2 atmosphere was followed by exposure to oxygen. The two lower lines are sensitivities observed when irradiation in a N_2 atmosphere was followed by exposure to H_2S. The vertical lines are optical aids for comparing the temperatures at which the radiation sensitivities of the two kinds of spores become temperature dependent. These spores are equilibrated to about 1 torr H_2O vapor pressure.

two kinds of molecules in their close-order, icelike relationships to complex cellular structures may differ in their stability with deuterium water's being removed with much difficulty. Experiments that involve heating at 80 C at less than 10^{-4} mm Hg for 16 hours prior to irradiation have no effect on these relations; and it seems unlikely that the deuterium effect is the reflection of removal of relatively less water from the deuterium spores. Furthermore, when the two kinds of spores are suspended in liquid water, the D spores still differ from the H spores, as shown in the first two columns of Table 2, in both the oxygenated and the nonoxygenated circumstances. Spores produced from cells grown in 100 per cent D_2O are less sensitive to radiation; this lessened sensitivity is probably not related to the amount of water in the cell.

TABLE 2

*Inactivation Constants Observed in Two Kinds of Spores when Suspended during Irradiation in Either Pure H_2O or D_2O, in the Presence and Absence of O_2**

MEDIUM / SPORES	H_2O				D_2O			
	O_2		N_2		O_2		N_2	
	k	S.E. × 10^4	k	S.E. × 10^4	k	S.E. × 10^4	k	S.E. × 10^4
H_2O	.02221	4.1	.01139	3.0	.02540	4.3	.01130	1.8
	.02355	2.7	.01100	1.4	.02454	2.7	.01239	2.6
	.02383	2.6	.01110	1.2	.02785	3.8	.01248	6.1
	.02212	7.1	.01157	2.3	.02702	3.2	.01193	3.4
	.02853	4.5	.01055	1.7	.02488	2.4	.00974	2.4
	.02589	3.5	.01100	.95	.02868	6.9	.01189	.96
					.02624	3.2		
	.0244 ± .0004		.0111 ± .0002		.0263 ± .0004		.0116 ± .0003	
D_2O	.01849	1.2	.00990	1.2	.02010	2.6	.01032	1.2
	.01854	1.7	.00932	.84	.01922	2.6	.01036	1.7
	.01798	3.0	.01023	3.7	.01864	1.9	.00987	1.3
	.01972	3.0	.01023	.91	.02004	2.1	.00975	1.2
	.01917	1.5	.01053	1.5	.01952	1.3	.01047	.89
			.01037	1.7			.01045	1.1
			.01020	1.8			.01016	.65
			.00995	1.9				
	.0188 ± .0001		.01009 ± .0002		.0195 ± .0002		.0102 ± .0001	

* Constants from individual experiments are written; the lowest number in each box is the mean and the standard error of the experimental values in the box.

One general question suggests itself immediately. To what extent does the deuterium effect depend upon the amount of water in the cell? In Figure 10, the change in sensitivity of H and D spores when equilibrated with H_2O are shown. The deuterium effect becomes larger as the total amount of water given to the cells prior to irradiation decreases. This is true for both Class II and Class III damage, because Class I is about the same value throughout the dry range. This shows that the three classes of damage are affected by deuterium presence, and for the oxygen dependent modes the magnitude of the difference is determined by the amount of H_2O given to the spores during the preirradiation equilibration process.

Then this question presents itself: Since the magnitude of the effect

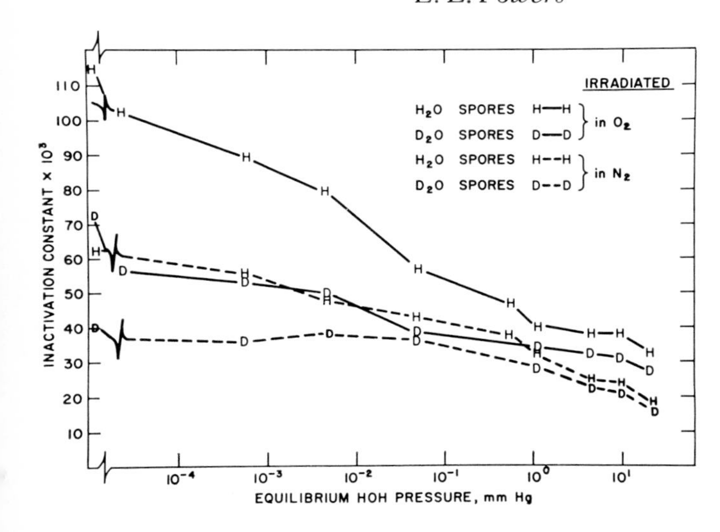

FIGURE 10. Radiation sensitivities of spores of two kinds irradiated in O_2 and in its absence after equilibration to gaseous H_2O.

of deuteriation depends upon the amount of H_2O added during the equilibration process, what, if any, is the effect of adding D_2O in equilibration? Figure 11 shows that the general relationships between amount of D_2O added to the cells and the deuterium effect is like that seen when H_2O is the additive. Figure 12 is a partial comparison of H_2O spores given H_2O and D_2O. In the dry spores (< 1 mm Hg H_2O vapor pressure), the facts presented in this figure and elsewhere indicate that the quality of the water added during equilibration prior to irradiation is not important to the effect. The isotope effect is related to deuterium incorporated in the spore at the time of its formation.

However, when the amount of water added is larger than that introduced at 1 torr equilibrium pressure, there is an appreciable effect of

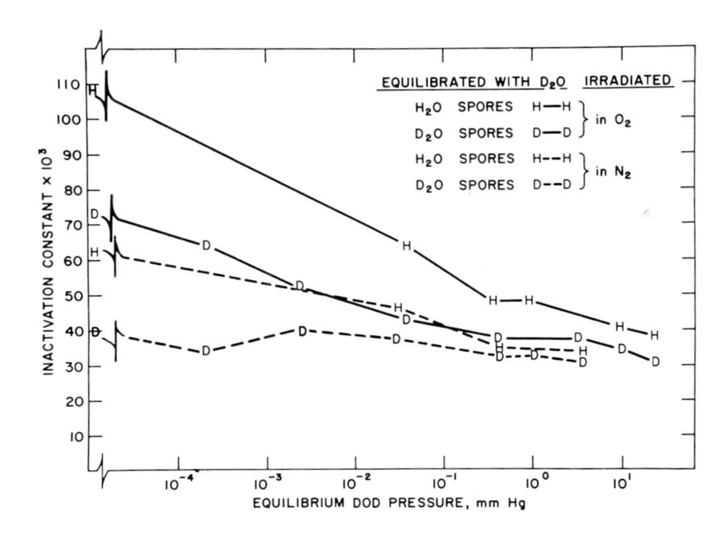

FIGURE 11. Radiation sensitivities of spores of two kinds irradiated in O_2 and in its absence after equilibration to gaseous D_2O.

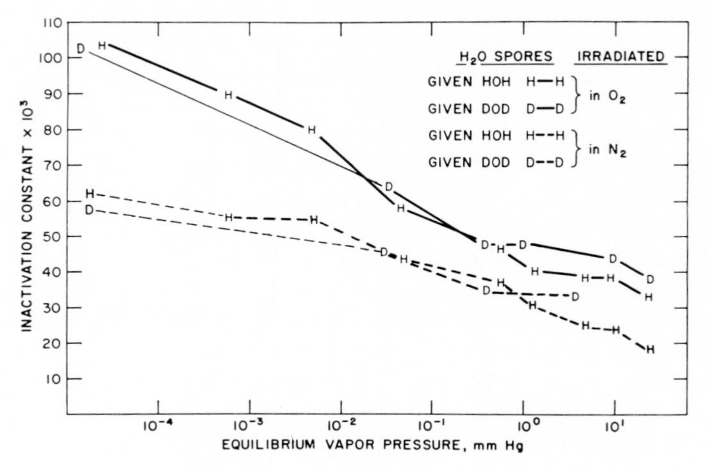

FIGURE 12. Radiation sensitivities of spores produced in H_2O equilibrated with either H_2O or D_2O as indicated.

deuterium addition. In this instance, the effect is in the opposite direction; namely, spores to which D_2O is added are more sensitive than those to which H_2O is added. D_2O is a sensitizing agent under these conditions.

The same comparison can be made for spores prepared in D_2O, and then equilibrated with either H_2O or D_2O prior to irradiation (Figure 13), and the same result is observed. Below about 1 mm Hg equilibration pressure, correspondence between D_2O-grown spores given H_2O and those given D_2O prior to irradiation is seen certainly in N_2 and probably in O_2 (note coincidence of H and D points on the O_2 curve in the very dry spores). But, as in the H_2O-grown spores, above about 1 torr, the D_2O spores are more sensitive when given D_2O than they are when given H_2O for both experimental conditions described. The absolute differences appear to be a bit smaller for the D_2O-grown spores than they are for the H_2O spores, but they are consistently higher for both the anoxic and the oxygenated experiments.

In these wet spores, the deuterium effect may be a double one: one operates to decrease the radiation sensitivity, observed in the dry spore, and the other operates to increase the radiation sensitivity, observed in the wet spore. The two certainly must be associated with different compartments in the cell, the sensitizing effect probably being a water effect in what we call the "juicy" compartment, and the protective effect probably a water effect in that water (not easily removed) associated intimately with cellular structures.

The results of a test of the extreme circumstance is presented in Table 2. Inactivation constants are given for spores produced in H_2O and D_2O irradiated when suspended in H_2O and D_2O, in the presence and the absence of oxygen. (In order to ensure penetrance of the beam, a filtered 250 kvp beam was used in these experiments. The inactivation constants are different from those seen after irradiation with 50 kvp x rays [Powers, Webb, and Ehret, 1958]).

The generalization holds that spores produced in H_2O are more sensitive than those produced in D_2O in all similar experimental conditions tested. The difference is small in one instance, but here also the H_2O spore value is the higher one. Consider now the H_2O spores only. When suspended in D_2O, they are more sensitive than when suspended in H_2O, whether oxygen is present or not. For the D_2O spores the differences are very small, but directionally the same, bearing out the sensitivities shown in Figure 13. In cells of this degree of wetness (more than 1 torr equilibration pressure), added D_2O has a net sensitizing effect.

From even this partial statement of our results in these experiments, there are a number of general statements possible concerning the effect of deuterium substitution on radiation sensitivity:

1. Over a very wide temperature range, deuterium substitution lowers radiation sensitivity by decreasing Class I (oxygen independent) damage. It is too early to suggest physical mechanisms by which this is accomplished.

2. In the D_2O spore, the temperature at which spores become temperature dependent is about 30° higher than it is in the H_2O spore. It is of interest, and perhaps of importance, that D_2O ice and H_2O ice differ in certain properties that are related to temperature in this way.

3. The deuterium effect becomes larger as the spore becomes drier. The increase in the effect is observed both in Class II and III, but not in Class I, in which it remains constant. So we seen that the three general components of damage are affected by deuterium presence—all in the same direction (protection in the dry region), but to different degrees. H_2O and D_2O added after spore production lessen the deuterium effect observed in the oxygen-dependent parts of damage (see point 4).

4. In dry spores (< 1 mm Hg water vapor equilibration), the kind of water (H_2O or D_2O) added to the spore is not important. They bring about equal quantitative changes. In this range of water content, the amount of

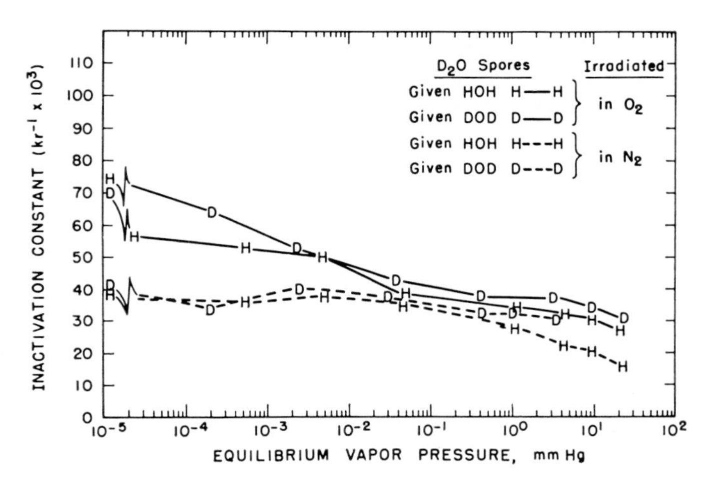

FIGURE 13. Radiation sensitivities of spores produced in D_2O equilibrated with either H_2O or D_2O as indicated.

water in the cell controls the degree to which the deuterium effect is expressed, but this controlling water can be either H_2O or D_2O. If the deuterium effect arises from a water compartment, as it may, we see here a nice distinction between two interacting water compartments—one being D-dependent and the other not.

5. In wet spores ($>$ 1 mm Hg water vapor equilibration), the kind of water (H_2O or D_2O) added to the spore is important. The changes are quantitatively and qualitatively different. Added D_2O in this range of wetness is a sensitizing agent, an opposite effect to that brought about by incorporated D_2O in the dry spore. The effect appears to be in Class I. What are the reasons? Is this an expression of differences in the radiolysis of D_2O and H_2O? Or, if these are the same, is this an expression of the greater protective capacity of liquid H_2O over that of D_2O? Is the radiation chemistry of D_2O and H_2O the same with O_2 present, but different in its absence?

6. The degree of hydration at which the sensitizing effect of added D_2O is appreciated ($\sim$ 1 torr) is an important point at which several aspects of the radiation biology of spores and bacterial cells change:

A. As water content changes from the very dry to the wet, a plateau in the sensitivity (in O_2) versus water content curve begins at this point (Tallentire and Powers, 1963). This marks the beginning of a state in the spore which is unchanged by a fourfold increase in equilibrium pressure of water.

B. As water content changes from the very dry to the wet, there begins at this point of hydration a small but definite increase in the anoxic (Class I) component of damage. The ways in which the exposed cells die change relatively, although total sensitivity in O_2 remains the same (point A above).

C. In vegetative cells of *Staphylococcus aureus*, the same qualitative phenomena listed in A and B above take place (Webb, 1964).

D. In both systems, there are seen deviations from the regular dose-response curves. These have not been systematized and cannot be described in detail at this time. But we must note here that, in the absence of oxygen, unexplained aberrancies occur and that these are rare in the presence of oxygen. These effects must be understood before we understand the role of water in the fully wetted system. The fact that D_2O sensitization in cells of this degree of hydration appears to be mostly in the oxygen-independent component of damage can be presumed, for working reasons, to be related with these apparent departures from exponential behavior.

Conclusion

There are good reasons to believe that some of the early events in cells that precede expression of biological damage will be described in detail in the near future. Investigation of dry biological systems has revealed already one definite fact: High-energy radiations cause radical formation, and these radicals when combined with oxygen are responsible for part of the biological damage observed. Other investigations have revealed that these systems respond to many experimental variables in ways that suggest strongly that other physical and chemical mechanisms will reveal themselves if we pursue the leads offered by the organisms.

This report necessarily has been limited to a brief description of parts of the work of our small group. It is unfortunate that other substantial work by others cannot be considered here. In other papers we have discussed the relationship of these results to ours. Many of us know that the work of many other investigators using a variety of test systems demonstrates like promise. Plant embryos, cellular systems other than bacteria, virus particles, isolated macromolecules, and other chemical systems (water, for instance) yield information that is important and that can be appreciated and integrated to lead us to an understanding of the bases of radiation sensitivity.

ACKNOWLEDGMENTS

This work was performed under the auspices of the United States Atomic Energy Commission.

Mrs. Barbara Kaleta Angelus, Mrs. June Blackwell, Mrs. Celestia Crawford and Miss Gloria Kokaisl, who participated in the experiments reported herein, and Miss Laurie Kusnik, who assisted with the manuscript, are due my thanks. The aid of Dr. Robert B. Webb in the experiments and in the preparation of this paper is gratefully acknowledged.

REFERENCES

Ehret, C. F., B. Smaller, E. L. Powers, and R. B. Webb. 1960. Thermal Annealment and Nitric Oxide Effects on Electron Spin Resonance Hyperfine Patterns Produced by Free Radicals in X-Irradiated Cells. *Science*, 132:1768–1796.

Kaleta, B. F., and E. L. Powers. 1958. "Modification of the Membrane Filter Technique for Studies of Radiation Effects in Spores of *Bacillus megaterium*," *Report of Division of Biological and Medical Research* (Argonne National Laboratory Publication No. 6093). Argonne, Illinois, Pp. 78–81.

Powers, E. L. 1961a. "Chemical Species Induced by X-Rays in Cells and Their Role in Radiation Injury," *The Initial Effects of Ionizing Radiations on Cells*, R. J. C. Harris, Ed. London, England, and New York, New York: Academic Press. Pp. 91–106.

———. 1961b. Reversible and Irreversible Radiation Injury in Dry Biological Systems. *Journal of Cellular and Comparative Physiology*, 58: Supplement on Gatlinburg Conference:13–25.

———. 1962. Considerations of Survival Curves and Target Theory. *Physics in Medicine and Biology*, 7:3–28.

Powers, E. L., and B. F. Angelus. 1962. The "Isotope Effect" in the Radiation Sensitivity of Bacterial Spores. Abstracts, *Second International Congress of Radiation Research* (Harrogate). Pp. 196–197.

Powers, E. L., C. F. Ehret, and A. Bannon. 1957. The Membrane Filter Technique in Radiation Studies of Spores of *Bacillus megaterium*. *Applied Microbiology*, 5:61–64.

Powers, E. L., C. F. Ehret, and B. Smaller. 1961. "The Role of Free Radicals in the Lethal Effects of X-Rays in Dry Bacterial Spores," *Free Radicals in Biological Systems* II (Proceedings of a Symposium Held at Stanford University, March 1960),

M. S. Blois, Jr., H. W. Brown, R. M. Lemmon, R. O. Lindblom, and M. Weissbluth, Eds. New York, New York, and London, England: Academic Press. Pp. 351–366.

Powers, E. L., and B. F. Kaleta. 1960a. Reduction of Radiation Sensitivity of Dry Bacterial Spores with Hydrogen Sulfide. *Science*, 132:959–960.

————. 1960b. An Isotope Effect in the Radiation Biology of *Bacillus megaterium.* (Abstract) *Proceedings of the Fourth Annual Meeting of the Biophysical Society*, p. 36.

Powers, E. L., C. A. Tobias, and J. Lyman. 1962. An Analysis of the Biological Damage Induced by Heavy Ions. *Radiation Research*, 16:608–609.

Powers, E. L., C. A. Tobias, J. Lyman, and T. Brustad. 1964. Damage Induced by Charged Particles in Bacterial Spores. (in preparation.)

Powers, E. L., R. B. Webb, and C. F. Ehret. 1958. "Modification of Sensitivity to Radiation in Single Cells by Physical Means," *Proceedings of the Second International Conference on the Peaceful Uses of Atomic Energy*, Geneva, Switzerland: United Nations Publication. Vol. 22. Pp. 404–408.

————. 1959. An Oxygen Effect in Dry Bacterial Spores and its Temperature Dependence. *Experimental Cell Research*, 17:550–554.

————. 1960. Storage, Transfer, and Utilization of Energy from X-Rays in Dry Bacterial Spores. *Radiation Research, Supplement* 2:94–121.

Powers, E. L., R. B. Webb, and B. F. Kaleta. 1960. Oxygen and Nitric Oxide as Modifiers of Radiation Injury in Spores of *Bacillus megaterium. Proceedings of the National Academy of Sciences of the U.S.A.*, 46:984–993.

Tallentire, A., and E. L. Powers. 1963. Modification of Sensitivity to X-Irradiation by Water in *Bacillus megaterium. Radiation Research*, 20:270–287.

Tyler, S. A., and M. H. Dipert. 1962. On Estimating the Constants of the "Multi-Hit" Curve Using a Medium Speed Digital Computer. *Physics in Medicine and Biology*, 7:201–212.

Webb, R. B. 1963. Glycerol and Water Effects on X-Ray Sensitivity in *Staphylococcus aureus. Radiation Research*, 18:607–619.

————. 1964. "Physical Components of Radiation Damage in Cells," *International Symposium on Physical Processes in Radiation Biology*. New York, New York: Academic Press, Inc. Pp. 267–285.

Webb, R. B., C. F. Ehret, and E. L. Powers. 1958. A Study of the Temperature Dependence of Radiation Sensitivity of Dry Spores of *Bacillus megaterium* between 5°K and 309°K. *Experientia*, 14:324–326.

Webb, R. B., and E. L. Powers. 1962. Glycerol and Water Effects in Bacterial Spores and Vegetative Cells. Abstracts, *Second International Congress of Radiation Research* (Harrogate). P. 42.

————. 1964. Protection Against Actions of X-Rays by Glycerol in the Bacterial Spore. *International Journal of Radiation Biology and Related Studies in Physics, Chemistry and Medicine*, 7:481–490.

Webb, R. B., E. L. Powers, and C. F. Ehret. 1960. Thermorestoration of Radiation Damage in Dry Bacterial Spores. *Radiation Research*, 12:682–693.

Sulfhydryl-Disulfide Protection Mechanisms and the Isolation of a Possible Target Structure from Mammalian Cell Nuclei

LORENTZ ELDJARN

Institute of Clinical Biochemistry, Rikshospitalet, University of Oslo, Oslo, Norway

In radiation therapy of cancer, there is an urgent need for procedures which may widen the narrow range between the curative radiation dose and the dose which will prove deleterious to the host. A promising approach toward this goal was opened up when Patt, Tyree, Straube, and Smith (1949) discovered that cysteine, in part, could protect mice against the lethal action of ionizing radiation. In subsequent years, the most significant advances probably have been the discovery of the protective action of cysteamine (Bacq *et al.*, 1951) and its S-guanido derivative, aminoethylisothiouronium bromide hydrobromide (AET) (Doherty and Burnett, 1955). However, despite hard work in many laboratories for a number of years, the progress in this field has been extremely slow, and compounds which might prove useful adjuvants in radiation therapy of cancer are still lacking.

At present the sulfur-containing protective agents offer the greatest hope for practical applicability in human beings, the realization of which, however, depends on progress in two fields: How can the toxic effect be reduced? Is it possible to increase the dose reduction factor beyond the magic figure of two? As a background for such work, I will present basic ideas concerning the mechanisms underlying the pharmacologic and radioprotective activity of the sulfur-containing protective agents. Some recent results which, in my opinion, shed light on our problems will be reviewed. Finally, I will comment on the search for "target molecules" of cell nuclei, which is currently under way in our laboratory.

CHEMICAL PROTECTION—RADIOCHEMISTRY OR CELLULAR PHYSIOLOGY?

The mechanisms which have been proposed to explain chemical protection against ionizing radiation fall into two categories. The most widely held view is that the S-containing protective agents ultimately take part in the physical dissipation of radiation energy in a nondeleterious way, *i.e.* a mode of action which involves purely radiochemical events. However, some authors have proposed that the chemical agents may increase the radioresistance of mammalian cells by a temporary interference with cellular metabolism. Fragmentary data have been published on the effect of S-containing protective agents on cellular metabolism, the radiobiological significance of which has recently been reviewed (Eldjarn, 1962).

A more mechanistic explanation emerged from the observations of Therkelsen (1958) e.g. that cysteamine and N-dimethyl cysteamine arrested mitoses in the metaphase in chicken heart fibroblast cultures, whereas the nonprotective compounds, S-methyl cysteamine and methyl-bis (β-mercaptoethyl)-amine, failed to do so. Eldjarn and Pihl (1960) discussed the possibility that such an effect might keep cells in a radioresistant phase during the period of irradiation. In fact, Pirie and Lajtha (1959) have presented evidence for such a view in the case of cysteine protection against cataract in rabbits. In the present discussion, which is mainly concerned with in vivo protection in mammals, several facts make it unlikely that an effect on mitoses should be responsible. In particular, it should be recalled that only minutes are needed after the administration of the protective agents to establish protection. If mitotic inhibition should be the mechanism of action, a much longer time interval would be expected in order to "collect" cells in a radioresistant phase.

Therefore, I believe that no likely hypothesis so far has emerged from the above data to account for the mechanism of action of the S-containing compounds. It appears most profitable to pursue this discussion on the assumption that the in vivo protection by the S-containing agents should be ascribed to some radiochemical events.

Radiochemical Protection Mechanisms

Basic radiobiology has profited enormously from the joint effort of scientists from the disciplines of physics, chemistry, biology, and medicine. As a result, our views on the mechanism of action of the S-containing protective agents are more detailed and perhaps more sophisticated than are those on most other pharmacologic agents. Four radiochemical mechanisms are presently under surveillance as explanations for the in vivo protection by the compounds of the cysteine-cysteamine group:

The "Radical Scavenger" Hypothesis

The concept of chemical protection was introduced by Dale (1940) on the basis of radiochemical studies on pure chemical systems containing two solutes. The results were correctly interpreted to demonstrate a competition between the two solutes for the "activated water."

Similar ideas were behind most of the early in vivo protection work, as clearly formulated by Brues and Patt (1953): "It may be significant that the amount of cysteine required for protection of animals against lethality is of the same order as the SH present in the body, while the reduction in biological effectiveness of radiation is of the order of 50 per cent. This suggests that we are simply doubling the absorbing material for the oxidants formed in irradiated water, or the buffer capacity for certain toxins."

In 1955 we attempted to test experimentally to what extent cystamine could actually capture free radicals in competition with the normal constituents of human serum, assuming that the nature and amounts of radiation products of cystamine would reflect this ability (Eldjarn, Pihl, and Shapiro, 1956). It was shown that when present in a concentration comparable to that obtained in vivo (1×10^{-3} M), only a small percentage of the radiation-induced radicals was inactivated by cystamine, whereas an inactivation of 50 per cent would have been needed to account for the in vivo dose reduction factor of about two. We therefore concluded that in vivo protection by S-containing agents apparently required selective concentration in organs, cells, and subcellular structures, and probably on the surface of the "target proper."

At present, an in vivo radical scavenging effect, comparable to that which occurs in simple in vitro systems, has been abandoned by most workers as the explanation for the cysteine-cysteamine protection. This conclusion clearly appears in the study of Nakken (1961), who, in carefully controlled radiochemical experiments, titrated the radical scavenging effect of protective thiols as well as of several nonprotective aromatic compounds. It was concluded that the lack of correlation between scavenging effect in vitro and protective effect in vivo indicated that other factors were decisive.

Repair of Ionized Target Molecules by Hydrogen Transfer Reactions

There is a definite time interval between the event in which target molecules have become excited or ionized by the direct or indirect action of radiation and the occurrence of stabilizing but destructive reactions. In particular, Charlesby and Alexander (1955), as well as Alper (1956), have advocated the view that the protective S-containing agents may act by way of salutary processes in this "methionic phase." No doubt such reactions can occur, as demonstrated in a striking way by Henriksen, Sanner, and Pihl (1963), who made use of a particular characteristic of the penicillamine electron spin resonance (ESR) "sulfur pattern" to demonstrate energy transfer in the dry state from proteins to adsorbed penicillamine (10 per cent by weight).

It has been stressed repeatedly that the S-containing agents demonstrate a striking and particular specificity with regard to chemical structure. Despite the testing of several hundred compounds (Doull, Plzak, and Brois, 1962; Huber and Spode, 1961), only those which conform to the cysteine-cysteamine group are active. The "repair theory" fails to account for these relationships.

The Anoxia Hypothesis

In cellular biology, oxygen serves as the terminal electron acceptor in the substrate oxidation to provide for energy production. Furthermore, molecular oxygen participates as an obligatory substrate in a number of biosynthetic processes (Bloch, 1962). The "oxygen effect" is generally ascribed either to interfering with the radiolysis of water or to rendering irreversible the energy absorption and damage to target molecules. Whatever the mechanism of the "oxygen effect," many investigators still believe it to be the common denominator for most protection phenomena.

In a recent review, Scott (1963), has given an excellent discussion of the present status of the relationship between chemical protection and the oxygen effect. In particular, he has reviewed the work by van der Meer and co-workers who used the Cater-electrode for oxygen tension measurements in vivo (van der Meer *et al.*, 1962; van der Meer and van Bekkum, 1959, 1962), as well as the careful studies by Vergroesen (1962) and Vos (1962). Despite his declared allegiance to the anoxia hypothesis, Scott concludes that the said investigators "appear to have proved almost conclusively that sulfhydryl drugs can protect cells even in the absence of oxygen, and high concentrations of cysteamine produced a greater DRF than anoxia alone." Unless some new pharmacologic effect of cysteine-cysteamine on a totally unknown and hypothetical oxygen transport mechanism in cells can be demonstrated (van den Brenk and Jamieson, 1962), it appears unreasonable to explain the in vivo protection by cysteine-cysteamine-AET on the basis of an oxygen effect. Conversely, it should be pointed out that the prophecies of Gray, Tew, and Jensen (1952) that pharmacologically active compounds, such as adrenalin and serotonin, owe their in vivo protection to tissue anoxia have been proved most elegantly by the Dutch investigators.

The Mixed Disulfide Hypothesis

The mixed disulfide mechanism was proposed by Eldjarn and Pihl (1956) as follows:

During the period of protection, the compounds of the cysteine-cysteamine group exist in the body largely in the form of mixed disulfides with SS and SH groups of tissue constituents. This binding is temporary, as is the protection. The mixed disulfide will be reduced by the disulfide-reducing system of the body, followed by metabolism and excretion of the protective agents.

An extensive formation of mixed disulfide with cellular constituents would temporarily interfere with enzyme activities and cellular metabolism. Pronounced toxic effects on cells and tissues will therefore be expected.

The conversion of target SS and SH groups with the protective agent to a mixed disulfide represents a particular form of concentration on specific cellular constituents, a concentration mechanism which can explain the striking requirements for the chemical structures necessary for protective activity in vivo.

Mixed disulfide groups had been shown to represent a partial protection of the target sulfur atom against attack by free radicals (Figure 1). The mixed disulfide bond was also assumed to protect the target sulfur group against that part of the ionizing energy inflicted elsewhere in the molecule, which reached the group by energy migration as proposed by Gordy, Ard, and Shields (1955) (Figure 1).

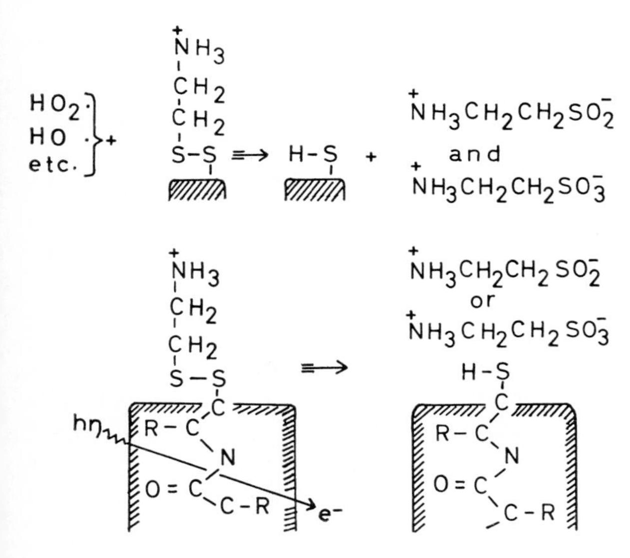

FIGURE 1. The mixed disulfide mechanism for protection against the indirect and direct action of ionizing radiation. (Eldjarn and Pihl, 1956.)

The theory also might offer a reasonable explanation for the moderate degree of in vivo sensitization which has been observed for certain sulfhydryl compounds. The indications are that protective thiols normally present in tissues (glutathione, cysteine) exist partly in the form of mixed disulfide with target molecules. Radiosensitizers of the cysteine-cysteamine group were believed to strip the target molecules of their protective residues because of a stronger tendency to form mixed disulfide with the naturally occurring "protectors," rather than with their target molecules.

VERIFICATION OF MACROMOLECULE PROTECTION BY MIXED DISULFIDE FORMATIONS

Barron and Dickman (1949), Barron and Flood (1950), and Barron and Johnson (1954) claimed that SH-enzymes, as well as small molecular thiols, were exceptionally susceptible to the indirect action of ionizing radiation. Much of their work was done on crystalline phosphoglyceraldehyde dehydrogenase (GAPDH) and alcohol dehydrogenase (ADH). Recently, Lange, Pihl, and Eldjarn (1959) did not succeed in repeating these experiments but reported that the over-all yields of inactivation under carefully controlled conditions fell in the same range as those reported for various non-SH enzymes. Our finding has been wrongly interpreted to mean that we, in general, reject the particular sensitivity of SH-enzymes to ionizing radiation (Scott, 1963). Rather, our studies indicate that there is a striking correlation between the accessibility and chemical reactivity of a protein SH group and its susceptibility to the indirect action of ionizing radiation. For papain, with a single reactive and essential SH group, a yield of inactivation as high as $G = 1.2$ was found (Pihl and Sanner, 1963a, b). With respect to GAPDH and ADH, a low G-value for inactivation was found despite a relatively high yield of destruction of each SH group. This could be ascribed to the great number of SH groups (11 and 21 respectively) and to special circumstances with respect to the dependence of the activity of these enzymes upon their integrity (Sanner and Pihl, 1963; Lange and Pihl, 1960).

Also, the hidden and nonreactive SH and SS groups of proteins appear to be susceptible to the indirect action of ionizing radiation, as is apparent from the considerable body of knowledge being accumulated on the radiochemistry of proteins in solution (Barron, Ambrose, and Johnson, 1955; Drake, Giffee, Johnson, and Koenig, 1957; Okada and Gehrmann, 1957; Jayko and Garrison, 1958; Kumta, Shimazu, and Tappel, 1962). These studies agree that cystine, methionine, and histidine are the most extensively degraded, but some damage was found in most of the amino acids. Clearly, SH and SS groups attract a greater share of radiation damage than that corresponding to their mole fraction. It is against this part of the radiation damage that mixed disulfide formation may offer partial protection.

Convincing examples of protein-SH sensitivity and protection by mixed disulfide formation has recently been reported by Pihl and Sanner (1963a, b). Papain in solution was found to be the most radiosensitive enzyme studied so far. When the single essential SH group of this enzyme is converted to a mixed disulfide with cysteamine, *i.e.* when a single cysteamine residue is attached to a protein of molecular weight 20,700 in a specific way and the enzyme is irradiated in solution, a dose reduction factor of 8.2 is obtained (5.5 in the presence of catalase). Coenzyme A (CoA) in solution was similarly protected with a dose reduction factor of 2.3 when converted to a mixed disulfide with cysteamine. These studies also demonstrate unequivocally that papain-S as mixed disulfide with cysteamine was effectively protected against the direct action of ionizing radiation. When irradiated in the dry state, the impressive dose reduction factor of 1.7 was obtained. The significance of the mixed disulfide attachment was strikingly apparent from the finding that no protection occurred when papain-SH and free cysteamine were freeze-dried in equimolar amounts and irradiated.

The proposed mechanism (Figure 1) for the mixed disulfide protection against direct hits was mainly based on the ESR studies of Gordy, Ard, and Shields (1955), which showed that "sulphur resonance patterns" were the dominating signal in a number of sulfur-containing proteins. Gordy's results have been seriously challenged by Libby, Ormerod, Charlesby, and Alexander (1961), who claimed the "sulphur patterns" to be an artifact caused by the formation of peroxide radicals. Henriksen, Sanner, and Pihl (1963) have recently unequivocally settled this question. A series of crystalline proteins were irradiated with doses up to 3.6×10^5 r in a vacuum at 77 K. After stepwise treatments for four minutes at increasing temperatures, the ESR spectra were recorded at 77 K. These spectra were resolved on the assumption that the low field part could be ascribed to a "sulphur pattern" only, to give results as shown for bovine serum albumin in Figure 2. The results of Gordy, Ard, and Shields (1955) were fully confirmed. At room temperature, two main types of ESR spectra were observed. The "sulphur pattern" and the "glycylglycine pattern" and the extent of their formation were related to the ratio cysteine-cystine/glycine in the protein. The temperature-dependency of the secondary processes which gave rise to these patterns could, according to the authors, be explained at least in part by a type of energy migration which involved intermolecular processes and radical fragments, rather than the intramolecular energy funneling as envisaged in Figure 1.

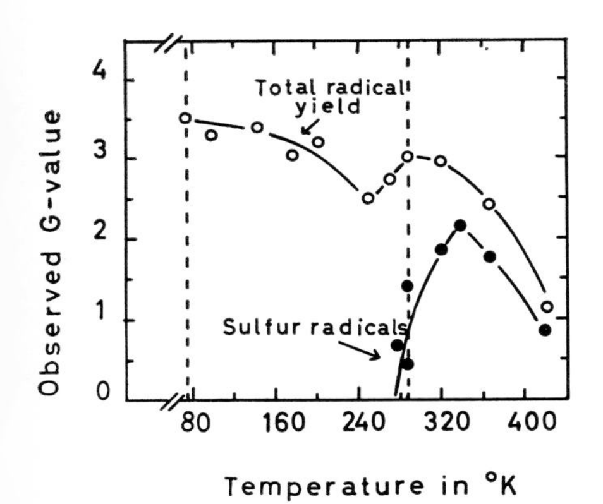

FIGURE 2. Bovine serum albumin under vacuum and in the dry state was irradiated (3.6×10^5 r) at 77 K. After successive and stepwise heat treatments, the ESR spectra were recorded at 77 K. (From Henriksen, Sanner, and Pihl, 1963.)

From the results here summarized, it seems warranted to conclude that the formation of mixed disulfides on essential SH or SS groups indeed protects these groups in an impressive way against both the direct and the indirect action of ionizing radiation.

THE CHEMICAL STATUS OF THE PROTECTIVE AGENTS IN CELLS AND TISSUES

It is likely that information on the chemical status of the S-containing protective agents in cells and tissues during the period of protection will give valuable indications of a radiochemical protection mechanism. The great number of publications which have been devoted to such studies permits reasonable conclusions on this point.

The Reduction of Disulfides by Erythrocytes

When tested in vivo a number of S-containing compounds are as protective when administered in the disulfide form as is the parent thiol (e.g. cystamine, di(guanidoethyl)-disulfide, and N,N,N′,N′-tetramethylcystamine). In the case of other disulfides (cystine-diethylester, and oxidized glutathione), no in vivo protection has been demonstrated despite the good protection offered by their thiol form. These results should be re-evaluated in the light of our finding that actively metabolizing erythrocytes from a number of mammalian species are capable of reducing those disulfides which possess protective ability in vivo with the appearance of the SH form in the suspending medium (Table 1) (Eldjarn, Bremer, and Börresen, 1962). Thus, the total erythrocyte mass of man is able to reduce approximately 0.25 g cystamine dihydrochloride per minute.

It is of particular interest that pronounced differences in this respect exist between erythrocytes from various mammalian species (Figure 3) (Börresen and Eldjarn, Unpublished data). Guinea pig, mouse, rat, and human erythrocytes are particularly effective in this regard, whereas the blood corpuscles of dog, rabbit, cow, sheep, and horse are very inefficient. Clearly, this is the reason why Fischer and Goutier-Pirotte (1954), in their studies on cysteamine and cystamine metabolism in rabbit and dog, concluded that whole blood in vitro was incapable of reducing cystamine. The species difference demonstrated should be borne in mind when protection experiments on various mammals are planned.

Organ Distribution

Since 1954, a series of researchers have tried to establish the distribution of the S-containing protective agents among various organs in the period of maximal protection (Eldjarn and Nygaard, 1954; Lauber, Zup-

TABLE 1

*Disulfide Reduction by Actively Metabolizing Erythrocytes and Liver Mitochondria from Rat**

Disulfide	μmoles SH produced per 10 min Erythrocytes (1 g)	Mitochondria (from 1 g liver)
None	0.0	0.7
Cystamine	3	7.8
NN′-Tetramethylcystamine	2.7	6.4
NN′-Tetraethylcystamine	3.6	6.9
NN′-Diacetylcystamine	2.8	2.4
Bis(hydroxyethyl)disulfide	1.7	1.8
Sodium tetrathionate	1.3	1.4
Cystine diethyl ester	0.4	6.4
L-CSSC	0	1.2
L-GSSG	0	1.0
L-Homocystine	0	1.3

* Substrates: glucose and α-ketoglutarate, respectively. (Eldjarn, Bremer, and Börresen, 1962; Eldjarn and Bremer, 1963.)

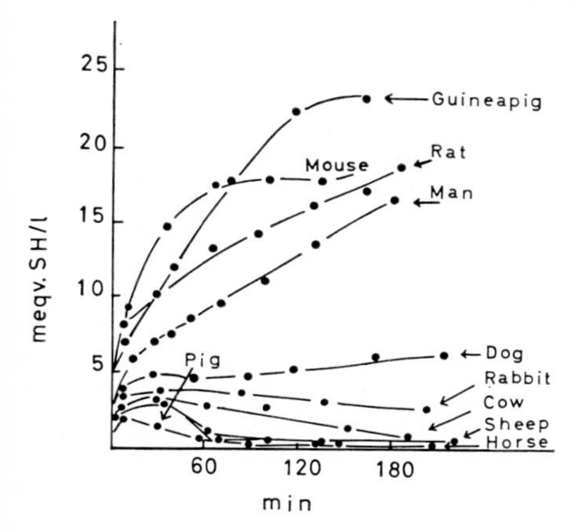

FIGURE 3. Species differences with respect to cystamine reduction by erythrocytes. (Börresen and Eldjarn, Unpublished data.)

pinger, and Aebi, 1958; Bradford, Shapira, and Doherty, 1961; Kollmann, Shapiro, and Schwartz, 1963; Mondovi, Tentori, De Marco, and Cavallini, 1962). These studies, which are concerned with cysteamine and AET in particular, agree on a number of essential points. In general, there is a remarkable difference in the organ distribution of these compounds, a difference which parallels the radioprotective activity observed. In bone marrow, spleen, intestinal mucosa, thyroid, submaxillary glands, and kidneys, high concentrations are found consistently. Conversely, low concentrations are generally reported in testes and in the lenses of the eyes. When blood concentration is used as unity, and cysteamine residues—whether free or protein-bound—are measured, the average tissue concentrations may vary from about 0.5 to 4.

Of particular significance in discussing the mechanism of action of these agents was the finding of Bradford, Shapira, and Doherty (1961) that the tissue distribution of mercaptoethyl-guanidine, D-mercaptobutyl-2-guanidine, and L-mercaptobutyl-2-guanidine hydrobromides, which differ by as much as 5 to 1 in their protective activity in mice, were similar both qualitatively and quantitatively. However, differences paralleling the protective abilities were observed with respect to their binding to subcellular particles. Similarly, Sörbo (1962) demonstrated a nearly identical increase in nonprotein sulfhydryl levels in liver, blood, and spleen after the administration of the protective compounds cysteamine, cystamine, and aminoethylthiosulfuric acid as after the administration of the nonprotective compounds mercaptoethanol and sodium thioglycolate.

Obviously, a selective accumulation of the protective agents in organs which play an important role in the radiation syndrome is a necessary but insufficient requirement for in vivo protection.

Disulfide Reduction in Cells and Tissues

Inside cells, most small molecular disulfides are rapidly reduced by the well characterized glutathione (GSSG) reductase system. This soluble enzyme is mainly confined to the particle-free supernatant fraction of cells, although indications of its occurrence in cell nuclei also exist (Stern and Timonen, 1954–1955; Wang, 1962). It is likely that the reduction of the disulfides is brought about via spontaneous exchange reaction with glutathione, since only oxidized glutathione can serve as a substrate of glutathione reductase. Even mixed disulfides containing glutathione were found to be inactive (Pihl, Eldjarn, and Bremer, 1957).

An indication as to the SH-SS redox situation in the cell sap may be found in the Michaelis-Menten constant of glutathione reductase for GSSG. We have recently determined this constant for a few human tissues (Table 2) (Börresen and Eldjarn, Unpublished data). In these studies, enzyme activity in crude cell preparations fortified with necessary cofactor and substrates was assayed by the increase in titratable SH groups at constant GSSG concentrations. This approach was made possible by the use of "GSSG-buffer systems" (Börresen and Eldjarn, Unpublished data) in which thiol-disulfide equilibria between glutathione and cystamine were used to attain a nearly constant concentration of GSSG at the desired level, despite the concomitant reduction of considerable amounts of disulfides. It appears from Table 2 that glutathione reductase from various organs shows different K_m values, a finding which demonstrates a new example of "iso-enzymes." The different K_m values may significantly influence the SH-SS redox potential of cytoplasm and may explain the finding by Bhattacharya, Robson, and Stewart (1955) that appreciable amounts of oxidized glutathione are present in the red cells of human, rabbit, and rat, whereas in liver, kidney, and pancreas tissues, measurable quantities of GSSG could not be found.

Glutathione reductase has so far been the only well-characterized disulfide-reducing system of mammalian cells. Recently we have demonstrated that isolated rat liver mitochondria rapidly reduce a number of low molecular disulfides, provided that substrates for the citric acid cycle enzymes are present (Eldjarn and Bremer, 1963). Our results indicate that this reduction occurs at the thioctic acid level of the α-keto acid oxidation. It appears from Table 1 that those disulfides which do not demonstrate in vivo protection are not effectively reduced by either erythrocytes or by iso-

TABLE 2

Michaelis-Menten Constant for GSSG of Glutathione Reductase from a Few Human Tissues

Source	K_m (M)	Author
Rat liver	5×10^{-5}	Mize and Langdon (1962)
Human erythrocytes	2.5×10^{-5}	Beutler and Yeh (1963)
Human liver	6.5×10^{-5}	Börresen and Eldjarn (Unpublished data)
Human erythrocytes	1.5×10^{-4}	
Human kidney	7.5×10^{-5}	
Human brain	2×10^{-4}	

lated mitochondria. Although no definite explanation can be given, it appears likely that these findings can be ascribed to membrane impermeability.

It thus appears likely that the S-protective agents are actively reduced in the body to their SH form, although smaller variations in the Michaelis constant of glutathione reductase for GSSG may lead to significant variations in the SH-SS redox potential of tissues. This conclusion is in agreement with the finding of Sörbo (1962) that whereas the nonprotein sulfhydryl level in spleen and liver showed significant increase after the injection of protective doses of cystamine, cysteamine, and aminoethylthiosulfuric acid, the nonprotein disulfide level remained practically unchanged. In this connection, it should also be recalled that Révész and Bergstrand (1963) demononstrated a nearly linear correlation between the increase of cellular nonprotein sulfhydryl and degree of radio protection in ascites tumor cells incubated in vitro with cysteamine.

The Intracellular Occurrence of Protein-Bound Protective Residues

The above series of studies also agree that the greater portion of the cellular cystamine residues occur bound to proteins in different cell fractions. By dialysis and exchange technique it has been found that at least 30 to 50 per cent of this fixation could be ascribed to mixed disulfide formation with protein SH or SS groups, whereas unspecific adsorption or electrostatic binding has been invoked to explain the additional binding. By increasing the dose of mercaptoethyl-guanidine, a marked increase in the protein-bound fraction was observed by Bradford, Shapira, and Doherty (1961). They also demonstrated that the poor protective compound aminothiazoline did not conform to the above behavior, but appeared, for the major part, free.

All cell fractions have been found to contain cysteamine residues, but with the lowest concentration in the microsome fraction and the highest in the nuclei when given relative to the nitrogen content. In our context, the nuclear residues may have particular importance. It should be stressed that by microautoradiographic localization studies using labeled cysteine and AET (Passalacqua and Koch, 1958; Maisin and Doherty, 1960), a nuclear concentration has also been shown to occur.

To my mind, the above results indicate that special attention should be given to the fixation of protective residues to nuclear constituents. Most likely, the protective agents in the thiol (or partly in the disulfide) form penetrate the nuclear membrane. Inside the nuclei, mixed disulfide formation then takes place with accessible protein disulfide and thiol groups. In this context, the following results and findings should be recalled:

1. The classical work by Rapkin (1931), as repeated and expanded by Mazia (1961), leaves no doubt that thioldisulfide interchanges play a central role in the formation of the mitotic apparatus. The histochemical results of Kawamura and Dan (1958) (Figure 4) demonstrate *ad oculos* that

the mitotic spindle contains a great number of sulfhydryl groups, which disappear later in the cell cycle.

2. In cellular radiobiology, a particular significance is ascribed to the nucleoproteins. In a recent review, Nygaard (1962) concluded that the synthesis of deoxyribonucleic acid (DNA), regarded as a metabolic process only, does not appear to be very sensitive to ionizing radiation. In a majority of the cases, the decreased DNA synthesis observed in a variety of cell populations can, according to Nygaard, be explained by an inhibition of mitosis. The radiation damage to the DNA-protein complex in the chromosome may be responsible for this failure or delay of mitosis.

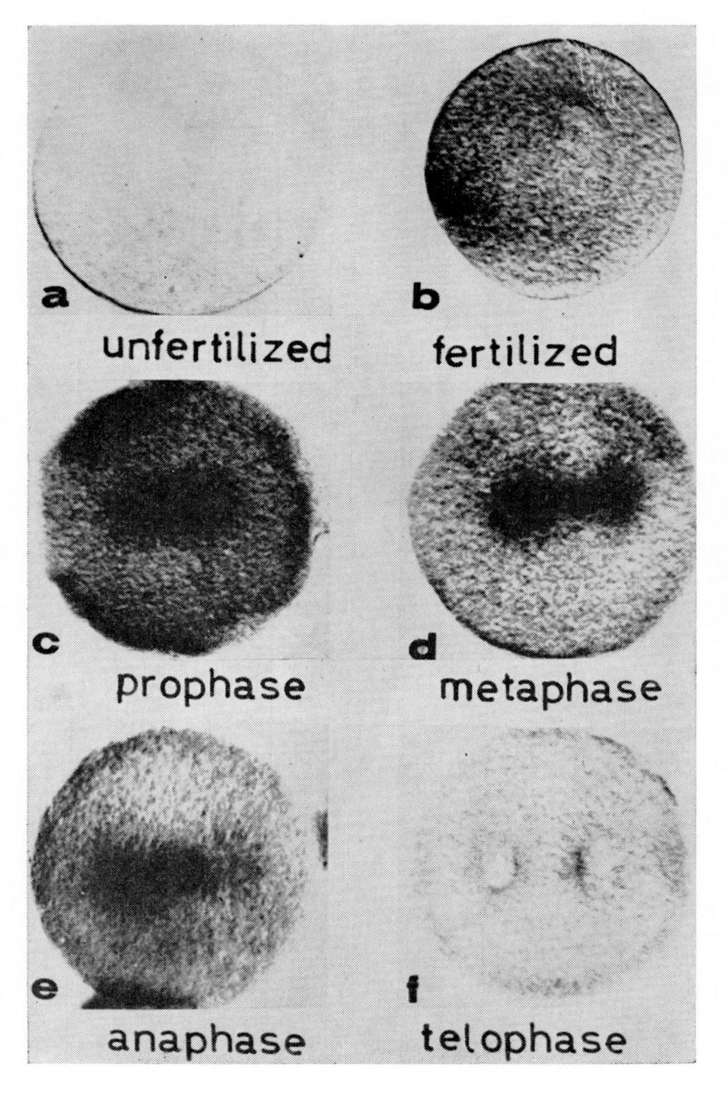

FIGURE 4. Protein SH staining in relation to mitotic cycle in sea urchin egg (*Clypeaster japonicus*). (From Kawamura and Dan, 1958.)

3. Ord and Stocken (1963), in a recent study on thiol distribution in rat thymus, came to the unexpected conclusion that about 70 per cent of the nuclear thiol groups are associated with the arginine-rich histone fraction as isolated by the method of Daly and Mirsky (1955).

With this background, we found it desirable to look for nuclear constituents capable of forming mixed disulfides with cysteamine or cystamine. Rat liver or calf thymus nuclei were isolated by gradient centrifugation in sucrose medium. When the nuclei were incubated with 1.7×10^{-3} M cysteamine-S^{35} or cystamine-S^{35} at pH 7.4, an extensive fixation to DNA nucleoproteins could be demonstrated (isolated by 1 M NaCl extraction and precipitation by dilution), (Jellum and Eldjarn, Unpublished data). This binding corresponded approximately to one cysteamine residue per molecular weight 100,000 of proteins. In these experiments, the DNA-nucleoproteins were isolated at pH 5 to prevent spontaneous SH-SS exchanges with the possible liberation of cysteamine residues.

That the fixation indeed could be ascribed to mixed disulfide formation was made likely in the following way: (1) The radioactivity could not be liberated by dialysis at pH 5. (2) The addition of surplus unlabeled cysteamine at pH 5 for one hour did not set free the radioactivity. (3) At pH 7.4 the addition of unlabeled cysteamine liberated the radioactivity within minutes. (4) Even without the addition of unlabeled carrier cysteamine, the radioactivity was set free at pH 7.4 in experiments in which a continous disulfide-reducing system was established outside the nuclear membrane.

In particular, the latter experiment should exclude the possibility that adsorption of radioactivity by noncovalent ionic binding could be responsible for the fixation.

Attempts to Isolate the Nuclear Components Responsible for the Mixed Disulfide Fixation of Cysteamine Residues

On the basis of the mixed disulfide hypothesis, suggestions may be made as to the chemical nature of "target molecules." In order to form extensive amounts of mixed disulfide, these molecules should carry accessible SH or SS groups which are sufficiently reactive to interact with the protective SS or SH compounds. It should be recalled that most disulfide groups of native proteins are completely unreactive towards cysteamine (Pihl and Eldjarn, 1959). Also, in the case of protein-SH-groups, it is the exception rather than the rule that they react with the weakly electrophilic disulfide group of cystamine.

The numerous methods for the isolation of proteins are largely based on the physico-chemical properties of the macromolecules considered *in toto*, *i.e.* on their size and shape, amphoteric properties, etc. The presence of particular groups such as thiols usually is without particular consequence for the fractionation. It would seem likely, however, that chromatographic material could be synthesized which would possess particular affinity for SH-groups. Such work has been undertaken by our laboratory and has resulted in an "organomercurial polysaccharide material" (Eldjarn and Jellum, 1963).

On Sephadex G-25, one SH group was introduced per 40 glucose units by amination of alcohol groups and thiolation of the amine groups with acetylamino-homocysteine thiolactone.

For the separation of proteins by means of their thiol groups, we decided to make use of the extreme reactivity of these groups toward mercury and of the well-known fact that, in the case of several organomercuric compounds (e.g. *p*-chloromercuribenzoate), this reaction is reversible without denaturation of the protein.

Upon treatment of the above thiolated Sephadex with the cyclic dimercurial 3.6-bis-(acetatomercurimethyl)-dioxane, the thiolated Sephadex was converted to an "organomercurial polysaccharide" which demonstrated the ability to separate a number of SH proteins and enzymes approximately according to the number of SH groups in the molecule (Eldjarn and Jellum, 1963).

In Figure 5 are shown the results of application of this chromatographic method to rat liver nuclei isolated in sucrose-$CaCl_2$ medium and subjected to ultrasonic vibration in 0.01 M phosphate buffer. The protein solution was applied to the organomercurial column in the acetate form and eluted with 0.35 M sodium phosphate buffer, with 0.5 M ammonium sulfate, and finally with cysteine solution. Four protein fractions were obtained which contained 2 SH, about 5 SH, 5 to 8 SH, and 22 to 25 SH per protein of a molecular weight of 100,000. It appears that the 5 to 8 SH fraction contains most of the DNA, whereas the ribonucleic acid (RNA) is found for the most part in the nonadsorbed fraction. Upon exposure to the air, the SH titer declined in the 5 to 8 SH fraction, a reduction reversible by cysteine. The addition of disulfides to this fraction resulted in a rapid

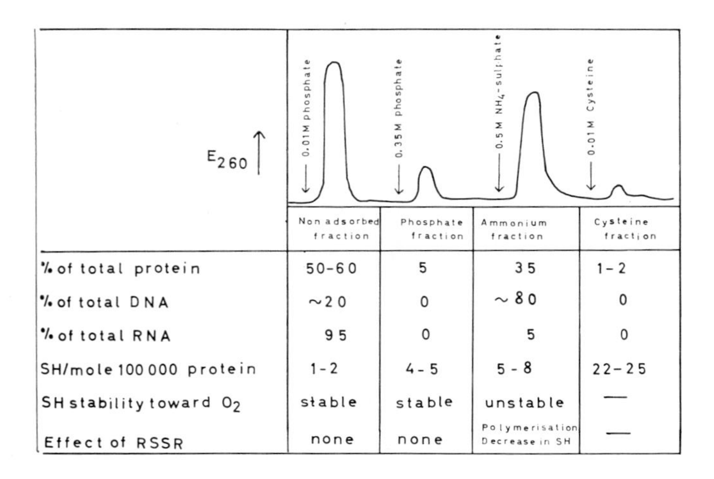

	Non adsorbed fraction	Phosphate fraction	Ammonium fraction	Cysteine fraction
% of total protein	50-60	5	35	1-2
% of total DNA	~20	0	~80	0
% of total RNA	95	0	5	0
SH/mole 100 000 protein	1-2	4-5	5-8	22-25
SH stability toward O_2	stable	stable	unstable	—
Effect of RSSR	none	none	Polymerisation Decrease in SH	—

FIGURE 5. The separation of sonicated rat liver nuclei on an organomercurial polysaccharide column. Elution of the column as indicated. (Jellum and Eldjarn, Unpublished data.)

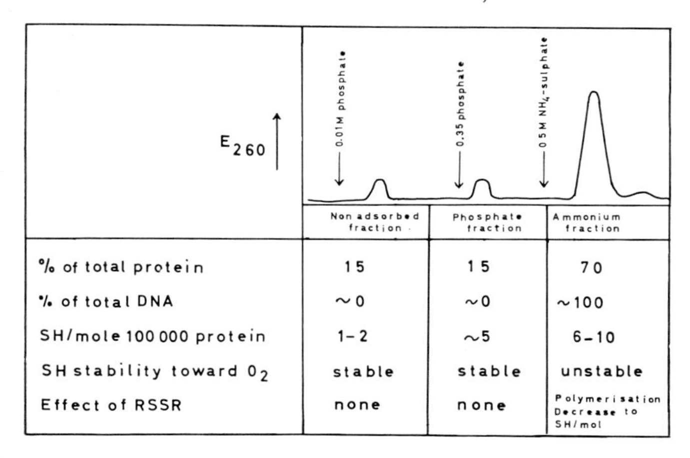

	Non adsorbed fraction	Phosphate fraction	Ammonium fraction
% of total protein	15	15	70
% of total DNA	~0	~0	~100
SH/mole 100 000 protein	1–2	~5	6–10
SH stability toward O_2	stable	stable	unstable
Effect of RSSR	none	none	Polymerisation Decrease to SH/mol

FIGURE 6. The separation of DNA-nucleoprotein (1 M NaCl) fraction of rat liver nuclei on organomercurial polysaccharide column. Elution of the column as shown. (Jellum and Eldjarn, Unpublished data.)

precipitation of all the DNA and proteins, possibly by a S-S polymerization.

Figure 6 shows an experiment in which the DNA-nucleoprotein fraction of rat liver nuclei was isolated by extraction with 1 M NaCl, followed by precipitation by dilution to 0.14 M, and subsequent separation on the organomercurial polysaccharide column. Again a DNA-nucleoprotein fraction containing 6 to 10 SH per protein of a molecular weight of 100,000 was isolated. Obviously, the DNA of interphase nuclei exists in an aggregate with histones and possibly with other proteins, on the surface of which a number of reactive and accessible SH-groups are found.

Further characterization of the 5 to 8 SH fraction is under way. It is suggested that this particular nuclear DNA-protein-SH complex may constitute a probable target for the extensive fixation of cysteamine residues in the nuclei, and may also represent a target for the protection offered by the S-containing protective agents against the deleterious action of ionizing radiation.

SUMMARY

Progress in the search for protective compounds which may prove useful adjuvants in radiation therapy of cancer, appears to be extremely slow. The S-containing agents at present seem to offer the greatest hope for practical application.

A review is given of the mechanisms which are under surveillance as explanation for the in vivo protection by the compounds of the cysteine-cysteamine group. A radiochemical explanation appears to be the more likely.

The mixed disulfide theory is discussed. Examples are given of impressive protection factors when essential SH groups are temporarily covered by cysteamine residues bound as mixed disulfides.

Our knowledge of the organ and cellular distribution of the S-containing agents is summarized. It seems justifiable to conclude that these agents demonstrate a favorable localization in cells and tissues of particular significance in the development of the radiation syndrome. The protective agents are effectively reduced to their SH form by erythrocytes, by the glutathione reductase system of most cells and tissues, as well as by actively metabolizing mitochondria. Intracellularly, the free protective residues, for the greater part, exist in SH form, although a certain amount of the disulfide forms may exist in particular tissues due to differences in the Michaelis-Menten constant of glutathione reductase for GSSG. At least 30 to 50 per cent of the protective residues are attached to protein fractions of subcellular structures, for a greater part in the form of mixed disulfides. A particularly high concentration of the protective residues are found in the cell nuclei. Upon incubation of isolated liver and thymus nuclei with cysteamine, an extensive mixed disulfide fixation to the nucleoprotein fraction was found to occur. Some results of our attempts to isolate and characterize SH/SS proteins of cell nuclei are presented. For this purpose an organomercurial polysaccharide chromatographic material was developed.

REFERENCES

Alper, T. 1956. The Modification of Damage Caused by Primary Ionization of Biological Targets. *Radiation Research*, 5:573–586.

Bacq, Z. M., A. Herve, J. Lecomte, P. Fischer, J. Blavier, G. Dechamps, H. Le Bihan, and P. Rayet. 1951. Protection contre le Rayonnement X par le β-Mercaptoéthylamine. *Archives internationales de physiologie*, 59:442–447.

Barron, E. S. G., J. Ambrose, and P. Johnson. 1955. Studies on the Mechanism of Action of Ionizing Radiations. XIII. The Effects of X-Irradiation on Some Physico-Chemical Properties of Amino Acids and Proteins. *Radiation Research*, 2:145–158.

Barron, E. S. G., and S. Dickman. 1949. Studies on the Mechanism of Action of Ionizing Radiations. II. Inhibition of Sulfhydryl Enzymes by Alpha, Beta, and Gamma Rays. *Journal of General Physiology*, 32:595–605.

Barron, E. S. G., S. Dickman, J. A. Muntzand, and T. P. Singer. 1949. Studies on the Mechanism of Action of Ionizing Radiations. I. Inhibition of Enzymes by X-Rays. *Journal of General Physiology*, 32:537–552.

Barron, E. S. G., and V. Flood. 1950. Studies on the Mechanism of Action of Ionizing Radiations. VI. The Oxidation of Thiols by Ionizing Radiation. *Journal of General Physiology*, 33:229–241.

Barron, E. S. G., and P. Johnson. 1954. Studies on the Mechanism of Action of Ionizing Radiations. XI. Inactivation of Yeast Alcohol Dehydrogenase by X-Irradiation. *Archives of Biochemistry and Biophysics*, 48:149–153.

Beutler, E., and M. K. Y. Yeh. 1963. Erythrocyte Glutathione Reductase. *Blood*, 21: 573–585.

Bhattacharya, S. K., J. S. Robson, and C. P. Stewart. 1955. The Determination of Glutathione in Blood and Tissue. *Biochemical Journal*, 60:696–702.

Bloch, K. 1962. Oxygen and Biosynthetic Patterns. *Federation Proceedings*, 21:1058–1963.

Börresen, H. C., and L. Eldjarn. 1963. A Test for the Disulphide Reducing Capacity of Red Blood Cells. *Acta chemica scandinavica*, 17:884–885.

————. Unpublished data.

Bradford, R. H., R. A. Shapira, and D. G. Doherty. 1961. The Intracellular Distribution and Binding of Radiation-Protective Mercaptoalkylguanidines. *International Journal of Radiation Biology and Related Studies in Physics, Chemistry and Medicine*, 3:595–608.

Brues, A. M., and H. M. Patt. 1953. Mechanisms of Protection against Mammalian Radiation Injury. *Physiological Reviews*, 33:85–89.

Charlesby, A., and P. Alexander. 1955. Reticulation des polymeres en solution aqueuse par les rayons gamma. *Journal de chimie physique et physico-chimie biologique*, 52:699–709.

Dale, W. M. 1940. The Effect of X-Rays on Enzymes. *Biochemical Journal*, 34:1367–1373.

Daly, M. M., and A. E. Mirsky. 1955. Histones with High Lysine Content. *Journal of General Physiology*, 38:405–413.

Doherty, D. G., and W. T. Burnett, Jr. 1955. Protective Effect of S, β-Aminoethylisothiuronium·Br·HBr and Related Compounds Against X-Radiation Death in Mice. *Proceedings of the Society for Experimental Biology and Medicine*, 89:312–314.

Doull, J., V. Plzak, and S. J. Brois. 1962. A Survey of Compounds for Radiation Protection. *U. S. Air Force School of Aerospace Medicine*, 62–29:124 pp.

Drake, M. P., J. W. Giffee, D. A. Johnson, and V. L. Koenig. 1957. Chemical Effects of Ionizing Radiation on Proteins. I. Effect of γ-Radiation on the Amino Acid Content of Insulin. *Journal of the American Chemical Society*, 79:1395–1401.

Eldjarn, L. 1962. "Chemical Protection Against Ionizing Radiation. Radiochemistry or Cellular Physiology?" *Strahlenwirkung und Milieu*, H. Fritz-Niggli, Ed. *Strahlentherapie. Sonderbände*, Supplement 51:232–242.

Eldjarn, L., and J. Bremer. 1963. The Disulphide-Reducing Capacity of Liver Mitochondria. *Acta chemica scandinavica*, 17:59–66.

Eldjarn, L., J. Bremer, and H. C. Börresen. 1962. The Reduction of Disulphides by Human Erythrocytes. *Biochemical Journal*, 82:192–197.

Eldjarn, L., and E. Jellum. 1963. Organomercurial-Polysaccharide, a Chromatographic Material for the Separation and Isolation of SH-Proteins. *Acta chemica scandinavica*, 17:2610–2621.

Eldjarn, L., and O. Nygaard. 1954. Cysteamine-Cystamine: Intestinal Absorption, Distribution among Various Organs and Excretion. *Archives internationales de physiologie*, 62:476–486.

Eldjarn, L., and A. Pihl. 1956. "On the Mechanism of Chemical Protection Against Ionizing Radiation. The Interaction of Cysteamine and Cystamine with Proteins," *Progress in Radiobiology*, J. S. Mitchell, B. E. Holmes, and C. L. Smith, Eds. Springfield, Illinois: Charles C Thomas, Publisher. Pp. 249–257.

———. 1960. "Mechanisms of Protective and Sensitizing Action," *Mechanisms in Radiobiology*, M. Errera and A. Forsberg, Eds. New York, New York: Academic Press, Inc. Vol. II. Pp. 231–296.

Eldjarn, L., A. Pihl, and B. Shapiro. 1956. Cysteamine-Cystamine: On the Mechanism for the Protective Action Against Ionizing Radiation. *Proceedings of the International Conference on the Peaceful Uses of Atomic Energy*. New York, New York: United Nations Publication. Vol. XI. Pp. 335–342.

Fischer, P., and M. Goutier-Pirotte. 1954. Metabolisme de la cysteamine et de la cystamine chez le lapin et le chien. *Archives internationales de physiologie*, 62:76–100.

Gordy, W., W. B. Ard, and H. Shields. 1955. Microwave Spectroscopy of Biological Substances. I. Paramagnetic Resonance in X-Irradiated Amino Acids and Proteins. *Proceedings of the National Academy of Sciences of the U.S.A.*, 41:983–996.

Gray, J. L., J. T. Tew, and H. Jensen. 1952. Protective Effect of Serotonin and of Para-Aminopropiophenone against Lethal Doses of X-Radiation. *Proceedings of the Society for Experimental Biology and Medicine*, 80:604–607.

Henriksen, T., T. Sanner, and A. Pihl. 1963. Secondary Processes in Proteins Irradiated in the Dry State. *Radiation Research,* 18:147–162.

Huber, R., and E. Spode. 1961. *Biologisch-chemischer Strahlenschutz; eine Übersicht in Tabellen.* Berlin, Germany: Akademie-Verlag. Vols. I-IV.

Jayko, M. E., and W. M. Garrison. 1958. Further Studies on the Formation of the $>C=O$ Bond in the Radiation-Induced Oxidation of Protein. (Abstract) *Radiation Research,* 9:134–135.

Jellum, E., and L. Eldjarn. Unpublished data.

Kawamura, N., and K. Dan. 1958. A Cytochemical Study of the Sulfhydryl Groups of Urchin Eggs during the First Cleavage. *Journal of Biophysical and Biochemical Cytology,* 4:615–625.

Kollmann, G., B. Shapiro, and E. E. Schwartz. 1963. The Mechanism of Action of AET. V. The Distribution and the Chemical Forms of 2-Mercaptoethylguanidine and Bis(2-Guanidoethyl) Disulfide Given Orally in Protective Doses to Mice. *Radiation Research,* 20:17–23.

Kumta, U. S., F. Shimazu, and A. L. Tappel. 1962. Decrease of Radiation Damage to Proteins by Sulfhydryl Protectors. *Radiation Research,* 16:679–685.

Lange, R., and A. Pihl. 1960. The Mechanism of X-Ray Inactivation of Phosphoglyceraldehyde Dehydrogenase. *International Journal of Radiation Biology and Related Studies in Physics, Chemistry and Medicine,* 2:301–308.

Lange, R., A. Pihl, and L. Eldjarn. 1959. The Inactivation of SH Enzymes by X-Rays. *International Journal of Radiation Biology and Related Studies in Physics, Chemistry and Medicine,* 1:73–79.

Lauber, K., A. Zuppinger, and H. Aebi. 1958. Distribution Pattern and Retention of Cysteamine S^{35} in Mammals. *Isotopes in Biochemistry and Physiology,* 225:96–99.

Libby, D., M. G. Ormerod, A. Charlesby, and P. Alexander. 1961. Prevention by Cysteamine of Radical Formation in Bovine Serum Albumin by γ-Rays. *Nature,* London, 190:998–999.

Maisin, J. R., and D. G. Doherty. 1960. Chemical Protection of Mammalian Tissues. *Federation Proceedings,* 19:564–572.

Mazia, D. 1961. "Mitosis and the Physiology of Cell Division," *The Cell,* J. Bracket and A. E. Mirsky, Eds. New York, New York, and London, England: Academic Press. Vol. III. Pp. 77–412.

Mize, C. E., and R. G. Langdon. 1962. Hepatic Glutathione Reductase. I. Purification and General Properties. *Journal of Biological Chemistry,* 237:1589–1600.

Mondovi, B., L. Tentori, C. De Marco, and D. Cavallini. 1962. Distribution of Cystamine-^{35}S in the Sub-cellular Particles of the Organs of the Rat. *International Journal of Radiation Biology and Related Studies in Physics, Chemistry and Medicine,* 4:371–378.

Nakken, K. F. 1961. The Relative Protective Effect of Pyridoxine, p-Aminobenzoic Acid, and Various Cysteamine Derivatives on the X-Ray Induced Degradation of Pyridoxal-5-Phosphate. *Strahlentherapie,* 116:628–637.

Nygaard, O. F. 1962. "Effects of Radiation on Nucleic Acid Metabolism. A Review of Current Concepts," *The Effects of Ionizing on Immune Processes,* C. A. Leone, Ed. New York, New York: Gordon and Breach Science Publishers. Pp. 47–73.

Okada, S., and G. Gehrmann. 1957. Inactivation of Desoxyribonuclease I by X-Rays. IV. Changes in Amino Acid Composition and Ultraviolet Light Absorption Induced by Ionizing Radiation. *Biochimica et biophysica acta,* 25:179–185.

Ord, M. G., and L. A. Stocken. 1963. Biochemical Effects of X-Irradiation and the Sulphydryl Hypothesis: A Re-appraisal. *Nature,* London, 200:136–138.

Passalacqua, F., and R. Koch. 1958. Untersuchungen über einen biologischen Strahlenschutz. XXII. Mitteilung: Mikroautoradiographische Untersuchungen über das Verhalten von S^{35}-Cystein. *Strahlentherapie,* 105:271–277.

Patt, H. M., E. B. Tyree, H. L. Straube, and D. E. Smith. 1949. Cysteine Protection Against X-Irradiation. *Science*, 110:213–214.

Pihl, A., and L. Eldjarn. 1959. "The Formation and Biological Role of Mixed Disulphides," *Fourth International Congress of Biochemistry*, O. Hoffmann-Osterhof, Ed. New York, New York; London, England; Paris, France; and Los Angeles, California: Pergamon Press. Vol. XIII. Pp. 43–62.

Pihl, A., L. Eldjarn, and J. Bremer. 1957. On the Mode of Action of X-Ray Protective Agents. III. The Enzymatic Reduction of Disulfides. *Journal of Biological Chemistry*, 227:339–345.

Pihl, A., and T. Sanner. 1963a. Protection of Sulfhydryl Compounds against Ionizing Radiation. *Biochimica et biophysica acta*, 78:537–539.

————. 1963b. X-Ray Inactivation of Papain in Solution. *Radiation Research*, 19:27–41.

Pirie, A., and L. G. Lajtha. 1959. Possible Mechanism of Cysteine Protection against Radiation Cataract. *Nature*, London, 184:1125–1127.

Rapkin, L. 1931. Sur les Processus chimiques au cours de la division cellulaire. *Annales de physiologie et de physicochimie biologique*, 7:382–418.

Révész, L., and H. Bergstrand. 1963. Radiation Protection by Cysteamine and Cellular Sulphydryl Levels. *Nature*, London, 200:594–595.

Sanner, T., and A. Pihl. 1963. Kinetics of Enzyme Inactivation by Ionizing Radiation. *Radiation Research*, 19:12–26.

Scott, O. C. A. 1963. The Modification of Tissue Response to Radiation Injury. *Annual Review of Medicine*, 14:371–380.

Sörbo, B. 1962. The Effect of Radioprotective Agents on Tissue Nonprotein Sulfhydryl and Disulfide Levels. *Archives of Biochemistry and Biophysics*, 98:342–344.

Stern, H., and S. Timonen. 1954–1955. The Position of the Cell Nucleus in Pathways of Hydrogen Transfer: Cytochrome C, Flavoproteins, Glutathione and Ascorbic Acid. *Journal of American Physiology*, 38:41–52.

Therkelsen, A. J. 1958. Studies on the Cytotoxicity of Cysteamine and Related Compounds in Tissue Culture. *Acta pathologica et microbiologica scandinavica*, 32:201–215.

Van den Brenk, H. A. S., and D. Jamieson. 1962. Studies of Mechanisms of Chemical Radiation Protection *in vivo*. II. Effect of High Pressure Oxygen on Radioprotection *in vivo* and its Relationship to "Oxygen Poisoning." *International Journal of Radiation Biology and Related Studies in Physics, Chemistry and Medicine*, 4:379–402.

Van der Meer, C., and D. W. van Bekkum. 1959. The Mechanism of Radiation Protection by Histamine and Other Biological Amines. *International Journal of Radiation Biology and Related Studies in Physics, Chemistry and Medicine*, 1:5–23.

————. 1962. A Study on the Mechanism of Radiation Protection by 5-Hydroxytryptamine and Tryptamine. *International Journal of Radiation Biology and Related Studies in Physics, Chemistry and Medicine*, 4:105–110.

Van der Meer, C., O. B. Zaalberg, O. Vos, A. J. Vergroesen, and D. W. van Bekkum. 1962. On the Mechanism of the Radioprotective Action of Cyanide. *International Journal of Radiation Biology and Related Studies in Physics, Chemistry and Medicine*, 4:311–319.

Vergroesen, A. J. 1962. "The Influence of Anoxia on the Radioprotection of Tissue Culture Cells by Cysteamine," Abstracts, *Second International Congress on Radiation Research* (Harrogate).

Vos, O. 1962. "Protection of Tissue Culture Cells Against X-Irradiation," Abstracts, *Second International Congress on Radiation Research* (Harrogate).

Wang, T.-Y. 1962. Free Amino Acids of Isolated Calf Thymus Nuclei. *Nature*, London, 195:1099.

DISCUSSION

Dr. Earle Gregg, Western Reserve University, Cleveland, Ohio: My question involves the mathematical analysis of the data in terms of the exponential equations used by Dr.

Powers and Dr. Alper: Dr. Powers in terms of adding rate constants, and Dr. Alper in terms of adding sensitivities. This is essentially adding probabilities linearly and one cannot do this unless one assumes independence. Are you both assuming independence in your formulation, or do you feel your results prove this assumption?

Dr. E. L. Powers, Argonne National Laboratory, Argonne, Illinois: I stated that our first premise is that there is independence, and noninteraction between and among the kinds of damage observed. Second, when one adds exponents, one does not add probabilities. Probability for survival is given by e raised to a minus product of the k and dose. The number k is a function of the probability of survival after dose D. The number is found by ascertaining the probability of survival. We do indeed assume independence and, I think are justified, since we have demonstrated this on at least two occasions.

Dr. Tikvah Alper, Medical Research Council, Hammersmith Hospital, London, England: To some extent my answer is the same as Dr. Powers'. The sensitivity components I added together were parts of the exponent in the expression: surviving fraction = function of $e^{-\lambda D}$. The λ in the exponent is made up of two or more components, e.g. $\lambda = \lambda_n + \lambda a$. However, my viewpoint is a little different from Dr. Powers'. I was considering these components principally in terms of their intrinsic oxygen enhancement ratios. If one thinks in terms of probability, my model would be consonant with the following: If there is a certain probability of producing a lethal event in the absence of oxygen, then that probability is multiplied by a given factor when oxygen is present, and that factor is, of course, the oxygen enhancement ratio. As regards the independence of the components of sensitivity, the analysis shows that it is consistent with the data that the components are independently modifiable. I do not know what independence means, apart from this, and it would really be more accurate to put it the other way around: that one assumes the total sensitivity to be made up of one part which is modifiable by a certain agent or treatment, while the other part is not so modifiable or is not modified in the given conditions. If one then uses this model to calculate values of the components, then the values are consistent for completely independent sets of data.

Dr. Bernard Shapiro, Albert Einstein Medical Center, Philadelphia, Pennsylvania: Dr. Eldjarn, how do you reconcile Dr. Alexander's belief that protective sulfhydryl compounds do not enter cells with your own belief that sulfhydryl compounds exert their protective action in the nuclei? How do you reconcile your belief in the mixed disulfide mechanism for protection with your observation that strong reducing systems in the cell reduce the protective agent to the thiol form which would be unlikely to react with protein thiols to produce mixed disulfides?

Dr. Lorentz Eldjarn, University of Oslo, Oslo, Norway: Dr. Alexander was using the ESR-spectrum technique in conjunction with ionizing radiation to demonstrate the presence or absence of the protective sulfur-containing compounds in his system. This appears to be an indirect and complicated analytical technique for sulfur compounds. By the use of sulfur-labeled protective agents, the nuclei isolated from mammalian tissues appear to be freely penetrable.

With respect to the second question we should bear in mind the complex system of compartments which exists inside cells, a situation which most probably results in different SH/SS redox situations in the different loci. For instance, glutathione reductase appears to be mainly confined to the cell sap. In particular, no glutathione reductase can be demonstrated in isolated mitochondria. Since the mitochondrial wall is impermeable to glutathione, it appears unlikely that the SH/SS redox situation should be identical in the cell sap and inside the mitochondria. Also it appears likely that in the cell sap the protective agents mainly occur in the thiol form, whereas in the nuclei higher concentrations of disulfides and mixed disulfides are obtained.

Dr. Peter Alexander, Chester Beatty Research Institute, Institute of Cancer Research, Royal Cancer Hospital, London, England: I have no doubt cysteamine penetrates into the nucleus of mammalian cells. There are much excellent data from many centers which prove this. What I said was that cysteamine did not penetrate into the interior of *E. coli* B/r. The possibility that radioprotective agents might be useful in radiotherapy has been considered by many authors over the last 15 years. Evidence for selective localization in the surrounding tissue of the tumor rather than the tumor cells themselves is equivocal. However, in those cases in which the high radioresistance of anoxic cells is the determining factor in the treatment, protective agents should be of help to the therapist even if all the cells, including those in parts of the tumor that are devoid of oxygen, are exposed to the protective chemical (*i.e.* even when there is no selective uptake). The reason for this is that these substances protect much better in the presence of oxygen than in its absence. Experiments done in many systems over the last 12 years have shown that once cells have been rendered less sensitive by removal of oxygen, the presence of a chemical protector does little to raise their radioresistance still more. Consequently, a protector will protect the normal tissue and thereby permit a higher dose of radiation to be tolerated without, at the same time, altering the radiation response of the anoxic cells in the tumor. Ideally, the protector should achieve all that could be hoped for from increased oxygenation during therapy. As yet, this principle cannot be applied to radiotherapy because all the effective agents give rise to most unpleasant side effects at the doses at which they need to be used.

We have, however, demonstrated that this method works in principle by irradiating primary benzpyrine-induced sarcoma in the rat. These tumors were irradiated under the conditions described by Haddow and Alexander (*Lancet*, February 29, 1964). The radiation response was assessed by the delay in growth, by measuring tumor diameters. Skin damage of the surface of the tumor was assessed as follows:

Grade 1 = Erythema
Grade 2 = Severe erythema
Grade 3 = Dry desquamation
Grade 4 = Moist desquamation
Grade 5 = Some skin loss
Grade 6 = 50% skin loss

With a local dose of 2,000 r, skin damage was confined to grades 1 and 2. With a local dose of 4,000 r, skin damage was in the grades 4 and 5. If the rats were given 150 mg/kg of cysteamine prior to 4,000 r locally, irradiation skin damage was reduced to grades 2 and 3. The tumor response was not affected by the injection of cysteamine. These tumors were very badly vascularized and probably highly anoxic. Our data therefore show that such tumors are not significantly protected by cysteamine, while the skin on top of them is well protected by cysteamine. Whether this selective action is due to the failure of the protector reaching the tumor, or whether it is due to the fact that the tumor is anoxic while the skin is not, cannot be decided from the present experiments.

Dr. Powers, could you tell us something about glycerol protection? Are DTO spores not poisoned when grown in pure D_2O?

Dr. Powers: Substitution of 100% D_2O does nothing that we can observe to the cells. We see normal sporulation and normal germination of the spores. I am not saying that some things aren't different, but with respect to the end point used, there are no reasons to suspect the D_2O spore is different from the H_2O spore.

Concerning glycerol, Dr. Robert Webb has found that glycerol does indeed reduce Class I, or oxygen independent, damage; but it also reduces oxygen dependent damage. Whether this oxygen dependent damage is in the Class II or Class III component cannot be decided at this time. These glycerol experiments necessarily have been done in aqueous suspension, and you recall from the Tallentire and Powers graph (*Radiation Research*, 20:270–287, 1963), at saturation levels of water the lifetimes of the free radicals formed are exceedingly short, and one sees no postirradiation oxygen effects. We can not distinguish between Class II and III under these circumstances; but the oxygen effect, the operational oxygen effect, is affected by the glycerol and it is reduced.

With respect to water content, Dr. Webb has taken these cells to 11 molar glycerol, and observed a slowly rising curve that plateaus as concentration increases. (Webb, R. B., *Radiation Research*, 18:607–617, 1963). I should recommend your attention to the relationship that he is able to recognize between glycerol content and total radiation sensitivity. It is obviously impossible to obtain infinite concentrations of glycerol within the cell; but he sets up the relationship between concentration of glycerol and effect on radiation sensitivity so that the reciprocal of the concentration of glycerol is plotted against a number which is derived from the rate constants seen at these concentrations (the Langmuir isotherm). At infinite glycerol concentration (zero water content on one assumption), there is zero radiation effect. This means, perhaps, that when a glycerol molecule is associated with something important, that that important thing is protected fully. It is important to emphasize that it is the *pressure of glycerol* and not the *absence of water* that is responsible for the protective effect. Recall that the *absence of water* results in a sensitive cell.

Dr. Herman Klouwen, Radiobiological Institute of the Organization for Health Research TNO, Rijswijk, Netherlands: Dr. Eldjarn, would you consider the possibility that protection of SH compounds is obtained by pharmacological action? I think this is well studied, especially by our group in Rijswijk, indicating that some of these protective actions, particularly by biological amines, can be explained on the basis of pharmacological action. I ask this also because I am a bit puzzled why we have to consider the possibility of the formation of SS bridges between the external added SH-substances is supposed to occur in preference to reactions within the cell between the SH protein groups and cellular SH groups which are present in all parts of the cell.

Dr. Eldjarn: The question has been raised whether in the case of the S-containing agents the phenomenon of protection should be ascribed to a pharmacological action. In a recent review (Chemical protection against ionizing radiation, Radiochemistry or cellular physiology? *Sonderband sur Strahlentherapie,* vol. 51, pp. 234–244, Ed. Hedi Fritz-Niggli) I have presented my own ideas on this point. It is obvious that, among other things, the extensive mixed disulfide formation temporarily brings about pronounced toxicological effect which may well affect the radioresistance of the cell. This probably also pertains to the above described mixed disulfide formation with nuclear DNA-protein-SH complexes. The very rapid onset of protection still makes me believe, however, that radiochemical mechanisms are at work in mammalian protection phenomena.

Dr. Barendsen: That is correct, but at very high LET it decreases again.

Dr. Robert J. Rutman, University of Pennsylvania, Philadelphia, Pennsylvania: I would like to discuss some evidence concerned with the mechanism of action of alkylating agents. This evidence may be relevant to the general question of the modalities available for modifying radiation damage. What we have done is to expose DNA in vitro to nitrogen mustard so that one in 1,000 to 2,000 nucleotides are alkylated and carry a C^{14} nitrogen mustard molecule. The alkylation has been carried out at 37 C for 5 minutes. The sample is then either kept at 37 C or brought to 0 to 5 C, and we can observe the course of further reaction with the DNA. The figure shows that the cross-linking is complete very quickly at 37 C; in fact, it takes less than 2 hours for the entire course of the cross-linking to occur at this temperature. The extent of cross-linking can be established by optical measurements of the remelting patterns of renatured DNA, by density gradient separation, or counter-current separation of single- and double-stranded molecules. However, at 0 C the process

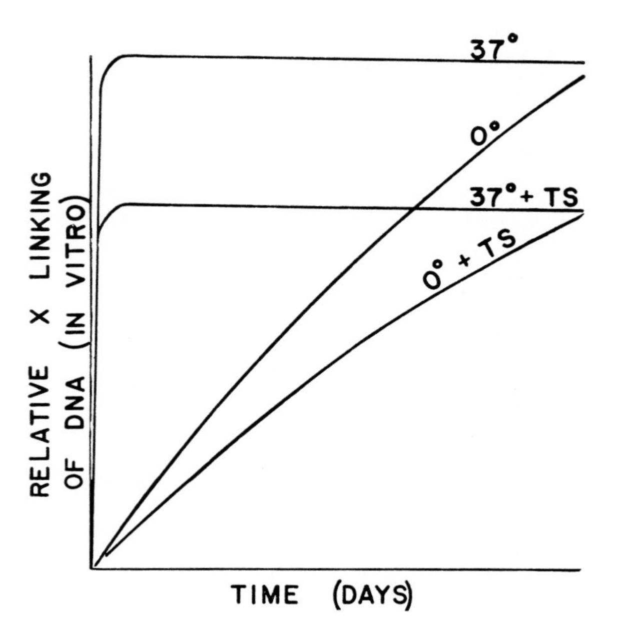

Calf thymus DNA reacted with C^{14}-HN_2 for 5 min at 37 C so as to produce 1 alkylation per 10^3 nucleotides. Aliquots held at 0 or 37 C for 2 hours, then dialyzed and held at 0–4 C with or without thiosulfate (TS) for 7 days.

of cross-linking which was initiated by the 5 minutes of exposure to HN_2 now takes 6 to 8 days to complete itself. A bifunctional alkylating agent, one arm of which has reacted with the DNA, is prevented from immediately reacting further with solvent or with DNA by the lower temperature and now takes a greatly prolonged time to react, but reaches the same end point. This also implies an unusual stability for the bound, but unreacted, functional group. Simultaneously with the change in the cross-linking due to the modification of circumstances, there is also a change in the splitting of C^{14} from the DNA. The C^{14} split is dialyzable and includes hydrolyzed HN_2, which is at first bound and then split off again. The loss of C^{14} therefore reflects to some extent, the chain splitting effects of alkylation. From this it can be seen that low temperatures reduce the splitting but that this reduction is less than the reduction of the cross-linking; and protective agents affect these two reactions differently. The protective agents were shown in the type of experiment to increase the C^{14} splitting and to decrease the cross-linking. My purpose in introducing these rather crude data is to show that in DNA itself there is a molecular basis for the modification of the kind of damage occurring when circumstances are changed. This is a molecular basis for low temperature effect which can provide also for a switching between deletions (mutations) and cross-linkings which affect whole sections of DNA. If this can be analogized to radiation, then any model which proposes to account for the effects of varying conditions has not only to consider different kinds of targets, but also different chemical reactions in a given target.

Dr. Thomas Wood, University of Pennsylvania, Philadelphia, Pennsylvania: I should like to describe briefly some unpublished work we have done on two systems, *E. coli* B and haploid yeast (*Sacch. cerv.*) which is quite similar to the elegant experiments of Dr. Powers and his collaborators. There are two reasons for mentioning these results. First, the experimental results are remarkably similar to those described by Dr. Powers; and second, the analysis which we have used, though quite speculative, is easy to visualize from a physical point of view. The two test systems were supported on cellulose acetate filters and exposed to X-irradiation under various conditions as indicated in the table. As the resulting survival curves were all exponential, we may describe the experimental results in terms of dose modifying factors taken relative to the radioresistance for wet, oxygenated cells.

Dose Modifying Factors for X-Ray Inactivation

Treatment	Dose Modifying Factors	
	Sacch. cerv.	*E. coli*
Wet-O_2	1.00[1]	1.00[1]
Wet-N_2	2.00	2.8
Wet-Glycerol[2]-O_2	2.8	2.3
Wet-Glycerol-N_2	5.0	3.7
Frozen[3]-O_2	2.5	2.7
Frozen-N_2	5.0	5.0
Dry[4]-O_2	0.7	1.1
Dry-N_2	0.7	1.2

[1] The LD_{10} for the yeast was 13.2 krad; for *E. coli*, 6.1 krad.
[2] Glycerol concentration: 6.9 M.
[3] Rapidly frozen at —35 C.
[4] *Sacch. cerv.* was dried to 0.1 mm Hg, and *E. coli* to 5.0 mm.

We had expected, in conformity with the prevailing ideas of a few years ago, that the drying would provide radiation protection even greater than that afforded by freezing or glycerol treatment; however, as shown in the table, it provides little protection, and may even sensitize to irradiation. Our earlier studies (*Review of Modern Physics*, 31:282–288, 1959) had suggested to us that freezing and glycerol protect by preventing a fraction of the cellular water from participating in the primary radiation events, perhaps by cellular dehydration or by binding. This fraction of the water that can be so affected had been designated as "free" water; the residual fraction, that which cannot be frozen or "bound up" by glycerol, as "bound" water. A portion of the bound water would be associated intimately with the radiation "targets" in the cell, and could only be removed from participation in the pertinent radiobiological events by vacuum drying.

The experimental results are consistent with a model based on the following assumptions: (1) In the "wet" state, radiation damage may be caused by radiation energy deposited directly in the cellular targets (direct action) or by the migration of radiation energy deposited in the cellular water near the targets (indirect action); (2) The "bound" water may serve to remove energy received by the targets by providing additional degrees of freedom for energy dissipation; (3) The "free" water may be operationally removed by freezing, by glycerol treatment, or by drying; (4) The "bound" water may be removed only by drying; and (5) There may be oxygen modifying effects on both direct and indirect actions. Thus in the "wet" condition, radiation energy from both direct and indirect action processes would be received by the targets; but a fraction, f, of this energy would be dissipated into the target environment by virtue of the presence of the "bound" water. With frozen or glycerol treated cells, indirect action would effectively be eliminated but the bound water would still act to dissipate energy received by the targets through direct actions processes; therefore, the cells would be greatly protected. If the cells are vacuum dried, indirect action events would be removed, but the concomitant removal of the "bound" water would prevent the dissipation of direct action energy from the target. Accordingly an over-all sensitization could result. A formal analysis using this model indicates that direct action events in the wet state are about twice as important as indirect action events and that f, the energy dissipation factor, is about 0.8.

Chairman Arthur Cole, The University of Texas M. D. Anderson Hospital and Tumor Institute, Houston, Texas: One can spatially separate or compartmentalize within the cell the effect of certain modifying agents. For example, using low-energy electron beams, we find "cytoplasmic" radiation damage (as judged by survival) generally is not oxygen-enhanced nor BUDR-enhanced. When one irradiates the sensitive region of a fibroblast cell with a low voltage beam which shows optimum efficiency for killing, one gets a value of BUDR potentiation which is larger than is observed for a uniform irradiation of the whole cell. We have interpreted this to mean that there are two spatially separated components in the cell which are involved in inactivation of mammalian cells. One component is BUDR potentiated and one is not.

Dr. Powers: It might be possible for us to talk about our results in terms of bound water and free water, but for what I think are good reasons we have always taken a very conservative attitude toward the use of these terms. It is impossible to define them. As a matter of fact, we have presented in the literature considerable evidence for *three* water compartments within the cell associated with radiation sensitivity. What these water compartments are physically remains to be demonstrated. While we might think of bound water, less bound water, and of free water, we, and others, have demonstrations to make, I think, before the terms are properly used. You will recall the Tallentire and Powers results (*Radiation Research,* 20:270–287, 1963) which I discussed in the lecture. Recall there are three levels of water as recognized by radiation sensitivity: there is that plateau of radiation sensitivity observed in the very dry state; there is a transition from that level to another plateau which is seen in the medium wet state; and there is another transition from that point to the very wet circumstance.

The deuterium substitution experiments indicate to me again three different water compartments within the spore. Substitution of D_2O for H_2O during sporogenesis results in spores that are always more resistant whatever the test circumstance. This is a water compartment that is not changeable by techniques used to date after the spore is formed. After formation, the spore in the dry state (below 1 mm. Hg water partial pressure) is not sensitive to the difference between D_2O and H_2O; this is another water compartment. But in the wet spore (above one torr) the spore is sensitive to the difference between D_2O and H_2O, and in a direction opposite to the effect demonstrated by incorporated D_2O; it is more sensitive if given D_2O. On the basis of deuterium substitution there are reasons for thinking of three water compartments, but we can hardly use the terms "bound" and "free," and associate them with "direct" and "indirect" actions.

RADIOSENSITIVITY IN THE REPLICATION CYCLE OF CELLS AND THE RELATION TO FRACTIONATION IN RADIOTHERAPY

The Influence of Oxygen on Damage to the Proliferative Capacity of Cultured Human Cells Produced by Radiations of Different LET

G. W. Barendsen

Radiobiological Institute TNO, Rijswijk, The Netherlands

The importance of oxygen with regard to the production of biological damage by ionizing radiations has been demonstrated with various cellular systems as well as with intact animals. In general, cells equilibrated with oxygen or air are more sensitive to radiation than cells in anoxic conditions. In addition, it has been found that this oxygen effect is smaller for radiations with a high linear energy transfer (LET), for instance densely ionizing alpha particles or fast neutrons, as compared with low LET radiations such as X or gamma rays. For mammalian cells, quantitative data on the relation between the oxygen enhancement ratio (OER) and the LET are scarce. This information is of interest because it is assumed that certain tumors contain a considerable proportion of anoxic cells which are relatively insensitive to X or gamma rays, and which consequently determine the radiocurability of these tumors. It is obvious that the use of high LET radiations with a lower oxygen enhancement ratio than X or gamma rays may have an advantage in this respect. This subject will be dealt with in more detail later during this symposium by Dr. Andrews, especially with a view of using fast neutrons in clinical radiotherapy.

In this contribution, information will be presented with regard to the fundamental aspects of the differences in OER between high and low LET radiations. We have used an established line of kidney cells of human origin which has been cultured during the past six years in our laboratory. The end point measured is impairment of the proliferative capacity of these cells. The plating technique developed by Puck, Marcus, and Cierciura (1956) allows quantitative determination of the fraction of cells which after irradiation have retained the capacity for clone formation. If this fraction is plotted as a function of the dose, a survival curve is obtained. The principal differences between high LET and low LET radiations are shown in Figure 1 (Barendsen and Beusker, 1960; Barendsen, Beusker, Vergroesen, and Budke, 1960; Barendsen, Walter, Fowler, and Bewley, 1963; Barendsen, 1961). In curves 1 and 2 of this figure, survival curves obtained with well-oxygenated cells and with anoxic cells, respectively, are presented for alpha particles of about 3.2 Mev energy, which have a LET of 140 kev/μ of unit density tissue. Both these curves are indistinguishable from exponentials and the ratio of two doses which result in the same percentage survival, *i.e.* the OER, in only 1.15 ± 0.10. Because the curves are exponential, this factor is also equal to the ratio of the slopes of the two curves.

With 250 kvp X rays, which have an average LET of about 2.5 kev/μ of unit density tissue, a much larger OER is found, as shown by comparison of curves 3 and 4 in Figure 1. The ratio of the two doses which results in the same percentage survival is about 2.6 ± 0.2. It will be clear that in this case it is not possible to give the ratio of slopes, for the slopes increase continuously with the dose. It is worthwhile noting, however, that even at low doses of between 200 and 500 rads, which are most frequently used as daily doses in clinical radiotherapy, the factor of 2.6 is found.

The point of interest which has now been investigated in more detail is concerned with the problem: At what LET between 2.5 and 140 kev/μ of tissue does the OER decrease from the high value of 2.6 to the low value of 1.15? In a publication which appeared some time ago, we have described in detail results obtained with alpha particles and deuterons of various LET's (Barendsen, Walter, Fowler, and Bewley, 1963). In cooperation with Dr. Bewley from the Medical Research Council Cyclotron Unit at Hammersmith Hospital in London, we have irradiated cells in equilibrium with

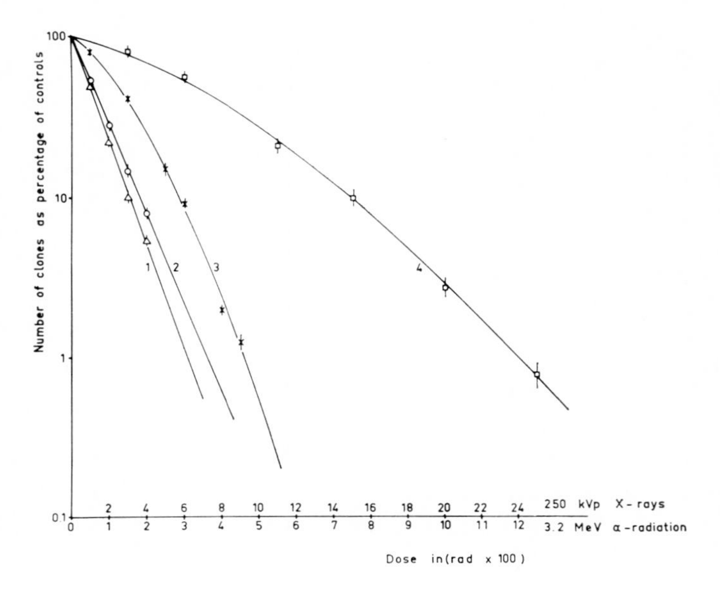

FIGURE 1. Survival curves of cultured human cells irradiated with alpha particles from Po^{210} and with 250 kvp X rays. Curves 1 and 2 were obtained with cells in equilibrium with air and nitrogen, respectively, after irradiation with alpha radiation. Curves 3 and 4 were obtained with cells in equilibrium with air and nitrogen, respectively, after irradiation with 250 kvp X rays.

air or nitrogen with alpha particles of different energies. Results of these experiments, which will be published in detail elsewhere, are summarized in the table, and presented graphically as a function of the LET in Figure 2. The OER is shown to decrease most rapidly between about 40 and 140 kev/μ of unit density tissue. In curve 2 of this figure, the relative effectiveness of the alpha radiation per unit dose is given, which is proportional to the relative biological effectiveness (RBE). This curve shows a maximum at about 105 kev/μ of unit density tissue, with a subsequent decrease at higher LET's. This decrease may be interpreted to result from a saturation effect. At very high LET's, a particle passing through a sensitive structure in the cell will deposit more energy in it than is required to produce the observed end point, and the excess energy is wasted. From Figure 2, it is clear that the OER approaches unity, *i.e.* the oxygen effect disappears, at a LET value beyond the maximum RBE, where the saturation effect starts. This is even more clearly demonstrated if the same data are presented in a different way. In Figure 3 the effectiveness per particle, which is proportional to the effective cross section, is given as a function of LET (curve 1), together with the OER's (curve 2). The saturation effect is, in this figure, demonstrated by the occurrence of a maximum in the effectiveness per particle, which is approached closely at about 150 kev/μ of tissue; at this LET the oxygen effect has almost disappeared. These results may be explained by the assumption that the decrease in OER as a function of the LET occurs

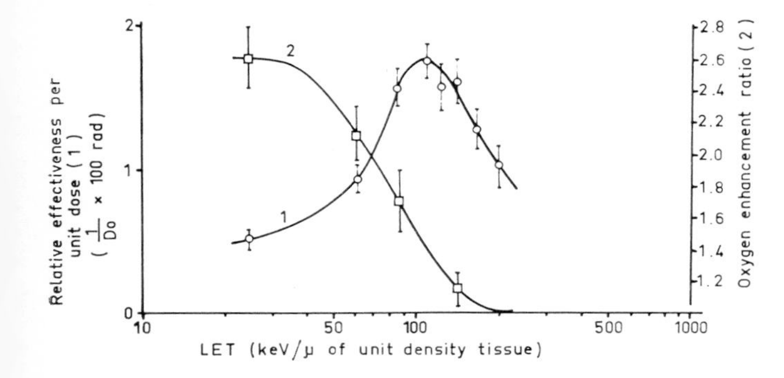

FIGURE 2. Relative effectiveness per unit dose of alpha radiation for inhibition of clone formation by cultured human cells (curve 1, left scale) and corresponding oxygen enhancement ratios (curve 2, right scale) as a function of LET.

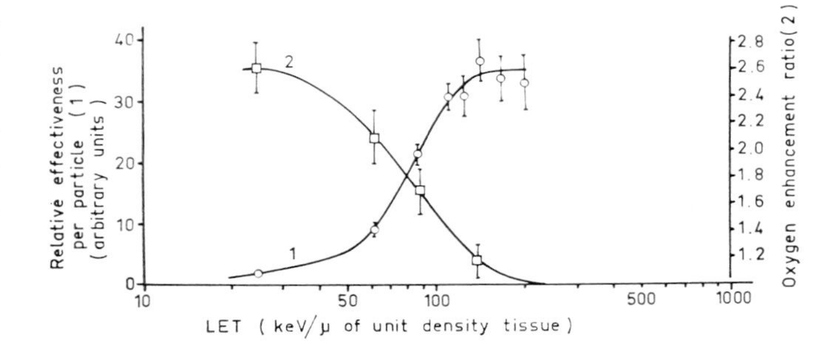

FIGURE 3. Relative effectiveness per particle for inhibition of clone formation by cultured human cells after alpha irradiation (curve 1, left scale) and corresponding oxygen enhancement ratios (curve 2, right scale) as a function of the LET.

because particles at a high LET produce so much damage in a sensitive site in the cell that prevention of part of these changes by anoxia is insufficient to diminish the residual damage to a level which can no longer impair the proliferative capacity of the cell. A quantitative estimate of this fraction of the damage which may be prevented by anoxia results in a value of about 30 per cent.

Oxygen Enhancement Ratios of α-Radiation for Impairment of the Proliferative Capacity of Cultured Human Cells

Energy (Mev)	LET (kev/μ of unit density tissue)	OER
3.2	140	1.15 ± 0.1
5.1	90	1.7 ± 0.2
8.3	60	2.1 ± 0.2
25.0	26	2.6 ± 0.2

Abbreviations: LET, Linear Energy Transfer; OER, Oxygen Enhancement Ratio.

Finally, a preliminary result may be mentioned of measurements of the OER of fast neutrons from Be^9 (d, n)B^{10} reaction, produced with the Medical Research Council cyclotron, which was estimated to be 1.5 ± 0.2. This value is lower than would be expected from the OER versus LET curve found for alpha particles, because the average LET of these neutrons is only about 20 kev/μ of unit density tissue (Bewley, 1963). The explanation of this difference may presumably be found in the fact that the average LET of these neutrons cannot be compared with the total LET's given for the alpha particles. More data about the energy dissipation characteristics of these radiations as measured by Rossi will be needed before this can be decided (Biavati, Rosenzweig, Rossi and Miyanaga, 1963).

ADDENDUM

With the same cellular system, the oxygen enhancement ratio has now been measured for fast neutrons from the D(T, n)He^4 reaction with an energy of 15 Mev. An OER of 1.7 ± 0.2 was obtained for these neutrons, which have a track average LET of about 12 kev/μ. Analogous to the result for Be^9 (d, n)B^{10} neutrons, this OER value is lower than the OER obtained with α-particles or deuterons in the LET range of 10 to 20 kev/μ. Although various factors concerning fractionation and recovery of normal and tumor cells have yet to be investigated, the OER values of these fast neutrons are favorable with regard to possibilities of their application to the radiotherapy for tumors.

REFERENCES

Barendsen, G. W. 1961. "Damage to the Reproductive Capacity of Human Cells in Tissue Culture by Ionizing Radiations of Different Linear Energy Transfer," *The Initial Effects of Ionizing Radiations on Cells*, R. J. C. Harris. Ed. New York, New York, and London, England: Academic Press. Pp. 183–194.

Barendsen, G. W., and T. L. J. Beusker. 1960. Effects of Different Ionizing Radiations on Human Cells in Tissue Culture. I. Irradiation Techniques and Dosimetry. *Radiation Research*, 13:832–840.

Barendsen, G. W., T. L. J. Beusker, A. J. Vergroesen, and L. Budke. 1960. Effects of Different Ionizing Radiations on Human Cells in Tissue Culture. II. Biological Experiments. *Radiation Research*, 13:841–849.

Barendsen, G. W., H. M. D. Walter, J. F. Fowler, and D. K. Bewley. 1963. Effects of Different Ionizing Radiations on Human Cells in Tissue Culture. III. Experiments with Cyclotron-Accelerated Alpha-Particles and Deuterons. *Radiation Research*, 18: 106–119.

Bewley, D. K. 1963. Physical Aspects of the Fast Neutron Beam. *British Journal of Radiology*, 36:81–88.

Biavati, M. H., W. Rosenzweig, H. H. Rossi, and I. Miyanaga. 1963. The Dependence of RBE on the Energy of Fast Neutrons. III. Evaluations of Radiation Quality. *Radiation Research*, 19:512–525.

Puck, T. T., P. I. Marcus, and S. J. Cierciura. 1956. Clonal Growth of Mammalian Cells *in vitro*. *Journal of Experimental Medicine*, 103:273–284.

The Effect of Cysteine upon the Radiation Sensitivity of Lysozyme at Two Temperatures and T2 Bacteriophage at Various LET

ROBERT J. SHALEK, CHARLES E. SMITH, S. J. SEDITA,* AND PETER ALMOND

Department of Physics, The University of Texas M. D. Anderson Hospital and Tumor Institute, and Physics Department, Rice University, Houston, Texas

A summary of the effect of cysteine upon the radiation sensitivity of T2r bacteriophage and lysozyme under several physical conditions of irradiation will be given here. Details of some of the experiments will be reported later.

RELATION OF CYSTEINE TO THE OXYGEN EFFECT

It was shown (Howard-Flanders, 1960) that in a solution of T2 bacteriophage in which no oxygen effect was apparent, added cysteamine caused a decrease in the radiation sensitivity in the absence of oxygen but caused no effect in the presence of oxygen. These results are similar to those found here, as shown in Table 1. The survival curves were exponential with dose, and radiation sensitivity was taken as the inverse of the inactivation dose, which is the dose required to reduce survival to 37 per cent (D_{37}). By analyzing the number of *Escherichia coli* killed by active and by inactive bacteriophage, it was demonstrated that the radiation damage was upon the deoxyribonucleic acid (DNA) of the bacteriophage and not upon the attachment mechanism in the tail.

In these experiments, the added cysteine reduced the radiation sensitivity in the absence of oxygen, but not in the presence of oxygen. The results are consistent with the hydrogen donor hypothesis for sulfhydryl action; namely, that a damaged site which is presumed to be the result of the removal of a hydrogen atom on a vital molecule may be restituted by re-

* Present address: University of Houston, Houston, Texas.

TABLE 1

Radiation Sensitivity of T2r Bacteriophage in Broth or in Cysteine Solutions at pH 7.0 by 250 kvp X Rays, HVL—5.3 mm Al, 24,000 rads/min (Survival Was Exponential with Dose)

	1% Broth 100 μg/ml Gelatin		10^{-2} M Cysteine 100 μg/ml Gelatin	
	N_2	O_2	N_2	O_2
D_{37}, krads	38.1	40.6	62.1	37.2
Relative sensitivity	1.00	0.94	0.61	1.02

Abbreviations: D_{37}, dose required to reduce survival to 37%; HVL, half-value layer; kvp, kilovolt peak.

action with sulfhydryl compounds, or confirmed as damaged by reaction with oxygen. In the absence of either sulfhydryl compounds or oxygen, it is postulated that the damaged molecule is inactivated by a slow but undefined reaction (Hutchinson, 1961).

Independence of the Protective Effect of Low Temperature and of Cysteine

Dry lysozyme and lysozyme-cysteine mixtures freeze-dried from 10^{-3} M HCl were irradiated by Cs^{137} gamma rays in the absence of oxygen at room temperature and at −196C. In preliminary experiments, 25 per cent by weight of cysteine conferred greater protection to the enzymatic activity of the lysozyme than did mixtures of greater or lesser amounts of cysteine. The inactivation doses, derived from the exponential survival curves, are shown in Table 2. It is seen that the radiation sensitivity is reduced more than a factor of 5 at −196 C from that at 23 C, and that the added cysteine confers about equal protection at both temperatures. These results are consistent with either the hydrogen donor or the mixed disulfide hypothesis for the radioprotective action of sulfhydryl compounds discussed by Dr. Eldjarn (see pages 305 to 323, this volume).

TABLE 2

Effect of Cysteine Upon the Radiation Sensitivity of Dry Lysozyme at Two Temperatures Cs^{137} Gamma Rays, 9,480 rads/min (Survival Was Exponential with Dose)

	D_{37} Megarads	Ratio
23 C		
Dry lysozyme	41.2	1.38
Dry, 75% lysozyme, 25% cysteine	57.0	
−195 C		
Dry lysozyme	220	1.47
Dry, 75% lysozyme, 25% cysteine	325	

The Radiation-Protective Action of Cysteine at Various LET

Co^{60} gamma rays, 250 kvp X rays, and accelerated protons from the 5.5 Mev Van de Graaff accelerator at Rice University were admitted into

TABLE 3

Inactivation of T2 Bacteriophage in Solutions of Broth or Cysteine at pH 7.0 by Various Ionizing Radiations (Survival Was Exponential with Dose)

Radiation source	Dose rate	Particle energy / Particle range Mev-cm²/g	1% broth 100 μg/ml gelatin D_{37}-kilorads	10^{-2} M cysteine 100 μg/ml gelatin D_{37}-kilorads	Ratio D_{37}-cysteine to D_{37}-broth
Co^{60} gamma	6,700 rads/min	2.5	42.2 ± 6.3	61.8 ± 1.6	1.46
250 kvp X ray HVL—5.3 mm Al	9,700 rads/min	≈25	42.0 ± 2.0	69.7 ± 3.6	1.66
4.689 Mev protons	5.1×10^{-8} amp/cm²	150	68.7 ± 3.1	90.5 ± 1.6	1.32
2.004 Mev protons	2.8×10^{-8} amp/cm²	266	111 ± 4	154 ± 8	1.39
0.993 Mev protons	3.4×10^{-8} amp/cm²	436	146 ± 4	176 ± 3	1.21

highly stirred solutions of T2r bacteriophage containing broth or cysteine, both in a nitrogen environment. A constancy of yield was demonstrated at various rates of stirring. The survival curves were exponential with radiation dose; the D_{37} values derived are shown in Table 3. It is seen that the radiation protective capability of cysteine is effective at various rates of linear energy transfer (LET), although there may be a decrease in the protection provided by cysteine at high LET. In these experiments, the environment of the bacteriophage at the time of irradiation was well defined; but the specific energy loss is not well defined, since the LET of the protons entering the solution increased as the particles slowed and came to rest. Other preliminary data taken in broth and in cysteine environments, but with the T2r bacteriophage deposited upon millipore filters, is roughly in agreement with the above data. However, at present the data are insufficient to test the hypothesis that the maximum in relative biological effectiveness (RBE) for cellular organisms at about 1,000 Mev-cm^2/g arises from competition between sulfhydryl compounds, oxygen, and radiation-produced radicals (Shalek, Humphrey, and Sedita, 1963). These results do seem, however, to be similar to the data upon bacteria irradiated by 28 Mev and 5.2 Mev alpha particles (Alper, Bewley, and Fowler, 1962), in which it was demonstrated that cysteine conferred about equal protection for both particles.

ACKNOWLEDGMENTS

This investigation was supported in part by the United States Atomic Energy Commission and by Public Health Service Research Grant CA 03283 from the National Cancer Institute.

REFERENCES

Alper, T., D. K. Bewley, and J. F. Fowler. 1962. Chemical Protection Against Alpha Particle Irradiation. *Nature*, London, 194:1245–1247.

Howard-Flanders, P. 1960. The Effect of Oxygen on the Radiosensitivity of Bacteriophage in the Presence of Sulfhydryl Compounds. *Nature*, London, 186:485–487.

Hutchinson, F. 1961. Sulfhydryl Groups and the Oxygen Effect on Irradiated Dilute Solutions of Enzymes and Nucleic Acids. *Radiation Research*, 14:721–731.

Shalek, R. J., R. M. Humphrey, and S. J. Sedita. 1963. A Suggested Mechanism for Relative Biological Effectiveness Involving the Participation of the Cellular Environment. (Abstract) *Radiation Research*, 19:214–215.

Radiosensitivity and Recovery of Radiation Damage in Relation to the Cell Cycle

WILLIAM C. DEWEY AND RONALD M. HUMPHREY

Department of Physics,
The University of Texas M. D. Anderson Hospital and Tumor Institute,
Houston, Texas

Reports indicate that the radiosensitivity based on both chromosomal damage and cell survival varies during the life cycle of the cell in both animals and plants. In plants, grasshopper neuroblasts, and spermatocytes, prophase appears to be more radiosensitive, judging by chromosomal damage, than do the other phases (Marshak, 1939; Neary and Evans, 1958; Sparrow, Moses, and Dubow, 1952; Carlson, 1954; Oakberg and DiMinno, 1960), although the recent work of Das and Alfert (1962) based on chromosomal damage at anaphase in *Vicia faba* indicates that the deoxyribonucleic acid (DNA) synthetic phase (S) is the most radiosensitive. In the mammalian systems the results differ, indicating that either the DNA postsynthetic phase (G_2) or the S phase is the most radiosensitive (Monesi, 1962; Dewey and Humphrey, 1962, 1963; Hsu, Dewey, and Humphrey, 1962; Sinclair and Morton, 1963a). However, Terasima and Tolmach (1963a) reported that for HeLa cells, the cells in mitosis were the most radiosensitive, followed by cells in either the latter part of the DNA presynthetic phase (G_1) or the early part of the S phase. In the present studies, the radiosensitivity during the cell cycle was studied in both the mouse L cell and the Chinese hamster cell growing in vitro. The different phases of the cell cycle were identified by using autoradiographic techniques to identify cells or colonies labeled with tritiated thymidine (H^3TdR).

The restitution of chromosomal breaks in plants (Giles, 1954; Sax and Mather, 1939; Sax, 1961; Wolff and Luippold, 1955; Wolff, 1960a, b), as determined by the change in frequency of exchanges when a given dose of radiation is delivered over different time intervals, can occur within 5 to 60 minutes after irradiation. In mammalian cells, data on the length of the restitution period are lacking, especially in relation to the different phases of the cell cycle. The present report concerns the investigation of this question utilizing Chinese hamster cells growing in vitro.

Elkind and Sutton (1960) have studied recovery or repair of sublethal damage as measured by colony survival following fractionated doses of irradiation. These studies show that the shoulder of the survival curve returns within two to four hours following irradiation. In the present studies, this recovery was investigated in cells irradiated in different phases of the cell cycle. The relationship between cell lethality and chromosomal damage was studied both in terms of radiosensitivity and of restitution of damage in different phases of the cell cycle.

Materials and Methods

The cell lines used in these experiments, the hypotetraploid mouse fibroblast strain L-P59, the hyperdiploid Lettré mouse ascites tumor (Dewey and Humphrey, 1962; Hsu and Kellogg, 1960a), and the quasi-diploid Chinese hamster fibroblast B14FAF28 (B-14) (Hsu and Kellogg, 1960b) have been described in detail. In our present studies, about 13 per cent of the hamster cells had more than 23 chromosomes. The Chinese hamster strain CH-24 was supplied by Dr. E. H. Y. Chu and differs from the B-14 line primarily in the extended length of the generation time (15 hours). The medium used was McCoy's 5a medium (McCoy, Maxwell, and Kruse, 1959) supplemented with 10 per cent calf serum for L-P59 and B-14 cells and 15 per cent fetal calf serum for CH-24 cells.

The general procedures used in the 10-minute pulse-labeling with H^3TdR, autoradiography, chromosome analysis, colony survival determination, and growth analysis have been described (Dewey and Humphrey, 1962, 1963; Hsu, Dewey, and Humphrey, 1962).

Colony Survival and Recovery

Both single- and double-labeling (1.0 μc/ml and 1.9 c/mmole H^3TdR) experiments were performed with L-P59 and B-14 cells. Following the initial pulse-labeling, T-flasks which were to receive a second pulse-labeling were washed once with fresh medium containing 10 μg/ml thymidine (TdR), the conditioned medium was replaced, and the flasks were returned to the incubator for three hours. Immediately after the final labeling, the cells were irradiated on a revolving disc (5 rev/min) under water maintained at 37 C in a water bath. The X-ray source was a General Electric "Maxitron" operated at 250 kvp, 15 ma, filtered with 0.5 mm Cu and 1.0 mm Al giving a half-value layer of 1.26 mm Cu with a dose rate of 500 r/min. For each experiment three flasks were used as controls, three received 300 r for L cells or 350 r for hamster cells, and three received 600 r for L cells or 700 r for hamster cells. Other flasks (two for each time interval) which were to receive two equal doses of irradiation (300 r or 350 r) were returned to the 37 C incubator for time intervals varying from 10 minutes to 12 hours between doses. Immediately following the final irradiation, the cells were plated to determine survival. By autoradiography, 100 to 200 colonies were identified at each dose point as labeled or unlabeled (Dewey and Humphrey, 1963). By comparing survival of cells irradiated on glass with survival of cells irradiated in suspension, a factor of 1.5 was obtained for converting r to rads.

Chromosome Analysis

Chinese hamster B-14 cells growing in T-flasks were pulse-labeled with H^3TdR and irradiated at 37 C with either an acute or a chronic dose of Co^{60} gamma rays (Dewey and Humphrey, 1964; Dewey, Humphrey, and Jones, 1964). For acute doses, the dose rate was 518 rads/min, and for chronic doses, the dose rate varied from 0.245 to 1.44 rads/min. The total doses ranged from 147 to 865 rads. During chronic irradiation, flasks were maintained at 37 C in a water bath. After nine hours of irradiation colcemid was added to the medium (0.06 μg/ml), and irradiation was continued for an additional hour. Cells were fixed and squashed by the hypotonic method (Hsu and Kellogg, 1960a), and 50 metaphases from each sample were analyzed for single breaks and exchanges.

L-P59 cells and ascites tumor cells were pulse-labeled with 0.1 μc/ml H^3TdR and immediately thereafter were irradiated at room temperature with Co^{60} gamma rays at a dose rate of 40 rads/min. The cells were fixed and scored at metaphase as described above.

For chromosome-restitution experiments (Dewey and Humphrey, 1964), three flasks containing B-14 cells were pulse-labeled with H^3TdR and then were irradiated with Co^{60} gamma rays either at 128 or 518 rads/min for total doses of either 300 or 600 rads. Other flasks were given 300 rads followed by another 300 rads after intervals of 10, 15, 30, and 60 minutes, with the flasks maintained at 37 C between doses. At either four to five hours or 10 hours after irradiation, the medium received colcemid, and the cells were fixed and squashed one hour later. In one experiment, the flasks were irradiated at 37 C with 250 kvp X rays (unfiltered) at a dose rate of 3,000 r/min and were sampled 5.5 hours later.

Procedure for Double Label with $C^{14}TdR$ and H^3TdR

Chinese hamster cells, strain CH-24, growing in T-flasks were pulse-labeled for 30 minutes with 0.25 μc/ml of $C^{14}TdR$ (0.025 c/mmole) and washed once with fresh medium. Conditioned medium (no TdR added) was replaced, and the flasks were incubated for three hours. The cells were then pulse-labeled for 10 minutes with 0.1 μc/ml of H^3TdR (1.9 c/mmole) and washed once with fresh medium containing 10 μg/ml TdR; conditioned medium containing 10 μg/ml TdR was returned to the flasks. Then the flasks were irradiated at 37 C with 600 rads Co^{60} gamma rays at a dose rate of 520 rads/min, and were incubated and sampled over an 18-hour period followed by the addition of colcemid one hour prior to fixation.

A modification of the double-stripping film technique described by Dawson, Field, and Stevens (1962), was used in which H^3 was detected in the first layer and C^{14} in both layers. Kodak AR-10 stripping film was applied to the slides and exposed for six days. The metaphases were then scored for damage. A second layer of film was applied over the first layer and was exposed for 30 days. The number of grains in each layer of film was counted for each metaphase cell which had been scored previously for damage. In the first layer of film, both the number of grains over the nucleus and the number of grains directly over the chromosomes were determined.

To distinguish between C^{14} and H^3 label in metaphase cells, the following relationships were established:

For cells labeled with C^{14} only:

$$\underset{\text{(from first layer only)}}{\text{Ratio A}} = \frac{\text{grains over chromosomes}}{\text{grains over nucleus}} = 0.44 \pm 0.06 \text{ (standard deviation)}$$

$$\text{Ratio B} = \frac{\text{grains in second layer}}{\text{grains over nucleus in first layer}} = 2.3 \pm 0.4$$

For cells labeled both with H^3 and C^{14}:

$$\text{Ratio A} > 0.50 \text{ and Ratio B} < 1.9$$

For cells labeled only with H^3:

> 5 grains in first layer over the chromosome and < 15 grains in second layer.

Results and Discussion

Studies with L-P59 Mouse Fibroblasts and Mouse Ascites Tumor Cells in Vitro

Radiosensitivity in Different Phases of the Cell Cycle-Chromosome Analysis

Studies on the radiosensitivity during the cell cycle, based on the criterion of percentage of cells with breaks and bridges at anaphase, indicate that the S phase is about 1.8 times more radiosensitive than the G_1 phase, and that the G_2 phase is intermediate in radiosensitivity (Table 1). The same results were obtained for mouse ascites tumor cells growing in vivo (Dewey and Humphrey, 1962). In these experiments, the cells were either pulse-labeled with H^3TdR and irradiated immediately thereafter as indicated in experiment A (Figure 1), or were pulse-labeled with H^3TdR and then allowed to incubate for 13 hours before they were irradiated (experiment B). In experiment A, the labeled cells were in the S phase at the time of irradiation, whereas in experiment B, the labeled cells were primarily in the G_1 phase at the time of irradiation. The anaphase figures were scored for damage at various time intervals after irradiation and were identified by autoradiography as labeled or unlabeled.

Wolff and Luippold (1957) reported that more radiation-induced ex-

TABLE 1

Chromosomal Aberrations in Mouse L-P59 Cells and Mouse Ascites H Tumor Cells Following 250 Rads of Co^{60} Gamma Rays (Cells were labeled with H^3TdR immediately prior to irradiation)

Cell description	L-P59 cells (Metaphases) Control	Lab. S cells	Unlab. G_2 cells	Ascites H cells (in vitro) (Metaphases) Control	Lab. S cells	Unlab. G_2 cells	Unlab. G_2 cells	Unlab.
Hours after irradiation when sampled	. .	8–14	8	. .	8–10	6	8	10
No. of cells	17	71	20	43	87	51	50	26
No. of breaks	1	9	9	3	5	15	5	3
No. of chromatid exchanges	1	8	8	1	8	16	13	4
No. of chromosome exchanges	0	0	0	0	0	0	0	0
Total no. of aberrations per cell	0.18	0.64	1.25	0.12	0.24	0.92	0.62	0.42
Per cent caused by exchanges	66	80	64	40	76	68	84	73
Per cent abnormal	12	46	50	9	15	47	30	23
	L-P 59 cells—anaphases*			Ascites H cells (in vivo)—anaphases*				
Per cent abnormal	26	80	65	11	90		70	. .
Aberrations per cell	0.40	1.9	1.3	0.12	1.8		1.2	. .

* From Dewey and Humphrey, 1962. A bridge was scored as two aberrations.
Abbreviations: Lab., labeled; Unlab., unlabeled; H^3TdR, tritium-labeled thymidine.

changes were observed at metaphase than at anaphase. Furthermore, at metaphase the frequency of exchanges was related to the square of the dose, whereas at anaphase the frequency was related to the first power of the dose. Therefore, we also analyzed for chromosomal damage in metaphase cells by scoring breaks and exchanges. The cells were labeled with H^3TdR and irradiated immediately thereafter as in experiment A (Figure 1). Results (Table 1) indicate that for both the L cell and the ascites tumor cell, the unlabeled G_2 cells had two to three times more aberrations than did the labeled S cells. The inverse relationship was found for the anaphase analysis. Therefore, there is clearly a difference in results between the metaphase and the anaphase analyses. This difference is also seen in comparisons of other studies. Das and Alfert (1962) pulse-labeled *Vicia faba* with H^3TdR and at anaphase found more radiation-induced damage in the S phase than

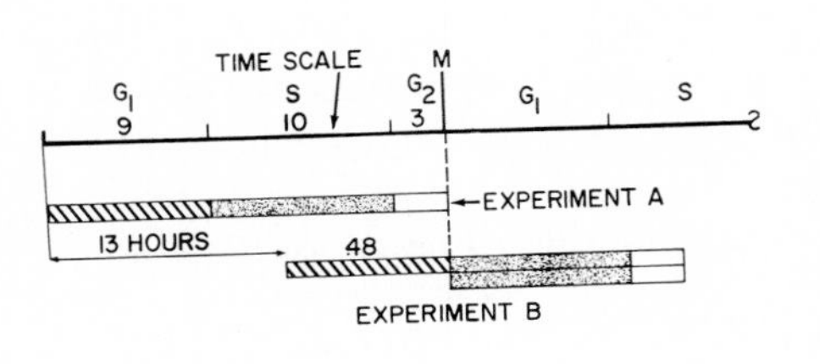

FIGURE 1. Position of L-P59 cells in the cell cycle at the time of irradiation. The duration of the various phases is indicated. In experiment A the cells were pulse-labeled with H^3TdR and irradiated immediately thereafter. In experiment B, the cells were pulse-labeled, incubated for 13 hours, and then irradiated. The labeled cells are indicated by the solid bar, and the unlabeled cells by the open and stippled bars.

in the G_1 and G_2 phases. However, Evans and Savage (1963), also studying *Vicia faba* with the H^3TdR-labeling technique, found at metaphase 1.5 times more damage in the G_2 phase than in the S phase, which had twice the damage of the G_1 phase. Possible reasons for the difference between the metaphase and the anaphase analyses will be discussed later.

Radiosensitivity in Different Phases of the L-P59 Cell Cycle-Colony Survival Analysis

The reproductive integrity of cells irradiated in different phases of the cell cycle was studied by labeling the cells with H^3TdR and irradiating them as indicated in Figure 1. The surviving colonies were identified by autoradiography as labeled or unlabeled. In experiment A (Figure 2), when the labeled cells were in the S phase at the time of irradiation, they were eliminated from the surviving population as the dose of irradiation increased. However, in experiment B, in which the labeled cells were in the G_1 phase at the time of irradiation, they persisted in the surviving population as the unlabeled cells were eliminated. Therefore, for irradiation under both oxygen and nitrogen, the S cells were more radiosensitive than the G_1 cells. When the results of experiments A and B were combined, it appeared that the G_2 cells were intermediate in sensitivity between the G_1 and S cells (Dewey and Humphrey, 1963).

To obtain more information on the relative radiosensitivities of the dif-

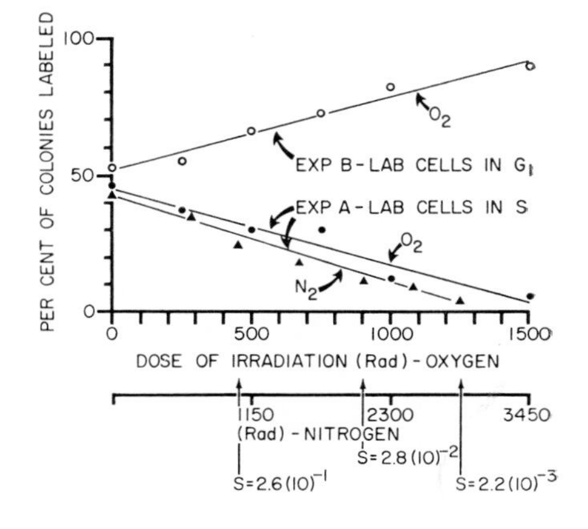

FIGURE 2. Per cent of L-P59 colonies labeled with H^3TdR as a function of radiation dose (250 kvp X rays) and survival. The cells were labeled and irradiated (either under oxygen or nitrogen) as illustrated in Figure 1.

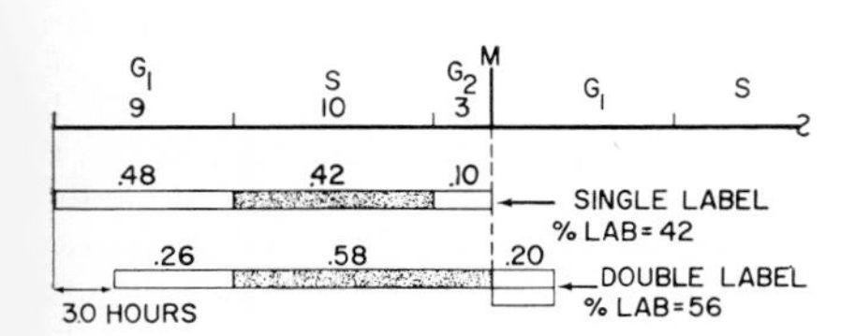

FIGURE 3. Position of L-P59 cells in the cell cycle at the time of the first dose of irradiation. The solid bar indicates cells labeled with H^3TdR, and the open bars indicate unlabeled cells. The length of each phase and the fraction of cells in the various phases are indicated; the values were determined considering logarithmic growth by the method of Edwards *et al.* (1960).

ferent phases, further experiments were conducted with L cells in which the cells were either singly labeled or doubly labeled with H^3TdR, as indicated in Figure 3. In the single-labeling experiment, only the S cells were labeled at the time of irradiation, whereas in the double-labeling experiment in which the two pulse-labels were separated by an interval of three hours, both the S and the G_2 cells were labeled at the time of irradiation. Calculations of colony survival were made as follows:

$$\text{Survival of all cells} = \frac{\text{number of colonies} \Big/ \text{number of irradiated cells plated}}{\text{number of control colonies} \Big/ \text{number of control cells plated}}$$

$$\text{Survival of labeled cells} = (\text{survival of all cells})\,(\text{fraction of colonies labeled})$$

$$\text{Relative survival of labeled cells} = \frac{\text{survival of labeled cells}}{\text{fraction of control colonies labeled}}$$

Similar calculations were made for the survival of unlabeled cells. Calculations of survival for cells in the individual phases, G_1, S, and G_2, at the time of irradiation were made as follows:

From the single-labeling experiments,

A = Survival of labeled cells = Survival of S cells

B = Survival of unlabeled cells = Survival of $G_1 + G_2$ cells

From the double-labeling experiment,

C = Survival of labeled cells = Survival of $S + G_2$ cells

D = Survival of unlabeled cells = Survival of G_1 cells

By combining the single- and double-labeling experiments,

Survival of G_2 cells = C − A or B − D

The relative survival, in which the survival is normalized to 1.0 for the controls, is given as follows:

$$\text{Relative survival of } G_2 \text{ cells} = \frac{\text{survival of } G_2 \text{ cells}}{\text{fraction of control cells in } G_2 \text{ phase}}$$

The same equation applies for the relative survival of G_1 and S cells; the fraction of control cells in the individual phases is obtained by using the survival values for the controls in the above equations.

Thus, it is seen that the survival of cells in the G_2 phase at the time of irradiation can be determined by comparing the results of the single- and double-labeling experiments. The results in Table 2 indicate that the percentage of the colonies labeled decreased as the dose of irradiation increased, and that more of the colonies were labeled in the double-labeling experiment than in the single-labeling experiment. Results, plotted in Figure 8, below, indicate that the S phase was the most radiosensitive, with the G_2 phase being intermediate between the G_1 and the S phases. Insufficient data were available to establish accurate survival curves, but it appears that the S and G_2 curves have about the same slope, which is one half to two thirds of the slope for the G_1 cells. Also, the extrapolation number (n) of the G_2 cells is about twice that of the S cells.

TABLE 2

Colony Survival of L-P59 Cells Irradiated with 250 kvp X Rays (Cells Were Pulse-Labeled with H^3TdR before Irradiation. Single Label-Immediately before. Double Label-Both Three Hours before and Immediately before).

	Dose (r)	0	300	600	
	Surv. all cells	1.00	0.224	0.014	
	Fract. lab.	0.37	0.21	0.058	
	Fract. unlab.	0.63	0.79	0.942	
Single labeling experiment 74 S	Surv. of lab.	0.37	0.047	0.000812	S cells
	(relative)	1.00	0.127	0.0022	
	Surv. of unlab.	0.63	0.176	0.0132	$G_1 + G_2$ cells
	(relative)	1.00	0.280	0.021	
Double labeling experiment 82 D	Fract. lab.	0.59	0.475	0.150	
	Fract. unlab.	0.41	0.525	0.850	
	Surv. of lab.	0.59	0.106	0.0021	$S_1 + G_2$ cells
	(relative)	1.00	0.181	0.0036	
	Surv. of unlab.	0.41	0.116	0.0119	G_1 cells
	(relative)	1.00	0.285	0.029	
	Surv. of G_2	0.22	0.059	0.00129	G_2 cells
	(relative)	1.00	0.272	0.0059	

Our results for the L cell are not greatly different from those reported by Terasima and Tolmach (1963a, b) for synchronized populations of HeLa cells. They reported that the most resistant phases were G_2 and early G_1 and that the most sensitive phases were mitosis, late G_1 and early S. Studies of Erikson and Szybalski (1963) indicate that in a human cell line synchronized with 5-fluorodeoxyuridine, radioresistance increased between late G_1 and late S or G_2. In our autoradiographic studies, we were not able to distinguish early G_1 from late G_1, and early S from late S; and thus could not detect increased radiosensitivity in late G_1 or early S. However, our results indicate that the most resistant cells in S phase were more sensitive than the most resistant cells in G_1 phase.

Recovery of Sublethal Damage, as Determined by Colony Survival of L-P59 Cells Irradiated in Different Phases of the Cell Cycle

Cells growing on the surface of T-flasks were either singly labeled or doubly labeled, as indicated in Figure 3, and were irradiated at 37 C with 300 r of 250 kvp X rays. They were maintained at 37 C for various periods of time prior to receiving a second dose of 300 r. Then, the cells were immediately plated and colony survival was determined for both labeled and unlabeled cells. The longest time interval between the two doses was 12 hours; and as shown in Figure 4, there was very little cell division occurring during this interval. The percentage of the colonies labeled as a function of time between the two doses of irradiation is shown in Figure 5. In the single-labeling experiment, the percentage labeled increase from 6 per cent to about 8 per cent at 30 minutes and reached a plateau of 20 per cent at two to three hours. This increase in percentage of colonies labeled indicates that there was more recovery of sublethal damage in the labeled S cells than in the unlabeled G_1 and G_2 cells. This is consistent with the survival curve for the S cells, which has more of a shoulder than have the G_1 and G_2 cells (see Figure 6). In a preliminary double-labeling experiment, the percentage of cells labeled started at 12 per cent and increased to 25 per cent at 30 minutes.

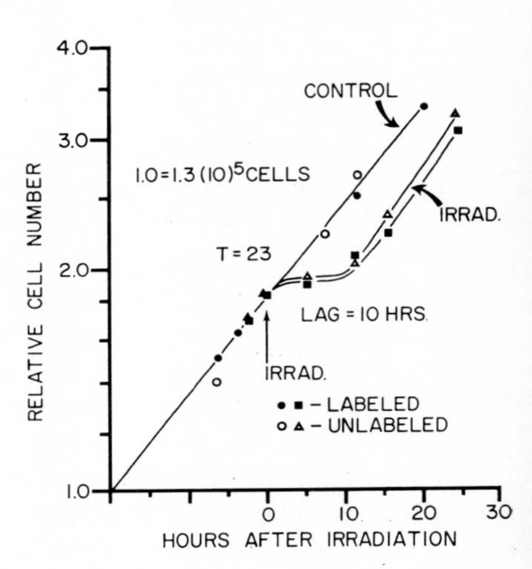

FIGURE 4. Increase in number of L-P59 cells after they received 300 r of 250 kvp X rays. The cells were counted repeatedly with the aid of a reticule in the same T-flasks. The doubling time in the controls was 23 hours, and a mitotic delay of 10 hours was observed. Two of the flasks were pulse-labeled with H^3TdR before irradiation, and two were unlabeled.

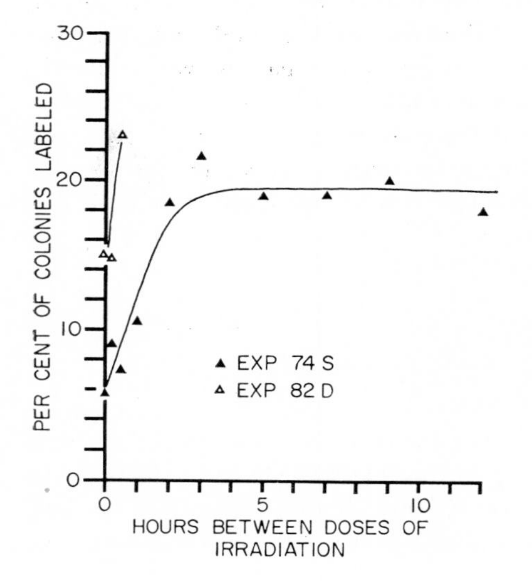

FIGURE 5. L-P59 cells were either singly labeled (experiment 74S) or doubly labeled (experiment 82D) with H^3TdR, as indicated in Figure 3, before they were irradiated with two 300 r doses of 250 kvp X rays. The per cent of the colonies labeled is indicated as a function of the time interval between the two doses.

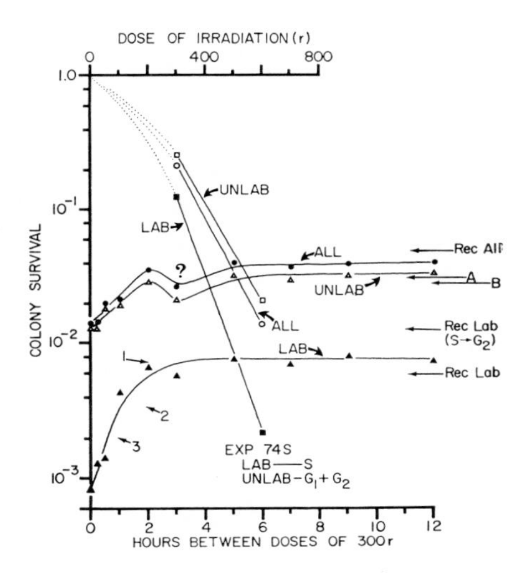

FIGURE 6. Survival and recovery of sublethal damage in L-P59 cells. The cells were irradiated with 250 kvp X rays immediately after they were singly labeled with H^3TdR, as indicated in Figure 3. The curves starting at a value of 1.0 indicate colony survival as a function of a single radiation dose. The survival is shown separately for the labeled and unlabeled populations of cells. The lower curves indicate colony survival as a function of the time interval between two equal doses of 300 r; note that the survival value for all the cells is equal to the sum of the labeled and unlabeled survival values. The arrows indicate survival values calculated, as described in the text, assuming recovery and progression of cells through the cycle.

The calculations for theoretical cell survival considering recovery are as follows:

S_A = survival following dose A

S_{2A} = survival following a single dose equal to 2 × dose A

Following two doses of dose A—

With recovery $S_R = S_A \times S_A$

For S, G_1 and G_2 cells—

S_R for G_1 cells = S_A for G_1 × relative S_A for G_1

If G_1 cells recovered in S Phase—

S_R for G_1 cells = S_A for G_1 × relative S_A for S cells

With no recovery $S_{NR} = S_{2A}$

If a certain fraction, f, of cells recover, $S = (1 - f)\ S_{2A} + f\ S_R$

For example, consider the values tabulated in Table 2 for experiments 74S and 82D.

(Fraction of control labeled = 0.37)

$S_{300} = 0.224$ (fraction labeled = 0.21)

$S_{600} = 0.014$ (fraction labeled = 0.058)

$S_R = 0.224 \times 0.224 = 0.0503$

$S_{NR} = 0.014$

S_A for S cells = 0.224 × 0.21 = 0.047

S_{2A} for S cells = 0.014 × 0.058 = 0.00081

Rel. S_A for S cells = 0.047/0.37 = 0.127

S_R for S cells = 0.047 × 0.127 = 0.006

S_{NR} for S cells = 0.00081

Suppose, for example, only one third of S cells recover. Then S_R for S cells = ⅔ (0.00081) + ⅓ (0.047) (0.127) = 0.0025

Suppose, for example, one third of S cells recover in G_2 and two thirds of S cells remain in the S phase with no recovery.

Rel. S_A for G_2 cells = 0.272 from experiments 74S and 82D

S_R for S cells = ⅔ (0.00081) + ⅓ (0.047) (0.272) = 0.0047

The survival results for the single-labeling experiment (74S) are indicated in Figure 6 in which recovery, as observed in all the cells without differentiating between labeled and unlabeled colonies, occurred in two to three hours and did not increase much thereafter. There was a questionable dip at about three hours. The observed survival of 0.04 following recovery very nearly approached the theoretical recovery of 0.05 (Rec all). Since 80 to 90 per cent of the colonies were unlabeled, the recovery observed primarily reflected recovery in unlabeled cells, e.g. cells in G_1 and G_2 phases at the time of irradiation. However, recovery also occurred in the labeled S cells and approached, within experimental error, the calculated recovery value (Rec lab). Again, it should be emphasized that cellular division did not occur during the recovery period.

The recovery observed for the unlabeled cells is difficult to interpret in terms of recovery in cells irradiated in G_1, as distinct from recovery in cells irradiated in G_2. Following the first dose of 300 r, 34 per cent of the unlabeled surviving cells were in G_2 and 66 per cent were in G_1 (calculated from Table 2). If all of the G_1 cells remained in the G_1 phase with no recovery while the G_2 cells recovered, the calculated survival would be 0.031 (Figure 6, arrow A). However, if all of the G_1 cells moved into the S phase, where they recovered, while the G_2 cells also recovered, the calculated survival would be 0.028 (Figure 6, arrow B). If the G_1 cells remained in the G_1 phase with no recovery in the G_2 cells, the survival would be between 0.013 and 0.034, depending on whether recovery occurred in the G_1 cells. The survival observed in unlabeled cells following maximum recovery was 0.033. Therefore, in this experiment it is not possible to distinguish between recovery in the G_1 and G_2 cells.

It is conceivable that the recovery observed in the labeled S cells did not occur in the S phase, but was related to the movement of the labeled S cells into the more radioresistant G_2 phase. If all the labeled cells moved into G_2 with recovery, the survival would be 0.013 (Rec lab., $S \rightarrow G_2$), greater than the observed maximum recovery of 0.0076. Calculations of survival for labeled cells were made assuming that the labeled cells moved from S into G_2 at a normal rate following irradiation, *i.e.*, 10 per cent of the labeled cells progress into G_2 at one hour and 22 per cent at two hours. The calculated survival values, assuming no recovery in S but complete recovery in G_2, are, as shown in Figure 6, 0.002 (arrow 3) and 0.0034 (arrow 2) for one and two hours respectively, which are less than the observed survival values. If the cells remaining in S also recovered, the survival value would be 0.0075 (arrow 1), slightly greater than that observed. However, our preliminary kinetic experiments (Dewey and Humphrey, Unpublished data) indicate that at six hours, only 29 per cent of the S cells had moved into G_2. The results of Mak and Till (1963) for the L cell irradiated with a comparable dose indicate a delay of three to four hours in moving from S into G_2. Therefore, recovery in labeled S cells occurred much more rapidly than would be predicted on the basis of movement from S into G_2, and it can be concluded that recovery occurred during the S phase.

Results for a double-labeling experiment (77D), in which both the S and G_2 cells were labeled, are shown in Figure 7. In this experiment, 53.4 per cent of the colonies in the controls were labeled as compared with 37 per cent in a single-labeling experiment (74D); therefore, unlabeled cells were definitely in the G_1 phase at the time of the first dose of irradiation. Complete recovery approximately equal to 0.033 calculated for G_1 cells (Rec G_1) occurred in these unlabeled G_1 cells over a period of two to three hours. Since it was shown (Figure 8) that the S phase is the most radiosensitive phase and the G_1 phase is the most radioresistant, the survival observed for the unlabeled G_1 cells would be expected to decrease as the G_1 cells moved into the S phase. If all of the G_1 cells moved into the S phase with complete recovery in either G_1 or S (Figure 7), the calculated survival for the unlabeled G_1 cells would be 0.016 (Rec $G_1 \rightarrow S$), much less than the value of 0.040 observed. If all of the G_1 cells recovered, but only one half moved into the S phase, the calculated survival would be 0.025 (Rec ½ $G_1 \rightarrow S$), a survival increment of 0.008 less than that calculated for all of the G_1 cells remaining in the G_1 phase (Rec G_1). A difference in survival of this magnitude (associated with sensitivity in S?) may be evident between five and eight hours. However, if one half of the G_1 cells remained in G_1 with no recovery, while the other half moved into S and recovered, the calculated survival would be only 0.014 (Rec ½ $G_1 \rightarrow S$, No Rec G_1). Since the survival observed for G_1 cells was 0.040, most of the G_1 cells must have remained in the G_1 phase where recovery occurred. Our preliminary kinetic experiments (Dewey and Humphrey, Unpublished data) and the results of Mak and Till (1963) indicate that at 10 hours after a dose of about 300 r (450 rads), about one half of the G_1 cells should have moved into the S phase. However, in this particular experiment (77D), the pH of the

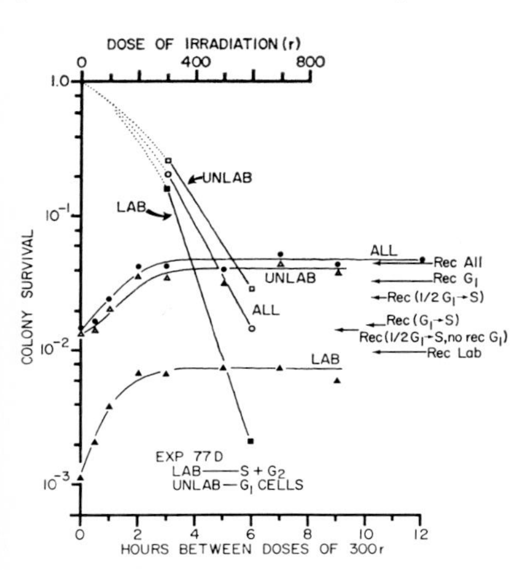

FIGURE 7. Survival and recovery of sublethal damage in L-P59 cells. The cells were irradiated with 250 kvp X rays immediately after they were doubly labeled with H^3TdR, as indicated in Figure 3. For further details see Figure 6.

medium had dropped into the acid range by seven to nine hours after irradiation; and it is possible that, as a result of this environmental change, less than one half of the G_1 cells moved into the S phase. Therefore, the results of the single-labeling experiment, 74S shown in Figure 6, were not compared with the results of the double-labeling experiment, 77D shown in Figure 7.

A preliminary double-labeling experiment (82D) appeared to be comparable to experiment 74S, and the results are compared in Figure 8, in which survival is shown separately for G_1, S, and G_2 cells. The survival for the S cells was taken from the data of experiment 74S in Figure 6. Data for G_1 and G_2 cells were available only over a 30-minute interval during which recovery appeared to occur in both the G_1 and G_2 cells. However, these data are too incomplete for definite conclusions. The theoretical recovery values of 0.033 (Rec G_1) and 0.015 (Rec G_2) are also indicated for G_1 and G_2 cells, respectively. If complete recovery occurred in G_2 cells, the survival for G_1 cells would have to increase to 0.019 (dotted line) in order to account for the observed value. It is also shown in Figure 8 (arrow b) that if 100 per cent of the G_1 cells moved into the S phase with complete recovery occurring in the S phase, the survival would decrease from 0.033 to 0.015. If one half of the G_1 cells moved into the S phase with complete recovery in both G_1 and S phases, the survival for G_1 cells would be 0.024 (arrow a); if one half moved into S with recovery while one half remained in G_1 with no recovery, the survival would be 0.013 (arrow c). Ideally, complete double- and single-labeling experiments should be conducted concurrently with an experiment studying the progression of the cells through the cell cycle, in order to choose between the alternatives proposed.

In summary, it appears that recovery of sublethal damage, as meas-

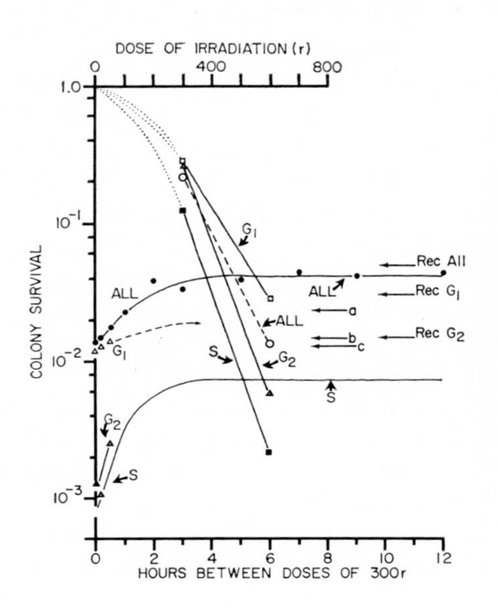

FIGURE 8. Survival and recovery of sublethal damage in L-P59 cells. The cells were irradiated with 250 kvp X rays immediately after they were either singly labeled (experiment 74S) or doubly labeled (experiment 82D) with H^3TdR, as indicated in Figure 3. In order to obtain the survival values for cells irradiated in the separate phases, G_1, S, and G_2, the results of the two experiments were compared as described in the text. The mean lethal doses were approximately 135 r for G_1 and 70 r for S. For further details see Figure 6.

ured by colony survival, occurred in both the G_1 and S phases during a period of two to three hours. However, as seen in Figure 7 and from the percentage of the colonies labeled in Figure 5, more recovery occurred in the S than in the G_1 phase. Sufficient data are not available to establish clearly recovery in the G_2 phase.

Studies with Chinese Hamster Cells In Vitro

Radiosensitivity in Different Phases of the Cell Cycle-Chromosome Analysis

Previous results indicated that in the hamster B-14 cells growing in vitro, the G_2 phase was more sensitive to ionizing radiation than the S phase, which was about equal in radiosensitivity to the G_1 phase (Hsu, Dewey, and Humphrey, 1962). Based on metaphase analysis, the G_2 phase was two to three times more radiosensitive than the S phase, whereas, based on anaphase analysis, the S phase was only about 1.2 times more radiosensitive. Differences between metaphase and anaphase analyses in Chinese hamster cells were also shown by Greenblatt (1961).

To differentiate more clearly between the radiosensitivities in the various phases of the cell cycle, CH-24 hamster cells were double-labeled, first with C^{14}TdR for 30 minutes and then with H^3TdR three hours later; the cells were irradiated with 600 rads of Co^{60} gamma rays immediately thereafter (Figure 9). One of the significant advantages of the double-labeling technique is the ability to distinguish clearly between cells irradiated in the G_1 phase and those irradiated in the G_2 phase. At the time of irradiation, cells in the G_2 phase were labeled only with C^{14}, whereas cells in the late and middle S phases were labeled with both C^{14} and H^3. The cells in early S phase were labeled only with H^3, and the G_1 cells were unlabeled. Samples were fixed at various time intervals following irradiation, and the metaphases were analyzed for chromosomal damage. By counting grains in the first and second layers of autoradiographic film, the phase in which the cell was located at the time of irradiation was determined (see Materials and Methods, above). The movement through mitosis of cells labeled with H^3 as a function of time after irradiation is indicated in Figure 10. This plot is similar to others reported previously (Hsu, Dewey, and Humphrey, 1962; Dewey and Humphrey, 1962) and is shown to indicate that it is possible to identify cells labeled with H^3 although they are also labeled with C^{14}. This cell line has a generation time of 15 hours with a G_1 phase of 6.2 hours, an S phase of 6.3 hours, and a G_2 phase of 2.5 hours. The 600 rad dose induced a mitotic delay of two to three hours. The movement through mitosis of cells in the different phases of the cell cycle at the time of irradiation is indicated in Figure 11. The cells labeled with C^{14} which divided at 14 to 16 hours probably consisted both of G_2 cells reaching division for the second time following irradiation, and of a few cells which moved into the G_1 phase before the radiation dose was delivered (See Figure 9). It is important to note that there was considerable mixing of the different populations; *i.e.*, many early S phase cells divided prior to many of the cells which were in the middle or late S phase. Even the unlabeled-G_1 cells started dividing before the middle S phase cells completed division.

The C^{14}-grain counts in the second layer (Figure 11) indicated that the first C^{14}-labeled cells to reach division had more grains than those dividing later. Normally the grain count is higher for cells labeled in middle S than for those labeled in early or late S phase (Humphrey, Dewey, and Cork, 1963; Terasima and Tolmach, 1963c). In the present experiment, the decrease in grain count was probably caused by labeling continuing for a period beyond the 30-minute pulse, since stable TdR was not added to the

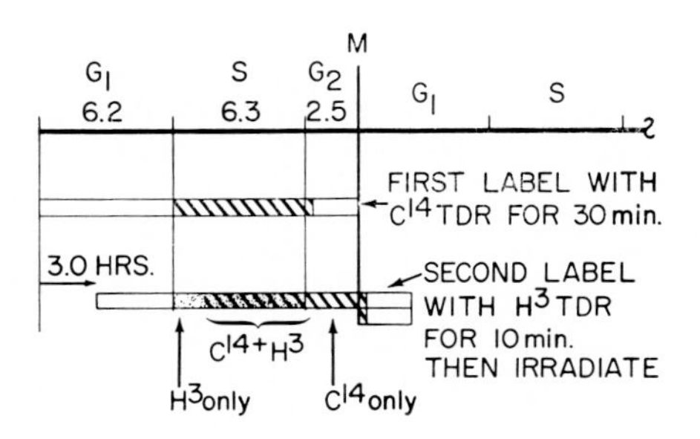

FIGURE 9. Position of CH-24 hamster cells in the cell cycle at the time of irradiation. The cells were labeled first with C^{14}TdR and three hours later with H^3TdR. Both labeled cells (H^3 only, C^{14} and H^3, and C^{14} only) and unlabeled cells (open bars) are indicated.

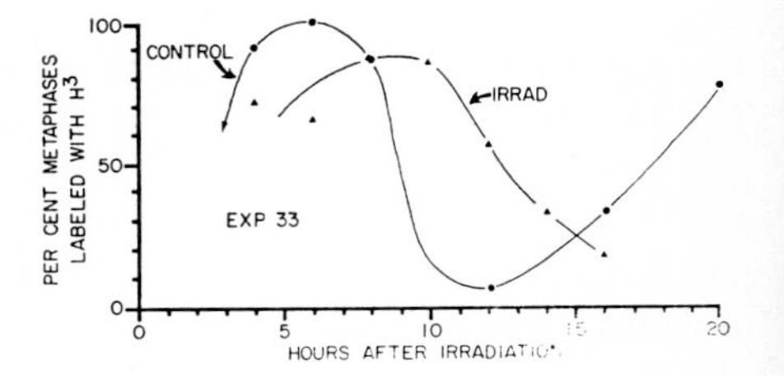

FIGURE 10. CH-24 hamster cells were irradiated with 600 rads of Co^{60} gamma rays immediately after double-labeling with C^{14}TdR and H^3TdR, as indicated in Figure 9. The per cent of metaphases labeled with H^3 (including those also labeled with C^{14}) is plotted as a function of time after H^3 labeling and irradiation.

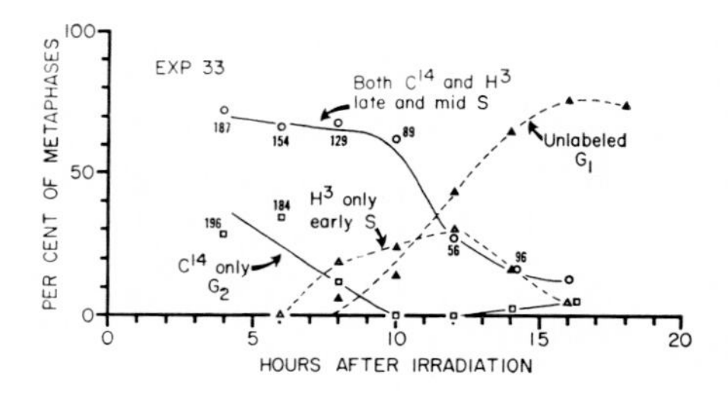

FIGURE 11. CH-24 hamster cells were irradiated with 600 rads of Co^{60} gamma rays immediately after double-labeling with C^{14}TdR and H^3TdR, as indicated in Figure 9. The per cent of metaphases which were in different phases of the cell cycle at the time of irradiation is indicated as a function of time after irradiation. To distinguish between C^{14} and H^3, the number of grains in each of two layers of film was determined (see text). The grain counts in the second layer (indicated by the numbers) decreased as the time after irradiation increased. Note that although the various populations were separated at the time of labeling, they became mixed after irradiation.

medium. Then, cells entering the S phase after pulse-labeling would be more lightly labeled. Therefore, the heavily labeled cells should have been in the G_2 and late S phases at the time of irradiation, and the lightly labeled cells should have been in the middle S phase.

Results of the chromosomal analysis at metaphase (Table 3) indicate, as reported previously (Hsu, Dewey, and Humphrey, 1962), that the G_2 cells had about 3.5 times more damage than the S-phase cells. Little difference in radiosensitivity was found between the G_1 and S phases as well as between the different parts of the S phase, although the early S phase may have been 10 to 20 per cent more sensitive than G_1 and late S. Also, it is important to note that both chromatid and chromosome (dicentric) exchanges were induced in the G_1 cells, and that chromosome exchanges were not induced in S and G_2 cells. This has been reported previously, and the implications involving chromosome structure have been discussed (Wolff, 1961; Dewey and Humphrey, 1964; Hsu, Dewey, and Humphrey, 1962; Humphrey, Dewey, and Cork, 1963). Essentially, our results are consistent with the hypothesis that the chromosome consists of two subunits which separate immediately as the cell enters the S phase.

TABLE 3

Chromosomal Aberrations in CH-24 Hamster Cells Irradiated with 600 Rads of Co^{60} Gamma Rays

Phase irradiated	No. of cells	No. of breaks	No. of chromatid exchanges	No. of chromosome exchanges	Total aberrations per cell	Per cent caused by exchanges	Per cent abnormal
G_2	29	38	32	00	3.5	62	93
Late and middle S	165	78	37	1	0.93	49	49
Early S	66	27	20	1	1.0	61	56
G_1	221	57	16	46	0.82	68	43
Late S cells > 126 grains/cell	74	44	11	0	0.89	33	. .
Middle S cells < 126 grains/cell	81	28	23	0	0.91	62	. .
Control	51	3	0	0	0.06	0	6

Radiosensitivity in Different Phases of the Hamster Cell Cycle-Colony Survival Analysis

It was reported (Dewey and Humphrey, 1963) that in the hamster cells the S and the G_1 phases had about the same radiosensitivity, as determined by colony survival. In addition, there was some evidence that the G_2 cells were more radiosensitive. These experiments have been extended in single-labeling and double-labeling experiments. In the single-labeling experiment, the labeled cells were in the S phase at the time of irradiation, whereas in the double-labeling experiment, the labeled cells were in both the S and G_2 phases (Figure 12).

The per cent of colonies labeled as a function of the dose of irradiation

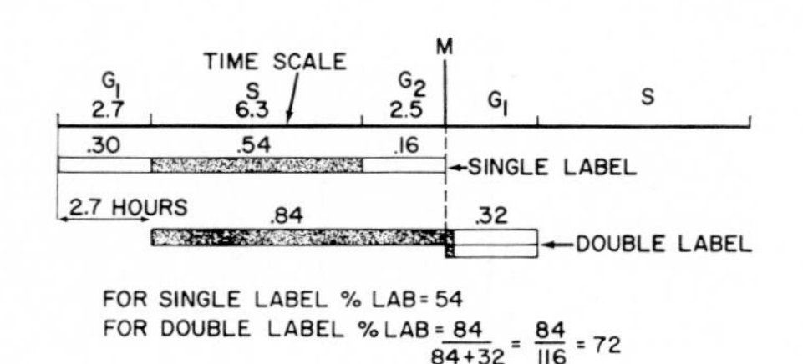

FIGURE 12. Position of B-14 hamster cells in the cell cycle at the time of the first dose of irradiation. The solid bar indicates cells labeled with H^3TdR, and the open bars indicate unlabeled cells. The length of each phase and the fraction of cells in the various phases are indicated; the values were determined considering logarithmic growth by the method of Edwards *et al.* (1960).

following a single labeling is indicated in Figure 13. For the controls, the percentage was 54; it increased to 65 per cent at a dose of 500 rads (survival $= 1.9\ (10)^{-1}$); and it decreased again to about 54 per cent at a dose of 800 to 1,200 rads (survival $= 10^{-2}$ to 10^{-3}). The difference between the percentage labeled for the controls and that for 500 rads is significant with $p = 0.005$. This rise in the percentage of colonies labeled indicates that some of the unlabeled cells were more radiosensitive and were being eliminated from the population of surviving cells. By comparing the results of the single-labeling experiment with those of the double-labeling experiment (Figure 14), it is possible to determine which group of unlabeled cells was the most radiosensitive. Although in the controls more of the colonies were labeled in the double-labeling experiment than in the single-labeling experiment (see also Figure 18), at doses of 350 and 700 r there was little difference between the single- and double-labeling experiments. Since the G_2 cells were unlabeled in the single-labeling experiments and were labeled in the double-labeling experiment, these results indicate that the G_2 cells were eliminated from the population of surviving cells as the radiation dose increased. Furthermore, the decrease in the percentage of colonies labeled at 800 rads compared to 500 rads (Figure 13) indicates that the S cells were slightly more radiosensitive than the G_1 cells. Survival calculations were made for cells in the separate phases (as in Table 2 for L cells), and the results (Table 4 and Figure 15) show that the G_2 cells were more radiosensitive than were the S and G_1 cells. The S cells were probably slightly more radiosensitive than the G_1 cells. With only one survival point for G_2 cells, it is not possible to ascertain if the greater G_2 radiosensitivity is related to a lower extrapolation number or to a lower mean lethal dose.

These results compare very well with those reported by Sinclair and Morton (1963a, b), who studied colony survival in synchronized Chinese hamster cells. Following a single dose of 750 r, the survival of the G_2 cells was a factor of three less than that of S cells. They reported that the differences in radiosensitivity were related more to changes in extrapolation number than to changes in the mean lethal dose.

Restitution of Radiation-Induced Chromosomal Damage in Different Phases of the Hamster Cell Cycle

It has been reported that in the B-14 cell line, restitution of chromo-

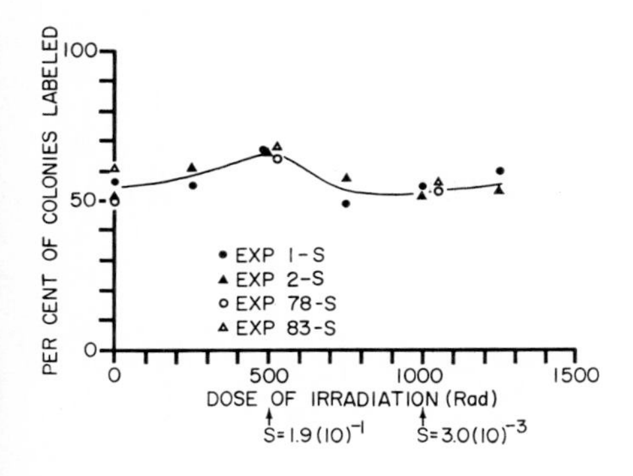

FIGURE 13. Per cent of B-14 colonies labeled with H^3TdR as a function of radiation dose (250 kvp X rays) and survival. The cells were singly labeled as indicated in Figure 12. The value at 500 rads is significantly different than the control value with $p = 0.005$.

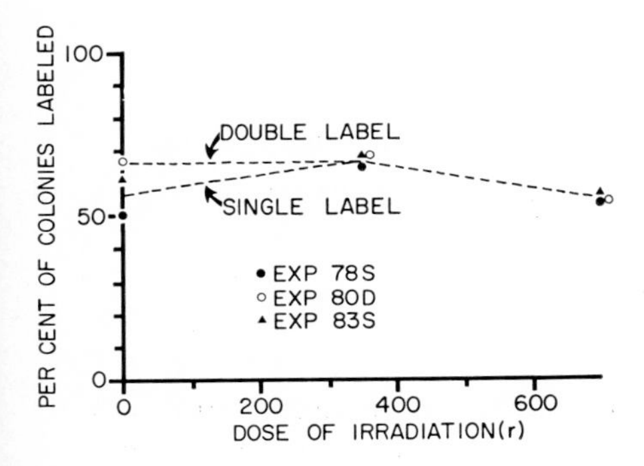

FIGURE 14. Per cent of B-14 colonies labeled with H^3TdR as a function of radiation dose (250 kvp X rays). The cells were either singly labeled (experiments 78S and 83S) or doubly labeled (experiment 80D), as indicated in Figure 12.

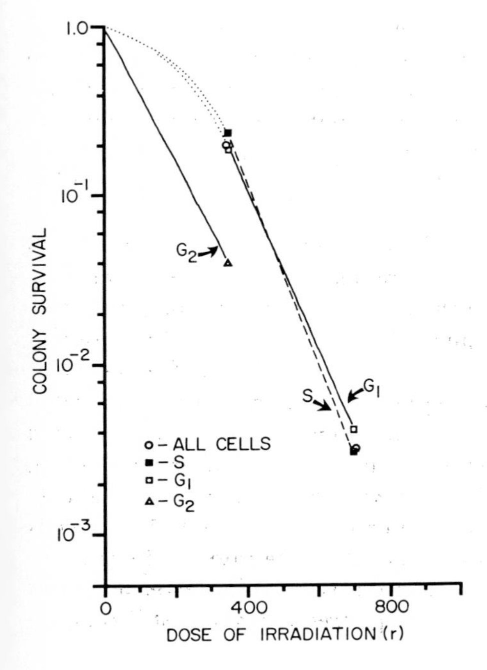

FIGURE 15. Survival of B-14 hamster cells. The cells were irradiated with 250 kvp X rays immediately after they were either singly labeled (experiments 78S and 83S) or doubly labeled (experiment 80D) with H^3TdR, as indicated in Figure 12. In order to obtain the survival values for cells irradiated in the separate phases of the cell cycle, the results of the single- and double-labeling experiments were compared as described in the text.

TABLE 4

Colony Survival of B-14 Hamster Cells Irradiated with 250 kvp X Rays (Cells Were Labeled with H^3TdR Before Irradiation. Single Label—Immediately Before. Double Label—Both Three Hours and Immediately Before.)

	DOSE (R)	0	350	700	
Single-labeling experiments 78S and 83S	Surv. all cells	1.00	0.201	0.0030	
	Fract. lab.	0.56	0.66	0.54	
	Fract. unlab.	0.44	0.34	0.46	
	Surv. of lab.	0.56	0.132	0.00162	S cells
	(relative)	1.00	0.236	0.0029	
	Surv. of unlab.	0.44	0.0684	0.00138	G_1+G_2 cells
	(relative)	1.00	0.155	0.00314	
Double-labeling experiment 80D	Fract. lab.	0.66	0.68	0.53	
	Fract. unlab.	0.34	0.32	0.47	
	Surv. of lab.	0.66	0.136	0.00159	$S+G_2$ cells
	(relative)	1.00	0.206	0.0024	
	Surv. of unlab.	0.34	0.0644	0.00141	G_1 cells
	(relative)	1.00	0.190	0.00415	
	Surv. of G_2	0.10	0.004	?	G_2 cells
	(relative)	1.00	0.04		

somal damage induced in cells in the G_1 phase occurred within 5 to 10 minutes, whereas little restitution in the S phase was demonstrated over a one-hour interval (Dewey and Humphrey, 1964). Results which are consistent with restitution occurring in the order of minutes in G_1 cells was reported by Brewen (1963). At this time, we can not explain the difference between S and G_1 on a biochemical basis. Taylor (1963b) reported that DNA synthesis seems to be involved in the formation of chromosomal exchanges, although this relationship admittedly is not clear (see also Wolff, pages 167 to 179, this volume). Wolff (1960b) reported that protein synthesis is necessary for restitution.

In our experiments, B-14 hamster cells were pulse-labeled with H^3TdR immediately before irradiation, and in autoradiographic studies it was possible to distinguish cells which were in the S phase at the time of irradiation from those cells which were in the G_1 phase. The restitution of chromosomal breaks following irradiation was observed by the change in frequency of chromosomal exchanges following two equal doses of irradiation separated by different time intervals. Additional experiments have been conducted in which the B-14 cells were sampled at 4.5 to 5.5 hours after irradiation, and the frequency of chromatid exchanges was observed in the unlabeled G_2 cells following fractionated doses. In one experiment (Table 5) the cells were irradiated at 37 C with Co^{60} gamma rays at a dose rate of 530 rads per minute. In the unlabeled G_2 cells, no restitution was evident over an interval of 30 to 60 minutes. However, the exchange frequency was still roughly proportional to the square of the dose, which implies an interaction between the events produced by the two doses. Brewen (1963), who studied chromosomal aberrations at metaphase in the corneal epithelium of the Chinese hamster, reported that restitution appeared to occur in the G_2 phase over an interval of one to two minutes. Therefore, our experiment was repeated with X rays at a dose rate of 3,000 r per minute, and the frequency of exchanges was determined for time intervals between the two doses varying from 2 to 30 minutes. Again no restitution was evident (Table 5). We could not demonstrate any reunion of breaks or restitution of chromosomal damage over a one-hour period in cells irradiated in the G_2 phase. Reports (Sax, 1939; Sax, King, and Luippold, 1955; Sax, 1961; Wolff and Luippold, 1955; Wolff, 1960b) indicate that in plants restitution may occur in the G_2 phase over an interval of 5 to 60 minutes, although Taylor (1963a) recently was unable to demonstrate any restitution in the G_2 phase of *Vicia faba* over a 30-minute interval. Obviously, exchanges do occur in cells irradiated in the G_2 phase, and our dose-squared results (Table 5) indicate an interaction between events separated by as long as one hour. Possibly, the reunion process itself occurs at the end of G_2 (prophase?); then, if the cells were irradiated while this reunion was occurring, restitution, as observed with fractionated doses, would be observed.

Further information was obtained on restitution occurring in the S and G_2 phases of the B-14 hamster cells by comparing the results of acute irradiation with those of chronic irradiation. In the chronic-irradiation experiment the cells were irradiated with Co^{60} gamma rays over a period of 10 hours, at which time they were fixed and the damage in the metaphase cells was scored. The aberration frequency was related to the 1.8 power of the dose (Dewey, Humphrey, and Jones, 1964), which implies interaction between increments of dose separated in time. For acute irradiation, the cells were irradiated at a dose rate of 518 rads per minute with either 250, 300,

TABLE 5

Restitution Experiments in G_2 Cells

	Co^{60} GAMMA RAYS, 530 RADS/MIN. UNLABELED CELLS SCORED AT 4.5 HOURS AFTER IRRADIATION.						
Dose (rads)	600	600	300 ↓ 30 min 300	300 ↓ 43 min 300	300 ↓ 60 min 300	300	300
Exchanges per cell	1.2	1.2	1.2	1.3	1.2	0.30	0.37
	X RAYS, 3,000 R/MIN. ALL CELLS SCORED AT 5.5 HOURS AFTER IRRADIATION.						
Dose (r)	500*	250 ↓ 2 min 250	250 ↓ 5 min 250	250 ↓ 30 min 250	250	250	Control
Exchanges per cell	1.63	1.40	1.56	1.65	0.38	0.35	0.08

* Although the conversion of roentgens to rads is not certain, the dose of 500 r equals aproximately 750 rads.

or 600 rads of Co^{60} gamma rays, and the cells were fixed either 4.5 or 10 hours after irradiation. In order to compare the acute and chronic exchange frequencies (Table 6), the acute values for S and G_2 were averaged; the S phase was weighted by two because it was twice as long as the G_2 phase. The average value for acute irradiation was 1.15 exchanges per cell, which was three times greater than that obtained for chronic irradiation occurring during the S and G_2 phases. The time for restitution can be estimated from Lea's (1956) G function which is equal to the exchange frequency for chronic irradiation divided by the exchange frequency for acute irradiation (when the dose is delivered in a time interval much shorter than the reunion time). At 600 rads, G was equal to 0.31, for which Lea has tabulated a value of 5.2 for the ratio of the radiation-time interval (10 hours) divided by the time for restitution. The mean time for restitution was therefore two hours (three to four hours for complete restitution), which applies to cells which were in the S and G_2 phases during the chronic-irradiation period.

TABLE 6

Reunion Time for Chromosomal Breaks Based on Comparison of Acute with Chronic Irradiation at 600 Rads of Co^{60} Gamma Rays. Acute—518 rads/min and Sampled 4.5 or 10.5 Hours Later. Chronic—1 rad/min Continuously over a 10-Hour Period.

	Acute			Chronic
Metaphases sampled	4.5 hr G_2	10 hr S	Avg.* G_2 and S	
Exchanges per cell	1.35	1.05	1.15	0.35

$$^{*}\ \text{Avg} = \frac{2\ (1.05) + (1.35)}{3} = 1.15$$

$$G = \frac{\text{Exchanges/cell for chronic}}{\text{Exchanges/cell for acute}} = 0.31$$

Reunion time (τ) = 2 hours

In summary, the restitution of chromosomal damage in the B-14 Chinese hamster cell line apparently occurs within five minutes when the cells are irradiated in the G_1 phase. In the combined S and G_2 phases, restitution appeared to occur with a mean time interval of two hours; however, with fractionated doses no restitution could be demonstrated over a one-hour period in the G_2 phase. Our restitution experiments, however, do not differentiate between a time interval during which breaks remain open and one during which damage responsible for the induction of chromosomal breaks is repaired.

Recovery of Sublethal Damage as Determined by Colony Survival for Hamster Cells Irradiated in Different Phases of the Cell Cycle

Experiments were conducted as described previously for mouse L cells in which survival was determined following single doses of 350 r and following two doses of 350 r separated by different time intervals. One major difference between the mouse cells and the hamster cells was seen in cell multiplication following irradiation. Although in the L cells there was no division for 10 hours following the first dose of irradiation, division commenced within one to three hours in the hamster cells (Figures 4, 16, and 17). Therefore, it is important to note that, in contrast to the L cells, division was occurring in the hamster cells during the time interval when recovery was being studied. The recovery pattern was not complicated by cellular multiplicity, *i.e.* two cells giving rise to the same colony (Elkind and Sutton, 1960), however, because the cells were counted and added to Petri dishes after the second dose of irradiation.

The cells were either singly or doubly labeled with H^3TdR, as shown in Figure 12. In the double-labeling experiments both the S and G_2 cells were labeled, while in the single-labeling experiments only the S cells were labeled (Figure 18). The division of labeled cells following irradiation was primarily responsible for the slight increase in the percentage of cells labeled as a function of time after irradiation.

The surviving colonies were identified by autoradiography as labeled or unlabeled; the percentage of colonies labeled as a function of the time interval between the two doses of 350 r is indicated in Figure 19. After a single dose of 350 r, 53 per cent of the colonies were labeled, and the per-

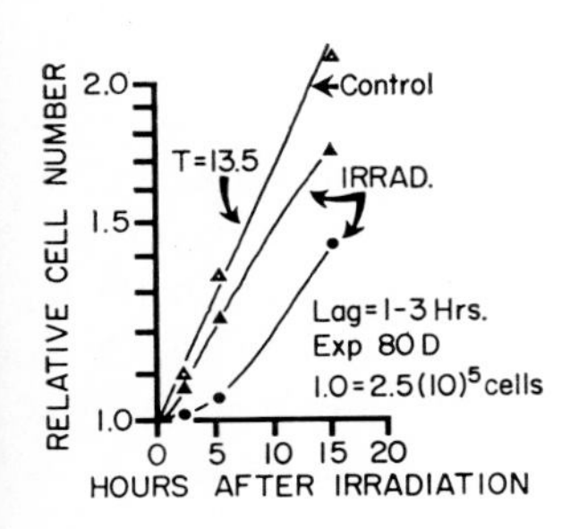

FIGURE 16. Increase in number of B-14 hamster cells after 350r of 250 kvp X rays. The cells were counted repeatedly with the aid of a reticule in the same T-flasks. The doubling time in the control was 13.5 hours, and a mitotic delay of one to three hours was observed.

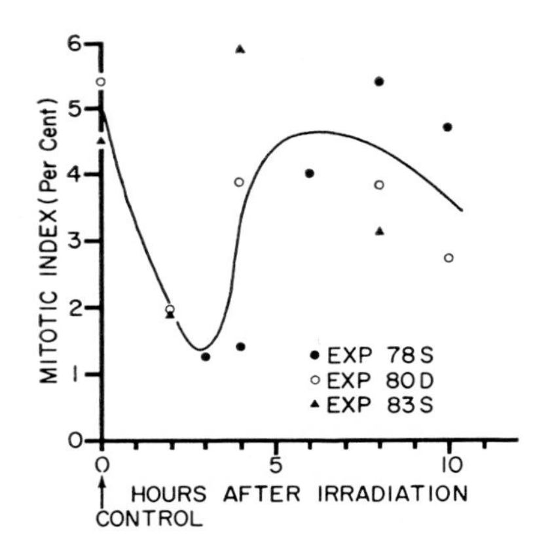

FIGURE 17. The mitotic index is indicated for B-14 hamster cells irradiated with 350 r of 250 kvp X rays.

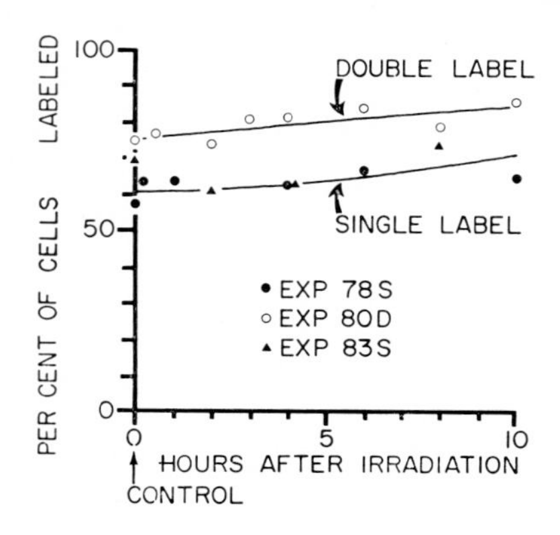

FIGURE 18. Per cent of B-14 hamster cells labeled with H^3TdR at various time intervals after irradiation with 350 r of 250 kvp X rays. The cells were either singly labeled (experiments 78S and 83S) or doubly labeled (experiment 80D), as indicated in Figure 12.

centage increased rapidly to 75 to 80 per cent when the two doses were separated by 30 minutes to one hour. The percentage decreased to about 50 per cent for a six-hour interval and again rose slowly between six and 10 hours; this second rise can be accounted for largely on the basis of the rise in percentage of cells labeled, as shown in Figure 18. In the double-labeling experiment the number of colonies labeled was no greater than in the single-labeling experiments, which would indicate that the G_2 phase was the most radiosensitive. The dip in the percentage of colonies labeled in the double-labeling experiment occurred earlier than in the single-labeling experiments; this may have been related to differences in the progression of the cells through the cell cycle (discussed below).

The survival of the labeled and unlabeled cells was calculated as described previously for L cells. In a single-labeling experiment (Figure 20) maximum recovery occurred in the cells, without distinguishing between labeled and unlabeled cells, at about two hours; then survival decreased to a minimum at four to six hours. The maximum recovery approached that

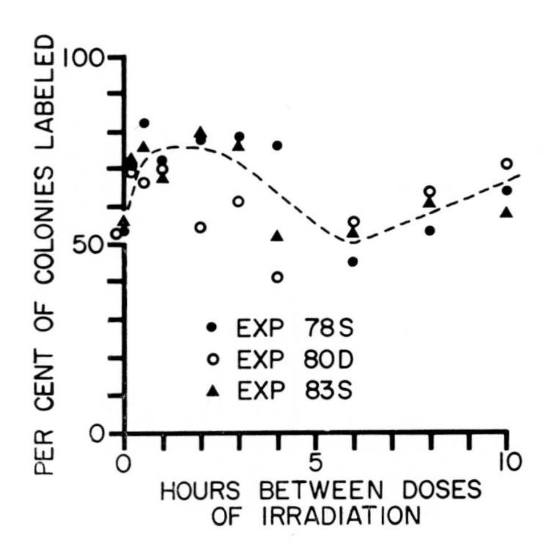

FIGURE 19. B-14 hamster cells were either singly labeled (experiments 78S and 83S) or doubly labeled (experiment 80D) with H^3TdR, as indicated in Figure 12, before they were irradiated with two 350 r doses of 250 kvp X rays. The per cent of the colonies labeled is indicated as a function of the time interval between the two doses. The initial increase in the per cent labeled signifies more recovery of sublethal damage in the labeled S cells than in the unlabeled G_1 cells.

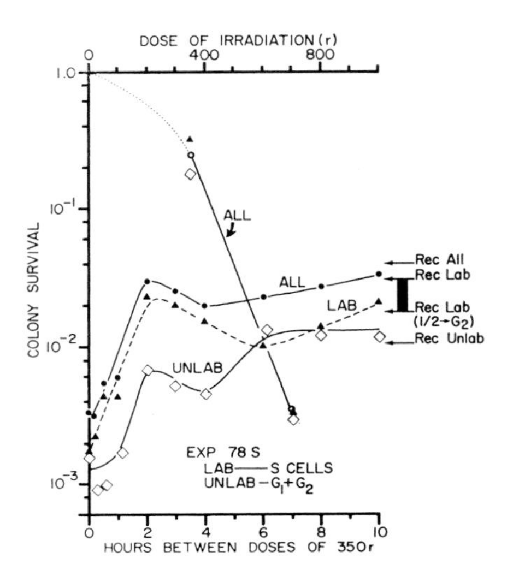

FIGURE 20. Survival and recovery of sublethal damage in B-14 hamster cells. The cells were irradiated with 250 kvp X rays immediately after they were singly labeled with H^3TdR as indicated in Figure 12. The curves starting at a value of 1.0 indicate colony survival as a function of a single radiation dose. The survival is shown separately for the labeled (solid triangles) and unlabeled (open diamonds) populations of cells. The lower curves indicate colony survival as a function of the time interval between two equal doses of 350 r; note that the survival value for all the cells is equal to the sum of the labeled and unlabeled survival values. The arrows indicate survival values calculated, as described in the text, assuming recovery and progression of cells through the cycle.

calculated for complete recovery (Rec all). In the labeled cells, which were in the S phase at the time of irradiation, recovery occurred very rapidly, reaching a peak at two to three hours; it decreased to a minimum at six hours and increased again to the maximum at about 10 hours. The survival approached but did not reach that calculated for complete recovery (Rec lab). In the unlabeled cells, there was continual recovery with a possible dip in survival at four hours; and a plateau of complete recovery was reached at six to 10 hours. Since only 5 per cent of the unlabeled cells surviving the first dose of 350 r were in the G_2 phase (calculated from data in Table 4), this unlabeled curve reflects recovery in cells irradiated in the G_1 phase.

Although detailed kinetic studies were not made of the progression of the cells through the cell cycle, there was almost a normal rate of division between 3 and 12 hours postirradiation (Figures 16 and 17). As shown by Elkind, Han, and Volz (1963), this would apply to both surviving and nonsurviving cells. Therefore, the labeled cells, which were in the S phase at the time of the first radiation dose, must have been moving into the relatively radiosensitive G_2 phase within two to three hours following irradiation. If survival is calculated on the basis of complete recovery and with one half of the labeled S cells moving into the G_2 phase ($\frac{1}{2}$ S → G_2), the dip in survival for labeled cells would be equal to an increment in survival of 0.013 which corresponds to the dip actually observed (Figure 20). Therefore, it is proposed that the minimum in survival observed for the labeled cells was caused by repair of sublethal damage in S phase followed by the movement of the labeled cells into the more radiosensitive G_2 phase. It is further postulated that the survival of labeled cells increased again at 10 hours as the labeled cells moved into the more radioresistant G_1 and S phases; the 10 per cent increase in percentage of cells labeled, as shown Figure 18, would not account for the observed 2.1-fold increase in surviv (correcting gives a 1.9-fold increase in relative survival).

It is possible that the recovery which was observed in the unlabel G_1 cells did not occur while the cells were in the G_1 phase, but only as th moved into the S phase. From the data in Figure 19 in which is shown increase in the percentage of colonies labeled from 53 to 75 during an int val of 30 minutes to 1 hour between doses, it is clear that there was mo recovery of sublethal damage in the S phase than in the G_1 phase. Furthe more, the S phase has about the same radiosensitivity as the G_1 pha (Figure 15), so that it is not possible to establish that recovery actual occurred while the unlabeled cells were in the G_1 phase.

In another single-labeling experiment (Figure 21), a dip in surviv was observed in both labeled and unlabeled cells. A double-labeling expe ment in which both S and G_2 cells were labeled (Figure 22) resulted in t dip in survival in the labeled cells, but none was evident in the unlabel G_1 cells.

The postulated cell kinetics following a single dose of irradiation the hamster cells are shown in Figure 23. It is postulated that, during t first three hours after irradiation, little movement of cells through the cy occurs. During this three-hour interval, recovery would occur in the label and unlabeled cells in the S and G_1 phases, respectively. Three hours la (6.5 hours after irradiation), the unlabeled G_1 cells would enter the S pha while the labeled S cells would enter the G_2 phase at the time of the seco radiation dose, thus causing the survival for the labeled cells to decrea At 9.5 hours after the first radiation dose, the labeled cells would be leavi the G_2 phase, and as they arrived in G_1 and S, survival following the s

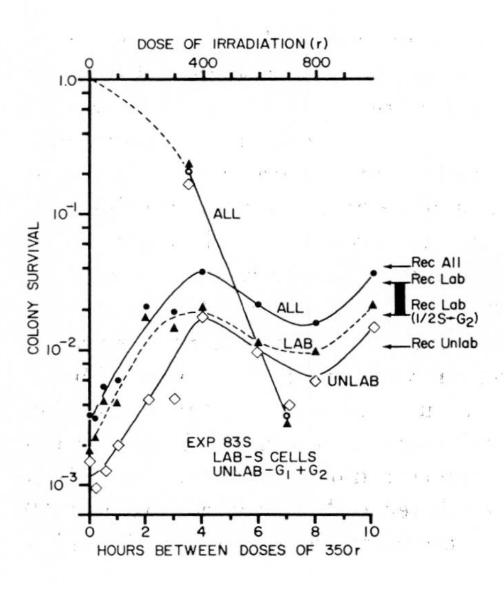

FIGURE 21. Survival and recovery of s lethal damage in B-14 hamster cells. other experiment was done as descri for Figure 20.

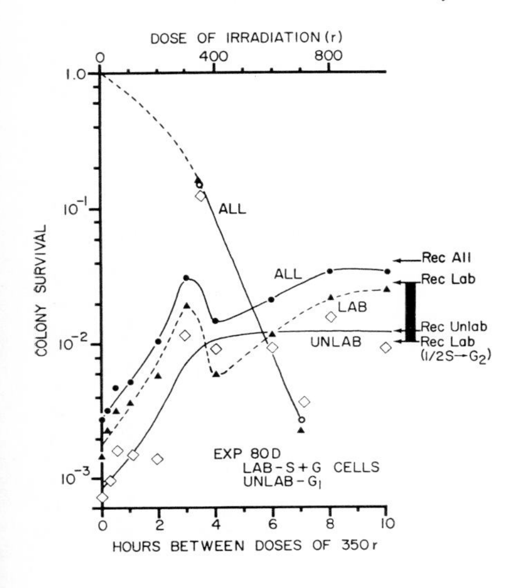

FIGURE 22. Survival and recovery of sublethal damage in B-14 hamster cells. Another experiment was done as described for Figure 20, except that the cells were doubly labeled with H^3TdR as indicated in Figure 12.

ond radiation dose would increase for the labeled cells. Nine to 10 hours following irradiation, the unlabeled G_1 cells would move into the G_2 phase, and a dip in the survival for the unlabeled cells should be seen. In one experiment (Figure 21) a dip in survival for the unlabeled G_1 cells was seen at about six hours; this could occur if the kinetics were as shown in Figure 24, in which it is postulated that the G_1 cells overtake the S cells. There is

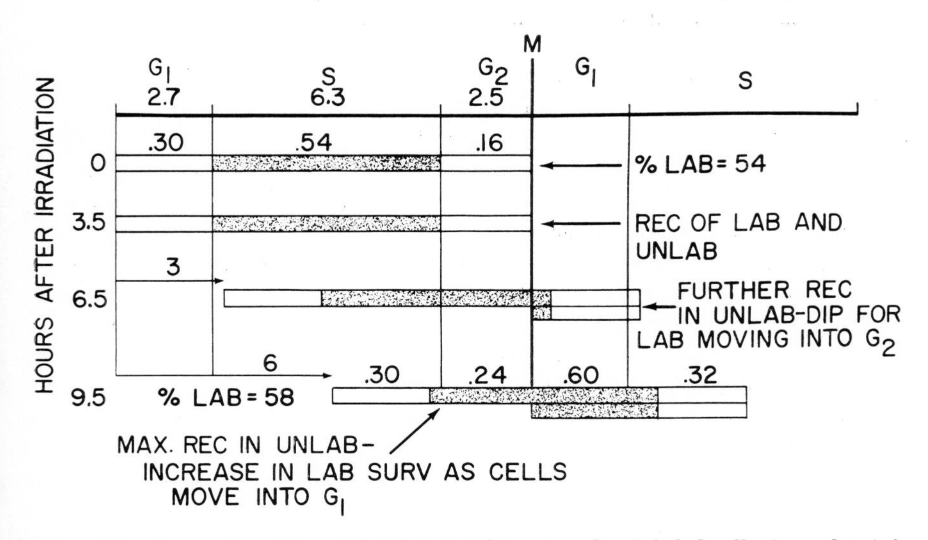

FIGURE 23. Assumed position of labeled (solid bars) and unlabeled cells (open bars) in the B-14 hamster cell cycle at various time intervals following the first dose of irradiation. It is assumed that cells in all three phases are delayed by three hours following irradiation. As explained in the text, the progression of labeled cells into the radiosensitive G_2 phase coincides with the minimum in survival shown in Figures 20, 21, and 22.

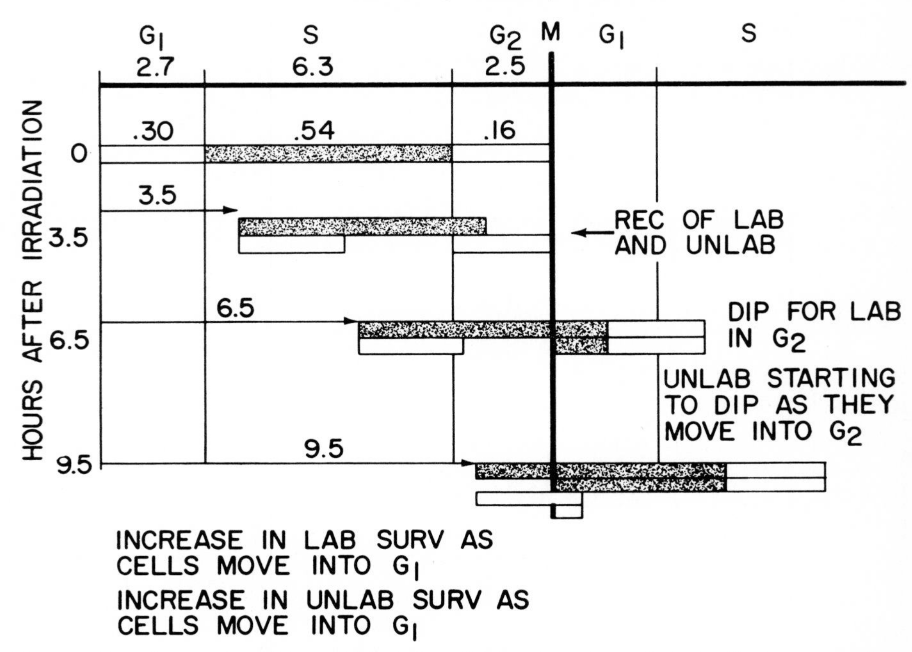

FIGURE 24. Assumed position of labeled (solid bars) and unlabeled cells (open bars) in the B-14 hamster cell cycle at various time intervals following the first dose of irradiation. It is assumed that cells in S phase are delayed about 2.5 hours following irradiation while cells in G_1 sustain no delay. As explained in the text, the progression of labeled and unlabeled cells into the radiosensitive G_2 phase roughly coincides with the minimum in survival of labeled and unlabeled cells shown in Figure 21.

some evidence that this may occur (Dewey and Humphrey, 1962; Mak and Till, 1963). In this case, survival in the unlabeled cells should begin to decrease at about six hours. To understand thoroughly the nature of the recovery survival curves, detailed kinetic studies of the progression of the cells through the cycle following irradiation should be conducted simultaneously with the colony-survival experiments.

The recovery curves shown in Figures 20, 21, and 22 are very similar to those reported by Elkind and Sutton (1960) for Chinese hamster cells with a generation time of 11 hours. After a dose of 500 rads, maximum recovery occurred at two to three hours, followed by a minimum at five to six hours. Elkind, Sutton, and Moses (1961) indicated that division commenced at about six to eight hours following the first dose of irradiation, although subsequent work (Elkind, Han, and Volz, 1963) would indicate that a mitotic delay of about five hours was obtained. Therefore, it is believed that their survival minimum can also be explained by movement of cells into the radiosensitive G_2 phase, followed by division and subsequent progression into the G_1 and S phases. When Elkind and Alescio (1963) allowed recovery to occur at room temperature, the dip in survival was eliminated, probably because the cells failed to move into the G_2 phase.

In summary, complete recovery as measured by colony survival occurred during the S phase within two hours. Recovery occurred somewhat slower in cells which were irradiateed in the G_1 phase, but it is possible that recovery occurred only as the G_1 cells entered the S phase. Recovery in the G_2 phase could not be studied in our autoradiographic experiments because the first dose of irradiation eliminated practically all of the G_2 cells. However, the apparent decrease in recovery observed following complete recovery was attributed to cells moving into the radiosensitive G_2 phase.

Cyclic Behavior of Recovery of Sublethal Damage

Reports indicate that recovery of radiation-induced sublethal damage is often followed by an apparent decrease in recovery, after which complete recovery is again observed. Examples of this for hamster cells (Elkind and Sutton, 1960) (Figures 20, 21, and 22) have been discussed. In addition, Berry and Oliver (1964), studying colony survival in vitro with HeLa cells following fractionated doses, observed a peak in survival (relative value of 1.5) with a two-hour interval between doses, followed by a dip in survival (relative value of 1.0) with a five- to seven-hour interval. With an 18-hour interval, survival again increased to the value of 1.5. Lockart, Elkind, and Moses (1961) obtained a maximum at two to three hours with HeLa cells in vitro, and a possible minimum at about five hours. Till and McCulloch (1963) observed a similar phenomenon in vivo with the formation of colonies in the spleen from irradiated mouse bone-marrow cells; the survival maximum of 2.0 occurred at five hours, the dip of 1.0 at 11 hours, and the return to 2.0 at 20 to 25 hours. Hornsey and Silini (1962), with Ehrlich ascites tumor cells in vivo, obtained a maximum in survival at five to seven hours, but they did not extend their studies beyond this time interval. Hall and Lajtha (1963), working with *Vicia faba* meristem cells, observed a maximum at five to six hours and a minimum at about 10 hours. Apparently the cyclic nature of the recovery-survival curve is quite general. It is postulated that the initial recovery is caused by repair of sublethal damage in surviving cells which are in a radioresistant phase of the cell cycle at the time of irradiation. As these cells move into a more radiosensitive phase at the time of the second dose of irradiation, recovery appears to decrease. Later, when they move into another radioresistant phase, recovery appears to increase again. This possibility was mentioned in previous papers (Elkind, Sutton, and Moses, 1961; Dewey and Humphrey, 1962) and was discussed at length by Kallman (1963). However, from our studies we conclude that these phases are not the same for all cell types. For cells behaving as did our L cells, the cells in the radioresistant G_1 phase would move into the sensitive S phase followed by movement into the resistant G_2 phase. For cells behaving as did our hamster cells, the cells in the radioresistant S phase would move into the sensitive G_2 phase followed by division and movement into the resistant G_1 and S phases.

Correlation Between Cell Killing and Chromosomal Damage

One purpose in the present studies has been to study the relationship between cell killing and chromosomal damage. Recently Till (1963) reviewed the evidence supporting the hypothesis that the principal target for cell killing lies in the chromosomes. In addition, Berry (1963) reported that, in leukemia cells irradiated under either oxygen or nitrogen, the extrapolation number for tetraploid cells was twice that for diploid cells, although the mean lethal doses were the same. Similar results were reported by Silini and Hornsey (1962). The increase in extrapolation number with increase in ploidy strongly supports the chromosomal target theory, and the failure of others (Till, 1961) to find this relationship may have been caused by complications relating to heteroploidy. Hall and Lajtha (1963) reported that the time interval required for recovery of radiation-induced sublethal damage in *Vicia faba* agreed well with the mean reunion-time interval of one hour observed for restitution of chromosomal breaks. In general, the results of our present studies implicate the chromosomes as a vital target in cell killing, although certain complications are evident.

Our results for the L cells (Table 7) indicate that 25 and 50 per cent of the cells in G_1 and S, respectively, lost their reproductive integrity after a dose of 250 rads; this agrees well with the finding of chromosomal damage at anaphase in 29 and 54 per cent of the cells in G_1 and S, respectively. Also, for chromosomal damage observed at anaphase and for cell killing, the S phase was 1.5 to 2.0 times more radiosensitive than was the G_1 phase; and the G_2 phase was intermediate in sensitivity (see also Figure 8). However, for chromosomal damage observed at metaphase, the G_2 phase was 1.1 to 2.0 times more radiosensitive than was the S phase (Tables 1 and 7). Therefore, except for the metaphase data, there is good correlation between

TABLE 7

Summary for Mouse L Cells in Vitro

GENERAL DESCRIPTION				
		G_1	S	G_2
Generation time = 22 hours ~ 64 chromosomes hypotetraploid		9.1 hours	9.9 hours	3.0 hours
PHASE RADIOSENSITIVITY				
		G_1	S	G_2
Per cent of cells abnormal at metaphase*	250 rads	. .	34	38
Per cent of cells abnormal at anaphase*	250 rads	29	54	39
Per cent of cells failing to form colonies	250 rads	25	50	. .
	450 rads	71	88	74
RECOVERY OF RADIATION DAMAGE				
		G_1	S	G_2
Time to approach complete recovery measured by colony survival		2–3 hours	2–3 hours	unknown

* Control per cent of 12 for metaphases and 26 for anaphases was subtracted.

chromosomal damage and cell killing.

The results for the hamster cells (Table 8) indicate that for doses of 250 and 600 rads, there is fair agreement between the percentage of cells which failed to form colonies and the percentage of cells which were abnormal as observed at metaphase. Also, for chromosomal damage observed at metaphase and for cell killing, the G_2 phase was about three times more radiosensitive than was the S phase, which had about the same sensitivity as the G_1 phase (see also Figure 15 and Table 3). For chromosomal damage observed at anaphase, however, the G_2 phase was only about 1.2 times more radiosensitive than the S phase. Restitution of sublethal damage was not studied in the G_2 phase, but for chromosomal damage observed at metaphase and for colony survival, significant restitution occurred in the S phase during a two-hour interval. In the G_1 phase, however, a discrepancy has been noted between cell killing and chromosomal damage; the restitution of chromosomal damage occurred within five to 10 minutes, whereas no recovery in sublethal damage was observed during this short interval. In fact, recovery of sublethal damage occurred more rapidly in the S phase than in the G_1 phase (Figure 19). Therefore, except for restitution data in the G_1 phase, there is good correlation between chromosomal damage and cell killing.

TABLE 8

Summary for Chinese Hamster Cells in Vitro

		G_1	S	G_2
General Description				
Generation time = 11.5 hours 22–23 chromosomes diploid		2.7 hours	6.3 hours	2.5 hours
Phase Radiosensitivity				
Per cent of cells abnormal at metaphase*	250 rads	41	29	76
	600 rads**	74	78	..
Per cent of cells abnormal at anaphase*	250 rads	30	40	48
Per cent of cells failing to form colonies	250 rads	30	30	72
	600 rads	88	88	97
Restitution and Recovery of Radiation Damage				
Reunion time based on frequency of exchanges at metaphase				
Determined with two radiation doses		5–10 minutes**	>1 hour**	>1 hour
Determined by comparing acute with chronic radiation		..	2 hours	
Time to approach complete recovery measured by colony survival		not 10 minutes 2–3 hours ?	2–3 hours	unknown

* Control per cent of 4 for metaphases and 40 for anaphases was subtracted; the large number of abnormal anaphases was probably caused by inclusion of polyploid cells which have a high incidence of dicentrics. (Hsu, Dewey, and Humphrey, 1962).

** From Dewey and Humphrey, 1964.

Our results, as well as those of Greenblatt (1961) and Davies (1963), indicate that the relationship between cell killing and chromosomal damage is not entirely clear. In the L cells, the radiosensitivity for cell lethality was greatest in the S phase and correlated well with the anaphase data; whereas in the hamster cells, the radiosensitivity for cell lethality was greatest in the G_2 phase and correlated well with the metaphase data. As illustrated by Thoday (1951), one half of the asymmetrical chromatid exchanges (the centromere on one chromosome is joined to the centromere on another chromosome) produce a bridge and a fragment at anaphase, and the other half form only one fragment; whereas none of the symmetrical exchanges (centromeres not joined) produce either a bridge or a fragment at anaphase. At metaphase both types of chromatid exchanges can be observed; therefore more of the exchanges should have been detected at metaphase than at anaphase. However, it is probable that many isochromatid breaks which were detected at anaphase were not detected at metaphase. As illustrated in Tables 1, 7, and 8, the main difference between metaphase and anaphase analyses of both mouse L cells and hamster cells was in the amount of damage in the S phase, which was less in the metaphase analysis. These results are relatively consistent with the data of Greenblatt (1962) for a Chinese hamster cell line. At six hours following irradiation (G_2 cells?), Greenblatt found more abnormal metaphases, including many isochromatid deletions, than abnormal anaphases; at 12 hours (S cells?) there was little difference between the anaphase and metaphase analyses. Thus, our differences could be caused by cells in the S phase sustaining more isochromatid breaks and a higher ratio of asymmetrical to symmetrical exchanges than cells in the G_2 phase. One can only speculate as to how such differences in types of breaks and exchanges might affect survival of the hypotetraploid L cell, which may have some duplication of genetic material in its 64 chromosomes, in contrast to survival of the diploid hamster cell, which has only 22 chromosomes and probably less duplication of genetic material.

It is possible that the differences in radiosensitivity observed between the mouse L cells and the hamster cells are related more to biochemical factors than to chromosomal differences. Casperson and Révész (1963) reported that a radioresistant cell line had a higher concentration of sulfhydryl compounds than a radiosensitive cell line; similar differences might occur during the cell cycle. Also, Konrad (1963) found that hamster cells had a higher rate of protein synthesis during prophase than did a human cell line.

Summary

Variations in sensitivity to ionizing radiation during the cell cycle were studied in vitro by autoradiographic techniques. Regarding cell lethality and chromosomal damage observed at anaphase in a mouse L fibroblast cell, the S phase was the most radiosensitive, the G_1 the most radioresistant, and the G_2 was intermediate in sensitivity. For chromosomal damage observed at metaphase, however, the G_2 phase was more radiosensitive than the S phase. For cell lethality and for chromosomal damage observed either at anaphase or metaphase in a Chinese hamster cell, the G_2 phase was more radiosensitive than the S phase, which had about the same sensitivity as the G_1 phase. Also, for chromosomal damage in the hamster cell, no difference in radiosensitivity could be detected between the early and late S phases.

Restitution of radiation damage during the cell cycle was also studied. Restitution of sublethal damage in the mouse L cell occurred over a period of two to three hours in both the S and G_1 phases. Insufficient data were available to demonstrate clearly recovery in the G_2 phase. In the Chinese hamster cells, both the restitution of chromosomal damage and the repair of sublethal damage occurred during S phase over a two- to three-hour interval. Although the repair of sublethal damage was not studied during the G_2 phase, no restitution of chromosomal damage could be demonstrated over a one-hour interval during the G_2 phase. During the G_1 phase the reunion of chromosomal breaks appeared to occur over a five- to ten-minute interval, but no repair of sublethal damage could be demonstrated during this interval.

The cyclic nature of recovery curves for sublethal damage, which increase to a maximum and then decrease to a minimum, was explained on the basis of surviving cells progressing through the cell cycle into a more radiosensitive phase. This radiosensitive phase may be either S or G_2, e.g. S for mouse L cells and G_2 for Chinese hamster cells.

ACKNOWLEDGMENTS

This work was supported in part by Grants CA-04484 and CA-06294 from the National Institutes of Health.

We greatly appreciate the assistance offered by Miss Ann Cork and Miss Beverly Ann Jones in conducting the experiments and preparing the manuscript.

ADDENDUM

It is possible that the discrepancy between the anaphase and metaphase data is related, to a certain extent at least, to rupture of the bridges before they are detected at anaphase (Conger, 1964). If this is true, our results would imply that bridges produced during the G_2 phase rupture more readily than do bridges produced during the S phase.

Experiments conducted subsequent to the work reported in this symposium indicate that in terms of cell lethality in the B-14 Chinese Hamster cells, the G_1 phase may be slightly more radiosensitive than the S phase (no difference in survival at 250 rads, but a factor of 5 at a dose of 750 rads). In our recent experiments, cells were synchronized with the H^3TdR suicide (window) technique described by Whitmore (see pages 423 to 441, this volume). The difference between the results obtained by the autoradiographic technique and those by H^3TdR window technique may be caused by increased sensitivity in early G_1, which would not be detected by the autoradiographic technique. These new results would not affect to any appreciable extent the basic conclusions reached concerning the cyclic nature of recovery curves.

REFERENCES

Berry, R. J. 1963. Quantitative Studies of Relationships between Tumor Cell Ploidy and Dose Response to Ionizing Radiation *in vivo*. Modification of Radiation Response in a Previously Irradiated Tumor. *Radiation Research*, 18:236–245.

Berry, R. J., and R. Oliver. 1964. Effect of Postirradiation Incubation Conditions on Recovery Between Fractionated Doses of X-Rays. *Nature*, London, 201:94–96.

Brewen, J. G. 1963. Dependence of Frequency of X-Ray-Induced Chromosome Aberrations on Dose Rate in the Chinese Hamster. *Proceedings of the National Academy of Sciences of the U.S.A.*, 50:322–329.

Carlson, J. G. 1954. "Immediate Effects on Division, Morphology, and Viability of the Cell," *Radiation Biology*, A. Hollaender, Ed. New York, New York: McGraw-Hill Book Company. Vol. I, Part 2. Pp. 763–824.

Casperson, D., and L. Révész. 1963. Cytochemical Measurement of Protein Sulphydryls in Cell Lines of Different Radiosensitivity. *Nature*, London, 199:153–155.

Conger, A. D. 1964. The Fate of Metaphase Aberrations. (Abstract) *Radiation Research*, 22:179.

Das, N. K., and M. Alfert. 1962. Sensitivity of Interphase Cells to Chromosome Breakage by X-Rays. *Nature*, London, 195:302–304.

Davies, D. R. 1963. Radiation-Induced Chromosome Aberrations and Loss of Reproductive Integrity in *Tradescantia*. *Radiation Research*, 20:726–740.

Dawson, K. B., E. O. Field, and G. W. W. Stevens. 1962. Differential Autoradiography of Tritium and Another β-Emitter by a Double Stripping Film Technique. *Nature*, London, 195:510.

Dewey, W. C., and R. M. Humphrey. 1962. Relative Radiosensitivity of Different Phases in the Life Cycle of L-P59 Mouse Fibroblasts and Ascites Tumor Cells. *Radiation Research*, 16:503–530.

———. 1963. Survival of Mammalian Cells Irradiated in Different Phases of the Life-Cycle as Examined by Autoradiography. *Nature*, London, 198:1063–1066.

———. 1964. Restitution of Radiation Induced Chromosomal Damage in Chinese Hamster Cells Related to the Cell's Life Cycle. *Experimental Cell Research*, 35:262–276.

———. Unpublished data.

Dewey, W. C., R. M. Humphrey, and B. A. Jones. 1964. Comparisons of Tritiated Thymidine, Tritiated Water, and Cobalt-60 Gamma Rays in Inducing Chromosomal Aberrations. *Radiation Research*. (in press.)

Edwards, J. L., A. L. Koch, P. Youcis, H. L. Freese, M. B. Laite, and J. T. Donalson. 1960. Some Characteristics of DNA Synthesis and the Mitotic Cycle in Ehrlich Ascites Tumor Cells. *Journal of Biophysical and Biochemical Cytology*, 7:273–282.

Elkind, M. M., and T. Alescio. 1963. Postirradiation Recovery Processes and Their Dependence on Metabolism in Cultured Mammalian Cells. (Abstract) *Radiation Research*, 19:216.

Elkind, M. M., A. Han, and K. W. Volz. 1963. Radiation Response of Mammalian Cells Grown in Culture. IV. Dose Dependence of Division Delay and Postirradiation Growth of Surviving and Nonsurviving Chinese Hamster Cells. *Journal of the National Cancer Institute*, 30:705–721.

Elkind, M. M., and H. Sutton. 1960. Radiation Response of Mammalian Cells Grown in Culture. I. Repair of X-Ray Damage in Surviving Chinese Hamster Cells. *Radiation Research,* 13:556–593.

Elkind, M. M., H. Sutton, and W. B. Moses. 1961. Postirradiation Survival Kinetics of Mammalian Cells Grown in Culture. *Journal of Cellular and Comparative Physiology,* 58: Supplement 1:113–134.

Erikson, R. L., and W. Szybalski. 1963. Molecular Radiobiology of Human Cell Lines. IV. Variation in Ultra-Violet Light and X-Ray Sensitivity During the Division Cycle. *Radiation Research,* 18:200–212.

Evans, H. J., and J. R. K. Savage. 1963. The Relation Between DNA Synthesis and Chromosome Structure as Resolved by X-Ray Damage. *The Journal of Cell Biology,* 18:525–540.

Giles, N. H. 1954. "Radiation-Induced Chromosome Aberrations in *Tradescantia,*" *Radiation Biology,* A. Hollaender, Ed. New York, New York: McGraw-Hill Book Company. Vol. I, Part 2. Pp. 713–761.

Greenblatt, C. L. 1962. The Evaluation of X-Ray-Induced Chromosome Aberrations in Cell-Cultures of the Chinese Hamster. *International Journal of Radiation Biology and Related Studies in Physics, Chemistry and Medicine,* 4:185–210.

Hall, E. J., and L. G. Lajtha. 1963. The Recovery of *Vicia faba* Meristem Cells from X-Radiation. *Radiation Research,* 20:187–194.

Hornsey, S., and G. Silini. 1962. Recovery of Tumor Cells Cultured *in vivo* After X-Ray and Neutron Irradiations. *Radiation Research,* 16:712–722.

Hsu, T. C., W. C. Dewey, and R. M. Humphrey. 1962. Radiosensitivity of Cells of Chinese Hamster *in vitro* in Relation to the Cell Cycle. *Experimental Cell Research,* 27:441–452.

Hsu, T. C., and D. S. Kellogg. 1960a. Mammalian Chromosomes *in vitro.* XII. Experimental Evolution of Cell Populations. *Journal of the National Cancer Institute,* 24:1067–1093.

————. 1960b. Primary Cultivation and Continuous Propagation *in vitro* of Tissues from Small Biopsy Specimens. *Journal of the National Cancer Institute,* 25:221–236.

Humphrey, R. M., W. C. Dewey, and A. Cork. 1963. Relative Ultraviolet Sensitivity of Different Phases in the Cell Cycle of Chinese Hamster Cells Grown *in vitro.* *Radiation Research,* 19:247–260.

Kallman, R. F. 1963. Recovery from Radiation Injury: A Proposed Mechanism. *Nature,* London, 197:557–560.

Konrad, C. G. 1963. Protein Synthesis and RNA Synthesis During Mitosis in Animal Cells. *The Journal of Cell Biology,* 19:267–277.

Lea, D. E. 1956. *Actions of Radiations on Living Cells.* 3rd Ed. London, England: Cambridge University Press. Pp. 261–276.

Lockart, R. Z., M. M. Elkind, and W. B. Moses. 1961. Radiation Response of Mammalian Cells Grown in Culture. II. Survival and Recovery Characteristics of Several Subcultures of HeLa S3 Cells After X-Irradiation. *Journal of the National Cancer Institute,* 27:1393–1404.

Mak, S., and J. E. Till. 1963. The Effects of X-Rays on the Progress of L-Cells Through the Cell Cycle. *Radiation Research,* 20:600–618.

Marshak, A. 1939. A Comparison of the Sensitivity of Mitotic and Meiotic Chromosomes of *Vicia faba* and its Bearing on Theories of Crossing-Over. *Proceedings of the National Academy of Sciences of the U.S.A.,* 25:510–516.

McCoy, T. A., M. Maxwell, and P. F. Kruse. 1959. Amino Acid Requirements of the Novikoff Hepatoma *in vitro.* *Proceedings of the Society for Experimental Biology and Medicine,* 100:115–118.

Monesi, V. 1962. Relation Between X-Ray Sensitivity and Stages of the Cell Cycle in Spermatogonia of the Mouse. *Radiation Research,* 17:809–838.

Neary, G. J., and H. J. Evans. 1958. "Gamma Radiation-Induced Mitotic Delay and Chromosome Breakage," *Proceedings of the Second United Nations International Conference on the Peaceful Uses of Atomic Energy*. Geneva, Switzerland: United Nations Publication. Vol. 22. Pp.303–307.

Oakberg, E. F., and R. L. DiMinno. 1960. X-Ray Sensitivity of Primary Spermatocytes of the Mouse. *International Journal of Radiation Biology and Related Studies in Physics, Chemistry and Medicine*, 2:196–209.

Sax, K. 1939. The Time Factor in X-Ray Production of Chromosome Aberrations. *Proceedings of the National Academy of Sciences of the U.S.A.*, 25:225–233.

————. 1961. Radiation Sensitivity of *Tradescantia* Microspore Chromosomes to a Second Exposure of X-Rays. *Radiation Research*, 14:668–673.

Sax, K., E. D. King, and H. Luippold. 1955. The Effect of Fractionated X-Ray Dosage on the Frequency of Chromatid and Chromosome Aberrations. *Radiation Research*, 2:171–179.

Sax, K., and K. Mather. 1939. An X-Ray Analysis of Progressive Chromosome Splitting. *Journal of Genetics*, 37:483.

Silini, G., and S. Hornsey. 1962. Studies on Cell-Survival of Irradiated Ehrlich Ascites Tumour. III. A Comparison of the X-Ray Survival Curves Obtained with a Diploid and a Tetraploid Strain. *International Journal of Radiation Biology and Related Studies in Physics, Chemistry and Medicine*, 5:147–153.

Sinclair, W. K., and R. A. Morton. 1963a. Variations in X-Ray Response During the Division Cycle of Partially Synchronized Chinese Hamster Cells in Culture. *Nature*, London, 199:1158–1160.

————. 1963b. Variations in X-Ray Response During the Division Cycle of Partially Synchronized Chinese Hamster Cells in Culture. (Abstract) *Radiation Research*, 19:217.

Sparrow, A. H., M. G. Moses, and R. J. Dubow. 1952. Relationships Between Ionizing Radiation, Chromosome Breakage and Certain Other Nuclear Disturbances. *Experimental Cell Research*, 2: Supplement: 245–262.

Taylor, J. H. 1963a. DNA Synthesis in Relation to Chromosome Reproduction and the Reunion of Breaks. *Journal of Cellular and Comparative Physiology*, 62:73–86.

————. 1963b. Effects of Inhibitors of Thymidylate Synthetase on Chromosome Breakage and Reunion. *Experimental Cell Research*, 9: Supplement: 99–106.

Terasima, T., and L. J. Tolmach. 1963a. Variations in Several Responses of HeLa Cells to X-Irradiation During the Division Cycle. *Biophysical Journal*, 3:11–33.

————. 1963b. X-Ray Sensitivity and DNA Synthesis in Synchronous Populations of HeLa Cells. *Science*, 140:490–492.

————. 1963c. Growth and Nucleic Acid Synthesis in Synchronously Dividing Populations of HeLa Cells. *Experimental Cell Research*, 30:344–362.

Thoday, J. M. 1951. The Effect of Ionizing Radiations on the Broad Bean Root. IX. Chromosome Breakage and the Lethality of Ionizing Radiations to the Root Meristem. *British Journal of Radiology*, 24:572–576; 622–628.

Till, J. E. 1961. Radiosensitivity and Chromosome Numbers in Strain L Mouse Cells in Tissue Culture. *Radiation Research*, 15:400–409.

————. 1963. Quantitative Aspects of Radiation Lethality at the Cellular Level. *The American Journal of Roentgenology, Radium Therapy and Nuclear Medicine*, 90:917–927.

Till, J. E., and E. A. McCulloch. 1963. Early Repair Processes in Marrow Cells Irradiated and Proliferating *in vivo*. *Radiation Research*, 18:96–105.

Wolff, S. 1960a. "Chromosome Aberrations," *Radiation Protection and Recovery*, A. Hollaender, Ed. New York, New York: Pergamon Press. Vol. VII. Pp. 157–174.

————. 1960b. Radiation Studies on the Nature of Chromosome Breakage. *American Naturalist*, 94:85–93.

———. 1961. The Doubleness of the Chromosome Before DNA Synthesis as Revealed by Combined X-Ray and Tritiated Thymidine Treatments. (Abstract) *Radiation Research*, 14:517.

Wolff, S., and H. E. Luippold. 1955. Metabolism and Chromosome Break Rejoining. *Science*, 122:231–232.

———. 1957. Inaccuracy of Anaphase Bridges As a Measure of Radiation-Induced Nuclear Damage. *Nature*, London, 179:208.

Yerganian, G., and M. J. Leonard. 1961. Maintenance of Normal *in situ* Chromosomal Features in Long Term Tissue Cultures. *Science*, 133:1600–1601.

X-Ray Sensitivity Changes During the Division Cycle of HeLa S3 Cells and Anomalous Survival Kinetics of Developing Microcolonies

L. J. TOLMACH, TOYOZO TERASIMA,* AND ROBERT A. PHILLIPS

The Edward Mallinckrodt Institute of Radiology, School of Medicine, and Committee on Molecular Biology, Washington University, Saint Louis, Missouri

THE SYNCHRONOUS HELA S3 SYSTEM

Although animal cells cultured under typical conditions usually grow firmly attached to the walls of the growth vessel, the bond to the wall is often greatly attenuated at the time a cell enters mitosis. Under favorable conditions, a gentle pipetting imparts sufficient shear to dislodge selectively a large fraction of the mitotic cells, e.g. about one per cent of a population of HeLa S3 cells can be recovered in this way (Terasima and Tolmach, 1961). Of the cells so harvested, 80 to 90 per cent are visibly in mitosis and rapidly complete division. They constitute a rather well-synchronized population; rarely more than five per cent divide during the next 18 hours (Terasima and Tolmach, 1963a). However, as shown in Figure 1, synchrony dissipates fairly rapidly, largely during the postmitotic (G_1) phase, as shown by autoradiographic detection of deoxyribonucleic acid (DNA) synthesis in individual cells, following brief exposures to H^3-labeled thymidine (H^3TdR). It takes six or seven hours from the first appearance of labeled cells until essentially all the cells show label; *i.e.* the duration of G_1 varies from about 6 to 13 hours among the cells of the population. Correspondingly, the spread in interdivisional times is also wide, about 18 to 26 hours, as shown by periodic count of the number of cells (Figure 1).

Thus the system has some severe limitations; nevertheless, it has useful features. (1) The synchronous cells seem to have properties that are

* Present address: National Institute of Radiological Sciences, Chiba City, Japan.

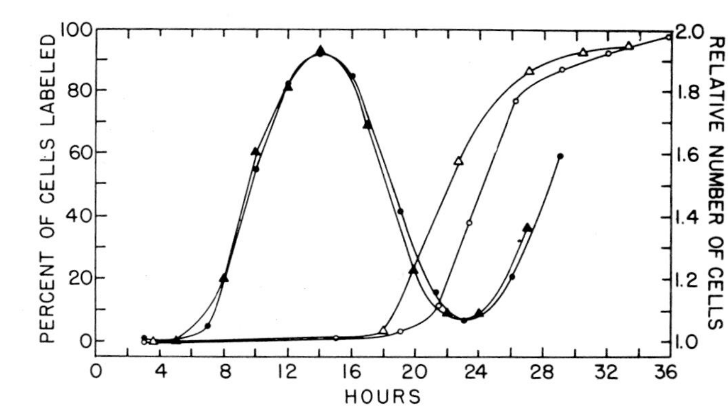

FIGURE 1. The pattern of DNA synthesis and of cell division in synchronously dividing cultures of HeLa S3, determined by pulse-labeling with H^3TdR. Mitotic cells were collected at zero hours. The triangles and circles refer to two separate experiments. Open symbols show the increase in cell number determined by repeated examination of a series of selected microscopic fields in parallel cultures. The solid symbols refer to the percentage of labeled cells determined by autoradiography of replicate cultures which were incubated with tracer for 20 minutes at various times, and then immediately fixed. The time scales have not been normalized. (From Terasima and Tolmach, 1963a.)

much the same as those of a randomly dividing population with respect to the average durations of the phases of the DNA cycle. Severe perturbations of the cells' metabolism are avoided, in contrast to the situation that obtains when synchrony is effected by cold or inhibitor treatments. (2) Although satisfactory study of the premitotic (G_2) phase is not feasible with this system unless additional manipulations are carried out, it is possible to study populations that are purely mitotic, or in G_1, or synthesizing DNA (S phase), and to study progressive changes throughout the cycle, although with limited resolution. (3) While the number of cells conveniently available for an experiment, about 10^5, is too few for many types of studies, it is sufficient for measuring several types of changes that occur in irradiated cells.

X-Ray Sensitivity Changes During the Division Cycle

Several observationally distinct responses of synchronized HeLa S3 populations to exposure to 220 kev X rays were examined (Terasima and Tolmach, 1963b). They can be grouped for convenience into three classes: (1) changes in proliferative patterns, (2) effects on DNA synthesis, and (3) loss of reproductive viability as measured by colony formation.

Changes in Proliferative Patterns

Measurement of cell proliferation by repeated counting of cells in specified microscopic fields revealed the well-known radiation-induced delay in division. Figure 2 shows growth curves obtained after irradiation of samples during mitosis (0 hours), G_1 (4 hours), S (14 hours), and late S or G_2 (19 hours) with 300 rad doses. The stage-dependence of the growth inhibiting effect is apparent. Mitotic cells are seen to be more sensitive than G_1 cells with respect to division delay. They are not delayed, however, in the completion of the division they are engaged in when irradiated (Terasima and Tolmach, 1963b). Data from several such experiments are shown in Figure 3, where the delay in division on a per rad basis is plotted against the time in the cycle at which cells were irradiated, each symbol referring to a different experiment. The increasing delay found as cells were irradiated progressively later in the cycle had been observed in other systems several years ago, and had been interpreted in terms of a repair mechanism that begins to operate immediately after irradiation (Lea, 1956). Such a model, if it is to accommodate our finding that the mitotic cell suffers more lag than the G_1 cell, must be modified to include either greater damage to

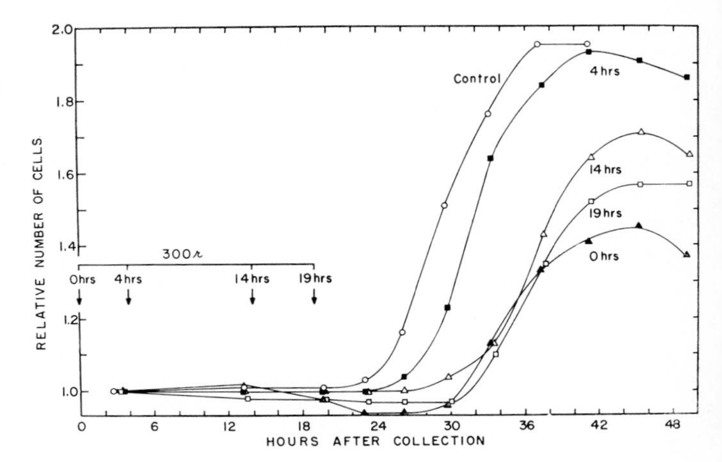

FIGURE 2. Growth curves of samples of a synchronous culture X-irradiated with 300 rads at the times after mitosis indicated above the arrows. The control curve refers to an unirradiated sample. (From Terasima and Tolmach, 1963b.)

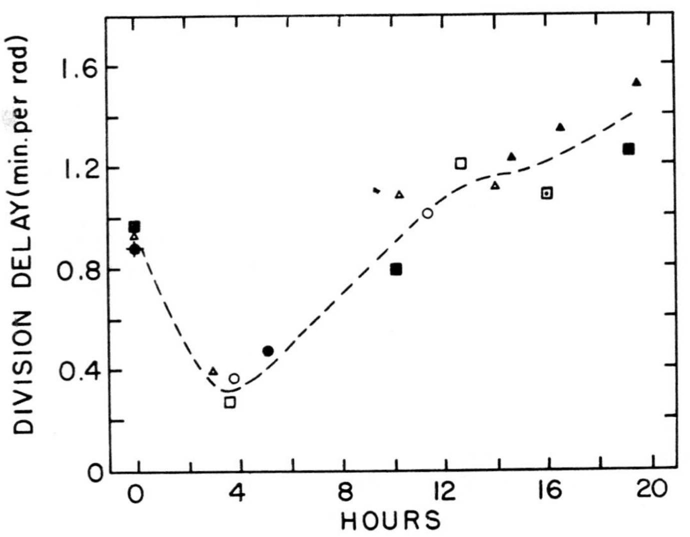

FIGURE 3. Delay in cell division measured in populations X-irradiated at the times after mitosis indicated. The time scales have been normalized to a minimum interdivisional time of 18 hours for each experiment, each denoted by a different symbol. Although delay is reported in units of minutes per rad, in most experiments only a 300 rad dose was administered. (From Terasima and Tolmach, 1963b.)

irradiated mitotic cells, or greater radiation sensitivity of the repair mechanism in such cells. Actually, the observation on which this model is based may be inadequate for cultured animal cells, for the measured mitotic delays may include delay in the DNA synthesis cycle which properly should be subtracted (see below).

Effects on DNA Synthesis

X-radiation produces complex perturbations in the pattern of DNA synthesis in HeLa S3 cells. In order to study them, synchronous cells were irradiated at times selected so that essentially all of the cells were in mitosis, G_1 or S. Autoradiography with H^3TdR was employed to determine the effect produced on the passage of cells from G_1 into S, on the rate of DNA synthesis, and on the duration of the S period.

Figures 4 and 5 show the kinds of results that were obtained when single doses of 300 rads were delivered:

1. Irradiation of mitotic cells scarcely affects the passage from G_1 to S, but measurably decreases the rate of synthesis and prolongs the S period.

2. Irradiation of cells in G_1 with this dose causes no measurable delay in the inception of DNA synthesis. In fact, a small acceleration of passage into S was noted; however, further measurements of this sort using C^{14}-thymidine (C^{14}TdR) and Geiger counting, rather than autoradiography, showed no effect at all at doses up to 1,000 rads. The rate and duration of DNA synthesis was scarcely affected by 300 rads administered at four hours. These results are at variance with those of Mak and Till (1963),

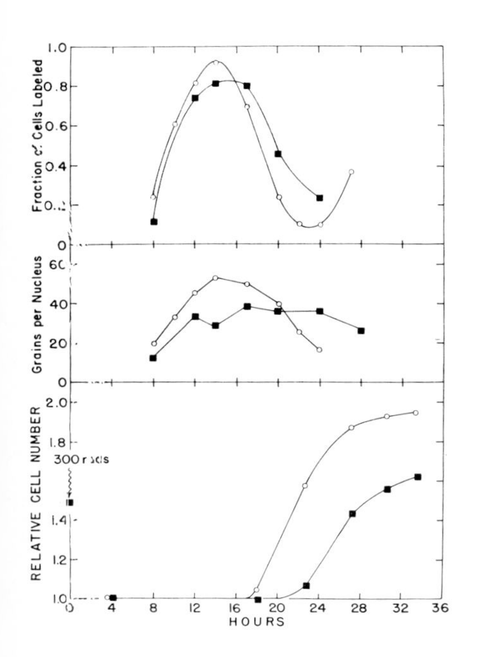

FIGURE 4. Solid squares show three effects of a 300 rad dose of X rays administered to synchronized cells during mitosis (zero hours). The open circles refer to an unirradiated control culture. The upper curves represent autoradiographic determinations of the fraction of cells synthesizing DNA at the times shown. The middle curves show the average rate of DNA synthesis in those cells which are in the S phase. The lower curves show cell division. (From Terasima and Tolmach, 1963b.)

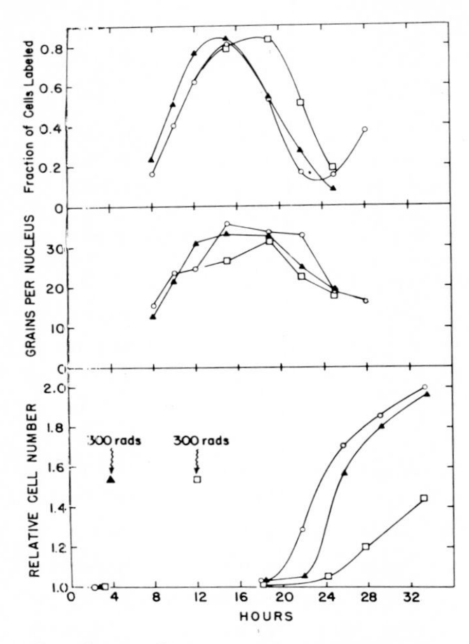

FIGURE 5. Similar to Figure 4, except that cells were irradiated during the G_1 phase (4 hours; solid triangles) or the S phase (12 hours; open squares). The open circles again refer to an unirradiated control culture. (From Terasima and Tolmach, 1963b.)

who showed in an autoradiographic analysis with randomly growing mouse L cells that irradiation slows down the transition from G_1 to S without causing a block, the effect saturating at a relatively low dose.

3. Irradiation of cells already synthesizing DNA causes a decline in rate and a prolongation of the S phase. The dose response is similar to that found by several other workers employing a variety of systems: when plotted on log response versus dose coordinates, a multicomponent curve is obtained. We have no information that bears on the interesting suggestion of Mak and Till (1963) that the extent of inhibition may be different for cells in various regions of the S period.

Obviously, further study is needed to assess quantitatively the contribution made by the delays in the passage of cells into and through the period of DNA synthesis to the over-all mitotic delay. Certainly, the magnitude of the G_2 block is not constant for cells irradiated at different times in the cycle, but it is not yet known just what shape the curve takes after the earlier delays are subtracted. Of course, it is not known either whether they should be subtracted; damage causing mitotic delay may well be repaired during the retention of cells in S. Our results shed no light on the question of the mechanism by which X-irradiation inhibits DNA synthesis.

Loss of Reproductive Viability

Figure 6 shows survival curves typical of those we reported previously (Terasima and Tolmach, 1963b). It is clear that sensitivity fluctuates during the division cycle; mitotic cells are apparently more sensitive than are interphase cells, and the latter, as well, show fluctuations in survival.

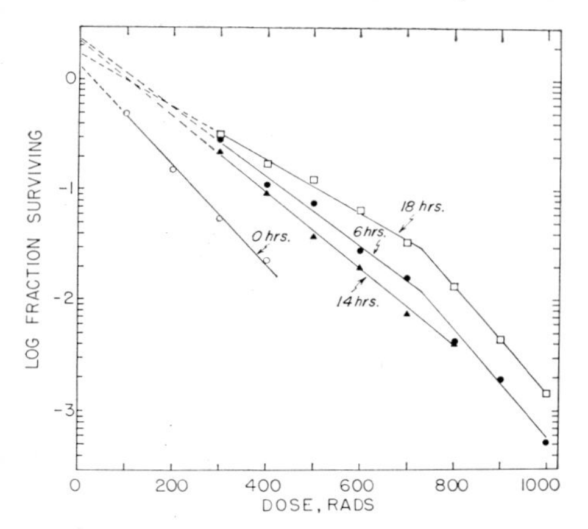

FIGURE 6. Survival of reproductive capacity in aliquots of a synchronous culture after X-irradiation at four different times during the cell cycle, measured from mitosis. The lines have been drawn by eye. (From Terasima and Tolmach, 1963b.)

These data are somewhat disturbing, however, because of the breaks in the curves that became apparent when sufficiently large doses were tested. Although survival curves showing increasing slopes have been reported for certain systems (Barendsen, 1962; Bender and Gooch, 1962), they are not generally observed, and in fact we do not see them when we irradiate randomly dividing populations. Our earlier suggestion (Terasima and Tolmach, 1963b) that the increasing slopes might have arisen from cell interactions must now be discarded (see below). Perhaps they are an experimental artifact; our more recent experiments do not show them.

It may also be noted that no serious changes in extrapolation number are apparent from these curves. However, the data are not precise enough to make any firm conclusions about this, and the breaks in the curves make extrapolation even less meaningful.

Ignoring, then, the distinction between changes in slope and in extrapolation number, we compared survival values after a single dose of 300 rads. The upper curve in Figure 7 summarizes the survival values found when this dose was delivered at different points in the cycle. In order to identify the sensitivity changes with specific stages of interphase, comparison was made with the time-course of DNA synthesis. The fraction of cells labeled with H^3TdR in 20-minute pulses is shown in the lower plot. It is seen that the interphase minimum in survival occurs at a time when about 60 per cent of the cells have begun synthesis, but it is apparent that because of the asynchrony already present by this time, precise identification of the most sensitive phase is not possible; it could be either late G_1 or early S.

It may be noted also that these data indicate no apparent increase in sensitivity during G_2. This matter is of some interest, as both Dewey and Humphrey (1963), and Sinclair and Morton (1963) have reported that Chinese hamster cells are highly sensitive during G_2. However, here again the loss of synchrony in our system would tend to mask a brief period of high sensitivity.

It was desirable, therefore, that resolution of the system be increased.

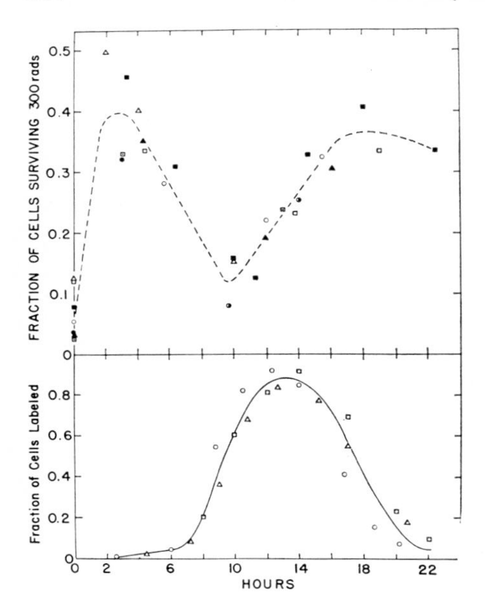

FIGURE 7. Survival and DNA synthesis during the cell cycle. The upper curve shows the fraction of cells surviving reproductively after receiving 300 rad doses of X rays at different times in the cell cycle. Mitosis is taken as zero hours. Each symbol represents a separate experiment, the time scales of which have been normalized to a minimum interdivisional time of 18 hours. The lower curve shows the pattern of DNA synthesis found in three separate experiments with synchronous cells. The fraction of cells that show incorporation of H^3TdR (0.02 to 0.2 μc/ml) after 20-minute sojourns in medium containing that tracer is plotted against the time after mitosis, normalized as in the upper curve. (From Terasima and Tolmach, 1963b.)

To this end, we added inhibitors of DNA synthesis early in the cycle, before any cells in the culture entered S, *i.e.* before six hours (Terasima and Tolmach, 1963c). Cells are thereby prevented from passing from G_1 into S; they collect at the transition point, ready to begin synthesis after the block is removed. Such a procedure has been employed successfully by others to yield synchronized populations in randomly growing cultures (e.g. Rueckert and Mueller, 1960).

When cells were irradiated in the presence of the inhibitor 5-fluoro-

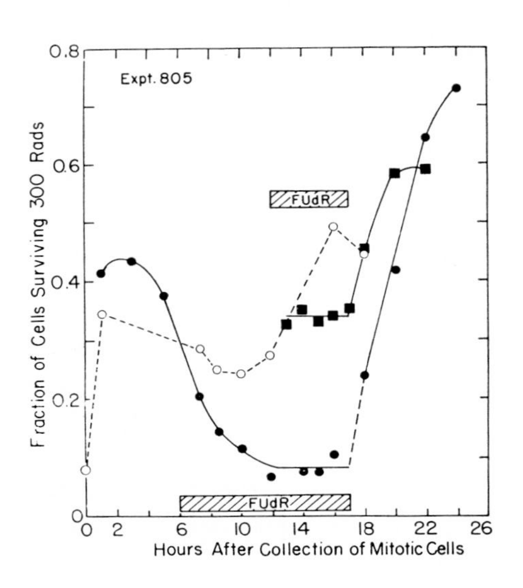

FIGURE 8. Survival of synchronous HeLa S3 cells after irradiation with 300 rad doses in the presence of 10^{-6} M FUdR during all (solid circles; lower bar), or only the latter portion (solid squares, upper bar), of the normal S period. The dashed lines connecting the points for the untreated controls (open circles) do not accurately portray the normal sensitivity fluctuations because survival values are lacking at several early times (compare Figure 7), but the typical minimum at 10 hours is apparent. (From Terasima and Tolmach, 1963c.)

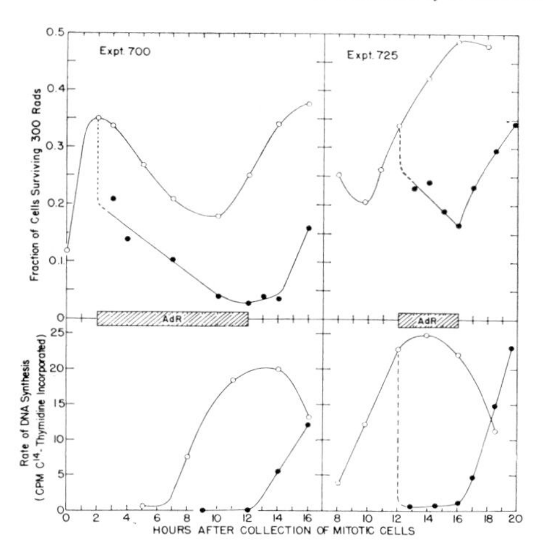

FIGURE 9. Effect of deoxyadenosine on the rate of DNA synthesis in synchronous HeLa S3 cells, as measured by incorporation of C^{14}TdR during 30-minute periods (lower curves), and on survival after 300 rad doses of X rays (top curves). Open circles are control values. Vertical dashed lines in the upper curves indicate the drop in survival caused by deoxyadenosine sensitization. (From Terasima and Tolmach, 1963c.)

deoxyuridine (FUdR) (Figure 8), we found that sensitivity continues to increase after 10 hours, and finally reaches a plateau at which cells are just about as sensitive as they are during mitosis. Release from the inhibition, with subsequent synthesis of DNA, results in a decrease in sensitivity. Similarly, the addition of the inhibitor at a time when cells had already begun synthesis caused a halt in the rise of the level of resistance. Essentially the same results were obtained when deoxyadenosine was used as the DNA inhibitor (Figure 9), but in this case there is the added complication of a generalized sensitization to X rays, so that the survival curves are displaced downward.

We have also attempted to increase resolution during the later portions of the cycle, in order to re-examine sensitivity during the G_2 period. The observation that mitotic cells harvested from a culture that has grown for three days, instead of only one day, spend a relatively longer time in G_2 provided the means for this attempt. Figure 10 shows the results of a large

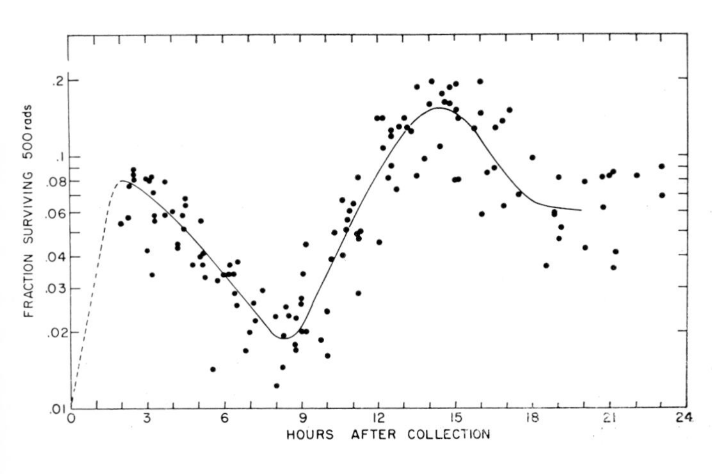

FIGURE 10. Fraction of reproductively viable cells following exposure to 500 rad doses of X rays at different times in the cell cycle. Zero hours corresponds to mitosis. The cells used in these experiments had grown for 72 hours before harvesting, instead of 16 hours, as was the case in the experiments shown in Figure 7.

number of survival determinations after 500-rad exposures, as carried ou with such cells. There does, indeed, seem to be an increase in sensitivity a the end of the cycle, but the decrease in the curve may well correspond to th increase in mitotic activity that synchronous populations show just prior t division (Terasima and Tolmach, 1961). That is, the resolution of th system is not yet adequate to define fully the sensitivity of these cells durin G_2. Still, as we have not been able to demonstrate convincingly an increas in sensitivity of HeLa S3 cells during G_2, the possibility that different cel types have qualitatively different patterns of radiation response during th cell cycle must be seriously entertained, as Dewey and Humphrey (1963 also concluded.

The foregoing results indicate (1) that the fluctuations in radiatio sensitivity of HeLa S3 cells are correlated with the DNA cycle, (2) tha sensitivity changes continuously throughout at least most of the cycle, *i.e* neither the G_1 nor the S phase can be characterized by a given sensitivity (3) that the end of G_1 is the most sensitive point during interphase, an (4) that the subsequent decrease in sensitivity is dependent on DNA syn thesis.

This last conclusion is consistent with the findings of other worker For example, Erikson and Szybalski (1963) measured sensitivity change in D98 cells synchronized by a 20-hour treatment with FUdR followed b the addition of thymidine, and found greater sensitivity at the end of th treatment period than at later times after DNA synthesis had taken place

The causes of the fluctuations in sensitivity during interphase remai to be elucidated; however, from the data presented, one tentative deductio seems warranted concerning the nature of the major target whose damag leads to reproductive cell deaths. When considered within the framework o the genetic damage theory of radiation inactivation (e.g. Puck, 1958, 1960) with which these data are certainly consistent, the close coupling of th sensitivity fluctuation cycle with the cycle of DNA synthesis suggests tha DNA itself may be that target (see also Szybalski and Lorkiewicz, 1962 Guild, 1963). The experiments of Erikson and Szybalski (1961), of Delihas Rich, and Eidinoff (1962), and of Humphrey, Dewey, and Cork (1963) which showed increased sensitivity of mammalian cells whose DNA con tained halogen-substituted analogs of thymidine, are consistent with thi identification, as is the demonstration by Szybalski and co-workers (Szy balski and Opara-Kubinska, 1961, and pages 232 to 240, this volume; Szybal ski and Lorkiewicz, 1962) that DNA is the principal target in bacteria.

Although it might have been predicted *a priori* that radiation sensitivit would increase during the S phase, since, according to the foregoing model the amount of target substance is increasing during this phase, it is possibl to rationalize the results in a number of ways. For example, the acquisitio by the cell of a second complement of information could lead to an increase resistance. Or, if cell killing does not involve loss of genetic determinant per se, the added DNA might tend somehow to stabilize the chromosom mechanically or permit the occurrence of repair mechanisms which can not function in a G_1 cell. Or, the fluctuations in both G_1 and S might reflect some sort of structural change that accompanies the initiation of DNA synthesis (Lark, 1963; Hsu, Dewey, and Humphrey, 1962; Evans and Savage, 1963). One could speculate further.

One other aspect of these results bears consideration. The existence of heterogeneity in a population—with respect to radiation sensitivity—does not necessarily imply that the population will display a complex survival curve. Calculations illustrating this have been presented by several workers (Zimmer, 1961; Dewey and Cole, 1962), and we have shown that this system (after making reasonable estimates of the sizes of each subgroup of cells having a particular sensitivity) yields an expected composite survival curve that can not conceivably be distinguished experimentally from a straight line down to survival levels of 10^{-5} on a semilog plot, once the shoulder is passed (Terasima and Tolmach, 1963b). In addition, the value of the extrapolation number for the composite curve need not bear any simple relation to those of the constituent subpopulations. Accordingly, survival curves, and the fact that they do or do not change under various conditions, must be interpreted with caution.

Nevertheless, it is to be anticipated that any procedure which causes a change in the composition of a cell population with respect to sensitivity states might alter the over-all radiation response, either transiently or permanently, (1) by changing the relative duration of the states, (2) by disturbing the phase relations between cells (*i.e.* inducing synchrony in a random culture), (3) by altering the metabolism of the cells so that the sensitivity of one or more of the states is changed, or (4) by selectively depleting one or another phase. A presumptive example of such a procedure is discussed in the next section.

Anomalous X-Ray Survival Kinetics of Developing Microcolonies

It has been reported (Person, Tolmach, and Sato, 1961) that under certain conditions the survival of microcolonies of L or HeLa S3 cells after X-irradiation does not increase in parallel with the increase in the number of cells per colony. Anomalous survival values may persist for as long as three days after plating single cells. Results typical of those reported earlier are shown in Figure 11, in which it is seen that rather than yielding a survival curve with terminal slope parallel to that for single cells but lying fivefold higher, microcolonies containing on the average 5.1 cells survived little better than did single cells, and possibly even less well at higher doses. The original data were not sufficient to draw a firm conclusion about changes in the extrapolation number, though they did suggest that it might be increasing as colonies got larger. However, even if an increase in extrapolation number had been definitely established, we would have hesitated to suggest that the radiation sensitivity of cells could change during three days of exponential growth. Rather, the findings were interpreted at that time as indicating that cells constituting the microcolonies were not independently killed, *i.e.*, that irradiated cells could cooperate to kill cells that otherwise would have suffered only sublethal damage.

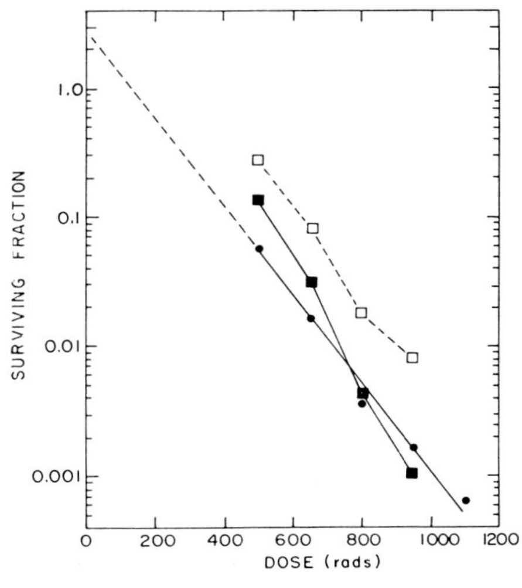

FIGURE 11. Survival of microcolonies containing 1.0 cell (solid circles) and a mean of 5.1 cells (solid squares). The open squares show the expected survival values for the 5.1-cell colonies.

Some support for this interpretation was provided by experiments of Elkind and co-workers in which they looked for interactions in irradiated Chinese hamster cells (Elkind and Sutton, 1960) and HeLa S3 cells (Lockart, Elkind, and Moses, 1961). Although they interpreted their results as providing no evidence for such interactions, they did find a transient increase in the sensitivity of Chinese hamster cells some six hours after plating, which was not inconsistent with the idea of cell interactions. In addition, Elkind, Sutton, and Moses (1961) observed a response to radiation in certain dose fractionation experiments that they interpreted as possibly indicating cell interactions. Although that phenomenon is not directly relevant to the matter under discussion, it did again suggest that cultured cell populations might show cooperative irradiation effects. Similarly, Bender and Gooch (1962) presented data that could be interpreted in terms of cell interactions. It appeared, then, that under our growth conditions, a marked interaction might be occurring, while under different conditions and with different material, it might be minimal or absent. In fact, Puck and Marcus (Personal communication) had observed no remarkable deviation from expected survival kinetics in developing HeLa S3 microcolonies at the time they made the first measurements of animal cell radiation sensitivity (Puck and Marcus, 1956).

If a toxic substance, which would be a logical mediator of any cell interaction, were released from irradiated cells, then exposure of cells plated on a monolayer previously killed by a large dose of X rays should result in more inactivation than treatment in the absence of such a feeder layer.

Bender and Gooch (1962) had found such an effect. However, as shown in Table 1, we found just the opposite to be true; the feeder cells apparently protect cells slightly from inactivation by either 400 or 800 rads.

TABLE 1

Effect of Feeder Layers on Cell Survival*

Time at which feeder layer was added	Fractional survival following 400 rads	800 rads	800 rads
	(Exp. 815)	(Exp. 860)	(Exp. 891)
Before irradiation	0.182	0.0159	0.0182
After irradiation	. .	.0102	.0118
No feeder layer	.136	.0084	.0088

* Feeder layers consisted of 10^6 cells that had received 2,000 rads.

Again, if there were cell interactions, then there might be a concentration dependence. In this case also Bender and Gooch (1962) found just such behavior. However, when we plated cells at densities ranging between 10^3 and 5×10^6 per dish and irradiated four hours later, the surviving fraction was essentially constant even though each cell was in contact with its neighbors at the higher concentrations.

Thus, in order to sustain the notion of co-operative effects, we were forced to postulate that irradiated cells could only practice fratricide, and had to proliferate together, *i.e.* be sisters or cousins, to be able to interact, perhaps through cytoplasmic bridges. Indeed, other experiments, in which cells were irradiated when they had reached the same confluent density but had grown over varying periods ranging up to three days to reach that density, showed that the period of incubation before irradiation, not the cell density, was the important factor in obtaining the enhanced killing effect (Table 2). Accordingly, the possibility of sister cell interactions also was tested (unlikely though it was, in view of the fact that under the conditions of growth then prevailing, our cells did not remain contiguous until the eight-cell stage or later, while the phenomenon of increased cell killing reached its maximum between the four- and eight-cell stage and then remained constant with increasing colony size). Conditions for that test were provided by the observation of Puck, Marcus, and Cieciura (1956) that

TABLE 2

Effect of Preirradiation Incubation on Cell Survival

Preirradiation incubation period	Survival*
4 hours	0.00418
1 day	.00512
2 days	.00195
3 days	.00185

* Replicate samples of a mass culture were grown for the times indicated, irradiated with 825 rads, trypsinized, counted, and plated. These values are the fraction of cells which gave rise to colonies.

cells grow much more tightly in the absence of human serum than in its presence. In several types of experiments, it was found that rather than enhancing the effect, growth in the absence of human serum apparently abolished it. Colony survival seemed to increase as expected from colony size, as shown in Figure 12.

In contrast, survival of microcolonies grown in medium containing human serum, where the cells were loosely aggregated, did not begin to parallel growth until two or three days after plating; this was shown in experiments similar to those reported by Lockart, Elkind, and Moses (1961) in which survival after a constant dose was measured as a function of microconoly size (Figure 13)).

Clearly, the explanation of the phenomenon in terms of cell interactions was no longer tenable. A more acceptable interpretation became apparent as the result of experiments in which the rate of DNA synthesis was followed with pulses of C^{14}TdR. It was observed (Figure 14) that although the cell number seemed to increase exponentially after about 10 hours, the rate of DNA synthesis did not increase in parallel with the cell number until after two or three days. Apparently, then, conditions of growth during the preirradiation incubation period influence both the radiation sensitivity of the developing microcolonies and the synthetic activities of the cells, and the two are affected simultaneously. That is, the sensitivity fluctuations appear to arise from fluctuations in the metabolic state of the culture. In view of the fluctuations in sensitivity that occur during the cell cycle, it seems reasonable to postulate that anomalous microcolony survival is caused by changes in the composition of the population which are induced by the trypsinization procedure and the subsequent cultural condi-

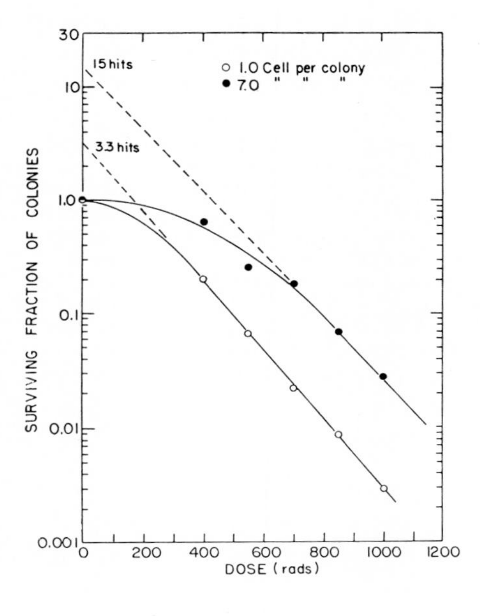

FIGURE 12. Survival of microcolonies containing 1.0 cell (open circles) and a mean of 7.0 cells (solid circles) that had grown in medium lacking human serum.

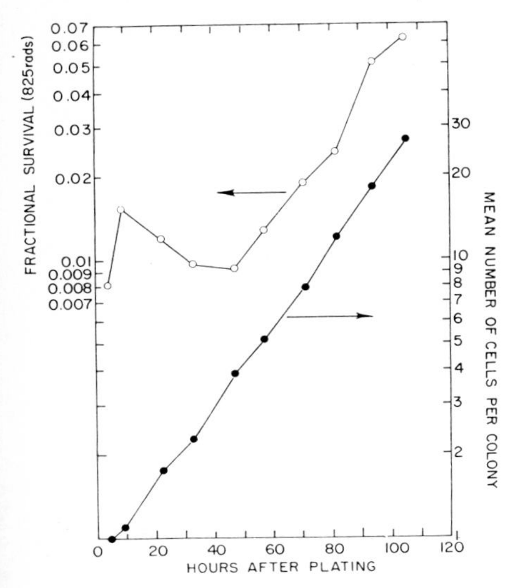

FIGURE 13. Changes in the X-ray sensitivity of developing colonies. The open circles (left ordinate) show the fraction of colonies surviving a dose of 825 rads at various times after plating single cells. The mean number of cells per colony at these same times is shown by the solid circles (right ordinate).

tions. Such fluctuations could, in principle, arise either from a partial synchronization of cells or from an actual change in their metabolic pattern, or both. We feel quite sure that their metabolism changes, as measurement of the duration of the phases of the DNA cycle show them to be appreciably different in cells after 72 hours of growth as compared with 16 hours (Table 3). Whether these changes in metabolic pattern only shift the composition of the population with respect to sensitivity state, or whether they also alter the radiation sensitivity of one or more of these phases, is unknown.

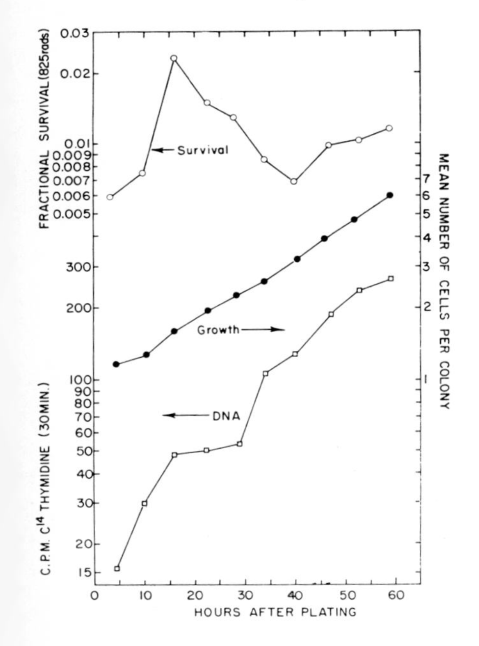

FIGURE 14. X-ray sensitivity and rate of DNA synthesis in developing microcolonies. The open circles (upper left ordinate) show the fraction of colonies surviving a dose of 825 rads at various times after plating single cells. The open squares (lower left ordinate) show the amount of C^{14}TdR incorporated in 30-minute pulses. The solid circles (right ordinate) indicate the mean number of cells per colony.

TABLE 3

Comparison of the Durations of the Phases of the DNA Cycle in Synchronous Cells Harvested after 16 or 72 Hours Growth

	16-HOUR CELLS				72-HOUR CELLS			
EXPERIMENT NUMBER	T_m* (HRS)	DURATION† (% OF T_m) G_1	S	G_2	T_m* (HRS)	DURATION† (% OF T_m) G_1	S	G_2
873	22.0	46	50	4	20.0	41	38	21
877	23.3	45	41	14	20.4	42	36	22
Average	22.7	45.5	45.5	9	20.2	41.5	37	21.5

* T_m, the median interdivisional time, is the interval between collection of mitotic cells and the subsequent division of half of the cells.

† Durations shown are median values determined from curves relating counts per minute of incorporated $C^{14}TdR$ (30 minute pulses) to time after collection of mitotic cells. Mitotic time is included in G_2, and because the collected cells are in mitosis, there is also some mitotic time included in G_1.

We suspect also that a culture becomes partially synchronized after trypsinization, as the fluctuations in sensitivity of microcolonies coincide with fluctuations in the rate of DNA synthesis, as mentioned above, and in addition, the mitotic index changes during this period. Furthermore, the notion that two distinct phenomena are occurring is consistent with the finding that short term (30 hour) fluctuations in rate of DNA synthesis, in mitotic index, and in X-ray sensitivity do, in fact, occur in medium lacking human serum, as well as in complete growth medium; whereas the long term (70 hour) fluctuations, which are described above, are found only in the complete medium (Figure 15).

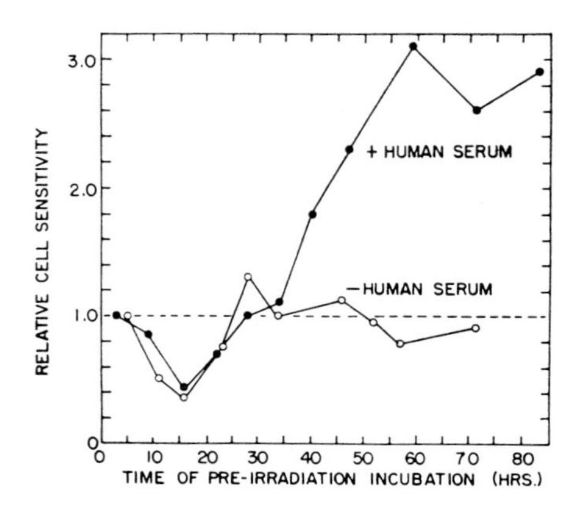

FIGURE 15. Relative sensitivity of cells grown in the presence and absence of human serum, as a function of time after plating. Survival at the earliest time (three or five hours) has been divided by the survival at the times indicated, after dividing the latter value by the mean number of cells per colony at each time. A dose of 800 rads was used.

There is a formal similarity between these sensitivity changes and those observed following a conditioning dose of radiation (Elkind and Sutton, 1960). If population changes account for the one, then they may well play a role in the other. Indeed, Elkind, Sutton, and Moses (1961), and Dewey and Humphrey (1962) have previously suggested that population shifts could be involved in recovery phenomena as studied in fractionated dose experiments, and Kallman (1963) has developed the theoretical aspects of this approach, and has correlated from this point of view data obtained from several different types of systems. Without implying that other phenomena, such as recovery of sublethal damage resulting in reappearance of the shoulder on the survival curve, are not also fundamental in producing the observed recovery curves (Whitmore, see pages 423 to 441, this volume), it would seem to be necessary that the possible role of population shifts be carefully explored.

ACKNOWLEDGMENTS

These investigations were supported by Research Grant CA 04483 from the National Cancer Institute, U.S. Public Health Service.

Mr. Phillips is a Trainee supported by U.S. Public Health Service Training Grant 2G-714.

REFERENCES

Barendsen, G. W. 1962. Dose-Survival Curves of Human Cells in Tissue Culture Irradiated with Alpha-, Beta-, 20 KV. X- and 200 KV. X-Radiation. *Nature*, London, 193:1153–1155.

Bender, M. A., and P. C. Gooch. 1962. The Kinetics of X-Ray Survival of Mammalian Cells *in vitro. International Journal of Radiation Biology and Related Studies in Physics, Chemistry and Medicine*, 5:133–145.

Delihas, N., M. A. Rich, and M. L. Eidinoff. 1962. Radiosensitization of a Mammalian Cell Line with 5-Bromodeoxyuridine. *Radiation Research*, 17:479–491.

Dewey, W. C., and A. Cole. 1962. Effects of Heterogeneous Populations on Radiation Survival Curves. *Nature*, London, 194:660–662.

Dewey, W. C., and R. M. Humphrey. 1962. Relative Radiosensitivity of Different Phases in the Life Cycle of L-P59 Mouse Fibroblasts and Ascites Tumor Cells. *Radiation Research*, 16:503–530.

————. 1963. Survival of Mammalian Cells Irradiated in Different Phases of the Life-Cycle as Examined by Autoradiography. *Nature*, London, 198:1063–1066.

Djordjevic, B., and W. Szybalski. 1960. Genetics of Human Cell Lines. III. Incorporation of 5-Bromo-, and 5-Iododeoxyuridine into the Deoxyribonucleic Acid of Human Cells and its Effect on Radiation Sensitivity. *Journal of Experimental Medicine*, 112: 509–531.

Elkind, M. M., and H. Sutton. 1960. Radiation Response of Mammalian Cells Grown in Culture. I. Repair of X-Ray Damage in Surviving Chinese Hamster Cells. *Radiation Research*, 13:556–593.

Elkind, M. M., H. Sutton, and W. B. Moses. 1961. Postirradiation Survival Kinetics of Mammalian Cells Grown in Culture. *The Journal of Cellular and Comparative Physiology*, 58: Supplement 1:113–134.

Erikson, R. L., and W. Szybalski. 1961. Molecular Radiobiology of Human Cell Lines. I. Comparative Sensitivity to X-Rays and Ultraviolet Light of Cells Containing Halogen-Substituted DNA. *Biochemical and Biophysical Research Communications*, 4:258–261.

————. 1963. Molecular Radiobiology of Human Cell Lines. IV. Variation of Ultraviolet Light and X-Ray Sensitivity during the Division Cycle. *Radiation Research*, 18:200–212.

Evans, H. J., and J. R. K. Savage. 1963. The Relation between DNA Synthesis and Chromosome Structure as Resolved by X-Ray Damage. *The Journal of Cell Biology*, 18:525–540.

Guild, W. R. 1963. The Radiation Sensitivity of Deoxyribonucleic Acid. *Radiation Research,* Supplement 3:257–269.

Humphrey, R. M., W. C. Dewey, and A. Cork. 1963. Effect of Oxygen in Mammalian Cells Sensitized to Radiation by Incorporation of 5-Bromodeoxyuridine into the DNA. *Nature,* London, 198:268–269.

Hsu, T. C., W. C. Dewey, and R. M. Humphrey. 1962. Radiosensitivity of Cells of Chinese Hamster *in vitro* in Relation to the Cell Cycle. *Experimental Cell Research,* 27:441–452.

Kallman, R. F. 1963. Recovery from Radiation Injury: A Proposed Mechanism. *Nature,* London, 197:557–560.

Lark, K. G. 1963. "Cellular Control of DNA Biosynthesis," *Molecular Genetics,* J. H. Taylor, Ed. New York, New York and London, England: Academic Press. Pp. 153–206.

Lea, D. E. 1956. *Actions of Radiations on Living Cells.* 2nd Ed. Cambridge, England: Cambridge University Press. 416 pp.

Lockart, R. Z., M. M. Elkind, and W. B. Moses. 1961. Radiation Response of Mammalian Cells Grown in Culture. II. Survival and Recovery Characteristics of Several Subcultures of HeLa S3 Cells after X Irradiation. *Journal of the National Cancer Institute,* 27:1393–1404.

Mak, S., and J. E. Till. 1963. The Effects of X-Rays on the Progress of L-Cells Through the Cell Cycle. *Radiation Research,* 20:600–618.

Person, S. R., L. J. Tolmach, and E. Sato. 1961. Interactions among Mammalian Cells Irradiated *in vitro.* (Abstract) *Radiation Research,* 14:491.

Puck, T. T. 1958. Action of Radiation on Mammalian Cells. III. Relationship between Reproductive Death and Induction of Chromosome Anomalies by X-Irradiation of Euploid Human Cells *in vitro. Proceedings of the National Academy of Sciences of the U.S.A.,* 44:772–780.

———. 1960. *In vitro* Studies on the Radiation Biology of Mammalian Cells. *Progress in Biophysics and Biophysical Chemistry,* 10:238–258.

Puck, T. T., and P. I. Marcus. 1956. Action of X-Rays on Mammalian Cells. *The Journal of Experimental Medicine,* 103:653–666.

Puck, T. T., P. I. Marcus, and S. J. Cieciura. 1956. Clonal Growth of Mammalian Cells *in vitro. The Journal of Experimental Medicine,* 103:273–284.

Rueckert, R. R., and G. C. Mueller. 1960. Studies on Unbalanced Growth in Tissue Culture. I. Induction and Consequences of Thymidine Deficiency. *Cancer Research,* 20:1584–1591.

Sinclair, W. K., and R. A. Morton. 1963. Variations in X-Ray Response during the Division Cycle of Partially Synchronized Chinese Hamster Cells in Culture. *Nature,* London, 199:1158–1160.

Szybalski, W., and Z. Lorkiewicz. 1962. On the Nature of the Principal Target of Lethal and Mutagenic Radiation Effects. *Abhandlungen der Deutschen Akademie der Wissenschaften zu Berlin, Klasse für Medizin.* Pp. 61–71.

Szybalski, W., and Z. Opara-Kubinska. 1961. DNA as Principal Determinant of Cell Radiosensitivity. (Abstract) *Radiation Research,* 14:508–509.

Terasima, T., and L. J. Tolmach. 1961. Changes in X-Ray Sensitivity of HeLa Cells during the Division Cycle. *Nature,* London, 190:1210–1211.

———. 1963a. Growth and Nucleic Acid Synthesis in Synchronously Dividing Populations of HeLa Cells. *Experimental Cell Research,* 30:344–362.

———. 1963b. Variations in Several Responses of HeLa Cells to X-Irradiation during the Division Cycle. *Biophysical Journal,* 3:11–33.

———. 1963c. X-Ray Sensitivity and DNA Synthesis in Synchronous Populations of HeLa Cells. *Science,* 140:490–492.

immer, K. G. 1961. "Generalized Formal Hit 'Theory'," *Studies on Quantitative Radiation Biology*. Edinburgh, Scotland: Oliver and Boyd. Pp. 16–47.

DISCUSSION

Dr. Sheldon Wolff, Oak Ridge National Laboratory, Oak Ridge, Tennessee: I might oint out that it has been known for quite some time that, from experiments with chromome aberrations observed at metaphase in *Vicia faba*, G_2 is more sensitive than S. It was mewhat disturbing to us that the hamster cell, which was like *Vicia faba* in this respect, ffered from the L cell. I was, therefore, quite glad to see the data Dr. Dewey presented hich showed that even in the L cell, if one looked at metaphase where one can really e all of the aberrations, the pattern is similar to that observed in Vicia and that in eneral all cell lines show a G_2 sensitivity greater than S.

There is, however, one thing disturbing about the data; this is the discrepancy in the ouse L cells between metaphase scoring and anaphase scoring. After all, anaphase abertions do come from metaphase aberrations. I wonder, if in the scoring of the slides, you bserved something in regard to the types of aberrations that would give you some clue as why, when you look at metaphase aberrations, you see more aberrations from G_2 than and yet have a switch when you look later on at anaphase. I wonder perhaps if you ould possibly be scoring gaps at metaphase that would not be true anaphase aberrations. wonder about this especially because L cells are mouse cells where scoring would be ard because they have a large number of very small chromosomes. It is much more diffilt to score these than it is to score hamster chromosomes.

Dr. William C. Dewey, The University of Texas M. D. Anderson Hospital and Tumor Institute, Houston, Texas: I wish we knew the answer to this. Personally, I think at we will not know the answer until we prepare idiograms of all cells and find out recisely what type of damage it is. One thing that I suspect or question is: Could it be ossible that the ratio of symmetrical to asymmetrical exchanges is different in the G_2 ells than it is in the S cells? This might account for some difficulties because we know at we would not score the symmetrical exchanges at anaphase. Also, the frequency of ochromatic breaks may be involved. Greenblatt (*International Journal of Radiation iology*, 4:185–210, 1961), who studied the aberrations in the Chinese hamster cell at etaphase, found that the frequency of isochromatid breaks rose with time, indicating at he may have had more isochromatic breaks in S than in G_2. I really think that we hould study this question carefully and precisely.

Dr. L. Lajtha, Holt Radium Institute, Manchester, England: I should like to question Dr. Dewey on a point of terminology. You have shown a slide, hamster cells, I believe, here the sensitivity of the G_2 cells was plotted against the sensitivity of the S cells. The rst showed a certain slope and very little or no shoulder, while the S cells had a very ronounced shoulder. The statement that you made was that therefore the G_2 cells are ore sensitive. However, if I remember your slide correctly, the D_0 slope of the S cells ppeared to be slightly steeper than that of the G_2 cells. If this is so, of course, after a ertain dose, the two curves would cross; therefore the sensitivity in respect of depopulaon would depend very much on the dose you would give to these two populations of cells. Now, this is not mere hair-splitting, since after all the aim of this very important work is give, if and when cell populations can be manipulated and synchronized, some indicaon to the radiotherapist when to treat. Radiotherapists will try to treat with relatively rge dose fractions and it may be that we might give them false information saying that he G_2 cells are more sensitive, if in fact the slope is shallower than that of the S cells nd if with the dose range that would be used we would get, in fact, a greater depopulaon with the S cells.

Dr. Dewey: I wouldn't venture to say anything at present about the differences in lopes and extrapolation numbers from the data that we have on the hamster cells. We ust do not have enough data. However, for a dose of 350 r the survival of the G_2 cells is bout one fifth that of the S cells. We were primarily interested in getting recovery data. n the process of doing that, we happened to have two doses so we got some survival data s well. I think your point is well taken. It must be studied now in great precision to fill n the points and to find out whether there are differences in slope or extrapolation number. I think that Dr. Sinclair has some data on this in the hamster cell.

Dr. Robert Kallman, Stanford University, Palo Alto, California: I would like to show some of the results of a single experiment that I undertook with Dr. Tolmach about a year ago in order to test a notion of what might be involved in the kinetics of recuperation. In a way, I hesitate to present this because the data are very preliminary, but I think that they bear on the discussion and tend to confirm the data that Dr. Dewey showed. We did this in order to test the validity of the notion that the recuperation kinetics observed in several systems result from a chain of events consisting of (1) an initial selective depopulation of a random sample of cells representing all phases of the cell cycle and, therefore, range of radiosensitivities; (2) a generation of stage-dependent delay in first dose-surviving cells such as to cause a piling up of these temporarily delayed but viable cells in a relatively radioresistant state at a point in G_2 shortly preceding their next mitotic division; and (3) a subsequent relatively synchronous passage of these survivors through the ensuing mitotic stages and into the next cycle. We selectively synchronized exponentially growing HeLa cells by the method that Dr. Tolmach described and seeded petri dishes with known numbers of cells which were incubated and allowed to progress synchronously through the next cycle. This particular experiment showed an excellent synchrony in the controls. We gave a first dose (D_1) of 300 rads between 16 and 18 hours after the start of synchronous growth, *i.e.* in G_2. (This range of time was necessitated by the limitations in the output of the X-ray machine and the number of dishes that we had to irradiate.) Immediately after that and roughly at 3, 5, 10, 13, and 20 hours, we gave a series of second doses.

In Figure 1, the survival curves are shown. These are fitted by eye because of the paucity of the data, but I think that the fits are reasonably good. The solid line (and solid circles) shows the survival curve for the cells exposed to a single dose, that is, for 0

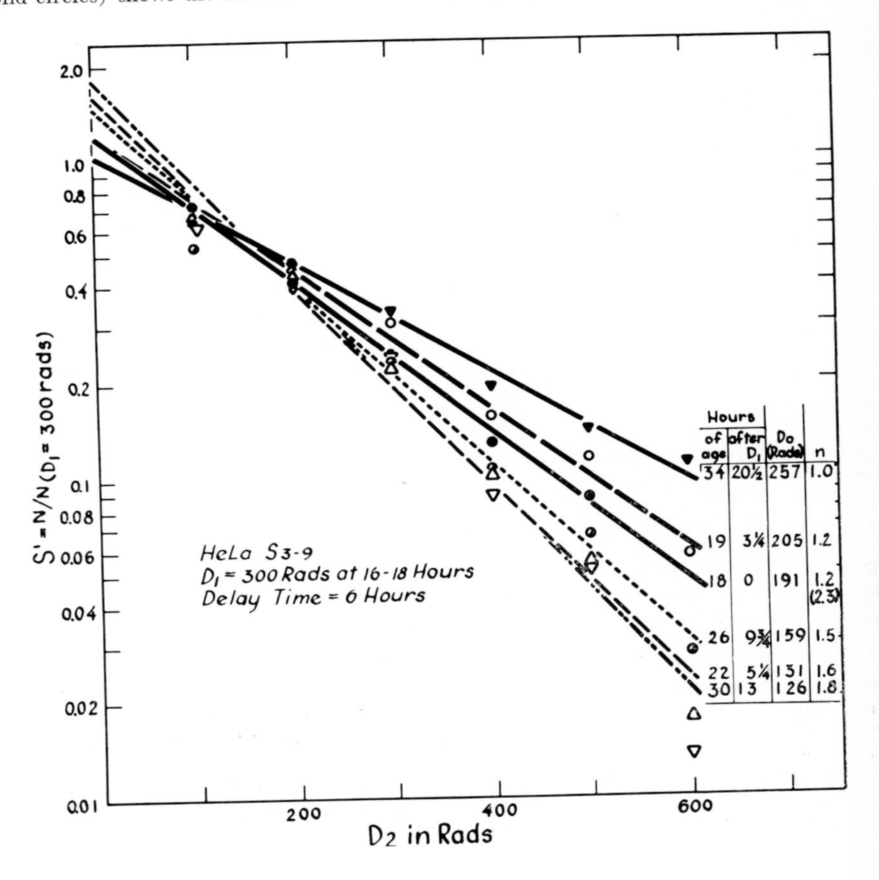

time between the two doses. You can see that the D_0 of these cells was 191 rads, and the extrapolation number, n, 1.2. Now these curves were plotted as the number of cells surviving the total dose ($D_1 + D_2$) divided by the number surviving the first dose of 300 rads. If we had used N_0 as the denominator, the extrapolation number would be 2.3. When we waited 3¼ hours, on the average, until giving the second dose, the D_0 was essentially the same and the extrapolation number had not changed. These cells (3¼ hours after D_1) happen to have been irradiated earlier in the 16 to 18 hour interval; that is why these numbers look so strange. When we waited 5¼ hours, the D_0 had decreased and the extrapolation number seems to have increased. When the D_2 was given at 9¾ hours, the D_0 was 159 rads and n was 1.5. At 13 hours the D_0 reached a minimum, and at 20½ hours we found a very high D_0, *i.e.*, the cells were quite resistant.

Figure 2 shows these data plotted somewhat differently, in the manner which Elkind has used so effectively. These are the same data that you just saw except that I have shown only the 100, 300, and 500 rad points. The controls are the half-solid circles and short-dashed line across the top. The lighter diagonal line is the survival curve of cells receiving a single dose at 18 hours after synchrony was started. You can see that the cells become more resistant at about three hours; Dr. Dewey just showed some similar results. Then, at five hours, they show a heightened sensitivity. Now the interesting thing about this is that this dose of 300 rads would be expected, based on Terasima and Tolmach's earlier findings, to induce a division delay of about six hours. This point was determined at about five hours, and our controls showed that division was indeed delayed for approximately six hours. These cells, then, would be just about in mitosis, probably in prophase; and, as you can see, for all of the doses that we tested, the cells at this time (and a little bit later with 100 rads) were more sensitive than cells given a single dose. We think that this is an interesting and significant point which tends to support the notion that the kinetics that one observes in a mixed population may be related to a shift in the proportions of

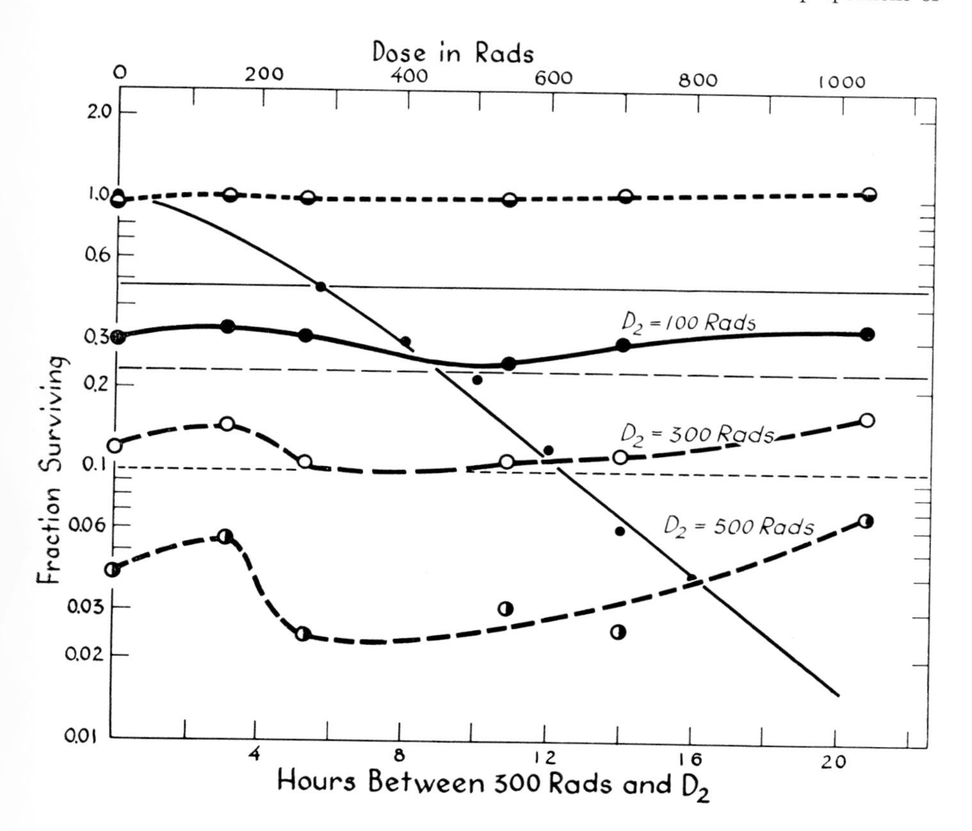

cells in different stages of the generation cycle. The fact that you get a heightened sensitivity at this particular time is consistent with the idea that the cells have now passed into a stage of heightened sensitivity which would presumably be the next mitotic stage.

Just before I left home, I had a letter from a colleague, Dr. William Caldwell, who is working in Dr. Lamerton's laboratory. He told me about some experiments that he has been doing with cells similar to those that Dr. Alexander talked about earlier, mouse lymphoma cells in vitro. These cells have a D_0 of about 50 rads and an extrapolation number of one; their doubling time is about 9 hours. He found, giving doses of 100 + 100 rads separated by increasing times, that when the two doses were separated by five hours the survival was 0.46, or 46 per cent, of the survival of cells given the same dose in a single session. Furthermore, he is able to get at least as high a degree of increased sensitivity by giving a first dose of 25 rads followed by a second dose of 175 rads, *i.e.* the same total dose. In other words, the first dose would appear to be, in effect, synchronizing the survivors and putting them into a sensitive state at about five hours, in this case, which coincidently happens at the same time as in our cells. The suggestion that these sensitivity changes are attributable to population shifts, or the induction of synchrony, is greatly strengthened by the fact that these cells have no shoulder on their survival curve, *i.e.* their extrapolation number is one. One would therefore expect no recovery in the usual sense that this term implies.

Dr. Arthur Cole, The University of Texas M. D. Anderson Hospital and Tumor Institute, Houston, Texas: This is certainly a premature report, but I suppose that is what this meeting is for. Dr. Carolyn Somers Cronenwett and I have been studying the structure of isolated mammalian metaphase chromosomes for the last year or so. This work was recently reported at the Biophysical Society Meeting. Our present interpretation is that the condensed mammalian metaphase chromosome appears to be a result of a sequence of folding back and twisting up operations of what is perhaps a fundamental fiber of an uncondensed configuration. The problem here is that such a metaphase configuration is not necessarily a linear expression of the relatively open state expressed in interphase. This means, for instance, in Dr. Hsu's work that one would not necessarily always expect a correlation between the location of radioactivity and the location of a break expressed in metaphase. Perhaps more importantly, such a configuration would immensely complicate the question of how an aberration which is induced in an uncondensed chromosome during interphase is subsequently expressed in metaphase. I have considered this, and no matter how you look at it, it is entirely speculative and difficult.

Effect of X Rays on Initiation of DNA Replication In Vivo

DANIEL BILLEN

Section of Radiation Biology, Department of Biology,
The University of Texas M. D. Anderson Hospital and Tumor Institute,
Houston, Texas

Recent studies with the thymine-requiring, multiauxotrophic *Escherichia coli* strain $15T^-A^-U^-$ have established that completion of replication of the bacterial chromosome may be achieved in the absence of protein and ribonucleic acid (RNA) synthesis (Maaløe and Hanawalt, 1961). The bacterial chromosome may be depicted as being replicated from a defined origin in a regular, orientated fashion. The sequential replication has been described for transformation markers in *Bacillus subtilis* by Yoshikawa and Sueoka (1963a,b) and in prophage induction in *E. coli* K-12 by Nagata 1963). Morphological proof of polarity in the replication sequence of deoxyribonucleic acid (DNA) in *E. coli* has been provided by the autoradiographic studies of Cairns (1963). Lark, Repko, and Hoffman (1963), who used biochemical methods to study *E. coli* strain $15T^-$ (555–7), reported results which substantiate the conclusion of Maaløe and Hanawalt (1961), who used *E. coli* strain $15T^-A^-U^-$, that in the absence of protein synthesis replication of the bacterial chromosome can proceed to completion and no further in these bacteria. Such a system then makes it possible to test for the existence of radiosensitive periods in the bacteria chromosomal cycle. This paper presents the results of experiments in which these multiauxotrophic, thymine-requiring bacteria have been utilized to study the effects of ionizing irradiations on the initiation of the subsequent cycle of chromosome replication.

That there are indeed times in the generation cycle in which the DNA-synthesizing system is more sensitive to a given dose of irradiation has been established in studies with plant and animal cells, which were recently reviewed by Ord and Stocken (1961). The so-called G_1 period (that period following mitosis but preceding DNA synthesis) appears to be a particularly sensitive period in the cell cycle, with regard to the effects of exposure to irradiation on the subsequent DNA-synthesizing (S) period.

Several years ago, it was observed in this laboratory that the blocking of protein synthesis by the addition of chloramphenicol prior to exposure to X rays brought about or resulted in a state such that doses of irradiation which while only partially inhibitory to the DNA-synthesizing system in growing cells could interfere substantially with the recovery of the DNA-synthesizing system usually observed in the unirradiated, but chloramphenicol-pretreated, cells. The effect of chloramphenicol on DNA synthesis in *E. coli* strain 15T⁻, used in these initial experiments, was somewhat different from that observed with the amino acid-starved cells. The use of chloramphenicol to block protein synthesis apparently allows the suspension of treated cells to continue into the next round of DNA synthesis before DNA replication will finally come to a halt. This is reflected in roughly a 100 per cent increase in DNA during protein synthesis inhibition, before DNA synthesis ceases. Maaløe and Hanawalt (1961), utilizing *E. coli* strain 15T⁻A⁻U⁻, showed that in the absence of the required arginine and uracil DNA synthesis continues to completion (condition B of Figure 1 and first nutritional shift of Figure 2). Recently *E. coli* strain 15T⁻ (555–7), which requires methionine, tryptophan, and arginine in addition to thymine, has been the subject of a similar investigation by Lark, Repko, and

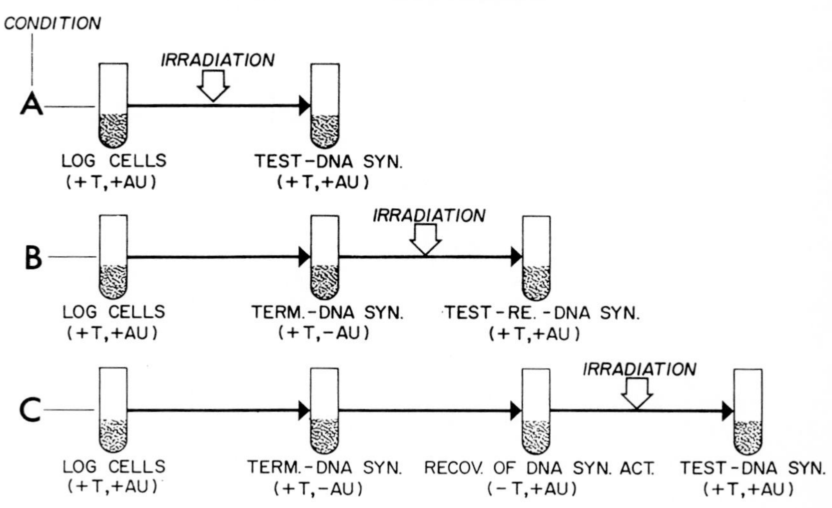

FIGURE 1. Diagrammatic representation of the nutritional shifts used to effect alteration of DNA replicating activity in *E. coli* strain 15 T⁻A⁻U⁻. For convenience the convention of Maaløe and Hanawalt (1961) has been adopted to describe the medium composition. Thus a thymineless medium containing both arginine and uracil has been designated (— T, + AU), and analogously for other combinations of thymine, arginine, and uracil. Abbreviations: T, thymine; A, arginine; U, uracil; DNA, deoxyribonucleic acid; Term.-DNA Syn, termination of DNA synthesizing capacity; Test-Re-DNA Syn, Test for the renewal of DNA synthesizing capacity; Recov. of DNA Syn Act., Restoration of DNA synthesizing activity.

Hoffman (1963). These investigators have concluded that amino acid starvation also leads to a similar completion of the chromosome in this strain. Reinitiation of the next round of replication of the DNA in these starved cells is dependent on renewed RNA and protein synthesis, which can be affected by the addition of the required nutrients (condition C of Figure 1 and the second shift of Figure 2). Using these two bacterial systems, we have looked at the effect of irradiation on the initiation of the next round of DNA replication.

The studies with *E. coli* strain 15T⁻ (555–7) (Billen, 1960) showed that if DNA synthesis were allowed to go to completion in the absence of the required amino acids, a dose of 10,000 roentgens was sufficient to increase the lag normally seen in the unirradiated control cells following amino acid starvation (Figure 3). This effect of ionizing irradiation on the reinitiation of the DNA-synthesizing system may result from one of several altered metabolic states: These include the following: (1) an effect on production of the necessary deoxyribonucleoside triphosphates required for the formation of the DNA polymer, (2) an interference with either the action or the synthesis of the enzymes involved in the polymerization step required for DNA formation, and (3) prevention of the conversion of the DNA into an effective replicative state. (An alternative explanation would

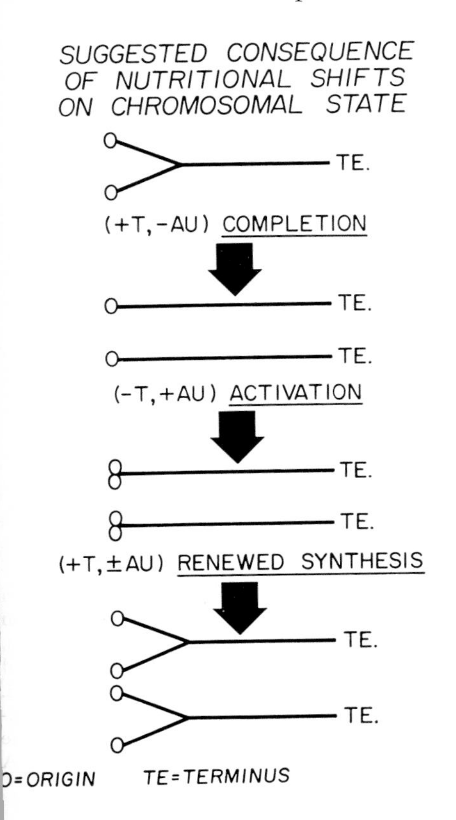

FIGURE 2. Diagrammatic representation of the various assumed states of the bacterial chromosome as a result of the nutritional shifts presented in Figure 1. "O" refers to the chromosomal origin (in regard to initiating site for DNA replication) and "Te" refers to the terminus of the chromosome. While a linear presentation is made, the diagrams would hold for a circular chromosome.

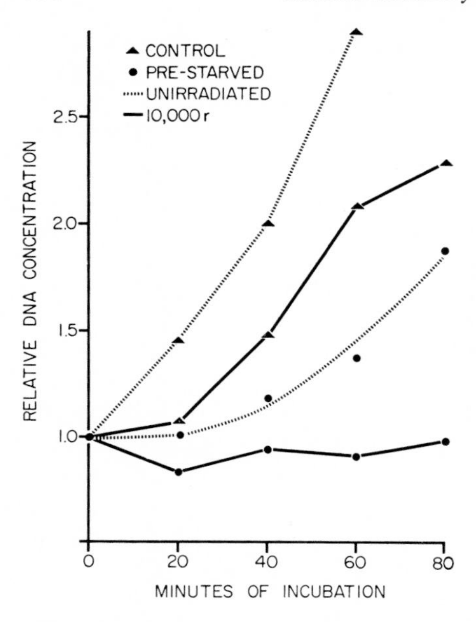

FIGURE 3. The effect of X-ray exposu on renewal of the DNA synthesis cyc in *E. coli* strain 15 T⁻ (555–7). The cel designated as "prestarved" were incubat at 37 C in a minimal salts, glucose mediu supplemented with thymine for 90 mi utes prior to irradiation (similar to co dition B of Figure 1). The control w cells in exponential growth at the time irradiation. The X-ray dose is given roentgens (r) delivered.

be offered by an enhanced degradation of the existing DNA, leading to a erroneous conclusion that DNA synthesis was inhibited. The latter poss bility is the subject of future experimentation and will not be discusse here [see Addendum].)

A study was undertaken to determine the availability of the kinas needed to phosphorylate thymidine and the deoxyribosides of cytosine, ad nine, and guanine to their respective triphosphates. In addition, the effe on DNA polymerase activity was explored. The nutritional shifts require to bring the cell population to one with full DNA complement (genera schema as for *E. coli* strain 15T⁻A⁻U⁻ shown in Figures 1 and 2) wer found not to alter markedly the measurable kinase or polymerase activit (Billen, 1962). Exposure of *E. coli* strain 15T⁻ (555–7), or extracts of suc cells, to 40,000 roentgens of X rays only partially interfered with the ac tivity of the enzymes responsible for the incorporation of thymidine int DNA (Table). On the basis of such studies and the findings in other labora tories indicating substrate accumulation following ultraviolet light exposur or X-irradiation (Kanazir and Errera, 1954; Ord and Stocken, 1958; Bisho and Davidson, 1957), we concluded that the effects of ionizing irradiatio at the dose required to kill 90 to 99 per cent of the population could not b accounted for by an insufficient supply of the enzymes responsible for pro viding the deoxyribonucleotide triphosphates and for subsequent conversio of the substrates into the DNA polymer. However, one additional poin must be considered in regard to the latter; that is, whether newly made poly merase is required for each round of DNA replication. Further studies i our laboratories are aimed at resolving this problem since it can easily b seen that, while X rays may have little effect on existing polymerase, the

Effect of X-Ray Exposure on DNA Synthesis by Extracts of Escherichia coli *Strain 15 T⁻ (555–7)*

Condition of exposure	X-ray dose (in roentgens)	Percentage of thymidine incorporating activity*
Whole cells	0	100
	40,000	82
Extracts	0	100
	10,000	105
	20,000	84
	40,000	61

* Average value of activities of extracts from three independent experiments (Billen, 1961).

may indeed exert a strong effect on synthesis of new polymerase. There is abundant evidence in the literature that the synthesis of new enzymes, particularly certain inducible enzyme systems, are especially sensitive to ionizing radiation (Billen and Lichstein, 1952; Novelli, 1962).

The third alternative, inhibition of activation of DNA-priming activity, appears at present to be the most reasonable explanation for our observations.

While experimental data related directly to the latter possibility are lacking, the following study with *E. coli* strain $15T^-A^-U^-$ illustrates the complex nature of the system under investigation. A study of this thymine-requiring auxotroph was undertaken in hopes of confirming our earlier results with *E. coli* strain $15T^-$ (using chloramphenicol) and *E. coli* strain $15T^-$ (555–7). The nutritional shifts involved in alignment of the cell population with regard to the state of DNA-synthesizing activity are diagrammatically presented in Figures 1 and 2. The system is essentially that used with *E. coli* $15T^-$ (555–7), except that a uracil requirement is introduced. When the effects of X rays on reinitiation of the DNA synthesis cycle (condition B) were assessed, it was found that the results were unlike those observed with *E. coli* $15T^-$ after chloramphenicol treatment or with *E. coli* strain $15T^-$ (555–7) after amino acid starvation (Billen, 1960). As shown in Figure 4, an X-ray dose of 13,600 roentgens did not greatly interfere with the recovery of DNA-synthesizing capacity in *E. coli* strain $15T^-A^-U^-$ (in other similar experiments some slight inhibition was noted with the irradiated cells).

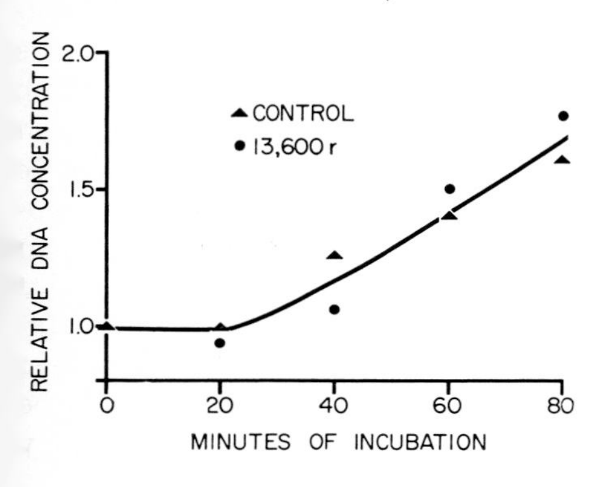

Figure 4. The effect of X-ray exposure on renewal of the DNA synthesis cycle in *E. coli* strain 15 $T^-A^-U^-$. The bacteria were incubated in a minimal salts, glucose medium supplemented with thymine for 90 minutes prior to irradiation (condition B of Figure 1). The X-ray dose is given in roentgens (r) delivered.

In light of this latter finding with *E. coli* strain 15T⁻A⁻U⁻, the preliminary conclusion that reinitiation of DNA replication was a relatively radiosensitive step in the cell cycle of these bacteria appears to need reevaluation. However, Kanazir, Barner, Flaks, and Cohen (1959) have found *E. coli* strain 15T⁻A⁻U⁻ to be a "leaky" mutant, *i.e.* some synthesis of arginine and uracil has been shown to occur (a 47 per cent increase in biuret-reactive material and 10 to 12 per cent increase in RNA in the absence of arginine and uracil). A later report from the same laboratory (Cohen, Sekiguchi, Stern, and Barner, 1963) indicates that both messenger and ribosomal RNA are synthesized under such conditions. While small amounts of protein and RNA are synthesized in the absence of the required amino acid and purine, this does not lead to a reinitiation of DNA-synthesizing capacity following completion of the chromosome (see condition B, Figure 1). For this latter event to occur, both arginine and uracil are required; neither is a sufficient supplement to accomplish this event individually (Billen, Unpublished data). The possibility exists that in *E. coli* strain 15T⁻A⁻U⁻ the radiosensitive event (limited protein and RNA synthesis) involved in initiating the next S period has occurred prior to completion of the chromosome. However, this step is only a part of the sequence of events related to the initiation of the S period, which requires full supplementation for completion. Additional studies with this strain, as well as with other auxotrophs, are being planned to determine whether the events leading to initiation of S period in the bacteria may have a special radiosensitivity.

ACKNOWLEDGMENT

This research was supported in part by Atomic Energy Commission Contract AT-(40-1)-2695.

LIST OF ABBREVIATIONS

Abbreviations used in this paper are as follows:

E. coli strain 15 T⁻A⁻U⁻—refers to a multiauxotrophic strain of *E. coli* requiring a supplement of thymine, arginine, and uracil for balanced growth

E. coli strain 15 T⁻ (555-7)—refers to a multiauxotrophic strain derived from the same parent as 15 T⁻A⁻U⁻, which requires thymine, arginine, tryptophan, and methionine for full growth

ADDENDUM

In cultures of *E. coli* strain 15T⁻ (555–7) grown for 90 min under amino acid deficient condition prior to exposure to 10,000 roentgens of X rays, there was no evidence of any greater degradation of DNA after 60 min postirradiation incubation (Frampton and Billen, Unpublished data).

REFERENCES

Billen, D. 1960. Effects of Prior Alteration in Nucleic Acid and Protein Metabolism on Subsequent Macromolecular Synthesis by Irradiated Bacteria. *Journal of Bacteriology*, 80:86–95.

———. 1961. Modification of the Capacity of Bacteria to Synthesize Deoxyribonucleic Acid Following X-Irradiation: An *in vivo-in vitro* Study. *Pathologie et Biologie*, 9:758–760.

———. 1962. Alteration in Deoxyribonucleic Acid Synthesizing Capacity in Bacteria: An *in vivo-in vitro* Study. *Biochimica et biophysica acta*, 55:960–968.

———. Unpublished data.

Billen, D., and E. W. Frampton. Unpublished data.

Billen, D., and H. C. Lichstein. 1952. The Effect of X Radiation on the Adaptive Formation of Formic Hydrogenlyase in *Escherichia coli*. *Journal of Bacteriology*, 63: 533–535.

Bishop, C. W., and J. N. Davidson. 1957. Changes in Deoxyriboside, Deoxyribotide and Nucleic Acid Content of Rabbit Appendix and Thymus after X-Irradiation. *British Journal of Radiology*, 30:367–370.

Cairns, J. 1963. The Bacterial Chromosome and its Manner of Replication as Seen by Autoradiography. *Journal of Molecular Biology*, 6:208–213.

Cohen, S. S., M. Sekiguchi, J. L. Stern, and H. D. Barner. 1963. The Synthesis of Messenger RNA without Protein Synthesis in Normal and Phage-Infected Thymineless Strains of *Escherichia coli*. *Proceedings of the National Academy of Sciences of the U.S.A.*, 49:699–707.

Kanazir, D., H. D. Barner, J. G. Flaks, and S. S. Cohen. 1959. Some Physiological and Genetic Properties of a Strain of *Escherichia coli* Requiring Thymine, Arginine and Uracil. *Biochimica et biophysica acta*, 34:341–353.

Kanazir, D., and M. Errera. 1954. Metabolisme des Acides nucleiques chez *E. coli* B apres Irradiation ultraviolete. *Biochimica et biophysica acta*, 14:62–66.

Lark, K. G., T. Repko, and E. J. Hoffman. 1963. The Effect of Amino Acid Deprivation on Subsequent Deoxyribonucleic Acid Replication. *Biochimica et biophysica acta*, 76:9–24.

Maaløe, O., and P. C. Hanawalt. 1961. Thymine Deficiency and the Normal DNA Replication Cycle. I. *Journal of Molecular Biology*, 3:144–155.

Nagata, T. 1963. The Molecular Synchrony and Sequential Replication of DNA in *Escherichia coli*. *Proceedings of the National Academy of Sciences of the U.S.A.*, 49:551–559.

Novelli, G. D. 1962. "Mechanisms Involved in the Control of Enzyme Synthesis," *The Molecular Basis of Neoplasia* (The University of Texas M. D. Anderson Hospital and Tumor Institute, Fifteenth Annual Symposium on Fundamental Cancer Research). Austin, Texas: University of Texas Press. Pp. 435–460.

Ord, M. G., and L. A. Stocken. 1958. Deoxyribotide Accumulation in Rat Thymus After X-Radiation. *Biochimica et biophysica acta*, 29:201–202.

———. 1961. "The Biochemical lesion *in vivo* and *in vitro*," *Mechanisms in Radiobiology*, M. Errera and A. Forssberg, Eds. New York, New York, and London, England: Academic Press. Vol. I. Pp. 259–331.

Yoshikawa, H., and N. Sueoka. 1963a. Sequential Replication of *Bacillus subtilis* Chromosome. I. Comparison of Marker Frequencies in Exponential and Stationary Growth Phases. *Proceedings of the National Academy of Sciences of the U.S.A.*, 49:559–566.

———. 1963b. Sequential Replication of *Bacillus subtilis* Chromosome. II. Isotopic Transfer Experiments. *Proceedings of the National Academy of Sciences of the U.S.A.*, 49:806–813.

Chromosome Aberrations Induced by Incorporation of Tritiated Thymidine

T. C. Hsu and Maria T. Zenzes*

Section of Cytology, Department of Biology,
The University of Texas M. D. Anderson Hospital and Tumor Institute,
Houston, Texas

Many investigators have found that incorporation of tritiated thym
dine (H^3TdR) into cellular deoxyribonucleic acid (DNA) induced chrom
some aberrations (McQuade, Friedkin, and Atchison, 1956; Wimber, 195
Natarajan, 1961). However, correlation has not been firmly established b
tween the site of incorporation and the site of chromosome damage. It
possible that the β emission of tritium from one chromosome induces da
age of a neighboring chromosome which contains no detectable incorpor
tion. In the light of the findings of asynchronous DNA replication sequen
in the Chinese hamster (Taylor, 1960; Hsu, 1964), the present study r
ports an analysis of the relationship between these two factors.

Material and Methods

A diploid Chinese hamster cell strain, strain Don (Hsu and Zenz
1964), was used in this study. Tritiated thymidine (New England Nucle
Corporation, specific activity 6.7 c/mmole, final dilution, 1 or 2 μc/ml) w
introduced to growing cultures and left in the medium until harvest. Ea
culture was also treated with Colcemid (CIBA Pharmaceuticals) for o
hour (final concentration, 0.06 μg/ml) before fixation. In one experime
H^3TdR labeling lasted for two hours, and the culture was washed a
grown for four additional hours in medium with nonradioactive thymidi
(10 μg/ml).

Aceto-orcein squash preparations were made with the convention

* International Atomic Energy Fellow. Permanent address: Laboratorio de Genética, Comisión Nacional
Energia Nuclear, México, D. F.

method. In recording chromosome aberrations, only obvious chromatid breaks and exchanges were scored, each chromatid break being counted as one break and each exchange, two breaks. A number of cells with aberrations (including incomplete breaks and constrictions) were photographed from cultures treated with 2 μc/ml H^3TdR before stripping film (Kodak AR 10) was applied. The exposure time of the film was four days. Autoradiographic technique and Giemsa staining method after film development followed the procedures described by Schmid (1963). The cells previously photographed were relocated and rephotographed.

Results

Brief Accounts of the Chromosomes of the Male Chinese Hamster

Hsu (1963) proposed a nomenclature system for the Chinese hamster chromosomes by arranging the diploid chromosomes in descending size order. Thus the two largest submetacentrics (1 and 2) form Group I, the medium-sized submetacentrics (X, Y, 4, and 5) form Group II, the subtelocentrics (6, 7, and 8), Group III, and the small metacentrics (9, 10, and 11), Group IV. Hsu and Zenzes (1964) made detailed measurements of the chromosomes and suggested a revised subdivision system but used the original chromosome numbers of Hsu.

The phenomenon of asynchronous DNA replication in this species was first described by Taylor (1960). Hsu (1964) analyzed autoradiographic patterns of many cells and found the following: The Y chromosome and the long arm of the X are very late replicating. Also late replicating are chromosomes 10 and 11, the short arms of chromosomes 7, 8, and 9, and regions in chromosomes 1, 2 and the distal portion of 6. Chromosomes 4 and 5 complete replication earlier than other elements.

Table 1 shows frequencies of chromatid breaks (breaks per cell) in the Don cells following treatment with tritiated thymidine at varying intervals.

TABLE 1

*Frequency of Chromatid Breaks (Breaks/Cell) in Chinese Hamster Cells (Strain Don) following Continuous Treatment with H^3TdR**

Dose of H^3TdR	Hours of treatment	Breaks/cell	Percentage of breaks forming exchanges
1 μc/ml	3	0.13	0.0
	4	0.33	6.2
	Control	0.01	0.0
2 μc/ml	3	0.32	6.4
	4	0.51	7.9
	6	2.24	16.1
	6(first 2 hours only)	0.72	11.1
	9(first 2 hours only)	1.90	25.3
	Control	0.03	0.0

* Each chromatid break was counted as 1 break; each exchange, 2 breaks. Cell number per sample, 100.

Several conclusions can be drawn from the data: (1) Frequency of aberrations increased with the increase of dose of tritiated thymidine. (2) Frequency of aberrations increased with the increase of duration of tritium treatment. (3) Percentage of exchanges increased more rapidly with the increase of duration than with that of dosage.

If H^3TdR induced randomized damage on chromosomes irrespective of the site of incorporation, the distribution of chromatid breaks should be proportional to the relative lengths of the chromosomes. Thus, the relative chromosome lengths of the Chinese hamster calculated by Hsu and Zenzes (1964) could be used as expected values for random distribution. If the production of chromatid aberrations is a direct result of thymidine incorporation, chromosomes showing higher DNA synthetic activity at the time of TdR treatment should sustain more damage than those showing low activity or no activity. The continuous incorporation method at the end stage of DNA synthesis used in this study would be more revealing than pulse labeling (especially at middle or early DNA synthetic period), because late replicating sites can be clearly demonstrated by heavy label. Thus the Y chromosome and the long arm of the X should show substantially higher frequency of damage than chromosomes 4 and 5. Furthermore, damage on the long arm of the X should show a higher frequency than damage on the short arm, on a comparative basis. Table 2 presents data showing nonrandom distribution of chromatid breaks among the chromosomes of male Chinese hamster treated with H^3TdR. The sex chromosomes sustained more damage in proportion to their lengths. This was especially so when the treatment period was short (three hours). Indication is, therefore, strong that the damage was positively related to the rate of H^3TdR uptake. Chromosomes 4 and 5, which generally complete DNA replication earlier than other chromosomes, showed less damage than expected on a random basis.

TABLE 2

*Percentage of Distribution of Chromatid Breaks among Chromosomes of Don Cells Treated with H^3TdR for Varying Intervals**

Chromosome number	Expected†	1 μc, 4 hr	2 μc			
			3 hr	4 hr	6 hour (1st 2 hours only)	9 hour (1st 2 hours only)
1	22.16	29.5	29.0	29.0	22.2	28.0
2	16.58	13.5	16.0	16.0	18.3	12.0
X	4.78	13.0	13.5	14.0	7.9	3.0
Y	4.25	10.0	13.5	10.0	6.4	1.0
4	10.14	7.5	5.0	6.0	10.3	14.0
5	8.94	5.0	4.5	5.0	6.3	10.0
6, 7, 8	20.74	17.0	14.0	15.0	18.3	24.0
9, 10, 11	12.44	4.5	4.5	5.0	10.3	8.0

* Minimum sample, 100 breaks.
† Based on percentage of mean chromosome length for diploid male cells. With the exceptions of X and Y chromosomes, the length for each chromosome is represented twice. (Hsu and Zenzes, 1964).

Since the Y chromosome and the long arm of the X chromosome do not replicate during the early S period (Taylor, 1960; Hsu, 1964), tritiated thymidine should not cause severe damage on these chromosomes during this stage if damage is correlated with active incorporation. An experiment was conducted to treat the cultures with H^3TdR for two hours, after which the cells were grown in medium containing nonradioactive thymidine and fixed four and seven hours thereafter. Thus the total time after the introduction of label was six and nine hours, respectively. The data, included in Table 2, show clearly that the damage on the sex chromosomes was greatly reduced, especially the sample harvested at hour 9.

Distribution of Breaks Along Chromosomes 1, X, and Y

According to Hsu's observation (Hsu, 1964), the Y chromosome is late replicating throughout its length, the X is late replicating only on the long arm, and chromosome 1 is relatively late replicating on its short arm. Therefore, one may be able to correlate the frequency of chromatid breaks and the late incorporation activities. The subdivision used in this report (Figure 1) follows the system suggested by Hsu and Zenzes (1964). Localization of the breaks was, of necessity, approximate. The long arm of chromosome 1, which is 1.20 times as long as the short arm, showed fewer breaks (51) than the short arm (61). The arm ratio (long arm/short arm) for the X chromosome is 1.30, but the distribution of breaks on this chromosome was 63 for the long arm and 22 for the short arm, approximately three times greater for the long arm. The Y chromosome has an arm ratio of 1.83, and the number of breaks was 51 for the long arm and 19 for the short arm. At least a part of the discrepancy between the expected and actual distribution can be explained on the basis of differential rate of incorporation of the tritiated DNA precursor.

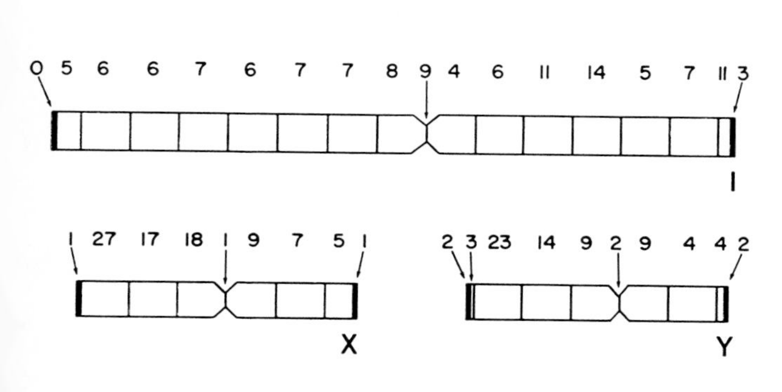

FIGURE 1. Frequency of chromatid breaks in regions of chromosomes, 1, X, and Y of the Chinese hamster. Cultures were treated continuously with H^3TdR (2 $\mu c/ml$) for four hours, and Colcemid (0.06 $\mu g/ml$) for the last hour. Zoning of chromosomes followed the system suggested by Hsu and Zenzes (1964).

Correlation between H^3TdR Incorporation and Chromatid Breaks in Autoradiographs

From cells showing aberrations photographed before and after film stripping, Figure 2 suggests positive correlation between sites of H^3 incorporation and chromosome damage. It must be pointed out that incorpora-

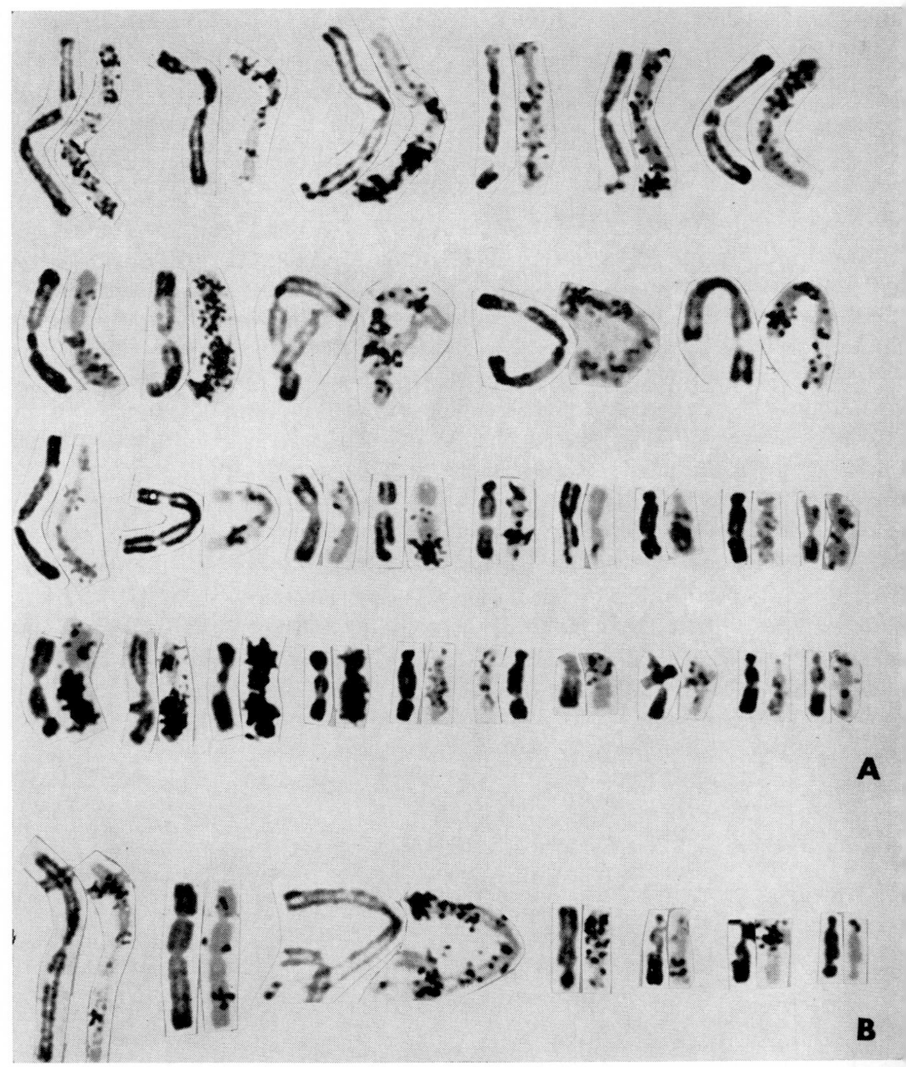

FIGURE 2. Cut-out chromosomes (before and after autoradiography) from cells of Chinese hamster treated with H^3TdR (2 μc/ml) continuously for four hours, and Colcemid (0.06 μg/ml) for the last hour.

A. Chromatid aberrations coinciding with tritium label.

B. Chromatid aberrations not coinciding with tritium label.

tion of H^3TdR does not always induce chromosome damage, but a high frequency of damage is seen to locate at the sites of radioactivity. The remaining breaks without label at their sites are probably caused by (1) spontaneous chromatid breaks which occur in regular cultures at a low frequency, (2) indirect induction by β emission from neighboring chromosomes which incorporated the isotope, and (3) actual incorporation of H^3 but lack of decay of the isotope during the exposure period (four days). However, the last possibility is not very likely, because, according to Dewey, Humphrey, and Jones (in press), to produce one visible aberration per cell over a 10-hour period, 1,730 disintegrations are needed. If a break had been induced by the β emission, there should have been sufficient incorporation to expose the film within the four-day exposure period.

Discussion

Our results established a strong correlation between sites of H^3TdR incorporation and chromatid breaks. Workers who claim to have found a lack of correlation employed methods different from the one used in this communication. Most workers are not concerned with the asynchronous DNA synthetic phenomenon, which appears important in this type of inquiry. Gilbert, Muldal, Lajtha, and Rowley (1962) observed in human cells that chromatid breaks seem to localize at replicating regions in late S cells, but appear to distribute at random among cells in the middle or early S phases. Since most chromosomes in the middle or early S phases take tritiated thymidine along their entire lengths (Dewey, Humphrey, and Jones, in press), aberrations are then possible on any part of the chromosome. The only question remaining is the direct relation between the location of the silver grains and the site of damage. When one wishes to study chromosome aberration from an autoradiograph without photographic recording before the application of the film, it becomes necessary to expose the film as lightly as practicable, thus allowing few H^3TdR molecules to decay. In so doing, many chromatid breaks would not show radioactivity even though incorporation of the precursor did take place. Our method of prerecording the aberrations, though more tedious, has a distinct advantage and would, consequently, provide more clear-cut data because heavy exposure to the film is allowed.

The data presented herein do not deny the possibility that chromosome aberrations may be indirectly induced; but it is clear that the sites of incorporation are the primary targets of the β particles.

ACKNOWLEDGMENTS

This work was supported in part by Grant E-286 from the American Cancer Society and Grant DRG-269 from the Damon Runyon Memorial Fund for Cancer Research.

ADDENDUM

After the submission of this paper, R. R. Klevecz and T. C. Hsu undertook an investigation on chromosome aberrations induced by H^3-uridine as an index of differential capacity for RNA synthesis among chromosomes. They repeated the H^3TdR work presented here and found comparable results (Klevecz and Hsu, 1964).

REFERENCES

Dewey, W. C., R. M. Humphrey, and B. A. Jones. 1964. Effectiveness of Tritiated Thymidine Compared with Tritiated Water and Cobalt-60 Gamma Rays for the Induction of Chromosomal Aberrations. *Radiation Research.* (in press.)

Gilbert, C. W., S. Muldal, L. G. Lajtha, and J. Rowley. 1962. Time-Sequence of Human Chromosome Duplication. *Nature,* London, 195:869–874.

Hsu, T. C. 1963. "Mammalian Chromosomes *in vitro.* XVI. Analysis of Chromosome Breakages in Cell Populations of the Chinese Hamster." *Canadian Cancer Conference (Proceedings of the Fifth Canadian Cancer Research Conference,* Honey Harbour, Ontario, June 10–14, 1962). New York, New York, and London, England: Academic Press. Vol. V. Pp. 117–127.

————. 1964. Mammalian Chromosomes *in vitro.* XVIII. DNA Replication Sequence in the Chinese Hamster. *Journal of Cell Biology.* (in press.)

Hsu, T. C., and M. T. Zenzes. 1964. Mammalian Chromosomes *in vitro.* XVII. Idiogram of the Chinese Hamster. *Journal of the National Cancer Institute,* 32:857–869.

Klevecz, R. R., and T. C. Hsu. 1964. The Differential Capacity for RNA Synthesis Among Chromosomes: A Cytological Approach. *Proceedings of the National Academy of Sciences of the U.S.A.,* 52:811–817.

McQuade, H. A., M. Friedkin, and A. A. Atchison. 1956. Radiation Effects of Thymidine-2-C^{14}. II. Chromosome Aberrations Caused by Thymidine-2-C^{14} and Thymine-2-C^{14} in the Onion Root Tip. *Experimental Cell Research,* 11:256–264.

Natarajan, A. T. 1961. Chromosome Breakage and Mitotic Inhibition Induced by Tritiated Thymidine in Root Meristems of *Vicia faba. Experimental Cell Research,* 22:275–281.

Schmid, W. 1963. DNA Replication Patterns of Human Chromosomes. *Cytogenetics,* 2:175–193.

Taylor, J. H. 1960. Asynchronous Duplication of Chromosomes in Cultured Cells of Chinese Hamster. *The Journal of Biophysical and Biochemical Cytology,* 7:455–463.

Wimber, D. E. 1959. Chromosome Breakage Produced by Tritium-Labeled Thymidine in *Tradescantia paludosa. Proceedings of the National Academy of Sciences of the U.S.A.,* 45:839–846.

Mathematical Models of the Recovery of Mammalian Cells from Radiation Injury, with Respect to Changes in Radiosensitivity

G. M. Hahn, J. R. Boen, R. G. Miller, S. F. Boyle, and R. F. Kallman

Departments of Radiology and Preventive Medicine,
Stanford University School of Medicine,
Palo Alto, California

The techniques of obtaining relatively precise quantitative data on the survival of mammalian cells after exposure to X rays are sufficiently advanced to warrant the construction of mathematical models to aid in the elucidation of the phenomena involved.

Given sufficient information about certain critical parameters (e.g. radiation sensitivity or D_0, extrapolation number, and division delay as a function both of dose and of cell state), we can then proceed to evaluate hypotheses to account for the time course of radiation-induced changes in the survival properties of different cell populations. In addition to these deterministic radiobiological quantities, statistical properties of the relevant variables are of importance, e.g. the durations of the several cell states and the rates of movement of cells through the cycle and its component parts. In tissue culture measurements, consideration of averages (or, more precisely, expected values) appears to be sufficient. If descriptions are to be extended to tissues and tumors, however, the stochastic properties of the proliferation processes will have to be more adequately defined and considered.

Using data obtained for the HeLa cell by Terasima and Tolmach (1963), we have constructed two different models in order to test the validity of the notion proposed in detail elsewhere (Kallman, 1963). Essentially, the hypothesis to be examined attempts to relate radiation-induced changes in radiosensitivity of originally random, or heterogeneous, cell populations with a changing pattern of redistribution of cell states among the individual cells surviving a first dose.

1. Stochastic Model

Assumptions

(1) Exponentially growing HeLa cells have a mean generation time of 22 hours, and individual cells display a delayed exponential distribution of generation times about this mean.

(2) The generation cycle may be divided into four states, *1*, *2*, *3*, and *4*, corresponding to G_1, S, G_2, and M, respectively.

(3) The duration of state *1* is a fixed minimum of 7 hours plus an exponential time. States *2*, *3*, and *4* are of fixed duration, lasting 6, 4, and 1 hours, respectively.

(4) Cells in each state are killed by radiation according to conventional hit theory, *i.e.* the surviving fraction $S = 1 - (1 - e^{-D/D_0})^n$; and n is assumed to be 2 for all states. The D_0's for the four states are 180, 100, 160, and 70 rads, respectively.

(5) All cells in states *1*, *2*, and *3* exposed to radiation will be delayed in reaching state *4* by intervals dependent upon their state at the instant of irradiation, but there will be no change in the rate of progress from state *1* to *2*, or *2* to *3*. The average delay times for a constant plus exponentially distributed time variables are: cells in state *1*, <0.1 minutes/rad; *2*, 0.4 minutes/rad; and *3*, 1.0 minutes/rad. Once a cell has entered state *4* it is assumed to be capable of progressing into the next cycle, provided it is not killed by the first radiation dose.

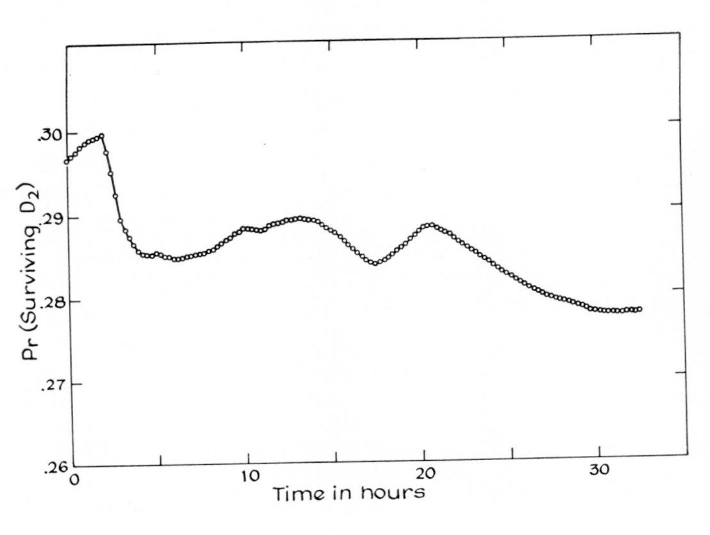

FIGURE 1. Probability of HeLa cells surviving a second dose (D_2) of 300 rads as a function of time after exposure to a first dose of 300 rads, as predicted according to the stochastic model.

Prediction

Assuming a heterogeneous population with the preceding characteristics, the model was solved for the composition of an exponentially growing HeLa cell population as a function of time after a dose of 300 rads. Given the predicted composition of the population at any time, with respect to the proportion of first-dose surviving cells of different states and therefore of different radiosensitivities as assumed above, the probability of surviving a second dose (D_2) of 300 rads was then computed (Figure 1).

The curve in Figure 1 indicates that the population becomes resistant for a very brief time (about two hours or less), then becomes more sensitive (reaching a maximum sensitivity at about 5 hours), then becomes more resistant, and finally becomes less resistant again. This progression of sensitivity changes offers some qualitative confirmation of expectation (Kallman, 1963) but does not agree with the limited experimental data available (Lockart, Elkind, and Moses, 1961) with respect both to the times at which the resistant and sensitive states supervene and to the magnitude of the degrees of resistance and sensitivity.

We feel that this disagreement is more apparent than real and can, to a large extent, be accounted for. This illustrates one of the fundamental weaknesses of this model at its present state of development. Obviously, cells do not change sensitivity abruptly between four arbitrary states. Rather, in fact, sensitivity during interphase is a continuously changing variable which reaches maxima and minima that hold for only very short periods. This model specifies a relatively long sensitive state (state *2*) into which state *1* survivors flow shortly after the differential depopulation at time 0. This kind of simplifying assumption is bound to predict a marked condition of sensitivity which would persist for an appreciable time; while such a state may indeed be brought about, it has not been observed, probably because it is of such short duration.

2. Phenomenological Model

We attempt to describe the behavior of cell populations under a variety of experimental conditions. Imagine that a heterogeneous population is subdivided into m subpopulations. The criterion used in establishing these subgroups is the position of the cell in its reproductive cycle. Mathematically we can then represent the cells by a vector $\vec{P}$ whose components, p_i, are the subpopulations. For convenience, the first component represents newly born cells, while the last is made up of cells about to divide. $\vec{P}$ is illustrated for three idealized populations: (a) the perfectly synchronized, (b) "perfectly random," and (c) exponentially growing population:

$$\vec{P}_{(a)} = \frac{N}{\sum_i p_i}\begin{bmatrix} 1 \\ 0 \\ \cdot \\ \cdot \\ \cdot \\ \cdot \\ \cdot \\ \dot{0} \\ \cdot \\ \cdot \\ \cdot \\ \cdot \\ \cdot \\ \cdot \\ \cdot \\ \dot{0} \end{bmatrix}; \quad \vec{P}_{(b)} = \frac{N}{\sum_i p_i}\begin{bmatrix} 1 \\ 1 \\ \cdot \\ \cdot \\ \cdot \\ \cdot \\ \cdot \\ \dot{1} \\ \cdot \\ \cdot \\ \cdot \\ \cdot \\ \cdot \\ \cdot \\ \cdot \\ \dot{1} \end{bmatrix}; \quad \vec{P}_{(c)} = \frac{N}{\sum_i p_i}\begin{bmatrix} 2^{-1/m} \\ 2^{-2/m} \\ \cdot \\ \cdot \\ \cdot \\ \cdot \\ \cdot \\ \dot{2}^{-i/m} \\ \cdot \\ \cdot \\ \cdot \\ \cdot \\ \cdot \\ \cdot \\ \cdot \\ \dot{2}^{-1} \end{bmatrix}$$

where N = total number of cells, and m = number of subdivisions in mean generation time T.

After some time, a measurement would show that the vector $\vec{P}$ has been changed to a vector $\vec{P}'$. This may be the result of radiation, drugs, or simply the passage of cells through the generation cycle. In the model we construct operators which affect transformations corresponding to specific events. Compound events are described by the sequential application of individual operators.

Unit Time Shift

Suppose we construct the vector $\vec{P}$ at time zero, and then sample the system again T/m time units later. Under conditions of exponential growth and in the absence of other events the only changes will be: a cyclic permutation of cell components, and a doubling of the number of cells in the process of permuting the last component to the first, *i.e.* those cells about to divide at $t = 0$ have divided by $t = T/m$. The operator which effects this transformation is the matrix Δ_1 followed by transposition.

Operating with this matrix on the three illustrative populations yields, except for constants,

$$\vec{P}' = [\Delta_1 \vec{P}]_{T_r} = \begin{bmatrix} 0 \\ 1 \\ 0 \\ \cdot \\ \cdot \\ \cdot \\ 0 \\ \cdot \\ \cdot \\ \cdot \\ \cdot \\ \cdot \\ 0 \end{bmatrix} ; \quad \begin{bmatrix} 2 \\ 1 \\ 1 \\ \cdot \\ \cdot \\ \cdot \\ 1 \\ \cdot \\ \cdot \\ \cdot \\ \cdot \\ \cdot \\ 1 \end{bmatrix} ; \quad 2^{1/m} \begin{bmatrix} 2^{-1/m} \\ 2^{-2/m} \\ 2^{-3/m} \\ \cdot \\ \cdot \\ \cdot \\ 2^{-i/m} \\ \cdot \\ \cdot \\ \cdot \\ \cdot \\ \cdot \\ 2^{-1} \end{bmatrix}$$

(a) (b) (c)

Here, T_r indicates transposition.

Radiation

The survival probability of irradiated cells is as stated above (*cf.* Model 1). In our scheme we generalize to the matrix $S(D)$:

$$S(D) = \begin{bmatrix} 1-(1-e^{-D/D_{01}})^{n_1} & 0 & \cdots & 0 \\ 0 & 1-(1-e^{-D/D_{02}})^{n_2} & \cdots & 0 \\ \vdots & & & \vdots \\ 0 & \cdots & \cdots & 1-(1-e^{-D/D_{om}})^{n_m} \end{bmatrix}$$

Delay

Radiation-induced delay is handled much in the manner of time shifts. Operators are defined which correspond to simple G_2 block (Whitmore, Stanners, Till, and Gulyas, 1961) or the more detailed stage-dependent delay (Terasima and Tolmach, 1963; Mak and Till, 1963). Details are somewhat cumbersome and are not presented here.

Dispersion

Because of the statistical variations of cell parameters, a measurement performed on a subgroup of cells at $t=0$ will not correspond precisely to the measurement made on the same subgroup some time later (recall the criterion for establishing subgroups, *i.e.* position within cell cycle). To account for this, we define a dispersion operator δ:

$$\delta = \begin{bmatrix} (1-\alpha-\beta) & \alpha & 0 & \cdots & \beta \\ \beta & (1-\alpha-\beta) & \alpha & \cdots & 0 \\ 0 & & & & \vdots \\ \vdots & & & & \vdots \\ \alpha & \cdots & & \beta & (1-\alpha-\beta) \end{bmatrix}$$

The dispersion operator is always associated with the unit shift operator. If $\alpha = \beta$, the cell parameters are symmetrically distributed. This is illustrated for $\alpha = \beta = .1$ by showing the effect of repeated operations of dispersion and time shift on $P_{(a)}$. Transposition and normalization constants are omitted.

$$\vec{P} = \begin{bmatrix} 1 \\ 0 \\ 0 \\ 0 \\ 0 \\ 0 \\ 0 \end{bmatrix} ; (\delta\Delta_1)\vec{P} = \begin{bmatrix} .1 \\ .8 \\ .1 \\ 0 \\ 0 \\ 0 \\ 0 \end{bmatrix} ; (\delta\Delta_1)^2\vec{P} = \begin{bmatrix} .01 \\ .16 \\ .66 \\ .16 \\ .01 \\ 0 \\ 0 \end{bmatrix} ; (\delta\Delta_1)^3\vec{P} = \begin{bmatrix} .001 \\ .024 \\ .195 \\ .560 \\ .195 \\ .024 \\ .001 \end{bmatrix}$$

Computer Results

The model was programmed on a CDC 1604. Data for HeLa cells were taken from Terasima and Tolmach (1963). The extrapolation number was assumed to be equal to two throughout the cycle. The cycle was subdivided into 22 stages, each of one-hour duration. The dispersion constants α and β were taken as .01 each; this yielded a standard deviation in generation times of 10 per cent, which is consistent with the observations of Puck and Steffen (1963). In particular, results were calculated for a hypothetical two-fraction experiment in which both first and second doses were 300 rads.

In terms of our model, this amounts to calculating the surviving fraction from the vector $\vec{P}_i'$, where L is the delay operator and

$$\vec{P}_i' = S(D_2)L_i(\delta\Delta_1)^i S(D_1)\vec{P}.$$

Figure 2 shows the results for $P_{(b)}$ and $P_{(a)}$ as the initial states of the population.

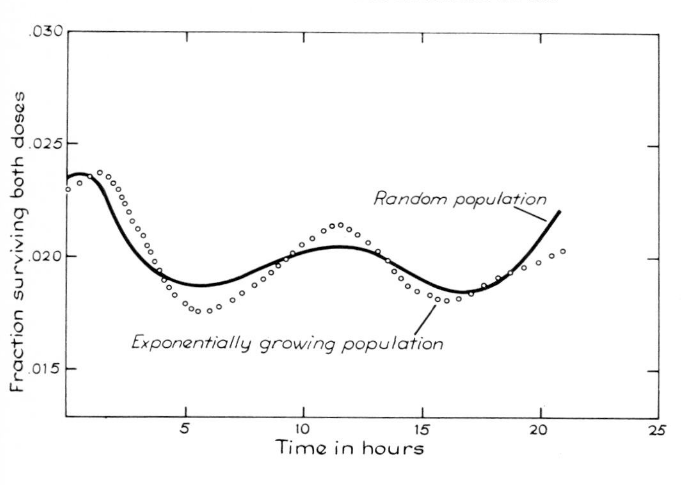

FIGURE 2. Expected fraction of HeLa cells surviving two doses of 300 rads as a function of time between exposure to the first and second dose, as predicted according to the phenomenological model.

CONCLUSIONS

It is concluded that the results, *i.e.* the predictions, from this model are in qualitative agreement with observation. The computer results do not show the exponential envelope, or trend, of the recuperation curves seen experimentally. It may be inferred, therefore, that the radiation-sensitivity changes, which occur during recuperation after a first dose, reflect two kinds of events: (1) shifts in the proportions of cell states which constitute the normal population, and (2) a true repair process taking place intracellularly in cells which have received a sublethal injury. Obviously, the approaches summarized in this report require extensive refinement by the incorporation of larger numbers of cell states and their relevant survival parameters.

ACKNOWLEDGMENTS

This investigation was supported in part by a Public Health Service training grant (number CA 5008) from the National Cancer Institute, Public Health Service. One of us (GMH) wishes to acknowledge a National Science Foundation Science Faculty Fellowship.

REFERENCES

Kallman, R. F. 1963. Recovery from Radiation Injury: A Proposed Mechanism. *Nature*, London, 197:557–560.

Lockart, R. Z., M. M. Elkind, and W. B. Moses. 1961. Radiation Response of Mammalian Cells Grown in Culture. II. Survival and Recovery Characteristics of Several Subcultures of HeLa S3 Cells after X Irradiation. *Journal of the National Cancer Institute*, 27:1393–1404.

Mak, S., and J. E. Till. 1963. The Effects of X-Rays on the Progress of L-Cells through the Cell Cycle. *Radiation Research*, 20:600–618.

Puck, T. T., and J. Steffen. 1963. Life Cycle Analysis of Mammalian Cells. *Biophysical Journal*, 3:379–397.

Terasima, T., and L. J. Tolmach. 1963. Variations in Several Responses of HeLa Cells to X-Irradiation during the Division Cycle. *Biophysical Journal*, 3:11–33.

Whitmore, G. F., C. P. Stanners, J. E. Till, and S. Gulyas. 1961. Nucleic Acid Synthesis and the Division Cycle in X-Irradiated L-Strain Mouse Cells. *Biochimica et biophysica acta*, 47:66–77.

Survival and Recovery in X-Irradiated Synchronized Chinese Hamster Cells

W. K. Sinclair and R. A. Morton

Argonne National Laboratory, Argonne, Illinois

We have synchronized Chinese hamster cell populations using a method similar to that described for HeLa cells by Tolmach, that is, by selecting for rounded-up cells. To accomplish this for hamster cells, a combination of procedures which includes temporary cooling and shaking under controlled conditions has been found necessary (Sinclair and Morton, 1963).

Various criteria may be used to describe the degree of synchrony achieved in such selected populations (Sinclair and Morton, 1964). One of these methods is demonstrated in Figure 1. The selected population is reincubated after inoculation, and at intervals thereafter plates are removed and pulse labeled with tritium-labeled thymidine (H^3TdR) (~ 0.2 μc/ml) for 15 minutes. At zero time, very few cells are labeled, but as the population enters the S period, the percentage of cells rises to about 90 per cent or more by five to six hours, remains high throughout S until $\sim$ 12 hours, and then falls again during the G_2 period. Most of the cells divide at about 15 hours. Figure 1 also shows the result of continuing pulse labeling into the second cycle. Slight desynchronization already occurs during the second cycle, with the maximum percentage of labeled cells a little lower, and the minimum percentage at the second division (26 to 27 hours) higher than in the first cycle.

In Figure 2 are shown X-ray survival curves over a range of more than two decades taken at different times, *i.e.* at different cell ages. The first curve is for cells at two hours, when most of the cells are in G_1. The next curve in order (curve No. 4) is at 15 hours when some of the cells have already divided, so that we have a mixture of G_2 cells and dividing cells. If we correct for the increase in cells per colony at this time, however, these cells give about the same survival curve as the G_1 cells. Cells in S at both 9 and 10 hours give rise to the curves labeled 2 and 3. It takes courage and some im-

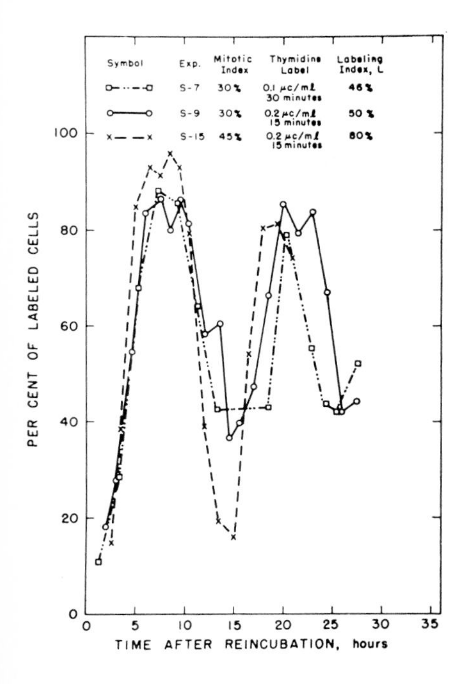

FIGURE 1. Partially synchronized populations of V79 Chinese hamster cells. Percentage of cells labeled with a pulse of tritiated thymidine versus incubation time. The labeling index $L = L_{max} - L^{f}_{min}$ is described elsewhere (Sinclair and Morton, 1964).

agination to fit the extrapolation number (n) and D_0 to the curve for S cells, but if this is done, to a first approximation, the slope is about the same as for the other curves [$D_0 \sim 200$ rad]; and n is greater by a factor of about 4. Now, insofar as Dr. Lajtha's question is concerned, we think in radiotherapy one is mostly interested in the first decade of survival, perhaps the first two decades; and we are not particularly concerned with whether it is the shoulder or the slope which has altered, or indeed whether it can be ascribed

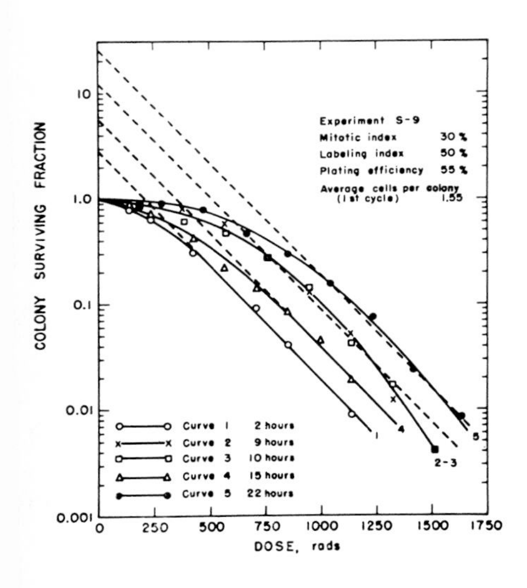

FIGURE 2. Colony survival curves at different times after incubation of partially synchronized V79 Chinese hamster cells. The dashed lines indicate the approximation obtained by fitting a multi-target, single-hit relation with a D_0 of 200 rad (Sinclair and Morton, 1964).

to either, but only whether at any given dose level in this range, these cells (*i.e.* S cells) are more resistant than those cells (G_1 and G_2). In the case of hamster cells, this is certainly true over at least two decades of survival.

The next curve (curve 5) shows a similar response for the S period in the second generation cycle, in which the extrapolation number has very properly gone up by about a factor of 2 over that for the S period in the first generation cycle.

There do not seem to be any major discrepancies between these responses and the data presented this morning for hamster cells by Dr. Dewey, except perhaps in G_1, where we think there is definitely a region of sensitivity in agreement with part of Tolmach's response in the HeLa cell in G_1. We do not see the period of resistance in G_1 which is seen in the HeLa cell by Dr. Tolmach, but this may only be because we do not have the length of G_1 to see it in. In fact, if you were to measure X-ray response back in time from the first division, *i.e.*, start at the end of 15 hours for the hamster cells (and later for HeLa cells) and go back in time, you would probably find that the HeLa cell response and hamster cell response to X rays are quite alike for a considerable period. The principal difference is that you can go further back in time with HeLa cells, and apparently an additional resistant period is then evident. It is worth noting, too, that the period of highest survival in the hamster is almost coincidental with the S period, whereas for L cells and for HeLa cells, both with longer generation times, early S is quite sensitive and middle-to-late S is quite resistant. The normal subdivisions of the cycle into G_1, S, and G_2 (and M) may not be the most suitable fractions with which to describe the X-ray response of mammalian cells with age.

The next point is concerned with recovery of cells following X-ray exposure. The real question in the work Elkind and Sutton (1960) have done is whether there is an actual phenomenon of intracellular recovery, or whether any of the changes that they have observed and documented so well can be explained by response changes during cellular movement from one cell age to another.

The top curve in Figure 3 shows the response to a single dose of 660 rads. The end of the first generation cycle occurs at about 15 hours. More than one cycle is shown on this graph, but let us concentrate on the first cycle only. The lower curve in Figure 3 is for a single dose of 1,320 rads. At various points on this curve (full circles), two fractionated doses of 660 rads plus 660 rads were given with various time intervals in between (the first open circle should be up on the 1,320 rads curve, but it is not, because the plates were handled slightly differently). I have shown only one of these two-dose response curves, that starting at 10.6 hours, because it occurs right at the peak of the single dose response curve. You can see the two-dose survival rises by a factor of something like 4, and thereafter follows very much the same pattern as that for 1,320 rads single dose, but displaced in time. Now this rise cannot be attributed to response changes during cellular movement. The first dose was given right at the peak of the response curve, and cell movement can only take the cell toward a lower level of survival probability. In fact, survival rises as the interval between first and second doses increases up to about 2.5 hours. Thereafter, the two-dose survival pattern (660 rad + 660 rad) is quite similar to that for a single dose of 1,320 rad, but displaced toward later times and higher survivals. Recovery, therefore, for cells in S is a real phenomenon which cannot be attributed to changing responses at different cell ages. Actually, we see this recovery rise at every cell age (2.5 hours, 7.0 hours, 10.6 hours, and 13.0 hours) which we have examined during the first cycle. Only one example is shown in Figure 3, to avoid confusion. We cannot say with certainty that the rise observed in the two-dose response at 2.5 hours is really caused by G_1 cells, because at this time a few cells are already beginning to synthesize deoxyribonucleic acid (DNA) (See Figure 1); and these are the primary survivors of the first dose, as we have already seen. We cannot be sure for cells in G_2 either, because we obviously have some residual S cells there. However, the fact that there is recovery and that it is approximately of the right magnitude to correspond to the return of the shoulder in S cells is, we think, unquestionable for these hamster cells.

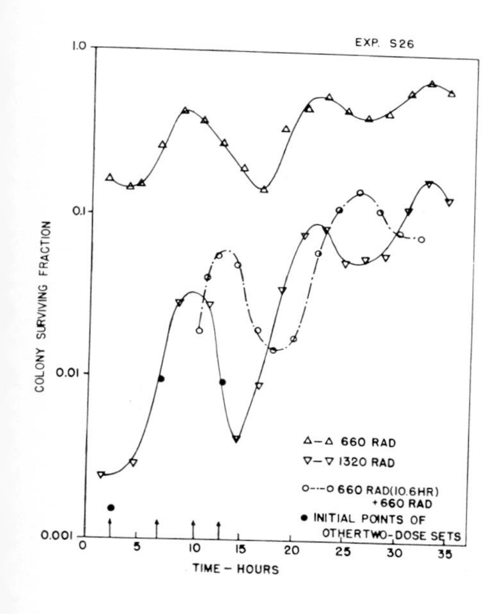

FIGURE 3. Colony surviving fraction in partially synchronized hamster cell population, against time after reincubating, following:

Δ———Δ 660 rad
∇———∇ 1320 rad
O—·—·—O 660 rad at 10.6 hr plus 660 rad at intervals thereafter

The arrows show when the first doses of 660 rad were given in the two-dose sets in this experiment (Sinclair and Morton, Unpublished data).

If we put the two-dose fractionation responses at the four different cell ages together and synthesize an asynchronous population with the appropriate cell density distribution, the response we should expect is indicated by the full line in Figure 4. The triangles are the points we actually observed in a two-dose fractionation experiment with an asynchronous population. Although they do not fit exactly, their general features are clearly similar.

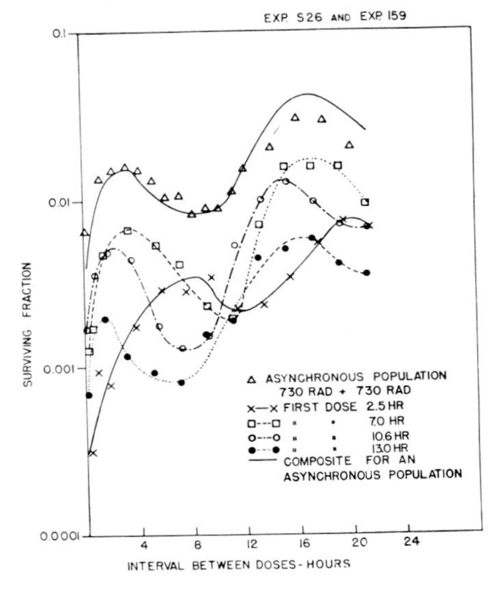

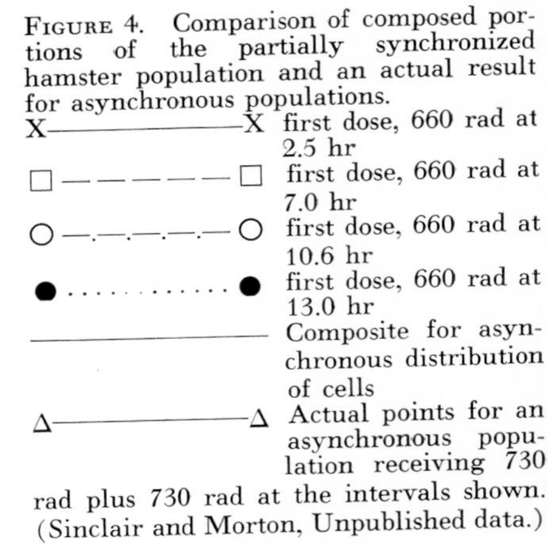

FIGURE 4. Comparison of composed portions of the partially synchronized hamster population and an actual result for asynchronous populations.
X——————X first dose, 660 rad at 2.5 hr
□ — — — — — — □ first dose, 660 rad at 7.0 hr
○ —.—.—.—.— ○ first dose, 660 rad at 10.6 hr
● . . . . ● first dose, 660 rad at 13.0 hr
—————— Composite for asynchronous distribution of cells
△——————△ Actual points for an asynchronous population receiving 730 rad plus 730 rad at the intervals shown. (Sinclair and Morton, Unpublished data.)

We can summarize our data for hamster cells as follows: Survival after X-irradiation varies with cell age and is greatest (over two decades at least) for cells in the S period. Recovery following a dose of X rays has been distinguished from the changing response resulting from varying cell age by the two-dose fractionation technique and has been shown to be quite definite for cells in S. It may also occur at other stages of the cell cycle, but further work is required to ascertain this.

ACKNOWLEDGMENT

This work was supported by the United States Atomic Energy Commission.

REFERENCES

Elkind, M. M., and H. Sutton. 1960. Radiation Response of Mammalian Cells Grown in Culture. I. Repair of X-Ray Damage in Surviving Chinese Hamster Cells. *Radiation Research,* 13:556–593.

Sinclair, W. K., and R. A. Morton. 1963. Variations in X-Ray Response during the Division Cycle of Partially Synchronized Chinese Hamster Cells in Culture. *Nature,* London, 199:1158–1160.

————. 1964. X-Ray and Ultraviolet Sensitivity of Synchronized Chinese Hamster Cells at Various Stages of the Cell Cycle. *Biophysical Journal.* (in press.)

————. Unpublished data.

Radiation Sensitivity Throughout the Cell Cycle and Its Relationship to Recovery

G. F. WHITMORE, S. GULYAS, AND J. BOTOND

Department of Medical Biophysics, University of Toronto, and Ontario Cancer Institute, Toronto, Canada

The response of mammalian cells exposed to ionizing radiation, either in vivo (Hornsey and Silini, 1962; Till and McCulloch, 1963) or in vitro (Elkind and Sutton, 1959, 1960; Elkind, 1961) depends greatly on whether the radiation is given during a single acute exposure or as several fractions separated by intervals of time. This was most clearly demonstrated by Elkind and Sutton (1959) in experiments in which Chinese hamster cells were given an initial exposure in vitro, incubated for various lengths of time, and then given a second exposure. When the fractional survival was plotted as a function of the time interval between the two doses, this value increased rapidly, and reached a maximum after about a one-hour time interval between the two doses. This experiment demonstrated that some sort of restoration occurred after the first irradiation. A delay of more than one hour between the two doses of radiation resulted in decreased survival which reached a minimum for an interval of five to six hours between the two doses, and then rose again.

Recovery from primary radiation damage seems to be a general phenomenon, having been observed in plant cells (Elkind, 1961; Hall and Lajtha, 1963) and in mammalian cells both in vivo and in vitro. It seems clear that an understanding of recovery processes will probably yield considerable insight into the mechanism or mechanisms responsible for the radiation killing of mammalian cells. An understanding of the recovery process and of the effects of fractionated doses of radiation is also of obvious importance to radiotherapy. For these reasons, we have embarked on a series of studies designed to elucidate the nature of the recovery process in vitro, and the purpose of this paper is to point out certain features of this process.

At least three possible explanations can be advanced to explain the general features of the kinetics of recovery observed in a dose fractionation experiment. The first theory would assume that all cells in a population show the same response to radiation, and therefore the kinetics observed for the two-dose fractionation curves represent a true restoration at early times followed by a sensitization and a subsequent recovery. A second model, first put forward by Elkind, Sutton, and Moses (1961) would assume that cells have different responses to radiation, depending upon their age in the mitotic cycle at the time of irradiation, and that the kinetics of recovery result from a true restoration process combined with a migration of cells from one sensitivity state to another. Variations in mammalian cell response to radiation as a function of cell age in the deoxyribonucleic acid (DNA) synthetic cycle were first demonstrated by Terasima and Tolmach (1963). Another possible explanation is that the kinetics of recovery are only a function of the progression of cells from one sensitivity state to another and that there is no true restoration of sublethal radiation damage.

As a working hypothesis in designing our experiments, we have assumed that cells do progress around the cell cycle following irradiation and that their radiation sensitivity does depend to a great extent on their age state at the time of irradiation. We have also assumed that there was a true restoration process which would reduce the radiation response of mammalian cells following a single dose of radiation, even in the absence of a concomitant shift in their age position within the cell cycle. With this hypothesis in mind, we have attempted to separate the true restoration process from changes in radiation response which were attributable to changes in cell age in the division cycle. Two methods of approaching this problem have been used. Working with asynchronous cultures, we have attempted to measure the effect of temperature changes on the kinetics of recovery. Also, since we felt that at least part of the kinetics of recovery was caused by changes in radiation response as cells progressed around the cycle, it became necessary for us to have methods of determining the radiation response of mammalian cells irradiated in various parts of the cell cycle and also to measure recovery as a function of cell age. These experiments required the development of synchronization techniques which could be applied to L cell populations in vitro. Consequently, a large part of this paper will be concerned with studies on radiation response as a function of cell age, and also with studies on recovery as a function of cell age in synchronized cultures.

Experimental Results

Recovery Curves in Asynchronous Populations

A typical two-dose fractionation curve for L cells is shown in Figure 1. For this experiment, cells were grown in suspension culture and irradiated in suspension at a concentration of approximately 2×10^5 cells/ml. They

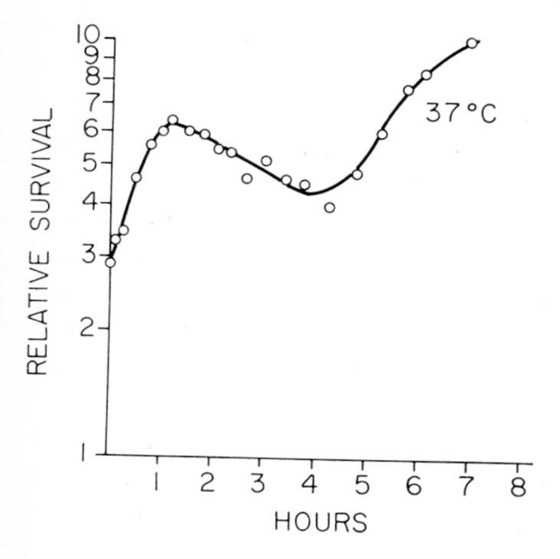

FIGURE 1. Recovery curve for L cells given an initial dose of 700 rads of X rays followed by 500 rads of Co^{60} separated by the time intervals shown. The cells were maintained in suspension culture at 37 C between exposures.

were first exposed to a dose of 700 rads of X rays (280 kv HVL of 1.2 mm Cu), allowed to incubate in suspension for varying lengths of time at 37 C, and then given a second dose of 500 rads of Co^{60}. The change of radiation sources was convenient for technical reasons. After the second dose, the cells were appropriately diluted and plated for colony survival.

The recovery curve shown in Figure 1 shows that as the interval between the first and second dose increases up to one hour, the number of survivors doubles. As the interval between the doses increases beyond one hour, the number of survivors decreases and reaches a minimum at four hours. There was then a steady rise to approximately seven hours, at which time the experiment was terminated. It should be pointed out here that there are quantitative differences between the hamster recovery curves reported by Elkind and Sutton (1959) and L cell recovery curves, and indeed, there are day-to-day and long-term variations in the curves obtained for either population. However, the qualitative features of the curve are always the same. There is an initial rise with decreasing slope, a maximum, followed by a minimum of greater or lesser extent and a subsequent rise.

In agreement with our previously mentioned hypothesis that recovery is a result of a restoration of sublethal damage coupled with changes in radiation response as cells move around the cell cycle, we interpret these recovery results as follows: The prompt increase in survival results mainly from the repair of sublethal damage in cells surviving the conditioning dose. At the same time as these cells are exhibiting these recovery processes, they are also progressing around the cycle; this progress at early times tends to shift the majority of surviving cells to regions of increased radiation response, thus causing the minimum in the recovery curve. Finally, the cells pass through the region of maximum radiation response and into a region of reduced response. It must be emphasized throughout all of the early experiments described in this paper that we are dealing with an asynchronous population, and therefore it is likely that some cells are moving into states of increased response at the same time as others are moving into states of reduced response.

As a partial test of the above hypothesis, experiments have been carried out to determine the effect of reduced temperatures on the kinetics of the recovery process. The assumption underlying these experiments was that reduced temperatures would probably inhibit the movement of cells around the cell cycle, but that they might not have as pronounced an effect on the actual restoration of radiation damage. The data in Figure 2, taken from Elkind, Whitmore, and Alescio (1964), compare the effect on net survival when Chinese hamster cells are kept at either 37 C or room temperature (approximately 25 C) between doses.

At both 25 C and 37 C, survival increased promptly and without delay. There appears to be very little difference either in the initial rate of recovery or in the height of the maximum. The principal difference appears to be that at room temperature the dip in the recovery curve is absent.

Figure 3 shows the results of a similar experiment carried out with L cells. For this experiment, the cells were grown and irradiated in suspension culture, and for the curves obtained at 25 C and 8.5 C, the cells were cooled to their respective temperatures 10 minutes prior to the first exposure, and were maintained at these temperatures between the 700 and 500 rad exposures. After the 500 rad exposure, cells were plated and assayed

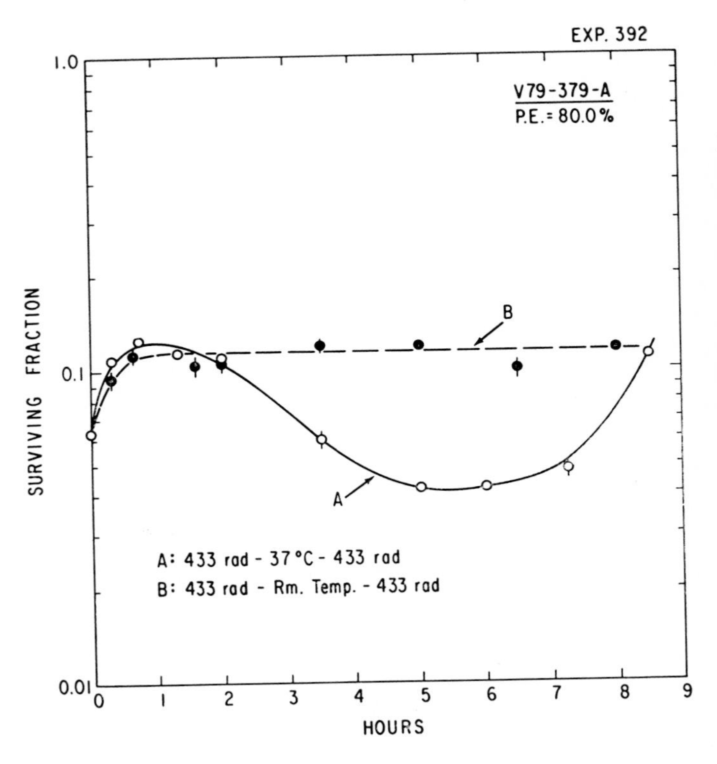

FIGURE 2. Fractionation survival of Chinese hamster cells, V79–379–A, attached to glass. Between two 433 rad doses administered at room temperature, cells were incubated at 37 C, curve *A*, or room temperature (approximately 25 C), curve *B*. After the second dose, the cells were incubated at 37 C for colony formation. (From Elkind, Whitmore, and Alescio, 1964.)

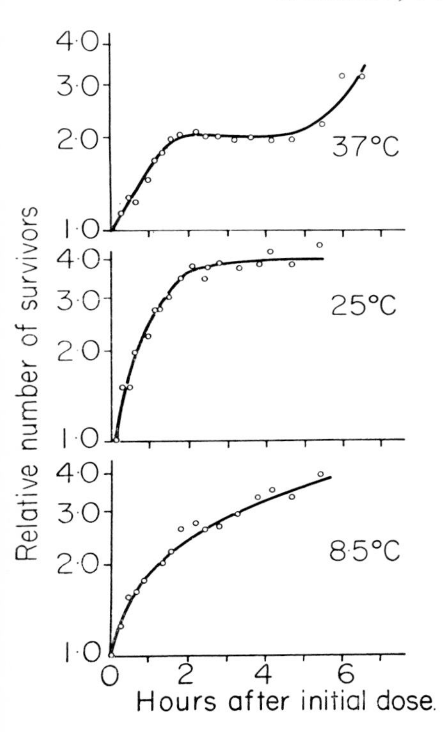

FIGURE 3. Recovery curve for L cells given an initial dose of 700 rads of X rays followed by 500 rads of Co^{60} separated by the time intervals shown. For each temperature, the cells were equilibrated at that temperature for 10 minutes prior to the initial irradiation, maintained at the temperature for the time interval between the two doses, and then incubated at 37 C for colony formation. All growth and incubation prior to the second dose of radiation was in suspension.

for colony-forming ability. The upper curve shows the results for 37 C; in this particular experiment, even at 37 C, the secondary dip was absent. At 25 C, the initial rise is almost as fast as at 37 C, and if anything, the extent of the recovery is even greater. At 8.5 C, the rate of recovery is appreciably reduced, but the total extent of the recovery appears about equal to that obtained at 25 C. These results may indicate that the initial recovery process is only weakly dependent upon active metabolic processes within the cell, since there is only a weak temperature dependence. We interpret the lack of a minimum in the recovery curve for Chinese hamster cells at 25 C as being caused by the absence of cell movement around the cell cycle at the low temperature; we attribute the lack of secondary increase in the L cell curves at low temperature to the same cause.

Synchronization Procedures

In order to examine rigorously the possibility that the kinetics of the recovery process are determined to some extent by the movement of cells through the mitotic cycle into different radiation response states, it was necessary to know the radiation response of cells in different parts of the cell cycle. For this latter purpose, it became important to obtain synchronized populations of L cells which had been subjected to the least possible degree of trauma during the synchronization procedure. Such synchronized populations were obtained as follows: A high concentration of high specific activity thymidine (2 μc/ml, 6 c/mmole) was added to cultures of L cells for a period of six hours. All cells which are in or pass through the S period during this six hours will pick up labeled thymidine. The level of the radioactivity is so high that all these cells are killed before they carry out a sufficient number of divisions to form a visible colony during a plating experiment. A small window consisting of those cells in late G_1 which did not synthesize DNA during the exposure to tritiated thymidine will remain viable. If a high concentration of unlabeled thymidine is added to the culture at the end of the six hours, then this will dilute the activity, allowing this small fraction of the total population to grow and to form a synchronized population. The advantages of this method of synchronization are that it can be made to yield a relatively large population of cells, and that these cells are apparently obtained without any associated trauma. We do not propose here to go into the details of the controls which have been used to establish the ideal conditions of thymidine incorporation, or of the controls which have been used to establish the validity of the method. These will all be published elsewhere (Whitmore and Gulyas, in preparation).

The extent of the synchronization obtained from this procedure can be assessed from the experimental results shown in Figure 4. Here, the high specific activity thymidine (2 μc/ml at 6.7 c/mmole) was added to an asynchronous L cell population growing in suspension culture, and was diluted with 100 μg/ml of unlabeled thymidine three hours (upper curve) or six hours (lower curve) later. Samples were then taken at various times, and

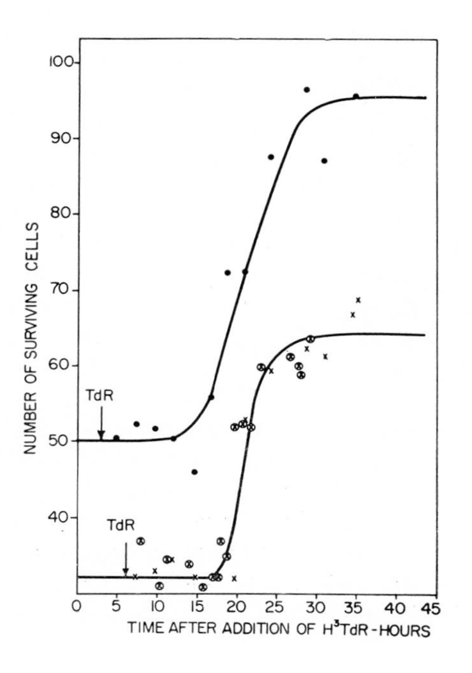

FIGURE 4. Number of colony-forming cells in a population of L cells given tritiated thymidine (2 μc/ml at 6 c/mmole) at time zero and unlabeled thymidine (10 μg/ml) at the times shown by the arrows.

measured for their colony-forming ability. It can be seen that in both cases, approximately 11 hours after the addition of the unlabeled thymidine, there was a burst of division in both cultures with the number of viable cells doubling in a short time; however, the rise time was appreciably longer in the culture which had a three-hour exposure to the labeled precursor than in the population which had a six-hour exposure. It is likely that the degree of synchronization could be even further enhanced by producing a smaller window, but such synchronization would be obtained at the expense of reduced cell yield. For this reason we have chosen to use a six-hour exposure in all of the experiments to be described here. This exposure will leave approximately 27 per cent of the cells viable.

The synchronized populations obtained by the above method were used to examine the effect of cell age or position in the cell cycle on radiation response to acute exposures, and on the recovery of cells between fractionated doses of radiation. In order to interpret such experiments, it was necessary to determine the duration of S, G_2, M, and G_1 in populations synchronized by the above procedure.

The duration of the various phases was determined by a combination of several methods. In a population of cells synchronized by the window method, the only viable cells in the culture at the beginning of the experiment, *i.e.*, when cold thymidine is added, are cells in late G_1. Although the specific activity of the medium is drastically reduced by the addition of the cold thymidine, uptake of some radioactive thymidine continues at a level too low to bring about cell killing but high enough to be detected autoradiographically. As the cells in the window move from G_1 into S, the fraction of unlabeled cells, detected autoradiographically, will decrease. This decrease will give a measure of the rate of flow of viable cells from G_1 into S. The rate of flow of cells from S into G_2 was also determined autoradiographically, but by a different procedure. In this case an aliquot was removed from the synchronized suspension, centrifuged lightly, and resuspended in a growth medium containing 2.0 μc/ml of tritiated thymidine (specific activity 6.7 c/mmole) for 30 minutes. This level of activity will give an autoradiograph in a time much shorter than is required to give autoradiographs of the cells which synthesized DNA in the presence of both the labeled and unlabeled precursors. The number of cells in the aliquot which failed to show label was then determined autoradiographically; this is a measure of the rate of flow of cells from S into G_2.

The results of this experiment are shown in Figure 5, in which it can be seen that the percentage of unlabeled cells falls very rapidly, reaches a minimum between three and four hours, and then rises steeply. We have determined the 50 per cent points of the rising and falling segments of this curve and have shown the nine-hour time duration between these two points as S. M was assumed to be 30 minutes in duration and was assumed to occur at the midpoint in the rise of viable cell number (Figure 4). This gave a G_2 value of 3 hours and a G_1 value of 4.5 hours, or a total generation

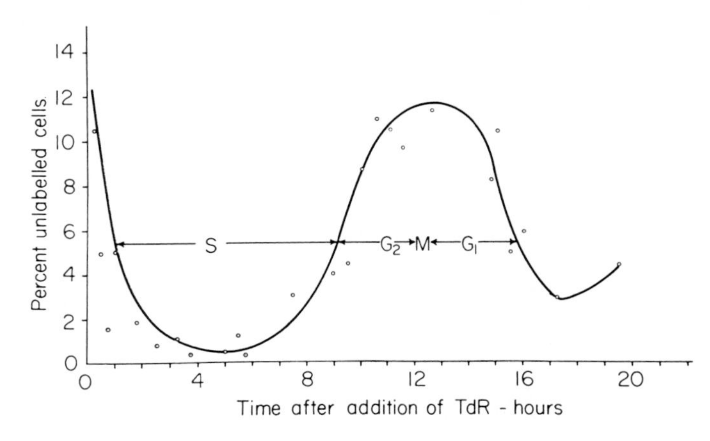

FIGURE 5. Percentage of cells which are not incorporating labeled thymidine as a function of the time after the addition of unlabeled thymidine in a culture given labeled thymidine six hours prior to the addition of unlabeled thymidine.

time of 17 hours. The durations of the various phases were equal to the values of the same periods determined by methods described before (Stanners and Till, 1960) for unsynchronized cells of the same cell line also having a doubling time of 17 hours.

Radiation Response in Synchronized Populations

With the availability of cultures synchronized as described above, it became possible to measure radiation survival curves as a function of age in the cell cycle. These have been measured at approximately two-hour intervals for 20 hours after the addition of cold thymidine, *i.e.* for slightly more than one generation time. All of the survival curves were sigmoidal in shape and both the extrapolation number and D_0 values varied with cell age. The data from all of these survival curves have been summarized in Figures 6 and 7.

Figure 6 shows the extrapolation numbers as a function of cell age

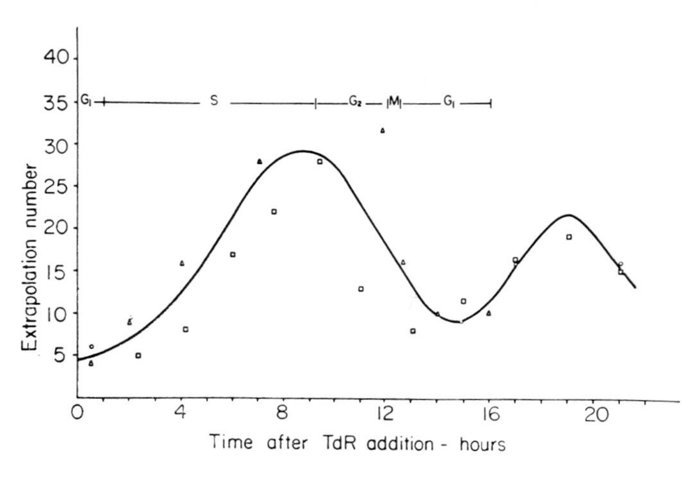

FIGURE 6. The extrapolation number as a function of cell age for L cell survival curves obtained for a partially synchronized population. Time zero in the figure refers to the time of addition of the unlabeled thymidine used to prevent uptake after a six-hour exposure to tritiated thymidine.

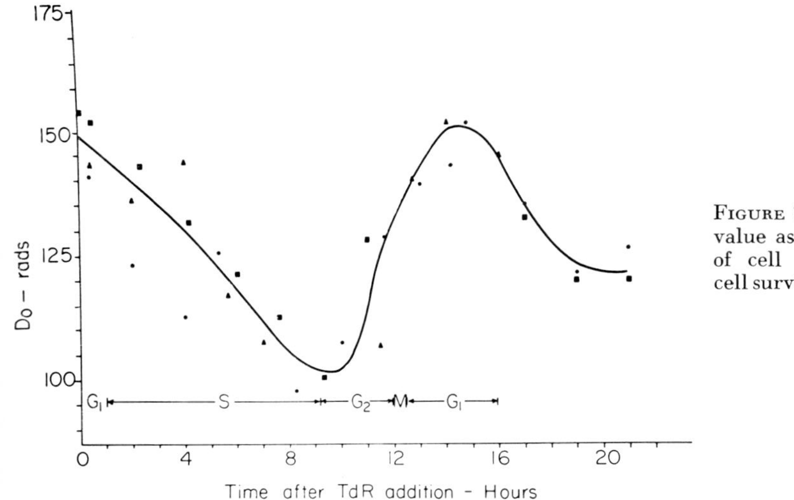

FIGURE 7. The D_0 value as a function of cell age for L cell survival curves.

and Figure 7 the D_0 values. Time zero in these curves refers to the time when the cold thymidine was added; at this time, therefore, the cells which have survived thymidine suicide are all in the latter part of the G_1 and just beginning to move into S. The phase of the cells in the cell cycle at the time of irradiation is indicated in the figure. It must be borne in mind that the window is of finite width; it is not possible to draw sharp boundaries, and as mentioned above, we have drawn the boundaries to correspond to the point at which 50 per cent of the cells in the window have passed into the particular phase.

It can be seen from Figure 6 that the extrapolation number for cells in G_1 is about 5 and increases to a maximum value of approximately 30 just prior to the end of S, and then falls throughout G_2, M, and G_1. Assuming a 17-hour generation time and that the synchronization could be maintained, then we would expect this curve to be repeated beginning at about 17 hours. In actual practice, synchronization is not maintained (Till, Whitmore, and Gulyas, 1963) and, therefore, while the shape of the curve shows a general tendency to repeat itself, the absolute values are not repeated. This we feel is the explanation for the fact that the minimum in the curve at 15 hours is not as low as the starting value, and the secondary maximum is not as high as the first. Of course as the synchronization decays, the extrapolation number will approach a constant value which for an asynchronous L cell population appears to be of the order of 10.

Figure 7 shows the variation in D_0 as a function of time after the addition of cold thymidine. The value of D_0 is at a maximum of 150 rads for cells in late G_1 and the beginning of S, falls to a minimum value of 100 rads at the end of S or the beginning of G_2, and then rises steeply throughout G_2, M, and early G_1.

The fact that the extrapolation number tends to increase throughout S, whereas the D_0 value decreases during this interval, means that the two parameters are exerting opposite effects upon cellular survival. The effect of these opposing forces can be seen in Figure 12, which we will have occasion to discuss later.

The Survival Curve of the Asynchronous Population

One test of the validity of radiation survival data as a function of cell age is that the survival curve of an asynchronous population must be equal to the sum of the survival curves of all of the subpopulations which comprise the total population. This being the case, we would expect that a summation of the number of cells with any particular radiation response multiplied by the survival for a particular dose under these response conditions, summed over all cell response states and for a series of doses would give the survival curve of the asynchronous population. We have attempted to construct the survival curve of an asynchronous population by assuming that cells were exponentially distributed around the cell cycle and had twice the cell density at the beginning of G_1 as they had at the end of G_2 (Stanners and Till, 1960). We have divided the cell cycle into two-hour intervals and have multiplied the cell number in each interval by the survival, as calculated from the extrapolation number and D_0 values given in Figures 6 and 7. The survival curve which we obtained is shown in Figure 8. It has an extrapolation number of 8.2 and a D_{10} in the exponential region of 322 rads. These values compare very favorably with the average values of these parameters obtained in a large number of experiments with asynchronous

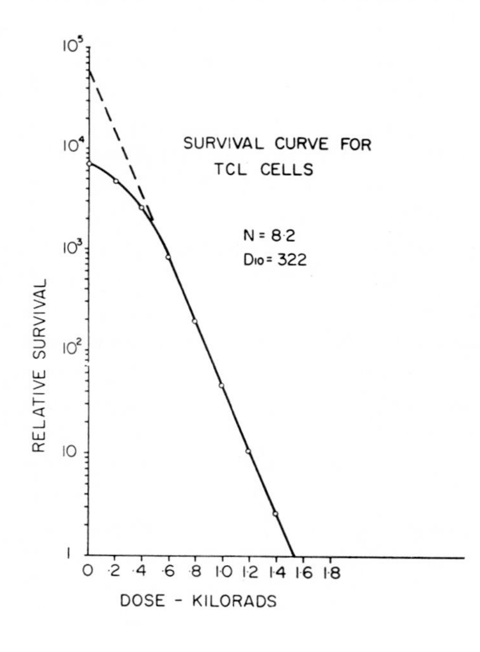

FIGURE 8. Composite survival curve for an asynchronous L cell population calculated on the basis of the extrapolation number and D_0 values given in Figures 6 and 7. The calculation assumes an exponential distribution of cells around the cell cycle and a 17-hour generation time. The caption TCL refers to the subline of L cells used throughout these experiments.

populations and which gave an average extrapolation number of 11 and a D_{10} of 334 rads. The theoretical survival curve appears to become strictly exponential on a semilog plot despite the fact that the population is composed of cells with widely different values of n and D_0. It should be pointed out that while it is a necessary condition that the sum of the survival curves of the various populations which make up the asynchronous population should yield a survival curve which is a good replica of the survival curve measured for the asynchronous population, this is in itself not a rigorous test of the experimental data, since such a survival curve, if carried to low enough values of survival, will certainly give a D_0 value which is characteristic of the subpopulation with the highest D_0 value.

Recovery in Synchronized Populations

Knowing the radiation response at various points in the cell cycle and using the synchronized populations, it was now possible to measure recovery as a function of cell age at the time of the first dose of radiation. For these experiments, a cell population was first given a six-hour exposure to high specific activity thymidine and then the label was heavily diluted by the addition of unlabeled thymidine. At five different times after the addition of unlabeled thymidine, *i.e.* at 0, 4, 6, 9, and 13 hours, large populations of cells were exposed to 700 rads of 280 kv X rays. Then at various intervals thereafter, aliquots were removed from the cultures and given a further dose of 500 rads of Co^{60}. After the second dose, the cells were diluted appropriately and then plated. The results of the experiment are shown in Figure 9.

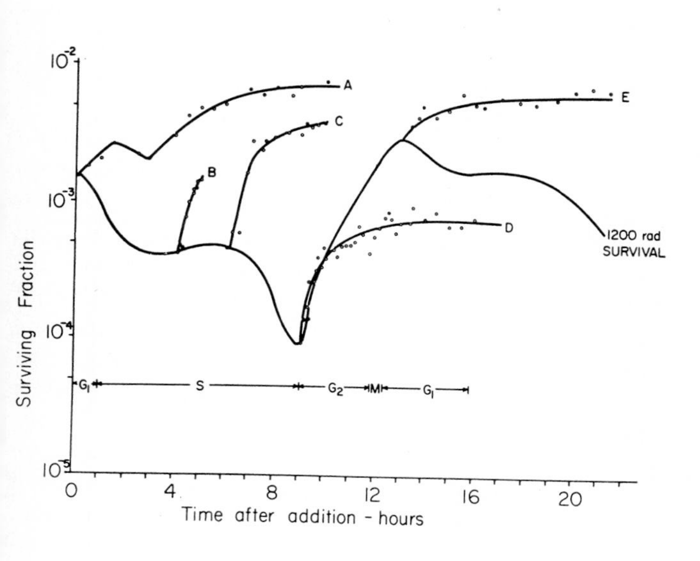

FIGURE 9. Recovery curves at 37 C for partially synchronized L cell populations. The population was synchronized by a six-hour exposure to tritiated thymidine. In each case, the cells were given an initial exposure of 700 rads followed by a second exposure of 500 rads. The curve labeled 1,200 rad survival is the survival curve of the synchronized population given a single dose of 1,200 rads of X rays at the times shown.

The surviving fraction of cells given an initial dose of 700 rads at either 0, 4, 6, 9, or 13 hours and given a second dose of 500 rads at various intervals thereafter is plotted against the time after the addition of unlabeled thymidine. The position of the cells in the cell cycle at the time of the first irradiation can be determined from the cell phases shown on the figure. The curve marked 1,200 rad survival is the survival curve for cells given a single acute exposure of 1,200 rads at various times in the cell cycle, and the recovery curves have all been normalized so that they begin at the correct survival value. The curves marked A, B, C, D, and E are the recovery curves obtained for populations given an initial exposure of 700 rads at 0, 4, 6, 9, and 13 hours after the addition of cold thymidine, respectively, and followed by a second dose of 500 rads at various times thereafter.

For a population of cells irradiated in late G_1, the kinetics of the subsequent recovery curve appear very similar to the kinetics of the random population in that they show an initial rise followed by a secondary minimum. For populations irradiated at 4, 6, or 9 hours (mostly cells in S), the recovery curve shows a steep initial rise followed by a more gradual increase in the case of the six- and nine-hour curves. For the 4-hour curve, the experiment terminated early because of a technical error. For a population of cells given a conditioning exposure at 13 hours, there is not as much recovery as in the 4-, 6-, and 9-hour curves, but again there seems to be an initial rapid increase followed by a more gradual increase. The important feature of the five curves would appear to be that in all cases there is an initial rise, and that this rise occurs in all parts of the cell cycle.

The Recovery Ratio

In a cell population that was given a single exposure to radiation and then allowed to incubate for a given time before a second exposure, we might expect that the response to the second dose would depend upon the results of three processes: (1) any true restoration process which tends to repair sublethal damage and which is independent of movement around the cell cycle; (2) changes in extrapolation number over and above those accounted for by (1) and which would probably result from progression around the cell cycle; and (3) changes in D_0 as a result of movement around the cell cycle. In an attempt to look for correlations between the over-all recovery curve, and the restoration of the extrapolation number and changes in extrapolation number as a result of cell progression around the cycle, we have attempted to calculate the total amount of restoration and changes in extrapolation number which occurs over and above any effect caused by changes in D_0. In order to eliminate changes in restoration resulting from these changes in D_0, it is necessary to calculate the survival to be expected from changes in this parameter alone and to compare the observed survival to this calculated value. The calculation is based on the assumption, which as yet remains to be rigorously tested, that a cell following a first dose of 700 rads will progress around the early part of the cell cycle at the same rate as it would have progressed had it never received the initial 700 rad exposure, and will assume the D_0 value characteristic of that point in the cell cycle. This assumption is certainly not valid for cells irradiated in early G_2, which even during a relatively short experiment would almost certainly be held up behind the radiation induced mitotic block which we know exists in G_2 (Whitmore, Stanners, Till, and Gulyas, 1960). It is probably reasonably valid for all other parts of the cell cycle. For the purposes of the calculation, we have used the survival curves for cells irradiated at 0, 4, 6, and 9 hours after the addition of unlabeled thymidine to calculate the number of cells which would survive the first 700 rad exposure. To obtain the theoretical value of the survival after a second dose of 500 rads administered at various times Δt after the initial 700 rads, we have multiplied the 700 rad survival by the survival to be expected from a dose of 500 rads. The survival for 500 rads was obtained by assuming that the survival curve is now strictly exponential and has the D_0 value obtained from the data given in Figure 7 for a time Δt after the initial 700 rad exposure. This merely means that we have calculated the survival curve for a cell which was given an initial exposure of 700 rads and then allowed to move to a position in which it had a survival curve characterized by the D_0 value read from Figure 7 but where the extrapolation number was unity and then given a further dose of 500 rads. The ratio of the measured survival value obtained from Figure 9 divided by this theoretical survival value is a measure of the extent of the recovery process which results from (1) and (2) above. We will refer to this ratio as the recovery ratio and will attempt to show that it does in fact consist of two parts, an initial rapid restoration of at least part of the original extrapolation number, and an increase or decrease in extrapolation number which is caused by the migration around the cell cycle and which parallels the increase or decrease of extrapolation number in unirradiated cells.

The recovery ratios calculated on the above basis have been plotted in Figure 10 as a function of the time after the addition of unlabeled thymidine. These are shown as the five lower curves, and on the same diagram we have redrawn the curve of Figure 6, relating the change in the extrapolation number to the time of addition of unlabeled thymidine. It should be pointed out at the outset that the latter curve represents the change in the extrapolation number of the survival curves of cells which have not had any previous radiation as they change their position in the cell cycle. If irradiated cells were capable of rapidly restoring the extrapolation number which existed at the time of the first 700 rad exposure and then moved around the cycle at the same speed as unirradiated cells, the recovery ratio curve should essentially superimpose upon the extrapolation number curve.

For cells irradiated at the end of G_1 there appears to be an initial rapid restoration, then a plateau, and then a period of rapid recovery in which the irradiated cells appear to recover somewhat more rapidly than the in-

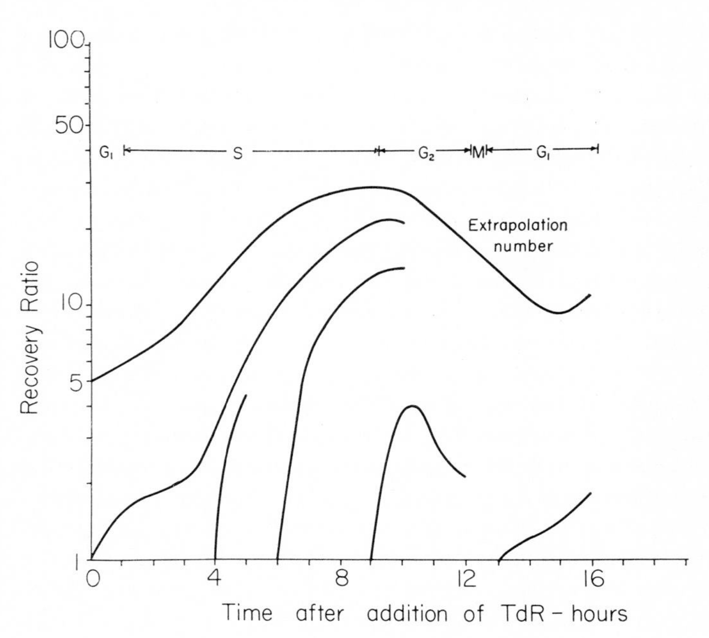

FIGURE 10. The recovery ratio as a function of cell age in a partially synchronized population of L cells. The experimental data used for the calculation were obtained from Figures 7 and 9, and the method of calculation is outlined in the text. The extrapolation number curve is a repeat of Figure 6.

crease in the extrapolation number which would have occurred in cells which had had no previous irradiation. Finally, however, the curves of recovery ratio and the extrapolation number appear to become parallel. For cells irradiated at 4, 6, and 9 hours there appears to be an initial period during which the curve for recovery rises much more steeply than the curve for extrapolation number, and at least for the 6- and 9-hour curves, this is followed by a period when the curve for recovery follows that of the extrapolation number. For the population given a conditioning exposure at 9 hours, there is a pronounced maximum in the recovery ratio at approximately the same time as the curve of extrapolation number passes through its maximum. The curve for cells given a conditioning dose at 13 hours, when most of the population would have been in G_1, suggests that at this time there is a decreased amount of true recovery and that the amount of recovery again begins to rise at about the same time as the extrapolation number begins to increase. The recovery ratio data plotted in Figure 10, which at least for cells irradiated in S appears to consist of an initial rapid restoration followed by more gradual changes which parallel changes in the extrapolation number, would appear to support the contention that immediately following a conditioning dose of radiation, cells do rapidly restore at least part of their original extrapolation number and from that time on their extrapolation number is parallel with that which would be expected for a population which had never been irradiated. From the data we have and because of certain technical limitations which limit the time at which we can obtain our first point after the original conditioning dose, we cannot say with certainty whether the recovery curve actually reaches to the same height as the extrapolation number curve.

If the recovery ratio is a product of two parts, a true restoration at early times after irradiation and a change in response resulting from cell movement, and if cell movement is retarded at 25 C but restoration is not, then the recovery ratio at 25 C should show the initial rapid rise but then should not follow the extrapolation number curve. Accordingly, we have measured the recovery curves for synchronized populations maintained at 25 C during the time interval between exposures. The results of these experiments are shown in Figure 11. The principal difference between the 25 C and the 37 C recovery curves appears to be that the zero time curve does not show the early maximum observed in the 37 C curve nor the secondary minimum, but instead appears to be increasing steadily. Also, the curves for irradiations given at 4, 6, and 9 hours do not rise as fast, nor do they rise as high as their 37 C counterparts. If our assumption that cells do not progress around the cycle at 25 C is correct, then the recovery ratio curves would be identical to the recovery curves but normalized to a starting value of unity. Accordingly, these ratios have not been plotted.

Discussion

Our radiation survival studies with L cells have indicated that, starting from the beginning of S, the extrapolation number increases at the same time as the D_0 value decreases. The extrapolation number appears to reach a rather broad maximum value somewhere close to the end of S. Conversely, the D_0 value reaches a minimum value at the end of S or the beginning of G_2. The apparently opposing nature of these two parameters may have some rather important consequences for the interpretation of some experiments

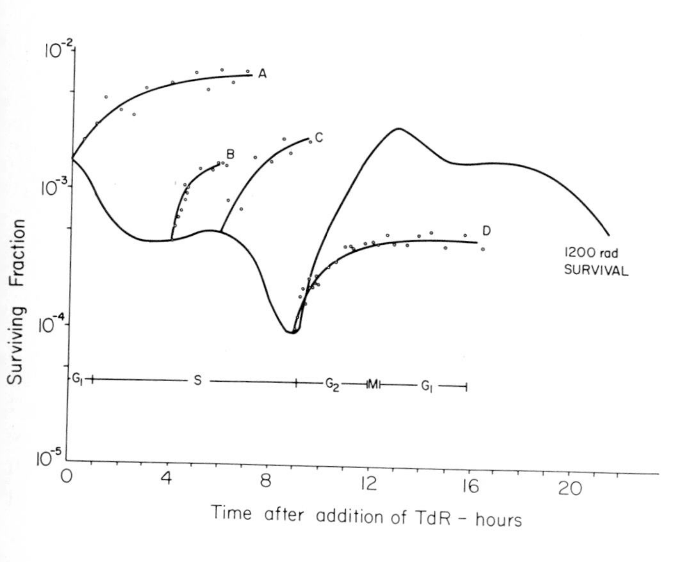

FIGURE 11. Recovery curves at 25 C for partially synchronized L cell populations. The cells were first synchronized by a six-hour exposure to tritiated thymidine and were maintained at 37 C until 10 minutes before the 700 rad initial exposure of each survival curve. Cells were maintained at 25 C between exposures and were plated at 37 C for colony formation.

appearing in the literature (Terasima and Tolmach, 1963; Sinclair and Morton, 1963). Some of these consequences can be seen with reference to Figure 12 in which we have plotted the survival of synchronized cells given 400, 800, or 1,200 rads at various times in the cell cycle. For low doses, the extrapolation number is the main determinant of survival, and therefore a population irradiated with a dose of 400 rads at different times in the cell cycle will show a minimum survival early in S and a maximum survival toward the middle or end of S. For a dose of 800 rads, the effect of D_0 becomes more important, giving rise to a minimum survival toward the end of S, but the effect of the changing extrapolation number is also apparent as an increased survival in mid-S. A dose of 1,200 rads gives a pronounced minimum at the end of S, but the effect of the maximum in the extrapolation number is still apparent in mid-S. From the data in Figure 12, it is apparent that it is misleading to speak of radiation sensitivity as a function of cell age without specifying whether one is referring to extrapolation number or to D_0; therefore we prefer to group the effect of the two parameters and speak of radiation response. But even here one can only speak of maximum and minimum response as a function of cell age by specifying the dose or dose ranges.

On the basis of the data which are now available, it is difficult to know whether there are significant differences in the age dependence of radiation response between HeLa cells, Chinese hamster cells, and L cells. With HeLa cells it has been reported (Terasima and Tolmach, 1963) that there are two

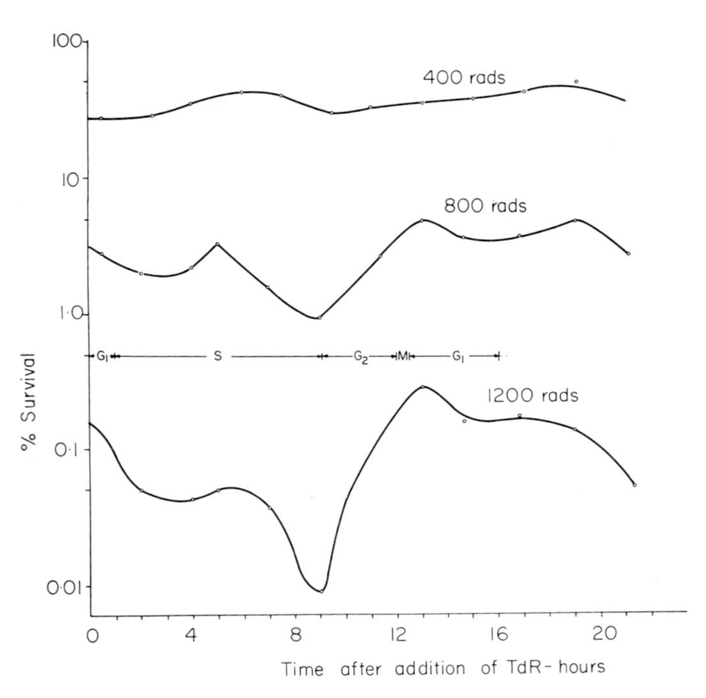

FIGURE 12. Survival curves as a function of cell age for partially synchronized L cells exposed to a single acute exposure of X rays. Synchronization conditions, etc. are the same as for Figure 9.

ensitivity maxima, one at mitosis and the second at a point half way hrough the cycle. However, these maxima were reported only for a single lose of 300 rads, and since this dose usually gave a survival greater than 10 per cent, it is likely that the extrapolation number was still the controlling feature. Terasima and Tolmach (1963) have also published a numper of complete survival curves for HeLa cells at various points in the cell cycle, and these seem to show that the values of D_0 have maxima at the beginning and end of S and a minimum value somewhere in the S phase. HeLa cells would therefore appear to have a minimum D_0 value somewhere n the S phase and probably a maximum extrapolation number somewhere n S, since for a single low dose of radiation, the survival appears to increase throughout S. These observations would then agree with the L cell observations reported here. With Chinese hamster cells, Sinclair and Morton (1963) have reported that after a single dose of 750 r there is a urvival maximum closely correlated with the time at which there is a naximum number of cells in the S phase. These data are also consistent vith the data obtained with HeLa and L cells. However, Sinclair and Morton believed from their early observations that this increase in survival vas largely attributable to an increase in the extrapolation number, and hat their results were compatible with an unchanging value of D_0. With he exception of the latter observation concerning the lack of change in D_0, hese observations would also appear to be consistent with the HeLa and L ell observations. Proof that the cyclic responses to radiation are the same or different in the three cell lines will have to await the acquisition of more data on all three cell systems.

The application of the window method of synchronization, reported n this paper, to the study of recovery phenomena indicates to us that immediately following irradiation, cells are able to restore at least a fraction of the sublethal damage which they have accumulated as a result of the rradiation. We are unable to say, as yet, whether the extent of this initial estoration is identical in all parts of the cell cycle. At 37 C it is difficult to ffect a complete separation between recovery and changes in extrapolation number brought on by cell movement. At 25 C where we have assumed, but as yet not proved, that cell movement around the cell cycle is either topped or reduced, the amount of recovery does appear to be a constant for ells irradiated in all parts of the S phase, even though there are pronounced hanges in the extrapolation number throughout S. This may mean that ecovery to the maximum of the initial extrapolation number is never obained, although the present experiments do not rule out complete recovery.

At 37 C, once the initial recovery is complete, the recovery curve for synchronized culture appears to parallel the extrapolation number. Again, the limitations of the experiments reported so far do not allow us to tell whether the restoration process will completely restore the extrapolation umber, in which case the recovery ratio should be equal to the extrapolation number.

In an earlier section of this paper, we mentioned that while the recovery curves appeared to be qualitatively similar in Chinese hamster and in L cells, there were quantitative differences between the two cell lines. Indeed, even within a single cell line there appeared to be day-to-day variations as well as long-term variations. Our studies with synchronized populations may indicate some reasons for these variations. If, as now seems possible, the radiation response as a function of cell age is qualitatively similar in HeLa, Chinese hamster, and L cells, then we would expect that differences in the recovery curves could come about because of differences in the manner in which cells are distributed in various parts of the cell cycle in the different cell lines. A population with a long G_1 may have a greatly different survival curve and recovery curve from a cell with relatively short G_1. It would be expected that changes in cell distribution around the cycle would exert their most pronounced effect on the extrapolation number of the survival curve, since the terminal slope of the survival curve is always characteristic of the cell population with the largest D_0 value. Since the total recovery measured in a population appears to be dependent upon the extrapolation numbers of the cells at the time of and following irradiation, it is obvious that anything which affects the extrapolation number will affect the shape of the recovery curve.

The day-to-day fluctuations in the shape of the recovery curves for one cell line are likely a result of the fact that it is extremely difficult to obtain a truly asynchronous population, and any degree of synchronization would be expected to give some variation in the recovery curve. In the same way, any factor which tends to affect the length of the various phases of the cell division cycle will also affect both the survival curve and the recovery curve. It appears that as cells go through many hundreds of generations in tissue culture, and because of improvements in growth media and methods for handling cells in tissue culture, the generation times are becoming shorter. In our laboratory this has resulted over a number of years in a shortening of the average doubling time for L cells from 24 to 16 hours. This increased growth rate appears to have resulted largely from a shortening of the G_1 phase without any appreciable change in duration of S or G_2. This means that the distribution of cells within the various phases has greatly altered; therefore we would expect that our current populations would have a recovery curve and a survival curve very different from those of the populations with which we worked a number of years ago.

In summary, we feel that the evidence presented in this paper strongly suggests that the kinetics of cellular recovery in a two-dose fractionation experiment is the result of two processes: (1) a true repair of sublethal damage, and (2) the migration of cells through different ages and into different radiation response states. The degree of recovery which will be seen in any population will depend upon the age distribution of the population at the time of irradiation. The nature of the biophysical or biochemical processes involved in this recovery mechanism has yet to be elucidated.

REFERENCES

Elkind, M. M. 1961. Radiation Responses of Mammalian Cells. *Brookhaven Symposia in Biology*, 14:220–245.

Elkind, M. M., and H. Sutton. 1959. X-Ray Damage and Recovery in Mammalian Cells in Culture. *Nature*, London, 184:1293–1295.

———. 1960. Radiation Response of Mammalian Cells Grown in Culture. I. Repair of X-Ray Damage in Surviving Chinese Hamster Cells. *Radiation Research*, 13:556–593.

Elkind, M. M., H. Sutton, and W. B. Moses. 1961. Postirradiation Survival Kinetics of Mammalian Cells Grown in Culture. *Journal of Cellular and Comparative Physiology*, 58: Supplement 1: 113–134.

Elkind, M. M., G. F. Whitmore, and T. Alescio. 1964. Actinomycin D Suppression of Recovery in X-Irradiated Mammalian Cells. *Science*. (in press.)

Hall, E. J., and L. G. Lajtha. 1963. The Recovery of *Vicia faba* Meristem Cells from X-Radiation. *Radiation Research*, 20:187–194.

Hornsey, S., and G. Silini. 1962. Recovery of Tumor Cells Cultured in vivo after X-Ray and Neutron Irradiations. *Radiation Research*, 16:712–722.

Sinclair, W. K., and R. A. Morton. 1963. Variations in X-Ray Response during the Division Cycle of Partially Synchronized Chinese Hamster Cells in Culture. (Abstract) *Radiation Research*, 19:217.

Stanners, C. P., and J. E. Till. 1960. DNA Synthesis in Individual L-Strain Mouse Cells. *Biochimica et biophysica acta*, 37:406–419.

Terasima, T., and L. J. Tolmach. 1963. Variations in Several Responses of HeLa Cells to X-Irradiation during the Division Cycle. *Biophysical Journal*, 3:11–33.

Till, J. E., and E. A. McCulloch. 1963. Early Repair Processes in Marrow Cells Irradiated and Proliferating *in vivo*. *Radiation Research*, 18:96–105.

Till, J. E., G. F. Whitmore, and S. Gulyas. 1963. Deoxyribonucleic Acid Synthesis in Individual L-Strain Mouse Cells. II. Effects of Thymidine Starvation. *Biochimica et biophysica acta*, 72:277–289.

Whitmore, G. F., and S. Gulyas. 1964. (in preparation.)

Whitmore, G. F., C. P. Stanners, J. E. Till, and S. Gulyas. 1961. Nucleic Acid Synthesis and the Division Cycle in X-Irradiated L-Strain Mouse Cells. *Biochimica et biophysica acta*, 47:66–77.

Oxygen, Nitrogen, Recovery, and Radiation Therapy

M. M. ELKIND, R. W. SWAIN, T. ALESCIO,* H. SUTTON, AND W. B. MOSES

Laboratory of Physiology and the Radiation Branch,
National Cancer Institute, National Institutes of Health,
Bethesda, Maryland

As other papers in this symposium have already demonstrated, cultured mammalian cells are popular experimental material in radiobiology. Perhaps the principal reason for this is that cultured cells afford many of the technical and interpretive advantages of simpler systems (e.g. bacteria and yeasts) while minimizing the biological extrapolation required in applying results obtained with cells to tissues. This is particularly true in connection with radiation therapy since the end point of major concern, *proliferative integrity*, is a cell property which can be effectively studied in vitro. Because of this, some years ago we switched our interest to the study of cultured cells. Also, we chose to examine the effect of fractionated exposures on survival to simulate procedures commonly used in therapy.

From the beginning, our fractionation experiments were conceived in the context of the biophysical fact that surviving mammalian cells are usually damaged cells. This follows from the shape of the single-cell survival curve alone, which for X rays and other low linear energy transfer (LET) radiations has a threshold region usually followed by a region of exponential response (Elkind and Sutton, 1959, 1960; Alper *et al.*, 1962). A threshold means that an effect is not produced until damage is accumulated. It is not possible to construct a curve with a threshold from the sums or products of exponential responses.

Since the publication of our initial recovery experiments (Elkind and Sutton, 1959, 1960), similar results have been reported for other lines of cultured cells (Lockart, Elkind, and Moses, 1961; Barendsen, 1962), for cells assayed in vivo (Hornsey and Silini, 1962; Till and McCulloch, 1963), and for plant cells (Hall and Lajtha, 1963). There seems little doubt, there-

* From the Comitato Nazionale per l'Energia Nucleare, Centro Studi Nucleari della Casaccia, Rome, Italy. Present address: Istituto di Anatomia Topografica, Universita di Napoli, Naples, Italy.

fore, that at least in mammalian cells, and probably in plant cells too, the fractionation responses which underlie the subject of this paper are general. Moreover, the predictions of tissue responses based upon cellular observations (Elkind, 1961; Till and McCulloch, 1964) appear to be borne out in connection with animal survival after whole-body exposures (see Elkind, 1961; and Kallman, 1963). These latter results illustrate that a knowledge of cell responses can contribute to our understanding of tissue responses.

Concerning the response of tumors during radiation therapy, the state of oxygenation of the target cells is of considerable importance for at least two reasons: (1) because of the oxygen effect, the survival resulting from any given acute exposure will be greater under anoxic* as opposed to oxygenated conditions (see Gray, 1957–1958, 1961; Alper, 1960) and (2), the absence of oxygen may affect a cell's ability to recover from sublethal damage. The importance of the oxygen effect in influencing many cellular responses, including survival, is well known, and its significance in radiation therapy now seems to be acknowledged. Concerning the dependence of recovery on oxygen tension, little if any quantitative information has been available.

In this paper, we report our initial findings dealing with the survival dependence on oxygen of mammalian cells subjected to fractionated exposures. Our presentation will be comparative (*i.e.*, the response under nitrogen versus the response under air) and will include the effect of reduced oxygen tension on the growth and division properties of mammalian cells, a brief review of the fractionation response of cells equilibrated with air, and a comparison of the survival kinetics of cells exposed to fractionated doses while under nitrogen as opposed to air. Finally, to relate these results to the question of interest in this session, we will present the elements of a model for tumor response to fractionated doses in radiation therapy.

Materials and Methods

In our earlier experiments, cells were grown and irradiated with 55 kv X rays while attached in Pyrex Petri dishes (Elkind and Sutton, 1959, 1960; Elkind, Sutton, and Moses, 1961). For studies under reduced oxygen tensions, we were required to devise a sealable container for cell growth and irradiation and to use, therefore, a harder source of X rays. Hence, except for the changes to be noted, our materials and methods were the same as those previously described.

Single-cell suspensions of the Chinese hamster cell line V79-379-A (a clonal derivative of line V79-1) were inoculated into 4 oz prescription bottles fitted with gauze plugs. The cells were grown overnight in a CO_2

* Throughout this paper the general terms *anoxic* and *under nitrogen* will be used interchangeably to mean an oxygen tension low enough to have a pronounced effect on response. The terms *oxygenated* or *under air* will mean an oxygen tension in the region of that corresponding to equilibration with air. Where equilibration with a particular anoxic atmosphere is referred to, the parts per million (ppm) of oxygen accurate to ~5 per cent will be noted.

incubator (15 to 18 hours). The number of cells inoculated was varied in order that ~100 visible colonies would result nine days after irradiation. For survival estimates, three or more bottles were used per dose point. (Standard errors in survival are shown on the figures to be discussed where larger than the points as plotted.) From earlier studies (Elkind, Han, and Volz, 1963), we knew that after an overnight growth period cells would be in log-phase growth.

Following the initial growth period, sample bottles were fitted with rubber stoppers for measurements under air, or with specially designed plastic stopcocks for measurements under nitrogen. The latter closures were sterilized with ethylene oxide at room temperature. After gassing with an appropriate mixture of $O_2 + N_2$ (including ~2 per cent CO_2 for pH control), valves were closed and cells were incubated (37 to 38 C) and/or irradiated (room temperature) as required. Colonial growth took place under air.

To reduce the oxygen content in the bottles to known concentrations, an apparatus was used which consisted of the following elements in series: (1) a gas handling and mixing system capable of delivering controlled flows of humidified mixtures of $O_2 + N_2$ (plus CO_2), (2) a sample bottle shaking apparatus to hasten gas exchange between the liquid and gas phases without bubbling, and (3) an oxygen measuring and recording instrument consisting of a KOH gas scrubber (to remove the CO_2) and a polarographic cell (Beckman Instruments, Model 80). This apparatus permits the alternate use of up to four different gas mixtures in one experiment (five, including air), the gassing of up to nine bottles at one time in less than 10 minutes, and the measurement of effluent gas oxygen concentrations to insure that steady state conditions have been reached.

Figure 1 is a photograph of our shaking board with two bottle assemblies in place and a valve alone for details. The outer end of each valve body (lucite) has tapered entrance and exit ports to which are connected

FIGURE 1. Photograph of the shaking board used to reciprocate sample bottles during gassing. Cells are attached to the underside of the upper surfaces of the bottles.

polyvinyl jumpers via 90° tapered metal connectors. The latter are greased with Kel-F and secured in place in the valve bodies by a piece of rubber hose running along the inner top ledge of the board. Each valve carries a pair of "O" rings greased with Kel-F for lubrication and to help make a gas-tight seal. During gassing the board is reciprocated ~125 strokes/min in a horizontal direction with the cells attached to the underside of the top surface. A plastic tube conducts the incoming gas to the upper corner of each bottle. Hence, during gassing, medium is sloshed up the sides of the bottles, but not over the cells, which yields good mixing as well as a surface area of about 60 cm^2 for gas exchange. Flow rates were ~2.5 l/min (about 150 volume changes per gassing run). As a result, the small leaks associated with the plastic tubing and mechanical joints used were of minor importance.

The details of irradiation of cells attached in Petri dishes (55 kv X rays, ~722 rads/min) have been described (Elkind and Sutton, 1960). For cells X-irradiated in 4 oz prescription bottles, we used a Van de Graaff accelerator (2.5 mv; HVL = 9.6 mm Pb; 750 to 800 rads/min). Bottles were irradiated from above while rotating on a lucite turntable with cell attachment surfaces up (*i.e.*, as shown in Figure 1). The turntable accommodates eight bottles; up to seven samples were exposed at one time with the eighth position used for a ferrous sulfate dose measurement for each exposure. The very thin layer of medium which covered the cells during exposure helped minimize any oxygen tension gradients which might result from the radiochemical depletion of dissolved oxygen (Dewey and Boag, 1959.

Experimental Results

The Oxygen Effect

Single-Dose Survival

Figure 2 shows an experiment, more or less typical of those performed by others, which demonstrates the oxygen-enhancing effect on single-dose survival (e.g. see Dewey, 1960; Hewitt and Wilson, 1961; Barendsen, 1961; Silini and Hornsey, 1962; Schneider and Whitmore, 1963; Belli and Andrews, 1963). The experiment number shown in the upper right corner indicates in this instance (as well as in others so noted) that all the data were obtained with the same starting suspension of cells. For each survival curve, bottles were withdrawn from the incubator as a group to minimize and roughly equalize the length of time that each group was at room temperature. Small adjustments in survival for varying initial growth periods were made to correspond in this case to an average cellular multiplicity, $\overline{N} = 3.3$.

Several features of the results in Figure 2 should be noted: (1) The average plating efficiency (P.E.) is high and the standard error small. This

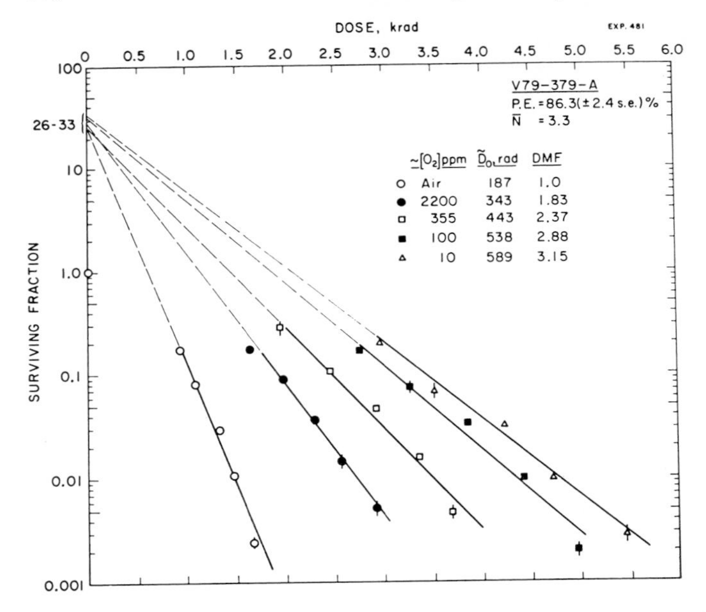

FIGURE 2. The oxygen effect for Chinese hamster cells, line V79–379–A, irradiated with 2.5 mv X rays at room temperature in the presence of the oxygen concentrations shown. PE stands for plating efficiency. $\bar{N}$ is the cellular multiplicity per potential colony-forming unit at the time of exposure.

means that the gassing procedure did not unfavorably affect viability. (2) The $\widetilde{D}_0$ values (*i.e.*, the doses required to reduce survival by a factor of 1/e along the straight lines shown) were estimated from lines fitted to the data by eye. (3) While the over-all extraploation numbers $\widetilde{nN}$ of the lines as drawn cover a range from 26 to 33, they do not differ significantly; hence these results are consistent with an oxygen effect which is strictly dose modifying. (4) The dose-modifying factors (DMF) listed (DMF's were obtained from ratios of $\widetilde{D}_0$'s) cover a range somewhat larger than that usually reported, although equal to the DMF reported for hypertetraploid Ehrlich ascites cells (Silini and Hornsey, 1962). (5) From these results, the oxygen concentration for a half-maximum effect is estimated to be ~8 μmole/liter at 24 C.

Division Rate and Division Delay

As shown by others, our results in Figure 2 confirm in a general way that mammalian cells have higher survivals when irradiated under anoxic than under oxygenated conditions. We now inquire what influence anoxia has on the division delay resulting from an acute exposure, and on the division rate of surviving (and nonsurviving) cells after the delay period.

In Figure 3, the growth of unirradiated cells is traced by the open and closed circles. At the time indicated by "X", anoxic and oxygenated cells were given approximately equal survival doses (8 to 10 per cent survival). Air + CO_2 was then introduced into the "anoxic bottles" and the subsequent increases in total and colony-forming cells were traced with time.

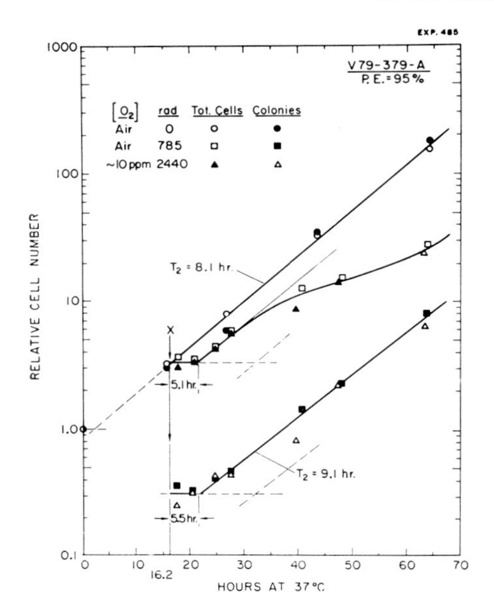

FIGURE 3. The relative effect of anoxia at the time of exposure only on division delay and division rates after the delay period (2.5 mv X rays). Total cell number measurements were made with a Coulter electronic cell counter. Colony formation data were obtained by plating appropriate aliquots of cells which had been suspended by trypsinization at the times shown. (T_2 = doubling time.)

Except for the modifications in techniques noted, this experiment was performed in the same way as a large series of similar experiments reported earlier (Elkind, Han, and Volz, 1963). In our earlier study we found that (1) division delays of total and colony-forming cells were equal and increased linearly with dose over the range examined, (2) surviving cells divided asynchronously after their delay and at an essentially unaltered rate compared to the controls, and (3) after the delay period, the initial division rate of the total population equaled that of the surviving fraction.

As expected, quite similar results are shown in Figure 3 for cells exposed under air. However, Figure 3 also contains the result that mammalian cells exposed only while hypoxic subsequently are delayed and divide in a manner quite similar to cells exposed under air. (A similar observation has been reported for *Shigella flexneri* by Alper [1961].) If the 3.1 times larger dose (2,440 rad/785 rad) had increased division delay in proportion to the dose, cells anoxic when exposed would have been delayed longer by approximately this same factor as sketched by the dashed lines. Clearly, this did not happen. This result extends the generality of the oxygen effect and further supports the view that oxygen enters into radiobiological effects between the initial absorption events and the biological fixation of the lesion.

Although the results in Figure 3 support our general notions about how cells are influenced by oxygen, they are of limited usefulness because cells were anoxic only during exposure. To examine the influence of reduced oxygen tensions on recovery, we have to know what are the postirradiation division properties of cells anoxic after, as well as during, exposure. Some insight into this question can be obtained from a knowledge of the dependence of respiration rates on oxygen tension (Dewey, 1963). We have not as yet measured respiration rates; instead we have measured the effect of anoxia on the division of control and irradiated cells.

In Figure 4, we show the effect of anoxia on the division of unirradiated cells which were initially in log phase growth (under air). The data show that initial anoxic division rates decrease with decreasing oxygen concentration; the data also suggest that these decreases are not attributable to reduced viability (*i.e.* colony-forming ability) since the total cell and colony formation data overlap. The last points on the anoxic curves may be spurious in that oxygen may have leaked into the bottles by the times shown. Alternatively, they suggest that the populations may have adapted to anoxia or that a fraction of the starting cells were able to divide at essentially unreduced rates. Although more data are needed to permit a choice between these possibilities, the point remains that after oxygen depletion, initial division rates are reduced. The possibility that respiration might have further significantly reduced the oxygen supply will be considered in connection with a later figure.

In Figure 5, the results in Figures 3 and 4 are extended to the case of anoxia during as well as after irradiation. Here are shown two experiments at ~355 ppm oxygen. The delays and cell-number increases after exposure which would be expected on the basis of Figure 3 (anoxia during exposure only) are also indicated. Consistent with the reduced division rates in Figure 4, after a dose which yielded approximately the same surviving fraction as in Figure 3, anoxia increased the division delay period by a factor of at least 2. Also, the division rate of surviving cells after the delay period is significantly less in Figure 5 than in Figure 3; this is probably also true for the nonsurviving moiety since 90 per cent or so of the "total cells" are nonsurvivars (noncolony formers). For completeness, we also note here that the results in Figure 5 might have been influenced by respiration-enhanced anoxia since we would not expect the doses used to have any effect on

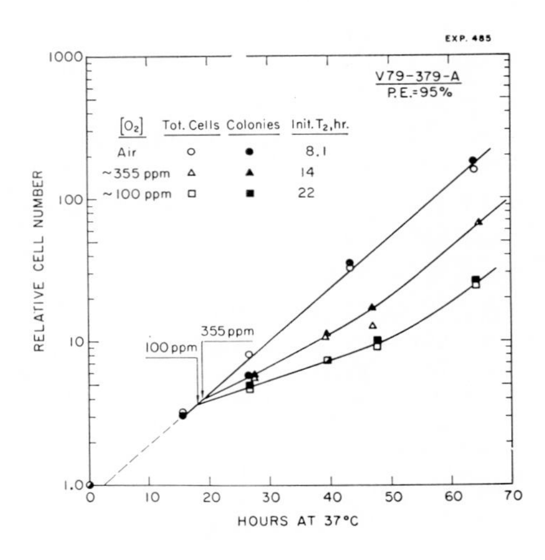

FIGURE 4. The effect of anoxia on the subsequent division of unirradiated cells. The times of gassing are indicated by arrows (T_2 = doubling time).

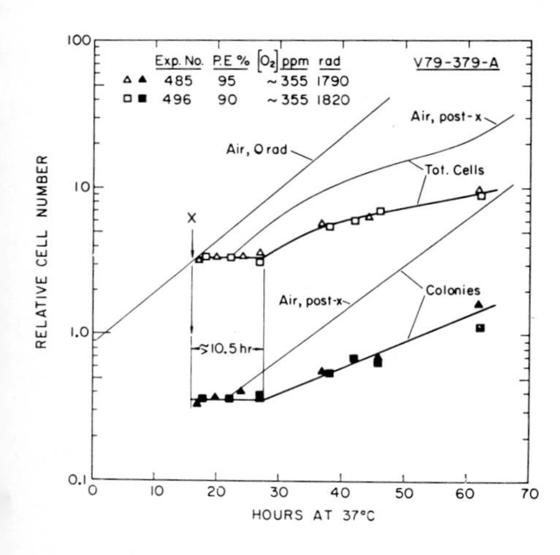

FIGURE 5. The effect on the postirradiation division of cells irradiated at time "X" and maintained anoxic until sampled. The results of two experiments are shown (2.5 mv X rays).

respiration rates (Cammarano, 1963; Coe, Garcia, Ibsen, and McKee, 1963). We discuss this possibility later.

Repair of Sublethal Damage

Oxygenated Cells

We turn now to the survival response of cells exposed to fractionated doses. Since it is helpful in analyzing results obtained under nitrogen to compare them to results obtained under air, we start by describing the fractionation survival properties of oxygenated cells.

Figure 6 shows an experiment from an earlier study (Elkind, Sutton, and Moses, 1961). This experiment was started when cells attached in Petri dishes were still essentially all single. The curve marked "Surv." traces the single dose survival determined at zero hours. (Arrows on the

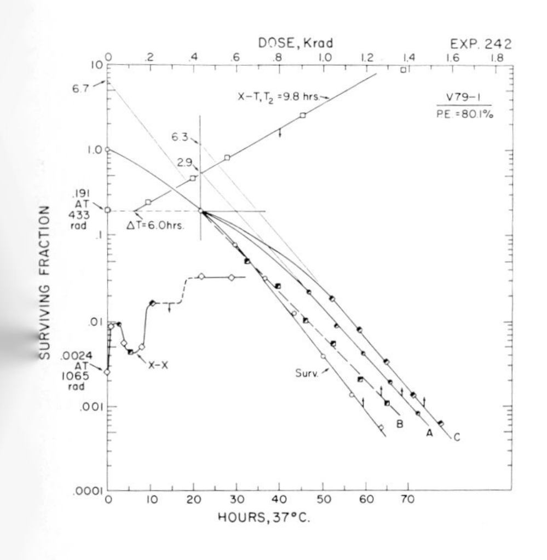

FIGURE 6. Single and two-dose survival data (55 kv X rays) for oxygenated, initially single, Chinese hamster cells. Surv., the initial survival curve after a 1 hour attachment period; A, survival curve 2.6 hours after 433 rads; B as for A at 5.3 hours; C as for A at 10.6 hours; X-T, division of cells surviving 433 rads determined by respreading developing colonies (T_2 = doubling time); X-X, net survival after 433 rads followed by 632 rads as a function of time between doses. Arrows indicate appropriate abscissae. (From Elkind, Sutton, and Moses, 1961.)

Description of Curves and Survival Parameters for Data in Figure 6

CURVE	DESCRIPTION	$\tilde{n}$* OR $(\widetilde{nN})$†	$\tilde{D}_0$‡
Surv.	Initial survival curve	6.74 ± 0.97§	134.5 ± 5.2§
A	433 rads; 2.6 hours, 37 C; Survival	2.9	155
B	433 rads; 5.3 hours, 37 C; Survival	1.0	165
C	433 rads; 10.6 hours, 37 C; Survival	6.28 ± 0.89§	147.2 ± 6.2§
X-T	433 rads; 37 C, trypsinization		
X-X	433 rads; 37 C; 632 rads		

* Single cell extrapolation number.
† Over-all extrapolation number after the onset of division.
‡ $\tilde{D}$—dose required to reduce survival by a factor of 1/e ($\underset{=}{\sim}$ 0.37).
§ From least square fits to a straight line of the terminal portions of the survival curve.

curves point to the appropriate abscissae.) The portion of the curve below 433 rads is essentially a straight line which indicates that cells surviving that dose were close to being saturated with sublethal damage (see Elkind and Sutton, 1960). The remainder of the data in Figure 6 refer to the survival or growth properties of cells which all received the same first or conditioning dose, 433 rads. In particular, the survival curves of those cells surviving 433 rads were measured 2.6, 5.3, and 10.6 hours later; these are traced by curves A, B, and C, respectively (see also table). Judging from the variation with time of the single-cell extrapolation $\tilde{n}$ (Alper, Gillies, and Elkind, 1960) or the overall extrapolation number $(\widetilde{nN})$, at 2.6 hours, about half the original value returned; at 5.3 hours, $\tilde{n} \simeq 1$; and by 10.6 hours, $(\widetilde{nN})$ is equal to the $\tilde{n}$ of cells which received no prior irradiation (the initial survival curve).

The reason for our designating the extrapolation number at 10.6 hours by $(\widetilde{nN})$ instead of $\tilde{n}$ is indicated by the curve marked "X-T" in Figure 6. This curve traces the division of cells surviving 433 rads and is quite similar to the postirradiation growth curves shown in Figure 3. By 10.6 hours after the conditioning dose, an appreciable number of surviving cells had divided; the average multiplicity of viable cells at that time was $\overline{N} = 1.4$.

The curve marked "X-X" in Figure 6 traces the net survival to 433 rads followed by 632 rads given at the times shown. The points at 0, 2.6, 5.3, and 10.6 hours come from the initial survival curve and curves A, B, and C, respectively. The shape of this curve from the minimum on does not reflect division alone, but rather the combined effects of division and cell progression, as recent studies have indicated (Elkind, Whitmore, and Alescio, 1964). (The dashed portion of the "X-X" curve is inferred from other experiments. In addition to a stepwise shape, in some experiments a minimum was observed between ~11 and ~19 hours.) However, starting at zero hours, the prompt initial rise in the two-dose fractionation curve results principally from repair of sublethal damage. This point is dealt with in more detail by other speakers in this session (Dewey and Humphrey, pp. 340 to 375; Sinclair and Morton, pp. 418–422; Whitmore, Gulyas, and Botond, pp. 423 to 441, this volume). The drop in net survival from the maximum to the minimum before the onset of division is probably caused by the progression of recovered cells into more responsive states as we suggested earlier (see p. 129 in Elkind, Sutton, and Moses, 1961). Kallman has offered a similar interpretation, except that he does not associate the prompt initial rise in survival with recovery from sublethal damage (Kallman, 1963). Studies with asynchronous cells make uncertain the extent of recovery in all surviving cells. However, the biophysics of damage accumulation which follows from a threshold-type response, plus the evidence cited by Elkind, Whitmore, and Alescio (1964), forces the conclusion that the initial rise in the "X-X" curve results from repair of sublethal damage.

Since our principal concern in this report is the applicability of fractionation survival data to radiation therapy, we can leave aside the detailed interpretation of results such as those in Figure 6. Suffice it to note that in periods of time of the order of a doubling time—*i.e.* by 10.6 hours in Figure 6—cells which survive a conditioning dose respond to subsequent exposures as though they had received no prior irradiation.

Anoxic Cells

Bearing in mind the results under air, we turn now to fractionation data under nitrogen. In these experiments, cells were kept in the atmospheres noted, from just before their first until just after their second doses.

In the experiment shown in Figure 7, the two-dose survivals in the presence of ~100 ppm and ~355 ppm oxygen are compared to air (lower curves). The data along the upper curve were obtained in the same way as

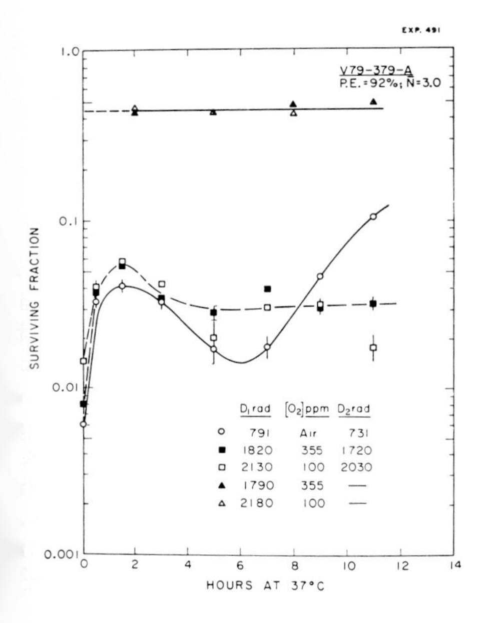

FIGURE 7. Net survivals as a function of doses D_1 and D_2 (lower curves) separated by the intervals shown (2.5 mv X rays). The reduced oxygen atmospheres were maintained from just before the first to just after the second dose. The upper points are based upon colony counts and were obtained in the same manner as those in Figure 5. $\overline{N}$ is the multiplicity after overnight growth.

the "colony" data in Figure 5. Before discussing these results, several technical points should be noted. First, although the cell multiplicity was 3.0 when exposures were started, the fractionation data trace net survivals of essentially single cells. This is certainly true for the nitrogen data since all survivals are <0.1 and no division occurred over the fractionation interval examined (upper curve). For the air data, division started at about the minimum (see Figure 3); hence the net survivals at 9 and 11 hours would be slightly higher than shown if adjusted to single surviving cells (see Elkind and Sutton, 1960, for the relevant mathematics). To be valid, these statements require that cells in groups survive independently as is the case for Chinese hamster cells (Elkind, Sutton, and Moses, 1961).

Second, the fractionation doses, D_1 and D_2 in Figure 7, are average values. Survivals for doses which differed from the averages were adjusted using the appropriate survival curve in Figure 2. This procedure is approximate, but since the resulting changes were usually <10 per cent of the surviving fraction, the approximation is not important.

Third, compared to results like those in Figure 6, the data in Figure 7 have appreciably larger uncertainties. This is a result, in part, of the lesser degree of control that we have over experiments of this type which involve the use of stoppered bottles (as opposed to plates in controlled CO_2 environments), and the transportation of samples to and from the Van de Graaff accelerator. Even for irradiations under air, large uncertainties occasionally result (e.g. $\pm$ 14 per cent standard error for the point at seven hours). Added to this is the possibility that bottles fitted with valves may occasionally have small leaks. Since in the range of oxygen concentrations used the oxygen effect on survival is quite pronounced, small leaks can lead to large uncertainties. Also, the effect of a leak would very likely be in the direction of reducing the number of colonies which grow out. Hence, in addition to increasing uncertainties, leaky valves tend to reduce the average survival of a given set of samples (e.g. the 5- and 11-hour points at 100 ppm oxygen). Because of this, when fitting nitrogen data, we have given less weight to points with large uncertainties (see also Figure 8). We should point out, that if a given bottle leaked appreciably, it is likely that no colonies would have been observed because of the large dose-modifying factors involved.

Returning to the results in Figure 7, we note first that the air fractionation curve is similar to the "X-X" curve in Figure 6. This is also true of the first few hours of the two nitrogen curves which both show a rapid increase in survival to a maximum. In the region from three to eleven hours, the 355 ppm oxygen curve is fairly flat and, while two of the 100 ppm points are low, for the reasons given it is likely that the 100 ppm curve is flat in this region also. Consistent with the results in Figure 5, the upper curve in Figure 7 shows that no division occurred in the interval examined after first doses close to those used for the fractionation results. (Note that the survival traced by the upper curve is higher than the single-cell surviving fractions by the multiplicity factor, $\overline{N} = 3$.)

Hence, although sublethally damaged anoxic cells appear to repair damage promptly, their two-dose response differs from that of cells under air from a short time after the maximum on. While not predictable, this latter difference is reasonable; the postirradiation division data show that anoxic cells are delayed longer than oxygenated cells for a survival-equivalent dose, and it has been shown that the development of the minimum in the air curve is a result of cell progression toward division (Elkind, Whitmore, and Alescio, 1964).

The results in Figure 8 show an extension of the 355 ppm data in Figure 7 and also a test of the possible influence of respiration on oxygen concentration. (No data were taken during the interval indicated by the dashed part of the curve.) Through the use of varying numbers of X-ray sterilized cells (2.0 krad under air), net survivals were determined with total cell numbers per bottle differing by 9 to 10 times when first doses were given. The curve was drawn to fit low titer data (solid circles). Since it has been shown that respiration rates under air are unaffected even after much larger doses than those used (Cammarano, 1963; Coe, Garcia, Ibsen, and McKee, 1963), high titer data (open circles) indicate that respiration had little if any effect on net survivals. Slightly increased survivals brought about by the larger number of sterilized cells per bottle may have resulted from an enhanced feeder cell effect. In view of these results, it seems unlikely that respiration affected the data in Figures 4, 5, and 7 since these experiments involved cell numbers considerably less than 1.7×10^5 per bottle.

Although the similar shapes of the beginning parts of the air and nitrogen two-dose curves in Figure 7 suggest that the single cell extrapolation number of anoxic cells increases between doses (e.g. as for oxygenated cells in Figure 6), we checked to see if this is true at an oxygen concentration even lower than in Figures 7 and 8. Figure 9 shows the initial survival curve (open circles, $\overline{N} = 3.2$) and fractionation survival curves after a conditioning dose of 2,430 rads at ~15 ppm oxygen. In spite of uncertainties in

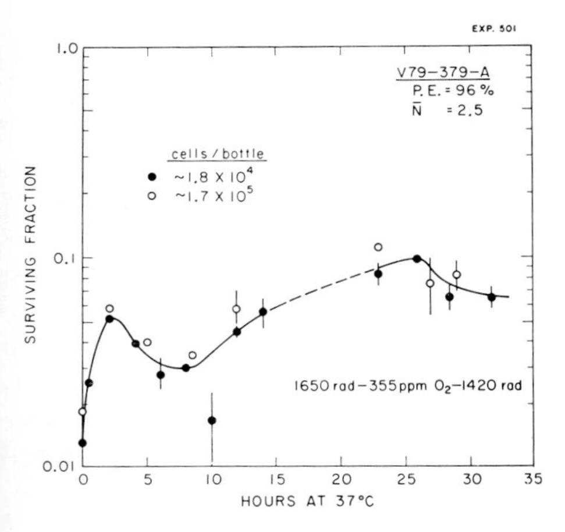

FIGURE 8. Net survivals as a function of time between two doses for two different cell concentrations. The format of this experiment is the same as for Figure 7 except that the number of X-ray sterilized cells ("feeder" cells) present at the time of gassing was adjusted to the values shown.

the data, it is clear that by 1.5 hours (open triangles) the extrapolation number is approximately four times larger than it is at zero hours (*i.e.* in the straight line regions, the curve at 1.5 hours is displaced upward by ~4 times compared to the initial survival curve). At 5.5 hours, the extrapolation number has dropped to a lower value than at 1.5 hours, but it is still higher by ~2 times compared to the value immediately after the conditioning dose.

The results in Figure 9 confirm that, even under anoxic conditions, sublethally irradiated cells can repair damage. We have also found that sublethally affected cells can undergo repair while maintained both anoxic and at room temperature. Apparently, recovery requires neither aerobic metabolism nor metabolism at optimal growth temperatures.

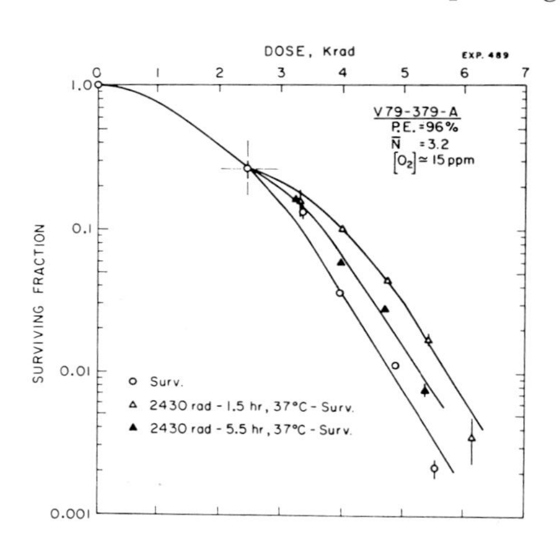

FIGURE 9. Fractionation survival curves at ~ 15 ppm oxygen. The open circles trace the initial survival curve of log phase cells ($\bar{N} \simeq 3.2$). The open and closed triangles trace the survival of those cells which survived a 2,430 rad conditioning dose and received graded second doses at 1.5 and 5.5 hours, respectively. (2.5 mv X rays.)

A Model for the Fractionation Response of Tumors

Repeated Recovery

Figure 10 consists of a series of fractionation survival curves which we will use to illustrate the basis of a first order model for the fractionation response of tumors (Elkind, 1960). The assumptions are the following:

1. As sketched in Figure 10, we assume that the intervals between successive treatments are long enough to permit surviving cells to survive additional exposures as though they had fully recovered. An example of this is curve C in Figure 6. This assumption means that if cells received the fractionated doses D_1, D_2-D_1, D_3-D_2, and so on, survival would fall off according to curve F (see Elkind and Sutton, 1960, for additional illustrations of repeated recovery).

2. We will assume that throughout a treatment course, cellular survival parameters remain essentially constant in time and uniform throughout the tumor. That is, we are assuming that oxygen tension remains constant and that curves A, B, C, D, E, and so on all have the same shape.

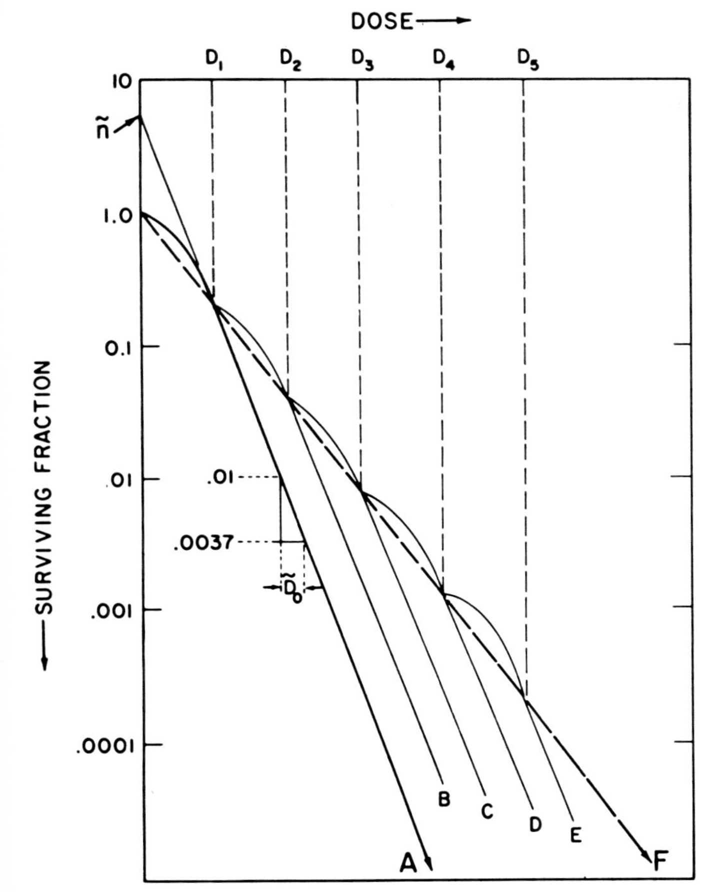

FIGURE 10. Theoretical fractionation survival curves to illustrate the analysis of tumor response according to a first order model. Curve A is a single-cell survival curve specified by the parameters ñ and $\tilde{D}_0$. Curves B, C, D, and so on are the fractionation survival curves of cells which survive and fully recover from the total doses D_1, D_2, D_3, and so on.

3. We will assume that a tumor will be sterilized when the number of cells still capable of unlimited proliferation is reduced below a certain level. Barring other effects which may be important in a given case (e.g. immune responses), the smallest number required for regrowth would be one cell.

4. We assume that cells are not induced to become malignant as a result of treatment. That is, aside from some amount of division that may occur between treatments (e.g. as noted in connection with curve C in Figure 6), we assume that no new cells are added to the tumor during treatment.

Isosurvival Curves

The easiest way to describe the model is to use an example. We will assume that a surviving fraction of 1×10^{-10} is required to sterilize a tumor. If a tumor consists of 1×10^{9} cells which have to be killed to suppress regrowth, a surviving fraction of 1×10^{-10} would insure that 9 out of 10 such tumors would be sterilized. Assuming equal dose fractions are used, we inquire: How does the total dose vary with the number of exposures? We call the latter curve an isosurvival curve since we require that the same survival be reached regardless of the number of exposures used. An isosurvival curve is equivalent to an isoeffect curve if the surviving fraction for tumor sterilization is independent of the number of treatments.

Figure 11 shows four isosurvival curves, each of which is completely specified if the single-cell survival curve is specified (e.g. curve A, Figure 10). For simplicity, we assume that the single-cell survival curves can be adequately described by parameters $\tilde{n}$ and $\tilde{D}_0$. To determine a point on an isosurvival curve, for a given number of treatments ν, we must determine the single dose D_1 which satisfies the equation,

$$S_c(D = D_1) = (S_T)^{1/\nu} \quad (1)$$

where S_c is the single-cell dose dependent survival (e.g. curve A, Figure 10) and S_T is the isosurviving fraction. The total dose D_T is then,

$$D_T = \nu D_1. \quad (2)$$

Several points are apparent in Figure 11: (1) For a given $\tilde{n}$, the curves are shifted upward roughly in proportion to $\tilde{D}_0$. (2) For a given $\tilde{D}_0$, increasing $\tilde{n}$ causes the curve to rise more rapidly. (3) The ranges of $\tilde{n}$'s and $\tilde{D}_0$'s used predict a range of total doses consistent with those used in practice. Since the single-cell survival parameters shown are similar to those observed experimentally, this point by itself supports the pertinence of mammalian cell studies to radiation therapy. (4) Assuming anoxic cells, like oxygenated cells, can recover between repeated exposures, the effect of anoxia would be evident in a shift from one isosurvival curve to another such that the $\tilde{D}_0$'s involved are in the ratio of the dose-modifying factor. For example, if the DMF = 3 for cells whose oxygenated response is specified by $\tilde{n} = 2$, $\tilde{D}_0 = 75$ rads, anoxia will cause a shift from the lowest to the uppermost curve in Figure 11 ($\tilde{n} = 2$, $\tilde{D}_0 = 225$ rads).

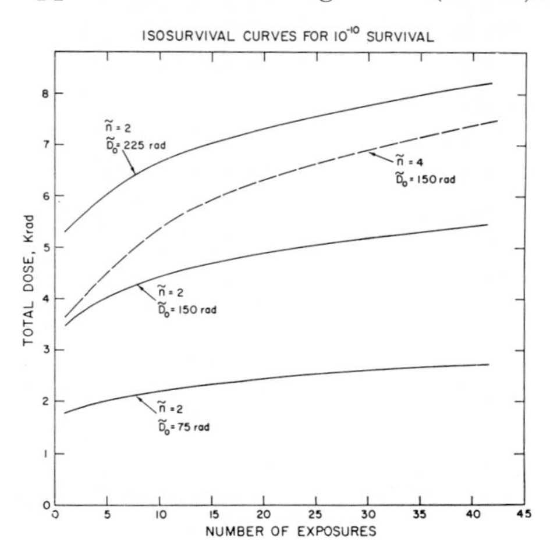

FIGURE 11. Isosurvival curves for a surviving fraction of 1×10^{-10}. Total dose versus number of exposures is plotted for different single-cell survival curves denoted by the $\tilde{n}$'s and $\tilde{D}_0$'s (see Curve A, Figure 10). The coordinates are linear; a similar curve using linear-log coordinates was published earlier (Elkind, 1960).

umor Studies

In the radiation therapy literature, it is difficult to find studies suffi-
ently controlled and documented to use as tests of this model. Many prac-
al considerations contribute to this, including: variations from tumor to
mor in size, survival properties of the constituent cells, and patterns of
oxia; complications resulting from systemic effects; and changes in the
ttern of anoxia or the properties of the surviving cells during the course
treatment. Of the studies which have been performed, the work of Fried-
an and Pearlman (1955) is of particular interest because of the larger
easure of experimental control afforded by their approach.

Friedman and Pearlman treated individual subcutaneous lesions which
curred after radical mastectomy. In one instance, 27 lesions in the same
tient were individually treated; the results are shown in Figure 12. The
en circles represent lesions which were not sterilized, and the closed
rcles lesions which were sterilized (see Addendum for a further discussion
the end point used by Friedman and Pearlman). The curve drawn is
riedman's and Pearlman's estimate of the isoeffct curve which, in this case,
ould be a line separating the region of "success" from "failure." These
ta are of particular interest because it is reasonable that all recurrences
ter mastectomy resulted from one or a few cell types.

Although a detailed comparison between the curve in Figure 12 and
ose in Figure 11 is not justified, two points are noteworthy: (1) The iso-
fect curve (Figure 12) has the same general shape as the isosurvival
rves (Figure 11); and (2) judging from the position the former curve
ould occupy if plotted relative to the latter curves, the single-cell survival

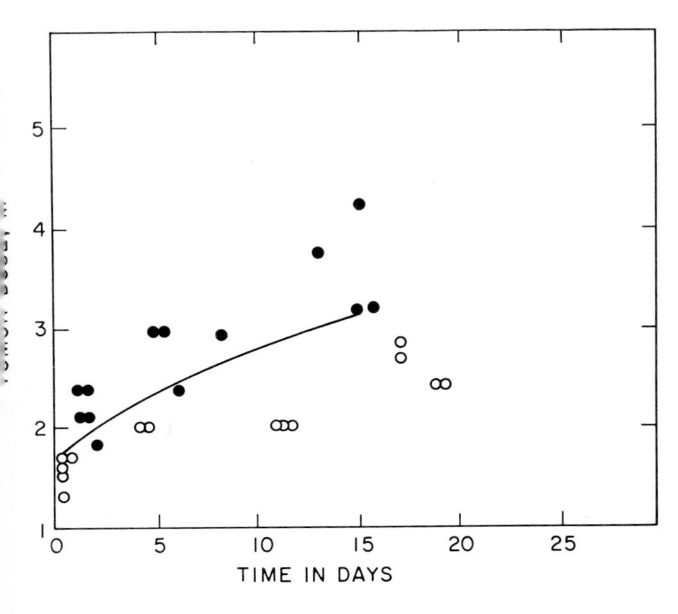

FIGURE 12. Total doses as a function of the duration of treatment for 27 subcutaneous nodules which recurred in the same patient after radical mastectomy. Nodules ranged in size from 0.5 to 2.0 cm in diameter. Open circles, treatments which failed to sterilize tumors; closed circles, treatments which succeeded. The doses are calculated tumor doses (200 kv X rays, HVL = 1 mm Cu) (Redrawn from Friedman and Pearlman, 1955).

parameters $\tilde{n} = 2–4$, $\tilde{D}_0 \simeq 75$ rads would fit the nodule data quite we
Similar isoeffect curves have also been reported for mycosis fungoid
(Friedman and Pearlman, 1956). Also, Kohn's plot (Kohn, 1958) of Ga
cia's carcinoma of the cervix data (Garcia, 1955) can be fitted by a simil
curve.

Discussion

Our results thus far support the view that anoxic cells recover in mu
the same way as do oxygenated cells. (By recovery, we refer to the prom
increase in threshold widths after an acute exposure; see Alper *et*
1962). This does not mean that the fractionation survival kinetics
oxygenated and anoxic cells are identical. Rather we believe that there a
differences, but that these may result from oxygen-dependent differences
postirradiation growth patterns rather than from differences in recovery pa
terns. For the therapy model presented, the critical point is that recover
as opposed to cell growth, is independent of oxygen tension.

Because our model is only a starting point, we have glossed over son
relevant considerations. These we mention here with the expectation
more fully dealing with them at a later date.

First, the conditions of our experiments with anoxic cells do not co
pletely simulate the conditions expected in a tumor. In our experimen
anoxia was brought about abruptly. In a tumor, varying degrees of anox
exist for longer periods before exposure depending upon the vasculari
and supportive tissue architecture (see Thomlinson, 1961). However, whi
this point should be checked, our findings that cells recover under reduc
metabolism (Elkind, Whitmore, and Alescio, 1964) as well as after rapid
induced anoxia suggest that the pattern of recovery will be roughly t
same in cells grown under nitrogen before their first exposure.

Second, when the number of treatments is large, the survival per trea
ment is in the threshold region of the single-cell survival curve. This mea
that the shape of the isosurvival curve for large numbers of fractions d
pends critically on the initial slope of the survival curve. If the initial slo
is zero, total doses will increase without limit as the number of fractions
increased. However, observed single-cell survival curves usually have neg
tive initial slopes, which means that total doses should approach consta
values. If the curves in Figure 10 had been drawn with initial slopes clos
to that of the curve marked "Surv." in Figure 6, the isosurvival curves i
Figure 11 would be flatter.

Third, when the number of treatments is small, the shape of the initi
part of the isosurvival curve is controlled by the shape of the terminal po
tion of the single-cell survival curve. If instead of being a straight line, th
terminal portion of the survival curve bends downward—for example, du
to "small colony" induction (Sinclair, 1964)—the beginning of the is
survival curve would rise more steeply than in Figure 11. This assum
"small colony" damage is repairable. If "small colony" damage is not con

letely repairable, isosurvival curves may first be concave upward, for nall numbers of treatments, and then become concave downward.

Last, the state of oxygenation may change during treatment depend-ıg upon a number of factors (see Gray, 1957–1958, 1961; and Thomlin-ɔn, 1961). If this occurs, the "static" or treatment number-independent ıodel depicted by Figure 11 must be replaced by a "dynamic" model to ccount for major shifts in survival parameters during treatment.

As a concluding statement, we note that the model as such is not a rescription for therapy. A principal objective in radiation treatment is to roduce the differential effect between normal and malignant tissue which ; therapeutically most favorable. Since, in general, proliferating normal nd malignant cells probably respond similarly to fractionation, an opti-ıum treatment schedule must account for their relative responses and, in articular, for changes in their relative responses which may be induced uring a treatment course (e.g. due to changes in oxygenation). In this con-ection, adjunctive techniques like drug therapy may be an effective way f enhancing relative responses.

ACKNOWLEDGMENTS

We wish to acknowledge with thanks the technical assistance of Jill Landon nd Frederick L. Faw.

ADDENDUM

Some additional comments are in order concerning the end point used y Friedman and Pearlman (1955). As pointed out by Dr. Powers in the liscussion (see page 463, this volume), sterilization of nodules was not orroborated although the criterion which was used (*i.e.*, regression for at east six months) may have been equivalent to sterilization. Nevertheless, egression for an appreciable interval must have resulted from a certain legree of cell killing and, hence, the curve shown in Figure 12 is still an soeffect curve. For purposes of the model presented, the point of interest is hat theoretical isosurvival curves have the same shape, and lie in the same lose range, as observed isoeffect curves.

In connection with our recovery data at reduced oxygen tensions, since his paper was prepared additional results have been published (Elkind *et ıl.*, 1964). These extend the observations reported here and lend further upport to our view that repair of sublethal damage is independent of oxy-gen tension.

REFERENCES

Alper, T. 1960. Cellular Radiobiology. *Annual Review of Nuclear Science*, 10:489–530.

———. 1961. "Effects on Subcellular Units and Free-Living Cells," *Mechanisms in Radiobiology*, M. Errera and A. Forssberg, Eds. New York, New York: Academic Press, Inc. P. 375.

Alper, T., J. F. Fowler, R. L. Morgan, D. D. Vonberg, F. Ellis, and R. Oliver. 1962. The Characteristics of the "Type C" Survival Curve. *British Journal of Radiology*, 35:722–723.

Alper, T., N. E. Gillies, and M. M. Elkind. 1960. The Sigmoid Survival Curve in Radiobiology. *Nature,* London, 186:1062–1063.

Barendsen, G. W. 1961. "Damage to the Reproductive Capacity of Human Cells in Tissue Culture by Ionizing Radiations of Different Linear Energy Transfer," *The Initial Effects of Ionizing Radiations on Cells,* R. J. C. Harris, Ed. New York, New York, and London, England: Academic Press. Pp. 183–194.

———. 1962. Dose-Survival Curves of Human Cells in Tissue Culture Irradiated with Alpha-, Beta-, 20 Kv. X-, and 200 Kv. X-Radiation. *Nature,* London, 193:1153-1155.

Belli, J. A., and J. R. Andrews. 1963. The Relationship between Tumor Growth and Radiosensitivity. *Journal of the National Cancer Institute,* 31:689–703.

Cammarano, P. 1963. Protein Synthesis, Glycolysis, and Oxygen Uptake in Hepatoma Cells Irradiated *in vitro. Radiation Research,* 18:1–11.

Coe, E. L., E. M. Garcia, K. H. Ibsen, and R. W. McKee. 1963. Respiration and Glycolysis in X-Irradiated Ehrlich Mouse Ascites Carcinoma Cells. *Radiation Research* 20:586–592.

Dewey, D. L. 1960. Effect of Oxygen and Nitric Oxide on the Radiosensitivity of Human Cells in Tissue Culture. *Nature,* London, 186:780–782.

———. 1963. The X-Ray Sensitivity of *Serratia marcescens. Radiation Research* 19:64–87.

Dewey, D. L., and J. W. Boag. 1959. Modification of the Oxygen Effect when Bacteria Are Given Large Pulses of Radiation. *Nature,* London, 183:1450–1451.

Elkind, M. M. 1960. Cellular Aspects of Tumor Therapy. *Radiology,* 74:529–541.

———. 1961. Radiation Responses of Mammalian Cells. *Brookhaven Symposia in Biology,* 14:220–245.

Elkind, M. M., T. Alescio, R. W. Swain, W. B. Moses, and H. Sutton. 1964. Recovery of Hypoxic Mammalian Cells from Sublethal X-Ray Damage. *Nature,* London, 202: 1190–1193.

Elkind, M. M., A. Han, and K. W. Volz. 1963. Radiation Response of Mammalian Cells Grown in Culture. IV. Dose Dependence of Division Delay and Postirradiation Growth of Surviving and Nonsurviving Chinese Hamster Cells. *Journal of the National Cancer Institute,* 30:705–721.

Elkind, M. M., and H. Sutton. 1959. X-Ray Damage and Recovery in Mammalian Cells in Culture. *Nature,* London, 184:1293–1295.

———. 1960. Radiation Response of Mammalian Cells Grown in Culture. I. Repair of X-Ray Damage in Surviving Chinese Hamster Cells. *Radiation Research,* 13:556–593.

Elkind, M. M., H. Sutton, and W. B. Moses. 1961. Postirradiation Survival Kinetics of Mammalian Cells Grown in Culture. *Journal of Cellular and Comparative Physiology,* 58: Supplement 1: 113–134.

Elkind, M. M., G. F. Whitmore, and T. Alescio. 1964. Actinomycin D Suppression of Recovery in X-Irradiated Mammalian Cells. *Science,* 143:1454–1457.

Friedman, M., and A. W. Pearlman. 1955. Time-Dose Relationship in Irradiation of Recurrent Cancer of the Breast. *The American Journal of Roentgenology, Radium Therapy and Nuclear Medicine,* 73:986–998.

———. 1956. Time-Dose Studies in Irradiation of Mycosis Fungoides, Iso-Effect Curve and Tumor Lethal Dose. *Radiology,* 66:374–379.

Garcia, M. 1955. Further Observations on Tissue Dosage in Cancer of the Cervix Uteri. *The American Journal of Roentgenology, Radium Therapy and Nuclear Medicine,* 73:35–60.

Gray, L. H. 1957–1958. "The Influence of Oxygen on the Response of Cells and Tissues to Ionizing Radiation," *Lectures on the Scientific Basis of Medicine.* London, England: The Athlone Press. Vol. VII. Pp. 314–347.

nsistent with what we see, and I would like to ask if you agree to this general hypothesis : the hamster cell.

Dr. Elkind: I think your description is borne out by the last figure presented by Dr. nclair. However, I would like to make another point. When we talk about the response cells to a first exposure (e.g., in terms of the fine experiments of Drs. Dewey, Sinclair, lmach, and Whitmore), we are usually talking about how they survive with respect their position relative to the DNA cycle. We can say they were in G_1, S, or G_2 and so . However, when we talk about the response of cells after a first dose which are then allenged by a second dose given at some later time, by and large the linear DNA map cell position breaks down. I presume, in the L cell judging from Dr. Whitmore's re- arks, there are data on the position of surviving cells with time after a first dose. But, general, the position correspondence between cells which have been irradiated and ose which have not been is not known. After all, division delay is one indication of the coupling effect of irradiation and there probably are others. For these reasons, I think is difficult at this time to specify the correspondence between cell cycle position after th that before a first exposure.

Dr. W. Powers, Washington University, St. Louis, Missouri: My understanding of e paper of Friedman and Pearlman (*The American Journal of Roentgenology, Radium erapy and Nuclear Medicine,* 73:986–998, 1955) was that the parameter they were easuring was resolution of the tumor rather than sterilization which is considerably dif- rent. I wonder if one should make any interpolation or extrapolation of D_0 from that pe of data?

Dr. Elkind: Dr. Powers' point is correctly taken. The endpoint used by Friedman d Pearlman was disappearance of a lesion for at least six months. Therefore, steriliza- n of the lesions was probably not assured. For purposes of the model presented, however, e nodule data cited are still pertinent. Even if the nodules indicated by the solid circles the last figure were not sterilized but only caused to regress markedly (*i.e.*, for at least months), they were probably more successfully treated than those nodules indicated by en circles. Hence, the line drawn still corresponds to an *isoeffect* curve. The similarity tween the latter curve and the theoretical *isosurvival* curves presented is the significant int with respect to our model.

Dr. Elkind: To be sure, the results which were shown this morning involve doses nich were purposely chosen to be large enough to get more or less beyond the initial oulder. In our more extensive studies with aerobic cells, we used smaller doses, doses nich were well within the initial shoulder. With doses within the initial shoulder re- on, we see results which are qualitatively quite the same as those which I have reported.

Dr. Alexander: I would like to draw attention to what I think may be a significant fference between the data Dr. Elkind just showed us and some data which are in the erature and particularly those of Drs. Dewey and Humphrey. They and some others ve found that the extrapolation number in nitrogen is very much less than the extrapo- tion number under air or oxygen. If that is the case, then I think the effect of fractiona- n will be to reduce the total benefit that is gained by having a tumor fully oxygenated. ne reason for this is illustrated diagrammatically in Figure 10 (page 455) which treats the sponse of a tumor as described by Dr. Elkind. If we have a tumor made up of 10^{10} cells, nich under nitrogen have an extrapolation number of 2 and in air an extrapolation num- r of 10, then the amount of radiation given in a single dose sufficient to cure the tumor, ., to kill 10^{10} cells, is very different for anoxic and aerated conditions. But if the treat- ent is given in 300 r fractions, then the advantage gained by oxygenation is very much ss. So far any tumor that has cells having the survival curve characteristics shown here cells of the type studied by Dewey and Humphrey, the benefit of oxygenation would t be very great if the radiotherapy was given in fractionated doses. Even for tumors ade up of cells of the kind which Dr. Elkind studied, where the extrapolation number the same in N_2 as in air, of course, fractionation would still reduce the advantage gained oxygenation below that expected from a single dose treatment because Dr. Elkind owed that anoxia reduces the amount of recovery between fractions.

Dr. Tikvah Alper, Medical Research Council, Hammersmith Hospital, London, Eng- nd: Hornsey and Silini (*Radiation Research,* 16:712–722, 1962) examined recovery of cites tumor cells from sublethal damage, and their figures for viable count as a function time are reminiscent of Dr. Elkind's curves for cells irradiated in anoxic conditions and kept anoxic between doses. In the experiments of Hornsey and Silini, the irradiated ce were inoculated intraperitoneally into adult mice between irradiations, and there is e dence that in this situation the cells are likely to be in very anoxic conditions. This m be the explanation of the fact that Hornsey and Silini's "recovery curves" did not demo strate the early peak and trough which appear to be characteristic for cells which are he aerobic between doses.

One aspect of these and other results is relevant to Dr. Alexander's suggestion th survival curves for anoxic and aerobic cells have different extrapolation numbers. Horns and Silini observed a tenfold increase in survival for split-dose experiments, compared wi single shots, an increase which agrees very well with the extrapolation number observ for both anoxic and aerobic survival curves. We have been using a computer progra (Pike and Alper, *British Journal of Radiology*, 37:458–463, 1964) to test this very poi namely whether it is in general true that anoxic and aerobic survival have the sar shape (*i.e.*, the same extrapolation numbers). So far about 40 sets of data have be handled by the computer and in only two cases (both referring to experiments with mic organisms) has there been a significant difference in the extrapolation number. In bo these cases, a spuriously *high* extrapolation number for the anoxic survival curve could attributed to inadvertent admission of oxygen to the system at the higher doses.

I should like to make another point about the results obtained by Hornsey and Sili With these particular cells, there was no difference in the shapes of the survival curves f X rays and for fast neutrons: The extrapolation numbers were the same, and this w verified for neutrons by "recovery" experiments. It would be as well, therefore, to be wa about assuming that with neutron irradiation the shoulder to the survival curve is nec sarily considerably reduced, as compared with X rays, although such a reduction is fairly common phenomenon.

Dr. Arthur Cole, The University of Texas M. D. Anderson Hospital and Tumor I stitute, Houston, Texas: It is perhaps a trivial but sometimes overlooked truism that terms of DNA content, the mammalian cell is an extremely radium-resistant system co pared with other systems. For example, the radiation inactivation volume of a nak molecule is roughly equal to the volume of the molecule, as Dr. Hutchinson pointed o earlier. The inactivation volume of a virus system, such as T2 bacteriophage, correspon to about 10 per cent of the DNA volume. The inactivation volume for bacterial syste corresponds to about only 1 per cent of the DNA volume and for mammalian systems co

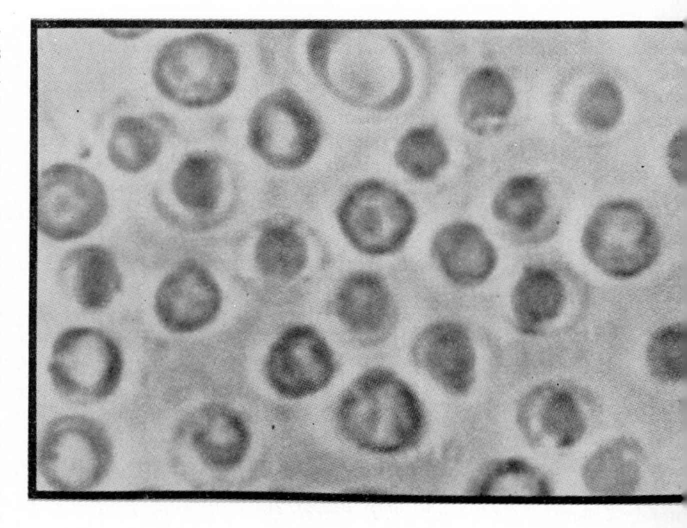

FIGURE 1. Leukemic lymphocytes irradiated with 1,000 r and incubated nine hours. The cell at the top, center, is a large red blood cell. A few lymphocytes are viable, as indicated by chromatin masses and nucleoli. The cytoplasm in these lymphocytes cannot be seen. A few cells have large intranuclear vacuoles surrounded by a dark chromatin ring. One cell near lower left shows an intranuclear vacuole and early rupture of the chromatin ring. Most of the cells are dead wit large dark, structureless pyknotic nuclei, surrounded by a narrow ring of cytoplasm. (Pri from a time-lapse cinemicrographic film.)

responds to only a few hundredths of a per cent of the DNA volume. So, in terms of the DNA content, the mammalian cell is an extremely radium-resistant system. In view of such results, one can implicate the DNA or the genetic structure as a major radiosensitive component if one supposes that recovery or protective mechanisms become increasingly more important as the complexity of the organism advances.

Dr. Robert Schrek, Veterans Administration Hospital, Hines, Illinois: There is one type of cell, the lymphocyte, which has not been discussed but which shows good synchronization of the G_1 and S phases and which shows good recovery. The lymphocyte as obtained from human blood does not show any DNA synthesis and does not show any mitotic divisions. If phytohemagglutinin is added, the cells go in two days into active DNA synthesis and division. Presumably, the cell as it exists in the human blood is in the G_1 stage. Now if this cell is irradiated with 1,000 r, the cell forms intranuclear vacuoles, the chromatin ring ruptures and condenses to form a pyknotic nucleus (Figure 1). This is the method used in this study. The lymphocyte is extremely sensitive and 2 r within six days produces an average effect of 13.6 per cent. Irradiation of the lymphocyte with 100 r kills about 98 per cent of the cells in six days. If phytohemagglutinin is added before irradiation (Figure 2), about 20 per cent of the cells remain alive despite irradiation with 1,200 or 2,400 r (Schrek and Stefani, *Journal of the National Cancer Institute*, 32:507, 1964). The lymphocyte becomes extremely resistant when it is thrown into DNA synthesis. Even if the phytohemagglutinin is added 24 hours after irradiation, there is still a considerable amount of recovery and increased resistance to X rays (Figure 3). From these studies, it would seem that the G_1 stage, or one part of the G_1 stage is very sensitive to irradiation, but when the lymphocyte is in DNA synthesis, it becomes quite resistant.

Chairman Kaplan: I think it should be pointed out, of course, that this is quite a different criterion, namely pyknosis. There is no real evidence under these circumstances that the cells have escaped reproductive death. They may simply express reproductive death in a quite different way.

Dr. Anna Goldfeder, New York University, New York, New York: I have carried out extensive experiments regarding the comparative effects of a massive X-ray dose applied in a single exposure to tumors *in situ* with those noted when this dose was employed in several fractions. The greatest effect was obtained when the dose required for total tumor

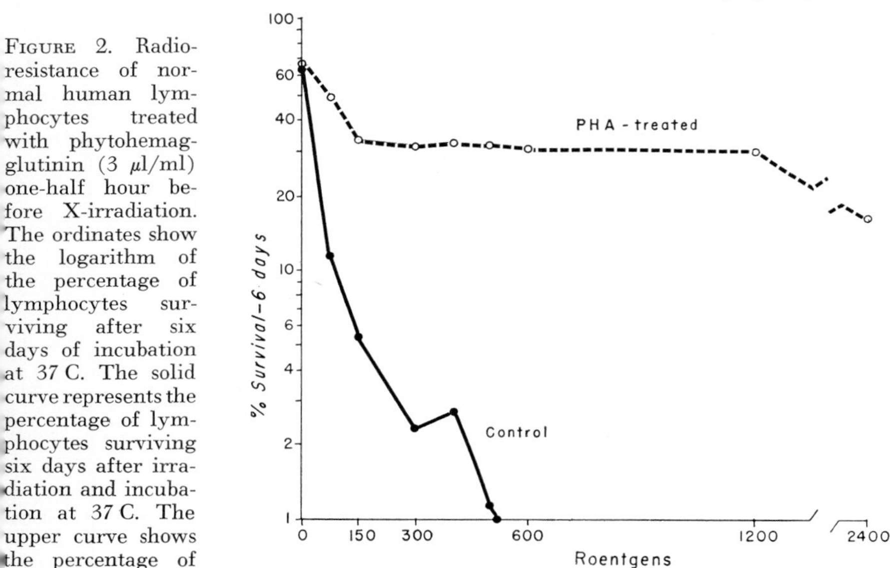

FIGURE 2. Radioresistance of normal human lymphocytes treated with phytohemagglutinin (3 µl/ml) one-half hour before X-irradiation. The ordinates show the logarithm of the percentage of lymphocytes surviving after six days of incubation at 37 C. The solid curve represents the percentage of lymphocytes surviving six days after irradiation and incubation at 37 C. The upper curve shows the percentage of lymphocytes surviving in suspensions which were irradiated one-half hour after addition of PHA (3 µl/ml).

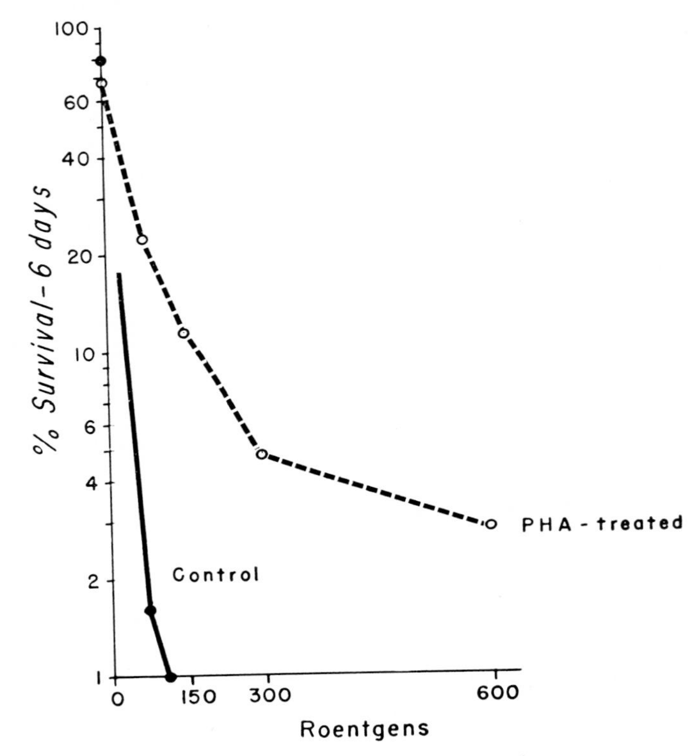

FIGURE 3. Curves are similar to those in Figure 2 except that PHA was added to the suspension 24 hours after irradiation. Counts of viable lymphocytes were made six days after addition of PHA.

destruction was employed in two equal fractions at 12-, 24-, or 48-hour intervals and the least effects when the dose was employed in eight equal fractions at 24-hour intervals.

Instances of metastatic spread to the internal organs, principally to the lungs, liver, and kidneys were more frequent when the dose was employed in six to eight fractions than when employed in a single or in two sessions. The results indicate that a higher degree of cellular sterilization or, conversely, a lower degree of recovery is achieved by employing the dose fractions within short intervals of time.

RESPONSES IN MAMMALIAN CELLS AND THE IMPLICATIONS FOR RADIOTHERAPY OF CANCER

Effects of Single and Repeated Low Doses of Ionizing Radiations on the Proliferative Capacity of Human Cells in Culture

G. W. Barendsen

Radiobiological Institute TNO, Rijswijk, The Netherlands

Since the development by Puck, Marcus, and Cieciura (1956), of a plating technique which yields accurate quantitative data on the proliferative capacity of mammalian cells, dose-response curves for several types of cells irradiated with X or gamma rays have been published. Usually the fraction of cells which have retained the capacity for clone formation, *i.e.* for unlimited proliferation, is plotted on a logarithmic scale as a function of the dose given on a linear scale. In general these survival curves show, between doses of 0 and 500 rads, a considerable curvature followed by a region in which this curvature is less pronounced or an exponential decrease is observed. Some disagreement exists about the correct shape of these curves, especially in relation to attempts to provide a mathematical description of these curves, based on "multitarget" or "multievent" models (Fowler, 1964).

The experimental results obtained by various authors point in apparently different directions (Barendsen, 1962; Dewey, Humphrey, and Cork, 1963; Bender and Gooch, 1962; Elkind and Sutton, 1960).

For the choice between the mathematical descriptions based on these two models, it is important to know whether the survival curves are exponential at high doses or whether they continue to bend. However, experimental determination of the shape of the curves at high doses depends critically on the homogeneity of the cell population which is irradiated and on the uniformity of the dose distribution. If, for instance, a few per cent of the cells are slightly less sensitive than the majority, which may be attributable either to their stage in the cell cycle or to their oxygenation condition, or if a small fraction of the cells receives a lower dose caused by inhomogeneity of the radiation field, the curve at low percentage survival tends to straighten or becomes concave upward (Powers and Tolmach, 1963).

In view of these difficulties, it is of interest to note that the mathematical descriptions based on the two different models may also predict differences in survival curve shapes at low doses. Curves 1 and 2 of Figure 1 provide examples of such differences. For a multievent model, it is assumed that radiation-induced damage results if a number of "events" (excitations, ionizations, or ion clusters) is produced in a sensitive site in the cell. This number of events may be produced by a single particle, for instance an alpha particle of high linear energy transfer (LET), or by two or more particles which each contribute part of the events. The end point observed, *i.e.* loss of reproductive capacity, may thus result partly from a "single particle" type of action involving the passage of a single ionizing particle through a sensitive site; and partly from a multiple particle or cumulative type of action involving the passage of two, three, or more ionizing particles through the sensitive site. For curve 1 of Figure 1, it is assumed that equal parts of the total damage are contributed by one-, two-, three-, four-, and five-particle types of action respectively and that the D_{37} is equal to 94 rads (Fowler, 1964). This curve matches closely the survival curve obtained experimentally in our laboratory with kidney cells of human origin (Barendsen, 1962).

For a multitarget model, it is assumed that radiation-induced damage results only if a number of sensitive sites, two, three, or more, are each damaged by the occurrence of events (excitations, ionizations, or ion clusters) produced in or near these sites. Curve 2 represents a "multitarget" type of survival curve with an extrapolation number $n = 5$ and a D_{37} equal to 150 rads. This is an arbitrary example which in the medium-dose region, *i.e.* between 500 and 1,200 rads, matches curve 1 closely. At low doses, how-

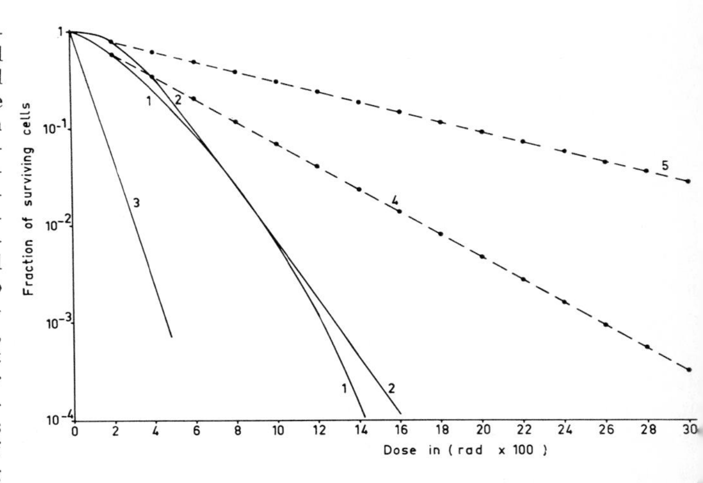

FIGURE 1. Theoretical survival curves of single and repeated exposure to X rays and alpha radiation. 1, multievent type of survival curve. 2, multitarget type of survival curve. 3, exponential survival curve pertaining to densely ionizing alpha radiation. 4, curve which might be obtained after fractionated irradiation with fractions of 200 rads of X rays, assuming curve 1 applies for single exposures. 5, curve which might be obtained after fractionated irradiation with fractions of 200 rads of X rays, assuming curve 2 applies for single exposures.

ever, a considerable difference between curves 1 and 2 is observed. A main feature of any multitarget type of survival curve is that its slope approaches zero at low doses, *i.e.* very low doses are almost ineffective for the production of biological damage. In contrast to this model, the assumption of a partly "single particle" type of action results in an initial negative slope of the survival curve at the intercept with the ordinate. Such a negative slope at low doses is in agreement with measurements of surviving fractions at low doses of 25, 50, 100, and 200 rads of 250 kvp X rays for cells derived from human kidney (Barendsen, 1962). At higher doses the slope increases, and this may be interpreted as a cumulative type of action through the cooperation of two or more particles which each cause only sublethal damage, but together produce inhibition of clone formation if the time interval between their passage is too short to allow for the recovery phenomenon discovered by Elkind to occur.

In addition to experiments with X and gamma rays at low doses, there is evidence from experiments with high LET radiations which supports the conclusion that part of the damage in mammalian cells from X or gamma rays is produced according to a "single particle" type of mechanism. As has been published previously, densely ionizing radiations produce exponential survival curves (represented by curve 3 of Figure 1) (Barendsen, Walter, Fowler, and Bewley, 1963). The wide LET distribution of X and gamma rays implies, however, that part of the energy is dissipated through low energy electrons which have a relatively high LET of between 20 and 60 kev/μ of tissue. This part of the energy, dissipated at a high ion density, must cause damage in the same way as densely ionizing alpha particles, and consequently a negative initial slope of the survival curve is implicated.

The shape of the survival curves at low doses is not only of theoretical radiobiological interest but may also be of clinical significance. In radiotherapy for patients with tumors, a general practice is to administer total doses in fractions of between 200 and 300 rads, separated by 24 hours. As discovered by Elkind and Sutton, this interval presumably allows for the recovery of sublethal damage which corresponds to a return of the initial radiosensitivity of the cells (Elkind and Sutton, 1960; Elkind, 1960). As a consequence, the effectiveness of the total dose is determined by the number of cells killed by the single fractions, *i.e.* by the shape of the survival curves at low doses. This is exemplified by curves 4 and 5 of Figure 1, where the effect of repeated doses of 200 rads of X rays is presented in case curve 1 or curve 2, respectively, is assumed to apply. It will be clear that the effect on a tumor may be vastly different in both cases. With cultured cells derived from human kidney, we have made a few measurements with three doses separated by four-hour intervals, to simulate such conditions of repeated exposure. The results, which have been published elsewhere, are presented in Figure 2 (Barendsen and Walter, 1964). It will be clear that with total doses not exceeding 300 rads in oxygenated condition and 1,000 rads in anoxic conditions, the observed surviving fractions agree well with those

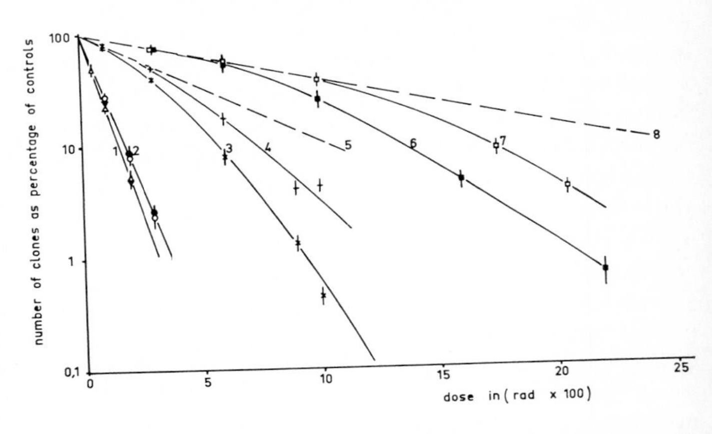

FIGURE 2. Effects of single and fractionated exposures of cultured human cells to Po^{210} alpha particles and 250 kvp X rays with cells in equilibrium with air and with nitrogen. Curve 1, survival after alpha irradiation of cells in equilibrium with air; closed triangles correspond to single exposures, and open triangles correspond to exposure with the total doses fractionated in three equal parts with time intervals of four hours. Curve 2, survival after alpha irradiation of cells in equilibruim with nitrogen; closed circles correspond to single exposures, and the open circles correspond to exposures with the total doses fractionated in three equal parts administered with time intervals of four hours. Curve 3, survival after 250 kvp X-irradiation; single exposures, cells in equilibrium with air. Curve 4, survival after 250 kvp X-irradiation; total doses fractionated in three equal parts administered with time intervals of four hours, cells in equilibrium with air. Curve 5, curve indicating initial slope of survival curve 3. Curve 6, survival after 250 kvp X-irradiation; single exposures, cells in equilibrium with nitrogen. Curve 7, survival after 250 kvp X-irradiation; total dose fractionated in three equal parts administered with intervals of four hours, cells in equilibrium with nitrogen. Curve 8, curve indicating initial slope of survival curve 6.

expected from the initial slopes of the survival curves. With alpha radiation from Po^{210} no recovery effect was observed at all.

Differences in initial slopes of survival curves as shown by curves 1 and 2 of Figure 1 might contribute to clinically observed differences between the radiosensitivity of tumors. It has been pointed out repeatedly that all of the survival curves determined so far in vitro and in vivo with various systems are very similar as far as their shape and the slopes of the curves beyond the initial low dose region are concerned, but that in contrast to this uniformity of response, clinical experience with the radiotherapy of patients with tumors points to great differences in radiosensitivity. Two factors at the cellular level have been considered to account for this discrepancy. First, few, if any, tumors in patients are known to have generation times as short as those of cells cultured in vitro. This may be because of differences in the length of the G_1, S, and G_2 phases of the cell cycle, and as these phases are known to show differences in radiosensitivity, different fractions of cells in a particular phase may cause variations in radiosensitivity of the tumor. A second factor is found in the fact that tumors are known to contain anoxic cells which are less sensitive to X or gamma rays than are well-oxygenated cells. Fluctuations in the fraction of anoxic cells might consequently influence the response of the tumor to irradiations. In addition to these factors, it should be pointed out that experimental survival curves obtained with different types of cultured cells have not been determined with sufficient accuracy at low doses and with fractionated exposures to conclude whether their shapes are the same. Important differences might well be found which may account for differences between the responses of various tumors and between tumors and normal tissue after fractionated irradiation.

REFERENCES

Barendsen, G. W. 1962. Dose-Survival Curves of Human Cells in Tissue Culture Irradiated with Alpha-, Beta-, 20 Kv. X- and 200 Kv. X-Radiation. *Nature*, London, 193:1153–1155.

Barendsen, G. W., and H. M. D. Walter. 1964. Effects of Different Ionizing Radiations on Human Cells in Tissue Culture. IV. Modification of Radiation Damage. *Radiation Research*, 21:314–329.

Barendsen, G. W., H. M. D. Walter, J. F. Fowler, and D. K. Bewley. 1963. Effects of Different Ionizing Radiations on Human Cells in Tissue Culture. III. Experiments with Cyclotron-Accelerated Alpha-Particles and Deuterons. *Radiation Research*, 18: 106–119.

Bender, M. A., and P. C. Gooch. 1962. The Kinetics of X-Ray Survival of Mammalian Cells *in vitro*. *International Journal of Radiation Biology and Related Studies in Physics, Chemistry and Medicine*, 5:133–145.

Dewey, W. C., R. M. Humphrey, and A. Cork. 1963. Comparison of Cell Multiplication and Colony-Formation as Criteria for Radiation Damage in Cells Grown *in vitro*. *International Journal of Radiation Biology and Related Studies in Physics, Chemistry and Medicine*, 6:463–471.

Elkind, M. M. 1960. Cellular Aspects of Tumor Therapy. *Radiology*, 74:529–541.

Elkind, M. M., and H. Sutton. 1960. Radiation Response of Mammalian Cells Grown in Culture. I. Repair of X-Ray Damage in Surviving Chinese Hamster Cells. *Radiation Research*, 13:556–593.

Fowler, J. F. 1964. Differences in Survival Curve Shapes for Formal Multi-Target and Multi-Hit Models. *Physics in Medicine and Biology*, 9:177–188.

Powers, W. F., and L. J. Tolmach. 1963. A Multicomponent X-Ray Survival Curve for Mouse Lymphosarcoma Cells Irradiated *in vivo*. *Nature*, London, 97:710–711.

Puck, T. T., P. I. Marcus, and S. J. Cieciura. 1956. Clonal Growth of Mammalian Cells in vitro. *Journal of Experimental Medicine*, 103:273–284.

The Importance of Cell Population Kinetics in Determining Response to Irradiation of Normal and Malignant Tissue

C. W. GILBERT AND L. G. LAJTHA

Paterson Laboratories,
Christie Hospital and Holt Radium Institute,
Manchester, England

Cell population kinetics is a term denoting the time sequence of changes in the composition or size of a cell population due to processes of growth, differentiation, aging, or recovery from an insult. It is customary to subdivide cells of similar functional states into "compartments," and much of the studies is concerned with the transit of cells from one to another of these functional compartments. Although functionally very real, in most instances the "compartments" have no anatomical meaning, and cells belonging to a growing and to a differentiating "compartment" may be mixed together, as they are, for example, in the bone marrow.

In the adult organism there are many different cell populations. Some are in an active state of turnover, others, while capable of turnover, do so only very slowly, again others may have no growth potential at all. Some cell types will differentiate, giving rise to cells with long or short life span; a life span may be of fixed duration or a mere "mean life" which is a statistical average, for example, in cases of random destruction.

Radiation may kill cells within a few hours—this is the so-called "interphase death"—or it may cause cell sterilization, that is the cells may divide one or more times before they stop growing or before they disintegrate. That some tissues are more radiosensitive than others is old knowledge. However, the recent exciting progress in radiobiology, initiated by Puck and Marcus (1956) and followed up by Hewitt and Wilson (1959), Elkind and Sutton (1959) and others, caused a considerable rethinking by demonstrating a remarkable similarity in the basic radiosensitivity of all mammalian cells in respect to reproductive integrity. This rethinking necessitates an investigation and better understanding of the population kinetics of cells in the various tissues in order to explain the observed radiation effects, and in order to use radiations perhaps in a more rational rather than merely empirical manner.

The purpose of this paper is first to consider certain principles on which cell population models may be constructed, then to examine experimental evidence for the existence of such cell populations, and, finally, to discuss the various response patterns which such cell populations may exhibit following irradiation.

As the next paper in this symposium is concerned with the kinetics of tumor cell populations, this paper will only briefly consider tumor cells and will be concerned mainly with normal tissues.

Several aspects of the problems have been discussed in earlier papers (Lajtha and Oliver, 1962; Lamerton, Lord, and Quastler, 1963) and in a recent elegant review by Patt and Quastler (1963). It is a tragic aspect of this review that in a sense it is also the swan song of Henry Quastler, with whose untimely death we have lost one of the founding fathers of cell population kinetic studies.

The Cell Cycle

Cell cycle time is defined as the time from the beginning of the growth phase (beginning of the G_1 period) to the end of mitosis (anaphase). The cell cycle as described by Howard and Pelc (1953) consists of three periods: G_1 or presynthetic period, S or deoxyribonucleic acid (DNA) synthetic period, and G_2 or post-DNA synthetic period, followed by mitosis. In the original concept mitosis was followed again by G_1 period, a period in which net cell growth (protein, ribonucleic acid [RNA], etc.) proceeds, as well as preparation for DNA synthesis. To this concept another period has recently been added: G_0 or "no growth" period (Lajtha, 1963; Quastler, 1963), signifying a time after mitosis but before the onset of growth processes ($G_1 - S - G_2$). The G_0 period is not part of the cell cycle; therefore it should not be included in the cell cycle time, which represents the growth

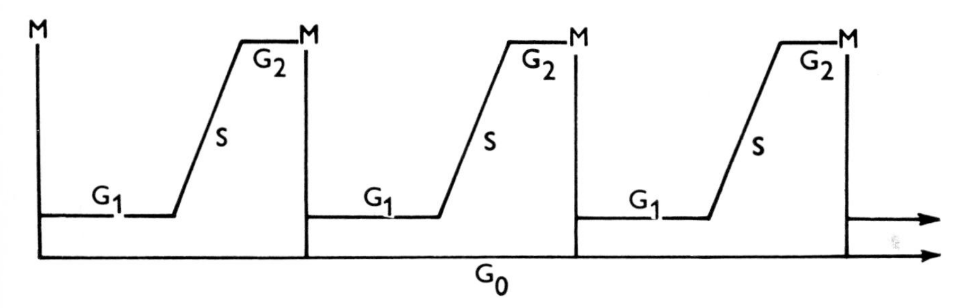

FIGURE 1. Illustration of the G_0 period. Following mitosis (M) a cell may immediately enter into cell cycle ($G_1 - S - G_2$ periods and mitosis) or into a state of no growth (G_0). From G_0 the cell may be at any time triggered into cell cycle. This triggering is random and the statistical chance for it (and therefore the mean time in G_0) will depend on the degree of population turnover.

cycle only, that is $G_1 - S - G_2 - M$ (Figure 1). There is a growing bulk of experimental evidence that cell cycle time remains substantially constant and is not shortened or lengthened to meet the pressing needs of the organisms.

Types of Cell Populations

Before any quantitative studies can be entered into on cell kinetics, one must be clear of what one means by a population, and make sure that there is a precisely defined population under study. In the following pages cell population will be defined as a number of either one type or, more usually, of several types of cells. The cell types which are included in the population, as well as the extent of the population, must be clearly stated, in both space and time. For example, the population could be limited to the malignant cells of a tumor in an early stage or to the erythroid cells in the bone marrow, and only during that part of the animal's life when a steady state prevails.

A population can often be divided into several subpopulations; hence a population will, in general, have cells entering it from outside, and likewise will pass cells into another population. Another important property of the cell population is the ability of some members of it to divide and to produce two new members. Thus, in general, the cell populations can often be characterized by the relative importance of these three properties: (1) cells entering (input), (2) cells leaving (output), and (3) cells dividing. Any one cell population may not have all these properties, so it is convenient to classify populations according to the various combinations of these properties.

The possible combinations are illustrated in Figure 2. The figure is self-explanatory, and names have been given to the various population types, except to the two types which have input but no output.

Examples may be quoted for these population types illustrated in Figure 2. To take first the four types in which no cell division takes place, a simple transit population would be the reticulocyte population in the bone marrow. Cells are fed into this population from the erythroid precursor cells, and cells are released from this population into the peripheral blood. No example is available for the second population type, except a hypothetical population of dead cells. For the third, the decaying population, one example would be the adult ovary, in which there is a release of cells throughout the functional life of the population, whose number therefore decays. The example for the fourth, the closed static population, would be the adult central nervous system where no cell production or cell release occurs during certain periods of the animal's life. It is understood, of course, that this is an oversimplification, for even in the adult central nervous system, cells are probably dying continuously, and cell death constitutes a release of cells from the population.

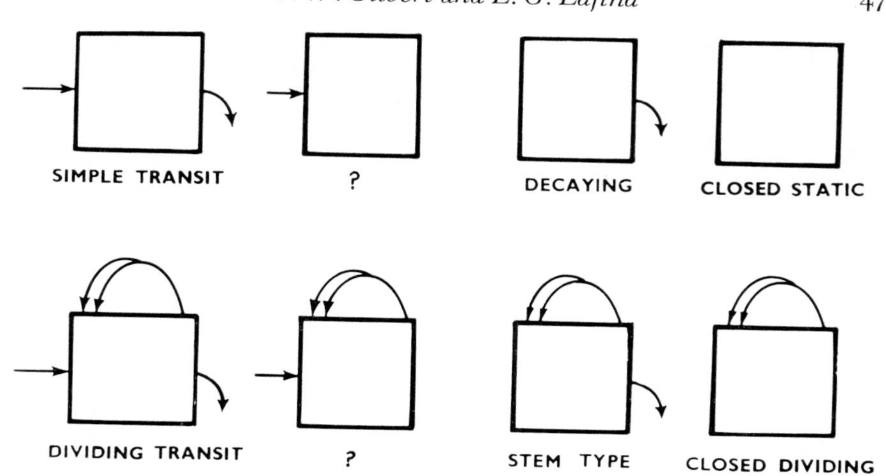

FIGURE 2. Diagrammatic representation of possible cell populations. Arrow entering indicates cells entering population, and arrow leaving, cells leaving. Double-headed arrow leaving and entering indicates cells leaving on division and daughter cells entering.

As to the examples for the population types with cell division, the dividing transit population could be illustrated by the nucleated red cells in the bone marrow: a population which is receiving cells from the stem cell population and which releases cells into, for example, the marrow reticulocyte pool, but in which population cells divide one or more times during transit. For the second type, again, no good example can be quoted for a dividing population with input but no output. The third type, the stem type population, is the classical example of a self-maintaining population which can produce cells at a steady rate for another population—this is the property of any stem cell, hence the name stem type population. This is one of the populations with which this paper will be mostly concerned. Finally, the closed dividing population is the type into which most tumor tissue would be classified. The best example for this, nevertheless, will be tissue culture in the exponential phase of growth. In most tumors, eventually there is a certain amount of cell death which would constitute a release of cells from the population; hence only a tumor in a very early state of growth would truly belong to the closed dividing population type.

The Compartment Concept

In order to be able to discuss the cell populations in a more quantitative way than the crude qualitative scheme presented above, the concept of a compartment has to be introduced. A compartment is a subpopulation in which all the cells are identical in all respects, or can be treated as such for the purposes of argument. A compartment will have input and output, but no cell division. A compartment is always assumed to be randomly mixed, so that cells emerging from it are uncorrelated with cells entering. For example, in a study of the kinetics of the reticulocytes circulating in the blood, the population of cells must first be broken into a number of compartments, each compartment consisting of cells of the same age or very nearly the same age. Compartments are very real entities, even though it will not usually be possible to identify the individual cells which belong to them.

A special case of the compartmental system, very usual in cell kinetics, is obtained by connecting a number of compartments in line. This is called a pipe; it represents a homogeneous group of cells going through the various compartments in a regular order, without cell division within the compartment. For example, cells in the cell cycle can be represented by a pipe if the cell cycle time is constant. The compartments in this case would be various short-time divisions of G_1, then S, and then G_2. The pipe, in fact, is nothing but a chain of compartments.

To study the kinetics of a cell population, it is necessary to break it down and represent it by a set of interconnected compartments. For each compartment, a balance sheet can be written down accounting for all the individual cells:

$$\frac{dN}{dt} = I - O$$

This states that the rate of increase of cells in the compartment $(\frac{dN}{dt})$ is equal to the net rate at which cells enter (I) less the rate at which they leave (O). The rate at which the cells leave the compartment will depend on the current size of the compartment and is often of the simple form

$$O = \lambda N$$

where λ is constant. In nonsteady state and particularly in regulated populations with some feedback control, λ may not be constant and may change not only with time but also in a complicated way with the current size of the compartment. Such a set of differential equations, two for each compartment, together with the initial values, will give a complete description of the kinetics of the cell population. For any but some of the simplest models of cell population, this set of differential equations may not yield solutions expressible in terms of known and tabulated functions; but these equations are of the form for which numerical solutions can be readily calculated by a modern computer, if numerical values can be assigned to the parameters involved, and if the number of compartments is finite (preferably small).

Quantitative Aspects of Cell Populations

It has already been noted that in order to make quantitative calculations of cell kinetics, it is necessary to represent the population by a model which consists of a manageable number of compartments. In this section, we shall consider the type of kinetics given by some very simple models consisting of a single compartment and/or a pipe.

Closed Dividing Populations

The simplest model is a single compartment in which cells divide at random, giving two daughter cells. The multiplication is represented by a parent cell leaving the compartment and being replaced by two daughter cells entering. This system can be worked out in detail fairly simply. The differential equations describing this model are:

$$\frac{dN}{dt} = I - O$$

$$O = \lambda N$$

$$\text{and} \quad I = 2O = 2\lambda N$$

where $1/\lambda$ is the mean time between cell divisions.
Hence:

$$\frac{dN}{dt} = \lambda N$$

$$\text{and} \quad N = N_0 e^{\lambda t}$$

where N_0 is the number of cells initially.

The population grows exponentially and doubles in a time $\ln 2/\lambda$. This model, in spite of its rather artificial random cell division mechanism, is, nevertheless, often very valuable because of its mathematical simplicity. This has been described in detail by Harris (1959).

A more realistic representation of the cell cycle time can be obtained by using a small number of random compartments in series followed by cell division. This permits some variation in the cell cycle time.

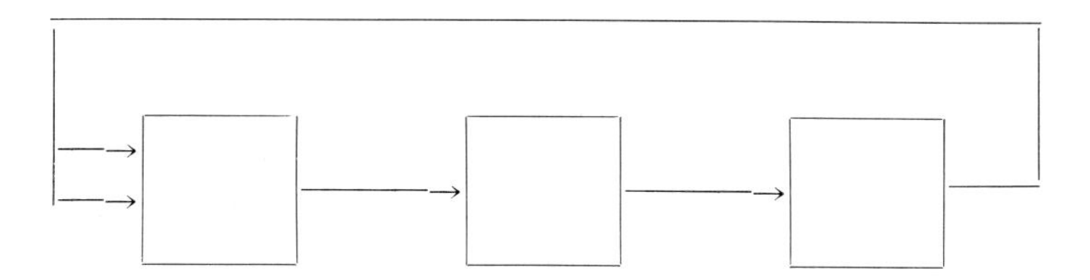

The use of a single pipe represents a model with a constant cell cycle time for all cells:

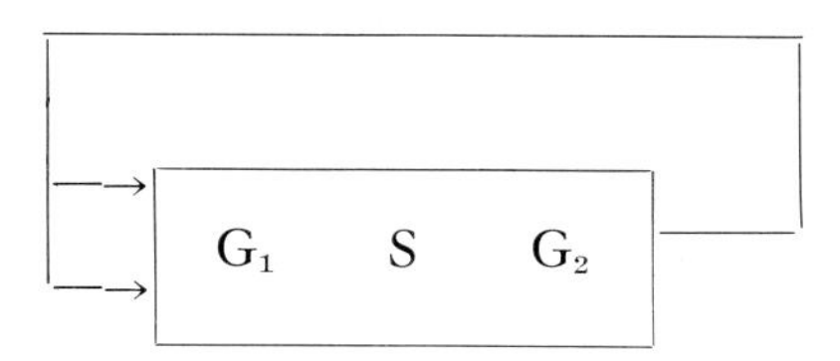

These two models can both be calculated in detail, though the mathematics is already somewhat tedious. Both lead to an exponential growth; for the pipe, the doubling time is equal to the cell cycle time and approximately equal to the mean cell cycle time for the series of random compartments.

In all the models discussed above, the new daughter cells immediately begin cell cycle. If, however, account is to be taken of a resting phase G_0, the model below can be used:

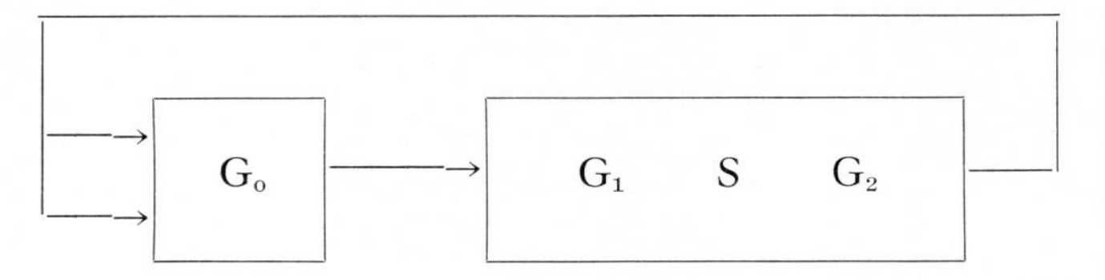

where G_0 is a single random compartment.

If the output from the G_0 compartment is proportional to G_0, then this model will also give an exponential growth but the population doubling time will be longer than the cell cycle time. This model can take account of the environment by making the output from the G_0 compartment vary with time and depend on the size of the population or on outside conditions.

In the case of tumor cells and in tissue cultures, the size of the population and the conditions outside may be closely related. A certain population density may influence the nutritional possibilities of cells by increasing the distance between cells and nutrient capillaries, or by partially exhausting the culture medium. This exhaustion may be general, as in suspension cultures, or local, as in cell clones growing on glass surfaces.

In these models the G_0 compartment acts as a store from which cells may be triggered into cell cycle. There is a possibility, however, that certain conditions may "hold" cells in a part of the cell cycle—possibly in the premitotic G_2 period. In such a case the G_2 period may act as a "store" population, from which cells can, if conditions permit, enter mitosis. Distribution studies of the DNA content of interphase tumor cells in populations in which the metaphase DNA values show a suitable population homogeneity indicate that such G_2 accumulation may take place. More evidence for G_2 stores have been published by Gelfant (1962) for skin epithelium.

In tumors, however, the ideal conditions for a closed dividing population are not always maintained. There is almost always some cell death occurring, and this constitutes a "leak" from the population, which thus ceases to be "closed" in the true sense.

If the tumors are considered as a pipe with a store and a leak, then the

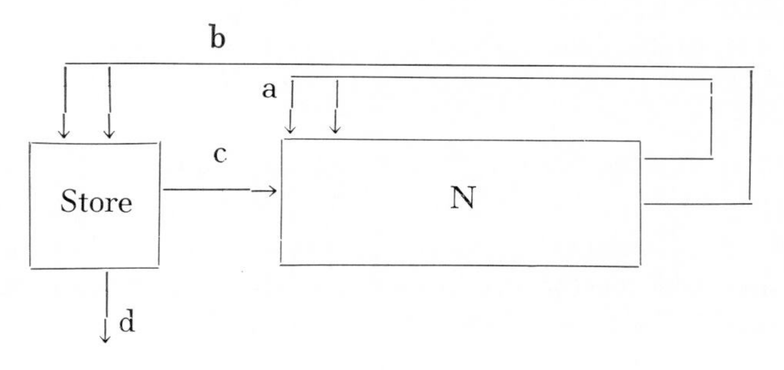

store may be constituted by cells held up in cycle, cells not in cycle, and cells degenerating. From this store, cells may feed back to the growing population at the rate c, and/or may die at the rate d. This store is fed at the rate b, which may depend in some way on the size of the growing population N. The rate of loss of cells (d) from the store may also depend on the size of N, or the size of the store, or both. This statement is also valid, of course, for the values of a, b, and c.

For this reason, tumor growth—especially in the case of solid tumors —will rarely follow a simple exponential growth for long, a statement amply corroborated by all investigators.

Radiation may influence this picture in various ways: Depopulation (decrease in N) may alter the values of a, b, c, and d, and result in a different rate of growth compared to the preradiation rate. This may be further complicated by the rate at which the sterilized cells die and disappear in a particular tumor. Taking two extreme examples, (1) in which the sterilized cells disappear slowly and b and d are decreased by the radiation effect, or (2) in which the sterilized cells disappear fast and b and d are increased following irradiation, we would get an apparently "radioresistant" or "radiosensitive" tumor (Figure 3), although the initial depopulation in N may have been the same in both cases. The only way to differentiate between these two cases would be by knowing the initial and postirradiation growth rate of N.

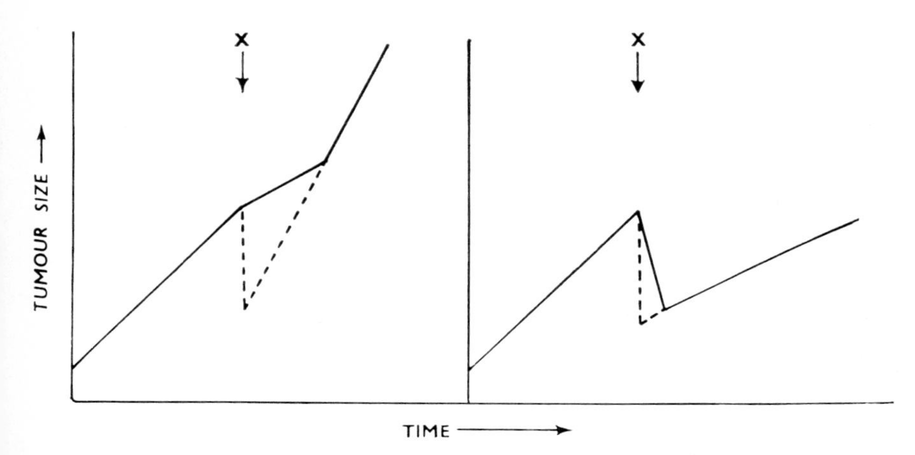

FIGURE 3. Tumor growth following radiation. *Left,* Sterilized cells disappear slowly; feed into and death rate from store population decreased. *Right,* Sterilized cells disappear fast; feed into and death rate from store population increased.

Stem Cell Populations

A stem cell population has output and the capacity for cell division of some of its members, but has no input from other populations. Such populations can, under the right conditions, be self-maintaining. They must, at some time, have been "created"; for example, a whole animal or organism could be considered a stem cell population, the system being created by the input of a single fertilized egg cell and then no more input. There are, however, a number of subpopulations in an adult animal which also would seem to have the characteristic of being self-maintaining, without the necessity of taking cells from other populations. The marrow, liver and skin, *i.e.* any cell population capable of recovery to original size following damage, must have this characteristic.

We can represent a stem cell population diagrammatically as follows:

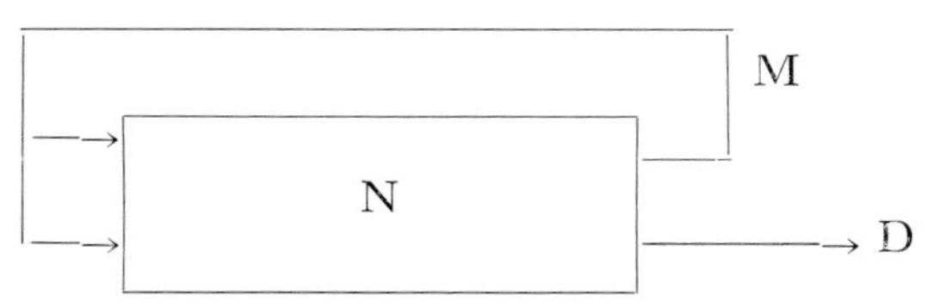

where M and D are the rates at which cells leave for multiplication (M) and differentiation (D).

Of the cells which leave the population, a fraction, α, divides to provide two daughter cells which return to the population, and the fraction $(1 - \alpha)$ goes into other populations ($\alpha = [\frac{M}{D+M}]$; $[1 - \alpha] = \frac{D}{D+M}$). It can readily be shown that if $\alpha > 1/2$, then the population must grow; if $\alpha < 1/2$, the population must decline, but will remain stationary for $\alpha = 1/2$. Thus for any workable stem cell population, α must change, depending on the circumstances of the moment. It is the output from the stem cell system to the other populations which can be thought of as the useful product (*i.e.* differentiation) and if more product is needed, it can be obtained by increasing the total output from the stem cell population but still preserving the fraction α near $1/2$.

If, however, the stem cell population itself suffers damage that results in ultimate loss of cells (e.g. decrease in N due to radiation), then a recovery can be made only if α becomes greater than $1/2$ for a period, but with the return of α to $1/2$ if and when a new steady state is achieved.

The rate D will depend in some way on the requirement for production of, for example, differentiated cells. Both D and M may depend in some way on the size or changes in size of the stem cell population N. If we plot the magnitude of D and M for different values of N, and if we get a plot similar to those shown in Figure 4, then we have a potentially stable stem cell system, and the population size will tend to adjust to the steady state value N_s where the two curves cross. For population sizes smaller than the steady state (N_s) value $\alpha > 1/2$ and so the population will tend to grow, and in a similar way an overpopulation will tend to diminish. A stem cell population must not only have a size to which it endeavors to approach (N_s), but it must do so in a well-behaved fashion and not go into violent and uncontrolled oscillations when disturbed.

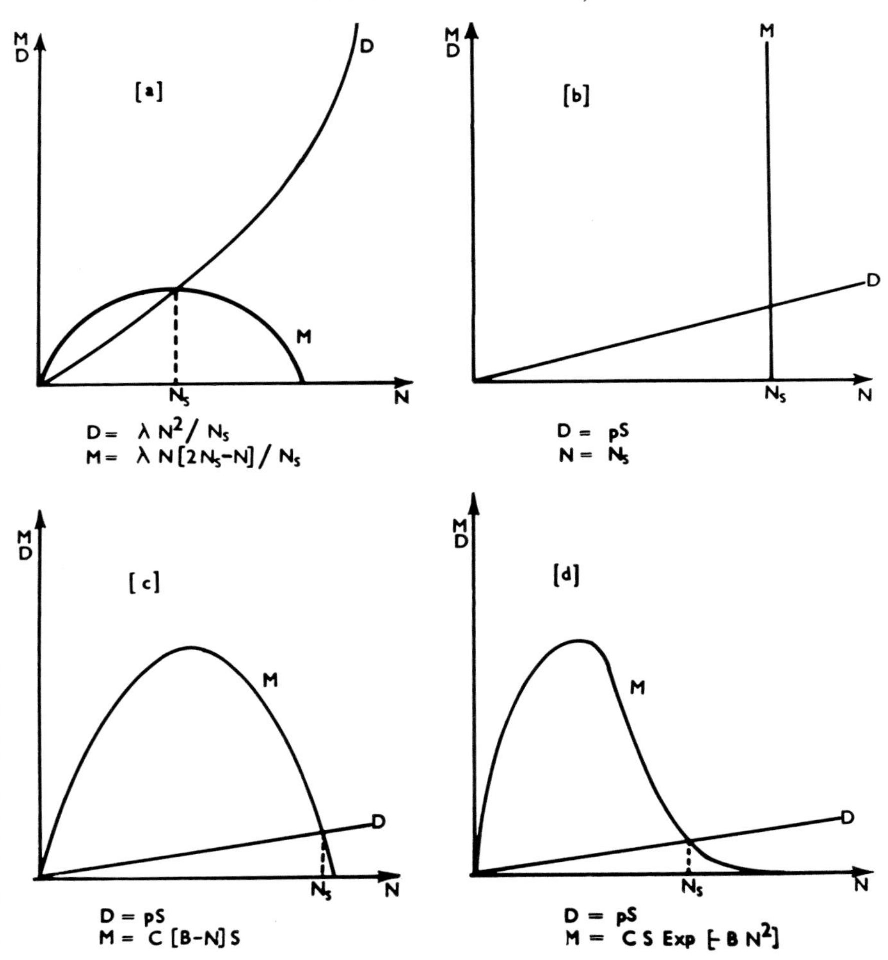

FIGURE 4. Relationships that determine steady state population size by relating rates of differentiation and entry to cell cycle to population size: a—bean root stem cell model; b—, c—, and d— bone marrow stem cell models.

In the following sections, some existing stem cell populations will be examined and attempts will be made to represent them in terms of simple models. For this we shall represent the population in question by a few simple compartments or pipes, and will assign some simple forms to the relationship of D and M to the stem cells' population sizes.

SOME PARTICULAR STEM CELL MODELS AND THEIR RESPONSE TO IRRADIATION

Bean Root

The simplest possible stem cell model consists of a single random compartment:

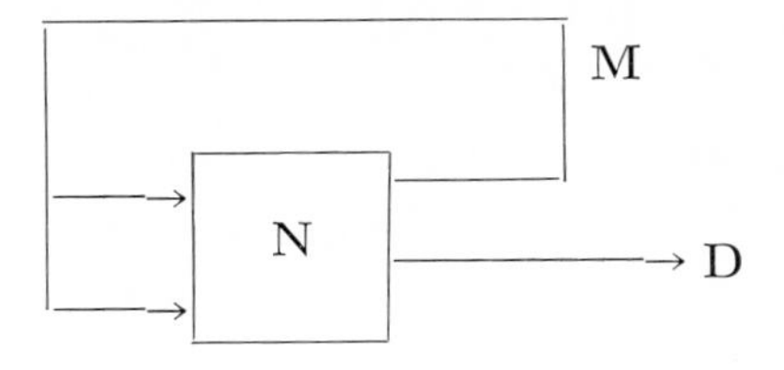

Here we have a population consisting only of stem cells all in cell cycle (Dewey and Howard, 1963). They divide at random times so that the number dividing is proportional to the size of the compartment. At division, a cell either reproduces two new stem cells which return to the population, or differentiates and produces two differentiated cells which leave the population. This model has been used by Hall, Lajtha, and Oliver (1962) to account for the changes in the growth rate of the root tip of *Vicia faba* following X-irradiation. The rates M and D were assumed to depend on the size of the stem cell population N (I in the paper quoted above) in the following way:

$$M + D = 2\lambda N$$
$$1 - \alpha = D/(M + D) = \tfrac{1}{2}\, N/N_s$$

where N_s is the stable size of the stem cell population, and $1/\lambda$ the mean cell cycle time. The way M and D vary with N is shown in Figure 4a.

Following a depletion of the stem cell population from N_s to N_o by X-irradiation, the stem cell population increases and returns in a well-damped way to the original stable size N_s, according to the expression

$$N = N_s[1 + (N_s/N_o - 1)e^{-\lambda t}]^{-1}$$

and the rate of production of differentiated cells which will be proportional to the rate of growth of the root tip is given by

$$D = \lambda N^2/N_s$$
or
$$D/\lambda\, N_s = [1 + (N_s/N_o - 1)e^{-\lambda t}]^{-2}$$

The latter expression is the more useful in making comparisons with the experiment, because it is the ratio of the recovery rate to the normal rate of an irradiated control, which is λN_s. The form of the recovery is shown in Figure 5.

In the calculation above, the cells, when sterilized by radiation, have been assumed to be immediately removed from the population. This is unrealistic and the model has been extended to allow for a limited number of divisions of the sterilized cells, and in particular, that the sterilized cells may differentiate (Hall, Lajtha, and Oliver, 1962).

In experimental studies, the growth rate of the bean root after irradiation is expressed as a fraction of that of the unirradiated controls (Figure

6). These curves may be analyzed as having two components, the first a decreasing contribution of cells from the sterilized population (cells which have lost their reproductive integrity) or from cells in the process of elongation, and the other an increasing contribution from the "surviving" fertile cells (which have retained their reproductive integrity). This scheme is illustrated in Figure 7.

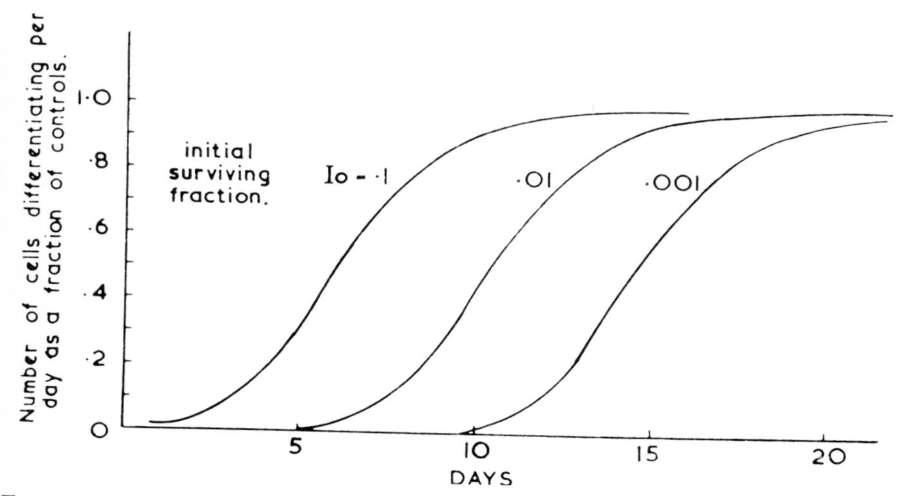

FIGURE 5. Recovery of the number of cells differentiating per day, corresponding to the growth rate of the bean root. (Redrawn from Hall, Lajtha, and Oliver, 1962.)

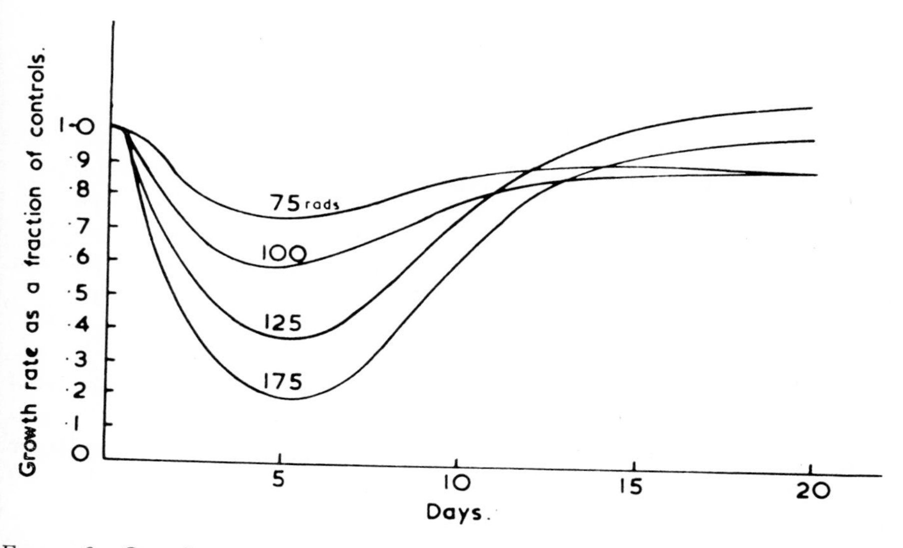

FIGURE 6. Growth rate of bean roots, after various doses of X-radiation, expressed as a fraction of that for controls of equal age. (Redrawn from Hall, Lajtha, and Oliver, 1962.)

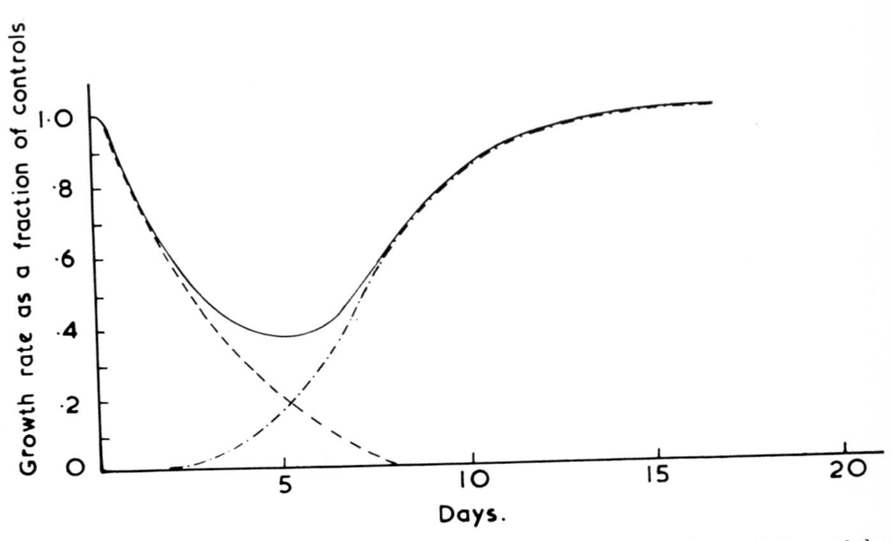

FIGURE 7. The curve for the growth rate of roots exposed to 125 rads as a fraction of that for controls (full line) is built up of two components. The broken line represents the decreasing contribution from cells which have lost their reproductive integrity; the chained line represents the increasing contribution from integer cells. (Redrawn from Hall, Lajtha, and Oliver, 1962.)

On the basis of such experimental curves and using the model outlined above (Figure 5), the degree of depopulation (sterilization) by various radiation doses can be calculated. Such calculations yield a dose response curve illustrated in Figure 8. The best fit would give a D_0 of 40 to 50 rads and an extrapolation number between 2 and 3.5. This is in good agreement with the curve obtained by an independent method, using fractionation experiments (Hall, 1962).

Another method of deducing a dose response curve consists of the following:

About 10 days after irradiation, the root tip is growing again at the same rate as the unirradiated controls. However, during the recovery period, the total output of differentiated cells is less than that of the controls. This difference may be represented as a temporary deficit equivalent to a time delay in the growth curve. This time delay may be expressed as a number of cell cycles lost.

The model considered above gives a definite algebraic form for the rate of growth of the root as expressed by the rate of production of differentiated cells (D). The difference between this growth rate and the control rate of production (λN_s) can be integrated to give the total number of cells by which the irradiated root is behind the control. This deficit expressed as cell cycles lost (T_l) yields the expression:

$$T_l = 1 - x - \ln x \qquad (1)$$

where $x = N_o/N_s$ (the depopulation fraction).

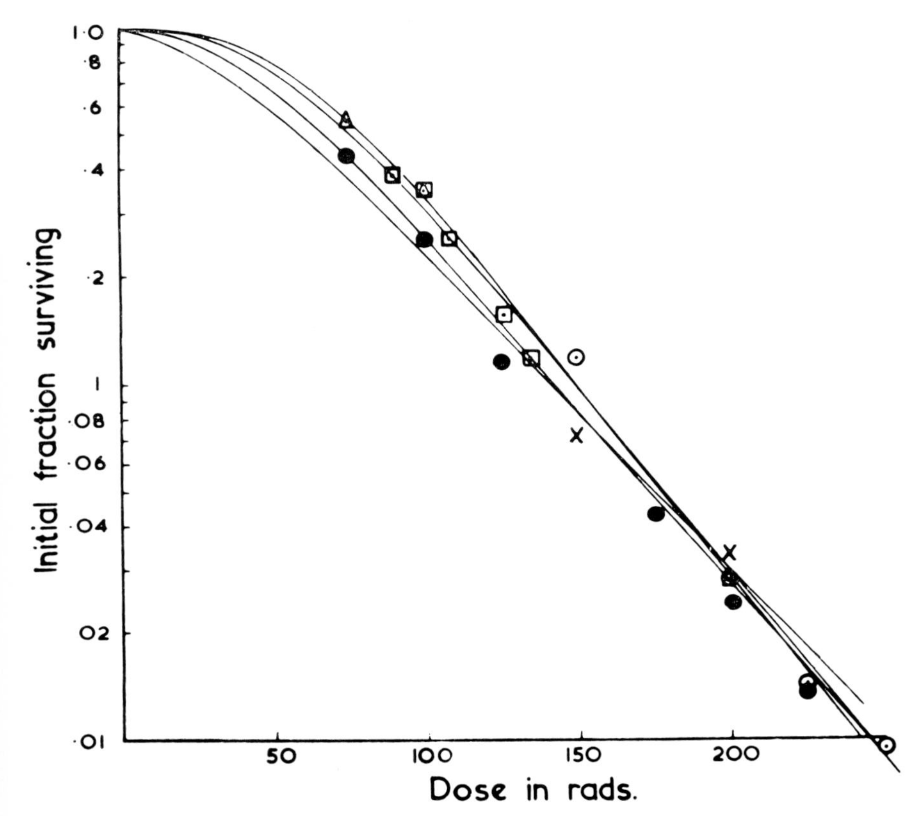

FIGURE 8. Initial surviving fraction of cells in the meristem plotted against dose. The five different symbols refer to data from five separate experiments. (Redrawn from Hall, Lajtha, and Oliver, 1962.)

Using this relationship, a dose response curve for the stem cells of the root meristem can be deduced from experiments which measure the total growth of control cells and irradiated cells over 10 days, the lost cell cycles being given from the measurements by

$$T_l = 8(L_c - L_r)/L_c$$

where L_c and L_r are the total growth of control and irradiated roots in 10 days.

In this system of growing the roots, 10 days is equivalent to eight cell cycles.

For each dose of radiation, the experimental T_l can be calculated, and then the theoretical depopulation fraction can be read from a graph of equation (1). Using the data of such an experiment (Hall and Lajtha, 1963) a dose response curve of the Puck type is obtained with a D_0 of 38 rads and an extrapolation number of about 2.5.

In the model, the bean root meristem is considered as a population in which all cells are in cell cycle. This is an oversimplification as there is evidence for a "quiescent center" in such a population, a zone in which cells rarely divide (Clowes, 1954). Although following irradiation the quiescent center takes an active part in recovery of the population (Clowes and Hall, 1962), the net contribution from the surviving quiescent cells is insignificant compared with the error of experimental measurements. The situation would be different if the quiescent center contained cells with lower radiosensitivity than the main meristem population, but experimental studies do not support such a hypothesis (Hall, Lajtha, and Clowes, 1962).

While the radiation effects discussed above refer specifically to the bean root meristem (*Vicia faba*), the bean root is by no means the only example for this type of cell population. The crypt cells in the intestinal epithelium may be another.

The experimental techniques available cannot give as good a measurement of population growth in the crypt cells as in the root meristem, but it is known that in the bottom half of the crypt (which represents the stem cell population in this system), most of the cells are in cell cycle all the time, and that during regeneration the cell cycle time does not alter significantly. The problem has been extensively investigated by Lamerton and his colleagues in a series of excellent papers (Wimber and Lamerton, 1963; Quastel, 1963; Lamerton, Steel, and Wimber, 1961), and their new application of crypt and villus cell population counts may furnish the additional quantitative information needed for the establishing of a dose response curve for X rays for the reproductive integrity of these cells.

It is important to realize that in many cases with such cell populations (the bean root par excellence), the experimental techniques measure D only (rate of differentiation), and give very scanty knowledge of the state or numbers of N (total cells in the stem compartment). This is a potentially misleading situation, as changes in the relation of D to N may thus give different apparent radiosensitivity values to the system.

In the model we have described, when the surviving fraction following radiation is small, virtually all the dividing cells are used for replenishing the population and not for differentiation. Since the major part of the recovery time is spent in increasing the stem cell population up to, for example, one tenth to one third of the normal value, one would expect this model to give as fast a recovery as possible with such systems.

If however, some proportionally significant differentiation is still maintained at very low survival values, then this differentiation occurs at the expense of cells available for restocking the population; hence, the over-all rate of recovery must be slower. Again, as the differentiation will not reach an experimentally measurable degree until the population is up to one tenth to one third of the normal value, this long recovery might be misinterpreted as a sign of greater initial depopulation, *i.e.* greater radiosensitivity.

For these reasons, the D_0 values deduced from experiments concerning our model must, to some extent, be sensitive to the exact form of differentiation at low survival values. Consequently, the values deduced from our model, if in error, would tend to be on the low side (*i.e.* having overestimated the intrinsic radiosensitivity of the bean root cells).

Bone Marrow

The model we have discussed for the stem cells of the bean root represents a model with all the stem cells in cell cycle. This model gives the maximum output of differentiated cells compatible with a regulated stem cell compartment size. This system is rigid insofar as it cannot alter the rate of cell production for differentiation in steady state without (1) lengthening cell cycle time, and (2) reducing the population size.

In the body, however, there are organs which are capable of regeneration without altering cell cycle time. This can simply be achieved by keeping at any time a part of the population out of cell cycle, that is in the G_0 state. There is very good experimental evidence that this is the case, for example, for liver after partial hepatectomy.

The stem cells in the bone marrow probably work in a similar way. Here the output of differentiated cells must be capable of adjustment to meet the changing demands of the organism.

Such a marrow stem cell system is shown diagrammatically in Figure 9A. S_0 represents a stock of stem cells in G_0 state and is a compartment which is randomly mixed. Stock cells differentiate at a rate D and leave the compartment, the rate being determined by the need of the animal (e.g. concentration of erythropoietin in the plasma). To maintain the stock, cells leave the compartment at a rate M to go into cell cycle. These are represented as entering the population of triggered cells T_0. After cell division, two daughter stem cells are produced and re-enter the stock S_0. We denote by M^* the rate at which cells leave the triggered population, and consequently new cells enter the stock population at a rate $2M^*$. As in the case of the bean root model, the stem cell population tries to maintain a fixed size by adjusting the rate M, depending on the population sizes. This model has now two populations, stock cells (S_0) and triggered cells (T_0); therefore M may depend on both of these numbers. In our investigations we have so far considered only linear combinations of these numbers, and have taken a total population size to be represented by N where

$$N = S_0 + AT_0$$

and A is a constant. Some of the values for the parameter A have fairly simple meanings. The case in which a cell in cell cycle is counted as a single member of the stem cell population corresponds to $A = 1$. The case $A = 2$ would correspond to the triggered cells being already counted as two, in anticipation of the subsequent cell division. The case $A = 1.5$ would be appropriate if it were the total DNA content or the total cell mass which determined the stable population size. If the triggered cells have no influence on the population size, then $A = 0$. It follows that A can be considered as the "signal value" of the triggered cells in respect of compartment size feedback control.

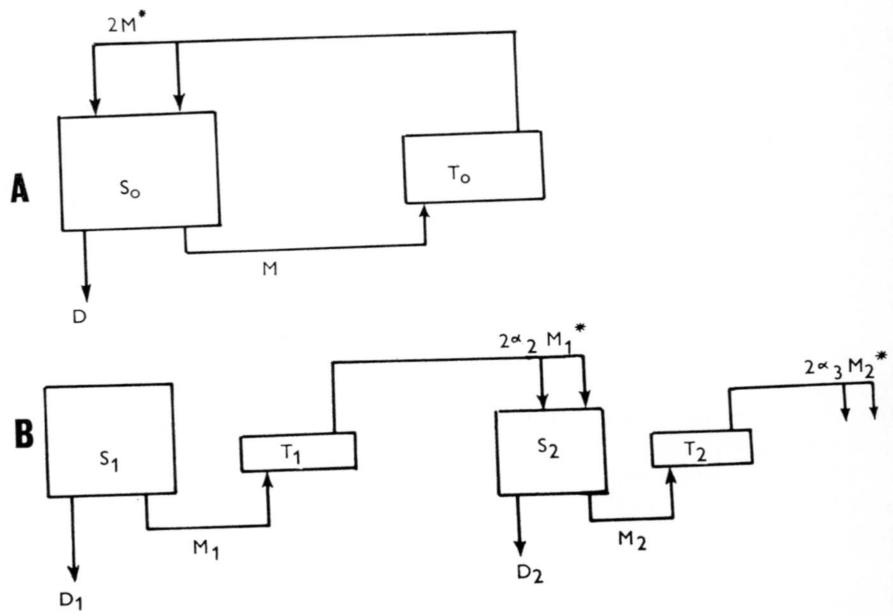

FIGURE 9. Model for the bone marrow stem cell population. A. The normal state or the integer cells after irradiation. B. The sterilized cell population after irradiation.

The rate at which cells from the stock differentiate, D, will depend on the need for differentiated cells and will vary from time to time. However, in investigations of the kinetics of the stem cell models, we shall normally take D to be

$$D = pS_o$$

where p is a constant, and represents a proportion of S_o.

This would be the case in erythropoiesis if, for example, a certain concentration of the humoral factor erythropoietin would cause a certain proportion of the available stock cells to differentiate. In the above formula, the cells in state of cell cycle (T_o) are not available for differentiation. The reason and experimental evidence for this has been discussed in an earlier communication (Lajtha, Oliver, and Gurney, 1962).

The triggered population (T_o) can be represented by a random compartment or by a pipe. In these two cases, the rate at which triggered cells divide, M*, is given by

$$M^* = \lambda T_o$$

or

$$M^*(t) = M(t - \tau)$$

respectively, where τ is the cell cycle time.

The second expression indicates that the rate at which cells are leaving at any time t is equal to the rate at which they were entering T_o one cell cycle earlier.

Although the random compartment for T_o has mathematical simplicity, ie pipe is nearer to the facts; therefore, this is the one we have used in our alculations. This can be used without extra trouble, since these models will sually only be amenable to numerical solution using a computer. We have mployed the Manchester University Atlas computer for this purpose.

The kinetics of this model describes the way in which the populations $_o$ and T_o will approach the steady state and are given by the differential quations

$$\dot{S}_o = \frac{dS_o}{dt} = -D - M + 2M^*$$

$$\dot{T}_o = M - M^*$$

$$D = pS_o \quad \text{and} \quad N = S_o + AT_o$$

nd an equation which describes the manner in which M depends on the opulation size.

Several models of the type for the bone marrow stem cells have been ivestigated, and the different models can be characterized by the way M epends on the compartment size.

The earlier work of Lajtha, Oliver, and Gurney (1962) assumed a form f D and M shown in Figure 4b. A value of $A = 2$ was used and a 'perfect' eedback mechanism was assumed which resulted in the total population ize being constant at N_s. This system shows a well-damped response to step hanges in the demands for differentiated cells, as represented by changes i the parameter p.

The size of the stem cell population of the bone marrow can be meas-red experimentally and its recovery after X-irradiation can be followed. n order to use our models to make comparisons with irradiation experi-ients, we must now make some simplifying assumptions about the effects f radiations on these stem cell populations. The major effect of the radia-ion is to divide the stock and triggered populations into two parts, (1) cells vhich retain their full reproductive integrity, which we shall continue to enote by S_o and T_o although initially very much reduced in number, and 2) sterile cells which, however, remain in the population, and contribute o the population size but produce none or small numbers of progeny. The terile cells will usually be lost at one of the first few divisions following rradiation. The scheme for the sterile cells is shown in Figure 9B. S_1 and T_1 epresent the population of sterile cells which have not yet made a division ince the radiation, S_2 and T_2 cells which have divided once but have made he second division, and so on. The sterile cells in the resting phase $S_1, S_2 \ldots$ re assumed to respond to the stimulations for differentiation or trigger in he same way as the integer cells S_o. However, at each division of the sterile ells, only a proportion $\alpha_2, \alpha_3 \ldots$ successfully produce daughter cells which nter the next sterile stocks $S_2, S_3 \ldots$. The rest of the cells are assumed lost i attempting the division. If $\alpha_2 = 0$, then all sterile cells are lost at the first ivision. The total population for control of the population size is

$$N = (S_0 + S_1 + \ldots) + A(T_0 + T_1 + \ldots).$$

The earlier model with D and M as shown in Figure 4b, in which $A = 2$ and $\alpha_2 = 0$ or $\alpha_3 = 0$, predicts rapid recovery from an irradiation sterilization of a large fraction of the population. Before the recovery, however, the available stem cell stock S_0 shows a postirradiation dip. This is a result of an increased rate of triggering when the sterile cells begin to be lost as they attempt cell division.

The experimental results showed the characteristics of a postirradiation dip followed by a rapid return to the normal population size (Gurney, Lajtha, and Oliver, 1962). However, the extension of the experimental work showed that this is followed by a considerable overshoot above the normal size with a slow return back to normal (Alexanian, Porteous, and Lajtha, 1963). In order to obtain a model which would predict this type of overshoot, population control responses, M, of the form shown in Figure 4c and d, were investigated, together with other values of A. The original model is only stable for values of A near 2, and it also seems that any model with A near 2 implies such a well-regulated population size control that recovery from a severe depopulation will always be rapid but also well damped, with little, if any, overshoot. Therefore $A = 1$ was tried, and the population size control shown in Figure 4c with

$$M = C\,(B - N)\,S$$

used. This gave a stable response provided C was not too large, but although this model predicts an overshoot, it was not very great. To obtain more overshoot, $A = 0$ was tried. This implies that the population size feedback control only operates on the S cells (they "signal" their existence, but the T cells do not). During recovery, triggering from S_0 into T_0 occurs at a greater rate than in steady state, and when the size of S_0 reaches normal, there will be a "surplus" of cells in T_0. This tends to give an overshoot because of the overstocking of the triggered population during recovery, but unless the population size control is chosen carefully, the system will be unstable.

Finally, for these reasons, the form shown in Figure 4d was chosen. This dependence of M on N and S has a low slope near the stable size N_s so that only a small change in the triggering rate results from a small change in population size from normal, but when the population is severely depleted there is a very great increase in the rate of triggering. This model can predict overshoots up to twice the normal size following a 90 per cent sterilizing dose of radiation.

The predicted behavior of such a cell population is illustrated in Figure 10, and the experimental results in Figures 11 and 12. This type of feedback regulation also enables a steady state to develop under conditions of chronic irradiation, simply by coping with the excess cell removal (caused by cell death) by increased population turnover. If an increased rate of differentiation is applied to the smaller than normal S_0, a normal rate of production of differentiated cells can be maintained. The increased turnover might be detected by an increased mitotic index, or by DNA specific ac-

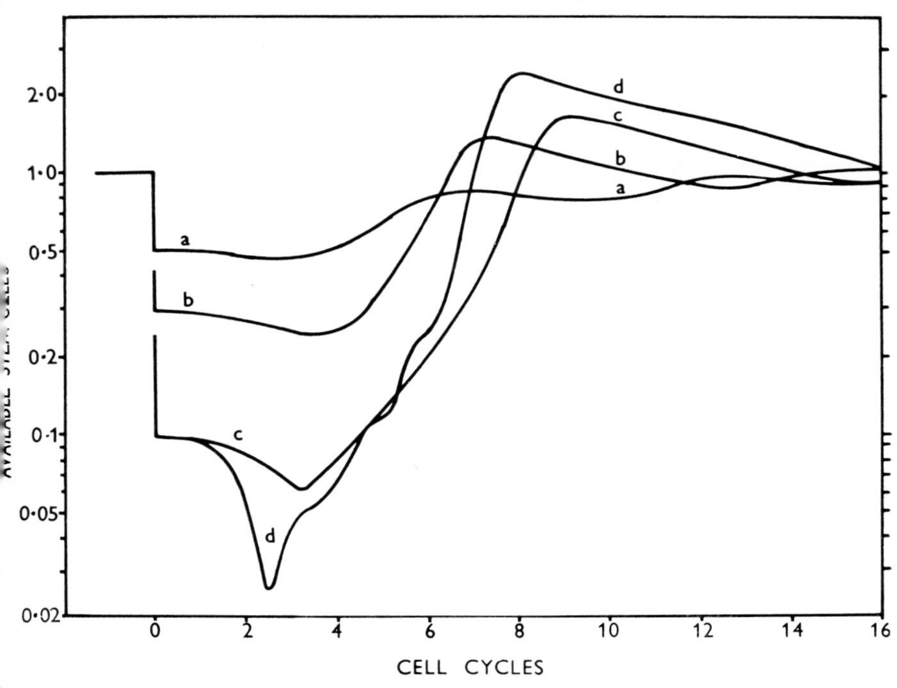

FIGURE 10. Computed recovery of the available stem cell population following a single radiation sterilization. Stem cell model with population size relationships of Figure 4d, and the following values of the parameters: A = 0, p = 0.1, $\alpha_2 = 0.5$, $\alpha_3 = 0$, and B adjusted to make the steady state population unity for all curves. For curves (a), (b), and (c), C = 2.5 with 50 per cent, 30 per cent, and 10 per cent surviving cells, respectively; for curve (d), C = 5.0 with 10 per cent surviving cells.

ivity following a suitable label. Such results were, in fact, obtained by Lamerton and his associates (Lamerton, Pontifex, Blackett, and Adams, 1959; Pontifex and Lamerton, 1960; Lamerton, Steel, and Wimber, 1961) during their continuous or interrupted chronic irradiation experiments.

Since the radiosensitivity in regard to reproductive integrity of the bone marrow stem cells is known (Hodgson, 1962; McCulloch and Till, 1960; Till and McCulloch, 1961; McCulloch and Till, 1962; Gurney, Lajtha, and Oliver, 1962; Gurney and Wackman, 1961; Alexanian, Porteous, and Lajtha, 1963; Porteous, Alexanian, and Lajtha, 1963), it is possible to establish quantitative correlation between experimental findings and computer predictions. As the recovery pattern will, to some extent, depend on the variation for demand for differentiation during recovery, this has to be taken into account in the computer calculations. Work in progress in our laboratory is conducted at present on the assumption that the organism will aim at maintaining the normal amount of differentiation. In this way, it might be possible to obtain some values for the normal proportion of stem cells differentiating, and thus for the absolute size of the bone marrow stem pool.

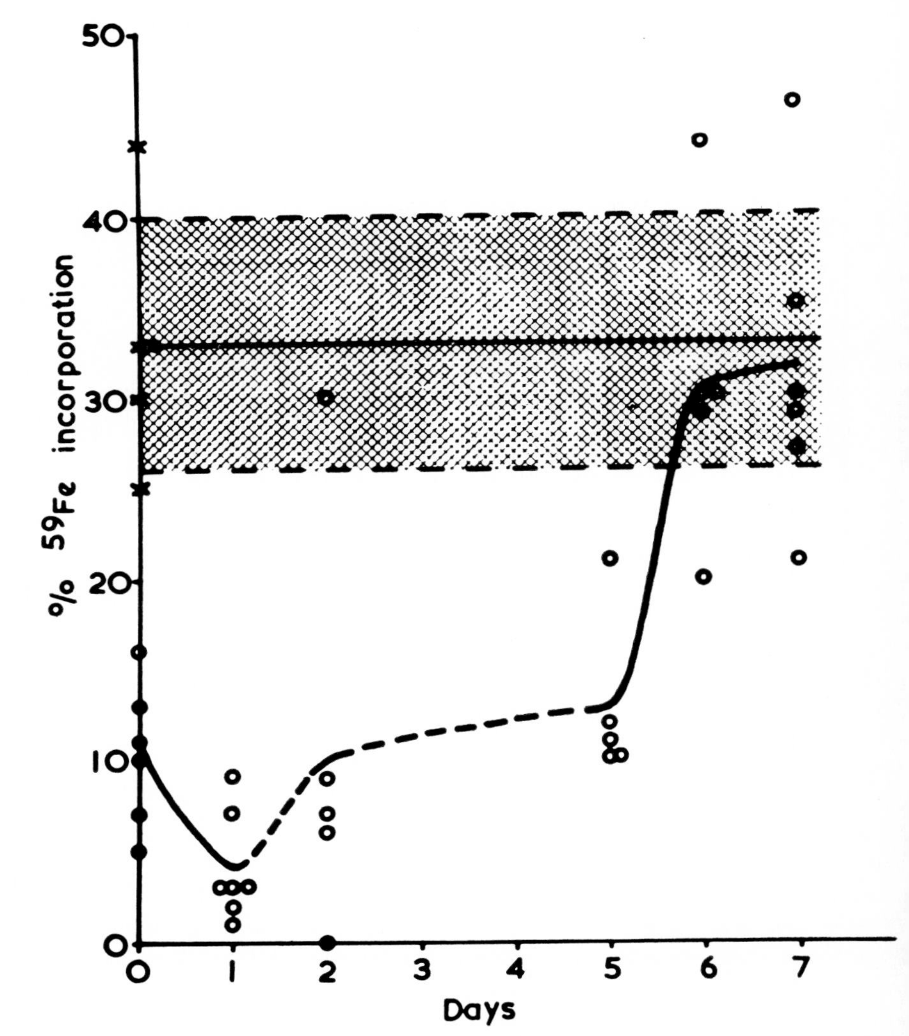

FIGURE 11. Stem cell recovery in the polycythemic mouse after 150 rads. Shaded area indicates range of response in control animals. (Redrawn from Gurney, Lajtha, and Oliver 1962.)

CONCLUSIONS

In the foregoing report, various models of cell populations were considered in regard to the modes of maintenance and variations of population size, proliferation, and differentiation.

Model construction consists essentially in building up a series of formulated questions, at first qualitative, then quantitative. It hinges on suitable experimental systems in which some answer to the questions raised may be obtained.

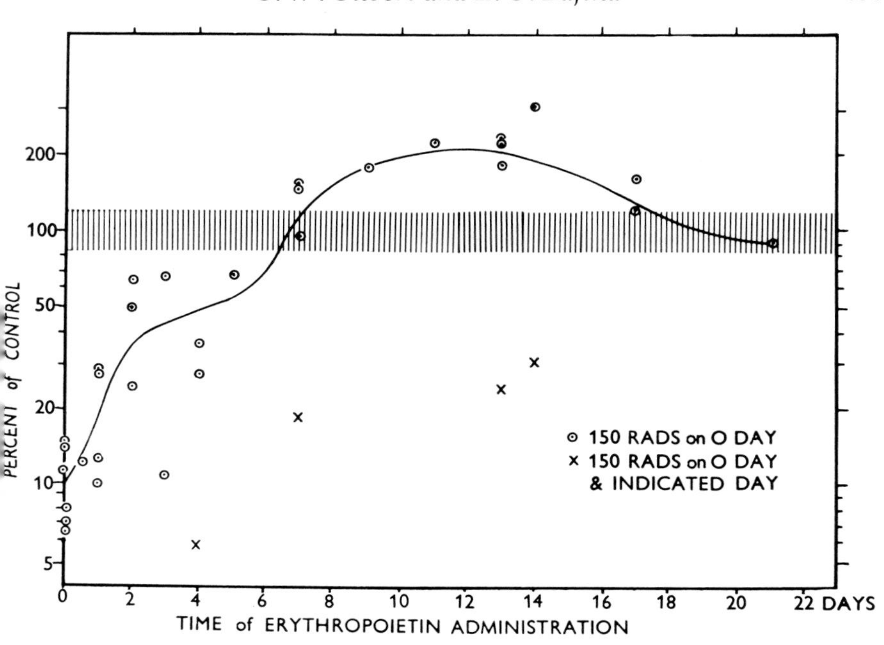

IGURE 12. Recovery and overshoot of stem cell response to erythropoietin after 150 rads. Iatched area indicates ± 1 standard error. (Redrawn from Alexanian, Porteous, and ajtha, 1963.)

The aim of this paper was to demonstrate that the response of various ell populations to irradiation is determined to a great extent by their popuation kinetic patterns. This can be complicated even in such "simple" sysems as tumors, but even more complicated in steady state populations vhich have feedback mechanisms controlling the various parameters of their ctivities. In such steady state populations, the problem is further compliated by the fact that the experimental systems available frequently do ot measure the populations in question, but measure their products instead.

The aim of this symposium is to obtain a better understanding of the asic effects of radiation on cellular systems. It has been attempted to indiate in this paper that for this purpose the study of cell population kinetics s an essential process. The circle is completed by saying that in the study f cell population kinetics, radiation is a powerful tool, by which perturbaions may be introduced into the systems in a specific way. It is the pattern f restitution from such perturbations that gives much useful information n the nature of the system under investigation.

REFERENCES

lexanian, R., D. D. Porteous, and L. G. Lajtha. 1963. Stem-Cell Kinetics After Irradiation. *International Journal of Radiation Biology and Related Studies in Physics, Chemistry and Medicine*, 7:87–94.

Clowes, F. A. L. 1954. The Promeristem and the Minimal Constructional Centre i Grass Root Apices. *New Phytologist*, 53:108–116.

Clowes, F. A. L., and E. J. Hall. 1962. The Quiescent Centre in Root Meristems c *Vicia faba* and its Behaviour After Acute X-Irradiation and Chronic Gamma Irradia tion. *Radiation Botany*, 3:45–53.

Dewey, D. L., and A. Howard. 1963. Cell Dynamics in the Bean Root Tip. *Radiatio Botany*, 3:259–263.

Elkind, M. M., and H. Sutton. 1959. X-Ray Damage and Recovery in Mammalia Cells in Culture. *Nature*, London, 184:1293–1295.

Gelfant, S. 1962. Initiation of Mitosis in Relation to the Cell Division Cycle. *Experi mental Cell Research*, 26:395–403.

Gurney, C. W., L. G. Lajtha, and R. Oliver. 1962. A Method for Investigation of Stem Cell Kinetics. *British Journal of Haematology*, 8:461–466.

Gurney, C. W., and N. Wackman. 1961. Impairment of Erythropoiesis by Irradiatior *Nature*, London, 190:1017–1018.

Hall, E. J. 1962. A Method of Deducing a Dose-Response Relationship for Reproductiv Integrity of Cells Exposed to Radiation by Means of Fractionation Experiment. *British Journal of Radiology*, 35:398–402.

Hall, E. J., and L. G. Lajtha. 1963. The Recovery of *Vicia faba* Meristem Cells fror X-Radiation. *Radiation Research*, 20:187–194.

Hall, E. J., L. G. Lajtha, and F. A. L. Clowes. 1962. The Role of the Quiescent Centr in the Recovery of *Vicia faba* Roots from Radiation. *Radiation Botany*, 2:189–194.

Hall, E. J., L. G. Lajtha, and R. Oliver. 1962. X-Ray Dose-Response Relationship fo Reproductive Integrity of *Vicia faba*. *British Journal of Radiology*, 35:388–397.

Harris, T. E. 1959. "A Mathematical Model for Multiplication by Binary Fission, *The Kinetics of Cellular Proliferation*, F. Stohlman, Jr., Ed. New York, New York and London, England: Grune and Stratton, Inc. Pp. 368–381.

Hewitt, H. B., and C. W. Wilson. 1959. A Survival Curve for Mammalian Leukaemi Cells Irradiated *in vivo* (Implications for the Treatment of Mouse Leukaemia b Whole-Body Irradiation). *The British Journal of Cancer*, 13:69–75.

Hodgson, G. S. 1962. Radiosensitivity of Marrow Cells Responsible for Reestablishin Erythropoiesis in Lethally Irradiated Mice. *Acta physiologica latinoamericana*, 12 365–369.

Howard, A., and S. R. Pelc. 1953. Synthesis of Deoxyribonucleic Acid in Normal an Irradiated Cells and its Relation to Chromosome Breakage. *Heredity*, 6: Supplemer on Chromosome Breakage: 261–273.

Lajtha, L. G. 1963. "On the Concept of the Cell Cycle," *Journal of Cellular and Com parative Physiology*, 62: Supplement 1: 143–145.

Lajtha, L. G., and R. Oliver. 1962. Cell Population Kinetics Following Different Re gimes of Irradiation. *British Journal of Radiology*, 35:131–140.

Lajtha, L. G., R. Oliver, and C. W. Gurney. 1962. Kinetic Model of a Bone-Marrow Stem-Cell Population. *British Journal of Haematology*, 8:442–460.

Lamerton, L. F., B. I. Lord, and H. Quastler. 1963. Studies of Cell Population Kinetic in Normal and Continuously Irradiated Animals. *Radioaktive Isotope in Klinik un Forschung*, 5:493–501.

Lamerton, L. F., A. H. Pontifex, N. M. Blackett, and K. Adams. 1959. Effects of Pro tracted Irradiation on the Blood-Forming Organs of the Rat. I. Continuous Exposure *British Journal of Radiology*, 33:287–301.

Lamerton, L. F., G. G. Steel, and D. R. Wimber. 1961. Sensitvity of Mammalian Tis sues to Continuous Exposure, *Brookhaven Symposia in Biology*, 14:158–175.

McCulloch, E. A., and J. E. Till. 1960. The Radiation Sensitivity of Normal Mous Bone Marrow Cells, Determined by Quantitative Marrow Transplantation into Ir radiated Mice. *Radiation Research*, 13:115–125.

————. 1962. The Sensitivity of Cells from Normal Mouse Bone Marrow to Gamma Radiation *in vitro* and *in vivo*. *Radiation Research*, 16:822–832.

Patt, H. M., and H. Quastler. 1963. Radiation Effect on Cell Renewal and Related Systems. *Physiological Reviews*, 43:357–396.

Pontifex, A. H., and L. F. Lamerton. 1960. Effects of Protracted Irradiation on the Blood-Forming Organs of the Rat. II. Divided Doses. *British Journal of Radiology*, 33:736–747.

Porteous, D. D., R. Alexanian, and L. G. Lajtha. 1963. The Fasted Mouse in the Study of Bone-Marrow Stem-Cell Kinetics. *International Journal of Radiation Biology*, 7:95–100.

Puck, T. T., and P. I. Marcus. 1956. Action of X-Rays on Mammalian Cells. *Journal of Experimental Medicine*, 103:653–666.

Quastel, M. R. 1963. Continuous Irradiation of the Rat at High Dose Rates: A Study of Jejunal Damage, Recovery and Radioresistance Using Tritiated Thymidine. *Radiation Research*, 18:46–57.

Quastler, H. 1963. "The Analysis of Cell Population Kinetics," *Guinness Symposium on Cell Proliferation*, L. F. Lamerton and R. J. M. Fry, Eds. Oxford, England: Blackwell Scientific Publications. Pp. 18–34.

Till, J. E., and E. A. McCulloch. 1961. A Direct Measurement of the Radiation Sensitivity of Normal Mouse Bone Marrow Cells. *Radiation Research*, 14:213–222.

Wimber, D. R., and L. F. Lamerton. 1963. Cell Population Studies on the Intestine of Continuously Irradiated Rats. *Radiation Research*, 18:137–146.

The Kinetics of Tumor Cell Proliferation

MORTIMER L. MENDELSOHN

Department of Radiology, University of Pennsylvania, Philadelphia, Pennsylvania

In his attempt to cure the patient who has cancer, the radiotherapist faces the difficult task of deliberately destroying an abnormal population of cells within the host while inflicting a minimum of damage to the surrounding normal tissues. In this context, recent developments in cellular radiation biology have been of great interest, initially reinforcing the hope that eventually the empirical foundations of radiotherapy would be replaced by a suitable theoretical foundation, and more recently suggesting what may become strategically important insights into the comparative radiosensitivity of cells.

This volume gives ample evidence of the growing awareness that radiation sensitivity and radiation recovery are closely linked to the cell cycle. As work in this area develops, there will be an increasing desire to extend the observations to radiotherapy and the tumor-host problem. Implicit in this extension is an intimate knowledge of the kinetics of cell proliferation in normal and tumor tissues.

Because of the individuality of spontaneous neoplasms and their disorderly, nonsteady state growth, the analysis of tumor kinetics is different from, and probably more difficult than, the analysis of normal tissues (see Mendelsohn, 1963, and Patt, 1963, for a review and discussion of the problem). In this paper, attention will be focused on two questions concerning the cell cycle in tumors:

1. Given an experimental tumor and the techniques of kinetic analysis, can the parameters of the cell cycle be determined for the tumor cells?

2. Can these methods be extended to a single tumor—such as a particular clinical neoplasm—or to categories of clinical tumors?

The experimental tumor to be described is the so-called "spontaneous" mammary tumor of C3H mice. The etiology of this lesion is complex, involving the mammary tumor agent, the endocrine milieu of the individual mouse, and the genetic constitution of the mouse strain. The tumors arise abundantly in appropriate females, have undisputed malignant properties, and display considerable heterogeneity of morphology and growth rate. They can be transplanted readily, but offer the considerable advantage of a system which can be studied conveniently in the animal of origin.

The Cell Cycle of Proliferating Tumor Cells

As will be discussed later, there is a high probability that only a fraction of C3H tumor cells are actually involved in the cell cycle. At this point in the argument, it is enough to realize that this may be so, and somehow to restrict the analysis specifically to proliferating cells. To accomplish this, we use the visible stages of mitosis as morphological criteria of a cell's involvement in the proliferative cycle, limiting the observations to those cells in the prophase to telophase portion of the cycle.

Our first description of the cell cycle in vivo in C3H mammary tumors was based on a series of 51 tumors fixed and sampled at various times within the first 24 hours after the parenteral injection of tritiated thymidine (Mendelsohn, Dohan, and Moore, 1960). T_S, the mean transit time of the cells through deoxyribonucleic acid (DNA) synthesis, and T_{G2M}, the mean transit time from the end of DNA synthesis to the midpoint of visible mitosis, were estimated from autoradiographs by following the incidence of labeling of mitotic cells as a function of time. In principle, the method assumes that a brief pulse of tritiated thymidine has labeled all cells in DNA synthesis, and that these labeled cells are initially synchronized at a specific portion of the cell cycle.

The availability of labeled thymidine to many, if not all, tumor cells in DNA synthesis is suggested by the 70 to 95 per cent labeling of mitotic figures from 4 to 10 hours after a single injection. However, the unlabeled mitoses could be exceptions to the rule, or could represent stragglers and rapidly cycling cells which were not in DNA synthesis at the time of injection. That the lack of saturation is attributable to the intersection of the ascending and descending limbs of the wave and not to mitotic cells out of reach of the tritiated thymidine is indicated by the observation that *all* mitotic tumor cells are labeled after infusing tritiated thymidine intraperitoneally at a rate of 5 μc/hr for 10 hours or more (Figure 1).

The evidence that a parenteral injection of thymidine represents a pulsed exposure has been available for several normal tissues and for ascites cells (Rubini, Cronkite, Bond, and Fliedner, 1960; Quastler and Sherman, 1959; Koburg, 1963; Kisieleski, Baserga, and Lisco, 1961). We have studied this problem in C3H tumors by isolating the tumors with clamps at the time of intravenous injection of the tritiated thymidine (Staroscik, Jenkins, and Mendelsohn, 1964). The uptake of tritium into the nuclei of mitotic tumor cells was determined autoradiographically and expressed as a function of the interval between injection and removal of the clamps. When the clamps were removed 40 minutes after initial injection, significant incorporation

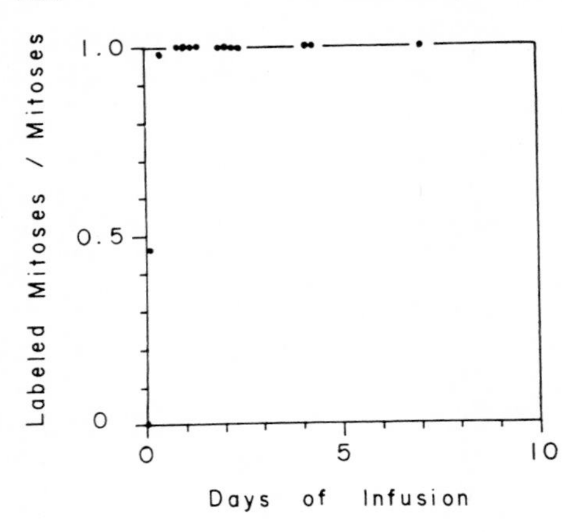

FIGURE 1. "Labeled mitoses/mitoses" as a function of duration of infusion in tumors removed immediately after the end of an intraperitoneal infusion of tritiated thymidine. This technique effectively demonstrates the leading edge of the first wave of labeled mitoses and indicates the availability of the label to all proliferating tumor cells. Two of the data points and the technical details have been described previously (Mendelsohn, 1962b).

of label in the tumor was observed, but this represented only 1 or 2 per cent of control uptake. In agreement with experiments in which tissues are removed at various times after injection, the clamping study indicated that 95 per cent of the uptake from a single intravenous injection of tritiated thymidine occurs within the first 25 minutes.

The final assumption, namely that the cells are initially synchronized, is borne out to a large extent by the residual synchrony still manifest hours later when the cells pass through visible mitosis. However, the synchrony at that time is clearly not perfect, and the possibilities remain that (1) individual tumor cells regularly partition their proliferative cycle in slightly different proportions, (2) the proportions of the cycle are somewhat indeterminate, being subject to local influences and random variation, and (3) the cells demonstrate stable or unstable variation in the velocity with which they proceed through the cycle.

The 1960 study was designed to show the first wave of labeled mitoses, thus giving direct information for T_S and T_{G2M}. To obtain the corresponding direct estimate for T_C (the mean transit time around the entire cycle) and T_{G1} (the mean transit time through the presynthetic portion of the cycle) would require the demonstration of a second wave of labeled mitoses. Twenty-eight tumors fixed anywhere from 1 to 14 days after labeling gave no indication of a second wave, and, if anything, suggested that the labeled cells had desynchronized by this time, distributing diffusely around the cycle (Mendelsohn, 1960, 1962a). If the cells had indeed desynchronized, Wright's hypothesis—that the frequency of cells in a phase of the cycle is proportional to the duration of the phase (Wright, 1925)—could be used to calculate T_C from the mean values of "labeled mitoses/mitoses":

$$\frac{\text{Labeled Mitoses}}{\text{Mitoses}} = \frac{T_S}{T_C}. \qquad (1)$$

Since T_S was estimated to be 9.97 hours (from the area under the first wave of labeled mitoses), and "labeled mitoses/mitoses" for 10 tumors fixed at 120 hours was 0.300 (Mendelsohn, 1962a), T_C calculated to 33.2 hours. This state of affairs left much to be desired, including a corroborative or more direct estimate of T_C, information on the rate at which the cells desynchronized, and the effect of variation from tumor to tumor.

In an as yet unpublished experiment, A. C. Waltman and I have recently added 92 tumors to this material, deliberately sampling at regular intervals in the period from 20 to 190 hours after labeling. Figure 2 summarizes these results, combining the new and old data into one plot. A complete analysis of this experiment is not appropriate at this time, but the following points can be made:

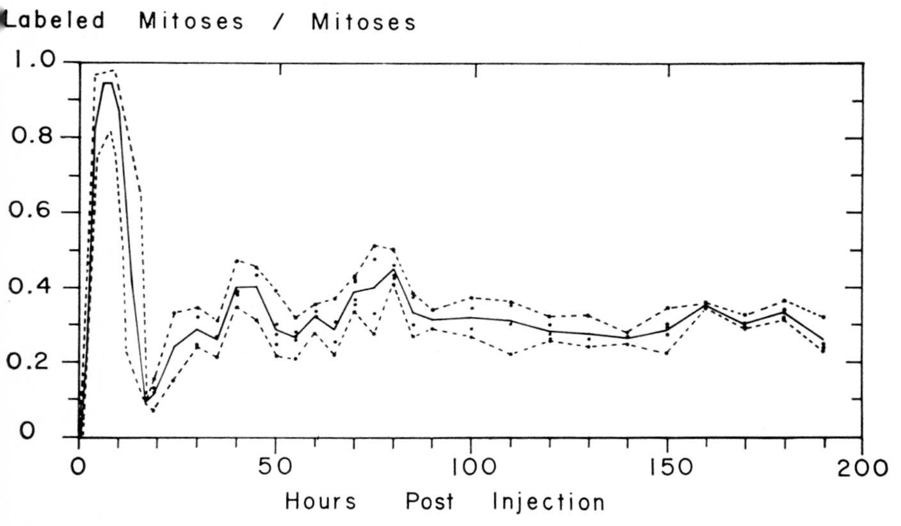

FIGURE 2. "Labeled mitoses/mitoses" in 143 mammary tumors at various times after the parenteral injection of tritiated thymidine. The means for tumors harvested at the same time period are joined by the solid line. The dashed lines join the extreme values. The individual tumors are represented as dots, but are shown only for the data extending from 20 to 190 hours.

1. By eye, it is apparent that the first wave is followed by two additional waves and then by a long, stable plateau. The three waves are equally spaced and are separated by approximately 35 hours. Judging from the shape of the waves, there is a considerable loss of synchrony between the first and second wave.

2. The visual impression of a repeating pattern is confirmed by statistical analysis. A calculation of autocorrelation in five-hour increments gave a significant positive correlation ($P < 0.05$) between values sampled at separations of 35 or 70 hours, and a significant negative correlation between values sampled at separations of 10 or 45 hours. The positive correlation at 35 hours matches the 35 hour separation of the three peaks seen by eye, and the negative correlation probably represents the interaction of peaks and troughs.

3. The mean value of "labeled mitoses/mitoses" for the 45 tumors sampled on the plateau from 85 to 190 hours after labeling was 0.301. This is in close agreement with the value of 0.300 mentioned earlier for 10 tumors sampled at 120 hours. Using equation (1) and a T_S of 9.97 hours, the plateau figure again gives a T_c of 33.2 hours. The close agreement between this estimate for T_c and the 35-hour value obtained from the autocorrelation analysis reinforces one's confidence in both of these techniques. (The correction factor [Hoffman, 1949; Johnson, 1961] for the nonlinear or quasi-exponential growth of these tumors is not called for in the above calculation. Since the method is based on the desynchronization of the labeled cells, the assumption that they accomplish this by distributing themselves symmetrically about their starting position eliminates the need for applying the correction term to Wright's hypothesis.)

4. The area under each of the peaks is roughly the same, and is equal to the area under the plateau for a 35-hour period. This is a good indication that a comparable proportion of the proliferating cells is cycling each 35 hours. Coupled to the high probability that the first synchronous wave contains all or almost all of the originally labeled cells, this must mean that the average cycle time of 33 to 35 hours is based on the preponderance of proliferating cells.

5. Prior to this experiment, we had interpreted the range of values of "labeled mitoses/mitoses" at 120 hours as an indication of variation in the mean cycle time from tumor to tumor. Coupled to the lack of evidence for second waves, this interpretation led to our making a false contrast between the apparent constancy of T_S and T_{G2M} (resulting in a sharply defined first wave) and a variable cycle time (resulting in the rapid loss of synchrony within and between tumors). We now find that the composite data from 143 tumors is consistent with three synchronous waves separated by 35 hours, and a plateau representing asychrony but with the same mean cycle time of approximately 35 hours. What is more, the individual tumor values (or the mean values for each time period) vary from the plateau mean by no more than what would be expected from the binomial sampling theorem. That these results go a long way toward characterizing the behavior of these tumor cells is indicated by the following examples of populations which would not conform to Figure 2: (a) tumors in which the variance of cell cycle times was very small would desynchronize slowly and would be likely to produce a scattering of points near 0 and 100 per cent labeled mitoses, either in or out of phase with the peaks shown in the figure; and (b) regardless of the variance of cycle time, tumors with widely divergent mean cycle times would not have collectively generated the second and third waves and would have individually shown more deviation from the plateau. We can only conclude that there is a common mean cell cycle time of approximately 35 hours applicable to all tumors in the series, that the variance of cell cycle time has a lower limit in these tumors, and that the magnitude of the variance is at least such that the position of the cells in the cycle is completely

reshuffled every three cycles.

As one of many possible models of tumor cell behavior, Figure 3 demonstrates an artificial system which closely mimics the behavior of the C3H mammary tumors. The model is based on a population of cells with a log normal distribution of cell cycle times, a T_C of 30 hours, and subdivisions of the cycle which are fixed fractions of the cycle time (G_2, 10 per cent; S, 30 per cent). After each mitotic division, the daughter cells are assigned a new cycle time according to chance and the predefined frequency distribution. Figure 3 shows "labeled mitoses/mitoses" as a function of time, with the initial labeling occurring at time zero. The progressive degeneration of the synchronous waves and the approach of the plateau toward the ratio of T_S/T_C is similar to the actual tumor data in Figure 2. Thus, the sharp first wave and the almost complete loss of synchrony in two to three generations can occur without any internal variation in the relative partitions of the mitotic cycle. The only source of variation in this model is in the time scale of the cell cycle, which is equivalent to a standard deviation of 46 per cent of the mean. The cells would desynchronize much more rapidly if the model included a positive correlation between successive cycle times for the same cell.

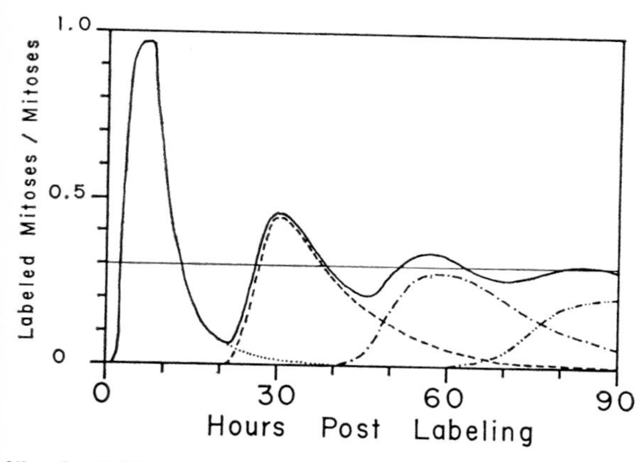

FIGURE 3. "Labeled mitoses/mitoses" as a function of time in an artificial model system. The cells have been given a log normal distribution of cycle times and a duration of DNA synthesis which is 30 per cent of the cycle. The mean cycle time of 30 hours and the variance of cycle time are reflected in the successive cycles of labeled mitoses (shown by the broken lines) and in the sum of these waves (shown by the solid line). The system is much like the C3H tumors in that the incidence of labeled mitoses shows a rapidly damped oscillation which eventually reaches a plateau of 0.300, the ratio of T_S/T_C.

There is at present no direct evidence for the frequency distribution of cycle times of the C3H mammary tumor cells (or, for that matter, of any other in vivo cell system). A crude indication of the long side of this distribution is suggested by data from chronic infusions shown in Figure 4. Unlike Figure 1, the incidence of labeling in these mitotic cells has been determined three to five days after the termination of infusions of tritiated thymidine. Thus the counts represent the frequency of labeling of proliferating cells after the cells have desynchronized. The dotted line joins the value 0.301 at time zero (single injection) with a value of 1.0 at time 1.04

days (35 hours minus 9.97 hours) and represents what would happen if the proliferating cells cycled with a mean of 35 hours and a variance of zero. The separation of the experimental points from this line represents the fraction of unlabeled proliferating cells in excess of this simple prediction, and is due to a combination of the variance of cycle time, the initial distribution of the cells in the cycle, and the effects of recycling. The pattern suggests that the distribution of cycle times is skewed toward the long values, extending out several multiples of the mean cycle time.

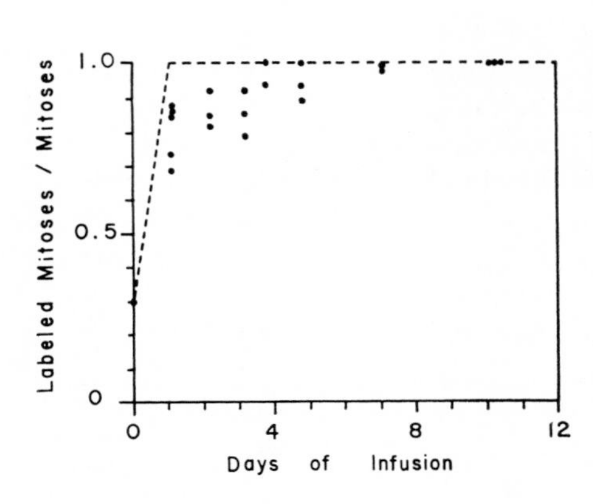

FIGURE 4. "Labeled mitoses/mitoses" as a function of duration of infusion in tumors removed three to five days after the end of an intraperitoneal infusion of tritiated thymidine. Each point represents the extent to which the proliferating population of tumor cells has been labeled by the infusion. The dotted line reflects what would happen if the cycle time was 35 hours and there was no variation. All proliferating cells have apparently been labeled in a number of tumors, but the pattern of points lying below the dotted line suggests the distribution of cells with cycle times in excess of the mean. Nine of the 22 points were reported previously (Mendelsohn, 1962b).

THE RELATIONSHIP BETWEEN PROLIFERATING AND TOTAL TUMOR CELLS

If the C3H mammary tumors consist exclusively of a closed system of proliferating, nondying cells, the fact that these tumors (selected without regard to age or size) all show a similar mean cell cycle time should result in the following predicted behavior:

1. The tumors should grow exponentially and all at a similar rate, with doubling time approximating the mean cell cycle time.

2. The indexes "labeled mitoses/mitoses" and "labeled cells/cells" should have comparable values in any one tumor at 85 to 190 hours after a single injection of tritiated thymidine.

3. After chronic infusions of tritiated thymidine, the behavior of "labeled cells/cells" should be similar to the behavior shown in Figure 4 for "labeled mitoses/mitoses."

In fact, evidence from this laboratory refutes each of these hypothetical predictions:

1. Only a small fraction of these tumors grows exponentially, as will be discussed in more detail below. Even if forced into an exponential growth pattern (*i.e.* by the best straight-line fit for a plot of log tumor volume versus time), the doubling times of 115 C3H mammary tumors show a wide range with a mean of 8.5 days (Figure 5). We have never seen a C3H mammary tumor double in 1.4 days (35 hours).

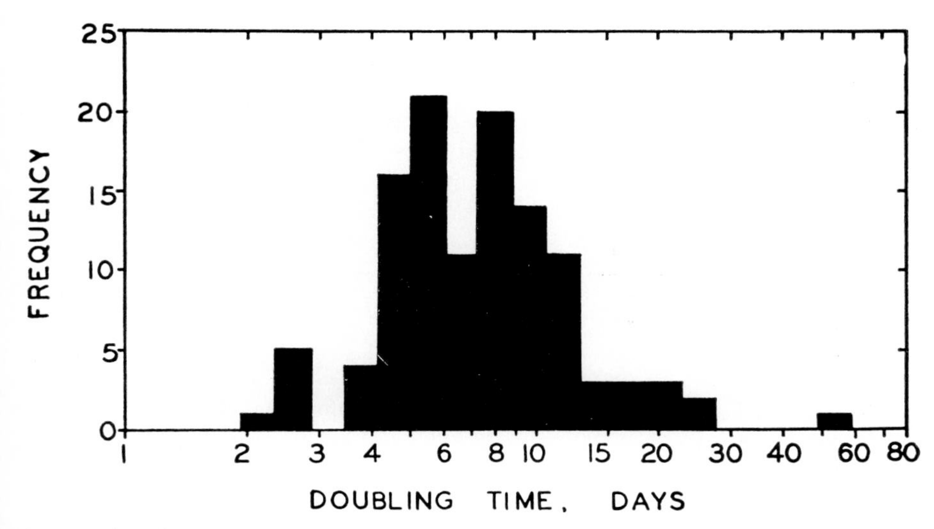

FIGURE 5. The frequency distribution of doubling times for 115 C3H mammary tumors. For each tumor, serial measurements of tumor volume were taken over several doublings and plotted against time on semilogarithmic paper. The doubling time was determined from a straight line of best fit drawn through the data points. Although the method is inappropriate for the mode of growth of most of these tumors, it does give a reasonable indication of the spectrum of growth rates. Note that the abscissa is a logarithmic scale.

2. After the labeled cells desynchronize, there is always a disparity between "labeled cells/cells" and "labeled mitoses/mitoses," with the latter consistently being the larger of the two. Thus the mean of "labeled cells/cells" at 120 hours for the 10 tumors previously studied was 0.182 (61 per cent of the mean for "labeled mitoses/mitoses"). In the new series, "labeled cells/cells" was measured in 28 tumors, ranging from 30 to 80 hours after labeling. A mean of 0.1416 (with a standard error of the mean of 0.0086) was obtained. This value is 47 per cent of the plateau mean for "labeled mitoses/mitoses." Under certain circumstances, the ratio of "labeled cells/cells" and "labeled mitoses/mitoses" leads to an estimate of growth fraction, proliferating cells/total cells (Mendelsohn, 1962a). The 10 tumors referred to above yielded a growth fraction of 0.4 when corrected for the growth which took place during the time between labeling and harvesting of the cells. A similar downward correction would be called for with the new data, thus reinforcing the impression that approximately a third of the C3H tumor cells behave as proliferating cells. In the original interpretation of growth fraction, the method was compromised by the suspicion that cycle time was varying greatly and transit time through DNA synthesis was varying very little. If, as was just indicated, the transit time through DNA synthesis may be proportional to the cycle time, then the growth fraction method takes on added significance.

3. Figure 6 shows the effect of chronic infusions of tritiated thymidine on "labeled cells/cells." The results reinforce the evidence from single in-

jection, indicating that the incidence of labeling is always less in the total cell population than in the proliferating cell population. Attempts to saturate the population by labeling all morphologically intact tumor cells have been notably unsuccessful even after infusions as long as 10 days. The interpretation of Figure 6 is compounded by the fact that intervening growth of the tumor inevitably dwarfs the fraction of cells which are neither labeling nor dividing.

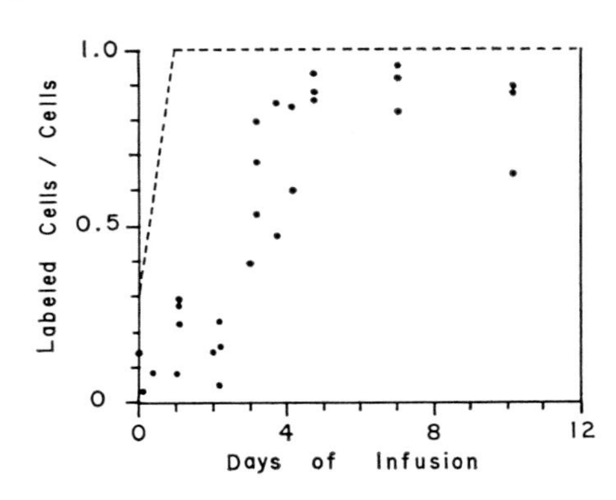

FIGURE 6. "Labeled cells/cells" as a function of duration of infusion in tumors fixed at various times after an intraperitoneal infusion of tritiated thymidine. The dashed line indicates what would occur if all the tumor cells were proliferating, and the cell cycle time was 35 hours without any variation. When compared with Figure 4, these results strongly suggest that a sizable fraction of the cells are nonproliferating. Twelve of the 28 points were reported previously (Mendelsohn, 1962b).

On the strength of these arguments, the original premise that the C3H mammary tumors consist exclusively of a closed system of proliferating, nondying cells must be rejected. The evidence points strongly to the presence of a large component of nonproliferating cells, but several other factors may be operating as well: (1) there is qualitative but not quantitative evidence of cell death, either in the form of regional necrosis, or in the more universal presence of about 1 per cent necrotic cells distributed through the tumor; (2) the occurrence of pulmonary metastases indicates that the tumor is not a completely closed system, but the magnitude of cell traffic out of the tumor is not known; and (3) some of the observations can be accounted for by cells with cycle times much longer than the mean cycle time, but these cells would have to represent a small fraction of the total proliferating cells to be compatible with the results in Figure 2.

Having gone to these great lengths to study the cellular kinetics of C3H mammary tumors, we are left with a reasonably clear picture of a proliferating compartment, and a rather confusing picture of a number of factors which complicate the impact of this proliferating compartment on the tumor as a whole. We would very much like to know if nonproliferation is an irreversible state, how and when the decision is made that a cell will no longer proliferate, and what determines the surprisingly reproducible behavior of the proliferating tumor cells. In approaching a new tumor system, we wonder if there is a more direct or less inconvenient way to arrive at the characteristics of the proliferating population. As matters stand, a few samples of an unknown tumor would not supply good evidence of the cycle time, since one either needs enough tumors to demonstrate multiple waves, or one must know T_S and be convinced that the tumors are also being sampled on the plateau after the labeled cells have desynchronized. Finally, we would like to relate behavior at the cellular level to the gross properties of tumor masses.

Tumor Growth Curves

This work is based on the assumption that the C3H mammary tumors consist of two subpopulations: a proliferating compartment characterized by a stable mean cell-cycle time, and a completely passive, nonproliferating compartment. Thus,

$$\frac{dN}{dt} = \frac{w}{T_C} N_p = \frac{w}{T_C}(GF)N \tag{2}$$

where dN/dt is the rate of change of total cells (N), T_C is the mean cell-cycle time, N_p is the number of proliferating cells, GF is the growth fraction (N_p/N), and w is a correction factor for the distribution of proliferating cells within the cell cycle. For a tumor growing exponentially under these conditions, GF is constant, w becomes $\ln(1 + GF)/GF$, and the equation simplifies to:

$$\frac{dN}{dt} = \frac{\ln(1 + GF_0)}{T_C} N. \tag{3}$$

For linear growth, w is equal to one, and N_p is a constant:

$$\frac{dN}{dt} = \frac{N_{po}}{T_C}. \tag{4}$$

Inspection of growth curves indicated from the beginning that the C3H tumors were usually not following either of these two growth modes. Within the context of the model, this suggested that N_p was likely to be some function of N other than a simple proportion. From among the many functions that could be chosen to expand this model, we selected

$$N_p = gN^b \tag{5}$$

where g is a constant of proportionality and b is an attribute controlling the mode of growth (Mendelsohn, 1963). The advantage of this particular function is that it reduces to linear growth when b equals zero, it is equivalent to exponential growth when b equals one, and it follows the so-called cube-root growth when b equals two thirds. Using this function, equation (2) can be restated as

$$\frac{dN}{dt} = \frac{wg}{T_C} N^b \tag{6}$$

and its integral becomes:

$$N^{1-b} = \frac{(1-b)\,wg}{T_C} t + C_0; \quad b \neq 1 \tag{7}$$

$$\ln N = \frac{\ln(1 + GF)}{T_C} t + C_1; \quad b = 1. \tag{8}$$

M. J. Marion and I have attempted to explore the relevance of this model by fitting actual tumor growth data to it. The crux of this experiment is the meticulous serial measurement of external dimensions of undisturbed C3H mammary tumors. The technique involves caliper measurements to the nearest 0.1 mm, measuring the maximum width, the width at right angles to the maximum, and the maximum height of the tumor. The product of these three dimensions is used as a relative volume. (Relative volume should be proportional to the true volume in tumors which do not change shape as they grow. For spherical or hemispherical tumors, true volume equals 0.52 times relative volume.)

A linear plot of volume (V) versus time for a single transplanted C3H mammary tumor is shown in Figure 7. The range of volumes, scatter of individual measurements, and upward bend of the curve are all typical of the results we obtain. That this tumor is not increasing exponentially is shown in Figure 8.

Our first concern was to study the effect of time on the mode of growth, b. From the smoothed curve drawn through the data points of the linear plot, tangents were taken to determine dV/dt. Assuming that volume is proportional to cell number, dV/dt can be used to find b by means of a logarithmic transformation of equation (6):

$$\log(dV/dt) = b \log V + C_2. \quad (9)$$

In Figure 9, a log-log plot of dV/dt versus V shows the data points lying in a reasonably straight line, implying that the slope, b, is constant during the period of observation. This can be confirmed, as in Figure 10, by inserting

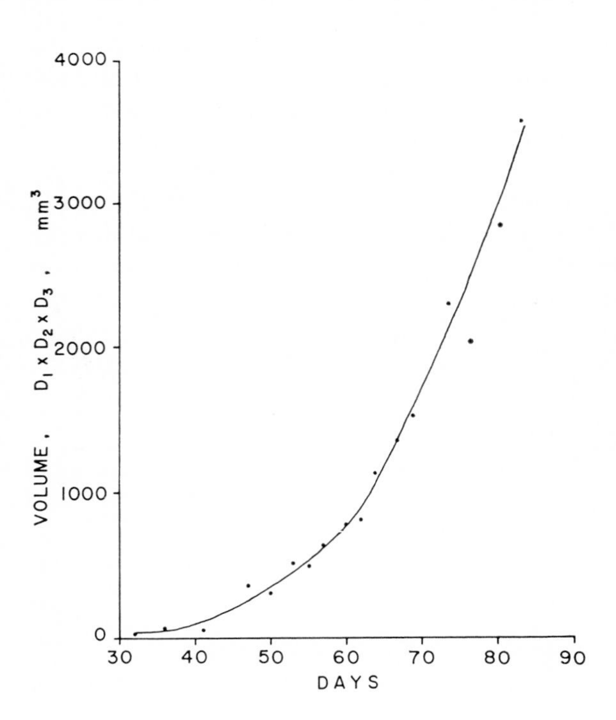

FIGURE 7. Relative tumor volume as a function of time. This C3H mammary tumor was transplanted subcutaneously into a C3H male on day zero. The growth curve is typical of both primary and transplanted C3H tumors. The smoothed line through the data points was used to determine dV/dt. Various transformations of these data are shown in Figures 8, 9, and 10.

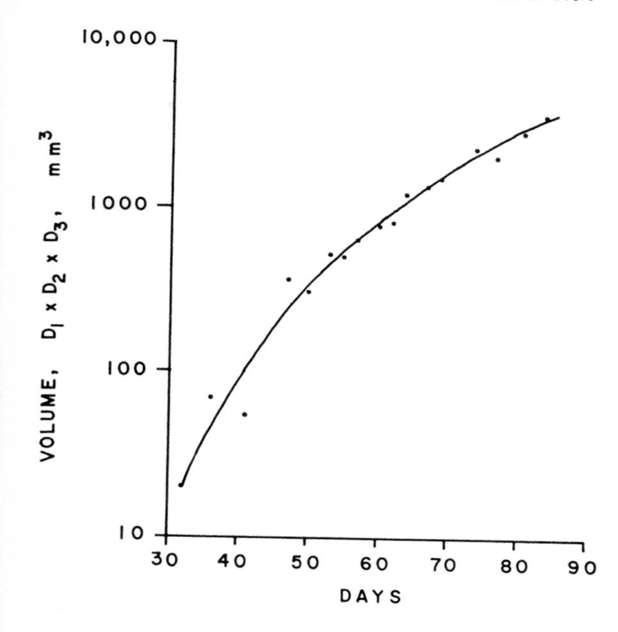

FIGURE 8. The log of relative tumor volume as a function of time. These are the same data as in Figure 7. The downward curve of the data points occurs in almost all C3H mammary tumors and is an indication that the tumors are not growing exponentially.

the measured value of b into equation (7) or (8) and observing the transformation of the original growth curve into a straight line.

Almost every C3H mammary tumor we have studied with this technique behaves as if b is constant throughout the interval when volume can be measured. A frequency distribution of the values of b for 92 tumors is shown in Figure 11. The data suggest a clustering of growth modes at b = two thirds, and a less pronounced cluster at b = 1.

This striking tendency for these mammary tumors to show the cube root of volume increasing as a linear function of time is very much like the growth pattern Mayneord described for Jensen's sarcoma in 1932. On the basis of the characteristic central necrosis of Jensen's sarcoma, Mayneord

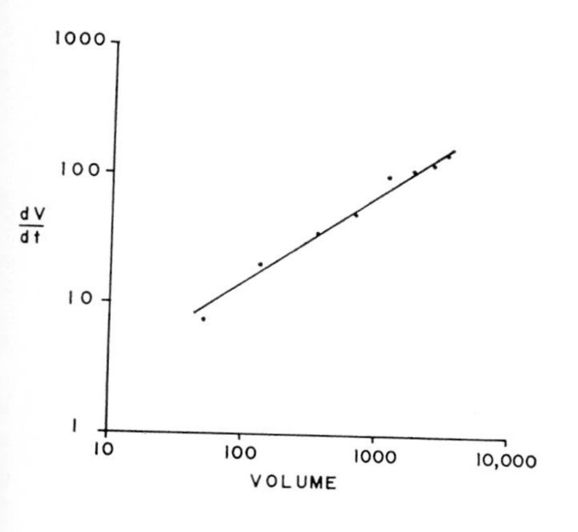

FIGURE 9. Log dV/dt as a function of log volume. Each data point was defined by a tangent to the linear plot in Figure 7. The points form a reasonably straight line on this plot, suggesting that dV/dt is proportional to V^b, where b is the slope of the line.

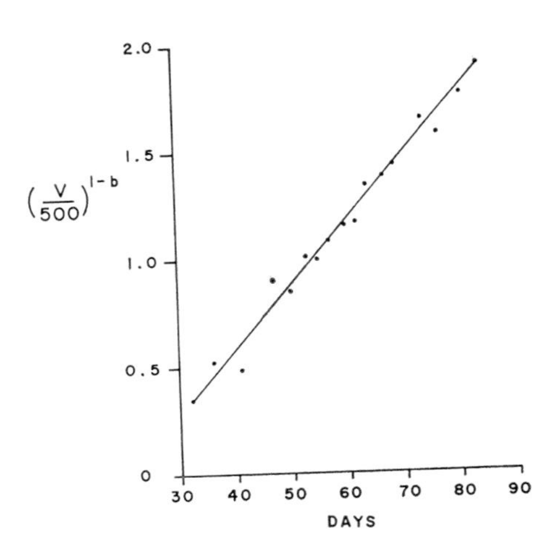

FIGURE 10. Normalized tumor volume raised to the 1 — b power and plotted as a function of time. The original data points are used in this graph and the b is taken from Figure 9. Dividing each volume by 500 mm^3 is a convenient device for comparing growth curves, and has no effect on the relative position of the transformed points. The curved growth pattern of Figure 7 has been transformed into a linear pattern by the choice of an appropriate b for this tumor; thus confirming that the tangent method is effective and that b is essentially constant during the 50 days over which this tumor was measured. This transformation has been very helpful in the analysis of experimental treatments which attempt to modify tumor growth (Mendelsohn, Dethlefsen, and Briddell, 1964).

constructed a model in which proliferating cells with a constant cycle time were localized to the viable outer rim of the tumor. When the rim was very thin, the model showed cube-root growth [as might be expected from equations (6) and (7), since the number of proliferating cells was then proportional to $N^{2/3}$]. Mayneord used these relationships to calculate the cycle time from the slopes of the growth curves. We hoped to follow Mayneord's example, but in attempting to apply his approach to the C3H mammary tumor, we were stopped by the evidence against a geometric equivalent of

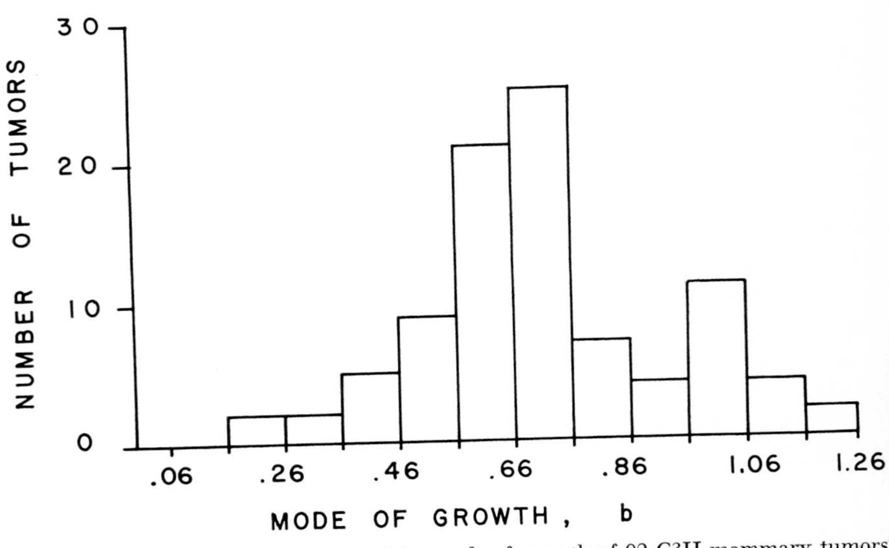

FIGURE 11. A frequency histogram of the mode of growth of 92 C3H mammary tumors. There is a wide range of b's, with a mode at values consistent with cube-root growth, and a second peak suggesting exponential growth.

a proliferating compartment: (1) the mammary tumors often show no central necrosis; (2) the evidence is strong that not all intact cells are proliferating; and (3) the distribution of proliferating cells is widespread throughout the tumor.

Returning to equation (6), the problem in the C3H tumors can be summarized by replacing N with V/v_c, where v_c is the mean volume of a single tumor cell:

$$\frac{dV}{dt} = \frac{wg\ v_c}{T_C}\left[\frac{V}{v_c}\right]^b. \tag{10}$$

The values of dV/dt, b, and V can be obtained from the growth curves, and estimates of cell volume can be made independently in a variety of ways. The correction term, w, is difficult to sort out since it is a function of b, V, v_c, and g; however, for b in the range of 0.7 or less, the correction is usually between 0.9 and 0.99 and can be taken as 1.0 for a first approximation. Finally, we are left with g and T_C undefined, and here the argument is forced into a dead end, since there are innumerable combinations of these two parameters which will fit any particular growth curve. The situation is much the same for exponential growth where cycle time and growth fraction contribute jointly to the growth constant and cannot be separated from the growth curve alone.

Although it would appear from this argument that cell cycle time cannot be extracted from growth curves without additional information about the tumor cells, we are at least in a position to test for compatibility between external growth and the various parameters of cell behavior already determined for the C3H mammary tumors. This can be approached directly by selecting those tumors in Figure 11 with a value for b in the range of 0.6 to 0.78. The 43 tumors in this category have an average b of 0.689, and an average dV/dt at a volume of 500 mm^3 of 60.17 mm^3/day (standard error of the mean, 7.1 per cent). Rearranging equation (10),

$$g = \frac{T_C\ (dV/dt)}{w\ v_c\left[\dfrac{V}{v_c}\right]^b}. \tag{11}$$

When $b = 0.689$, $T_c = 1.4$ days, $v_c = 1000\ \mu^3$ (a rough estimate of relative volume based on cell dimensions of $10 \times 10 \times 10\ \mu$), $V = 500\ mm^3$, dV/dt = 60.17 mm^3/day, and $w = 0.95$, g calculates to 90. Under these circumstances, the average growth fraction for tumors of this size is

$$GF = \frac{gN^b}{N} = 0.18. \tag{12}$$

Although slightly lower than the direct estimates of growth fraction, the similarity between these two totally different ways to measure growth fraction is very reassuring and suggests that this mathematical model is reasonably appropriate for the C3H mammary tumors.

Further work is in progress to evaluate the significance of b and the other parameters of the growth curve. Of particular interest to us is whether one can distinguish between the role of the host and the role of the tumor in terms of these parameters. Hopefully, the growth curve equations will eventually prove to be relevant in other tumor systems, both for the analysis of tumor growth and the quantitative assessment of therapeutic attempts to alter growth.

Summary and Conclusions

Returning to the two questions posed at the outset, the answer to the first appears to be that information about the cell cycle can be obtained from experimental tumors using a variety of laboratory techniques. With the possible exception of the growth fraction method, the approaches we have used require multiple samples of tumor over extended periods of time. These are complex procedures and are ill-suited for clinical application. Thus a partial answer to the second question is that these particular techniques have little or no applicability to the evaluation of the individual clinical neoplasm. Unfortunately, once one has accepted the concept of nonproliferating tumor cells, one is committed to the proposition that cell-cycle time cannot be estimated from growth curves, mitotic index determinations, or techniques such as colchicine blockade and accumulation of mitotic figures as a function of time. Perhaps new methods will be developed in the future, but the outlook at present is decidedly pessimistic for the analysis of the individual tumor.

In the case of the C3H mammary tumors, the success of the analysis was due in large measure to the conformity of behavior of proliferating cells from tumor to tumor. This came as a surprise to us, since we had assumed initially that primary tumors would have unique attributes both at the gross and cellular levels. We have been surprised in a similar way by the apparently uniform behavior of tumor cells in primary epidermoid cancers induced in the hamster cheek pouch (Reiskin and Mendelsohn, 1964). These two examples suggest the hypothesis that tumors of common origin have common cell cycles, and the results from the hamster study also indicate that the cell cycle in the tumor can be very different from the cell cycle in the tissue of origin. Speculating about the possible meaning of these relationships, perhaps the crucial difference between normal and malignant tissues is that the normal cells are subject to modulation of their cell cycles, whereas the tumor cells proliferate at a maximum rate determined by the degree of differentiation, the tissue of origin, or some other feature of the tumor type. Local and systemic restraints continue to operate on the tumor as a whole, determining the growth mode and the fraction of cells proliferating, but to the individual cell it is an all-or-nothing situation. The importance of the hypothesis in the present context is that it offers the hope that the underlying similarities between tumors of common origin can be the basis for accumulating a relevant body of kinetic data for different types of human tumors. When and if this day comes, we can look forward to a rewarding application of cellular radiation biology to the welfare of mankind.

ACKNOWLEDGMENTS

This investigation was supported by the Cancer Institute of the United States Public Health Service through Research Grant CA-03896 and Research Career Award K6-CA-18,540.

REFERENCES

Hoffman, J. G. 1949. Theory of the Mitotic Index and Its Application to Tissue Growth Measurement. *Bulletin of Mathematical Biophysics*, 11:139–144.

Johnson, H. A. 1961. Some Problems Associated with the Histological Study of Cell Proliferation Kinetics. *Cytologia*, 26:32–41.

Kisieleski, W. D., R. Baserga, and H. Lisco. 1961. Tritiated Thymidine and the Study of Tumors. *Atompraxis*, 7:81–86.

Koburg, E. 1963. "The Use of Grain Counts in the Study of Cell Proliferation," *Cell Proliferation*, L. F. Lamerton and R. J. M. Fry, Eds. London, England: Blackwell Scientific Publications. Pp. 62–76.

Mayneord, W. V. 1932. On a Law of Growth of Jensen's Rat Sarcoma. *American Journal of Cancer*, 16:841–846.

Mendelsohn, M. L. 1960. Autoradiographic Analysis of Cell Proliferation in Spontaneous Breast Cancer of C3H Mouse. II. Growth and Survival of Cells Labeled with Tritiated Thymidine. *Journal of the National Cancer Institute*, 25:485–500.

———. 1962a. Autoradiographic Analysis of Cell Proliferation in Spontaneous Breast Cancer of C3H Mouse. III. The Growth Fraction. *Journal of the National Cancer Institute*, 28:1015–1029.

———. 1962b. Chronic Infusion of Tritiated Thymidine into Mice with Tumors. *Science*, 135:213–215.

———. 1963. "Cell Proliferation and Tumor Growth," *Cell Proliferation*, L. F. Lamerton and R. J. M. Fry, Eds. London, England: Blackwell Scientific Publications. Pp. 190–210.

Mendelsohn, M. L., L. A. Dethlefsen, and J. D. Briddell. 1964. Transformation of Tumor Growth Curves. (Abstract) *Proceedings of the American Association for Cancer Research*, 5:43.

Mendelsohn, M. L., F. C. Dohan, Jr., and H. A. Moore, Jr. 1960. Autoradiographic Analysis of Cell Proliferation in Spontaneous Breast Cancer of C3H Mouse. I. Typical Cell Cycle and Timing of DNA Synthesis. *Journal of the National Cancer Institute*, 25:477–484.

Patt, H. M. 1963. Quantitative Aspects of Radiation Effects at the Tissue and Tumor Level. *The American Journal of Roentgenology, Radium Therapy and Nuclear Medicine*, 90:928–937.

Quastler, H., and F. G. Sherman. 1959. Cell Population Kinetics in the Intestinal Epithelium of the Mouse. *Experimental Cell Research*, 17:420–438.

Reiskin, A. B., and M. L. Mendelsohn. 1964. A Comparison of the Cell Cycle in Induced Carcinomas and Their Normal Counterpart. *Cancer Research*, 24:1131–1136.

Rubini, J. R., E. P. Cronkite, V. P. Bond, and T. M. Fliedner. 1960. Metabolism of H^3-Thymidine in Man. *Journal of Clinical Investigation*, 39:909–918.

Staroscik, R. N., W. H. Jenkins, and M. L. Mendelsohn. 1964. Availability of Tritiated Thymidine after Intravenous Administration. *Nature*, London, 202:456–458.

Wright, C. P. 1925. The Relative Duration of the Various Phases of Mitosis in Chick Fibroblasts Cultivated *in vitro*. *Journal of the Royal Microscopical Society*. Pp. 414–417.

Radiation Response of C3H Mouse Mammary Carcinoma Evaluated in Terms of Cellular Radiation Sensitivity

H. D. Suit, R. J. Shalek, and R. Wette

Departments of Radiology and Physics and Office of Research, The University of Texas M. D. Anderson Hospital and Tumor Institute, Houston, Texas

As a result of the series of advances made in cellular radiation biology over the recent decade, it is now appropriate to inquire of the experimentalist: Do the constituent cells of a solid tumor respond to irradiation on an individual cellular basis, or are there factors inherent in the relationship between the cells of a tumor and/or between the cell and the organism of which it is a part that modify that response? This may be restated as follows: Is the relationship between surviving fraction of cells of tumor tissue irradiated in vivo and radiation dose described by the same multihit survival curve that would be obtained if the cells were suspended individually in vitro at the time of irradiation? The multihit survival curve is described by the relationship: $S = 1 - (1 - e^{-D/D_{37}})^n$ (Puck and Marcus, 1956), where S = surviving fraction, D = dose, D_{37} = dose which reduces the surviving fraction in the exponential part of the curve by a factor of 0.37, and N = extrapolation number (Alper, Gillies, and Elkind, 1960). If, in fact, this relationship did obtain for cells constituting tissue in vivo, then the probability of a tumor lethal response to a specified single radiation dose could be predicted by knowing only the number of cells and their radiosensitivity (in terms of D_{37} and N) determined by in vitro studies on individual cells in suspension, provided that a single surviving cell would produce a recurrence. If so, the experimentalist should find that there is an orderly relationship between the number of cells in a tumor and the dose required to control half the tumors irradiated, *i.e.* the TCD_{50}. This relationship should be that shown in Figure 1, which is a plot of log tumor cell number against

$$\frac{TCD_{50}}{D_{37}} - \ln N + \ln \ln 2.$$

This paper presents an analysis of TCD_{50} (tumor control $dose_{50}$) data from experiments based on tumors varying in volume at the time of irradia-

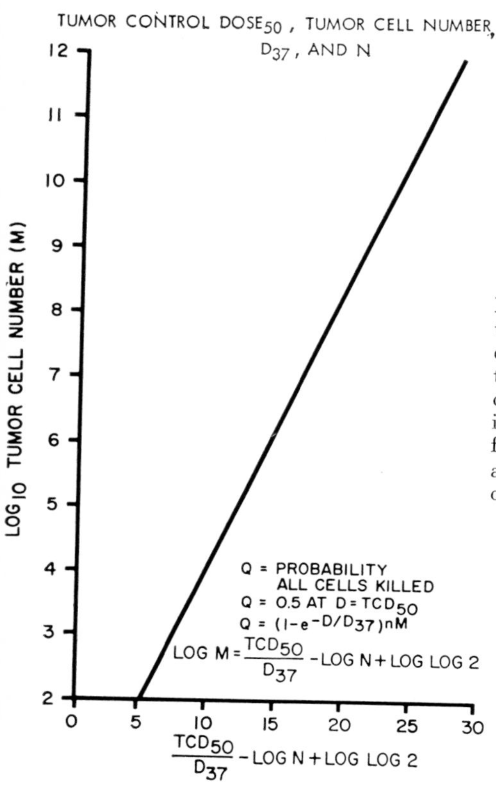

FIGURE 1. The curve describes the relationship between TCD_{50} (tumor control dose for infinite time periods for half of treated tumors) and number of viable cells in a tumor at the time of irradiation if these conditions obtain: (1) survival fraction of cells, $S = 1 - (1 - e^{-D/D_{37}})^N$, and (2) a recurrence always develops if one or more cells survive.

tion by a factor of more than 10^3. These experiments have been planned so that all radiations have been given as single doses, under conditions of local tissue anoxia, with a uniform distribution of radiation dose throughout the irradiated tumor, and with a negligible likelihood of an immunologic reaction by the host against the tumor.

Materials and Methods

Animal Tumor System

Spontaneous Mammary Carcinomas

Adult female mice of the inbred C3H and Strong A strains (mammary tumor agent positive) that carried a single spontaneous mammary carcinoma were supplied by the Texas Inbred Mouse Company, Houston, Texas, and the Roscoe B. Jackson Memorial Laboratories, Bar Harbor, Maine. A separate dose-response experiment was set up for spontaneous mammary carcinomas of each of the two strains of mice. These animals were maintained at a constant temperature and humidity in the animal facility of M. D. Anderson Hospital and Tumor Institute. Standard Purina pellets and water were supplied ad libitum; the animals were housed five per box. The occasional pregnant mouse was excluded from these studies. The diagnosis of mammary carcinoma in each of these animals was confirmed by histological study based on a needle biopsy. Details of animal care, histological studies, selection of animals for the study, and assignment to one of the radiation dose groups have been given previously (Suit and Shalek, 1963a).

Early Generation Isotransplants

Weanling female mice of the inbred C3H strain were supplied by the above listed sources. When the animals were approximately four months old, tumor transplants were made as first or early generation isotransplants into the outer portion of the ear or into the dermis of the flank region. An inoculum of one to two microliters containing 2.5 to 7.5×10^4 viable cells was injected into the tissue spaced between the cartilage plate and the skin of the ear, or directly into the dermis of the flank region. The details for preparation of the cell suspension and counting of "viable" cells have been described elsewhere (Suit and Shalek, 1963b). The tumor cell suspensions were prepared from either freshly excised tumors or from tumor tissue (first or second generation isotransplants) that had been stored in a frozen tissue bank. For the latter, tumor fragments had been suspended in McCoy's 5a medium supplemented with 10 per cent calf serum and 10 per cent glycerol, and then stored in sealed glass vials at − 69C.

Experimental Groups. Groups of 60 to 120 sequentially numbered animals were arbitrarily placed into one of the radiation dose-tumor response studies: radiation was given when the average tumor diameter reached 0.75, 1.0, 2.0, or 4.0 mm in the ear transplants or 3.0, 5.0, or 10.0 mm in the flank transplants. However, at the time of transplantation, animals within each dose response experiment were assigned to one of five radiation dose levels by use of a random number table. During the time that the increasing tumor volumes were approaching the size at which they were to be irradiated, tumors were measured three or more times per week. Thus, the tumors in any one dose response study were irradiated over a period of several days. The volume of tumor at the time of irradiation was computed according to the formula $V = (\pi/6) \times D_1 \times D_2 \times D_3$. Ear Tumors were measured by use of a stereomicroscope (× 10) fitted with a reticle. Vernier calipers were used for measurement of flank tumors.

Definition of Recurrence. All animals were examined following irradiation at least once weekly, and the presence and the size of residual or recurrent tumor were noted. Local recurrence was counted only if there was an increase of size of the residual tumor on two successive weeks, or if tumor reappeared in the irradiated area. Thus, an animal dying with a residual tumor mass which had shown no signs of increase in size was counted as a local control. The very occasional animal showing a marginal recurrence in the flank tumor groups was excluded from the study.

Production of Anoxia. A circular brass clamp was fitted across the base of the ear or the root of the skin flap containing the tumor and maintained for one minute prior to the initiation of the irradiation. As an additional precaution during irradiation of ear tumors, oxygen in the air surrounding the ear was displaced by a stream of nitrogen passing above and below the ear. The resultant O_2 concentration in the region of the ear was less than 1 per cent, as determined by measurements with a miniaturized Clark electrode.

Immunologic Status of the Isotransplanted Animals. In an attempt to virtually eliminate the likelihood of a weak immunologic reaction by the host against the isologous tumor, 400 r total-body irradiation were given 24 hours before transplantation in all instances, except where otherwise indicated.

X-Irradiation. Physical factors of radiation treatments were: 250 kv constant potential X rays; 7.8 mm Al HVL, no added filtration, 24 and 25.6 cm target tumor center distance. The radiations were delivered by two 250 kv X-ray units fixed to each other by a specially designed device so that the tumor and its supporting tissues were suspended in air at nearly midpoint between the two targets, and were thereby irradiated simultaneously by a pair of colinear opposed 250 kv X-ray beams. The dose rate in air at the position of the tumor center was 1,430 r/min. Details of the design of mouse holder device, dose distribution across the treatment field, dose distribution throughout the irradiated tumor, and measurements of the radiation output by ionization and chemical methods are given in an additional paper (see Nunnally, Worsnop, and Shalek, pages 531 to 535, this volume). Radiation doses as listed are the minimum tumor dose in rads and are estimated to have a standard deviation of less than $\pm$ 4 per cent due to errors from all causes. The ratio of maximum/minimum dose throughout a tumor did not exceed 1.03 for tumors up to 15 mm diameter. Figure 2 shows a treatment field localization film which illustrates a typical positioning in the X-ray beam of a mouse ear bearing a small isotransplant. Anesthesia for these animals was achieved by an intraperitoneal injection of 0.07 mg Nembutal per gram of mouse.

The animals in 12 of the dose-response experiments received 400 r total-body irradiation 24 hours before they were injected with the tumor cell suspension. Physical factors of these irradiations were: 250 kv half wave, 3 mm Cu HVL, 38.5 cm target to upper surface of animal distance, and 44 r/min in air at the midportion of the animal. During the irradiation, the mice were in a Lucite mouse holder, containing 12 wedge-shaped individual compartments. This holder was positioned on a rotating platform during the exposure in order to assure the delivery of the same dose to each mouse.

Statistics. For the estimation of the tumor control-dose relationship, especially for the TCD_{50}, at each time after treatment, use was made of the observation that in the dose ranges covering data points, this relationship could be described closely by the logistic log-dose response law: P(D) =

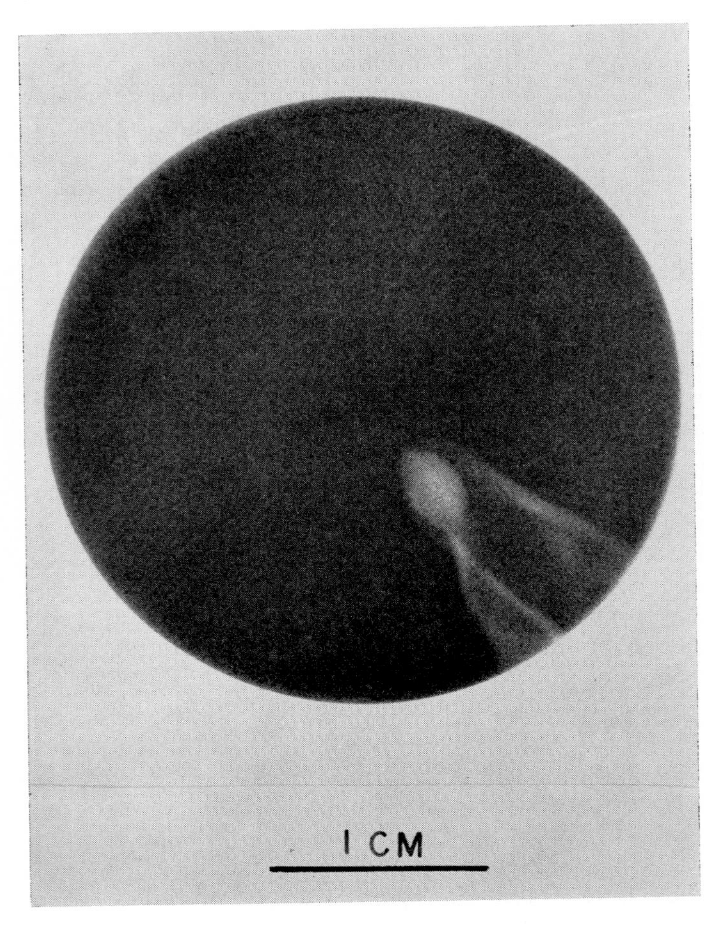

FIGURE 2. Treatment field localization film which shows a typical setup of a mouse ear bearing a small isotransplant. Radiation dose distribution across the area of the field used for tumor irradiation was uniform to within ± 1 per cent. The line is 1 cm in length.

$[1 + \exp(\alpha + \beta \cdot \log D)]^{-1}$, where P is the expected proportion of temporary controls, D the dose, $\exp(x) = e^x$, and α and β are intrinsic parameters to be estimated. The (logit) transformation $Y_i = \log \frac{P(D_i)}{1 - P(D_i)} = \alpha + \beta \cdot \log D_i$ then gives a linear regression of the so-called logit Y on the logarithm of dose D; with intersection α and slope β. Estimation of the two parameters α and β gives the $TCD_{50} = \exp(-\alpha/\beta)$, and was achieved by the method of maximum likelihood under the usual assumption of a binomial distribution of the number of temporary controls around the expected logistic.

No adjustments were made to account for the loss of animals due to accidental death prior to tumor recurrence. The evaluation was based on the number of animals alive without recurrence, with exclusion of the animals lost prior to evaluation. This procedure is valid under the assumption that the proportion of temporary control is the same for both lost and remaining animals (the latter comprising the recurrences and the ones alive without recurrence), and admissible at least from a heuristic point of view.

The estimated TCD_{50} — time after treatment relationship exhibited asymptotic behavior for increasing observation time in the more complete experiments. A tentative extrapolation for this asymptote, which would correspond to the TCD_{50} for "ultimate control" (*i.e.* cure), was done by eye. An extrapolation by numerical or statistical methods was not attempted, particularly in view of the fact that consecutive TCD_{50} estimates are not independent, being based on the same (though decreasing in number) animals.

Results

Transplant Take Rates and Tumor Growth Rates

Radiation dose-response curves using local control or failure of recurrence as the end point have been determined for 13 experiments employing isotransplants of the C3H mammary carcinoma, and three experiments based on spontaneous mammary carcinomas of the mouse (C3H strain—two tumor volume groups; Strong A—one tumor volume group). This represents a total of 1,155 isotransplanted tumors and 361 animals with spontaneous mammary carcinomas. The isotransplants were derived from two spontaneous carcinomas. Those that developed from the first were "slow" growing and from the second "fast" growing, *i.e.* tumor volume doubling times of eight days and three days, respectively, over the tumor volume range of 0.6 to 10 mm^3. These tumors transplanted into the ear reached a volume of 4 mm^3 at a median time of 92 and 21.5 days, respectively, following transplantation (Figure 3).

Table 1 gives a detailed account of the tumor transplant take rate, indicating the transplantation site, transplantation generation number, the source of the tumor tissue, and inoculum volume, as well as the number of "viable" cells in the inoculum. Inspection of the data reveals that where fresh tumor tissue was employed as a source for the tumor cell suspension, the transplant take rate at 90 days following transplantation was 100 per cent (743/744). However, where the tumor tissue had been stored in a frozen tissue bank for three to six months, the transplant take rate was reduced. The total transplant take rate for two experiments, in which frozen tissue was used to prepare the cell suspension, was 156 out of 251 (62 per cent) ear transplants and 255 out of 291 (88 per cent) flank transplants were successful. Although the inocula in these isotransplants into the mouse ear were 0.7 to 1 μl and contained only 2 to 3 $\times$ 10^4 "viable" cells, the low transplant take rate indicates that our count of "viable" cells was falsely high in cell suspension prepared from frozen tissue.

In no instance was spontaneous regression of tumor observed. However, in several instances a decrease in size of the recurrent tumor was observed which had resulted from partial cannibalization of the tumor by other animals in the box. Cause of the occasional decrease in volume of the

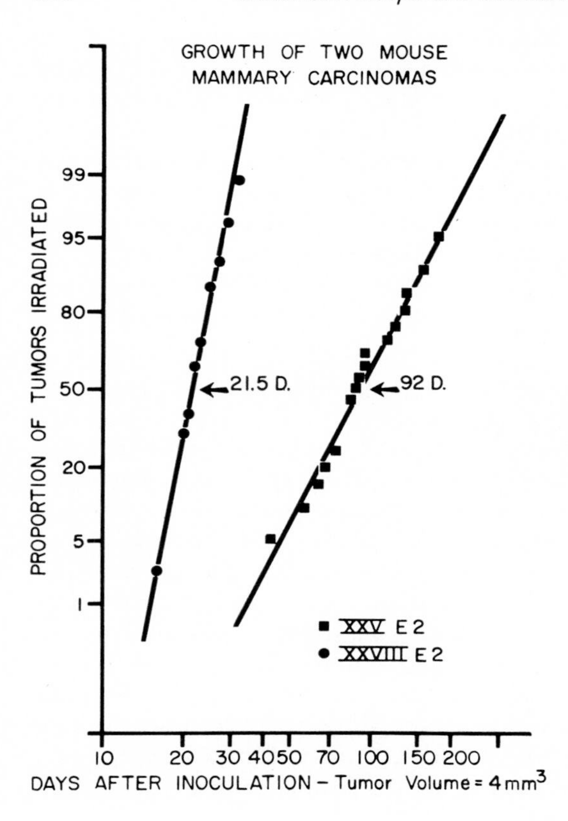

FIGURE 3. Time after isotransplantation required for two mouse mammary carcinoma lines to reach a volume of 4 mm³. Median times were 92 and 21.5 days.

TABLE 1

Tumor Transplant Take Rate

Experiment number	Transplant site	Transplant generation number	Tumor tissue source	Inoculum volume (μ1)	Inoculum no. viable cells	Tumor incidence following transplantation 90 days	180 days
XXV	Ear	2	Frozen	1	20,000	73/156	96/156 (62%)
	Flank	2	Frozen	2	60,000	90/113	102/113 (90%)
XXVII	Ear	1	Fresh	2	75,000	119/119	(100%)
	Flank	1	Fresh	2	75,000	55/55	(100%)
XXVIII	Ear	2	Fresh	2	50,000	424/424	(100%)
	Flank	2	Fresh	2	90,000	146/147	146/147 (99%)
XXVIII	Ear	3	Frozen	0.7	30,000	55/95	60/95 (63%)
	Flank	3	Frozen	2.0	80,000	152/178	153/178 (89%)

TOTAL $\frac{1,155}{1,287} = 90\%$

ar transplant was indicated by the ulcerated area in the tumor and the loss f substance of the ear. This did not present any real difficulty in the simple es or no evaluation of recurrence, but it did make futile the attempts to ıeasure growth rates of the recurrent tumor. In the rare instance of an ear eing lost entirely from this cause during the stage of acute radiation re- ction, the animals were discarded from the study. In earlier studies with ımor transplants growing in the ear (Suit and Shalek, 1963b) partial annibalization of the ear tumor was not observed. No explanation for this ontrast is offered. The only obvious difference between the two series of xperiments is that the radiation doses are higher in the present series.

'umor Control Dose$_{50}$

The results in terms of TCD_{50} for tumors of various volumes growing ı the ear or in the flank and irradiated under conditions of local tissue noxia are illustrated in Figures 4, 5, and 6 and are listed in Table 2. As ıdicated, the TCD_{50} studies have been completed on tumors whose me- ian volume ranged from 0.16 mm^3 to 1,000 mm^3. The 95 per cent confi- ence limits around the median volume of each experiment fell within $\pm$ 0 to 20 per cent of the indicated volume.

A plot of log-TCD_{50} against days after irradiation has given, in each f the experimental groups, a curved line which approaches an asymp- ɔte at 80 to 150 days. Local recurrences have been noted in every dose re- ponse study following day 120, except for the Strong A spontaneous mam- ıary carcinoma study, in which only nine animals that had received a dose ≤6,600 rads survived for more than that time. Recurrences in a few animals

TABLE 2

Tumor Control Dose$_{50}$ Results

XPERIMENT NUMBER	TYPE OF TUMOR	SITE OF TUMOR	MEDIAN TUMOR VOLUME (mm^3)	TCD_{50} $\approx$ 180 DAYS	CALCULATED SURVIVAL FRACTION
XVE	Transplant	Ear	0.2	4,200	5×10^{-6}
			5	4,750	2×10^{-7}
			31	5,250	3.2×10^{-8}
XVF	Transplant	Flank	70	5,100	1.4×10^{-8}
XVIIE	Transplant	Ear	4	5,200	2.3×10^{-7}
			30	5,825	3.3×10^{-8}
XVIIIE	Transplant	Ear	0.16	4,250	6.2×10^{-6}
			0.7	4,800	1.4×10^{-6}
			4.0*	5,600	2.5×10^{-7}
			33	6,100	3.0×10^{-8}
XVIIIF	Transplant	Flank	8	4,900	1.2×10^{-7}
			70	5,900	1.4×10^{-8}
			400	6,350	2.5×10^{-9}
V C_3H	Spont.	Mammary gland	300	6,200	3.3×10^{-9}
			1000	6,600	1×10^{-9}
V Strong A	Spont.	Mammary gland	300	6,200	3.3×10^{-9}

* These animals received no total-body irradiation prior to transplantation.

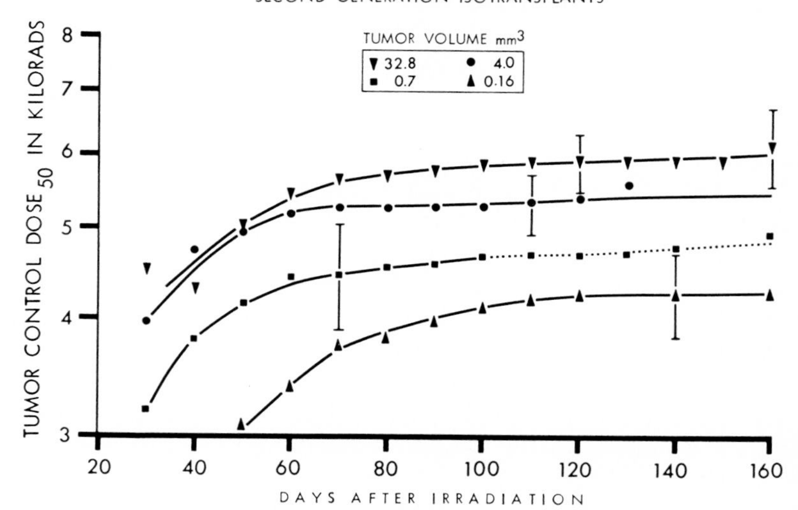

FIGURE 4. TCD_{50} and time after irradiation for ear isotransplants of four different tumor volumes at the time of treatment.

have been observed as late as 200 days following irradiation. In each ex periment there was observed an increase in TCD_{50} with increase in tumo volume for a given transplant site. However, between experimental group there was overlapping of results. As an example, the 4 mm^3 ear tumors o Exp. XXVII and XXVIII had a higher TCD_{50} value than did the 8 mm flank tumor of XXVIII; these are first and second generation isotransplant of the same mammary carcinoma.

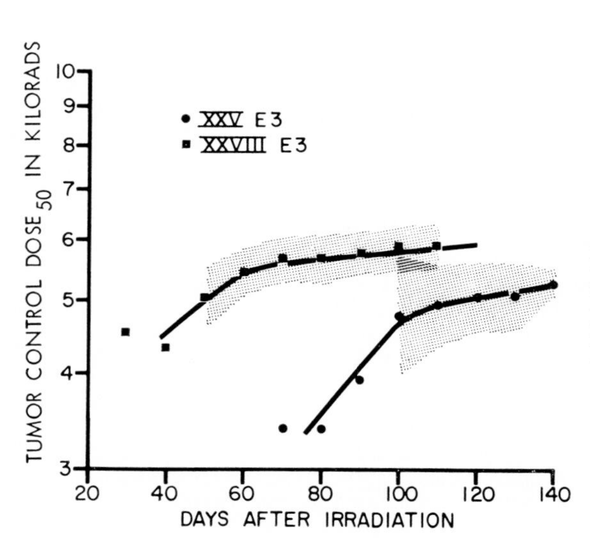

FIGURE 5. Relationship of com puted TCD_{50} and time after ir radiation for transplants grow ing in the ear. Tumor volum doubling time: three days fo XXVIII and eight days fo XXV.

This presentation of results in terms of TCD_{50} against time has the merit of indicating the recurrence time distribution. Figure 5 compares the relationship between TCD_{50} and time for a "fast" and a "slow" growing tumor (tumor volume doubling time of three and eight days, respectively). It is noted that the curves would indicate that the TCD_{50} of the "slow" tumor was less than that for the "fast" tumor at 80 days. However, the curves tend to approach the same TCD_{50} at 180 days; this results from the greater incidence of late appearing recurrences in the "slow" growing tumors. Unfortunately, only a small proportion of these animals have survived past the 180 day point, so that information on the probability of a recurrence at quite late time periods will not be obtained. Statistical methods are being developed to analyze the distribution of recurrences in time in order to compare observed results with those predicted on the basis of various models of tumor cell proliferation.

Figure 6 shows that the plot of log-TCD_{50} values against time for spontaneous mammary carcinomas of the C3H and the Strong A strains of mice yielded nearly identical curves. The tumors for both dose-response curve studies were 300 mm^3 at time of treatment. The shaded area around the curve for the C3H tumors covers the 95 per cent confidence limits around the individual points in the curve. From this curve the TCD_{50} value at 180 days is taken at 6,200 rads and is based on the response of 171 irradiated

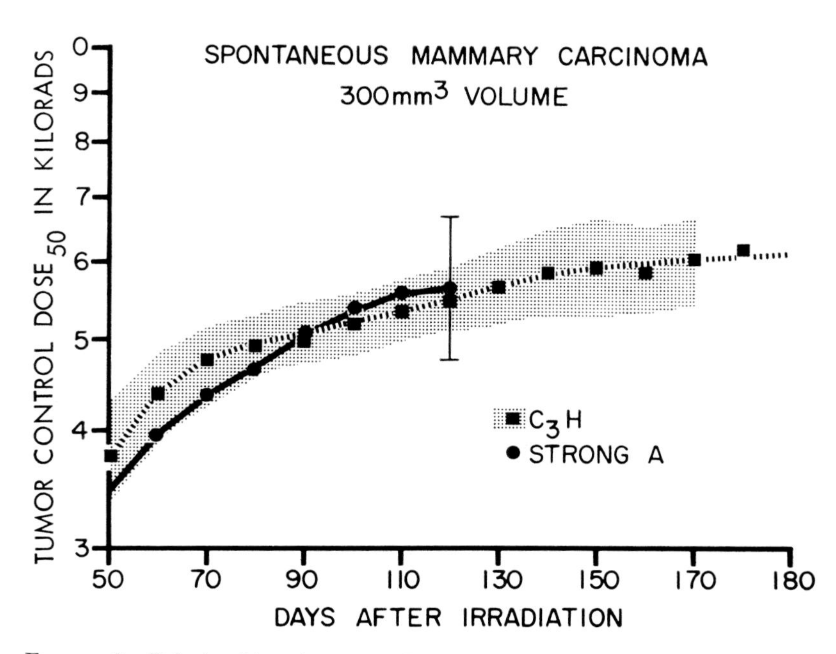

FIGURE 6. Relationship of computed TCD_{50} and time after irradiation for spontaneous mammary carcinomas of the C3H and Strong A strains of mice. Median tumor volume at time of irradiation was 300 mm^3 for both experiments.

tumors. By contrast, the Strong A data are derived from 77 tumors and the confidence limits are correspondingly wider. In these two studies there have been 15 animals that have survived recurrence-free for more than 200 days, eight for more than 250 days, and four for more than 300 days. No recurrences have been detected after the two-hundredth posttreatment day.

As pointed out in the introduction, the analysis of data of greatest interest to this study was to determine the relationship between tumor cell number (tumor volume) and TCD_{50}. A plot of log tumor volume against TCD_{50} for 16 dose-response experiments is shown in Figure 7. Because of the density of the points, confidence limits around each point have not been shown. The right ordinate indicates an assumed $\log_{10}$ tumor cell number (M). The C3H mammary carcinoma cell is 9 μ in diameter (ranging from 8 to 11 μ), when measured as individual cells in a cell suspension; a sphere of 9 μ diameter would be $\approx$ 400 μ^3. We have assumed that approximately 40 per cent of the tumor volume is composed of viable tumor cells and that the remaining 60 per cent consists of nonviable cells, connective and vascular tissue, and of necrotic or cystic areas. These mouse tumors are therefore considered as having one viable tumor cell per 1,000 μ^3 of tumor volume, and that this value is independent of tumor volume. Thus, each 1 mm^3 of tumor would contain $\approx 10^6$ viable cells.

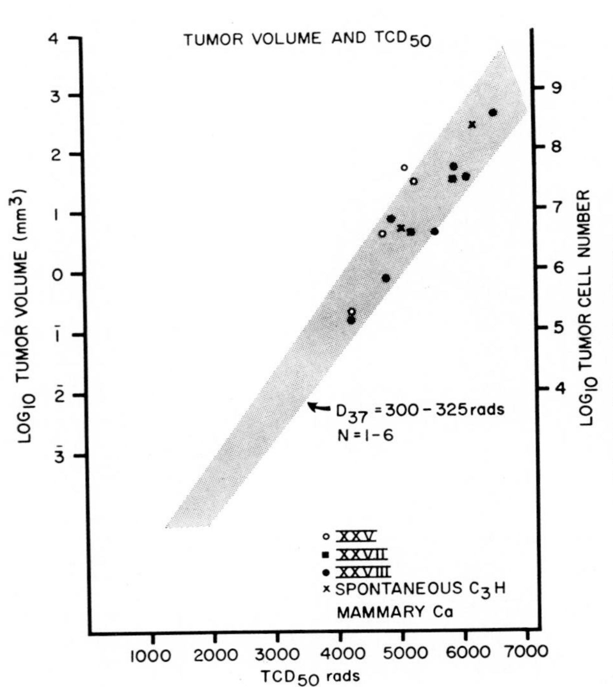

FIGURE 7. A plot of $\log_{10}$ tumor volume against TCD_{50} in rads. Shaded area enclosed by curves which were calculated on these assumptions: (1) one viable cell per 1,000 μ^3 tumor volume; (2) one surviving cell produces an observed recurrence; and (3) $TCD_{50} = D_{37}$ (ln M + ln − ln ln2).

Provided the multihit survival curve describes the relationship between adiation dose and surviving fraction of tumor cells, and that a recurrence vill develop when the survival fraction corresponds to one or more tumor ells, the relationship between TCD_{50}, D_{37}, N, and M (tumor cell number) s developed below:

$$S = 1 - p$$
$$S = 1 - (1 - e^{-D/D_{37}})^N$$
probability of killing a single cell is $(1 - e^{-D/D_{37}})^N$
$$Qp = \text{probability that all cells are killed}$$
$$Qp = (1 - e^{-D/D_{37}})^{N \cdot M}$$
$$= 0.5 \text{ where } D = TCD_{50}$$
$$-\ln Qp = N \cdot M \cdot [-\ln(1 - e^{-D/D_{37}})]$$
$$-\ln(1 - e^{-D/D_{37}}) \approx e^{-D/D_{37}},$$
where $D/D_{37} >> 1$, *i.e.* > 3
$$\approx N \cdot M \cdot e^{-D/D_{37}}$$
$$\ln(-\ln Qp) \approx \ln N + \ln M - D/D_{37}$$
$$\ln M \approx D/D_{37} - \ln N + \ln(-\ln Qp)$$
$$\ln M \approx TCD_{50}/D_{37} - \ln N + \ln\ln 2$$
(where $D = TCD_{50}$; $Qp = 0.5$).

Employing this derived relationship between M, TCD_{50}, D_{37}, and N, the haded area in Figure 7 defines the limits on the TCD_{50} values for tumors f various volumes if the tumor cell D_{37} varied between 300 and 325 rads nd N varied between one and six. Fifteen of the 16 points from these exeriments fall within the shaded area. Three points are shown on the graph vith the spontaneous tumor marker: (1) the C3H mouse mammary carinoma at 300 mm^3 volume. The point for the Strong A spontaneous mamnary carcinoma would be superimposed on the C3H point; (2) autotranslants of the C3H tumor (5 mm^3); this point is taken from a separate study Suit and Caton, 1964); and (3) the C3H mouse mammary carcinoma at ,000 mm^3 volume.

The data in Figure 7 have been replotted in Figure 8 to show the relaionship between tumor cell number and TCD_{50} in terms of a calculated suriving fraction of irradiated tumor cells and TCD_{50}. In this figure, the right rdinate indicates the $\log_{10}$ tumor volume, but increasing from above downvards. The survival fraction S when dose equals TCD_{50} has been computed ccording to the relationship $\ln S = -\ln M + \ln\ln 2$. Of course the points re observed again to fall within the shaded area described for $D_{37} = 300$ to 25 rads and N = 1–6. Also shown in Figure 8 is the point indicating the TCD_{50} obtained for 4.6 mm^3 ear tumors irradiated in normal isologous nimals (no whole-body irradiation prior to receiving the tumor transplant) s reported earlier (Suit and Shalek, 1963b). That this value is quite similar o those for isotransplants in whole-body irradiated animals and to the one alue for autotransplants indicates that immunologic factors have not afected measurably the tumor lethal responses in this animal tumor system.

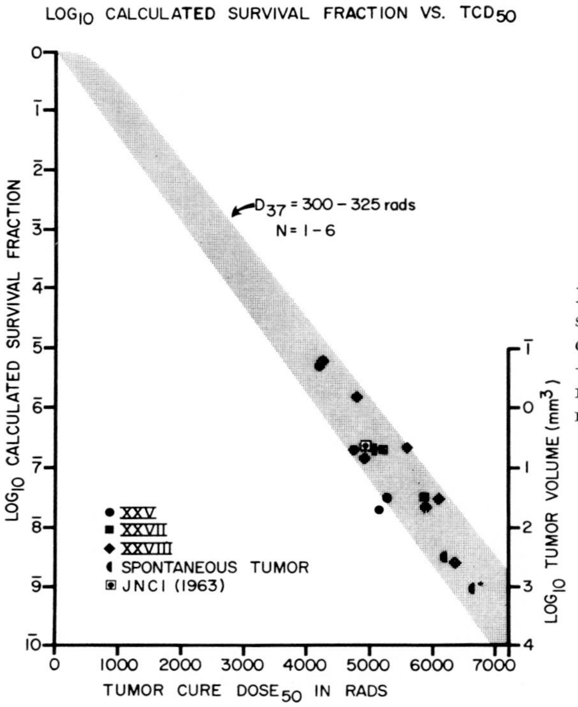

FIGURE 8. A plot of calculate survival fraction (S) of tumo cells against TCD^{50}. $\ln S = -\ln M + \ln\ln 2$. Measured tu mor volume is indicated on th right ordinate.

DISCUSSION

A measure of radiation sensitivity of special interest to tumor radio biology is the cell lethal response to radiation. The extensive body of dat on cellular radiation biology that has appeared following the now classi report of Puck and Marcus (1956) has established that, with few exceptions the lethal response of mammalian cells to radiation can be described b multihit survival curves.

Of particular relevance to this report are the experiments which hav shown that, for several cell lines, the D_{37} values derived from in vivo an in vitro irradiation studies did not differ. Results on three cell lines whic have been irradiated in vivo and in vitro in the same laboratory are liste in Table 3. It is pertinent to these considerations to point out that the D_3 has been estimated for the cells of three normal tissues by methods whic did not disturb the integrity of the tissue (see Table 4). The D_{37} for mous bone marrow stem cells was estimated in vivo by indirect methods as 11 rads (Gurney, Lajtha, and Oliver, 1962). This value is not considered to b different from the measured value of 87 rads (in vitro irradiation [Sch neider and Whitmore, 1963]) or 81 rads (in vivo and in vitro irradiatio [Till, 1963]). Results from the two experiments using plant tissues give D_3 estimates that are within or close to the usual value for mammalian cells.

TABLE 3

*Radiation Sensitivity of Mammalian Cells Irradiated in vivo and in vitro**

Cell line	In vitro irradiation D_{37} (250 kv rads)	In vivo irradiation D_{37}	Reference
Murine lymphosarcoma	95	110	Powers and Tolmach, 1964
Murine bone marrow	95 × 0.85** = 81	81	Till, 1963
Murine leukemia	115 × 0.85 = 98	98	Bush and Bruce, 1963

* Cell viability assayed by in vivo methods.
** RBE factor of 0.85: Co^{60} rads × 0.85 = 250 kv rads.

TABLE 4

Radiation Sensitivity of Cells of Intact Tissue

Tissue	D_{37} (250 kv rads)	N	Reference
Murine bone marrow stem cells	110	1.2	Gurney, Lajtha, and Oliver, 1962
Vicia faba	40–48	2–4	Hall, Lajtha, and Oliver, 1962
Tradescantia meristem	149	1.6	Davies, 1963

Our experiments were designed to yield data for the analysis of the lethal response of tumor cells to irradiation, in which the tissue was not manipulated after irradiation, and the viability of surviving cells was assayed by their ability to proliferate and produce a recurrence in the irradiated tissue. In order to minimize variations of cellular D_{37} throughout the tumors, all irradiations were performed under conditions of local tissue anoxia. Only the spontaneous tumor or early generation isotransplants were employed in these studies.

The TCD_{50} values obtained under these conditions were in the range that would be predicted if the multihit survival curve described the relationship between cell lethal response and radiation dose and $D_{37} = 300$ to 325 rads and $N = 1$ to 6. These results were therefore consistent with the proposal that cells of this tumor respond randomly and on an individual cellular basis, and that a single surviving cell will proliferate to produce a recurrence. An estimate of the radiosensitivity for the anoxic mammary carcinoma cell as $D_{37} \approx 310$ and $N \approx 2$ to 4 is near the middle of the range of the reported D_{37} values for seven lines of mammalian cells irradiated under anoxic conditions either in vivo or in vitro, as listed in Table 5. The results range from 212 rads for bone marrow to 350 rads for the $L\text{-}P_{59}$ cell line and the Ehrlich ascites carcinoma cell.

We are aware that the multihit survival curve is only descriptive of the data, and that other models of variable biological plausibility can be proposed which would also be consistent with these data.

TABLE 5

Radiation Sensitivity of Anoxic Mammalian Cells

CELL LINE	EXPERIMENTAL CONDITIONS (VIABILITY ASSAY)	N	D_{37} (250 KV RADS)	REFERENCE
Murine leukemia	in vivo	2	313*†	Hewitt and Wilson, 1959
Murine leukemia	in vivo	1.6	310†	Berry and Andrews, 1961
Murine lymphosarcoma	in vivo		260	Powers and Tolmach, 1964
Murine bone marrow	in vivo	1.5	212†	Till, 1963
Human liver cell	in vitro	16	263	Dewey, 1960
Ehrlich ascites	in vivo	10	353	Hornsey and Silini, 1961
L-P_{59} cell	in vitro	3	350	Humphrey, Dewey, and Cork, 1963

* Co^{60}: roentgen to rad conversion factor of 0.97.
† RBE factor of 0.85: Co^{60} rads × 0.85 = 250 kv rads.

A point of interest in an analysis of tumor lethal dose is a consideration of the maximum number of "surviving cells" that would permit local cure or no recurrence, and whether this maximum number is a function of tumor cell number. As the latter increases, so also do the TCD_{50} and the proportion of lethally irradiated cells to surviving cells. Cells in the surviving fraction following a radiation dose equivalent to the TCD_{50} for a tumor of 10^9 cells will have accumulated more "sublethal" damage than the cells of the surviving fraction in a tumor of 10^5 cells that had also received a radiation dose equivalent to its TCD_{50}. In addition, a single surviving cell in a tumor of 10^9 cells might be in a more vulnerable position with respect to availability of nutrient or there may be a greater "toxic" effect from the larger number of lethally irradiated cells than in the instance of the small tumor.

The experiments of Révész (1958) are relevant to this last point. Studying early transplant generation of the mouse mammary carcinoma, he found that large numbers of lethally irradiated tumor cells injected with a small number of viable cells increased the transplant take rate. In a complex series of experiments there was no suggestion of a "toxic" effect by the radiation-killed cells on the viable ones; the effect, where demonstrated, was in the opposite direction.

Sinclair (1964) has found in his in vitro studies on a hamster cell line that the clones produced by the cells that constitute the surviving fraction after doses of some 1,500 rads are often composed of cells which are small in size, have a markedly prolonged mean cell generation time, and have an increased probability of daughter cell death. Should similar changes occur in vivo, the cells of the surviving fraction of tumor cells irradiated in vivo to doses of TCD_{50} to TCD_{90} might display patterns of proliferation kinetics that differed from those of the cells in the unirradiated tumor. If this indeed occurred, the time distribution of recurrences at these high doses would be quite delayed when compared to those following lower doses. Our analyses of recurrence time distribution have not been completed. However, the data do show that following the TCD_{50} or greater dose, recurrences have been unexpectedly delayed and usually have a distinctly slower growth rate (tumor volume doubling time) than the unirradiated tumor.

Summary

Cellular radiosensitivity of the C3H mouse mammary carcinoma cell has been investigated by analysis of 16 radiation dose-response experiments using as the end point the permanent local control of tumor. Pertinent aspects of the experimental design were: all radiations were given as single doses and under conditions of local tissue anoxia; the distribution of radiation dose throughout the tumor was uniform, *i.e.* $\pm$ 4 per cent; and the likelihood of an immunologic reaction by the host against the tumor negligible. The tumors employed in these studies have been in the range of 0.16 mm^3 to 1,000 mm^3 at the time of irradiation; these were either spontaneous carcinomas or early generation isotransplants. Radiation response (proportion of local cure at each dose level for each tumor volume used) has been assessed at 10-day intervals from day 30 to $\approx$ 200 after treatment. These results have been used to compute a TCD_{50} (tumor dose that controls half of the tumors) at each time interval. The plot of TCD_{50} against time after irradiation showed that the TCD_{50} approached an asymptote at 80 to 150 days. A plot of $\log_{10}$ tumor volume, at the time of irradiation, against TCD_{50} yielded a scatter of points within the area that would be enclosed by curves predicted on these considerations: (1) survival fraction of tumor cells $S = 1 - (1 - e^{-D/D_{37}})^N$, (2) a recurrence always develops if one or more cells survive, and (3) radiosensitivity of the anoxic mouse mammary carcinoma cell: $D_{37} = 300$ to 325 rads and $N = 1$ to 6. These data are interpreted as being consistent with the proposal that the cells of this tumor tissue respond to radiation randomly and on the basis of individual cellular radiosensitivity; that is, the results do not indicate a tissue effect on cellular radiosensitivity, tumor bed effect on tumor curability, or nonspecific host-tumor effect. They also indicate in this animal tumor system that cells which survive in a reproductive sense also have a high probability of surviving metabolically long enough to proliferate and produce a recurrence of tumor.

ACKNOWLEDGMENTS

This investigation was supported in part by Grant C-5047 from the National Cancer Institute, National Institutes of Health, United States Public Health Service. We are pleased to acknowledge the excellent technical assistance of Mary Eby, Donna Dixon, Terrance Boone, and Walter Bennett.

REFERENCES

Alper, T., N. E. Gillies, and M. M. Elkind. 1960. The Sigmoid Survival Curve in Radiobiology. *Nature*, London, 186:1062–1063.

Berry, R. J., and J. R. Andrews. 1961. Quantitative Studies of Radiation Effects on Cell

Reproductive Capacity in a Mammalian Transplantable Tumor System *in vivo* *Annals of the New York Academy of Sciences*, 95:1001–1008.

Bush, R. S., and W. R. Bruce. 1963. The Radiosensitivity of Murine Lymphoma Cells *in vivo* as Determined by a Splenic Colony Method. (Abstract) *Radiation Research* 19:217–218.

Davies, D. R. 1963. The Relationship Between Radiation-Induced Chromosome Damage and Loss of Reproductive Integrity. (Abstract) *Radiation Research*, 19:185–186.

Dewey, D. L. 1960. Effect of Oxygen and Nitric Oxide on the Radiosensitivity of Human Cells in Tissue Culture. *Nature*, London, 186:780–782.

Gurney, C. W., L. G. Lajtha, and R. Oliver. 1962. A Method for Investigation of Stem-Cell Kinetics. *British Journal of Haematology*, 8:461–466.

Hall, E. J., L. G. Lajtha, and R. Oliver. 1962. X-Ray Dose-Response Relationship for Reproductive Integrity of *Vicia faba*. *British Journal of Radiology*, 35:388–397.

Hewitt, H. B., and C. W. Wilson. 1959. The Effect of Tissue Oxygen Tension on the Radiosensitivity of Leukaemia Cells Irradiated *in situ* in the Livers of Leukaemic Mice *The British Journal of Cancer*, 13:675–684.

———. 1961. Survival Curves for Tumor Cells Irradiated *in vivo*. *Annals of the New York Academy of Sciences*, 95:818–827.

Hornsey, S., and G. Silini. 1961. Studies on Cell-Survival of Irradiated Ehrlich Ascites Tumour. II. Dose-Effect Curves for X-Ray and Neutron Irradiations. *International Journal of Radiation Biology, and Related Studies in Physics, Chemistry and Medicine*, 4:135–141.

Humphrey, R. M., W. C. Dewey, and A. Cork. 1963. Effect of Oxygen in Mammalian Cells Sensitized to Radiation by Incorporation of 5-Bromodeoxyuridine into the DNA. *Nature*, London, 198:268–269.

Powers, W. E., and L. J. Tolmach. 1964. Demonstration of an Anoxic Tumor Cell Component Population by *in vivo* Assay of Cell Survival. *Radiology*. (in press.)

Puck, T. T., and P. I. Marcus. 1956. Action of X-Rays on Mammalian Cells. *Journal of Experimental Medicine*, 103:653–666.

Révész, L. 1958. Effect of Lethally Damaged Tumor Cells Upon the Development of Admixed Viable Cells. *Journal of the National Cancer Institute*, 20:1157–1186.

Schneider, D. E., and G. F. Whitmore. 1963. Comparative Effects of Neutrons and X-Rays on Mammalian Cells. *Radiation Research*, 18:286–306.

Sinclair, W. K. 1964. Colony Size and Heritable Damage Among Survivors of X-Irradiated Mammalian Cells Grown in Culture. *Radiation Research*. (in press.)

Suit, H. D., and C. Caton. 1964. Autotransplants of the C3H Mouse Mammary Carcinoma: Transplant Take Rate, Growth Rate, and Response to X-Irradiation. (in preparation.)

Suit, H. D., and R. J. Shalek. 1963a. Response of Spontaneous Mammary Carcinoma of the C_3H Mouse to X-Irradiation Given Under Conditions of Local Tissue Anoxia. *Journal of the National Cancer Institute*, 31:497–509.

———. 1963b. Response of Anoxic C_3H Mouse Mammary Carcinoma Isotransplants (1–25 mm^3) to X-Irradiation. *Journal of the National Cancer Institute*, 31:479–495.

Till, J. E. 1963. Quantitative Aspects of Radiation Lethality at the Cellular Level. *The American Journal of Roentgenology, Radium Therapy and Nuclear Medicine*, 90: 917–927.

Dose Determination for X-Irradiation of Mouse Tumors

JAMES NUNNALLY, RALPH WORSNOP, AND ROBERT J. SHALEK
Department of Physics,
The University of Texas M. D. Anderson Hospital and Tumor Institute,
Houston, Texas

For the analysis of the data presented in the foregoing paper to have alidity, it was important that the distribution of radiation dose throughout he tumor be as uniform as possible and that the minimum tumor dose be nown within close limits. To accomplish this result, the collimated beams f two Westinghouse 250-kvp constant potential X-ray machines of half-alue layer 0.5 mm copper (60 kev effective energy) were directed so that hey were collinear and opposite to each other.

The irradiation device is shown alone in Figure 1 and in position be-ween the X-ray machines for simultaneous irradiations in Figure 2. The nouse holder shown in Figure 3 consists of a brass ring clamp of the same iameter as the X-ray field, mounted on a brass plate. When the holder is lid into the collimating device, between the tracks provided, the ring is ocked in line with the X-ray beams. The ring is wrapped externally with .0 mm of lead to reduce the 90° scatter from the brass ring and tumor, hus reducing the dose to points at 1 cm. outside the beam to about 0.1 per ent of that in the useful beam. The clamp, besides fixing the irradiation osition of the tumor, restricts the blood supply and thus produces anoxia n the tumor. In addition, plastic cylinders with the machine end closed are ocated above and below the mouse so that a stream of nitrogen gas may rovide nearly anoxic conditions at the skin surface.

The primary dosimetry has been done with 250 r Victoreen chambers tilizing calibration factors derived from standardizations by the National ureau of Standards. A chamber was exposed for various periods of time in rder to permit correction of differences between the time of X-ray exposure nd the time indicated on the timer. During calibration, the ring clamp vhich holds the tumor in position was simulated. The tumors did not always ccupy the center of the field; however, measurements indicated that the lose rate at a point 0.5 cm inside the periphery was only 0.7 per cent less

FIGURE 1. Irradiation device for small mouse tumors. From the top, the parts, are: primary lead collimator, secondary lead collimator, gas control cup, tracks for holding clamp (Figure 3), secondary lead collimator, gas control cup, primary lead collimator. The total length of the device is 19.6 cm.

than that at the center of the field. Figure 4 is a presentation of isodose distributions across the treatment field in air, obtained by optical densitometer measurements of Translite film exposed at the irradiation position. The nonsymmetry is due primarily to the fact that the X-ray target in one of the machines is slightly off center. However, the 99 per cent curve comes very close to one edge of the field; fortunately this is the edge from which tumors extend. The nominal exposure dose rate from both machines operating simultaneously was 1,470 roentgens per minute.

The profile of dose through the tumor, as shown in Figure 5, was derived from calculations based on Victoreen exposure measurements from

FIGURE 2. Irradiation device located between two 250-kvp constant potential X-ray machines. The beams are collinear and in opposition.

FIGURE 3. Mouse holder. A lead-lined ring is utilized to clamp the tumor in the irradiation position and to produce anoxia in the tumor.

each machine, the backscatter factors (*British Journal of Radiology*, Supplement No. 10, 1961) corrected for the variations in backscatter with thickness of tissue (Quimby and Laurence, 1940) and the depth dose values (*British Journal of Radiology*, Supplement No. 10, 1961). The conversion

MOUSE TUMOR IRRADIATOR
ISODOSE CURVES OBTAINED FROM PHOTOGRAPHIC FILMS
DIAMETER: 2.85 cm

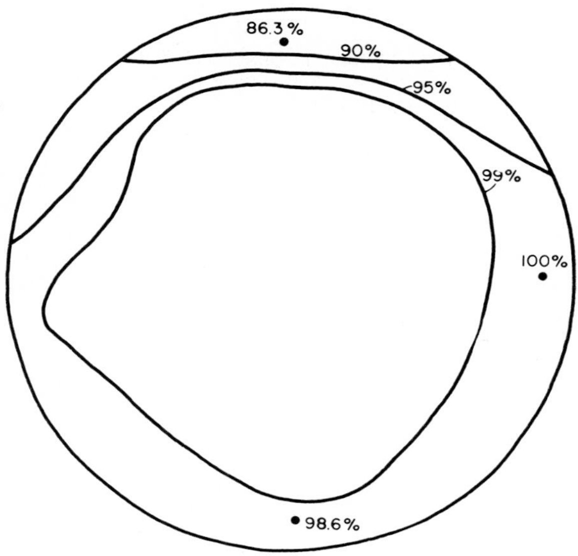

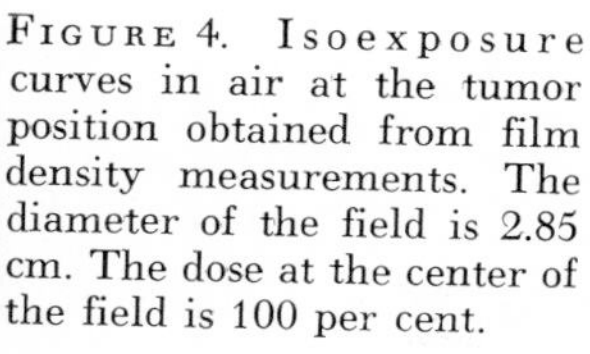

FIGURE 4. Isoexposure curves in air at the tumor position obtained from film density measurements. The diameter of the field is 2.85 cm. The dose at the center of the field is 100 per cent.

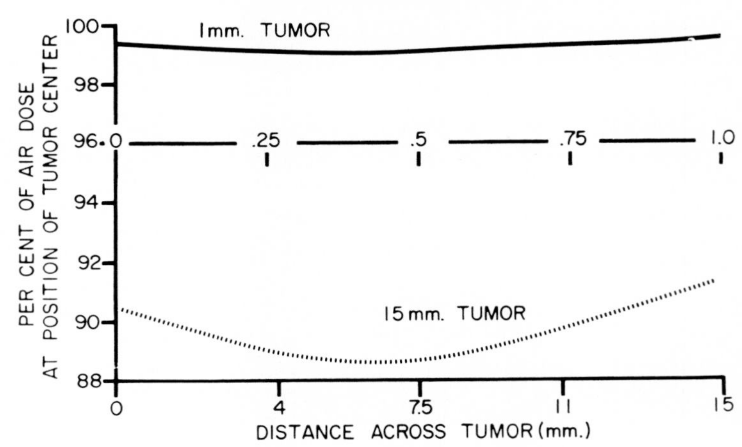

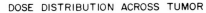

FIGURE 5. Calculated relative dose distribution through the tumor on a line parallel to the X-ray beams. For calculation a right circular cylinder with a diameter and length of 1 mm or 15 mm is situated at the tumor position with its principal axis coincident with the target-target line. The minimum tumor dose does not occur at the center of the tumor because the outputs of the machines differ and the distances to the targets differ.

to rads in muscle was taken as 0.929 rads/r (U. S. National Bureau o Standards, 1963). For these calculations the tumor was considered to be a right circular cylinder with the length equal to the diameter and the princi ple axis collinear with the X-ray beam. The focal-center distance wit respect to the upper and lower machines was 23.8 cm and 23.5 cm, re spectively. In Figure 6, the variation of maximum to minimum tumor dos with tumor size is shown. For large tumors (15 mm) the maximum dos

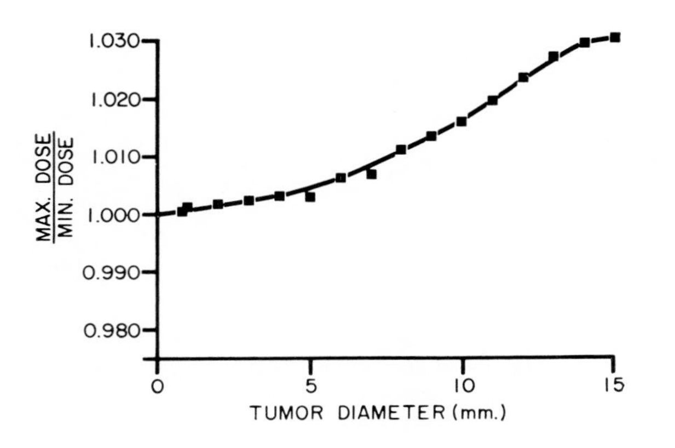

FIGURE 6. The ratio of max imum tumor dose to mini mum tumor dose for tumor of various sizes calculated b the method of Figure 5.

vas only about 3 per cent larger than the minimum dose, and the differ-
nce between the maximum and minimum dose was less for smaller tumors.

The above method of measurement with the Victoreen r-meter and
ssociated calculations were compared to measurements with the Fricke
:hemical dosimeter (0.8 N H_2SO_4, 1 mM $FeSO_4$, 1 mM NaCl) utilizing a
Teflon cup, 1 cm in diameter and 1 cm in length. In calculating the aver-
ige dose received by the chemical dosimeter, the following factors were
mployed (Shalek, Sinclair, and Calkins, 1962):

Extinction coefficient of ferrous sulfate dosimeter—
2177 1 $mole^{-1}$ cm^{-1} at 25C.

G = 14.9 molecules Fe^{+++} produced per 100 ev absorbed.

Ratio of energy absorption coefficients in muscle to that in
0.8 N H_2SO_4 = 0.951

The average dose measured by the chemical dosimeter was 4 per cent
iigher than the average dose calculated by the ionization method.

Tumor doses are given as the minimum in the tumor and are estimated
o have a standard deviation of about 5 per cent in individual exposures due
o errors from all causes.

ACKNOWLEDGMENTS

This investigation was supported in part by United States Public Health
ervice Research Grant CA 06294 from the National Cancer Institute.

REFERENCES

ritish Journal of Radiology, Supplement No. 10. 1961. *Depth Dose Tables for Use in Radiotherapy* (A Survey Prepared by the Scientific Sub-Committee of the Hospital Physicists' Association). London, England: British Institute of Radiology, 96 pp.

uimby, E. H., and G. C. Laurence. 1940. Radiological Society of North America Standardization Committee, Technical Bulletin No. 1. *Radiology*, 35:138–159.

halek, R. J., W. K. Sinclair, and J. C. Calkins. 1962. The Relative Biological Effectiveness of 22-Mevp X-Rays, Cobalt-60 Gamma Rays, and 200-Kvcp X-Rays. II. The Use of Ferrous Sulfate Dosimeter for X-Ray and Gamma-Ray Beams. *Radiation Research*, 16:344–351.

J. S. National Bureau of Standards. 1963. *Clinical Dosimetry* (U. S. National Bureau of Standards Handbook No. 87). Washington, D. C., 61 pp.

DISCUSSION

Dr. Reimut Wette, The University of Texas M. D. Anderson Hospital and Tumor nstitute, Houston, Texas: If we assume that we have considerable variation of generation me, or growth rates, among the cells within a tumor, and if we assume a multihit or orresponding dose-response law (in the simplest case, and exponential response law), then we irradiate a mass of cells the response law for tumor survival will no more be a ultihit. In fact, it would exhibit decreasing efficiency with increasing dose as compared the multihit. You showed the distribution of estimated b's (modes of growth). Could ot it be possible that if you assume that the mode of growth is constant for all tumors, that e observed distribution is due to estimation errors rather than a true variation of the b's mong tumors?

Dr. Mortimer Mendelsohn, University of Pennsylvania, Philadelphia, Pennsylvania: Vith regard to your first statement, are you also assuming that there is a variation in nsitivity of the cells in relation to their position in the proliferative cycle?

Dr. Wette: Yes. Since you have a variable generation time, I think that you can safely assume that the sensitivity of your cell varies with time, as we have seen today and yesterday. Then the probability that you hit a certain sensitivity with a single dose is different for different generation times.

Dr. Mendelsohn: Given these assumptions, I would agree that you would probably get a survival curve such as you described. With regard to your second point—that the C3H mammary tumors all might have the same mode of growth, b, and that the variation we are observing may be due entirely to measuring error—I think this is very unlikely. Obviously there is uncertainty in the way we measure b, but the enormous range of measured values, their correlation with the shape of the growth curves, and their apparent reproducibility when estimated by different observers (including an IBM 7040 computer programmed for us by Mrs. J. Prewitt) all lead me to conclude that the differences in b are real.

Chairman Warren K. Sinclair, Argonne National Laboratory, Argonne, Illinois: I assume that you have irradiated some of these tumors. Can you say anything about the effect of exposure on generation time?

Dr. Mendelsohn: We have not as yet studied the kinetics of irradiated tumors. In fact, it is only in the last 3 weeks in getting ready for this meeting that we learned we could say anything worthwhile about the kinetics of unirradiated tumors. Experiments with X rays will be started in the near future, but this is going to be a difficult and tedious job.

Chairman Sinclair: Yes, I realize that but I think this is very important; one of the biggest steps we have to take is from the in vitro work that we were hearing about this morning, to in vivo responses, and I think that however difficult this is, it is something that must be pursued. Dr. Suit, if I might summarize, the net result of your work is that you have in tumors a D_{37} which corresponds to that of anoxic cells in vitro and that you must give appropriate doses in order to cure it.

Dr. Herman Suit, The University of Texas M. D. Anderson Hospital and Tumor Institute, Houston, Texas: What I would say would be that these data are consistent with a conventional D_{37} anoxic value and that they are also consistent with the proposal that a single surviving cell will produce a recurrence.

Dr. Robert Kallman, Stanford University, Palo Alto, California: Dr. Suit, have you looked for any correlations between radiation treatments and the occurrence of metastases, distant metastases of the treated tumors, particularly the one treated *in situ* in the flank?

Dr. Suit: No detailed study has been made of this. However, we have observed, after doses of the order of TCD_{50} and higher, 15 animals for more than 200 days and 5 for more than 300 days after irradiation without apparent metastases. These tumors were originally confirmed by histological diagnosis. Our control animals have all died within 125 days from the time of assignment to a control group. Part of these were of course death due to the local growth of the tumor, but many of those did have demonstrated metastases.

Dr. Arthur Cole, The University of Texas M. D. Anderson Hospital and Tumor Institute, Houston, Texas: Do your tumors grow as Dr. Mendelsohn's tumors grow? Does the volume increase with the cube of the time?

Dr. Suit: No. The growth curves for the isotransplanted tumors are straight lines on a log-linear plot over the volume range of 0.5 to 50 mm^3. The growth points usually fit nicely on a straight line. For the spontaneous tumors, the majority of the tumors also show a growth curve as a straight line over the range of 100 to 1,000 mm^3. We have had several of them that have gone up another decade with the points exactly on a straight line. That these points usually fall on a straight line over the limited volume range of 1 to 2 decades does not mean that the growth rate of the tumor is constant for the entire range of 8 to 10 decades.

Dr. Anna Goldfeder, New York University, New York, New York: In reference to Dr. Mendelsohn's presentation, it is the only paper available in the literature which deals with the use of intact tumors growing in the animal host to be used in experiments with tritiated thymidine. I have carried out similar experiments. I have a test system consisting of two types of tumors, an epithelial type which is similar to Dr. Mendelsohn's but is growing in mice of a different strain. The other is a spindle cell type rapidly growing in the mice of the same inbred strain as the epithelial tumor. Figure 1 shows the curve from which the division cycle of the epithelial tumor cells was constructed. I noticed something which is rather puzzling to me and I would appreciate an explanation of this problem by the experts who are present. I would draw particular attention to the synthesis (S) time

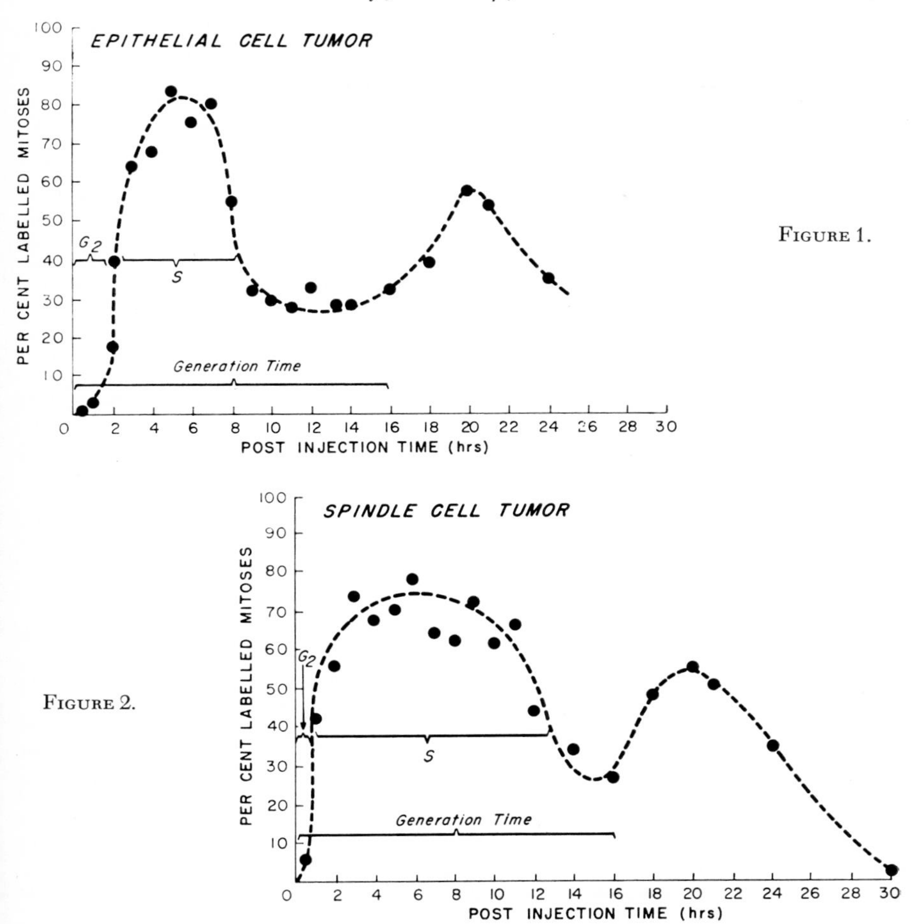

FIGURE 1.

FIGURE 2.

which is about 6 hours regarding the epithelial tumor. Figure 2 shows the division cycle of the spindle cell type tumor. Note that S is about 12 hours. The spindle cell type tumor is more rapidly growing. The question is how to explain this discrepancy. The spindle cell type tumor grows about twice as fast as the epithelial tumor. Why is S twice as long as for that of the epithelial tumor? I would like to offer an explanation and ask if I am right.

The spindle cell tumor has about 60% tetraploids mixed with octaploids. Is there a possibility that the cell which needs to synthesize DNA for 4 or 8 daughter cells needs more time than a cell which has to synthesize DNA only for 2 daughter cells?

As I indicated previously, the spindle cell type tumor is fast growing. It doubles its size in a much shorter time than the epithelial tumor. I have counted the labeled nuclei of the spindle cell and epithelial cell tumors at ½ hour after the injection of label and found that the spindle cell tumor contained about 28% of labeled nuclei and the epithelial tumor contained about 13% of labeled nuclei, which is about one half. Since the spindle cell tumor contains about 50% more labeled nuclei at about ½ hour after injection of the label, this indicates that this tumor possesses about 50% more of potentially dividing cells or stem cells, and this might explain why this tumor grows more rapidly than the epithelial tumor regardless of the long synthesis time.

Dr. Mendelsohn: Dr. Goldfeder, if the cells of one of your tumors are spending a longer time in DNA synthesis, you would expect them to show a higher incidence of labeled cells. The tumor may be growing faster because it has a larger pool of proliferating cells, but I think that you will need better evidence to show this.

Dr. Goldfeder: If I have no labeled cells, you expect that the tumor will grow?

Dr. Mendelsohn: The longer time spent in DNA synthesis would give you a higher fraction of labeled cells without there necessarily being any difference in the size of the proliferative pool.

Dr. Goldfeder: And what if the mitotic index is double?

Dr. Mendelsohn: Well, all these things point in the same direction and certainly are encouraging. However, our experience with mitotic index is that it is a very difficult parameter to interpret, again because of the duration that is involved. We have run into situations where similar cell systems show variations of as much as four times in the duration of visible mitosis; this, of course, will distort the relationship between the mitotic index and cell cycle time enormously.

Dr. Goldfeder: How would you explain the growth-speed of the tumor in this case? It would seem that more potential dividing cells must be present.

Dr. Mendelsohn: The best estimate of generation time, I would have thought taking a quick look at your data, was the distance between the double waves you have for each of your tumors.

Dr. Goldfeder: No.

Dr. Mendelsohn: And these looked about the same. They were something like 15 hours?

Dr. Goldfeder: About, yes.

Dr. Mendelsohn: So that if one tumor is growing much faster than the other, I do not think you can blame it on generation time. You are going to have to think in terms of growth fraction or the survival of cells.

Dr. Goldfeder: The G_2 was 2½ hours for the slow growing tumor, and for the faster growing was one hour. It seems once DNA is synthesized, the cells divide rapidly in the fast growing tumor.

Chairman Sinclair: I do not think that ploidy *per se* necessarily requires twice the synthesis time. I am sure many other people have the same thing as we in this respect: we have, for example, two sublines of the hamster, one of which is a relatively pure diploid and the other a rather pure tetraploid; both sublines double in cell number in exactly the same time and also have the same length of DNA synthetic period.

Dr. Bradford N. Craver, E. R. Squibb & Sons, New Brunswick, New Jersey: Theoretically, mitotic poisons should enhance the susceptibility of an organism's cells to the effect of X rays or γ rays. Several such poisons are available. The classical example is, of course, colchicine. Less well known and probably less toxic would be griseofulvin which Paget and Walpole demonstrated some years ago would produce mitotic arrest in animals (I believe in the stage of metaphase). Fortunately the doses employed vastly exceeded those that have to be attained in the clinical treatment of dermatophytic infections.

What proportion of an organ's cells can be left in mitotic arrest without serious toxic or even lethal effects? I appreciate that even if the suggested experiment has been performed or were to be performed, this proportion might be so low that the results of the experiment would be equivocal.

Has this approach been employed in the treatment of human beings with rapidly growing cancers? With a rapidly proliferating neoplasm, it might be possible to leave a sufficiently high proportion of the cells in mitotic arrest to make this approach to therapy useful.

Dr. Henry S. Kaplan, Stanford University, Palo Alto, California: I expect to touch on this in my talk (see pages 584 to 595, this volume), and perhaps we could defer the further discussion of this interesting set of questions until that time.

The Integrity of Cytoplasmic Ultrastructures: A Factor in Cellular Radiosensitivity

ANNA GOLDFEDER

Cancer and Radiobiological Research Laboratory, Department of Hospitals, City of New York, and Department of Biology, New York University, New York, New York

The existing difference in cellular radiosensitivity is one of the baffling problems in the field of radiobiology which remains to be elucidated. The variation in response of various tissue types to ionizing irradiation was noted by the pioneer investigators shortly after the discovery of X rays. The actively dividing and the least differentiated cells proved to be the most radiosensitive. However, there are cells which are not actively dividing but are very radiosensitive, e.g. oöcytes, lymphocytes, mammalian spermatogonia, certain cells of the small intestines, and others. Furthermore, there exists a significant difference in radiosensitivity not only between various somatic cell types, but also between cells of the same classification. For example, small lymphocytes are more radiosensitive than are large lymphocytes; epithelial cells of the small intestines are more radiosensitive than the epithelial cells of the kidneys.

My personal interest is mainly focused on unraveling the factors responsible in differential cellular radiosensitivity. This interest evolved from my earliest experiments in which it was demonstrated that when a mixed cell population was exposed in vitro to ionizing radiation (X rays or radium), the lymphocytes, leukocytes, macrophages, and fibroblasts were destroyed by gradually increased doses of irradiation, whereas the epithelial cells of the kidneys continued to proliferate.

The results of subsequent experiments demonstrating a difference in radiosensitivity between two analogous mammary tumors, *i.e.* tumors of the same histological classification, potentiated the interest in shedding light on the inherent properties of the cell which might be responsible for differential cellular radiosensitivity. Such information may also serve to elucidate some basic mechanism(s) involved in radiation-induced cellular injury. It was therefore tempting to undertake investigations by means of modern techniques in the hope of providing information which would shed light on the following baffling questions: (1) Why do cells differ in their response to ionizing radiation? (2) Where is the primary site of cellular injury caused by irradiation? (3) What is the mechanism(s) leading to cell death?

With these questions in mind, we have undertaken investigations concerning the detection of a possible relationship between cellular structure, function, and radiosensitivity.

The detection of morphologic changes is important because they are usually either the results of functional changes or are accompanied by them. In our present studies, the structural and functional parameters are closely related as criteria.

Whereas previous investigations were concerned with changes induced by ionizing radiation in the nuclear material, the present studies focus the main attention on the changes taking place in the cytoplasmic constituents.

The modern techniques, such as electron microscopy which permit the visualization of cellular ultrastructures and ultracentrifugation, which facilitates the isolation and separation of some of the cytoplasmic components for testing their function were employed.

Two types of malignant mouse tumors, a slowly growing epithelial tumor and a rapidly growing spindle-cell type constituted the basic test material for these studies. Both tumors are of the same genetic origin, and both are propagated in isologous parent hosts of an inbred DBA/212 strain of mice. Thus, this material offers an ideal model system for studying inherent properties of two different cell types in which a possible influence of heterologous host factors on these properties are eliminated. Structural properties of cells from lymph nodes of normal, nonirradiated and of whole-body irradiated mice have been studied electron microscopically for comparative purposes. The observations gathered so far on this experimental material are briefly summarized and discussed.

Endogenous Cytoplasmic Ultrastructures

The principal cytoplasmic components, namely mitochondria, Golgi apparatus, centrioles, membranes and vesicles of the endoplasmic reticulum, and ribonucleoprotein (RNP) particles, were noted in the cytoplasm of both types of tumors as well as in the cells of the lymph nodes. Although these ultrastructures were similar in appearance, differences in their quantity and structural integrity were noted. Specifically, the mitochondria of the epithelial tumor cells (Figure 1) are more numerous and contain more internal membranes (cristae) than the cells of the spindle-cell tumor (Figure 2). Further, the vesicles of the spindle-cell tumor appear more dilated, forming cisternae. The RNP particles of the spindle-cell tumor are also fewer as compared to those of the epithelial tumor. (The significance of these observed differences regarding cellular radiosensitivity will be discussed later.)

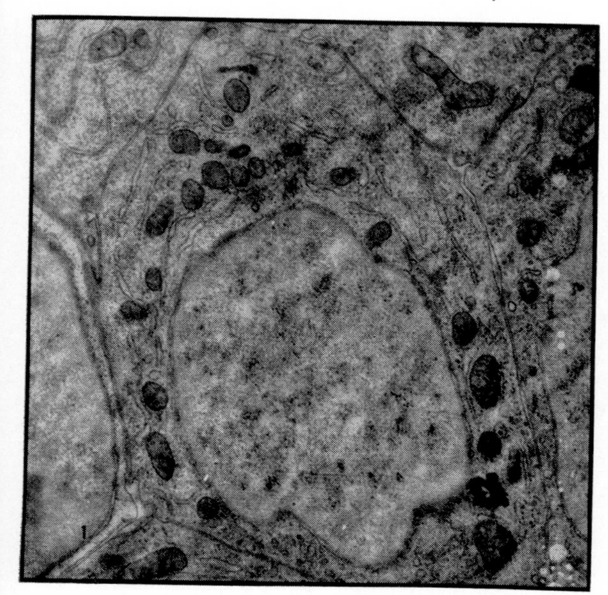

FIGURE 1. Three adjacent cells of epithelial tumor. Note the cell in the center containing a significant number of mitochondria filled with cristae, vesicles, membranes, and ribonucleoprotein particles (RNP). Note also the double nuclear membrane and nuclear pores. Reduced from × 20,000

The inguinal lymph nodes of normal mice consist mainly of lymphocytes and plasma cells. The cytoplasm of the lymphocytes was poorly differentiated, consisting of few mitochondria filled with cristae, a few vesicles, and RNP particles. A typical example is seen in Figure 3. Plasma cells were identified by containing an array of paired membranes to which ribonucleoprotein particles are attached; mitochondria are sparcely distributed. Figure 4 exemplifies such a cell.

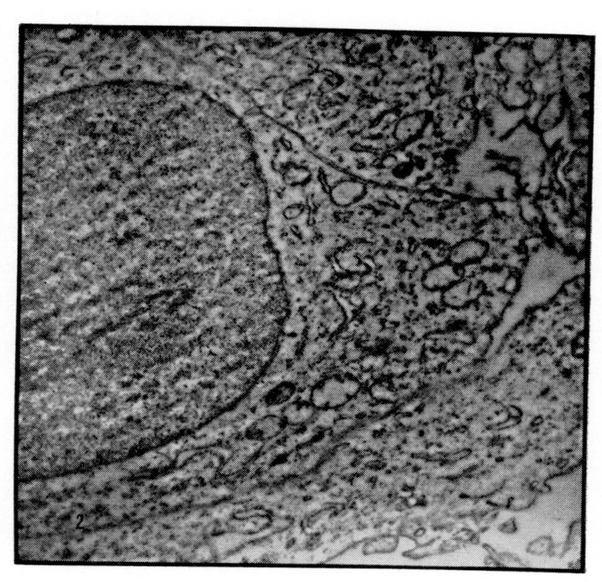

FIGURE 2. Three adjacent cells of the spindle-cell tumor. Note the mitochondria with few cristae, the vesicles are dilated forming cisternae, RNP particles, double nuclear membrane, and nuclear pores. Reduced from × 22,000

Effects of X-Irradiation on the Cytoplasmic Ultrastructures

The alterations which took place in the morphology of the cytoplasmic organelles following X-irradiation can best be seen in the accompaning electron micrographs. For brevity, only a few examples are presented. Swelling of mitochondria was a general occurrence in irradiated cells. This phenomenon can readily be seen in electron micrograph Figure 5 in which is

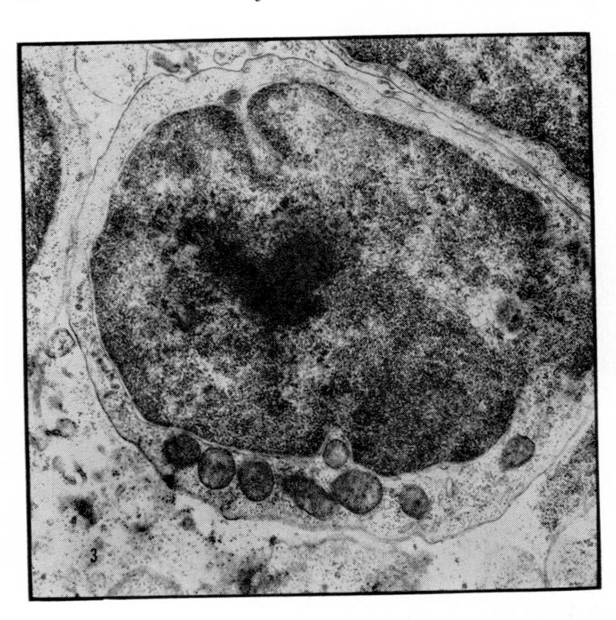

FIGURE 3. Lymphocyte. Note the narrow brim of cytoplasm, the relatively few mitochondria filled with cristae, and fine granules presenting RNP particles. Reduced from × 26,800

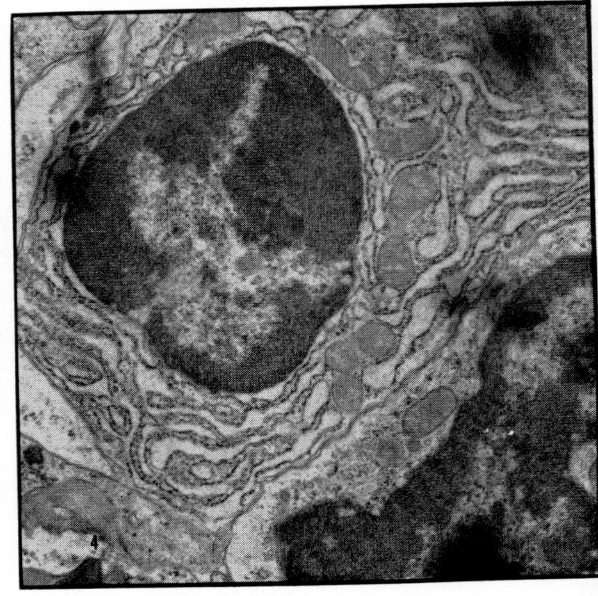

FIGURE 4. An electron microscopic field showing cells of an inguinal lymph node. Note the plasma cell which is characterized by numerous lamellae to which RNP particles are attached. Note the sparsely distributed mitochondria filled with cristae. Reduced from × 20,000

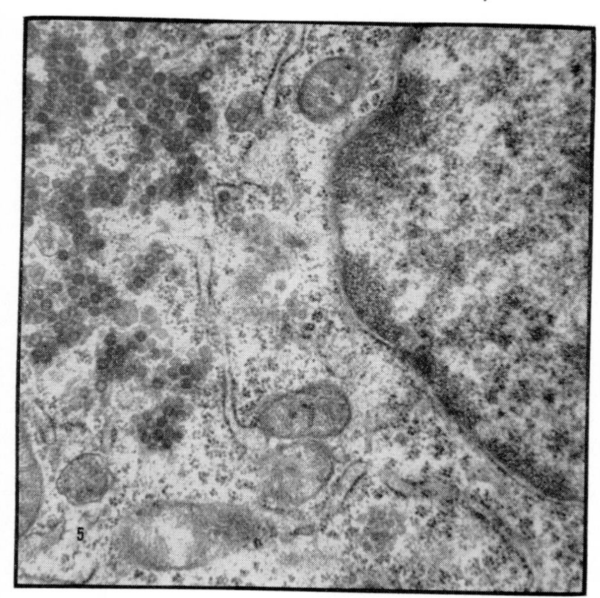

FIGURE 5. A portion of a cell of the epithelial tumor which received 5,000 rads and was fixed 25 hours later. Note the swollen mitochondria, the broken cristae, the dilated vesicles, and the coalesced RNP particles. The round structures showing electron lucite center present viruslike particles usually present in the epithelial type tumor. Reduced from × 30,000

shown a portion of a cell of the epithelial tumor which received 5,000 rads *in situ* and was fixed 25 hours later. A comparison of this figure with that of a nonirradiated control (Figure 1) reveals not only swelling of mitochondria, but also breakages of their cristae and their disappearance in some of the mitochondria. Detailed inspection also reveals some widening of the boundary mitochondrial membranes of these swollen mitochondria, whereas the double boundary membrane of the nonirradiated mitochondria (Figure 1) appears as a single electron dense line. Further, the vesicles of the endoplasmic reticulum in this cell appear dilated; the RNP particles are coalesced in many areas of the cytoplasm.

Alterations similar to those of the epithelial tumor were induced in the cytoplasmic organelles of the irradiated spindle-cell tumor, but these changes appeared to a greater extent. Specifically, swelling of mitochondria, destruction of their cristae, dilatation of the vesicles, and breakages in the plasma membrane were more prevelant after relatively smaller doses of X-irradiation (2,000 to 3,000 rads) as compared with those noted in the epithelial tumor after 5,000 rads.

The irradiation-induced changes in the cytoplasmic organelles of the cells in the irradiated lymph nodes are similar in nature to those in the tumor cells, but those appear to a far greater extent following relatively small doses of irradiation, 200 to 400 rads. An example is given in Figure 6.

EFFECTS OF X-IRRADIATION ON THE FUNCTION OF CYTOPLASMIC ULTRASTRUCTURES

Three cytoplasmic components, mitochondria, microsomes and cell sap, were separated by the aid of ultracentrifugation. The activities of two en-

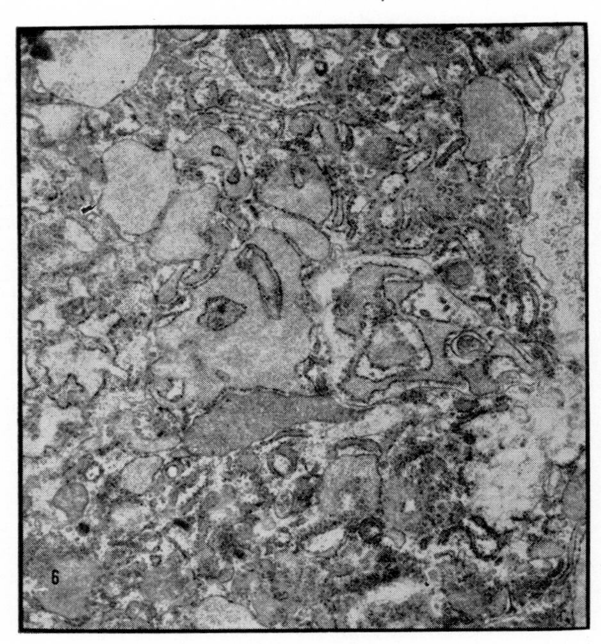

FIGURE 6. A portion of a plasma cell of a lymph node which received 400 rads and which was fixed 20 hours later. Note the dilated vesicles of the endoplasmic reticulum which seem to be filled with amorphous material, several swollen mitochondria, and the coalesced RNP particles. Note also on the right upper corner of the photograph several lamellae which resemble those of a nonirradiated plasma cell in Figure 4. Reduced from × 30,000

zyme systems, catalase and adenosinetriphosphatase (ATPase), of the epithelial and spindle-cell tumors were determined.

The endogenous catalase activity was highest in the mitochondrial fraction of the epithelial tumor, whereas the activity of this enzyme (catalase) was highest in the cell sap fraction of the spindle-cell tumor. The relatively high catalase activity in the cell sap fraction of the spindle-cell tumor can be explained by leakage of this enzyme through the mitochondrial membrane during homogenization and centrifugation procedures, since it is well established that the catalase particles reside within the mitochondria. This explanation finds support in the electron micrographs showing that the mitochondria of the spindle-cell tumor are of inferior quality, and possess a greater aptitude for swelling than do those of the epithelial tumor. This interpretation finds further support by the increase of catalase activity in the cell sap fraction of irradiated tumors. In fact, an increase in catalase activity of the cell sap fraction was detected within ten minutes after a dose as low as 25 to 50 rads delivered to the epithelial tumor *in situ*.

The effects of X-irradiation on the mitochondrial ATPase of both types of tumor (epithelial and spindle-cell) resulted in an initial increase in activity of this enzyme as early as ten minutes after irradiation of the tumors with a dose of 1,000 rads. The initial increase in the mitochondrial ATPase activity following irradiation can also be explained by the release of this enzyme from the mitochondrial membrane to which it is known to be attached. Since the tumors were X-irradiated while the rest of the animal body was shielded with 6 mm lead, an abscopal influence can be excluded.

Comments

To date, there are no ways which would enable the investigator to follow precisely the intervening steps of events which are taking place from the time a quantum of radiation energy is absorbed by a molecule of a cellular structure. Therefore, we must use imagination and understanding to interpret results on the basis of what we see or determine quantitatively.

Morphologic alterations in the cytoplasmic organelles which occur following irradiation and which are revealed electron microscopically and illustrated in the accompanying micrographs include the following: (1) swelling of mitochondria and loss of their internal membranes (cristae); (2) change in permeability of the boundary membranes as revealed by the release of the enzyme investigated (catalase and ATPase); (3) dilatation of the vesicles of the endoplasmic reticulum; (4) breakages in the plasma membrane; and (5) in some cases, aggregation of RNP particles.

In evaluating cellular radiosensitivity, we should take into consideration the quantity and quality of the cytoplasmic organelles. This is borne out from the observations presented here. It follows that if the cell is equipped with many organelles such as mitochondria, of which only a few are destroyed by irradiation, the cell may be able to function and reproduce new mitochondria. Conversely, if the cell is equipped with only a small number of vital organelles and a portion of them are destroyed, the results of irradiation will be severe. Good examples for such a possibility can be found in the three cell types presented. The cytoplasmic components such as mitochondria are more prevalent in the epithelial tumor cells than in those of the spindle tumor cells. Furthermore, the mitochondria of the epithelial tumor cells contain more internal membranes (cristae) and appear of better quality than those of the spindle-cell tumor. The superior quality of the epithelial cell tumor mitochondria is also borne out by their superior oxidative phosphorylation as determined by P:O ratios and by their quantitative enzymic activities. The epithelial tumor proved to be more radioresistant than the spindle-cell tumor as far as total regression following irradiation *in situ* is concerned.

It can be seen in the electron micrograph (Figure 3) which presents a typical lymphocyte that it is surrounded by a narrow brim of cytoplasm containing a few mitochondria and sparsely distributed RNP particles, in addition to membranes, vesicles, and a large nucleus. This cell type is known to be very radiosensitive. Conversely, cells of the heart muscle and those of the kidneys are known to be very radioresistant. These cells possess large numbers of mitochondria closely packed with cristae (Figure 7). These observations do not bear out the prevailing opinion that the larger the nucleus, the more radiosenstive the cell. On the contrary, it seems more likely that the cells poor in mitochondria and in other cytoplasmic organelles are the most radiosensitive. The lymphocytes serve as an example. Furthermore, the intrinsic strength or permeability of the boundary membranes is an important factor in cellular radiosensitivity.

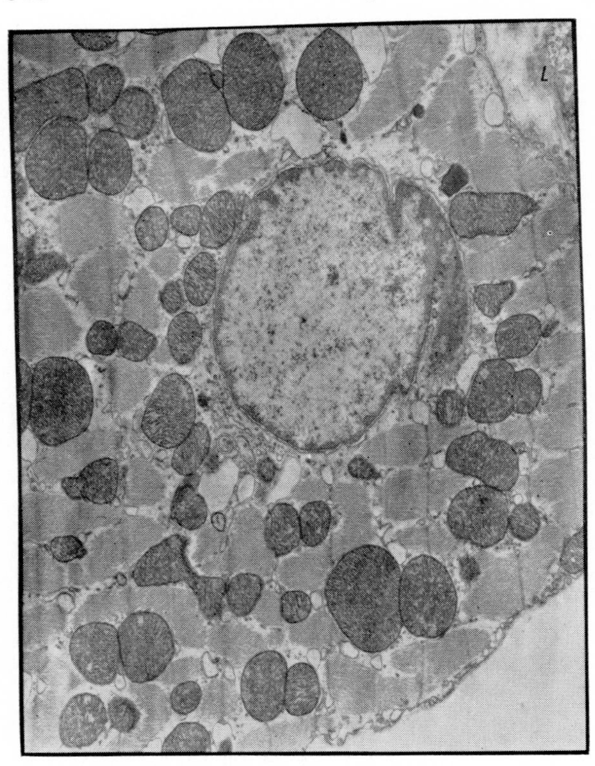

FIGURE 7. A heart muscle cell of a normal mouse. Note the numerous mitochondria filled with cristae. Reduced from × 18,750

Generally, on the basis of the observations made on the test material discussed, it is conceivable to conclude that the integrity and quantity of the cytoplasmic composition which pertain particularly to the intrinsic membrane system, including mitochondria, are determining factors in cellular radiosensitivity.

A Comparison of the Cell Generative Cycle in Normal, Hyperplastic and Neoplastic Mammary Gland of the C3H Mouse

Francesco Bresciani

Biology Department, Brookhaven National Laboratory, Upton, New York, and Institute of General Pathology, University of Naples, Naples, Italy

From a kinetic point of view, a neoplastic cell population is essentially characterized by an irreversible prevalence of cell birth rate over cell death rate (irreversible progressive growth), as opposed to the equivalence of these rates in a normal cell population of an adult animal (steady state condition). This pathological imbalance of rates could be the consequence of a relative decrease of the duration of the generative cycle (generation time). However, factors other than generation time can change a cell system from a state of balance to that of progressive growth. For example, an alteration of the mechanism controlling the relative flow of newborn post-mitotic cells into the reproductive cycle again, or away from the cycle to differentiation and eventually death.

Comparison of generative cycles of normal and neoplastic cells deriving from different tissues can be of little help in an attempt to find differences between the cell cycles of normal and tumor cells. Generation time of normal, different cell types can vary greatly—in the mouse, from 12 hours in the hair follicle (Cattaneo, Quastler, and Sherman, 1961) to 24 days in the epidermis of the ear (Sherman, Quastler, and Wimber, 1961) —and in theory, a small irreversible change of generation time would be sufficient to produce a state of progressive growth. Generation times of tumors also show conspicuous variations and are generally longer than those of several normal tissues. In the mouse, for example, the generation time of the mammary gland tumors is about 33 hours (see Mendelsohn, pages 498 to 513, this volume, as well as this presentation) and that of Ehrlich ascites tumor, 18 hours (Baserga, 1963), in comparison, for instance, with those of cells in the growing hair follicle, 12 hours (Cattaneo, Quastler, and Sherman, 1961), myeloblasts, nine hours (Patt and Maloney, 1959), and cells in the intestinal crypts, 12 to 18 hours (Quastler and Sherman, 1959). Thus differences in cycle time between dissimilar cell types can obscure differences between normal and neoplastic cells.

From the previous considerations and results, it follows that a comparison of the generative cycle of neoplastic cells with that of the corresponding normal cell type is needed. The comparative study of the phases into which the cycle can be subdivided* could also bring some further useful information on the mechanism of the neoplastic change.

The mammary gland of the C3H mouse is a suitable system for this investigation. In fact, in adult females, neoplastic and hyperplastic tissues and their normal counterparts can be obtained from the mammary gland. The hyperplastic nodules in the glands were demonstrated to be precancerous lesions (DeOme, Faulkin, Bern, and Blair, 1959). These hyperplastic, precancerous cells add further interest to the study. Moreover, the growth in the mammary gland can be stimulated by administration of ovarian hormones and, therefore, the use of the mammary gland also offers the possibility of comparing the modification due to hormonal stimulus with the modification of cancer.

Material and Methods

In the experiments with the double-labeling techniques of Hilscher and Maurer (1962) and Wimber and Quastler (1963) the following procedure was followed. C3H adult female mice bearing tumors were first injected with 100 μc of thymidine methyl-H^3 (H^3TdR, specific activity, 6.7 c/mM), and 90 minutes after the first injection, a second one of 50 μc of thymidine-C^{14} (C^{14}TdR, specific activity, 25 mc/mM) was made. The mice were sacficed 30 minutes after the last injection.

In the experiment aimed at the study of the waves of labeled mitoses after pulse labeling, a single injection of H^3TdR (2.3 $\mu c/g$ body weight) was administered intraperitoneally to a homogeneous group of animals and followed by serial killing. These animals had been ovariectomized and were under continuous stimulation of subcutaneously injected 17-β-estradiol (1 μg/day) and progesterone (1 mg/day).

In all experiments, the animals were killed by cervical dislocation, and the integument with all five pairs of mammary glands and tumors attached was rapidly removed and placed in a cold mixture of absolute ethanol with glacial acetic acid (3:1) for about one hour. The tumors were sliced to assure homogeneous fixation. The glands and tumors were then dissected from the skin and placed again in the ethanol acetic acid mixture for an

* The generative cell cycle is typically subdivided into the following phases: M = mitotic phase; S = DNA synthetic phase; G_1 = postmitotic presynthetic phase; G_2 = postsynthetic premitotic phase. C (for cycle) = M + G_1 + S + G_2. T_C = duration of the generative cycle = transit time through the entire cycle = generation time. T_S, T_{G_1}, T_{G_2}, T_M = transit times through S, G_1, G_2, M; e.g. S-time, G_1-time, etc. (Quastler, 1963).

additional 12 to 24 hours. The fixed glands and tumor slices were carried through a descending series of ethanols to water, and Feulgen-stained in bulk. The treelike structure of the glands and the hyperplastic nodules are clearly visible after Feulgen coloration. Generally, the third pair of thoracic glands was picked out for further processing. Under the dissecting microscope, single alveoli or groups of alveoli were dissected using fine needles. The preparations were practically free from connective tissue, as the epithelial structures can be made to slip away from the connective tissue after some experience. At any rate, connective cells can generally be distinguished from epithelial cells in the final preparations, and, when found, were disregarded. Small bits of tissue were obtained from the cortical shell of tumors. The dissected structures were squashed in a drop of 45 per cent acetic acid between a slide and a cover slip by the pressure of the thumb. The squash preparations were checked under the microscope, waved over a flame, and immediately frozen over dry ice.

Preparations of normal cells from different parts of the glands as well as from different hyperplastic noduli and tumors were made. The cells spread out apart from each other nicely in most of the squashes. Unsatisfactory squashes were discarded. The cover slips were removed from the frozen slides, the slides placed for 10 minutes in 100 per cent ethanol, and then carried through a descending series to water and dipped in nuclear photographic emulsion (Kodak NTB). The slides of the double-labeling experiment were dipped a second time after drying. After the final drying, the slides were placed in lightproof boxes with dryrite, exposed conveniently, then developed (Kodak D19, six minutes), fixed (Kodak acid fixer, ten minutes), washed (one hour or more), and made into permanent preparations (Euparol).

The estimation of T_S for normal alveolar cells, cells from hyperplastic nodules, and mammary tumors was carried out with the double-labeling technique. Briefly, this method consists of a first pulse labeling with thymidine-H^3 (H^3TdR) followed by a second pulse with thymidine-C^{14} ($C^{14}TdR$) after a short time. The cells in the S phase at the time of the first injection will be labeled with H^3TdR. During the interval between the two injections (t_a), a portion of the H^3 cells will have passed out of the synthetic phase and will be labeled with H^3 only, not with the subsequently injected C^{14}. If the interval between the injections is kept short and no labeled cells have divided at the time of sacrifice, then the duration of deoxyribonucleic acid (DNA) synthesis can be calculated from the simple relationship

$$\frac{H}{C} = \frac{t_a}{t_s} \tag{1}$$

where H indicates the H^3 cells and C the cells labeled with C^{14} alone or with both C^{14} and H^3. Equation (1) was also applied as such in the case of tumor cells. In fact, even assuming a population growing exponentially and a duplication time of 30 hours, it was calculated that the size of the S compartment would change about 4 per cent between the two injections; this introduces only a negligible error in the computation of T_S.

Squash preparations are particularly suitable for the double-labeling technique, which relies on the possibility of distinguishing between H^3- and C^{14}-labeled cells. The cells in the squash preparations are generally spread well apart and the H^3-labeled cells, not being in close range of the more energetic β-rays from C^{14}-labeled cells, can be easily spotted. A photograph of a squash preparation from a tumor is presented (Figure 1). Duration of DNA synthesis in normal alveolar cells, cells from hyperplastic lesions, and tumor cells from six C3H mice are presented in Table 1. When possible, different preparations from different hyperplastic nodules and tumors were made from the same animal. At the same time, the labeling index (C^{14}-labeled cells/total cells) and the mitotic index were measured. The duration of DNA synthesis of normal alveolar cells varies greatly from animal to animal. This result was not unexpected because of previous unsuccessful trials to identify coherent waves of labeled mitoses after pulse labeling.

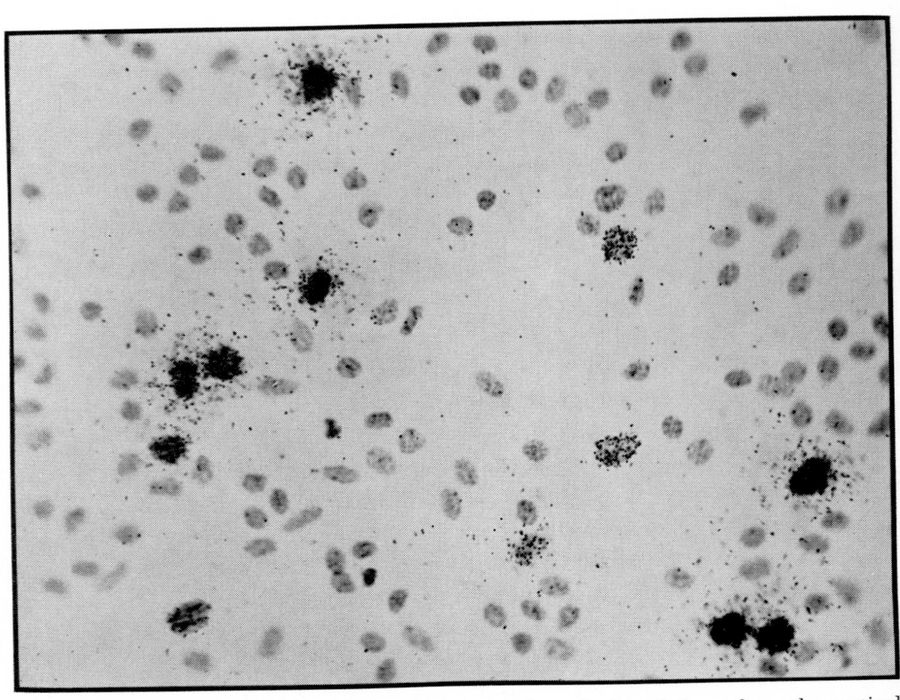

FIGURE 1. Photograph of a typical squash preparation of a bit of tissue from the cortical shell of a mammary tumor. The tissue was Feulgen-stained in bulk prior to squashing. The nuclei which have incorporated C^{14}TdR shows a spray of tracks in many planes (mean energy of C^{14} beta ray, 49 kev; mean distance traveled 50 μ); the nuclei labeled with H^3TdR only show grains exclusively in their immediate vicinity, essentially in one plane over the nuclear material (mean energy H^3 beta ray, 5.7 kev; mean distance traveled 1 μ).

TABLE 1

Duration of DNA Synthesis, Labeling Index† and Mitotic Index in Cells of Normal, Hyperplastic and Neoplastic Mammary Gland Cells of the C3H Mouse*

		Normal alveoli			Hyperplastic nodules‡			Tumors‡		
Exp. no.	Animal no.	T_S (hours)	L.I. (%)	M.I. (%)	T_S (hours)	L.I. (%)	M.I. (%)	T_S (hours)	L.I. (%)	M.I. (%)
114A	1	20.4	4.8	0.40	12.8	18.2	0.00	11.4	19.4	1.47
					19.4	6.6	0.14	11.6	5.7	0.54
					13.8	8.0	1.14	8.6	6.2	0.26
								13.5	6.5	0.55
	2	13.0	3.3	0.70	14.2	9.3	0.84	13.2	18.9	1.52
					15.6	13.4	0.17	10.4	26.4	1.54
								10.3	19.2	2.68
	3	28.2	7.4	0.11	16.3	6.4	0.31	13.4	7.5	0.94
								12.0	18.5	1.05
105	1	31.2	7.6	0.71	14.6	5.8	0.87	10.4	14.6	1.00
					20.1	10.2	0.46	10.6	18.4	0.82
								13.9	8.0	1.24
	2	18.3	2.7	0.00						
	3	19.2	3.5	0.30						
Averages (and maximal variations)		21.7 (13.0–31.2)	4.9 (2.7–7.6)	0.37 (0.0–0.7)	15.9 (12.8–20.1)	9.7 (5.8–18.2)	0.49 (0.0–1.14)	11.6 (8.6–13.9)	14.1 (5.7–26.4)	1.13 (0.26–2.68)

* Determined by the double-labeling technique (see text). In each case at least 100 H^3-labeled cells were counted, but generally many more, and this corresponds to scoring of several hundred C^{14}- and $C^{14}H^3$-labeled cells and a total scanning of several thousand cells.
† C-cells/total cells. C-cells = sum of cells tagged with C^{14} only or both H^3 and C^{14}.
‡ Each value corresponds to a different nodule or a different tumor. Animals with multiple tumors were purposefully selected for the experiment.
Abbreviations: L.I., labeling index; M.I., mitotic index; T_S, duration of DNA synthesis.

In an ideal system in which the entire cell population is proliferating,

$$\frac{N_s}{N_c} = \frac{T_S}{T_C} \qquad (2)$$

where N_s = number of labeled cells; N_c = total number of cells; and T_S and T_C, synthetic time and cycle time, respectively. Knowing T_S, T_C and N_s, the equation (2) can be solved for N_c. If N_c thus calculated actually corresponds to the total number of cells counted, then the whole cell population is actually proliferating. If the calculated number of cells, N'_c, is smaller than the total number of cells, N_c, then the ratio

$$\frac{N'_c}{N_c} = \text{growth fraction} \qquad (3)$$

Knowing T_S, the labeling index, and mitotic index, the cycle time can be computed from equation (2) and the mitotic time from the equation:

$$\frac{N_M}{N_c} = \frac{T_M}{T_C} \qquad (4)$$

where N_M = number of mitoses; T_M = mitotic time, and N_c and T_C have the same meaning as in equation (2). In the case in which only a portion of the total cells are proliferating, the value of the growth fraction has to be used instead of N_c in order to obtain a correct calculation. Mendelsohn (1962) has found that the growth fraction in the mammary tumors of the C3H mouse corresponds to 40 per cent of the population, and this value is used for tumors in the present calculations. From data in this paper (see following), the growth fraction for the normal alveolar cells under hormonal stimulation was computed to be 16 per cent. This value is used in the calculation of cycle time in normal alveolar cells from intact animals, with the understanding that it probably represents a ceiling value for the normal cell population. To date, the growth fraction is not estimated for hyperplastic growth, but it is realistic to assume that it lies between the values for normal and neoplastic growth. Cycle times for hyperplastic cells for both the growth fraction values (16 and 40 per cent) were calculated, in addition to computation of cycle time for an average of the two growth fraction values $(16 + 40/2 = 28)$. T_{G_2} for tumors was taken from Mendelsohn, Dohan, and Moore (1960); for normal and hyperplastic cells, T_{G_2} was estimated from the preliminary unsuccessful trials in search of coherent waves of labeled mitoses after pulse labeling. T_{G_1} was finally calculated as follows:

$$T_{G_1} = T_C - (T_{G_2} + T_M + T_S) \qquad (5)$$

The results on duration of the generative cycle and its phases are presented in Table 2.

Results

Preliminary attempts to study the generative cycle by the method of pulse labeling with thymidine-H^3 and identification of the waves of labeled cells through mitosis (Quastler and Sherman, 1959) in normal and hyperplastic alveoli of intact animals were unsuccessful. On the contrary, a coherent second wave was easily obtained in experiments with mice under treatment with 17-β-estradiol and progesterone. The percentage of labeled mitoses (only metaphases and anaphases are scored as "mitoses") after pulse labeling is plotted as a function of time in Figure 2. The circles indicate mitotic labeling indexes after subtraction of background grains only, while the triangles represent the labeling indexes obtained adopting the commonly used device of a high grain count as a criterion of labeling (five or more grains). The distance on the abscissa between the midpoints on the successive curves gives T_C. T_{G_2} can be estimated as the distance on the abscissa between pulse labeling (time 0) and the appearance of the first labeled mitoses; T_M can be approximated as the distance between appearance of the first labeled mitoses and saturation of the mitotic compartment by labeled cells; the number of hours between the 50 per cent points of the ascending and descending parts of the first wave of labeled mitoses gives an estimate of duration of DNA synthesis. However, a more precise estimation of T_S is obtained by measuring the area of the first wave (Bresciani, 1964), and this technique was applied here. Measurements of T_{G_2}, T_M, and T_S were

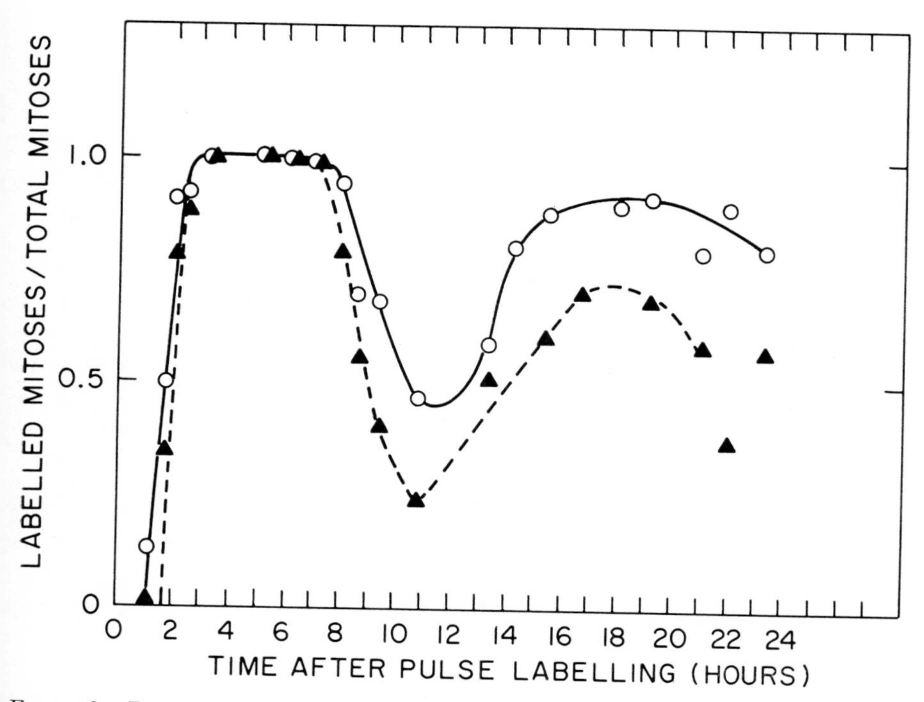

FIGURE 2. Percentage of H^3TdR-labeled mitoses as a function of time after pulse labeling in mammary gland alveoli from C3H mice under continuous stimulation with 17-β-estradiol (1 μg/day) and progesterone (1 mg/day). Circles indicate labeling indexes after subtraction of background grains only. Triangles represent the labeling indexes using a high grain count as criterion of labeling (5 or more grains) (see text).

made from the curve fitted to the circles, because if cycle time is clearly not affected by adopting a high grain count labeling criterion, other transit times are. T_{G_1} was finally calculated according to equation (5). Once the previous parameters are obtained, the growth fraction (Mendelsohn, 1962), e.g. the fraction of actually proliferating cells in the total cell population can also be calculated according to equation (2).

The calculated parameters for the cell cycle of alveolar cells under hormonal treatment are given in Table 2. It is important to point out that doses of hormones 10 times larger (10 mg of progesterone + 10 μg of 17-β-estradiol per day) than those used in the experiments presented here give the same results (Bresciani, in press).

TABLE 2

Duration of the Generative Cycle and Its Phases in Cells of Normal, Hyperplastic and Neoplastic Mammary Gland Cells of the C3H Mouse*

		T_S	T_{G_1}	T_{G_2}	T_M	T_C	GROWTH FRACTION**
Intact mice†	Normal alveoli	21.7	~45.7	~3††	~1.6	~71	
	Hyperplastic nodules	15.9	~26.8	~2††	~1.3	$\sim 46^{26}_{65}$	
	Tumors	11.6	16.5–19.5	1.4‡	~0.9	~33	40%‡
17-β-estradiol and progesterone treated mice§	Normal alveoli	9.2	1.3	1.5	1	13	16%

* In hours. T_S = duration of the DNA synthesis; T_{G_1} = duration of the presynthetic postmitotic period; T_{G_2} = duration of the postsynthetic premitotic period; T_M = duration of mitosis; T_C = duration of the generative cycle = $T_{G_1} + T_{G_2} + T_M + T_S$.

** Defined as proliferating cells/total cells in the tissue.

† T_{G_1}, T_M, T_C based on average values of T_S, Labeling Index and Mitotic Index from six mice (see Table 1). For normal alveoli a growth fraction = 16 per cent was used, on the basis of the data from hormone-treated mice; for tumors a growth fraction = 40 per cent was used on the basis of data from Mendelsohn (1962). For hyperplastic cells an average value of (16 + 40/2 = 28) was used, but the cycle times computed using both values of growth fraction are also given as indexes to the average.

†† Data from unpublished results using single radioactive pulse with H^3TdR and studying the appearance of the leading edge of a labeled mitoses wave.

‡ Data from Mendelsohn (1962).

§ Data obtained by the waves of labeled mitoses method (Figure 2).

A comparison of DNA synthesis in alveolar cells of intact mice and of mice under continuous hormonal stimulation with 17-β-estradiol and progesterone shows that the hormones decrease the time of DNA synthesis to an average of 9.2 hours. This time, however, is not much different from the duration of DNA synthesis, 13 hours, measured in one of the intact mice (no. 114-A-2) and it is difficult to avoid concluding that this mouse was probably in a moment of peak secretion of ovarian hormones. Implicitly, it is suggested that variation of transit times of cells in intact female mice depends upon the cyclic changes in the hormonal titer. The observation of cyclic morphologic changes in the female mouse mammary gland is well known (Nandi, 1958). The average duration of DNA synthesis decreases in hyperplastic cells and is very much reduced in tumor cells; the variation in the synthetic times clearly follows the same trend.

Conclusions

1. DNA synthesis proceeds at a faster pace in hyperplastic and neoplastic cells in comparison with corresponding normal alveolar cells. The average synthetic time (T_S) is reduced to about three fourths of the normal value in hyperplastic cells and to about one half in neoplastic cells.

2. The average duration of the presynthetic postmitotic period (T_{G_1}) is also decreased in hyperplastic and neoplastic cells in comparison to normal cells. The hyperplastic cells show a value intermediate between normal and neoplastic cells.

3. The durations of the postsynthetic premitotic period (T_{G_2}) and the mitotic time (T_M) do not show clear changes in hyperplasia and neoplasia. If at all, these phases seem slightly shorter in the pathological cells.

4. The average duration of the generative cycle (T_C) is therefore shorter in hyperplastic and neoplastic cells in comparison with the normal counterpart of the mammary gland. The hyperplastic cells show a T_C value intermediate between those of normal and neoplastic cells. The decrease of cycle time in the pathological cells is brought about by a reduction of duration of both the S phase and the G_1 phase, with a possible slight contribution from G_2 and mitosis. The noticeable "contraction" of the DNA synthetic time indicates that, contrary to a current idea, synthetic time also can vary conspicuously under different conditions.

5. Under hormonal stimulation, the generative cycle time of normal alveolar cells is greatly reduced and is considerably below the value of neoplastic cells. Doses of hormones 10 times larger do not further decrease the cycle time, nor change the relative contribution of its phases to the total generative cycle time. The result suggests that a "minimum" value is reached under this condition. The cell spends 70 per cent of the cycle time in DNA synthesis and clearly this process is now the limiting factor of the generation time. G_1 is greatly reduced; in fact G_1, G_2, and mitosis all last about the same time, *i.e.* one to one and one-half hours.

6. Comparison of the cell cycle parameters for neoplastic cells and normal alveolar cells under hormonal stimulation clearly indicates that the generative cycle time in tumor cells does not correspond to the potential "minimum" of the normal cells from which they originated. The duration of DNA synthesis seems, however, to have reached the "minimum" value in tumors, as the difference of T_S between neoplastic cells and normal cells under hormonal stimulation does not appear to be significant. If the generation time is shorter in hormone-stimulated normal cells than in neoplastic cells, the growth fraction is, however, only about one half of that of tumors.

Summary

The duration of the cell generative cycle is reduced in tumors of the mammary gland in comparison to normal alveolar cells and this, in all probability, plays a role in the dynamics of neoplastic growth. The hyperplastic preneoplastic cells show a generation time intermediate between those of normal and tumor cells. Factors other than an increased generative cycle rate are not excluded by these results. The duration of both the DNA synthetic period and the postmitotic presynthetic period and possibly the postsynthetic premitotic period and mitosis decrease in neoplastic cells and in normal cells under hormonal stimulation. This result points out that the control of the cell cycle rate does not depend exclusively on variation of G_1. In fact, hormones as well as neoplastic transformation seem to act via a general mechanism which affects equally biochemical processes in the different phases of the cycle.

ACKNOWLEDGMENTS

The author thanks Mrs. Dale Cummings for her skillful assistance and endurance in scanning about one fourth million cells.

The research was carried out at Brookhaven National Laboratory under the auspices of the United States Atomic Energy Commission.

REFERENCES

Baserga, R. 1963. Mitotic Cycle of Ascites Tumor Cells. *Archives of Pathology*, 75: 156–161.

Bresciani, F. 1964. Duration and Rate of DNA Synthesis in the Mammary Gland of the C3H Mouse as Studied by Incorporation of H^3-Thymidine. (Abstract) *Sixth International Congress of Biochemistry*, New York. Abstract I-19.

———. 1965. Effect of Ovarian Hormones on Duration of DNA Synthesis in Cells of the C3H Mouse Mammary Gland. *Experimental Cell Research*. (in press.)

Cattaneo, S. M., H. Quastler, and F. G. Sherman. 1961. Proliferative Cycle in the Growing Hair Follicle of the Mouse. *Nature*, London, 190:923–924.

DeOme, K. B., L. J. Faulkin, Jr., H. A. Bern, and P. B. Blair. 1959. Development of Mammary Tumors from Hyperplastic Alveolar Nodules Transplanted into Gland-Free Mammary Fat Pads of Female C3H Mice. *Cancer Research*, 19:515–520.

Hilscher, W., and Maurer, W. 1962. Autoradiographische Bestimmung der Dauer der DNS-Verdopplung und ihres zeitlichen Verlauf bei Spermatogonien der Ratte durch Doppelmarkierung mit C^{14}- und H^3-Thymidin.

Mendelsohn, M. L. 1962. Autoradiographic Analysis of Cell Proliferation in Spontaneous Breast Cancer of C3H Mouse. III. The Growth Fraction. *Journal of the National Cancer Institute*, 28:1015–1029.

Mendelsohn, M. L., F. C. Dohan, Jr., and H. A. Moore, Jr. 1960. Autoradiographic Analysis of Cell Proliferation in Spontaneous Breast Cancer of C3H Mouse. I. Typical Cell Cycle and Timing of DNA Synthesis. *Journal of the National Cancer Institute*, 25:477–484.

Nandi, S. 1958. Endocrine Control of Mammary-Gland Development and Function in the C3H/He Crgl Mouse. *Journal of the National Cancer Institute*, 21:1039–1063.

Patt, H. M., and M. A. Maloney. 1959. "Kinetics of Neutrophil Balance," *The Kin-*

etics of Cellular Proliferation, F. Stohlman, Ed. New York, New York: Grune and Stratton, Inc. Pp. 201–207.

Quastler, H. 1963. "The Analysis of Cell Population Kinetics," *Guinness Symposium on Cell Proliferation*, L. F. Lamerton and R. J. M. Fry, Eds. Oxford, England: Blackwell Scientific Publications. Pp. 18–36.

Quastler, H., and F. G. Sherman. 1959. Cell Population Kinetics in the Intestinal Epithelium of the Mouse. *Experimental Cell Research*, 17:420–438.

Sherman, F. G., H. Quastler, and D. R. Wimber. 1961. Cell Population Kinetics in the Ear Epidermis of Mice. *Experimental Cell Research*, 25:114–119.

Wimber, D. E., and H. Quastler. 1963. A ^{14}C- and ^{3}H-Thymidine Double Labeling Technique in the Study of Cell Proliferation in *Tradescantia* Root Tips. *Experimental Cell Research*, 30:8–22.

Physical, Biological, and Clinical Aspects of Fast Neutron and Other High LET Radiations and Implications for Fast Neutron Beam Clinical Radiotherapy

J. ROBERT ANDREWS*

Radiation Branch, National Cancer Institute, National Institutes of Health, Department of Health, Education, and Welfare, Bethesda, Maryland

I wish to commence this presentation with some thoughts about radiosensitivity for, fundamentally, all that I shall try to develop finally concerns itself, in any conceivable application to human cancer radiotherapy, with the exploitation of radiosensitivity. It is essential, therefore, that I try to define precisely what I mean by this term radiosensitivity. I mean by it cellular susceptibility to radiation injury but not the expression of this injury. In cell colonial radiobiological experiments of the type which have contributed so greatly to our understanding of irradiation effects the expression of radiation injury must be recognized for the expression itself is often, in these experiments, the only evidence of the injury. Ancel and Vitemberger (1925) were, I believe, the first to make a clear distinction between susceptibility to and the induction of the radiation injury and the expression of this injury. In the contextual sense this injury may be either sublethal, from which recovery may be effected, or lethal. By the latter is meant the effect which, upon the stimulus (whatever it is or by whatever homeostatic mechanism invoked) to cell division, will result in the death of the irradiated cell, itself, or of its progeny. The expression of this lethal injury may be immediate or it may be long delayed with preservation of the cellular capacity to carry on some of its normal life processes.

This failure to distinguish induction from expression of injury has been the cause of what I now believe to be a serious misconception which has obtained for decades in clinical cancer radiotherapy where the expression

* Presently Professor of Radiology and Director of Radiotherapy, Georgetown University Medical Center, Washington, D.C.

of the radiation injury was interpreted as synonymous with susceptibility to the induction of the injury and where a prompt expression of the injury was given the connotation of radiosensitivity. When the expression of the radiation injury was interpreted in this manner there were believed to be great differences in the degrees of radiosensitivities between both different human normal tissues and different human cancer tissues. If, however, susceptibility to the induction, only, of the radiation injury is considered to be the index of radiosensitivity, then the interpretation may be quite different, and it is this susceptibility to radiation injury which must next be examined.

The exact macromolecular lesion of the radiation injury has not yet been precisely identified but there is, however, a growing acceptance that the radiation injury is somehow related to effects exerted upon the macromolecular nucleic acids, an interpretation first proposed by Epstein in 1953, and upon chromosomes. Such effects are manifested by aberrations of the self-replicating systems of cells. If this interpretation is valid, then, conceptually, the two following corollaries ought to obtain. The first is that susceptibility to radiation injury should be dependent upon the condition, *i.e.* the synthesis, of the macromolecule, or in other words, upon the temporal relationship of the irradiation to the cell life cycle; the second is that susceptibility to radiation injury should bear some relationship to the macromolecule (deoxyribonucleic acid [DNA]) content or chromosome number or volume. There is some experimental evidence, sometimes contradictory, in support of both corollaries and such evidence in support of the first is presented summarily in Table 1 and graphically in Figure 1. However, as will be seen, the results are inconsistent; variations in susceptibility to injury do occur in relationship to the cell life cycle, but thus far there has not emerged a consistent pattern in these variations. Human cell populations, whether of normal or cancer tissues, have not been shown to be synchronous in respect of their life cycles. It may be concluded, then, that such populations will display the average radiosensitivities of the component cells of these populations in respect to variations within life cycles. It has been suggested that some degree of synchrony might be induced either by prior

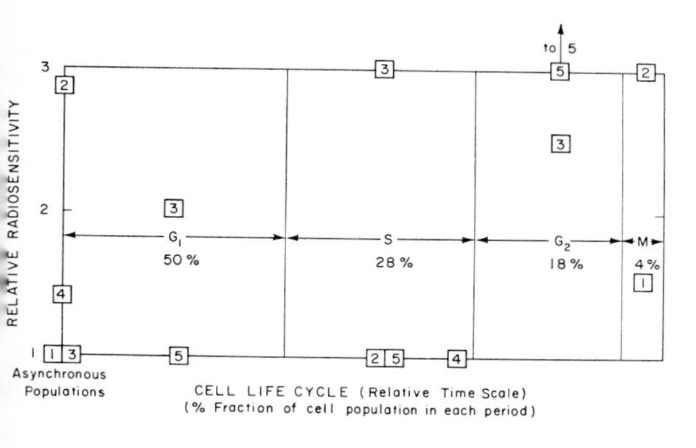

FIGURE 1. The relationship of radiosensitivity to the mammalian cell life cycle: graphical display of data from Table 1. Numbers in squares coded to reference numbers in Table 1. Relative radiosensitivity: radiosensitivity ratio as defined in Table 1. Cell life cycle: relative time in each period and fraction of a cell population (S3 HeLa) in each (Puck and Steffen, 1963).

TABLE 1

The Relationship of Radiosensitivity to Mammalian Cell Life Cycle

Reference number in Figure 1	Reference	Characteristics	Criteria and values	Radiosensitivity ratio*
1	Terasima and Tolmach 1961	HeLa		
		Synchronous, in mitosis:	D_0: 59–82 rads	1.6
		Asynchronous:	D_0: 100–120 rads	1.0
2	Sinclair and Morton 1963	Chinese hamster	Surviving fraction to 750 rads	
		Synchronous, in mitosis:	.1	3
		Synchronous, in S period:	.3	1
		Asychronous:	.12	3
3	Dewey and Humphrey 1962	Mouse fibroblasts and ascites	Percentage of abnormal chromosomes	
		G_1 period:	56	2
		S period:	80	3
		G_2 period:	65	2.5
		Asynchronous:	26	1
4	Erikson and Szybalski 1963	Human cells in culture	Ratio of D_0's	
		Partially synchronized:	1.4	1.0
		Asynchronous:	1.0	1.4
5	Chu, Giles, and Passano 1961		Ratio of chromosomal abnormalities	
		G_1 period:	1	1
		S period:	1	1
		G_2 period:	5	5

* Radiosensitivity ratio: Either as direct ratios or as ratios of the reciprocals of the lowest numerical values of the end effect criteria to the reciprocals of the values of the ones with which they are compared, as fit the criteria.

irradiation or the administration of drugs and that subsequent irradiation could be given in such a pattern of periodicity as to take the maximum advantage of recurring cycles of radiosensitivity. Such concepts are, however, wholly speculative at this time.

Evidence in support of the second corollary has been developed by Terzi (1961), Guild (1963), and Sparrow, Schairer, and Sparrow (1963). The first has collated D_0 inactivation doses* and nucleic acid content for a wide range of organisms extending from the single-stranded DNA or ribonucleic acid (RNA) viruses to the cells of vertebrates, including man. Four different levels of inactivation efficiency could be demonstrated which corresponded with the degrees of complexity of the genetic structure and from which the conclusion may be drawn that for a given order of nucleic acid content there is a specific order of radiosensitivity. The second has calculated the ionizations occurring in nuclear DNA which result from in-

* D_0 dose: that dose of radiation which, on the exponential portion of the survival curve, results in the reduction of a surviving fraction of a population to e^{-1} of that population.

activation by a D_0 dose for a variety of organisms ranging in DNA content from 6×10^{-11} to 4×10^{-18} g/DNA cell and these two parameters are shown to have a log-log relationship. This relationship is shown graphically in Figure 2. The third, while finding an inverse log-log relationship between interphase chromosome volume and radiosensitivity in 16 different plant species, concluded that the absorbed energy per chromosome at lethal radiation exposures approached a constant in spite of wide ranges of lethal exposures (0.6 to 75 kr), of nuclear volumes (43 to 1,758 μ^3), and of chromosome numbers (6 to 136). It may be concluded, therefore, that there exists some fixed relationship between radiosensitivity and nuclear DNA content or chromosomal number or volume.

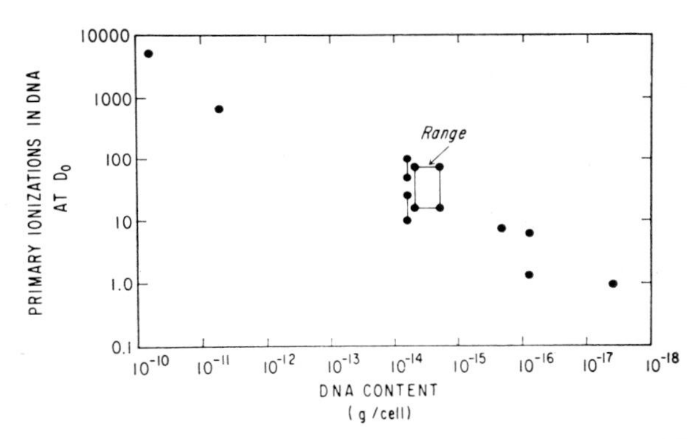

FIGURE 2. The relationship of the primary ionizations in cellular DNA at D_0 doses to the DNA content. (From Guild, 1963.) Primary ionizations in DNA at

$$D_0 = \frac{\text{primary ionizations}}{\text{g rad}} \times D_0 \text{ (rads)} \times \frac{\text{g DNA}}{\text{cell}}$$

Thus far, inherent radiosensitivity is defined, in the context employed in this presentation, as cellular susceptibility to the induction of radiation injury; this susceptibility varies inconsistently with the cell life cycle and it is some function of the nuclear nucleic acid content or of chromosome number or volume.

However, in human cancer radiotherapy we are dealing not with single cell but with cell population effects and not with synchronous but with asynchronous cell populations in respect to the life cycles of the cells composing the populations. At the same time, all of the cells composing the diverse cell populations of both normal and cancer tissues have, within the relatively narrow limits of a factor of two, the same nucleic acid content and chromosome number or volume. The evidence of this is as follows:

Atkin and Richards (1956) studied the DNA content of human normal (leukocyte, lymphocyte, plasma cell, fibroblast, and cervical and endometrial epithelium) and cancer (cervix, endometrium, breast, anus, vagina, cheek, tongue, melanoma, leiomyosarcoma, stomach, skin, and rectum) cells. The DNA content of the blood cells and fibroblasts was identical and that of the normal epithelium was 10 per cent greater, while bimodal values 30 and 100 per cent greater were found for the cancer cells. Stich, Florian, and Emson (1960) also studied the nuclear DNA content of human normal and cancer cells. This was found to be similar for lymphocytes, epithelium, and adenomatous polyps but adenocarcinoma cells had modal values in the hyperdiploid and hypertetraploid regions. Hauschka (1961) examined the karyotypes of 104 human neoplasms, the cells being fixed for study immediately upon removal and without recourse to culture or colchicine treatment; 76 of the 104 showed aneuploid and 28 of the 104 showed diploid or pseudodiploid modal karyotypes. Bell (1964) has described a form of polyploidy occurring in cultures of human leukocytes after irradiation which results in four-stranded chromosomes, a process he has termed "endoreduplication." Petrakis, Bostik, and Siegel (1959) have described findings in Hodgkin's disease showing that the DNA content of the nuclei of individual Sternberg-Reed cells ranged from 2 times to, exceptionally, 15 times the normal lymphocyte value with the DNA content bearing a direct relationship to the nuclear size and the degree of its lobulation. Koller (1963), in an extensive review of the literature on the nucleus of the cancer cell, concludes that there is a parallelism between nuclear DNA content and chromosome number.

It is found in man, then, that nuclear DNA content and chromosome number are directly related and that the variation of their values does not exceed, excepting the characteristic cells of Hodgkin's disease, a factor of two. The effect of such a factor on the radiation response of mammalian cells has been studied in our laboratory by Berry (1963). Diploid and tetraploid lines of the P-388/DBA tumor cells were irradiated and assayed in vivo under identical conditions and radiation dose-cell survival curves were constructed. The tetraploid line had approximately double the cellular nucleic acid, DNA, and protein content of the diploid line. The D_0 doses for both oxygenated and anoxic conditions were not significantly different for the two lines (oxygenated: 160 and 180, anoxic: 360 and 380 rads for, respectively, the diploid and tetraploid lines) but the extrapolation numbers* differed by a factor of two (1.6 and 3.1 for, respectively, the diploid and tetraploid lines). One may conclude, then, from the preceding development of the relationship of inherent cellular radiosensitivity to the cell life cycle, to the nuclear DNA content or chromosomal number or volume, and to variations of the latter that the inherent radiosensitivity, defined as an inverse function of the D_0 dose, of human cell populations is essentially invariant but that the number of the units which are determinant of inherent radiosensitivity may vary by a factor of as much as two (exceptionally, in certain cells, 15), and that this variation is reflected by a similar variation of the extrapolation number of the survival curve. If this number is small, it will not

* Extrapolation number, n: the number to which, at zero dose, the exponential portion of the survival curve may be extrapolated.

be possible to demonstrate differences in human radiotherapy responses due to variations of it. I (Andrews, 1965a) have suggested that n for human cells may have a value of around 12.

I conclude, therefore, with the premise that insofar as human cancer radiotherapy is concerned the inherent susceptibility to radiation injury of both different normal and different cancer tissues is essentially invariant. For a given dose, observed differences in effects are the results of differences in the expression of injury at the tissue level. The probability of the occurrence of radiation-induced lesions in any irradiated human cell populations, asynchronous in respect to cell life cycles, is a dose-dependent random one; the postirradiation expression of this lesion is a nonrandom process dependent upon the stem cell population number, stem cell proliferative characteristics, and homeostatic regulators or homeostatic regulatory mechanisms.* In general, because of the manifestation of lethal injury by failure of cell division of the lethally irradiated cell or its progeny, if the proliferative characteristics of an irradiated cell population are such that normal tissue steady state cell renewal, cell removal systems' cell population turnover times or cancer tissue cell population doubling times are very short, the expression of radiation injury will be prompt. Conversely, in those cell population systems, such as nervous tissues, in which perhaps cell population renewal does not occur the expression of radiation injury may never, within the lifetime of the individual, become manifest. This is not to say, however, that the injury did not occur or that the cell population system is not radiosensitive. Till (1963) has shown experimentally that such distinctions in the expression of radiation injury may be demonstrated quantitatively by differences in the rates of restitution of different cell populations. This is shown graphically in Figure 3.

This aspect, or condition, of radiosensitivity which, effectively, is a constant within the human species I term inherent radiosensitivity (Andrews, 1962); it is a consequence of intrinsic characteristics. Without, however, alteration of intrinsic characteristics, the susceptibility of cells to radiation injury may be affected by the extrinsic conditions of the irradiation. To this aspect, or condition, of radiosensitivity I have given the term apparent radiosensitivity.

The increase in the degree of this apparent radiosensitivity when mammalian cells are irradiated with either X rays or gamma rays under oxygenated, as compared with anoxic, conditions is now so well known as to constitute a fundamental law of radiobiology. Our own experiments (Belli and Andrews, 1963) with the P-338/DBA mouse lymphocytic leukemia

---

* Proliferative characteristics, *i.e.* cell population turnover times in normal tissue steady state cell renewal, cell removal systems, and cancer tissue cell population doubling times, may be considered to be under some regulatory mechanism, whether intrinsic or extrinsic, and the postirradiation expression of the radiation lesion will be some function of the degree (sublethal or lethal) and type (recoverable or nonrecoverable) of injury and, therefore, of the capacity to respond to the regulatory mechanism. The present state of knowledge does not permit any inference to be drawn as to whether the regulatory mechanism itself may be injured.

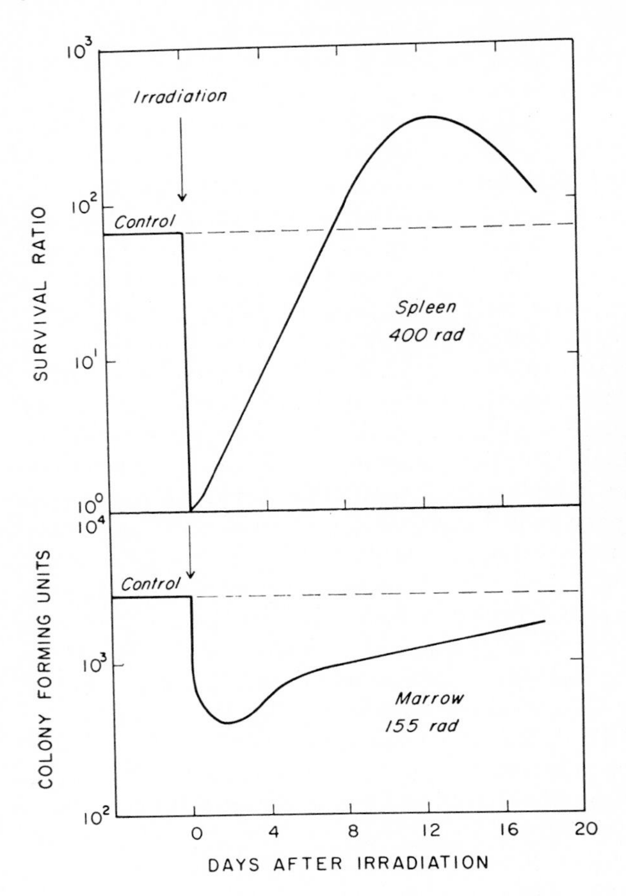

FIGURE 3. The kinetics of the postirradiation proliferation of colony-forming mouse spleen and marrow cells. (From Till, 1963.) Spleen: colony-forming cells in spleen following dose of 400 rads. Marrow: colony-forming units per two femurs, following 155 rads.

cells have shown that the degree of apparent radiosensitivity may be increased by the oxygen effect by as much as a factor of 2.7. It should be emphasized that essentially the maximum oxygen effect is attained when mammalian cells are irradiated while exposed to those oxygen partial pressures which obtain in the earth's atmosphere at sea level; a further increase in oxygen partial pressure increases the apparent radiosensitivity only insignificantly.

The transfer of radiation energy to biological materials is effected by processes of ionization and excitation, the relative proportions of which are the same for all ionizing particles. While the relative proportions of these two processes are fixed, their concentration, or density, is not and the degree of apparent radiosensitivity of mammalian cells is also related to the concentration, or density, of these two processes. The density of these processes is a function of the charge and is inversely proportional to the velocity of the ionizing particles producing them; it may be described in terms of the mean linear energy transfer (mean LET) in units of kev/μ. The velocity of charged particles having a given amount of energy is an inverse function of their mass. Our own experiments (Andrews and Berry, 1962; Berry and Andrews, 1963; Andrews, Correa, and Belli, 1964) have shown an increase in the degree of apparent radiosensitivity due to LET by factors of 4.6 and 2.7, the ratios of the reciprocals of the D_0 doses, for fission-spectrum fast neutron and Co^{60} irradiations performed under anoxic and oxygenated conditions, respectively. That these ratios are not identical is due to the fact that the oxygen effect ratio (OER) is greater, having a value of 2.7 in our experiments (Belli and Andrews, 1963), for the low mean LET Co^{60} irradiation than for the high mean LET fission-spectrum fast neutron, OER 1.2 (Andrews, Correa, and Belli, 1964) irradiation. The high LET's are, then, in the biological effectiveness of a given dose, less oxygen-dependent than the low LET radiations. Thus, there exists an interrelationship between apparent radiosensitivity, the oxygen effect, and ionization density. This interrelationship is shown graphically in Figure 4.

The exact biochemical mechanism responsible for this interrelationship is not known at present. It is tempting, of course, to attempt the development of a model but the proposal of such is not essential to the purposes of this presentation. The empirical evidence of the interrelationship seems irrefutable; the exact reason for it is unknown. The graphical display (Figure 4) of the experimental observations does seem to allow the theorem that there is a continuously variable inverse ratio between the oxygen effect and LET with limiting values of the former, for mammalian cell-killing effects, of 3 or near 3 at low values and of 1 or near 1 at high values of LET. I say 3 or near 3, for the actual number, 3, has not been found and of 1 or near 1, because a small oxygen effect at high values of LET always seems to have been found. This latter may be presumed, as a working hypothesis, to be a

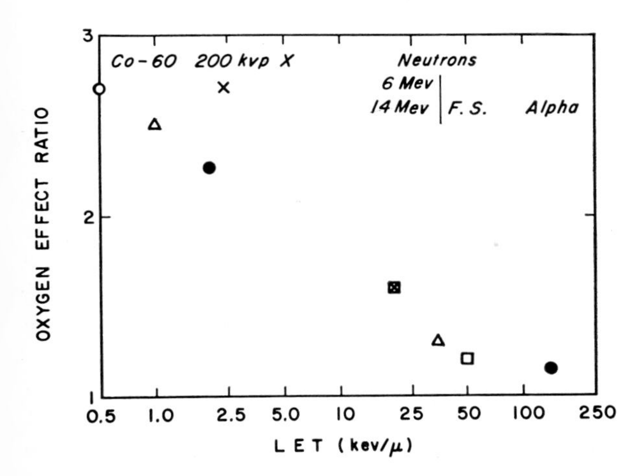

FIGURE 4. The interrelationship of the oxygen effect and LET for mammalian cells. Oxygen effect ratio: the ratio of the reciprocal of the D_0 dose for the oxygenated to the reciprocal of the D_0 dose for the anoxic condition of irradiation at various LET'S. (F.S., fission spectrum.)

Sources:

□ Andrews, Correa, Belli, 1964

● Barendsen and Walter, 1963

○ Belli and Andrews, 1963

X Bewley and Hornsey, 1964

△ Schneider and Whitmore, 1963

⊠ combined □ and ×

result of the presence of a component of oxygen-dependent, relatively low LET delta rays.*

The transfer of radiation energy to matter, whether through the medium of quantum (X ray and gamma ray photons) or particle (negatively charged heavy, proton, alpha, stripped nuclei, fission fragment, and neutron) radiations, is effected by charged particles by the processes of ionization and excitation. These processes are not qualitatively different whether effected by negatively or positively charged, light or heavy particles. As these energy transfer processes occur the kinetic energy of the charged particle is reduced and it is continually slowing down. As a consequence, it remains longer in one vicinity to react with increasing effect on the vicinal orbital electrons until, finally, combination results and no further ionization occurs. Ionization density is not, therefore, constant along the entire particle track but is increasing as the particle approaches the end of its range and is at its maximum, the Bragg (1912) peak, at the end of its track, as shown in Figure 5 (from Schaefer, 1964). Electrons, because of their light mass,

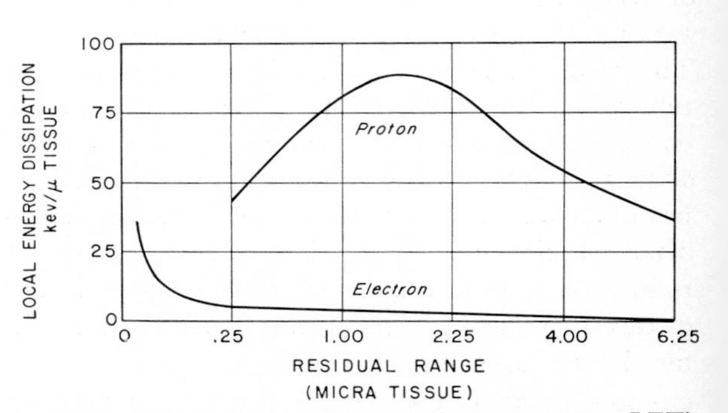

FIGURE 5. The local energy dissipation of electron and proton in termin sections of tracks in tissue. (From Schaefer, 1964.) The LET of the electron approaches that of the proton only at the very end of its track and for only a minute portion of this track. The proton attains a high LET much earlier in terms of residual track length and maintains it over a much longer distance. The proton, in its residual range, is at LET's independent of, or nearly so, the oxygen effect while the electron is not.

undergo more marked deflections than other particles; their paths are not straight lines; and, in addition, they may lose a large fraction of their energy in a single interaction with an orbital electron. These statistical variations in individual track characteristics, termed straggling, are much more pronounced for electrons than for heavy negatively or positively charged particles. As a result of the differences in the straggling phenomena for light and heavy charged particles a monoenergetic electron beam will not show a Bragg peak and its range, while finite, will not be sharply defined. Conversely, a monoenergetic heavy charged particle beam will show a pronounced Bragg peak and a relatively sharply defined range.

---

* Delta rays: any secondary ionizing particle ejected by recoil when a primary ionizing particle passes through matter.

Neutrons, being uncharged particles, generally will not react with orbital electrons but will interact instead with atomic nuclei. These interactions are of two main types, the one being absorption, in which a neutron enters the nucleus but other particles leave and quantum energy may or may not be emitted, and the other being scattering, by which a neutron interacts with and transfers a fraction of its energy to the nucleus but remains free after the process. The scattering process most important to the intention of this presentation is that termed elastic collision, by which process most of the energy of neutrons with energies between about 20 kev and 20 Mev is lost in tissue. In such an elastic collision the neutron will transfer some or all of its kinetic energy to the nucleus, this depending upon the geometry of the interaction and the atomic number of the nucleus. It so happens that hydrogen nuclei have the highest so-called collision cross section, or probability, for interactions with fast neutrons and from 94 per cent at a neutron energy of 0.3 Mev to 70 per cent at 14 Mev of fast neutron energy is transferred to tissue as recoil protons, in other words, as positively charged heavy particles. Such a recoil proton may emerge with an energy of anywhere from almost zero to that of the incident neutron, but, on the average, its energy will be equal to one half of the incident neutron energy. The mean linear energy transfer of each recoil proton will then be a function of its respective Bragg curve and its length of path a function of its energy. Other positively charged heavy particles characteristic of the nuclei or their components, of other atomic elements of tissue may also be ejected, but at substantially reduced yields compared with those of protons. Finally, after a series of such elastic scatterings, the energy of the neutron will be reduced to thermal levels upon which it will be "captured" by a nucleus; a different atomic nucleus will be formed; and energy will be released, either by the emission of one or a number of photons or by the ejection of a charged particle, commonly a proton or alpha particle. While, then, there are several components of dose; recoil protons, other recoil positively charged heavy particles, and gamma rays; this last is relatively unimportant, because of its relatively low yield and low mean LET in respect to the radiation responses of tissue, and, therefore, fast neutron beam irradiation may be considered, effectively, to be positively charged heavy particle irradiation in relation to its biological effects. These and other aspects of high energy radiations have been reviewed by Metz (1962).

The reactions which produce monoenergetic beams of fast neutrons and the yields which may be anticipated have been developed (Radiation Dynamics, 1963); desirable target characteristics have been defined (Coon, 1960); and problems connected with fast neutron beam collimation and shielding have been elaborated (Langsdorf, 1960; Rosen and Stewart, 1957; Ahn and Roberts, 1957). Target technology is the present limiting factor in respect to the yield of some monoenergetic fast neutron beams, especially the $H^3(d,n)He^4$ reaction (referred to as the D-T reaction) giving 14 Mev monoenergetic neutrons, of potential interest in human cancer radiotherapy. Desirable target characteristics may be listed (Coon, 1960) as high neutron yield, small physical size, small neutron energy spread together with small differences in angular distribution, minimum contamination by nuclei which yield neutrons by a different reaction, minimum amount of scatter near target, long lifetime, and ease of replacement. At 14 Mev neutron energy the proportion of energy deposited by recoil protons is, because of the falling collision cross section, or probability, for the process, only 70 per cent, while there is a significant energy deposition by other interactions yielding higher LET alpha particles, notably from the reaction $O^{16}(n,\alpha)C^{13}$ (Bewley, 1963a).

In respect to π^--mesons, it suffices for the purposes of this presentation to say that their capture by light nuclei, especially by C^{12} and N^{16}, leads to an exceptionally large release of energy in the form of short-range, high mean LET alpha particles. In common with other heavy charged particle beams, the Bragg peak phenomenon is manifested with peak to plateau relative ionization ratios of from 5 to 7:1 with the half value width of the peak not exceeding a centimeter or two (Fowler and Perkins, 1961). The Gatlinburg Conference of 1962, informally reported by Zucker and Snell (1963), on advances in meson and nuclear research below I Bev developed the state of the art and reported work in progress on accelerators which, among other research applications, would be appropriate for the generation of π^--meson beams for biomedical research.

Brustad (1962) has developed Bragg curves for the absorption, in tissue equivalent material, of the stripped nuclei, Ne^{20}, O^{16}, C^{12}, and B^{11}, of total energies of 208, 166, 124, and 112 Mev, respectively. Bragg peak to plateau relative ionization ratios were about 4.

The characteristics of the energy distribution, in either water or tissue equivalent material, of several different quantum and particle radiation beams are shown as depth dose curves in Figure 6.

In every case, including even the very densely ionizing fission fragments and regardless of the ionization density, the relative proportions of ionization and excitation produced by ionizing particles remains the same. This simplifies certain biological considerations for it is, then, only necessary to examine the possible effects on biological material of the compression of more ionization and excitation into a given length of track. Attention can be fixed, therefore, on a single physical parameter—regardless of the radiation source—the ionization density or linear energy transfer. In relation to its importance in human cancer radiotherapy, the prinicipal effects on biological material of compression of more ionization and excitation into a given length of track are reduction in the oxygen effect ratio and change in the shape of the survival curve for cell reproductive capacity. The former, reduction in the oxygen effect ratio, has already been discussed. Many different investigators have demonstrated that the survival curves for mammalian cell reproductive capacity undergo a change in their characteristics from cumulative, or threshold, to exponential types as the radiations by

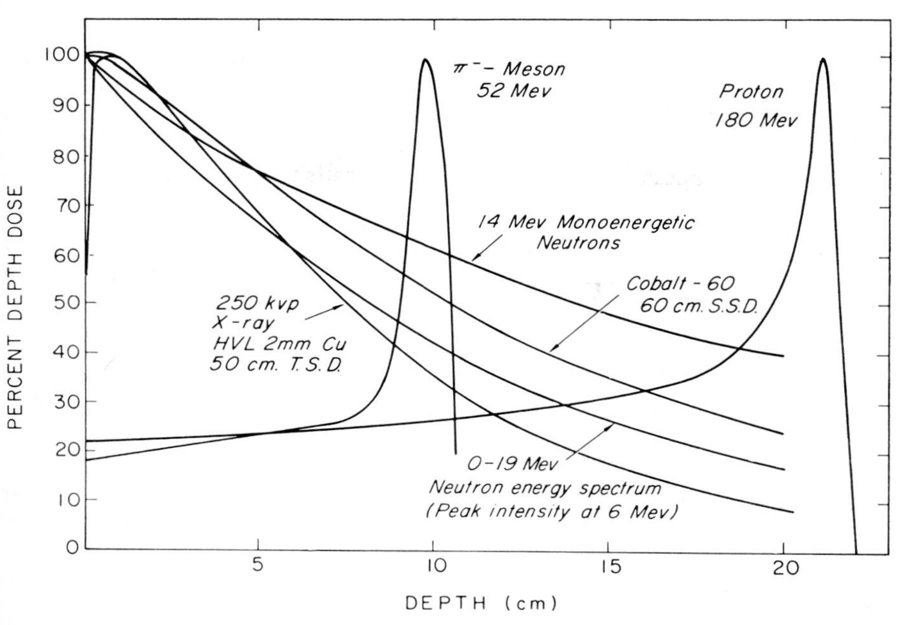

FIGURE 6. Relative depth dose curves for:
Co^{60} gamma ray (British Institute of Radiology, 1961).
250 kvp X ray, HVL: 2 mm. Cu, 50 cm. TSD (British Institute of Radiology, 1961).
180 Mev proton (Naeslund *et al.*, 1963).
52 Mev π^--meson (Fowler and Perkins, 1961).
14 Mev monoenergetic neutron (Smith and Boot, 1962).
0 to 19 Mev neutron energy spectrum, peak intensity at 6 Mev (Bewley, 1963b).

which they are determined are changed from low to high mean LET (Barendsen, Beusker, Vergroesen, and Budke, 1960; Andrews and Berry, 1962; Deering and Rice, 1962; Berry and Andrews, 1963; Schneider and Whitmore, 1963; Barendsen, 1963; Barendsen, Walter, Fowler, and Bewley, 1963). Our own experiments covered a range of mean LET's from the low of Co^{60} to the high of fission spectrum fast neutrons and the effect increased, as measured by the reciprocals of the D_0 doses of the survival curves, as LET increased. The experiments of Deering and Rice extended similar observations of the effects of the high LET's of 40 Mev He^4, 69 Mev Li^7, 105 Mev C^{12}, and 130 Mev O^{16} accelerated nuclei with, however, a reversal of effectiveness, as measured by the reciprocals of the D_0 doses, at the highest LET, 350 kev/μ, that of 130 Mev O^{16} particles, studied. Barendsen, using the 5.3 Mev alpha particles from Po^{210}, observed the same reversal of effectiveness at an LET of about 140 kev/μ. The investigators cited above have found that the extrapolation number, n, also drops to 1 as this peak of LET effectiveness is approached. The preceding discussion concerning the oxygen effect ratio developed the observation that this ratio also approaches 1 as this peak of LET effectiveness is approached.

From the point of view of human cancer radiotherapy these precepts emerge from the preceding development:

1. There are no significant differences in radiosensitivity, as judged by susceptibility to the induction of radiation injury, between human different normal or different cancer tissues;

2. The extrapolation number of human cells may vary by as much as a factor of two or, very exceptionally, more;

3. The significant biological effect of high, as distinct from low, LET radiations on mammalian cells is the induction of an exponential response or, stated another way, of nonrecoverable* injury as compared with the recoverable injury of low LET radiations; and

4. There is a continuously variable inverse relationship between the oxygen effect ratio and LET with limiting values of the former of near 3 at low values and of near 1 at high values of LET.

It is presumed that there does exist the potentiality for some differential modification, possibly by pharmacological agents, of both the radiosensitivity and the extrapolation number of human normal and cancer tissues but any consideration of such potentiality is outside the scope of this presentation. From the point of view of human radiotherapy applications we are limited, then, to a consideration of the practical implications of the LET and oxygen effects previously developed.

The existence of the oxygen effect in cell radiobiology is not in question; the importance of the oxygen effect in human cancer radiotherapy and the best means for exploiting it, if important. are, however, moot. This is for the reason that the evidence for its importance is indirect and not direct in the sense of a demonstrated improvement in radiotherapeutic effects due to oxygenation of presumed anoxic or severely hypoxic cancer cells and because alternative methods, which have not been fully explored, are available for the equalization of differences in radiation responses due to the oxygen effect. Alternative methods for the latter include high pressure oxygen breathing, the induction of localized or generalized hypoxia, 95 per cent oxygen and 5 per cent carbon dioxide breathing at ambient pressures, and irradiation with oxygen independent (high LET) radiations.

Hollcroft, Lorenz, and Matthews (1952) presented the first demonstration of the oxygen effect in a mammalian cell system, showing quantitatively a progressively greater reduction, due to X-ray irradiation, of the size of a transplantable mouse lymphosarcoma when irradiation was done as the animals breathed 8, 20, or 95 per cent oxygen at ambient pressures. Gray (1961) has presented a comprehensive and lucid review of the

---

* In this and the discussion which follows, I have given special meaning to certain terminology, as follows:
Irradiation injury—cellular radiation effects which may be either: (1) lethal, resulting in the loss of cell reproductive capacity and the subsequent death of either the irradiated cell or its progeny, or (2) sublethal, from which recovery will be effected.
Recovery—restoration, after sublethal radiation injury, of preirradiation parameters of cellular reproduction and radiation response.
Repair—cellular repopulation of normal or tumor tissues after recovery from injury.
Restitution—recovery and repair.

radiobiologic basis of oxygen as a modifying factor in radiation therapy; Churchill-Davidson, Sanger, and Thomlinson (1957) were the first to introduce high pressure oxygen breathing into clinical radiotherapy practice; the current state of the practice is reviewed in a symposium on high pressure oxygen radiotherapy (Madigan *et al.*, 1963); and physiological problems associated with high pressure oxygen breathing are examined in some detail in the Report of the *Ad Hoc* Committee on Hyperbaric Oxygenation of the National Academy of Sciences—National Research Council (Division of Medical Sciences, 1963). Potentialities for the converse of high pressure oxygen radiotherapy, that is, radiotherapy performed under induced anoxia, have been examined in some detail by the British Institute of Radiology at its meeting on "Hypoxia in Radiotherapy" (British Institute of Radiology, 1962) and the conclusion was reached that a generalized anoxia could not be induced in man because of the lethal effect of oxygen deprivation on the brain. Suit (1962) has shown, however, a reduced radiation effect on human skin after the induction of anoxia in a limb by application of an arterial tourniquet. Under these conditions double the X-ray dose was required to produce the effects observed without the tourniquet. Suit (1963) has also observed that under similar tourniquet conditions 12,000 rads could be administered to cases of osteogenic sarcoma as 12 fractions in 36 days with only slight skin reactions and with local control of the cancer.

It is not clearly evident that it is essential to breathe oxygen under high pressure in order to induce oxygenation of presumed hypoxic sites. Respiratory stimulation and vasodilatation result from the breathing of carbon dioxide. Du Sault (1963) irradiated spontaneous mammary tumors of mice with X rays while they were breathing either oxygen at three atmospheres of pressure, 95 per cent oxygen and 5 per cent carbon dioxide at three atmospheres, or 95 per cent oxygen and 5 per cent carbon dioxide at one atmosphere; all conditions gave the same cure rate without increasing the normal tissue reactions over those occurring when performing the irradiations while the mice were breathing air at ambient pressure. Conversely, Suit, Schlachter, and Andrews (1960) had shown that an increase in the cure rate of a transplantable mouse mammary carcinoma by X-irradiation under high pressure oxygen breathing was attained only when the tumors were still very small (7 to 10 mm. diameter) in size. Finally, van den Brenk, Elliott, and Hutchings (1963) have shown an actual differential effect between normal and cancer tissue responses by demonstrating that for equal cancerocidal effects on a mouse transplantable tumor, when the irradiations were performed under conditions of either air at ambient pressure, high pressure oxygen, or tourniquet anoxia with appropriate adjustments of X-ray dose for equal cancerocidal effects, skin, that is, normal tissue, reactions were less by a factor of from three to four for the conditions of hyperoxia or anoxia as compared with the reactions following irradiation while breathing air.

The most convincing evidence, to me, of the importance of the oxygen effect in human cancer radiotherapy, as distinct from its existence in cell radiobiology, are the experiments of Goldacre and Sylvén (1962) and of Evans and Naylor (1963). The former have presented some confirmation of the hypothesis upon which the original proposal for high pressure oxygen radiotherapy rested and that is that there are, in human cancers, zones of anoxic but viable, and therefore capable of unlimited reproduction, cells which will show the reduced apparent radiosensitivity response, due to the oxygen effect, to radiotherapy. These investigators studied the distribution of a diffusible dye, lissamine green, into transplantable cancers of rodents and determined that there were uncolored zones of tumor cells into which the dye did not diffuse but from which tumor cells which produced tumor implants in other animals could be dissected. The findings can be interpreted as indicative of impairment of the blood supply or of diffusion phenomena with anoxia but without cell death. Evans and Naylor were able to show, by platinum electrode oxygen polarography, an increase in tumor pO_2 in 30 of 32 measurements on four patients breathing oxygen at ambient pressure with a mean change from 48 to 311 mm of mercury. My own studies of the dose and time relationship and of a small series of patients with cancer of the head and neck irradiated to tumor exposures of 9,000 r in 100 days with thrice weekly increments of only 210 r (Andrews, 1965a) suggest to me that the oxygen effect may be least important at small increments of dose. This is because small increments of dose lie on the curvilinear portions of the two, oxygenated and anoxic, survival curves, where they are approaching each other with diminishing ratios of response and where, despite the magnification factor of repeated small increments on the different, oxygenated and anoxic, surviving fractions, the differences may be so little and such high tumor doses may be attained as to have cancerocidal effects. I believe that this should be systematically investigated.

Finally, I may say that I am especially privileged in having permission to present the preliminary results of high oxygen pressure radiotherapy attained by van den Brenk (1964), of the Cancer Institute Board of Melbourne, who has been studying this technique for two years in a very active radiotherapy clinic. Some 250 patients with advanced cancer have been irradiated with 4 Mev X rays under high pressure oxygen. Of these, 84 had comparable, advanced cancer of the head and neck with lymph node metastases in the neck; three months after irradiation, 56 of 59 patients receiving high pressure oxygen and 11 of 25 patients receiving conventional irradiation had complete retrogression of the presenting cancer to the same pattern of fractionation and total dose. This must be considered as direct evidence of the importance of the oxygen effect in human cancer radiotherapy.

My personal opinion of the oxygen effect and its importance in human cancer radiotherapy with X rays, gamma rays, or electrons, all low LET radiations, is that it probably is important; that it should be explored by carefully planned and, hopefully, definitive human studies rather than by the wholesale adoption of high pressure tanks and high pressure oxygen radiotherapy on a routine basis; that there are alternative ways of exploiting the effect and that these, especially 95 per cent oxygen and 5 per cent carbon dioxide breathing and high LET radiations, should be investigated on a research basis by competent groups; and that more needs to be known about the radiobiological aspects of fractionated irradiation with increments of dose at the very low dose ends of the survival curves where oxygenated:anoxic response ratios may be approaching unity.

Mammalian cell survival curves for low LET, as X-ray and gamma-ray, radiations are characterized by an initial region of zero or of very slight negative slope and then increasing slope to an exponential, or straight line when plotted on semilogarithmic coordinates, relationship of surviving fraction to dose and by extrapolation numbers greater than 1. A common feature of the mammalian cell survival curves which have been developed for high LET radiations by the several investigators previously cited is that they do not show this initial variation in negative slope or "shoulder region" but are of the exponential type with extrapolation numbers of 1 or very near 1 and their negative slopes are steeper. Mammalian cell radiation dose fractionation studies with Po^{210} alpha particles (mean LET, 170 kev/μ) (Barendsen, 1961), fission-spectrum fast neutrons (Andrews and Berry, 1962), Be^{9}(d,n)Be^{10} (bimodal, 1.5 and 6 Mev) fast neutrons (Schneider and Whitmore, 1963), and 14 Mev monoenergetic fast neutrons (Berry and Andrews, 1963), have shown, in general, that fractional increments of dose of the highest LET radiations yield the same surviving fractions as a single dose of the same amount as the total of the fractionated dose increments or, in other words, no recovery occurred between increments; at the lower end of mean LET of these radiations, 14 Mev monoenergetic fast neutrons, some recovery between fractions was demonstrated. These characteristics are reflected in the extrapolation numbers. Low LET radiations are not fully cumulative in their effects and the surviving fractions resulting from fractional increments of dose will be greater than those resulting from a single dose of the same amount. The kinetics of the changes which occur in populations of mammalian cells and which result in this noncumulative type of effect have been elaborated by Elkind and Sutton (1960) who have also found that surviving cells may undergo repeated cycles of sublethal injury and recovery when irradiated with low LET radiations. However, with high LET radiations there is no recovery and the response remains exponential.

The important consequence of this last to human cancer radiotherapy is in relationship to what might be postulated as differences in the kinetics of the restitution of both normal and cancer tissues. Certain cancers, notably those of epithelial origin, have relatively long cell population doubling times as compared with the cell population turnover times of certain normal steady state cell renewal, cell removal populations. The significance of this is that during a radiotherapy course of ordinary duration, e.g. 6 weeks, the cell population numbers of such cancers are not changing importantly due to proliferation of cells not inactivated by prior increments of radiation dose. This situation does not obtain, however, in respect to those normal tissues with very short cell population turnover times which, in the epithelium of the human duodenum (Bertalanffy and Nagy, 1961), colon, and rectum (Lipkin, Bell, and Sherlock, 1963), may be as short as two (duodenum) to four (colon and rectum) days. If the maintenance of a functioning essential organ is prerequisite, as it generally is, to successful cancer radiotherapy, then it is quite apparent that a given dose of high LET radiations, these being fully cumulative in their cell-killing effects, will have a greater depleting effect on these essential normal cell populations than will the same dose of low LET radiations which are not fully cumulative in their cell-killing effects; this difference will be magnified in repeated, small dose fractionation. This, besides the oxygen effect, is the important practical difference, in respect to radiotherapy applications, between high and low LET radiations. That the consequences of such effects may already have been observed in human radiotherapy situations will be touched upon in my remarks about fast neutron beam radiotherapy.

Human radiotherapy applications of high energy positively charged particle beams are now being studied, both with and without the exploitation of the high LET regions of their Bragg peaks, for it is only in these relatively narrow regions, which generally have half value widths of about 2 cm, that high LET, oxygen independent, and n = 1 radiations are present. The Bragg peak for any charged heavy particle radiation can be "transformed;" that is, it can be shifted proximally by the introduction of absorbers into the beam. The consequence of this will be widening of the peak, reduction of the peak to incident or plateau relative intensity ratio, and lowering of the mean LET of this widened and reduced peak region. The relative radiation intensity of the plateau builds up with increasing thickness of the absorber to the point at which it may equal or even very slightly exceed the terminal, now no longer a peak, relative intensity of the beam. As this progressive change occurs, the high LET of the peak is continuously and rapidly reduced to an LET not significantly different from that of X-ray or gamma-ray radiations in respect to mammalian cellular responses. When such transformations are effected, it may be expected that high LET effects will disappear. This has been the observation of the group in Uppsala (Falkmer *et al.*, 1962) which has been studying 187 Mev proton beam radiotherapy of human pelvic cancer. Pelvic cancer, because of its extent or potential extent, requires very broad beam and large volume irradiation and in order to effect a deep and broad zone of homogeneous irradiation in the pelvis the Bragg peak had to be transformed. This was accomplished by means of an ingenious variable thickness water absorber. As a result of the required transformations, the peak to incident relative radiation intensity ratio was reduced to 1.25 and nothing suggestive of high LET radiation effects on tissue was observed. It was concluded by Falkmer and his colleagues that the principal usefulness of such a transformed beam was the production of a cylinder or block of uniform dose and of uniform ionization density, or LET, not effectively different from that of X rays or gamma rays but, unlike them, with a sharp cutoff at the end of the beam range. This cutoff characteristic is shared by low LET electron beams.

Similar requirements, because of the finite size of the human body and the anatomic relationships of most cancers to it, for effecting the transformation of the Bragg peak, and the loss, thereby, of the oxygen independence of high LET radiations, probably will be the limiting factor, exclusive of cost factors, in the general development of heavy charged particle beam radiotherapy sources. Where exploitation of the Bragg peak is not essential or where other characteristics, such as sharp definition and deep penetration, of very high energy heavy charged particle beams are advantageous or where the zone of critical effect is small, as in the irradiation of the pituitary gland, and the Bragg peak can be exploited, such beams may find their greatest usefulness. The application of high energy proton and alpha particle beams for the destruction of the pituitary gland is being studied systematically by Lawrence and his associates (Lawrence *et al.*, 1963) and the same investigators and Kjellberg and his associates (as cited by Lawrence *et al.*, 1963) are studying possibilities for the exploitation of the Bragg peak in the direct, high energy proton beam irradiation of brain cancers. Preliminary results have been reported and depth dose curves have been published which show very high tumor to other tissues dose ratios of the order of 8 to 1 and peak dose half-value widths of about 8 cm, these relationships being achieved by the use of multiple fields, 13 in number, and the exploitation of the Bragg peak.

Prospects for and problems either associated with or to be anticipated with fast neutron beam human cancer radiotherapy may now be considered. So far, it is postulated that the inherent radiosensitivity of human, different normal and cancer tissues is invariant, that extrapolation numbers may vary within very narrow limits as functions of nuclear deoxyribonucleic acid (DNA) content or chromosomal number or volume, that apparent radiosensitivity is a direct function of LET, that capacity for cellular recovery from sublethal injury and, therefore, the potentiality for tissue restitution is an inverse function of LET, and that the oxygen effect is also an inverse function of LET. It follows, then, that if the oxygen effect is to be circumvented by the exploitation of high LET radiations, it is to be expected that normal tissue radiation effects will be different because of the different recovery, and, therefore, repair and restitution, characteristics associated with these radiations. For the exploitation of high LET radiations by the clinical application of fast neutron beam irradiation to human cancer radiotherapy an adequate depth dose must be attained; this limits, of course, the minimum energy of such a beam. It has alreadv been shown by Stone (1948) and his associates that cancer in a variety of anatomic locations could be cured by direct irradiation with a fast neutron beam generated by 16 Mev deutrons from a 60-inch cyclotron impinging upon a beryllium target. The depth dose of such a beam is probably comparable to that published by Bewley (1963b) for the Hammersmith cyclotron and shown in Figure 6. This beam is generated by 15 Mev deuterons on beryllium; the neutron energy spectrum extends from 0 to about 19 Mev with peak intensity at 6 Mev. The depth dose of such a beam is not superior to that of 250 kvp X rays and it probably would be considered by most radiotherapists to be at the absolute minimum of acceptability. A depth dose curve, developed by nuclear emulsion detector responses, for a 14 Mev monoenergetic neutron beam has been published (Smith and Boot, 1962) and is shown in Figure 6. It is superior to that for 250 kvp X rays and is comparable to that for Co^{60} gamma rays but without the subsurface ionization buildup, or skin-sparing effect, of the latter. Bewley (1963b) has stated, however, that there is some subsurface increase in ionization, due to proton buildup, similar to that for Cs^{137} gamma rays with the 0 to 19 Mev neutron energy spectrum fast neutron beam. In any event, it would appear that at least somewhat acceptable depth-dose relationships could be attained by fast neutron energies of 6 or greater Mev but that 14 Mev fast neutrons would provide substantially superior depth-dose relationships. But as neutron energy is increasing mean LET is decreasing and the oxygen effect ratio is increasing. Therefore it is necessary to know the distribution of neutron dose in various ranges of LET for specific neutron sources. A comparable analysis of this has not been made but calculations of the LET distributions of the first collision proton recoil doses have been published by Snyder and Neufeld (1963) for both fission-spectrum and 14 Mev monoenergetic fast neutrons. These calculations are shown in Table 2. It is apparent from this analysis that fission-spectrum fast neutrons are preponderantly high LET radiations while the 14 Mev monoenergetic fast neutron LET's are almost equally distributed between low and high. One may presume that the LET distribution of dose for fast neutrons of energies intermediate to the two shown in Table 2 would vary accordingly. We

TABLE 2

LET Distribution of Fast Neutron Dose

LET (KEV/μ)	PERCENTAGE OF DOSE FOR SPECIFIED NEUTRON SOURCE: MODIFIED FISSION-SPECTRUM NEUTRONS	14 MEV MONO-ENERGETIC NEUTRONS
3.5	0.29	0.031
3.5–7	0.11	42.0
7–25	12.00	7.5
25–50	34.00	14.0
50–100	47.00	7.3
100	6.6	29.0

(From Snyder and Neufeld, 1963.)

(Berry and Andrews, 1963; Andrews, Correa, and Belli, 1964) have found, in mammalian cell survival curve studies, both LET effects, per se, on the negative slopes of survival curves and an oxygen effect for both fission-spectrum and 14 Mev fast neutrons, the oxygen effect ratios being 1.2 and 1.6, respectively. In the same experiments, we found extrapolation numbers of 1 for fission-spectrum and of greater than 1 for 14 Mev monoenergetic fast neutrons. An oxygen effect ratio of a value similar to that for 14 Mev monoenergetic fast neutrons has been found (Bewley and Hornsey, 1964) for the cyclotron, 0 to 19 Mev neutron energy spectrum, fast neutrons. Bewley (1963b) has made calculations, which are shown in Table 3 and which are based upon human tissue composition, of the relative energy absorption from the 0 to 19 Mev neutron energy spectrum fast neutron beam by different tissues. It is apparent that these absorption characteristics are a reversal of those obtaining with 250 kvp X rays and are such as would not be disadvantageous in human cancer radiotherapy.

The prior experience of Stone (1948) and his colleagues with human cancer radiotherapy using 0 to about 19 Mev neutron energy spectrum fast neutrons may be summarized as follows: 226 patients with cancer of various anatomic sites, and generally very advanced in respect to extent and metastasis, were irradiated; of these, 17 survived five or more years. Therefore adequate observations of both immediate and late effects could be observed. Acute erythematous and, more generally, lytic effects were deliberately induced in the skin for it was felt that the fully realizable dosage had not been attained if such effects were not produced. Changes in normal tissues occurring months and years later were more marked than were expected in relationship to the acute reactions; these late lesions included persistent ulceration in the mouth, pharynx, and larynx, mandibular osteitis, and intestinal fibrosis with rigidity and loss of control. Eight patients had so much fibrotic induration in the region of the original tumor that it could not be determined whether residual cancer might be present. None of the 17 patients surviving were free from distressing symptoms related to late, normal tissue damaging effects.

It is of very great importance, in any consideration of the resumption of fast neutron beam human cancer radiotherapy studies, that Stone was able to deduce certain characteristics of the responses to these radiations related to what has already been developed although the determinative radiobiological characteristics themselves, the relationship of LET to re-

TABLE 3

Calculated Relative Energy Absorption of Fast Neutrons by Different Tissues

TISSUE	RELATIVE ENERGY ABSORPTION
Muscle	100
Fat	122
Bone	83

(From Bewley, 1963b.)

covery phenomena and the oxygen effect, were not known when the studies were done. This means that the observed differences in response compared with X-irradiation experience were gross; they were not overlooked; and reasons for them were deduced. Most notable of these observations were:

1. The ratio of the doses required to destroy the cancers to those causing severe damage to normal tissues was very small;
2. the regenerative capacity of the normal tissues was severely damaged;
3. the distribution of the neutron radiation in time was not sufficiently well understood; and
4. the relative degree of late tissue damage, compared with X rays, was even greater than for acute. All of these observations may be interpreted today as being related to the proliferative characteristics of normal steady state cell renewal, cell removal systems with short cell population turnover times and of cancer, nonsteady state cell proliferative, cell populations with relatively long cell population doubling times and to the effects of high LET radiations on cell population restitution potentialities and kinetics. Without the recovery phenomenon associated with low LET radiations the high LET radiations will, for a given dose appropriately adjusted for the increase in apparent radiosensitivity associated with these radiations, impair normal tissue restitution phenomena severely and the degree of impairment may be relatively greater for fractionated than for single dose irradiations. Further, increasing disabling effects, progression of the damage, and failure of healing would be expected to be noted with an increase in time, that is, late effects would be observed where severe injury to tissue restitution phenomena has occurred. That an oxygen effect in respect to improved cancer responses was observed cannot be inferred from Stone's reports. That only 17 of 226 patients survived for five or more years and that a better therapeutic ratio, in the sense of Number 1, above, was not observed suggest that the smaller oxygen effect ratio associated with the neutron beam employed by Stone, as compared with the higher ratio for X rays, did not result in a greater potentiality for cure. This raises, of course, some doubt about the importance of the oxygen effect in human cancer radiotherapy. One further thing may have happened in Stone's cases: there may have been, due to the spectral range, 0 to about 19 Mev, of the neutron energies, an LET effects gradient from high at incidence to low at depth. Theoretically this must occur even if its effects cannot be observed. Such effects would be less for 14 Mev monoenergetic fast neutron beams and this, together with their greater depth dose, would give them some advantages in human cancer radiotherapy. In addition, the oxygen effect ratio is essentially the same for 14 Mev monoenergetic and for 0 to 19 Mev neutron energy spectrum fast neutrons. Fowler (1964) has made an extensive review of the radiobiological and practical clinical aspects of fast neutron beam cancer radiotherapy. In a series of papers he and his associates have described and discussed the experiments performed as pre-

liminary to their announced intention (introduced by Fowler, Morgan, and Wood, 1963) to inaugurate human cancer fast neutron beam radiotherapy studies at the Hammersmith Hospital with the Medical Research Council cyclotron at a 0 to 19 Mev neutron energy spectrum.

Finally, it may be stated that there are certain human normal and cancer tissue radiation responses associated characteristically with LET and oxygen effects. The LET effects result in changes in apparent radiosensitivity and in cellular recovery, and, therefore, in tissue restitution phenomena, and the oxygen effect is inversely related to LET. The oxygen effect, per se, may be important in human cancer radiotherapy but this has not yet been proved. High LET radiations are relatively independent of this oxygen effect and, if the effect is important in human cancer radiotherapy, then they may be used to circumvent it. Satisfactory and, in some instances, greatly improved depth-dose ratios may be attained with high LET radiations. The changes in the cellular recovery phenomena associated with high LET radiations will have to be carefully considered in respect to both the size and spacing of dose increments in human cancer radiotherapy. The radiotherapeutic applications of heavy positively charged particle beams are being studied and similar applications of a 0 to 19 Mev neutron energy spectrum fast neutron beam will be studied by competent investigators. A heavy negatively charged particle, π^--meson beam is not presently available for such applications. To complete the scope of such studies, the development of 14 Mev fast neutron beam radiotherapy should now be undertaken.

ADDENDUM

In respect to the design of a 14 Mev fast neutron beam irradiation facility for human cancer radiotherapy, there are certain common problems of a general technical nature inherent in such radiotherapy which must be solved regardless of the type (photon or particle) or energy (low or high) of the radiations employed.

These common problems are concerned with the precise orientation of the patient and the radiation beam, the collimation of the beam, the protection of personnel, and the shielding of those parts of the patient where radiation is not wanted. A possible solution of these common problems in reference to specific design characteristics for a 14 Mev fast neutron beam human cancer radiotherapy facility has been proposed (Andrews, 1965b).

REFERENCES

Ahn, S. H., and J. H. Roberts. 1957. Energy and Angular Distributions of Neutrons from the Interaction of 14.1-Mev Neutrons with Zirconium. *Physical Review*, 108: 110–113.

Ancel, P., and Vintemberger. 1925. Sur la Radiosensibilité cellulaire. *Comptes rendus des séances de la Société de biologie*, 92:517–520.

Andrews, J. R. 1962. A Concept of Radiosensitivity. *The American Journal of Roentgenology, Radium Therapy and Nuclear Medicine*, 87:601–605.

———. 1965a. Dose-Time Relationships in Cancer Radiotherapy: A Clinical Radiobiology Study of Extremes of Dose and Time. *The American Journal of Roentgenology, Radium Therapy and Nuclear Medicine*, 93:84–97.

———. 1965b. The Potentialities for Fast Neutron Beam Radiotherapy. *The American Journal of Roentgenology, Radium Therapy and Nuclear Medicine*, 93:77–84.

Andrews, J. R., and R. J. Berry. 1962. Fast Neutron Irradiation and the Relationship of Radiation Dose and Mammalian Tumor Cell Reproductive Capacity. *Radiation Research*, 16:76–81.

Andrews, J. R., J. N. Correa, and J. A. Belli. 1964. "Fast Neutron Irradiation, Cell Reproductive Capacity, and the Oxygen Effect," *Proceedings of the International Atomic Energy Agency Symposium on the Biological Effects of Neutron Irradiations.* Vienna, Austria: International Atomic Energy Agency.

Atkin, N. B., and R. M. Richards. 1956. Deoxyribonucleic Acid in Human Tumours as Measured by Microspectrophotometry of Feulgen Stain: A Comparison of Tumours Arising at Different Sites. *The British Journal of Cancer*, 10:769–786.

Barendsen, G. W. 1961. "Damage to the Reproductive Capacity of Human Cells in Tissue Culture by Ionizing Radiations of Different Linear Energy Transfer," *The Initial Effects of Ionizing Radiations on Cells.* R. J. C. Harris, Ed. New York, New York and London, England: Academic Press. Pp. 183–194.

———. 1963. The Saturation Effect at High LET's for Radiation-Induced Inhibition of Clone-Formation by Human Cells in Culture. (Abstract) *International Journal of Radiation Biology, and Related Studies in Physics, Chemistry and Medicine*, 6:481.

Barendsen, G. W., T. L. J. Beusker, A. J. Vergroesen, and L. Budke. 1960. Effects of Different Ionizing Radiations on Human Cells in Tissue Culture. *Radiation Research*, 13:841–849.

Barendsen, G. W., and H. M. D. Walter. 1963. Differences Between Densely and Sparsely Ionizing Radiations with Regard to Modification of Radiation Damage in Human Tissue Culture Cells. In Review by L. F. Lamerton, "Linear Energy Transfer." *Radiation Effects in Physics, Chemistry, and Biology*, M. Ebert and A. Howard, Eds. Amsterdam, The Netherlands: North-Holland Publishing Company. Pp. 1–13.

Barendsen, G. W., H. M. D. Walter, J. F. Fowler, and D. K. Bewley. 1963. Effects of Different Ionizing Radiations on Human Cells in Tissue Culture. III. Experiments with Cyclotron-Accelerated Alpha-Particles and Deuterons. *Radiation Research*, 18: 106–119.

Bell, A. G. 1964. Diploid and Endoreduplicated Cells: Measurements of DNA. *Science*, 143:139–140.

Belli, J. A., and J. R. Andrews. 1963. The Relationship between Tumor Growth and Radiosensitivity. *Journal of the National Cancer Institute*, 31:689–703.

Berry, R. J. 1963. Quantitative Studies of Relationships between Tumor Cell Ploidy and Dose Response to Ionizing Radiation *in vivo*. Modification of Radiation Response in a Previously Irradiated Tumor. *Radiation Research*, 18:236–245.

Berry, R. J., and J. R. Andrews. 1963. The Effect of Radiation Ionization Density (LET) Upon the Reproductive Capacity of Mammalian Tumour Cells Irradiated and Assayed *in vivo. British Journal of Radiology*, 36:49–55.

Bertalanffy, F. D., and K. P. Nagy. 1961. Mitotic Activity and Renewal Rate of the Epithelial Cells of the Human Duodenum. *Acta anatomica*, 45:362–370.

Bewley, D. K. 1963a. A Fast-Neutron Source for Radiotherapy. *Nature*, London, 200: 701.

———. 1963b. Physical Aspects of the Fast Neutron Beam. *British Journal of Radiology*, 36:81–88.

Bewley, D. K., and S. Hornsey. 1964. Radiobiological Experiments with Fast Neutrons, with Reference to the Possible Value of Neutron Therapy. *Proceedings of the International Atomic Energy Agency Symposium on the Biological Effects of Neutron Irradiations.* Vienna, Austria: International Atomic Energy Agency.

Bragg, Sir W. 1912. *Studies in Radioactivity*. New York, New York: The Macmillan Co., 196 pp.

British Institute of Radiology. 1961. Depth Dose Tables for Use in Radiotherapy. *British Journal of Radiology*. Supplement 10: 1–96.

———. 1962. Hypoxia in Radiotherapy, Abstracts of Papers. *British Journal of Radiology*, 35:505–507.

Brustad, T. 1962. "Heavy Ions and Some Aspects of Their Use in Molecular and Cellular Radiobiology," *Advances in Biological and Medical Physics*. New York, New York: Academic Press, Inc. Vol. VIII. Pp. 161–224.

Chu, E. H. Y., N. H. Giles, and K. Passano. 1961. Types and Frequencies of Human Chromosome Aberrations Induced by X-Rays. *Proceedings of the National Academy of Sciences of the U.S.A.*, 47:830–839.

Churchill-Davidson, I., C. Sanger, and R. H. Thomlinson. 1957. Oxygenation in Radiotherapy. II. Clinical Application. *British Journal of Radiology*, 30:406–422.

Coon, J. H. 1960. "Targets for the Production of Neutrons," *Fast Neutron Physics. Part I: Techniques*, J. B. Marion and J. L. Fowler, Eds. New York, New York: Interscience Publishers, Inc. Pp. 677–721.

Deering, R. A., and R. Rice, Jr. 1962. Heavy Ion Irradiation of HeLa Cells. *Radiation Research*, 17:774–786.

Dewey, W. C., and R. M. Humphrey. 1962. Relative Radiosensitivity of Different Phases in the Life Cycle of L-P59 Mouse Fibroblasts and Ascites Tumor Cells. *Radiation Research*, 16:503–530.

Division of Medical Sciences, National Academy of Sciences—National Research Council. 1963. *Report of the* Ad Hoc *Committee on Hyperbaric Oxygenation.* (National Academy of Sciences, National Research Council). Washington, D.C., 37 pp.

Du Sault, L. A. 1963. The Effect of Oxygen on the Response of Spontaneous Tumours in Mice to Radiotherapy. *British Journal of Radiology*, 36:749–754.

Elkind, M. M., and H. Sutton. 1960. Radiation Response of Mammalian Cells Grown in Culture. I. Repair of X-Ray Damage in Surviving Chinese Hamster Cells. *Radiation Research*, 13:556–593.

Epstein, H. T. 1953. Identification of Radiosensitive Volume with Nucleic Acid Volume. *Nature*, London, 171:394–395.

Erikson, R. L., and W. Szybalski. 1963. Molecular Radiobiology of Human Cell Lines. IV. Variation in Ultraviolet Light and X-Ray Sensitivity During the Division Cycle. *Radiation Research*, 18:200–212.

Evans, N. T. S., and P. F. D. Naylor. 1963. The Effect of Oxygen Breathing and Radiotherapy upon the Tissue Oxygen Tension of Some Human Tumours. *British Journal of Radiology*, 36:418–425.

Falkmer, S., B. Fors, B. Larsson, A. Lindell, J. Naeslund, and S. Stenson. 1962. Pilot Study on Proton Irradiation of Human Carcinoma. *Acta radiologica*, 58:33–51.

Fowler, J. F. 1964. "Neutrons in Radiotherapy: Slow Neutrons, Fast Neutrons, and Other Heavy Particles," *Proceedings of the International Atomic Energy Agency Symposium on the Biological Effects of Neutron Irradiations*. Vienna, Austria: International Atomic Energy Agency.

Fowler, J. F., R. L. Morgan, and C. A. P. Wood. 1963. I. The Biological and Physical Advantages and Problems of Neutron Therapy. Introduction to Series: Pre-Therapeutic Experiments with the Fast Neutron Beam from the Medical Research Council Cyclotron. *British Journal of Radiology*, 36:77–80 (complete series: 77–121).

Fowler, P. H., and D. H. Perkins. 1961. The Possibility of Therapeutic Applications of Beams of Negative π-Mesons. *Nature*, London, 189:524–528.

Goldacre, R. J., and B. Sylven. 1962. On the Access of Blood-Borne Dyes to Various Tumour Regions. *The British Journal of Cancer*, 16:306–322.

Gray, L. H. 1961. Radiobiologic Basis of Oxygen as a Modifying Factor in Radiation

Therapy. *The American Journal of Roentgenology, Radium Therapy and Nuclear Medicine*, 85:803–815.

Guild, W. R. 1963. The Radiation Sensitivity of Deoxyribonucleic Acid. *Radiation Research, Supplement* 3: 257–269.

Hauschka, T. S. 1961. Chromosomes in Ontogeny and Oncogeny. *Cancer Research*, 21: 957–974.

Hollcroft, J. W., E. Lorenz, and M. Matthews. 1952. Factors Modifying the Effect of X-Irradiation on Regression of a Transplanted Lymphosarcoma. *Journal of the National Cancer Institute*, 12:751–763.

Koller, P. C. 1963. The Nucleus of the Cancer Cell: A Historical Review. *Experimental Cell Research*, Supplement 9: 3–14.

Langsdorf, A., Jr. 1960. "Neutron Collimation and Shielding for Experimental Purposes," *Fast Neutron Physics. Part 1: Techniques*, J. B. Marion and J. L. Fowler, Eds. New York, New York: Interscience Publishers, Inc. Pp. 721–807.

Lawrence, J. H., C. A. Tobias, J. L. Born, A. Gottschalk, J. A. Linfoot, and R. P. Kling. 1963. Alpha Particle and Proton Beams in Therapy. *Journal of the American Medical Association*, 186:236–245.

Lipkin, M., B. Bell, and P. Sherlock. 1963. Cell Proliferation Kinetics in the Gastrointestinal Tract of Man. I. Cell Renewal in Colon and Rectum. *Journal of Clinical Investigation*, 42:767–776.

Madigan, J. P., N. M. Cass, K. H. Clarke, K. L. Biggs, R. C. Kerr, D. Jamieson, and H. A. S. van den Brenk. 1963. Symposium on Oxygen Barotherapy. *Journal of the College of Radiologists of Australasia*, 6:94–121.

Metz, D. J. 1962. *Introductory Lectures on the Properties, Detection, and Chemical Effects of High Energy Radiations.* (Brookhaven National Laboratory Publication No. 748 [T-274]. Upton, New York: Brookhaven National Laboratory.

Naeslund, J., S. Stenson, S. Falkmer, A. Lindell, B. Larsson, and T. Svedberg. 1958. Concerning the Effects of Proton Radiation on Vx2 Carcinoma and Normal Skin in Rabbit Ears. *Acta Societatis medicorum upsaliensis*, 3–4:155–139.

Petrakis, N. L., W. L. Bostik, and B. V. Siegel. 1959. The Deoxyribonucleic Acid (DNA) Content of Sternberg-Reed Cells of Hodgkin's Disease. *Journal of the National Cancer Institute*, 22:551–554.

Puck, T. T., and J. Steffen. 1963. Life Cycle Analysis of Mammalian Cells. I. A Method for Localizing Metabolic Events within the Life Cycle, and its Application to the Action of Colcemide and Sublethal Doses of X-Irradiation. *Biophysical Journal*, 3:379–397.

Radiation Dynamics, Incorporated. 1963. *The Production of Monoenergetic Neutrons. Radiation Review*, Volume III. Westbury, L. I., New York, 4 pp.

Rosen, L., and L. Stewart. 1957. Neutron Emission Probabilities from the Interaction of 14 Mev Neutrons with Be, Ta, and Bi. *Physical Review*, 107:824–829.

Schaefer, H. J. 1964. "Local LET Spectra in Tissue for Solar Flare Protons in Space and for Neutron Produced Recoil Protons," *Proceedings of the International Atomic Energy Agency Symposium of the Biological Effects of Neutron Irradiations.* Vienna, Austria: International Atomic Energy Agency.

Schneider, D. O., and G. F. Whitmore. 1963. Comparative Effects of Neutrons and X-Rays on Mammalian Cells. *Radiation Research*, 18:286–306.

Sinclair, W. K., and R. A. Morton. 1963. Variations in X-Ray Response during the Division Cycle of Partially Synchronized Chinese Hamster Cells in Culture. *Nature*, London, 199:1158–1160.

Smith, J. W., and S. J. Boot. 1962. The Variation of Neutron Dose with Depth in a Tissue-Equivalent Phantom. *Physics in Medicine and Biology*, 7:45–67.

Snyder, W. S., and J. Neufeld. 1963. "Studies Concerning the Relation of RBE to LET," *Annual Progress Report of the Health Physics Division* (Oak Ridge National Laboratory Publication No. 3492). Oak Ridge, Tennessee, pp. 123–124.

Sparrow, A. H., L. A. Schairer, and R. C. Sparrow. 1963. Relationship between Nuclear Volumes, Chromosome Numbers, and Relative Radiosensitivities. *Science*, 141:163–166.

Stich, H. F., S. F. Florian, and H. E. Emson. 1960. The DNA Content of Tumor Cells. I. Polyps and Adenocarcinomas of the Large Intestine of Man. *Journal of the National Cancer Institute*, 24:471–482.

Stone, R. S. 1948. Neutron Therapy and Specific Ionization. Janeway Memorial Lecture. *The American Journal of Roentgenology and Radium Therapy*, 59:771–785.

Suit, H., L. Schlachter, and J. R. Andrews. 1960. "Oxygen Effect" and Tumor Size as Related to Response of C3H/Ba Adenocarcinoma to Local X-Irradiation. *Journal of the National Cancer Institute*, 24:1271–1281.

Suit, H. D. 1962. "Oxygen Effect Factor" of Human Skin. *Radiology*, 79:118–119.

————. 1963. Personal Communication.

Terasima, T., and L. J. Tolmach. 1961. Changes in X-Ray Sensitivity of HeLa Cells During the Division Cycle. *Nature*, London, 190:1210–1211.

Terzi, M. 1961. Comparative Analysis of Inactivating Efficiency of Radiation on Different Organisms. *Nature*, London, 191:461–463.

Till, J. E. 1963. Quantitative Aspects of Radiation Lethality at the Cellular Level. *The American Journal of Roentgenology, Radium Therapy and Nuclear Medicine*, 90:917–927.

Van den Brenk, H. A. S. 1964. High Pressure Oxygen Radiotherapy. *Proceedings of the International Congress on Clinical Application of Hyperbaric Oxygen*. Amsterdam, The Netherlands: Elsevier Publishing Company. (in press.)

Van den Brenk, H. A. S., K. Elliott, and H. Hutchings. 1963. Further Observations on Radiocurability of a Solid Ehrlich Tumour and Tissue Reactions in the Mouse with Fractionated Radiation Doses and the Effects of Oxygen. *The British Journal of Cancer*, 17:281–286.

Zucker, A., and A. H. Snell. 1963. Meson Factories? *Physics Today*, 16:19–24.

Clinical Potentialities of Recent Advances in Cellular Radiobiology

HENRY S. KAPLAN

Department of Radiology,
Stanford University School of Medicine,
Palo Alto, California

Recent experimental investigations in cellular radiobiology have yielded at least three significant general approaches to the improvement of end results in clinical radiotherapy; these are: (1) differential chemical radiosensitization; (2) differential chemical radioprotection; and (3) cell cycle-modulated dose fractionation. Each of these approaches has certain potential advantages and limitations (Kallman, 1961; Bagshaw, 1961). It is the purpose of this paper to discuss the problems associated with their clinical application.

DIFFERENTIAL CHEMICAL RADIOSENSITIZATION

The rationale of this approach hinges on the possibility that significantly greater concentrations of certain chemical radiosensitizers might be introduced into tumor tissue, as contrasted with the adjacent normal tissues within the field of irradiation. The expectation of differential concentration or incorporation of the chemical agent is based upon vascular and tissue diffusion considerations in the case of oxygen and on the presumably greater general frequency of deoxyribonucleic acid (DNA) synthesis in tumor versus stromal cells in the case of pyrimidine and purine analogues. The major problems in each instance center around the delivery of the chemical agent to the tumor.

Oxygen

It is well established that the radiosensitivity of a great many biologic systems may be enhanced approximately threefold by oxygen. Gray (1959, 1961) has ably presented the thesis that many tumors, as a consequence of local overgrowth of blood supply, contain severely hypoxic, partially necrotic regions in which the surviving tumor cells may be expected to be appreciably more radioresistant and thus to serve as foci for recrudescent tumor growth after radiotherapy. Physiological considerations indicated that breathing 100 per cent oxygen at normal atmospheric pressure would probably not significantly improve the oxygenation of these hypoxic regions. Accordingly, some years ago, a group at St. Thomas' Hospital in London undertook a courageous pioneering effort to utilize hyperbaric oxygen in conjunction with radiotherapy (Churchill-Davidson, Sanger, and Thomlinson, 1957). The complexity of the procedure demanded that the frequency of treatment be drastically reduced to two or three sessions, separated by intervals of one to two weeks. Unfortunately, a randomized control group treated without oxygen on the same unorthodox fractionation schedule was not simultaneously established. It is to be hoped that controlled clinical trials utilizing hyperbaric oxygen, which are now underway in other centers, will yield more definitive evidence on the value of this technique.

It has been pointed out that the highly fractionated radiotherapeutic technique introduced many years ago by Coutard may have had the unappreciated advantage of circumventing the oxygen problem, at least in part, by continuing treatment during the gradual regression of a tumor and the restoration of a more adequate blood supply to its previously less well-vascularized internal regions. If so, the improvement in cure rates from the use of hyperbaric oxygen, beyond those already achieved by variations of the Coutard method, will be relatively small.

The great practical difficulties of delivering oxygen under increased pressure have stimulated a search for other solutions to the problem. One such approach, now being actively explored by Fowler and his colleagues (Fowler and Morgan, 1963), involves the use of higher linear energy transfer (LET) radiations (specifically, neutrons), whose action is less oxygen-dependent. The usefulness of this approach will depend on three factors: (1) the availability of neutron generators suitable for clinical operation; (2) radiobiological evidence that the oxygen effect associated with neutrons of the energies generated by such apparatus is suitably low; and (3) neutron beam tissue distributions, particularly at depth, which compare not too unfavorably with those of supervoltage X rays.

Finally, practical considerations make it desirable to continue efforts to utilize oxygen at normal atmospheric pressure more effectively. Possible avenues for further study include hypertransfusion of washed red blood cells to increase blood hemoglobin concentration and oxygen-carrying capacity to maximal levels, the use of pharmacologic agents to modify tumor blood flow differentially (Abrams, 1964), and possibly the deliberate utilization of a longer interval between a suitable initial dose of radiation and the subsequent completion of the radiotherapy course to allow more time for partial tumor regression and the re-establishment of a better blood supply to the interior of the tumor.

Pyrimidine Analogues

The halogenated pyrimidines have provided us with agents of unusual selectivity. The three heavier halogen derivatives, 5-chlorouracil (ClU), 5-bromouracil (BU), and 5-iodouracil (IU) and their corresponding deoxyribosides (5-chlorodeoxyuridine [ClUdR], 5-bromodeoxyuridine [BUdR], and iododeoxyuridine [IUdR]) behave as analogues of thymine and thymidine, respectively, and are therefore selectively incorporated into DNA. In contrast, 5-fluorouracil (FU) is selectively incorporated into ribonucleic acid (RNA) in place of uracil. FU and its deoxyriboside (5-fluorodeoxyuridine [FUdR]) powerfully inhibit the enzyme thymidylate synthetase, thus blocking a main pathway for thymidylate (and DNA) synthesis. After the incorporation of ClU, BU, IU, or their deoxyribosides into cellular DNA, bacterial and mammalian cells become appreciably more sensitive to the lethal action of ultraviolet (UV) and ionizing radiations (Greer, 1960; Djordjevic and Szybalski, 1960; Kaplan and Tomlin, 1960; Kaplan, Smith, and Tomlin, 1962). In contrast, FU has no sensitizing effect on bacterial cells (Kaplan, Smith, and Tomlin, 1962). The degree of radiosensitization is clearly related to the extent of incorporation of the analogue into DNA; sensitivity increases with increasing time of incubation of bacteria in the analogue-containing medium, and sensitivities of intermediate degree are obtained when reciprocal 9:1 mixtures of thymine and BU are employed. Although very extensive incorporation of BU is required to elicit significant radiosensitization in wild-type *Escherichia coli* B/r grown in sulfanilamide medium supplemented with BU, a much lower extent of BUdR incorporation sufficed for significant radiosensitization of mammalian cells (Delihas, Rich, and Eidinoff, 1962). The radiosensitization elicited by the halogenated pyrimidines has been shown to be oxygen-independent (Kaplan, Zavarine, and Earle, 1962; Humphrey, Dewey, and Cork, 1963).

The halogenated deoxycytidine derivatives, 5-bromodeoxycytidine (BCdR) and 5-iododeoxycytidine (ICdR), are converted intracellularly into BUdR and IUdR, respectively, and thereafter incorporated into DNA (Calabresi, Creasey, Prusoff, and Welch, 1963). These compounds also proved to be effective radiosensitizers of mammalian cells in vitro (Bagshaw, 1962; Cramer, *et al.*, 1962).

The rationale for the use of the halogenated pyrimidines in clinical radiotherapy depends upon the fact that they are incorporated only into DNA newly synthesized by cells preparing to divide. It has seemed a reasonable assumption that many of the supporting stromal cells in the immediate vicinity of the tumor divide infrequently, if at all, and would thus be expected to incorporate little or none of the analogue into their DNA. A larger fraction of the cells of the tumor would be expected to undergo DNA synthesis and thus to incorporate significantly greater amounts of analogue during any finite period of time. However, tumor-cell generation times are variable and may be greatly prolonged (Mendelsohn, 1962). It seems unlikely that a majority of the randomly dividing cells of a tumor could be labeled prior to any single radiation exposure, except by the use of inconveniently long infusion periods involving the use of large, possibly toxic amounts of analogue. Kriss and his co-workers (Kriss and Révész, 1962; Kriss *et al.*, 1963) have shown that intravenously administered BUdR and IUdR undergo rapid enzymatic degradation in the liver, and that BCdR and ICdR are deaminated by an enzyme present in human and mouse blood. Recent unpublished investigations by Kriss, employing a $C^{14}O_2$ gas analyzer to monitor the retention of tracer doses of 2-C^{14}-labeled thymidine, BUdR, and IUdR, indicate that BUdR is retained and presumably incorporated into DNA of human tissues as well as thymidine or better and severalfold more efficiently than IUdR.

Thus, the following clinical strategy is emerging: (1) the analogue of choice appears to be BUdR or BCdR, although the corresponding chloro-compounds have not yet been excluded as candidates; (2) the analogue must be given by intra-arterial infusion to enable a high concentration to reach the tumor before the analogue's passage through the liver, where enzymatic degradation would be expected; (3) competition by endogenous thymidine should be blocked by the prior administration of FUdR (the optimal temporal relationships of FUdR and subsequent BUdR administration and the optimal duration of BUdR infusion remain to be elucidated); and (4) x-irradiation should be administered within a few hours after the BUdR infusion to avoid dilution of the incorporated BUdR by a second round of DNA replication in the next generation cycle.

It would be desirable to time each successive cycle of FUdR and subsequent BUdR administration as accurately as possible to the onset of a wave of DNA synthesis. Effective techniques for externally monitoring the onset of DNA synthesis are not presently available, and recourse must now be had to liquid scintillation counting of DNA extracted from biopsy specimens after serial tracer doses of tritiated thymidine. Perhaps, as experience with the method grows, it will be possible to define the time interval to the next round of DNA synthesis with reasonable precision for different classes of tumors and thus to eliminate the need for serial biopsy. Alternatively, if external monitoring techniques were available, the onset of DNA synthesis could be detected at each successive cycle in individual patients. With appropriate timing, a progressively greater fraction of the tumor cells should incorporate the analogue, and the average radiosensitivity of the tumor cell population should increase significantly.

The selection of optimal radiation doses and fractionation schedules will also demand some thought. To the extent that the interior of a tumor has an impaired blood supply, it will not only tend to be relatively hypoxic, and thus more radioresistant, but will tend to have a lower mitotic and DNA synthetic activity. In addition, the inadequacy of the blood supply would interfere with delivery of adequate concentrations of the analogue to this part of the tumor. There is thus an argument to be made for selecting radiation doses and intervals which will cause regression of the peripheral, well-vascularized portions of the tumor and improve the blood supply to previously ischemic regions between successive infusions of the analogue.

Purine Analogues

Certain purine analogues are also known to be incorporated into nucleic acids, though much less selectively than the pyrimidine analogues, since they enter both RNA and DNA. Accordingly, we have investigated the radiation response of bacterial cells grown in the presence of purine analogues and found that several of these compounds are powerful radiosensitizers (Kaplan, Smith, and Tomlin, 1961). In contrast to the pyrimidine analogues, the radiosensitization which they cause is highly oxygen-dependent (Kaplan, Zavarine, and Earle, 1962). The most extensively studied of the active compounds are 6-thioguanine (TG), 6-mercaptopurine (6-MP), and 2-aminopurine (2-AP). The incorporation of C^{14}-labeled thioguanine into both DNA and RNA of ascites tumor cells has been reported by LePage (1960), and we have confirmed this in bacterial cells with S^{35}-labeled TG (Kaplan and Earle, unpublished data). The extent of incorporation, calculated in terms of guanine replacement, is less than 1 per cent. There is a nonlinear correlation between the extent of incorporation of TG-S^{35} and the degree of radiosensitization of the bacterial cells. Incorporation of 2-AP into *E. coli* DNA has been reported to occur to a very slight extent (Gottschling and Freese, 1961); we are still investigating the incorporation of 6-MP into *E. coli* nucleic acids. The disproportionately greater radiosensitizing effect of the purine analogues may, of course, be due to mechanisms other than incorporation. Feedback inhibition and other purine pathway antimetabolic actions of these analogues (Gots and Gollub, 1959; Henderson, 1963), coupled with our recent discovery of the phenomenon of radiosensitization by purine starvation (Kaplan and Howsden, 1964), suggest that the sensitizing effect of these compounds may result, at least in part, from their induction of a secondary purine starvation at the cellular level.

The purine analogues are known to be highly toxic in man (Philips, Sternberg, Hamilton, and Clarke, 1954). For this reason, unless they present significant advantages (other than their low cost), such as greater resistance to enzymatic degradation and/or greater rapidity of action, they would probably be less desirable candidates for clinical use than the pyrimidine analogues. The same considerations of the timing of successive drug and radiation exposures would apply, and the problem of inhomogeneity of blood supply within the tumor would be even more critical, in view of the strong oxygen dependence of their radiosensitizing action.

Miscellaneous Agents

Actinomycin D

This agent has now been used for several years in conjunction with radiation in treatment for certain tumors, particularly Wilms's tumor and neuroblastoma in children, on the basis of its experimental and clinical potentiation of radiation effect (D'Angio, Farber, and Maddock, 1959; Bases, 1959). However, conclusive proof of its efficacy in terms of significantly improved long-term cure rates is not yet available, although many radiotherapists have now confirmed certain of the initial clinical observations, notably the curious reactivation by the antibiotic of cutaneous erythema in areas previously exposed to radiation. It has recently been demonstrated (Goldberg and Rabinowitz, 1962; Haselkorn, 1964; Reich, 1964) that the antibiotic selectively inhibits the enzyme RNA polymerase, thus interfering with messenger RNA and protein synthesis, by binding to the minor groove of DNA and thus excluding the enzyme from its normal binding site. Perhaps, now that its molecular interactions are becoming better understood, its interaction with radiation can be more fully elucidated.

Hydrogen Peroxide

The intra-arterial infusion of hydrogen peroxide has been investigated by Mallams and his associates (Mallams, Finney, and Balla, 1962), and encouraging clinical observations have been reported. It has been presumed that any effect of hydrogen peroxide would be attributable to its release of nascent oxygen in the tissues, perhaps with preferential distribution into previously hypoxic regions in the tumor. However, on the basis of known dissociation constants and diffusion rates, physiologists have expressed doubt that significant amounts of oxygen could reach hypoxic tumor cells under these conditions. Direct polarographic measurements with microelectrodes planted into the tumor may help to resolve this question. At the clinical level, a randomized therapeutic trial will be required to establish the efficacy of hydrogen peroxide infusion as an adjunct to radiotherapy.

Differential Chemical Radioprotection

Sulfhydryl Compounds

The radioprotective action of cysteine, glutathione, mercaptoethylamine, 2-aminoethylisothiouronium bromide hydrobromide (AET), and related compounds has been well documented for a number of years (Patt, 1953; Bacq and Alexander, 1961). The compounds must be present in the cells in adequate concentration at the moment of irradiation; even seconds after the radiation exposure, their administration is without effect. Although the action of these compounds has been thought to involve binding or competition with oxygen, there are indications that they protect even under anoxic conditions, probably by acting as hydrogen donors to quench free radicals (Howard-Flanders, 1961). Early attempts to demonstrate differentially greater radioprotection in normal tissues than in experimental tumors met with discouraging results (Straube, Patt, Smith, and Tyree, 1950), and the considerable systemic toxicity of these agents also represented a serious limitation. Recently the question of the tissue distribution of such compounds in tumors and normal tissues has been reinvestigated, and some indications of differential distribution have been obtained (Schwartz, Shapiro, and Kollmann, 1964; Kollmann, Shapiro, and Schwartz, 1964), although perhaps not of sufficient magnitude to be clinically useful. If related compounds of less systemic toxicity were to become available, clinical applications for them might well emerge.

Polyhydroxyl Alcohols

Glycerol and other polyhydroxyl alcohols have been shown to be effective in protecting bacterial and mammalian cells from the lethal effects of ionizing radiation (Marcovich, 1958; Webb, 1963). The mechanism of action is still debated, but is apparently independent of the oxygen effect. Although glycerol is nontoxic, the extremely high concentrations which are required for effective radioprotection (approximately 1 M) have not seemed attainable under clinical conditions.

Hypoxia

Wright and Bewley (1960) have suggested, on the basis of animal experiments, that tumor-bearing animals or patients breathing nitrogen or hypoxic gas mixtures would, if their normal tissues were better vascularized than the tumors, undergo a preferential washing out of oxygen from the normal tissues and would thus be expected to exhibit differential radioprotection, if they could be irradiated rapidly during a brief period of exposure to anoxia or to severe hypoxia. This prediction has been confirmed experimentally by Zatz (1963), using minimally tolerated concentrations (6.5 to 7.5 per cent) of oxygen. While such low oxygen concentrations might be tolerated by healthy young adult patients on a single-exposure basis, anesthesiologists and physiologists whom we have consulted have expressed grave concern about the ability of the human brain, particularly in elderly and frail individuals, to tolerate repeated hypoxic exposures, such as would be required for the multiple radiation treatments. The prior induction of hypothermia would enable such gas mixtures to be used with greater safety, but this would add appreciably to the complexity of treatment. The limited tolerance of the brain for hypoxia would also create a demand for radiation beams of exceedingly high intensity, to enable the treatment to be completed in a few seconds, after which oxygenation could be restored. Further experimental work with high-intensity electron beams, such as are provided by linear accelerators, may help to define circumstances in which this approach might be clinically exploited.

Cell Cycle-Modulated Dose Fractionation

Pelc and Howard (1955) proposed the experimental analysis of the mitotic cycle in terms of four phases of unequal duration: M—the actual process of mitosis; G_1—the interval or time gap between telophase and the onset of DNA synthesis; S—the DNA synthetic period, during which isotope-labeled precursors are incorporated into DNA; and G_2—the interval between the end of DNA synthesis and the next mitosis. New techniques for synchronizing one or more cell divisions in mammalian cell cultures have made it possible to study the radiosensitivity of cells at different stages of the mitotic cycle (Terasima and Tolmach, 1963a, b; Sinclair and Morton, 1963). There is agreement to date that cells are more sensitive to the lethal effects of ionizing radiations at some stages than at others. However, it appears that cells differ with respect to their most sensitive stage, although sensitivity during M seems a rather general feature. As Terasima and Tolmach have pointed out, the radiosensitivity of a randomly dividing population is a composite of the individual sensitivities of cells in various stages of division at the moment of irradiation.

The methods of achieving synchrony in mammalian cell cultures in vitro do not seem clinically applicable. However, radiation itself has long been known to delay the mitotic progress of intermitotic cells (Friedenwald and Sigelman, 1953; Terasima and Tolmach, 1963a; Mak and Till, 1963; Yamada and Puck, 1961). Since the principal block occurs in G_2, irradiated cells tend to accumulate in that phase. After relatively low doses of irradiation, the mitotic block is reversible, and cells may escape from the G_2 block in a partially synchronized pulse. Kallman (1963) has suggested that advantage might be taken of this radiation-induced mitotic arrest in G_2, despite the fact that the synchrony of the subsequent escape is far from perfect, to deliver a second dose of radiation at the moment when a maximal fraction of the cells are in the sensitive M phase. The same general concepts would apply to additional fractionated radiation exposures, each timed to occur during a mitotic wave.

The clinical usefulness of this concept hinges on several critical questions. Obviously, if all normal tissues and tumors exhibited exactly the same degree of mitotic delay and all escaped from the mitotic delay at the same time, no differential advantage would thus be gained, since the radiosensitivity of both the normal and the tumor tissues would be comparably augmented. However, the rates of cell division in the various normal tissues of the body are appreciably different, as are those of many kinds of tumors, and it is therefore to be expected that certain timing sequences would be differentially advantageous for the killing of tumor versus normal cells. Preliminary results from our laboratory (Frindel, Kallman, and Kaplan, 1963) for mouse intestine, bone marrow, and mammary tumors are encouraging on this score. Moreover, it has been shown that treatment with colchicine at an appropriate time *after* irradiation enables strikingly greater bunching in M of cells escaping from the radiation-induced G_2 block. Many years ago, Brues and associates (Brues, Marble, and Jackson, 1940) suggested the use of colchicine to block cells in mitosis and thus achieve radiosensitization. Experimental attempts yielded discouraging results, because of the toxicity of colchicine and the fact that the colchicine was being applied to an initially randomly dividing population. Perhaps the use of colchicine after irradiation, when many of the cells have been blocked in the colchicine-sensitive G_2 period, would enable smaller, less toxic doses of the drug to be employed successfully to achieve secondary bunching in M, thus enabling more effective timing of the second radiation exposure. It is obvious that methods for monitoring of impending cell mitosis in a partially synchronized population would be of the utmost assistance in implementing these concepts in clinical radiotherapeutic practice. The cyclic fluctuations of tumor radioactivity observed by Hale and his colleagues (Bullen *et al.*, 1963) in P^{32}-injected patients bearing indwelling probe counters are of interest in this connection, despite the fact that the physiological mechanism of the cycling activity has not been established.

Finally, it should be pointed out that some of the approaches discussed here are not mutually exclusive. For example, there is no reason why radiosensitization with the pyrimidine analogues could not be coupled to cell cycle-modulated radiation dose fractionation. Thus, FUdR applied to a randomly dividing cell population would block the onset of DNA synthesis and thus trap and bunch cells at the transition from G_1 to S, whereupon BUdR would be given to release the block and become incorporated into DNA. If the sensitized cells were then irradiated, they would again be blocked in G_2, and could then be treated with colchicine and finally reirradiated after they had become bunched in M. There is obviously still a vast amount of work to be done, however, before we can hope to implement such elaborate schemes for the artificial modification of radiotherapeutic response.

REFERENCES

Abrams, H. L. 1964. Altered Drug Response of Tumour Vessels in Man. *Nature*, London, 201:167–170.

Bacq, Z. M., and R. Alexander. 1961. *Fundamentals of Radiobiology*. New York, New York; London, England; and Paris, France: Pergamon Press, 55 pp.

Bagshaw, M. A. 1961. Possible Role of Potentiators in Radiation Therapy. *The American Journal of Roentgenology, Radium Therapy and Nuclear Medicine*, 85:822–833.

———. 1962. Modification of the Radiosensitivity of Hamster Cells *in vitro*. *Nature*, London, 193:389–391.

Bases, R. E. 1959. Modification of the Radiation Response Determined by Single-Cell Techniques: Actinomycin D. *Cancer Research*, 19:1223–1229.

Brues, A. M., B. B. Marble, and E. B. Jackson. 1940. Effects of Colchicine and Radiation on Growth of Normal Tissues and Tumors. *The American Journal of Cancer*, 38:159–168.

Bullen, M. A., H. F. Freundlich, B. T. Hale, D. H. Marshall, and R. C. Tudway. 1963. The Activity of Malignant Tumours and Response to Therapeutic Agents, Studied by Continuous Records of Radioactive Phosphorus Uptake. *Postgraduate Medical Journal*, 39:265–277.

Calabresi, P., W. A. Creasey, W. H. Prusoff, and A. D. Welch. 1963. Clinical and Pharmacological Studies with 5-Iodo-2′-Deoxycytidine. *Cancer Research*, 23:583–592.

Churchill-Davidson, I., C. Sanger, and R. H. Thomlinson. 1957. Oxygenation in Radiotherapy: Clinical Considerations. *British Journal of Radiology*, 30:406–422.

Cramer, J. W., W. H. Prusoff, A. C. Sartorelli, I. W. Delamore, P. K. Chang, C. F. von Essen, and A. D. Welch. 1962. Studies on the Biochemical Pharmacology of 5-Iodo-2′-Deoxycytidine *in vitro* and *in vivo*. *Biochemical Pharmacology*, 11:761–768.

D'Angio, G. J., S. Farber, and C. L. Maddock. 1959. Potentiation of X-Ray Effects by Actinomycin D. *Radiology*, 73:175–177.

Delihas, N., M. A. Rich, and M. L. Eidinoff. 1962. Radiosensitization of a Mammalian Cell Line with 5-Bromodeoxyuridine. *Radiation Research*, 17:479–491.

Djordjevic, B., and W. Szybalski. 1960. Genetics of Human Cell Lines. III. Incorporation of 5-Bromo- and 5-Iododeoxyuridine into the Deoxyribonucleic Acid of Human Cells and its Effect on Radiation Sensitivity. *Journal of Experimental Medicine*, 112:509–531.

Fowler, J. F., and R. L. Morgan. 1963. Pre-therapeutic Experiments with the Fast Neutron Beam from the Medical Research Council Cyclotron. VIII. General Review. *British Journal of Radiology*, 36:115–121.

Fowler, J. F., R. L. Morgan, and C. A. P. Wood. 1963. Pre-therapeutic Experiments with the Fast Neutron Beam from the Medical Research Council Cyclotron. I. The Biological and Physical Advantages and Problems of Neutron Therapy. *British Journal of Radiology*, 36:77–80.

Friedenwald, J. S., and S. Sigelman. 1953. The Influence of Ionizing Radiation on Mitotic Activity in the Rat's Corneal Epithelium. *Experimental Cell Research*, 4:1–31.

Frindel, E., R. F. Kallman, and H. S. Kaplan. 1963. DNA Synthesis and Mitotic Activity in Bone Marrow, Intestine, and Mammary Tumors of Mice after X-Irradiation. (Abstract) *Radiation Research*, 19:205.

Goldberg, I. H., and M. Rabinowitz. 1962. Actinomycin D Inhibition of Deoxyribonucleic Acid-Dependent Synthesis of Ribonucleic Acid. *Science*, 136:315–316.

Gots, J. S., and E. G. Gollub. 1959. Purine Analogs as Feedback Inhibitors. *Proceedings of the Society for Experimental Biology and Medicine*, 101:641–643.

Gottschling, H., and E. Freese. 1961. Incorporation of 2-Aminopurine into the Desoxyribonucleic Acid of Bacteria and Bacteriophages. *Zeitschrift für Naturforschung; Teil B*, 16B:515–519.

Gray, L. H. 1959. Oxygenation in Radiotherapy: Radiobiological Considerations. *British Journal of Radiology*, 30:403–406.

———. 1961. Radiobiologic Basis of Oxygen as a Modifying Factor in Radiation Therapy. *The American Journal of Roentgenology, Radium Therapy and Nuclear Medicine*, 85:803–815.

Greer, S. 1960. Studies on Ultraviolet Irradiation of *Escherichia coli* Containing 5-Bromouracil in Its DNA. *The Journal of General Microbiology*, 22:618–634.

Haselkorn, R. 1964. Actinomycin D as a Probe for Nucleic Acid Secondary Structure. *Science*, 143:682–684.

Henderson, J. F. 1963. Feedback Inhibition of Purine Biosynthesis in Ascites Tumor Cells by Purine Analogues. *Biochemical Pharmacology*, 12:551–556.

Howard-Flanders, P. 1961. Factors Affecting Radiation Injury to DNA in Bacteria and Bacteriophage Systems. *Brookhaven Symposia in Biology*, 14:18–30.

Humphrey, R. M., W. C. Dewey, and A. Cork. 1963. Effect of Oxygen in Mammalian Cells Sensitized to Radiation by Incorporation of 5-Bromodeoxyuridine into the DNA. *Nature*, London, 198:268–269.

Kallman, R. F., Editor. 1961. *Research in Radiotherapy. Approaches to Chemical Sensitization.* (National Academy of Sciences, National Research Council Publication No. 888.) Washington, D. C., 275 pp.

Kallman, R. F. 1963. Recovery from Radiation Injury: A Proposed Mechanism. *Nature*, London, 197:557–560.

Kaplan, H. S., and J. Earle. Unpublished data.

Kaplan, H. S., and F. L. Howsden. 1964. Sensitization of Purine-Starved Bacteria to X-Rays. *Proceedings of the National Academy of Sciences of the U.S.A.*. (in press.)

Kaplan, H. S., K. C. Smith, and P. A. Tomlin. 1961. Radiosensitization of *E. coli* by Purine and Pyrimidine Analogues Incorporated in Deoxyribonucleic Acid. *Nature*, London, 190:794–796.

————. 1962. Effect of Halogenated Pyrimidines on Radiosensitivity of *E. coli*. *Radiation Research*, 16:98–113.

Kaplan, H. S., and P. A. Tomlin. 1960. Enhancement of X-Ray Sensitivity of *E. coli* by 5-Bromouracil. (Abstract) *Radiation Research*, 12:447–448.

Kaplan, H. S., R. Zavarine, and J. Earle. 1962. Interaction of the Oxygen Effect and Radiosensitization Produced by Base Analogues Incorporated into Deoxyribonucleic Acid. *Nature*, London, 194:662–664.

Kollmann, G., B. Shapiro, and E. E. Schwartz. 1964. The Distribution and the Chemical Forms of the Radiation-Protective Agent AET in Leukemic Mice. *Cancer Research*, 24:120–124.

Kriss, J. P. Unpublished data.

Kriss, J. P., Y. Maruyama, L. A. Tung, S. B. Bond, and L. Révész. 1963. The Fate of 5-Bromodeoxyuridine, 5-Bromodeoxycytidine, and 5-Iododeoxycytidine in Man. *Cancer Research*, 23:260–268.

Kriss, J. P., and L. Révész. 1962. The Distribution and Fate of Bromodeoxyuridine and Bromodeoxycytidine in the Mouse and Rat. *Cancer Research*, 22:254–265.

LePage, G. A. 1960. Incorporation of 6-Thioguanine into Nucleic Acids. *Cancer Research*, 20:403–408.

Mak, S., and J. E. Till. 1963. The Effects of X-Rays on the Progress of L-Cells through the Cell Cycle. *Radiation Research*, 20:600–618.

Mallams, J. T., J. W. Finney, and G. A. Balla. 1962. The Use of Hydrogen Peroxide as a Source of Oxygen in a Regional Intra-arterial Infusion System. *Southern Medical Journal*, 55:230–232.

Marcovich, H. 1958. "Activité radioprotectrice de la glycérine chez les bactéries," *Organic Peroxides in Radiobiology*, R. Latarjet, Ed. London, England, and New York, New York: Pergamon Press. Paris, France: Masson et Cie. Pp. 117–123.

Mendelsohn, M. L. 1962. Chronic Infusion of Tritiated Thymidine into Mice with Tumors. *Science*, 135:213–215.

Patt, H. M. 1953. Protective Mechanisms in Ionizing Radiation Injury. *Physiological Reviews*, 33:35–76.

Pelc, S. R., and A. Howard. 1955. Effect of Various Doses of X-Rays on the Number of Cells Synthesizing Deoxyribonucleic Acid. *Radiation Research*, 3:135–142.

Philips, F. S., S. S. Sternberg, L. Hamilton, and D. A. Clarke. 1954. The Toxic Effects of 6-Mercaptopurine and Related Compounds. *Annals of the New York Academy of Sciences*, 60:283–296.

Reich, E. 1964. Actinomycin: Correlation of Structure and Function of Its Complexes with Purines and DNA. *Science*, 143:684–689.

Schwartz, E. E., B. Shapiro, and G. Kollmann. 1964. Selective Chemical Protection against Radiation in Tumor-Bearing Mice. *Cancer Research*, 24:90–96.

Sinclair, W. K., and R. A. Morton. 1963. Variations in X-Ray Response during the Division Cycle of Partially Synchronized Chinese Hamster Cells in Culture. *Nature*, London, 199:1158–1160.

Straube, R. L., H. M. Patt, D. E. Smith, and E. B. Tyree. 1950. Influence of Cysteine on the Radiosensitivity of Walker Rat Carcinoma 256. *Cancer Research*, 10:243–244.

Terasima, T., and L. J. Tolmach. 1963a. Variations in Several Responses of HeLa Cells to X-Irradiation during the Division Cycle. *Biophysical Journal*, 3:11–33.

———. 1963b. X-Ray Sensitivity and DNA Synthesis in Synchronous Populations of HeLa Cells. *Science*, 140:490–492.

Webb, R. B. 1963. Glycerol and Water Effects on X-Ray Sensitivity in *Staphylococcus aureus. Radiation Research*, 18:607–619.

Wright, E. A., and D. K. Bewley. 1960. Whole-Body Radioprotection of Mice to 8-Mev Electrons Produced by Breathing Nitrogen for Brief Periods. With a Note on the Dosimetry of Whole-Body Irradiation of Mice with Fast Electrons. *Radiation Research*, 13:649–656.

Yamada, M., and T. T. Puck. 1961. Action of Radiation on Mammalian Cells. IV. Reversible Mitotic Lag in the S3 Hela Cells Produced by Low Doses of X-Rays. *Proceedings of the National Academy of Sciences of the U.S.A.*, 47:1181–1191.

Zatz, L. M. 1963. The Radioprotective Effects of Combined Hypoxia and AET in Mice. *International Journal of Radiation Biology and Related Studies in Physics, Chemistry and Medicine*, 6:105–115.

DISCUSSION

Dr. Ronald M. Humphrey, The University of Texas M. D. Anderson Hospital and Tumor Institute, Houston, Texas: Dr. Kaplan, have you tested deoxythioguanosine as a sensitizing agent in tissue culture cells in view of the rather good results obtained with thioguanine and bacteria?

Dr. Henry S. Kaplan, Stanford University, Palo Alto, California: About 2½ years ago, I worked for about 6 months to synthesize a small amount of this compound, which we used in bacterial studies. We have since obtained a gift of a few more milligrams from Dr. Leon Goodman of the Stanford Research Institute, who worked out the synthesis to which you referred. The compound does sensitize our purine-requiring bacterial strains but is not any more effective than thioguanine, perhaps actually somewhat less so. However, the little we have had to work with has not been isotope-labeled; therefore we are uncertain as to the ability of the organism to destroy it. In work with the sulfur-containing purine analogues, one must consider the fact that many microorganisms and mammalian cells can metabolize the analogue by stripping off the sulfur and then converting the molecule to a natural purine base. One would then not expect to see an effect. In a general way, the effectiveness of these purine analogues as sensitizers seems to parallel their growth inhibitory activity. If they are inhibitory, they probably are not being metabolized by the cell, and under these conditions I would rather expect them to be effective sensitizers.

Dr. Bradford N. Craver, E. R. Squibb & Sons, New Brunswick, New Jersey: I was quite surprised at Dr. Kaplan's observation that the vessels of a renal cancer do not respond to epinephrine in the same manner as do the vessels of normal renal tissue. He has used this to improve the oxygen supply of the tumor and I would suggest that perhaps a reverse approach might also be a fruitful area for investigation. If one could diminish the oxygen supply to the tumor to the extent that one produced ischemia, this might be beneficial and also could lead to a concentration of radioprotective agent in the normal tissue as opposed to the tumor tissue. I believe it was Waugh and Pearl who first announced a few years ago that large doses of serotonin, administered to animals, would produce a potentially lethal renal corticonecrosis. Antiserotonin agents are now available that will prevent this effect completely. It is conceivable, in view of this differential vascular reaction, that the serotonin would constrict both the tumor vessels and the normal vessels but a suitable antiserotonin might inhibit the response of the normal vessels, but not the response of the tumor vessels. If there is an oncologist here that would be interested in this approach, we have an experimental drug available that would be helpful in implementing this study.

Dr. Kaplan: This is a very interesting suggestion. However, the toxicity of the sulfhydryl radioprotective compounds would still represent a formidable barrier to this approach.

Dr. William C. Dewey, The University of Texas M. D. Anderson Hospital and Tumor Institute, Houston, Texas: One problem that concerns me very greatly, and many other people I am sure, is this problem in which Dr. Mendelsohn is so actively engaged, that is, the proliferating pool versus the nonproliferating pool in the tumor. How does the radiation sensitivity of the proliferating cells compare with the radiosensitivity of the cells which are in the so-called G_0 or extended G_1? If there is a different radiation response in these two pools, this will certainly be very important. It will also be important in trying to get sensitizing agents incorporated into tumor cells to establish how cells move into the proliferating pool from G_0 and back again into G_0. Possibly Dr. Mendelsohn would like to comment on this.

Dr. Mortimer Mendelsohn, University of Pennsylvania, Philadelphia, Pennsylvania: This is a very important question, but unfortunately I am unable to supply the answer. We have been thinking about the problem for several years, but because of the limitations of available methods, we have not been able to design a definitive experiment. I reported in an abstract five years ago (*Radiation Research*, 11:454, 1959) that 500 r to the C3H mammary tumors abolished mitotic activity for at least 5 hours, but did not interfere with the uptake of tritiated thymidine injected 2 hours postirradiation. Three hours after labeling, such tumors show an incidence of labeling in pycnotic cells which is approximately twice the incidence in intact cells. In retrospect, I would attribute this to the possibility that acute postirradiation pycnosis occurs only in proliferating cells. But like so many similar responses in radiation biology, the rapidity of its appearance need not bear any relation to its radiosensitivity. One would much prefer to know the proliferative potential of the various types of cells in the irradiated tumor or perhaps find some way to identify which cells are responsible for postirradiation recurrences. The traffic between the proliferating and nonproliferating compartments, and particularly the reversibility of nonproliferation, are also problems for which we have no answers at the moment.

Mr. Paul Todd, University of California, Berkeley, California: In Dr. Andrews' last illustration we saw depth dose distribution curves for neutrons, mesons, protons, gamma rays, and X rays. The remark that went with the figures was that the further development of neutron generators for therapeutic use should be considered. I am wondering about the reason for singling out neutron generators on the basis of these curves.

Dr. Robert Andrews, National Institutes of Health, Bethesda, Maryland: These are some of the data which are available today on depth dose distributions in water or tissue equivalent materials (see Andrews, pages 558 to 583, this volume). They leave a lot to be desired. If it is considered that 250 kv X-irradiation is no longer suitable, in respect to its dose distribution, for internal cancer radiotherapy, then certain conclusions can be drawn by comparing the lines. Now I don't make this conclusion, each of you looking at the paper can make this decision independently. If it is concluded that the depth dose provided by cobalt-60 is adequate, then certain other comparisons can be made here on the drawing. I don't have to make this conclusion; you can make it individually. If it is concluded that only the depth dose characteristics of the 6 Mev or greater circular or linear accelerator is useful then other conclusions have to be drawn. Now, in respect to the exploitation of the Bragg peak of either heavy negatively charged particles or heavy positively charged particles there is another consideration. In human situations where the peak can be exploited, and you see the half-value width of the peak is only a couple of centimeters, then as in pituitary irradiation, the peak may very well be exploited. If, as the Upsala group did in order to irradiate a volume of tissue in the pelvis, the peak has to be transformed, that is, by scanning the peak back and forth by the introduction of absorbers, you see quite obviously that the peak to the plateau dose ratio is going to diminish very rapidly, that as this ratio diminishes the average LET of the peak diminishes also, and as the average LET diminishes, the irradiations are no longer oxygen independent.

Dr. John S. Laughlin, Division of Biophysics, Sloan-Kettering Institute for Cancer Research, New York, New York: In addition to the development of higher LET radiations, I should like to call attention to desirable extensions of some of the existing radiations. Both Dr. Kaplan and Dr. Andrews have discussed the biological advantages to be achieved by the use of higher LET radiation. They have also called attention to a loss of some of the physical advantages which are now available with X rays and electrons. These various advantages presently enjoyed can be retained and certain other biological advantages gained by the exploitation of the time dimension with electrons. This is technically feasible since sources of high energy electrons can now be built with intensities many orders of magnitude greater than those now in use.

Dr. Melvin L. Griem, University of Chicago, Chicago, Illinois: We have a linear electron accelerator which delivers a pulse in the range mentioned by Dr. Laughlin. We have seen some very unusual reactions in the lung which we cannot explain. The electron beam is scanned over the treatment area so that each cell receives an average of 23 pulses with a dose rate of 10 to 1,000 rads per micro second per pulse. The biological reaction in the lung is greater than the physical dose would suggest.

Dr. Herman D. Suit, The University of Texas M. D. Anderson Hospital and Tumor Institute, Houston, Texas: Dr. Laughlin, if I understood correctly, you implied that it would be possible to use an exceedingly high dose rate to overcome in part the oxygen effect. My understanding was that the total dose had to be in excess of 50,000 to 80,000 rads before there would be any change of this oxygen effect, and therefore even clinically maximal doses would not be in that range.

Dr. Laughlin: I was not suggesting the use of the high intensity doses to diminish the oxygen effect in the lesion. Rather, I was suggesting the use of the short pulse in order to make it convenient to obtain temporary hypoxia or anoxia of the surrounding healthy tissue to bring its oxygen content down to that of the lesion. Actually, I think the work of Dewey and Boag (*Nature*, London, 183:1450, May 23, 1959) and of Kirby-Smith and Dolphin (*Nature*, London, 182:270, July 26, 1958) have shown that pulses of the order of a few kilorads can produce appreciable oxygen depletion, but that was not the objective of this high intensity approach. I should like also to add that in order to produce a high intensity instantaneously over a large field it is necessary to produce a higher intensity source than now is available for research or therapy.

Mr. Todd: There are three brief remarks I would like to make. They may bear some relevance to the future therapeutic use of high LET radiations and are related to some of the earlier informal remarks about basic experiments with high LET radiations. These comments are based on our experience with the aerobic and anoxic irradiation of human cells in culture (kindly supplied by Dr. Barendsen) with heavy ions having LET's from 70 to 17,000 Mev cm^2/g (10 Mev cm^2/g is equal to 1 kev per micron divided by the density of wet tissue).

First, within the accuracy of our data, the oxygen enhancement ratio drops to 1.00 for radiations of LET greater than 3,000 Mev cm^2/g. In Dr. Powers' terms this means that the oxygen-dependent component of the inactivation constant becomes zero.

Second, there is no increase in radiosensitivity due to the incorporation of iododeoxyuridine when cells are exposed to radiations of LET greater than 2,000 Mev cm^2/g. This may have some relevance to Dr. Kaplan's discussion as well, although such densely ionizing radiations will not be available for clinical use for some time, if ever.

The third comment is a very general one. Dr. Alper's treatment of differential modification of radiation response may be applicable to the modification by increasing LET of the response of mammalian cells in culture. It cannot be unequivocally stated that increasing LET decreases the extrapolation number of mammalian cell survival curves. It can be argued that the extrapolation number, if such exists, remains constant until the shoulder of the survival curve is too narrow to observe, due to the increased importance of the initial slope which becomes very steep at high LET. I refer to figures which Dr. Barendsen showed us in an earlier discussion and in which the importance of the initial slopes of the survival curves was carefully pointed out. Evidently this initial slope is related to irreversible inactivation and is very sensitive to increasing LET. There is no evidence for cellular recovery at very high LET. These observations lead to the following question: Do mammalian cells lose their reproductive integrity by two (or more) independent means, one of which is irreversible and characterized by an exponential inactivation curve and the other, reversible and characterized by a "sigmoid" inactivation curve and cellular recovery?

Dr. G. Barendsen, Radiobiological Institute of the Organization for Health Research TNO, Rijswijk, Netherlands: I am afraid I can't answer this question unequivocally because we haven't carried out sufficient studies with fractionated doses at LET's between 10 and 60 kev/μ of tissue, which is the LET region where we have found the change from sigmoid to exponential survival curves. We do know however that with α-particles at 140 kev/μ of tissue an exponential survival curve and no recovery are observed. Furthermore with 250 kvp X rays at low doses up to 100 rads all inhibition of clone formation produced seems to be of the nonrecoverable type, *i.e.* if a total dose of 100 rads is given in two, three or more fractions with intervals of 4 hours, no increase in percentage survival is found as compared with a single dose of 100 rads. At higher doses, e.g. 300 rads or more, fractionation of a given dose has a clear effect, *i.e.* part of the damage produced by a single dose of 300 rads is not effective if fractionation is employed. This does not imply, however, that there should be two different biochemical or biological processes. This may be the case but the difference might also be due to different primary physical events of energy deposition, *i.e.* the required number of ionizations may be produced in a certain critical volume by one single particle or by two or more particles (*Nature*, London, 193:1153, 1962). We have no data to distinguish between these possibilities however.

Dr. Carl F. Tessmer, The University of Texas M. D. Anderson Hospital and Tumor Institute, Houston, Texas: Since the matter of high energy electrons has come up for discussion, and particularly in view of the comment of the one clinical experience where difficulty was encountered, I would like to call attention to some observations we have made in this area. Using 2 Mev electrons which by general physical criteria one would say penetrated 1 cm in tissue, approximately 0.5 cm/Mev, we confirmed that these effectively produced extensive tissue damage (in swine) to a depth of at least 3 centimeters. This report (*Radiation Research*, 14:167, 1961) suggests that there are some unknown factors which, as far as I know, have still not been adequately explained.

High Intensity Electrons for Research and Therapy

JOHN S. LAUGHLIN

Departments of Medical Physics and Biophysics,
Memorial Hospital for Cancer and Allied Diseases, and
Sloan-Kettering Institute for Cancer Research,
New York, New York

In connection with some of the cellular radiobiology studies discussed in this symposium, and partly as a consequence of some of them, it is pertinent to describe briefly some implications for both research and therapy involved in electron irradiation carried out at ultrahigh dose rates. Both Dr. Andrews (see pages 558 to 583, this volume) and Dr. Kaplan (see pages 584 to 595, this volume) have discussed biological advantages to be expected in the therapeutic use of higher linear energy transfer (LET) radiations. Dr. Kaplan has also called attention to therapeutic possibilities in the use of either sensitizing or protective agents coordinated in time of administration with tumor cell cycle stage. The possibilities offered by the use of high energy electrons delivered in high dose rate pulses should also be reviewed in connection with such considerations. Technical developments now make it feasible to construct sources of high energy electrons whose dose intensities are several orders of magnitude greater than those with presently available sources. Such electrons can be administered at high intensities over a broad field at energies from 5 Mev to 40 Mev.

Some of the features of electrons in doses up to several kilorads delivered in pulses a microsecond or less in width for radiobiological research and cancer therapy are briefly itemized here.

Irradiation can be carried out in a sufficiently short time so as to facilitate the temporary modification of the environment. This can include the production of anoxia or hypoxia in a local region containing both the lesion and unavoidably irradiated surrounding healthy tissue. As shown by Gray and others (Gray, 1961; Hewitt and Wilson, 1959; Powers and Tolmach, 1963; Thomlinson, 1963), and in further evidence summarized by Gray at this symposium, lesions are often in various stages of hypoxia, with a consequently higher radiation resistance. The nonlinear relation of radiation sensitivity and oxygen pressure is such that the relative biological response of lesion and surrounding healthy tissue will be made more similar with either an increase or a decrease in the general oxygen pressure. This local hypoxia can be achieved not only in extremities, but also can be achieved internally in some organs by using modern surgical techniques.

The possible treatment of lesions with electrons during the local injection or infusion of radiation sensitizers in the lesion region is also facilitated by pulsed dose irradiation. In the same manner, the temporary administration of protective agents in the surrounding healthy tissue is also made more feasible.

Hypothermia has been shown to cause a reduction in oxygen pressure in various organs of the mouse (Cater and Weiss, 1959), and has been correlated with radiation protection (Weiss, 1960). Reduction in radiation sensitivity has been demonstrated in the skin of patients by Liebner, Moos, Hochhauser, and Harvey (1962) and used by them for patient therapy. The therapeutic use of this technique is also facilitated by pulsed irradiation.

The existence of a recovery effect has been discussed in this symposium in detail. The inefficiency of low doses inherent in the shoulder of mammalian cellular survival curves is reduced by the employment of large doses spaced far apart in time. This nonlinear dose response, in conjunction with a higher dose in the target volume than in the surrounding healthy tissue, results in a greater biological effect per unit dose in the target volume than in the surrounding tissue. The greater biological effectiveness of a few large doses has been well brought out in the earlier paper by Elkind (see pages 442 to 461, this volume), and has also been treated by Ellis (1963), Oliver (1963), Lajtha and Oliver (1961), and others.

There should be some further enhancement of the biological effect, of a magnitude not now known, due to the influence of such factors as the local saturation of free radical scavengers during a large pulse of short duration. Because of the higher dose in the target volume, this threshold effect would be expected to result in a more biologically effective dose in the lesion region than in the surrounding healthy tissue.

In this connection it should be pointed out that the results of relative biological effectiveness (RBE) experiments carried out with existing radiations cannot be carried over directly to predict the biological effect of the high energy electron pulsed doses. We have made some calculations with various models of electron track and cluster arrangements in an attempt to facilitate such a comparison. Although on one model of randomly oriented tracks, it appears that a roughly equivalent LET of about 10 kev per micron can be obtained with a 10 kilorad pulse, the volume distribution of energy is more diffuse. Therefore, the RBE versus LET experimental results discussed here earlier cannot be carried over directly. For some systems this more diffuse distribution of dose may result in a further enhancement in RBE and, in some other systems, will result in a lesser degree of enhanced biological effect. The degree of this enhanced biological effectiveness can be determined only by construction of such sources and the carrying out of the pertinent experiments.

All of the above considerations which are pertinent to therapeutic applications of high intensity electrons are also applicable to research studies in various biological systems. The availability of sources capable of delivering large doses in time intervals comparable to the lifetimes of the free radicals would make possible significant experiments on radiation mechanisms in both chemical and biological systems.

A further major consideration which is relevant when various radiations, including neutrons, protons, mesons, *etc*., are being contemplated for therapy is that of the very real physical advantages which exist in the present use of electrons. Some of these factors are unique (Harvey, Haas, and Laughlin, 1952) and are sufficiently important to justify a brief listing here.

Definite range. This insures that beyond a certain depth there is a negligible insult to underlying tissue. In treating breast carcinoma patients with electron beams, for instance, a major decrease in pneumonitis and lung fibrosis has been demonstrated in comparison with radiation treatment with the best X-ray techniques (Chu, Nisce, and Laughlin, 1963).

Adjustable depth. The depth of penetration is proportional to energy and is conveniently adjustable.

Minimal interface discontinuities. In contrast with the dose buildup in superficial regions characteristic of high energy X rays, electrons exhibit a limited buildup. Consequently, for the frequent case of internal discontinuities, e.g. air cavities, contained within the target volume, high energy X rays may produce a low relative dose on the distal surface due to lack of electron equilibrium, which results in a cold spot in the center of the lesion. With high energy electrons a more uniform dose is maintained. This has proved important in many treatment sites.

Absence of increased absorption in bone. The absorption of electrons is primarily determined by the electron density of the absorbing material. Since the number of electrons per gram is almost the same in most materials, the absorbed dose in bone is no greater than in surrounding tissue.

Other practical advantages result from the fact that electron beams can be readily shaped with regard to the intricate configurations often required in therapy. The depth of penetration is readily adjusted across the surface of a field by the use of differential absorbers. Further, with the availability of sufficient intensity, the use of focusing becomes feasible and permits the simultaneous application of electrons in several different directions through different fields.

Some of these features are unique and make it possible to achieve a higher localization of dose in the target volume relative to the surrounding healthy tissue than can possibly be achieved with neutrons or conveniently with X rays. Furthermore, electron accelerators are relatively compact and inexpensive.

In conclusion, it would appear that the study of mechanisms of both biological and chemical effects of radiation would be aided by the use of radiation doses delivered in pulses of duration comparable to that of the life times of the radiation produced free radicals. Moreover, such high intensity electrons have promising therapeutic applications.

REFERENCES

Cater, D. B., and L. Weiss. 1959. Measurements of Oxygen Tension in the Tissues of Mice Cooled at 1° C. *Nature,* London, 183:1521–1522.

Chu, F. C. H., L. Nisce, and J. S. Laughlin. 1963. Treatment of Breast Cancer with High Energy Electrons Produced by 24 Mev Betatron. *Radiology,* 81:871–880.

Ellis, F. 1963. The Dose-Time Relationship in Radiotherapy. *British Journal of Radiology,* 36:153–162.

Gray, L. H. 1961. Radiobiologic Basis of Oxygen as a Modifying Factor in Radiation Therapy. *The American Journal of Roentgenology, Radium Therapy and Nuclear Medicine,* 85:803–815.

Harvey, R. A., L. L. Haas, and J. S. Laughlin. 1952. Betatron Cancer Therapy. *Radiology,* 58:23–33.

Hewitt, H. B., and C. W. Wilson. 1959. The Effect of Tissue Oxygen Tension on the Radiosensitivity of Leukaemia Cells Irradiated *in situ* in the Femurs of Leukaemic Mice. *The British Journal of Cancer,* 13:675–684.

Lajtha, L. G., and R. Oliver. 1961. Some Radiobiological Considerations in Radiotherapy. *British Journal of Radiology,* 34:252–257.

Liebner, E. J., W. S. Moos, M. Hochhauser, and R. A. Harvey. 1962. Refrigeration and Irradiation: Lowering Skin Temperature of Irradiated Field. *Radiology,* 78: 258–259.

Oliver, R. 1963. Theoretical Implications of Cell Survival Data in Relation to Fractionated Radiotherapy Treatments. *British Journal of Radiology,* 36:178–182.

Powers, W. E., and L. J. Tolmach. 1963. A Multicomponent X-Ray Survival Curve for Mouse Lymphosarcoma Cells Irradiated *in vivo. Nature,* London, 197:710–711.

Thomlinson, R. H. 1963. A Comparison of Fast Neutrons and X-Rays in Relation to the "Oxygen Effect" in Experimental Tumours in Rats. *British Journal of Radiology,* 36:89–91.

Weiss, L. 1960. The Alteration of Radiosensitivity of the Intact Mouse Spleen by Extreme Hypothermia. *British Journal of Radiology,* 33:32–35.

INDEX

INDEX

B

C

I

J

K

L

M

S

T

U

V

W